MATHS   0200 1963 H

MATHEMATICAL METHODS

Mathematical Methods
in
Science and Engineering

J. HEADING
M.A., Ph.D.

Senior Lecturer in Applied Mathematics
University of Southampton

LONDON
EDWARD ARNOLD (PUBLISHERS) LTD.

First Published 1963

To

JEREMY AND PETER

Printed in Northern Ireland at The Universities Press, Belfast

PREFACE

In presenting to students this single-volume text on mathematical methods, containing all the more important mathematical material necessary for the majority of first and second year degree students of science and engineering, the author would draw attention to the following features.

(*a*) It is written for the large numbers of average students who require routine mathematical procedure. Having marked hundreds of examination scripts at this level, the author is painfully aware of the fact that so many students never seem to grasp even routine methods. The main object of the book is to present blackboard material in a concise way and to help students to solve problems.

(*b*) A knowledge at Advanced Level standard is assumed in the calculus, in algebra, co-ordinate geometry and in trigonometry, although many of the fundamental results in these subjects are restated and briefly derived.

(*c*) The exposition has not been unduly condensed in order that all the relevant subject matter should be included in one volume; rather the text has not been expanded unnecessarily. The author has sought to include what *should* be written and not what *could* be written, bearing chiefly in mind the present syllabuses of the University of London for engineering, chemical engineering, ancillary mathematics for special physics and chemistry, and for the part I of the general degree in science. Part II of the general degree and part III of the engineering degree must of necessity be excluded from any one-volume work.

(*d*) Each subject is treated as an entity in itself, being confined to its own individual chapter. This facilitates ease of reference, and also rapid revision when each subject can be surveyed as a whole.

(*e*) An attempt has been made to treat certain subjects with greater clarity than that found in other texts—the chapter on partial differentiation being an example in question.

(*f*) For all subjects, the theory given is concise, thereby making the text suitable for learning, reference and revision. Every topic dealt with is illustrated by means of worked examples, there being some 400 such examples throughout the text.

(*g*) At the end of each chapter sets of examples are provided, all the questions being of the type set in modern examinations. The questions have been carefully graded in order of difficulty, and also in subject matter, the order and grouping being identical with that in the text itself. The author has attempted to make these sets of examples more useful and more complete than other existing sets, and students are advised to use them systematically, not only when learning the subjects originally, but also for exercises in order to retain and revise methods learnt many months previously.

(*h*) Answers are provided at the end of each set of examples, thereby avoiding the usual awkward fumbling of pages at the end of the book.

(*i*) Since the stress is on *methods* throughout, the author has omitted both formal theory which has very little application at these elementary levels, and applications to science and engineering problems which lecturers may discuss according to the taste and interests of their classes. The author does not believe in hiding a simple exposition of fundamental techniques behind actual physical applications, however interesting and important these applications may be. The techniques are grasped in their own context first of all; then the applications rightly follow.

(*j*) The chapters on applied mathematics at the end of the book are limited in order to provide in one text a complete mathematics course according to the revised London syllabuses, which nowadays for engineering students are more restricted in applied mathematics than in former years.

(*k*) The final chapter on statistics is necessary these days, and it is thought that such a chapter is new in omnibus texts for degree students.

(*l*) Finally, the text is not meant for the few mathematical specialists who attend science and engineering courses. Such students require a more advanced treatment of all topics, including more rigour and a greatly extended syllabus. Many excellent texts are already available for such students.

The author would state that a large portion of this text was written when he was Senior Lecturer in mathematics at the West Ham College of Technology, London. He would express his thanks to Mr. D. C. Salinger, M.Sc., also Senior Lecturer in mathematics at that college, who kindly read the text and offered many useful comments and corrections. Very grateful acknowledgment is due to the Syndics of the Cambridge University Press and to the Senate of the University of London for permission to reproduce examination questions selected from papers set in the respective universities; such questions are marked with an asterisk.

J. HEADING

The University of Southampton

CONTENTS

CHAPTER 1

THE THEORY OF DETERMINANTS

1.1 The solution of two simultaneous linear equations

Determinants are introduced into algebra in order to simplify the manipulation and evaluation of otherwise complicated algebraical expressions. The theory may be developed by considering first of all determinants of the second order.

The two simultaneous equations containing the ratios $x:y:z$

$$a_1x + b_1y + c_1z = 0$$
$$a_2x + b_2y + c_2z = 0 \tag{1}$$

may be solved immediately by eliminating x and y in turn, yielding

$$\frac{x}{b_1c_2 - b_2c_1} = \frac{-y}{a_1c_2 - a_2c_1} = \frac{z}{a_1b_2 - a_2b_1}. \tag{2}$$

In the three denominators of these expressions, we have maintained the coefficients a, b and c in the order in which they occur in the given equations. These denominators contain expressions similar in form one to another, and in anticipation of the usefulness of the notation, we are led to write such expressions in the form

$$\begin{vmatrix} a_1 & b_1 \\ a_2 & b_2 \end{vmatrix} \equiv a_1b_2 - a_2b_1. \tag{3}$$

The expression on the left is called a *second order determinant*, while the expression on the right is the *expansion* or value of this determinant. The four symbols a_1, a_2, b_1 and b_2 are called the *elements* of the determinant, while a_1 and b_1 form the first *row*, a_2 and b_2 the second row, a_1 and a_2 the first *column*, b_1 and b_2 the second column. The diagonal from the top left to the bottom right is termed the *leading diagonal*. The value of the determinant is then the product of the two elements occurring in the leading diagonal *minus* the product of the two elements in the remaining diagonal.

In this new notation, the ratios (2) may be written

$$\frac{x}{\begin{vmatrix} b_1 & c_1 \\ b_2 & c_2 \end{vmatrix}} = \frac{-y}{\begin{vmatrix} a_1 & c_1 \\ a_2 & c_2 \end{vmatrix}} = \frac{z}{\begin{vmatrix} a_1 & b_1 \\ a_2 & b_2 \end{vmatrix}}. \tag{4}$$

The alternating signs $+$, $-$, $+$ occurring in the numerators should be carefully noticed. The reader is recommended to remember the solution (4) in the verbal form:

x divided by the determinant formed from the coefficients by eliminating the coefficients of x

$= -y$ divided by the determinant formed from the coefficients by eliminating the coefficients of y

$=$ z divided by the determinant formed from the coefficients by eliminating the coefficients of z.

In equations (1), it should be noticed that *all* terms must be placed on the left hand side. In particular, if z is placed equal to 1, we evidently have the solution of two linear equations in the two unknowns x and y; if $a_1b_2 - a_2b_1 = 0$, either no solution exists at all, or no unique solution exists.

Example 1 We have the following three expansions:

$$\begin{vmatrix} 5 & 8 \\ 4 & 7 \end{vmatrix} = 5.7 - 4.8 = 3; \qquad \begin{vmatrix} 4 & -5 \\ 3 & 6 \end{vmatrix} = 4.6 + 3.5 = 39;$$

$$\begin{vmatrix} -2 & -3 \\ 7 & 5 \end{vmatrix} = -2.5 + 7.3 = 11.$$

Example 2 Find the ratios $x:y:z$ in the equations

$$2x + y - 2z = 0, \qquad 5x - 2y - 8z = 0.$$

We may write the solution immediately as

$$\frac{x}{\begin{vmatrix} 1 & -2 \\ -2 & -8 \end{vmatrix}} = \frac{-y}{\begin{vmatrix} 2 & -2 \\ 5 & -8 \end{vmatrix}} = \frac{z}{\begin{vmatrix} 2 & 1 \\ 5 & -2 \end{vmatrix}};$$

that is, $x/(-12) = -y/(-6) = z/(-9)$,

or $x:y:z = 4:-2:3.$

Example 3 Solve the equations

$$7x - 9y = -41, \qquad 10x + 3y = -11.$$

The equations should first be rearranged with all terms on the left hand side thus

$$7x - 9y + 41 = 0$$
$$10x + 3y + 11 = 0.$$

Then

$$\frac{x}{\begin{vmatrix} -9 & 41 \\ 3 & 11 \end{vmatrix}} = \frac{-y}{\begin{vmatrix} 7 & 41 \\ 10 & 11 \end{vmatrix}} = \frac{1}{\begin{vmatrix} 7 & -9 \\ 10 & 3 \end{vmatrix}},$$

or $x/(-222) = -y/(-333) = 1/111.$

Hence $x = -2, \quad y = 3.$

1.2 Properties of second order determinants

Property i. If the rows and columns of determinant (3) are respectively changed to columns and rows, the rearranged determinant has the same value as the original, for

$$\begin{vmatrix} a_1 & a_2 \\ b_1 & b_2 \end{vmatrix} = a_1 b_2 - b_1 a_2.$$

Property ii. If the two columns (or the two rows) in determinant (3) are interchanged, the sign of the determinant is changed, for

$$\begin{vmatrix} b_1 & a_1 \\ b_2 & a_2 \end{vmatrix} = b_1 a_2 - b_2 a_1 = -(a_1 b_2 - a_2 b_1).$$

Property iii. If the two columns (or the two rows) are identical, the value of the determinant is zero, for

$$\begin{vmatrix} a_1 & a_1 \\ a_2 & a_2 \end{vmatrix} = a_1 a_2 - a_2 a_1 = 0.$$

Property iv. If all the elements in one column (or row) are multiplied by a constant p, the original determinant is merely multiplied by p, for

$$\begin{vmatrix} pa_1 & b_1 \\ pa_2 & b_2 \end{vmatrix} = pa_1 b_2 - pa_2 b_1 = p \begin{vmatrix} a_1 & b_1 \\ a_2 & b_2 \end{vmatrix}.$$

Property v. If each element in a given column (or a row) is split into two distinct parts, the determinant may be expressed as the sum of two determinants, for

$$\begin{vmatrix} a_1 + c_1 & b_1 \\ a_2 + c_2 & b_2 \end{vmatrix} = (a_1 + c_1)b_2 - (a_2 + c_2)b_1$$

$$= (a_1 b_2 - a_2 b_1) + (c_1 b_2 - c_2 b_1)$$

$$= \begin{vmatrix} a_1 & b_1 \\ a_2 & b_2 \end{vmatrix} + \begin{vmatrix} c_1 & b_1 \\ c_2 & b_2 \end{vmatrix}.$$

Property vi. If a constant multiple of the elements of one column (or row) is added to the respective elements of the other column (or row), the value of the determinant is unchanged. For example, if p times the elements of column 2 are added to the elements of column 1, we have

$$\begin{vmatrix} a_1 + pb_1 & b_1 \\ a_2 + pb_2 & b_2 \end{vmatrix} = \begin{vmatrix} a_1 & b_1 \\ a_2 & b_2 \end{vmatrix} + \begin{vmatrix} pb_1 & b_1 \\ pb_2 & b_2 \end{vmatrix} \quad \text{(from property } v\text{)}$$

$$= \begin{vmatrix} a_1 & b_1 \\ a_2 & b_2 \end{vmatrix} \quad \text{(from properties } iv \text{ and } iii\text{)}.$$

This property may be used to simplify the elements of a determinant before it is evaluated numerically, as the following examples show.

Example 4   Evaluate the determinant

$$D = \begin{vmatrix} 213 & 210 \\ 357 & 351 \end{vmatrix}.$$

Although from the original definition it is correct that D equals $213.351 - 357.210$, we use property vi to simplify the arithmetic. Subtracting column 2 from column 1, we have

$$D = \begin{vmatrix} 213 - 210 & 210 \\ 357 - 351 & 351 \end{vmatrix} = \begin{vmatrix} 3 & 210 \\ 6 & 351 \end{vmatrix} = 3 \begin{vmatrix} 1 & 210 \\ 2 & 351 \end{vmatrix}$$

$$= 3(351 - 420) = -207.$$

When property vi is used, a brief note should always be made concerning what has been done. The author would use a note such as $(\text{col}_1 - \text{col}_2)$, to indicate to an independent reader the manipulation that has taken place.

Example 5   Evaluate the determinant

$$D = \begin{vmatrix} 433 & 140 \\ 215 & 67 \end{vmatrix}.$$

We have
$$D = \begin{vmatrix} 3 & 6 \\ 215 & 67 \end{vmatrix} \quad\quad\quad (\text{row}_1 - 2\text{row}_2)$$

$$= \begin{vmatrix} 3 & 0 \\ 215 & -363 \end{vmatrix}. \quad\quad (\text{col}_2 - 2\text{col}_1)$$

$$= -1089.$$

The reader should note that, if a zero element can be obtained by this process, the arithmetic is immediately simplified.

1.3   The definition of a third order determinant

A *third order determinant* consists of nine elements arranged in the form of a square consisting of three rows and three columns thus:

$$D = \begin{vmatrix} a_1 & b_1 & c_1 \\ a_2 & b_2 & c_2 \\ a_3 & b_3 & c_3 \end{vmatrix}. \quad\quad\quad (5)$$

Its expanded form is suggested by the following considerations.

If any one of the nine elements is chosen, and if the row and column containing that element are deleted, there remains a second order determinant, called the *minor* of the chosen element. Thus the minor of a_1 is $(b_2c_3 - b_3c_2)$, being the value of the determinant formed when the first row and the first column are deleted in D. The minor of b_3 is $a_1c_2 - a_2c_1$.

The *cofactor* of an element in D is its minor with a special sign attached, chosen in keeping with the following scheme:

$$\begin{matrix} + & - & + \\ - & + & - \\ + & - & + \end{matrix} .$$

We choose the sign occupying the same position as the element chosen in D. Thus the elements a_1, c_1, b_2, a_3, c_3 require a plus sign to be attached to their minors to yield the corresponding cofactors, while the elements a_2, b_1, b_3, c_2 require minus signs. We shall denote the cofactors of an element by the corresponding capital letters. Thus

$$A_1 = +(b_2c_3 - b_3c_2), \quad B_3 = -(a_1c_2 - a_2c_1), \quad C_2 = -(a_1b_3 - a_3b_1).$$

Let us now add together the three elements of any row (or column) after multiplying these elements by their respective cofactors. Six such sums may be formed; the first row yields

$$a_1A_1 + b_1B_1 + c_1C_1 = a_1(b_2c_2 - b_3c_2) - b_1(a_2c_3 - a_3c_2)$$
$$+ c_1(a_2b_3 - a_3b_2), \quad (6)$$

while the second column yields the sum

$$b_1B_1 + b_2B_2 + c_2C_2 = -b_1(a_2c_3 - a_3c_2)$$
$$+ b_2(a_1c_3 - a_3c_1) - b_3(a_1c_2 - a_2c_1).$$

If the reader inspects these two sums he will find that they are identical. Moreover, if the sums for the second and third rows and for the first and third columns are written down, it will be seen immediately that all the six sums are identical. This sum is taken to be the definition of the value of the third order determinant. Usually considerations of numerical simplicity determine which row or column should be used to expand the determinant, but the first row is often chosen.

Consider now the nine possible sums formed from the three elements of a row (or column) after multiplication of these elements by the respective cofactors of a distinct row (or column). For example, taking the elements of the first row and the cofactors of the second row, we have

$$a_1 A_2 + b_1 B_2 + c_1 C_2 = -a_1(b_1 c_3 - b_3 c_1)$$
$$+ b_1(a_1 c_3 - a_3 c_1) - c_1(a_1 b_3 - a_3 b_1) = 0,$$

since all terms in this expansion cancel out. Similarly, all nine such sums vanish identically.

Example 6 The determinant

$$D = \begin{vmatrix} 4 & 2 & 3 \\ 7 & 5 & 4 \\ 9 & 2 & 6 \end{vmatrix}$$

may be expanded along all three rows and all three columns thus:

Along row 1: $D = 4(5.6 - 2.4) - 2(7.6 - 9.4) + 3(7.2 - 9.5) = -17$;

along row 2: $D = -7(2.6 - 2.3) + 5(4.6 - 9.3) - 4(4.2 - 9.2) = -17$;

along row 3: $D = 9(2.4 - 5.3) - 2(4.4 - 7.3) + 6(4.5 - 7.2) = -17$;

along column 1: $D = 4(5.6 - 2.4) - 7(2.6 - 2.3) + 9(2.4 - 5.3) = -17$;

along column 2: $D = -2(7.6 - 9.4) + 5(4.6 - 9.3) - 2(4.4 - 7.3) = -17$;

along column 3: $D = 3(7.2 - 9.5) - 4(4.2 - 9.2) + 6(4.5 - 7.2) = -17$.

1.4 Properties of third order determinants

The following six properties are identical with those proved in section 1.2 for second order determinants.

Property i. If the rows and columns of the determinant (5) are respectively changed to columns and rows, the rearranged determinant has the same value as the original, for expanding along the first column we have

$$\begin{vmatrix} a_1 & a_2 & a_3 \\ b_1 & b_2 & b_3 \\ c_1 & c_2 & c_3 \end{vmatrix} = a_1(b_2 c_3 - c_2 b_3) - b_1(a_2 c_3 - c_2 a_3) + c_1(a_2 b_3 - b_2 a_3).$$

The six terms in this expansion are identical with expression (6), which is the expansion of D along its first row.

Property ii. If two columns (or two rows) in determinant (5) are interchanged, the sign of the determinant is changed. For if this new determinant and D are expanded down the column (or along the row) that remains unchanged, the cofactors used in the two cases are merely changed in sign.

Property iii. If two columns (or two rows) are identical, the value of the determinant is zero. For if D is expanded down the remaining column (or along the remaining row), all the cofactors used are zero.

Property iv. If all the elements in one column (or row) are multiplied by a factor p, the original determinant is multiplied by p. Upon expansion down this particular column (or along the row), the factor p occurs in all six terms in the expansion; this factor p may then be removed, leaving the original determinant D in expanded form.

Property v. If the elements in a column (or a row) are split into two distinct parts, the determinant may be expressed as the sum of two determinants. Let

$$D = \begin{vmatrix} a_1 + d_1 & b_1 & c_1 \\ a_2 + d_2 & b_2 & c_2 \\ a_3 + d_3 & b_3 & c_3 \end{vmatrix}.$$

If the cofactors of the three elements down the first column are denoted by A_1, A_2, A_3 respectively, we have

$$D = (a_1 + d_1)A_1 + (a_2 + d_2)A_2 + (a_3 + d_3)A_3$$

$$= (a_1A_1 + a_2A_2 + a_3A_3) + (d_1A_1 + d_2A_2 + d_3A_3)$$

$$= \begin{vmatrix} a_1 & b_1 & c_1 \\ a_2 & b_2 & c_2 \\ a_3 & b_3 & c_3 \end{vmatrix} + \begin{vmatrix} d_1 & b_1 & c_1 \\ d_2 & b_2 & c_2 \\ d_3 & b_3 & c_3 \end{vmatrix}.$$

It can be seen that if both columns 1 and 2 are split up, the determinant may be separated into 4 determinants, while if all three columns are each split into two parts, the given determinant may be expressed as the sum of 8 determinants.

Property vi. If a constant multiple of the elements of one column (or row) is added respectively to the elements of a distinct column (or row), the value of the determinant is unchanged. The proof is identical with that given for property *vi*, section 1.2, *mutatis mutandis*.

This property is used to simplify the elements of a complicated determinant before numerical expansion. There is of course no unique method for simplifying such a determinant.

Example 7 Simplify and evaluate the determinant

$$D = \begin{vmatrix} 87 & 42 & 3 \\ 45 & 18 & 7 \\ 50 & 17 & 3 \end{vmatrix}.$$

We have
$$D = \begin{vmatrix} 0 & 42 & 3 \\ 2 & 18 & 7 \\ 13 & 17 & 3 \end{vmatrix} \qquad (\text{col}_1 - 2\text{col}_2 - \text{col}_3)$$

$$= 3\begin{vmatrix} 0 & 14 & 1 \\ 2 & 18 & 7 \\ 13 & 17 & 3 \end{vmatrix}$$

$$= 3\begin{vmatrix} 0 & 0 & 1 \\ 2 & -80 & 7 \\ 13 & -25 & 3 \end{vmatrix} \qquad (\text{col}_2 - 14\text{col}_3)$$

$$= 6\begin{vmatrix} 1 & -40 \\ 13 & -25 \end{vmatrix} = 30\begin{vmatrix} 1 & -8 \\ 13 & -5 \end{vmatrix}$$

$$= 30(-5 + 104) = 2970.$$

Example 8   Solve the third order determinantal equation

$$D = \begin{vmatrix} x+1 & 2x & 1 \\ x & 3x-2 & 2x \\ 1 & x & x \end{vmatrix} = 0.$$

We have
$$D = \begin{vmatrix} 1-x & 2x & 1 \\ 2-2x & 3x-2 & 2x \\ 1-x & x & x \end{vmatrix} \qquad (\text{col}_1 - \text{col}_2)$$

$$= (1-x)\begin{vmatrix} 1 & 2x & 1 \\ 2 & 3x-2 & 2x \\ 1 & x & x \end{vmatrix}$$

$$= (1-x)\begin{vmatrix} 1 & 2x & 1-x \\ 2 & 3x-2 & 0 \\ 1 & x & 0 \end{vmatrix} \qquad (\text{col}_3 - x\text{col}_1)$$

$$= (1-x)^2\begin{vmatrix} 2 & 3x-2 \\ 1 & x \end{vmatrix}$$

$$= (1-x)^2(2-x) = 0;$$

hence $x = 1, 1, 2$.

1.5 Fourth order determinants

Fourth and higher order determinants are defined in a manner similar to that given for third order determinants, and they enjoy exactly similar properties. The minor of an element in the determinant

$$D = \begin{vmatrix} a_1 & b_1 & c_1 & d_1 \\ a_2 & b_2 & c_2 & d_2 \\ a_3 & b_3 & c_3 & d_3 \\ a_4 & b_4 & c_4 & d_4 \end{vmatrix}$$

is the value of the third order determinant formed by deleting the row and column through that element. The cofactor of the element is formed from its minor by attaching the appropriate sign drawn from the extended scheme:

$$\begin{matrix} + & - & + & - \\ - & + & - & + \\ + & - & + & - \\ - & + & - & + \end{matrix}.$$

If these cofactors are again denoted by capital letters, the value of D is defined to be the unique sum obtained by expanding the determinant along any one of its four rows or down any one of its four columns. For example:

$$D = a_1 A_1 + b_1 B_1 + c_1 C_1 + d_1 D_1 = a_1 A_1 + a_2 A_2 + a_3 A_3 + a_4 A_4.$$

Property vi may be used to simplify the elements in the determinant before numerical expansion.

Example 9 Evaluate the determinant

$$D = \begin{vmatrix} 4 & 9 & -1 & 3 \\ 3 & -7 & 2 & 5 \\ 2 & 5 & -3 & 7 \\ 1 & -3 & 4 & 9 \end{vmatrix}.$$

Using property vi repeatedly, we have

$$D = \begin{vmatrix} 4 & 9 & -1 & 3 \\ -1 & -16 & 3 & 2 \\ -1 & 12 & -5 & 2 \\ -1 & -8 & 7 & 2 \end{vmatrix} \qquad (\text{row}_4 - \text{row}_3, \ \text{row}_3 - \text{row}_2, \ \text{row}_2 - \text{row}_1)$$

$$= \begin{vmatrix} 4 & 9 & -1 & 11 \\ -1 & -16 & 3 & 0 \\ -1 & 12 & -5 & 0 \\ -1 & -8 & 7 & 0 \end{vmatrix} \quad (\text{col}_4 + 2\text{col}_1)$$

$$= -11 \begin{vmatrix} -1 & -16 & 3 \\ -1 & 12 & -5 \\ -1 & -8 & 7 \end{vmatrix} \quad (\text{expanding along row 1})$$

$$= -11 \begin{vmatrix} -1 & -16 & 3 \\ 0 & 28 & -8 \\ 0 & 8 & 4 \end{vmatrix} \quad (\text{row}_2 - \text{row}_1, \text{row}_3 - \text{row}_1)$$

$$= 11 \begin{vmatrix} 28 & -8 \\ 8 & 4 \end{vmatrix}$$

$$= 1936.$$

1.6   Factorization of symmetrical determinants

If a, b and c are three given symbols, consider the various homogeneous polynomials that may be formed from them with the property that if a is replaced by b, b by c and c by a the polynomial is unchanged.

Symmetrical polynomials have the additional property that if a and b, or b and c, or c and a are interchanged the polynomial remains unchanged.   For example,

$$a + b + c$$

is a homogeneous symmetrical polynomial of degree 1,

$$a^2 + b^2 + c^2, \quad bc + ca + ab$$

are distinct homogeneous symmetrical polynomials of degree 2,

$$a^3 + b^3 + c^3, \quad b^2c + bc^2 + c^2a + ca^2 + a^2b + ab^2, \quad abc$$

are distinct homogeneous symmetrical polynomials of degree 3.

An arbitrary linear combination of, say, the 3 independent polynomials of degree 3 is also a homogeneous symmetrical polynomial of degree 3, and is in fact the most general homogeneous symmetrical polynomial of degree 3 that may be formed from the 3 symbols a, b and c, namely

$$A(a^3 + b^3 + c^3) + B(b^2c + bc^2 + c^2a + ca^2 + a^2b + ab^2) + Cabc. \quad (7)$$

On the other hand, homogeneous polynomials of degree 3 in 3 symbols exist with completely different properties. Consider

$$(b - c)(c - a)(a - b) \equiv -a^2(b - c) - b^2(c - a) - c^2(a - b). \qquad (8)$$

This is called an *alternating* polynomial, since the interchange of any two symbols (b and c for example) changes the sign of the polynomial. This is in addition to the property that if a is replaced by b, b by c and c by a the polynomial is unchanged.

If a symmetrical homogeneous polynomial is multiplied by an alternating polynomial thereby forming a polynomial whose degree equals the sum of the degrees of its two polynomial factors, the product must evidently be an alternating polynomial, since the interchange of any two symbols produces a change in sign in the product. Conversely, if an alternating homogeneous polynomial is given for which a factor, also an alternating polynomial, can be found, the remaining factor must be a symmetrical polynomial.

Considerations such as these, together with the remainder theorem, enable determinants of a special character to be factorized without explicit expansion.

The reader should recall the remainder theorem: If, in a polynomial containing symbols a, b, c, ..., we replace a by b, and if the polynomial then vanishes identically, we conclude that $(a - b)$ is a factor of the polynomial.

Suppose a third order determinant is given whose elements are formed from the symbols a, b and c. Let its expansion be noticed by inspection to be a homogeneous polynomial of degree n; moreover, let the determinant have the property that the replacement of a by b, of b by c and of c by a leaves its value unchanged, a fact noticed by a judicious interchange of rows and columns. Various considerations are now used to find the factors. If a is placed equal to b, causing the determinant to vanish, we conclude that $(a - b)$ is a factor; similarly, $(b - c)$ and $(c - a)$ will be factors. The combined factor $(b - c)(c - a)(a - b)$ is a homogeneous alternating polynomial of degree 3, so the remaining factor must be a homogeneous polynomial of degree $n - 3$. If this is of degree 1, the factor must be of the form $A(a + b + c)$, while if it is of degree 2, the factor must have the general form

$$A(a^2 + b^2 + c^2) + B(bc + ca + ab).$$

If one of degree 3 is required, either factor (7) or (8) or a sum of both (7) and (8) is required, depending on whether the factor is symmetrical, alternating or neither. The constants A, B, C are found by various simple methods, for example by direct inspection or by putting a, b and c equal to special numerical values.

If $(a - b)$, $(b - c)$, $(c - a)$ are not factors, a different approach is necessary. If by placing a equal to zero the determinant vanishes, we conclude that a is a factor; similarly, b and c are factors. The factor $(a + b + c)$, or even $(a + b + c)^2$, may often be taken out of the determinant, either by suitable combinations of rows or columns, or by placing a equal to $-b - c$ and showing that the determinant then vanishes.

Similar arguments apply to fourth order determinants.

Example 10   Factorize the alternant determinant

$$D = \begin{vmatrix} 1 & 1 & 1 \\ a & b & c \\ a^2 & b^2 & c^2 \end{vmatrix}.$$

Since every term in the expansion consists of a product of elements one from each row, the expansion must be a homogeneous polynomial of degree 3. If we place a equal to b, the first two columns are identical, so D vanishes. Hence $(a - b)$ is a factor; similarly, $(b - c)$ and $(c - a)$ are factors. But $(b - c)(c - a)(a - b)$ is a homogeneous polynomial of degree 3, so no further factor remains to be found save a constant; hence

$$D = A(b - c)(c - a)(a - b).$$

The term down the leading diagonal is evidently bc^2, while in the factorized form the equivalent term is Abc^2. To be identical, we must choose $A = 1$.

Example 11   Factorize the determinant

$$D = \begin{vmatrix} a & b & c \\ a^2 & b^2 & c^2 \\ a^5 & b^5 & c^5 \end{vmatrix}.$$

Firstly we remove a, b and c as factors respectively from the three columns, giving D as the product of abc and the determinant

$$E = \begin{vmatrix} 1 & 1 & 1 \\ a & b & c \\ a^4 & b^4 & c^4 \end{vmatrix}.$$

This is a homogeneous polynomial of degree 5, and as before, $(b - c)(c - a)(a - b)$ is an alternating factor of degree 3. But E must be an alternating polynomial since, for example, the interchange of a and b changes the sign of E, column 1 and column 2 merely being interchanged. The remaining factor must be symmetrical of degree 2, so

$$E \equiv (b - c)(c - a)(a - b)[A(a^2 + b^2 + c^2) + B(bc + ca + ab)].$$

To find the constants A and B, we may either inspect various terms, or we may put $a = 0$ in this identity. The determinant E may then be expanded down its first column giving

$$bc^4 - b^4c \equiv (b - c)c(-b)[A(b^2 + c^2) + Bbc],$$

or, cancelling $bc(c - b)$

$$b^2 + bc + c^2 \equiv A(b^2 + c^2) + Bbc.$$

Hence $A = B = 1$, so

$$D = abc(b - c)(c - a)(a - b)(a^2 + b^2 + c^2 + bc + ca + ab).$$

Example 12   Factorize the determinant

$$D = \begin{vmatrix} 1 & p^3 & p \\ p & p^5 & p^4 \\ p^4 & p^{11} & p^{13} \end{vmatrix}.$$

First we remove the factor p^3 from column 2, p from column 3 and then p from row 2 and p^4 from row 3, obtaining

$$D = p^9 \begin{vmatrix} 1 & 1 & 1 \\ 1 & p & p^2 \\ 1 & p^4 & p^8 \end{vmatrix}.$$

This is a disguised form of the determinant D in example 10, with $a = 1$, $b = p$, $c = p^4$. Using this result, we have immediately

$$D = p^9(p - p^4)(p^4 - 1)(1 - p)$$
$$= p^{10}(p + 1)(p - 1)^3(p^2 + 1)(p^2 + p + 1).$$

Example 13   Factorize the third order *circulant*

$$D = \begin{vmatrix} a & c & b \\ b & a & c \\ c & b & a \end{vmatrix}.$$

This is symmetrical and homogeneous of degree 3. If a and b, for example, are interchanged, D remains unchanged, for the subsequent interchange of row 1 and row 2, and then of column 2 and column 3, reproduces the original form of D.

If column 2 and column 3 are both added to column 1, it can be seen that $(a + b + c)$ is a factor down column 1. D must then consist of this factor together with a symmetrical factor of degree 2, namely

$$D = (a + b + c)[A(a^2 + b^2 + c^2) + B(bc + ca + ab)].$$

To find A and B, put $a = 0$. Then

$$b^3 + c^3 = (b + c)[A(b^2 + c^2) + Bbc],$$

yielding $A = 1$, $B = -1$.

If ω and ω^2 are the two complex cube roots of unity, this quadratic factor $a^2 + b^2 + c^2 - bc - ca - ab$ may be further resolved into the two linear factors $(a + \omega b + \omega^2 c)(a + \omega^2 b + \omega c)$. These may be extracted directly from the determinant D by considering in turn the combinations of columns: column 1 + ωcolumn 2 + ω^2column 3 and column 1 + ω^2column 2 + ωcolumn 3.

Example 14   Factorize the determinant

$$D = \begin{vmatrix} (b+c)^2 & a^2 & a^2 \\ b^2 & (c+a)^2 & b^2 \\ c^2 & c^2 & (a+b)^2 \end{vmatrix}.$$

This is symmetrical in a, b, c and homogeneous of degree 6. If a and b are interchanged for example, the original form of D may be reproduced by interchanging rows 1 and 2 and then columns 1 and 2.

If we put $a = 0$, columns 2 and 3 are proportional, so D vanishes. Hence a is a factor; likewise b and c are factors, giving abc as a joint factor.

If column 2 is subtracted from column 1 and the differences of two squares thus obtained factorized, the common factor $(a + b + c)$ emerges. Similarly, if column 3 is subtracted from column 2, a second factor $(a + b + c)$ is obtained. The reader should note that it is not now permitted to subtract column 3 from column 1 to obtain this factor a third time, since column 1 has already been mutilated when the first factor was extracted.

We have therefore found the symmetrical factor $abc(a + b + c)^2$ of degree 5, indicating that the remaining factor must be symmetrical and linear. We take

$$D = abc(a + b + c)^2 . A(a + b + c).$$

If we put $a = b = c = 1$, D has the value 54, so $D = 9 \times 3A$, yielding $A = 2$.

Example 15   Factorize the determinant

$$D = \begin{vmatrix} \cos \alpha & \cos \beta & \cos \gamma \\ \sin 2\alpha & \sin 2\beta & \sin 2\gamma \\ \cos 3\alpha & \cos 3\beta & \cos 3\gamma \end{vmatrix}.$$

Expressing the trigonometrical functions of multiple angles in terms of functions of single angles, we have

$$D = \begin{vmatrix} \cos \alpha & \cos \beta & \cos \gamma \\ 2 \sin \alpha \cos \alpha & 2 \sin \beta \cos \beta & 2 \sin \gamma \cos \gamma \\ 4 \cos^3 \alpha - 3 \cos \alpha & 4 \cos^3 \beta - 3 \cos \beta & 4 \cos^3 \gamma - 3 \cos \gamma \end{vmatrix}$$

$$= \cos \alpha \cos \beta \cos \gamma \begin{vmatrix} 1 & 1 & 1 \\ 2 \sin \alpha & 2 \sin \beta & 2 \sin \gamma \\ 4 \cos^2 \alpha - 3 & 4 \cos^2 \beta - 3 & 4 \cos^2 \gamma - 3 \end{vmatrix}$$

$$= \cos \alpha \cos \beta \cos \gamma \begin{vmatrix} 1 & 1 & 1 \\ 2 \sin \alpha & 2 \sin \beta & 2 \sin \gamma \\ 1 - 4 \sin^2 \alpha & 1 - 4 \sin^2 \beta & 1 - 4 \sin^2 \gamma \end{vmatrix}$$

$$= -8 \cos \alpha \cos \beta \cos \gamma \begin{vmatrix} 1 & 1 & 1 \\ \sin \alpha & \sin \beta & \sin \gamma \\ \sin^2 \alpha & \sin^2 \beta & \sin^2 \gamma \end{vmatrix} \quad (\text{row}_3 - \text{row}_1)$$

$$= -8 \cos \alpha \cos \beta \cos \gamma (\sin \beta - \sin \gamma)(\sin \gamma - \sin \alpha)(\sin \alpha - \sin \beta)$$

from example 10.

1.7 The solution of homogeneous equations

Linear equations of the form

$$a_1x + b_1y + c_1z = 0$$
$$a_2x + b_2y + c_2z = 0 \qquad (9)$$
$$a_3x + b_3y + c_3z = 0$$

are termed *homogeneous* equations, since no constants exist in them apart from the nine coefficients of x, y and z. The solution $x = y = z = 0$ is trivial, so we investigate conditions under which solutions exist for which x, y and z are not all zero. If $z = 1$, we have a similar problem concerning the *consistency* of three equations in two unknowns x and y:

$$a_1x + b_1y + c_1 = 0$$
$$a_2x + b_2y + c_2 = 0 \qquad (10)$$
$$a_3x + b_3y + c_3 = 0$$

To find the condition, we solve the first two equations of the set (9) for the ratios $x:y:z$, and then substitute into the third equation to ascertain if it is satisfied. We have

$$\frac{x}{\begin{vmatrix} b_1 & c_1 \\ b_2 & c_2 \end{vmatrix}} = \frac{-y}{\begin{vmatrix} a_1 & c_1 \\ a_2 & c_2 \end{vmatrix}} = \frac{z}{\begin{vmatrix} a_1 & b_1 \\ a_2 & b_2 \end{vmatrix}}$$

from equation (4), section 1.1. Placing this ratio equal to λ, we have

$$x = \lambda \begin{vmatrix} b_1 & c_1 \\ b_2 & c_2 \end{vmatrix}, \quad y = -\lambda \begin{vmatrix} a_1 & c_1 \\ a_2 & c_2 \end{vmatrix}, \quad z = \lambda \begin{vmatrix} a_1 & b_1 \\ a_2 & b_2 \end{vmatrix}.$$

Finally, the value of the left hand side of the third equation is

$$a_3x + b_3y + c_3z = \lambda a_3 \begin{vmatrix} b_1 & c_1 \\ b_2 & c_2 \end{vmatrix} - \lambda b_3 \begin{vmatrix} a_1 & c_1 \\ a_2 & c_2 \end{vmatrix} + \lambda c_3 \begin{vmatrix} a_1 & b_1 \\ a_2 & b_2 \end{vmatrix}$$

$$= \lambda \begin{vmatrix} a_1 & b_1 & c_1 \\ a_2 & b_2 & c_2 \\ a_3 & b_3 & c_3 \end{vmatrix}$$

where this determinant is expanded along its third row. Placing this left hand side equal to zero, we obtain the condition for non-zero solutions, namely

$$\begin{vmatrix} a_1 & b_1 & c_1 \\ a_2 & b_2 & c_2 \\ a_3 & b_3 & c_3 \end{vmatrix} = 0. \tag{11}$$

Under these circumstances, the ratios $x:y:z$ may be obtained from the cofactors using *any* two rows of set (9), provided the two rows are not merely proportional.

Stated otherwise, equation (11) is the result produced when x, y and z are eliminated from the set (9). Similarly, if $z = 1$, the same condition (11) is necessary for the set (10) to be consistent.

Example 16 Test the set of equations

$$3x + 5y - 2z = 0$$
$$2x - 4y + 5z = 0$$
$$x - 13y + 12z = 0$$

to find whether non-zero solutions exist, and if so, find the ratios $x:y:z$.

Expanded along its top row, the determinant of the coefficients has the value

$$\begin{vmatrix} 3 & 5 & -2 \\ 2 & -4 & 5 \\ 1 & -13 & 12 \end{vmatrix} = 3(-48 + 65) - 5(24 - 5) - 2(-26 + 4) = 0.$$

Hence the equations possess non-zero solutions. These may be found by solving any two equations of the set; choosing the first two equations, we obtain

$$\frac{x}{\begin{vmatrix} 5 & -2 \\ -4 & 5 \end{vmatrix}} = \frac{-y}{\begin{vmatrix} 3 & -2 \\ 2 & 5 \end{vmatrix}} = \frac{z}{\begin{vmatrix} 3 & 5 \\ 2 & -4 \end{vmatrix}},$$

or

$$x:y:z = 17:-19:-22.$$

Example 17 Find the condition for the equations

$$(b + c)x - ay - a = 0$$
$$-bx + (c + a)y - b = 0$$
$$-cx - cy + (a + b) = 0$$

to be consistent. When this is so, show that the equations have infinitely many common solutions.

The required condition is

$$\begin{vmatrix} b + c & -a & -a \\ -b & c + a & -b \\ -c & -c & a + b \end{vmatrix} = 0.$$

Column 1 minus column 2, and then column 2 minus column 3, demonstrate that $(a + b + c)^2$ is a factor of this determinant. Since this is symmetrical of degree 3, the remaining factor must also be $(a + b + c)$. It follows that $a + b + c = 0$. The three equations then become

$$-a(x + y + 1) = 0$$
$$-b(x + y + 1) = 0$$
$$-c(x + y + 1) = 0.$$

Evidently every point on the line $x + y = -1$ satisfies the given equations, so an infinite number of common solutions exist.

Condition (11) leads to various applications.

Application i. Dependent linear expressions. The three linear expressions

$$a_1x + b_1y + c_1z$$
$$a_2x + b_2y + c_2z \tag{12}$$
$$a_3x + b_3y + c_3z$$

are given. If three constants l, m and n, not all zero, exist such that l times the first expression plus m times the second plus n times the third vanishes identically we say that the three expressions are *linearly dependent*. This merely means that each of the three expressions is a linear combination of the other two. We require

$$l(a_1x + b_1y + c_1z) + m(a_2x + b_2y + c_2z) + n(a_3x + b_3y + c_3z) \equiv 0$$

for all values of x, y and z. In other words,

$$a_1l + a_2m + a_3n = 0$$
$$b_1l + b_2m + b_3n = 0$$
$$c_1l + c_2m + c_3n = 0,$$

these being the coefficients of x, y and z respectively. The condition that a non-trivial set of ratios $l:m:n$ should exist is

$$\begin{vmatrix} a_1 & a_2 & a_3 \\ b_1 & b_2 & b_3 \\ c_1 & c_2 & c_3 \end{vmatrix} = 0.$$

This condition is the same as demanding that the determinant of the coefficients occurring in set (12) should vanish.

If this determinant does not vanish, the three linear forms (12) are said to be *linearly independent*.

Application ii. Characteristic roots and vectors. In certain theoretical investigations, the three linear expressions (12) arise, and it is required to find special values of x, y and z such that, if possible, the three expressions should be respectively proportional to x, y and z, with the same constant of proportionality for each expression, namely

$$a_1x + b_1y + c_1z = \lambda x$$
$$a_2x + b_2y + c_2z = \lambda y$$
$$a_3x + b_3y + c_3z = \lambda z.$$

These are three homogeneous equations, and may be rewritten thus:

$$(a_1 - \lambda)x + b_1y + c_1z = 0$$
$$a_2x + (b_2 - \lambda)y + c_2z = 0 \qquad (13)$$
$$a_3x + b_3y + (c_3 - \lambda)z = 0.$$

The condition for non-trivial solutions is

$$\begin{vmatrix} a_1 - \lambda & b_1 & c_1 \\ a_2 & b_2 - \lambda & c_2 \\ a_3 & b_3 & c_3 - \lambda \end{vmatrix} = 0.$$

Expanded, this is a cubic equation in λ, possessing three solutions. Each of these three values, when substituted in turn into equations (13), provides a set of ratios $x:y:z$.

The values of λ are called the *characteristic roots*, while the corresponding ratios $x:y:z$ are called the *characteristic vectors*.

Example 18 Find the characteristic roots and vectors of the three linear expressions

$$3x - 2y + 4z$$
$$-2x - 2y + 6z$$
$$4x + 6y - z.$$

Placing these equal to λx, λy and λz respectively, we have the three equations

$$(3 - \lambda)x - 2y + 4z = 0$$
$$-2x + (-2 - \lambda)y + 6z = 0 \qquad (14)$$
$$4x + 6y + (-1 - \lambda)z = 0.$$

The equation for λ is given by the determinant

$$\begin{vmatrix} 3 - \lambda & -2 & 4 \\ -2 & -2 - \lambda & 6 \\ 4 & 6 & -1 - \lambda \end{vmatrix} = 0.$$

Expanding this determinant, we obtain the cubic equation

$$-\lambda^3 + 63\lambda - 162 = 0,$$

or

$$(\lambda - 3)(\lambda - 6)(\lambda + 9) = 0,$$

possessing the roots 3, 6, -9.

When $\lambda = 3$, equations (14) become

$$-2y + 4z = 0$$
$$-2x - 5y + 6z = 0$$
$$4x + 6y - 4z = 0.$$

The ratios $x:y:z$ may be found from any two of these equations; the first two give

$$\frac{x}{\begin{vmatrix} -2 & 4 \\ -5 & 6 \end{vmatrix}} = \frac{-y}{\begin{vmatrix} 0 & 4 \\ -2 & 6 \end{vmatrix}} = \frac{z}{\begin{vmatrix} 0 & -2 \\ -2 & -5 \end{vmatrix}},$$

or $x:y:z = 8:-8:-4.$

These ratios may be simplified to

$$x:y:z = 2:-2:-1.$$

Similarly, when $\lambda = 6$, $x:y:z = 2:1:2$, and when $\lambda = -9$, $x:y:z = 1:2:-2$.

1.8   The solution of inhomogeneous equations

Three linear equations in the three unknowns x, y and z are given:

$$a_1 x + b_1 y + c_1 z + d_1 = 0$$
$$a_2 x + b_2 y + c_2 z + d_2 = 0$$
$$a_3 x + b_3 y + c_3 z + d_3 = 0.$$

The solution of these equations is readily obtained by the use of the theory of determinants, but the reader is warned that arithmetically this may not be the simplest method of solving the equations, since four third order determinants must be evaluated. It may be simpler merely to use elementary algebraical methods of elimination.

To find x, we rearrange the equations thus:

$$(a_1 x + d_1) + b_1 y + c_1 z = 0$$
$$(a_2 x + d_2) + b_2 y + c_2 z = 0$$
$$(a_3 x + d_3) + b_3 y + c_3 z = 0.$$

The results of section 1.7 enable us to eliminate y and z, obtaining

$$\begin{vmatrix} a_1 x + d_1 & b_1 & c_1 \\ a_2 x + d_2 & b_2 & c_2 \\ a_3 x + d_3 & b_3 & c_3 \end{vmatrix} = 0$$

or

$$x \begin{vmatrix} a_1 & b_1 & c_1 \\ a_2 & b_2 & c_2 \\ a_3 & b_3 & c_3 \end{vmatrix} + \begin{vmatrix} d_1 & b_1 & c_1 \\ d_2 & b_2 & c_2 \\ d_3 & b_3 & c_3 \end{vmatrix} = 0.$$

Rearranging the second determinant so the letters in the rows are in alphabetical order, we may write the solution for x in the form

$$\frac{x}{\begin{vmatrix} b_1 & c_1 & d_1 \\ b_2 & c_2 & d_2 \\ b_3 & c_3 & d_3 \end{vmatrix}} = \frac{-1}{\begin{vmatrix} a_1 & b_1 & c_1 \\ a_2 & b_2 & c_2 \\ a_3 & b_3 & c_3 \end{vmatrix}}.$$

Similarly, y and z may be found, yielding finally

$$\frac{x}{\begin{vmatrix} b_1 & c_1 & d_1 \\ b_2 & c_2 & d_2 \\ b_3 & c_3 & d_3 \end{vmatrix}} = \frac{-y}{\begin{vmatrix} a_1 & c_1 & d_1 \\ a_2 & c_2 & d_2 \\ a_3 & c_3 & d_3 \end{vmatrix}} = \frac{z}{\begin{vmatrix} a_1 & b_1 & d_1 \\ a_2 & b_2 & d_2 \\ a_3 & b_3 & d_3 \end{vmatrix}} = \frac{-1}{\begin{vmatrix} a_1 & b_1 & c_1 \\ a_2 & b_2 & c_2 \\ a_3 & b_3 & c_3 \end{vmatrix}}. \quad (15)$$

If the fourth determinant does not vanish, a unique solution exists. If the last determinant does vanish, but at least one of the first three determinants does not vanish, no finite solution exists; the three given equations are inconsistent. If all four determinants vanish, the three given equations are linearly dependent; the third equation, for example, is merely a linear combination of the first two. No unique solution exists in this case; any two of the equations should then be arranged in their simplest possible form.

Example 19   Solve the equations

$$x + y + pz - q = 0$$
$$-3x + y + 2z + 1 = 0$$
$$6x + 2y + z - 4 = 0$$

for three cases (*i*) $p = 2, q = 1$; (*ii*) $p = 1, q = 2$; (*iii*) $p = 1, q = 1$.
   First, we must test the determinant of the coefficients of x, y and z:

$$\begin{vmatrix} 1 & 1 & p \\ -3 & 1 & 2 \\ 6 & 2 & 1 \end{vmatrix} = 12 - 12p.$$

Case i. When $p = 2$, this determinant does not vanish, so a unique solution exists. This is

$$\frac{x}{\begin{vmatrix} 1 & 2 & -1 \\ 1 & 2 & 1 \\ 2 & 1 & -4 \end{vmatrix}} = \frac{-y}{\begin{vmatrix} 1 & 2 & -1 \\ -3 & 2 & 1 \\ 6 & 1 & -4 \end{vmatrix}} = \frac{z}{\begin{vmatrix} 1 & 1 & -1 \\ -3 & 1 & 1 \\ 6 & 2 & -4 \end{vmatrix}} = \frac{-1}{\begin{vmatrix} 1 & 1 & 2 \\ -3 & 1 & 2 \\ 6 & 2 & 1 \end{vmatrix}},$$

or, upon expansion $x/6 = y/6 = z/0 = 1/12,$

so $x = \tfrac{1}{2}, \quad y = \tfrac{1}{2}, \quad z = 0.$

Case ii. The determinant of the coefficients vanishes, so no unique solution can exist. It may be checked that the three determinants in the denominators of x, y and z have the values 9, 9 and 12 respectively, so no finite solution exists. The three equations are in fact inconsistent, for 3 times the first equation minus the second equation yields

$$6x + 2y + z - 7 = 0,$$

clearly inconsistent with the third equation.

Case iii. Both the determinant of the coefficients and the other three determinants now vanish, so the three equations are linearly dependent. In fact, 3 times the first equation minus the second yields the third equation, so all the available information is contained in, say, the first two equations only. To simplify these, we may solve for x and y in terms of z, to obtain

$$\frac{x}{\begin{vmatrix} 1 & z-1 \\ 1 & 2z+1 \end{vmatrix}} = \frac{-y}{\begin{vmatrix} 1 & z-1 \\ -3 & 2z+1 \end{vmatrix}} = \frac{1}{\begin{vmatrix} 1 & 1 \\ -3 & 1 \end{vmatrix}},$$

or

$$x = \tfrac{1}{4}(2+z), \quad y = \tfrac{1}{4}(2-5z).$$

Expressed parametrically in terms of t, let $z = 4t$, then

$$x = t + \tfrac{1}{2}, \quad y = -5t + \tfrac{1}{2}, \quad z = 4t.$$

EXERCISES

(1). Evaluate the determinants

(i) $\begin{vmatrix} 15 & 19 \\ 13 & 16 \end{vmatrix}$,　　(ii) $\begin{vmatrix} 21 & -16 \\ -17 & 12 \end{vmatrix}$,　　(iii) $\begin{vmatrix} -99 & 97 \\ -97 & 95 \end{vmatrix}$,

(iv)$\star$ $\begin{vmatrix} 76 & -23 & 53 \\ 103 & 199 & 302 \\ 176 & 177 & 353 \end{vmatrix}$,　　(v)$\star$ $\begin{vmatrix} 3 & 5 & 7 & 9 \\ -1 & 2 & -3 & 4 \\ 9 & -7 & 5 & -3 \\ 4 & 3 & 2 & 1 \end{vmatrix}$.

(2). Evaluate the determinants

$$D = \begin{vmatrix} 1 & 3 & 2 \\ 2 & 1 & 3 \\ 3 & 2 & 1 \end{vmatrix}, \quad E = \begin{vmatrix} 2 & 1 & 5 \\ 1 & 3 & -2 \\ 5 & -2 & 4 \end{vmatrix}.$$

Replace each element in D by its cofactor, and show that the value of the new determinant is D^2. Do the same thing for E.

(3). (i) Prove $\begin{vmatrix} 2\cos\theta & 1 & 0 \\ 1 & 2\cos\theta & 1 \\ 0 & 1 & 2\cos\theta \end{vmatrix} = \dfrac{\sin 4\theta}{\sin \theta}$.

(ii) Eliminate x, y and z from the three equations

$$p = (y+z)/x, \quad q = (z+x)/y, \quad r = (x+y)/z.$$

(4). Solve the determinantal equations:

(i)★
$$\begin{vmatrix} x & -3 & 2 \\ 2 & x & -3 \\ -3 & 2 & x \end{vmatrix} = 0,$$

(ii)★
$$\begin{vmatrix} x+1 & 2x & 1 \\ x & 3x-2 & 2x \\ 1 & x & x \end{vmatrix} = 0,$$

(iii)★
$$\begin{vmatrix} a-x & b-x & c \\ a-x & c & b-x \\ a & b-x & c-x \end{vmatrix} = 0,$$

(iv)★
$$\begin{vmatrix} x & 2 & 3 \\ 2 & x+3 & 6 \\ 3 & 4 & x+6 \end{vmatrix} = 0,$$

(v)
$$\begin{vmatrix} 6-5d & -2+d & 4-4d \\ -2+d & 2-d & 0 \\ 4-4d & 0 & 3-5d \end{vmatrix} = 0,$$

(vi)★
$$\begin{vmatrix} x+1 & \omega & \omega^2 \\ \omega & x+\omega^2 & 1 \\ \omega^2 & 1 & x+\omega \end{vmatrix} = 0$$

where ω is a cube root of unity, considering the two cases (a) ω real, (b) ω complex.

(5). Using determinants, solve the equations
   (i) $x + y + z = 2, x + 2y + 3z = 6, 3x + 2y - z = -4.$
   (ii) $3x - 2y + z = -4, 2x + 4y - 7z = 44, x + 3y - 2z = 19.$
   (iii)★ $4x + 3y + 5z = 11, 9x + 4y + 15z = 13, 12x + 10y - 3z = 4.$
   (iv)★ $5x + 4y + 2z = 16, 7x - 8y + 3z = -45, x + 6y - 4z = 16.$

(6). (i) Solve the given equations when (i) $a = 1, b = 0$; (ii) $a = b = 1$; (iii) $a = 0, b = 1$:

$$x + y + x + b = 0, \quad 3x + 2y + z = 0, \quad 2x + y + az - 1 = 0.$$

(ii)★ Find the condition for the equations

$$(a - b - c)x + 2ay + 2a = 2bx + (b - c - a)y + 2b$$
$$= 2cx + 2cy + (c - a - b) = 0$$

to have a common solution, and show that when this condition is satisfied the equations have infinitely many common solutions.

(7). Find the characteristic roots and vectors of the following sets of three linear expressions:
   (i)★ $x + 2y + z, \quad 2x + y + z, \quad x + y + 2z.$
   (ii)★ $y + \sqrt{2}z, \quad x + \sqrt{2}z, \quad \sqrt{2}x + \sqrt{2}y - 2z.$
   (iii) $5x - y - z, \quad x + 3y + z, \quad -2x + 2y + 4z.$

(8). Factorize the following determinants

(i)★
$$\begin{vmatrix} a & b & c \\ a^2 & b^2 & c^2 \\ a^4 & b^4 & c^4 \end{vmatrix},$$

(ii)★
$$\begin{vmatrix} x^3 & y^3 & z^3 \\ yz & zx & xy \\ 1 & 1 & 1 \end{vmatrix},$$

(iii)
$$\begin{vmatrix} 1 & b+c & b^2+c^2 \\ 1 & c+a & c^2+a^2 \\ 1 & a+b & a^2+b^2 \end{vmatrix},$$

(iv)
$$\begin{vmatrix} 1 & b+c & (b+c)^2 \\ 1 & c+a & (c+a)^2 \\ 1 & a+b & (a+b)^2 \end{vmatrix},$$

(v)★ $\begin{vmatrix} 1 & 1 & 1 \\ a^2 & b^2 & c^2 \\ (b+c)^2 & (c+a)^2 & (a+b)^2 \end{vmatrix}$, (vi)★ $\begin{vmatrix} (a-x)^2 & (a-y)^2 & (a-z)^2 \\ (b-x)^2 & (b-y)^2 & (b-z)^2 \\ (c-x)^2 & (c-y)^2 & (c-z)^2 \end{vmatrix}$,

(vii)★ $\begin{vmatrix} b^2c^2 + a^2d^2 & bc+ad & 1 \\ c^2a^2 + b^2d^2 & ca+bd & 1 \\ a^2b^2 + c^2d^2 & ab+cd & 1 \end{vmatrix}$, (viii)★ $\begin{vmatrix} 1 & a+bc & a^2 + b^2c^2 \\ 1 & b+ca & b^2 + c^2a^2 \\ 1 & c+ab & c^2 + a^2b^2 \end{vmatrix}$,

(ix)★ $\begin{vmatrix} x+y+nz & (n-1)x & (n-1)y \\ (n-1)z & y+z+nx & (n-1)y \\ (n-1)z & (n-1)x & z+x+ny \end{vmatrix}$, (x)★ $\begin{vmatrix} a^3 & a^2 & a & 1 \\ 3a^2 & 2a & 1 & 0 \\ b^3 & b^2 & b & 1 \\ 3b^2 & 2b & 1 & 0 \end{vmatrix}$.

(9). Show that the adjoined expression is a factor of the respective determinant, and hence factorize completely each determinant:

(i)★ $\begin{vmatrix} a & b-c & c+b \\ a+c & b & c-a \\ a-b & b+a & c \end{vmatrix}$, $(a+b+c)$;

(ii)★ $\begin{vmatrix} (y+z)^2 & x^2 & x^2 \\ y^2 & (z+x)^2 & y^2 \\ z^2 & z^2 & (x+y)^2 \end{vmatrix}$, $x, (x+y+z)$;

(iii)★ $\begin{vmatrix} x & 2y-z & -z \\ y & 2x-z & -z \\ y & 2y-z & x-y-z \end{vmatrix}$, $(x-y)^2$;

(iv)★ $\begin{vmatrix} y+z & -y & 2z \\ -x & z+x & -z \\ 2x & 2y & x+y \end{vmatrix}$, $(x+y+z)$;

(v) also prove that

$$\begin{vmatrix} 0 & a & b & c \\ -a & 0 & d & e \\ -b & -d & 0 & f \\ -c & -e & -f & 0 \end{vmatrix} = (af - be + cd)^2.$$

(10)★. Prove that

$$\begin{vmatrix} 3 & 3x & 3x^2 + 2a^2 \\ 3x & 3x^2 + 2a^2 & 3x^3 + 6a^2x \\ 3x^2 + 2a^2 & 3x^3 + 6a^2x & 3x^4 + 12a^2x^2 + 2a^4 \end{vmatrix}$$

is independent of x.

(11). (i)⋆ Find all the values of x in the range 0 to $\frac{1}{2}\pi$ for which

$$\begin{vmatrix} \cos^2 2x & \cos^2 4x & \cos^2 6x \\ \sin 2x & \sin 4x & \sin 6x \\ 1 & 1 & 1 \end{vmatrix} = 0.$$

(ii)⋆ Express the determinant

$$D = \begin{vmatrix} \cos^2 \alpha & \cos \alpha \sin \alpha & \sin^2 \alpha \\ \cos^2 \beta & \cos \beta \sin \beta & \sin^2 \beta \\ \cos^2 \gamma & \cos \gamma \sin \gamma & \sin^2 \gamma \end{vmatrix}$$

as a product of sines, and show that if $D = 0$ the determinant must have two equal rows.

(iii)⋆ Prove that the following determinant is independent of x:

$$\begin{vmatrix} \cos (x + \alpha) & \sin (x + \alpha) & 1 \\ \cos (x + \beta) & \sin (x + \beta) & 1 \\ \cos (x + \gamma) & \sin (x + \gamma) & 1 \end{vmatrix}.$$

ANSWERS TO EXERCISES

(1).   (i) -7.   (ii) -20.   (iii) 4.   (iv) 0.   (v) 1936.

(2).   (i) $D = 18, E = -83$.

(3).   (ii) $pqr - p - q - r - 2 = 0$.

(4).   (i) 1, $\frac{1}{2}(-1 \pm 5\sqrt{5}i)$.   (ii) 1, 1, 2.   (iii) 0, $b - c$, $\frac{1}{2}(a + b + c)$.
      (iv) 1, $-5 \pm \sqrt{34}$.   (v) 1, 2, -1.   (vi) (a) $-3, 0, 0$;   (b) 0, 0, 0.

(5).   (i) $x = 1, y = -2, z = 3$.   (ii) $x = 2, y = 3, z = -4$.
      (iii) $x = -5, y = 7, z = 2$.   (iv) $x = -2, y = 5, z = 3$.

(6).   (i) $x = 1, y = -2, z = 1$;   no solution; $x = t, y = 1 - 2t, z = t - 2$
      (ii) $a + b + c = 0$.

(7).   (i) 1, -1, 4; $x:y:z = 1:1:-2, 1:-1:0, 1:1:1$.
      (ii) -1, 2, -3; $x:y:z = 1:-1:0, \sqrt{2}:\sqrt{2}:1, 1:1:-2\sqrt{2}$.
      (iii) 2, 4, 6; $x:y:z = 0:1:-1, 1:1:0, 1:0:-1$.

(8).   (i) $abc(b - c)(c - a)(a - b)(a + b + c)$.
      (ii) $(y - z)(z - x)(x - y)(x^2 + y^2 + z^2 + yz + zx + xy)$.
      (iii) $(b - c)(c - a)(a - b)$.   (iv) $-(b - c)(c - a)(a - b)$.
      (v) $2(b - c)(c - a)(a - b)(a + b + c)$.
      (vi) $2(b - c)(c - a)(a - b)(y - z)(z - x)(x - y)$.
      (vii) $(b - c)(c - a)(a - b)(a - d)(b - d)(c - d)$.
      (viii) $(b - c)(c - a)(a - b)(1 - a)(1 - b)(1 - c)$.
      (ix) $n(x + y + z)^3$.   (x) $(a - b)^4$.

(9).   (i) $(a + b + c)(a^2 + b^2 + c^2)$.   (ii) $2xyz(x + y + z)^3$.
      (iii) $(x - y)^2(2x + 2y - 3z)$.   (iv) $3z(y - z)(x + y + z)$.

(11).   (i) 0, $\pi/2$, $\pi/6$, $\pi/8$, $3\pi/8$, $\pi/10$, $3\pi/10$.
      (ii) $\sin (\beta - \alpha) \sin (\alpha - \gamma) \sin (\gamma - \beta)$.

CHAPTER 2

THE THEORY OF EQUATIONS

2.1 Polynomials

A *polynomial* of degree n in the variable x is a linear combination of the $n + 1$ terms $1, x, x^2, x^3, \ldots, x^{n-1}, x^n$. If we denote the constants by $a_0, a_1, a_2, \ldots, a_{n-1}, a_n$, and the polynomial by $f_n(x)$, we may write

$$f_n(x) \equiv a_0 + a_1 x + a_2 x^2 + a_3 x^3 + \ldots + a_{n-1} x^{n-1} + a_n x^n,$$

where it is understood that a_n does not vanish.

If a polynomial $f_n(x)$ is divided by a linear factor $(x - \alpha)$, the quotient is a polynomial of degree $n - 1$, and the remainder is a constant independent of x. If $q_{n-1}(x)$ is the quotient and r the remainder, we may write

$$f_n(x) \equiv (x - \alpha)q_{n-1}(x) + r.$$

This is an *identity* in x; that is to say, if the right hand side is expanded, exactly the same terms are produced as appear on the left hand side. Any value of x may be inserted into the identity, always preserving the equality.

If we place x equal to α, we obtain

$$f_n(\alpha) = r.$$

This result is known as the remainder theorem; it yields the remainder when $f_n(x)$ is divided by $(x - \alpha)$ without the necessity of explicit long division. In particular, if $f_n(\alpha) = 0$, the remainder vanishes, in which case $(x - \alpha)$ is a factor of the given polynomial.

Example 1 Let the polynomial

$$f(x) \equiv x^4 + x^3 - 5x^2 - x - 2$$

be a given polynomial of degree 4. When divided by $(x - 3)$, the remainder is given by $f(3) = 58$. On the other hand, if $x = 2$, we find $f(2) = 0$, showing that $(x - 2)$ is a factor. Long division then yields the remaining cubic factor

$$f(x) \equiv (x - 2)(x^3 + 3x^2 + x + 1).$$

The remainder theorem may be generalized to embrace quadratic divisors. If $f_n(x)$ is divided by $(x - \alpha)(x - \beta)$, where $\alpha \neq \beta$, the quotient $q_{n-2}(x)$ will be a polynomial of degree $n - 2$, while the remainder must now be a linear expression in x, say $rx + s$. This gives the identity

$$f_n(x) \equiv (x - \alpha)(x - \beta)q_{n-2}(x) + rx + s.$$

25

We place x equal to α and β in turn, giving

$$f_n(\alpha) = r\alpha + s,$$
$$f_n(\beta) = r\beta + s.$$

The solution of these equations for r and s is

$$r = \frac{f_n(\alpha) - f_n(\beta)}{\alpha - \beta}, \quad s = \frac{\alpha f_n(\beta) - \beta f_n(\alpha)}{\alpha - \beta}.$$

The remainder then takes the form

$$rx + s = \frac{[f_n(\alpha) - f_n(\beta)]x + \alpha f_n(\beta) - \beta f_n(\alpha)}{\alpha - \beta}. \tag{1}$$

If $\alpha = \beta$ this result breaks down; we require a modified method to find the remainder when the divisor is $(x - \alpha)^2$. The remainder being again of the form $rx + s$, we have

$$f_n(x) \equiv (x - \alpha)^2 q_{n-2}(x) + rx + s.$$

Differentiating this identity with respect to x, we obtain

$$f_n'(x) \equiv 2(x - \alpha)q_{n-2}(x) + (x - \alpha)^2 q_{n-2}'(x) + r,$$

where the prime $(')$ denotes differentiation with respect to x. We may now place x equal to α in these two identities to obtain

$$f_n(\alpha) = r\alpha + s,$$
$$f_n'(\alpha) = r,$$

so

$$s = f_n(\alpha) - \alpha f_n'(\alpha).$$

The remainder finally takes the form

$$rx + s = x f_n'(\alpha) + f_n(\alpha) - \alpha f_n'(\alpha). \tag{2}$$

Example 2　Find the remainder when the polynomial

$$f(x) \equiv x^5 + x^4 + x^3 + x^2 + x + 1$$

is divided (i) by $(x - 1)(x + 2)$, (ii) by $(x + 2)^2$.

Case i. When $\alpha = 1$, $f(1) = 6$, and when $\beta = -2$, $f(-2) = -21$. Substitution into formula (1) yields

$$rx + s = 9x - 3.$$

Case ii. We have $f(-2) = -21$, and

$$f'(x) = 5x^4 + 4x^3 + 3x^2 + 2x + 1,$$

so $f'(-2) = 57$. From formula (2), the remainder is

$$rx + s = 57x + 93.$$

2.2 The general polynomial equation

The general polynomial of degree n, when equated to zero, provides an equation of the nth degree in x:

$$a_0 + a_1 x + a_2 x^2 + \ldots + a_n x^n = 0. \tag{3}$$

Any value of x satisfying this equation is called a *root* of the equation. If α is a root then $(x - \alpha)$ is a factor of the polynomial. The general theory of the roots of such equations requires the use of *complex numbers*. Only in the language of complex numbers is it possible to prove what is known as the *fundamental theorem of algebra*, namely that a polynomial of the nth degree can be resolved into n linear factors, this being equivalent to the statement that such a polynomial equation of the nth degree has n roots, some perhaps repeated in various groups.

In this section, we shall assume that equation (3) has n roots, designated by the symbols $\alpha_1, \alpha_2, \ldots, \alpha_n$. We shall later consider methods by which these roots may be calculated in simple cases.

Let us rearrange equation (3) so that the coefficient of x^n is unity:

$$x^n + c_1 x^{n-1} + c_2 x^{n-2} + \ldots + c_{n-1} x + c_n = 0. \tag{4}$$

In terms of the n roots $\alpha_1, \alpha_2, \ldots, \alpha_n$, this left hand side may be factorized into n linear factors:

$$(x - \alpha_1)(x - \alpha_2) \ldots (x - \alpha_n) = 0.$$

Clearly the left hand sides of these two equations are equal and identical and not merely proportional, since the coefficient of x^n is unity in each case. A little consideration on the part of the reader will show that these n factors may be multiplied together, yielding the polynomial

$$x^n - x^{n-1} \sum \alpha_1 + x^{n-2} \sum \alpha_1 \alpha_2 - x^{n-3} \sum \alpha_1 \alpha_2 \alpha_3 + \ldots$$
$$+ (-1)^n \alpha_1 \alpha_2 \ldots \alpha_n, \tag{5}$$

where $\sum \alpha_1$ denotes the sum of the n roots, $\sum \alpha_1 \alpha_2$ denotes the sum of all the $_nC_2$ products formed from the roots by taking every combination of two, $\sum \alpha_1 \alpha_2 \alpha_3$ denotes the sum of all the $_nC_3$ products formed from the roots by taking every combination of three, and so on. These n sums are known as the *elementary symmetrical functions* of the roots.

Equating coefficients of respective powers of x in expressions (4) and (5), we obtain the n relations between the roots of equation (4) and the coefficients:

$$\sum \alpha_1 = -c_1$$
$$\sum \alpha_1 \alpha_2 = +c_2$$
$$\sum \alpha_1 \alpha_2 \alpha_3 = -c_3 \tag{6}$$
$$\cdots \cdots \cdots \cdots \cdots$$
$$\alpha_1 \alpha_2 \ldots \alpha_n = (-1)^n c_n.$$

For the quadratic equation $x^2 + ax + b = 0$, we have

$$\alpha_1 + \alpha_2 = -a, \qquad \alpha_1\alpha_2 = b. \tag{7}$$

For the cubic equation $x^3 + ax^2 + bx + c = 0$, we have

$$\alpha_1 + \alpha_2 + \alpha_3 = -a, \quad \alpha_2\alpha_3 + \alpha_3\alpha_1 + \alpha_1\alpha_2 = b, \quad \alpha_1\alpha_2\alpha_3 = -c. \tag{8}$$

For the quartic equation $x^4 + ax^3 + bx^2 + cx + d = 0$, we have

$$\alpha_1 + \alpha_2 + \alpha_3 + \alpha_4 = -a,$$

$$\alpha_1\alpha_2 + \alpha_1\alpha_3 + \alpha_1\alpha_4 + \alpha_2\alpha_3 + \alpha_3\alpha_4 + \alpha_4\alpha_2 = b, \tag{9}$$

$$\alpha_2\alpha_3\alpha_4 + \alpha_1\alpha_3\alpha_4 + \alpha_1\alpha_2\alpha_4 + \alpha_1\alpha_2\alpha_3 = -c,$$

$$\alpha_1\alpha_2\alpha_3\alpha_4 = d.$$

We shall use these fundamental relations throughout the chapter.

2.3 Sums of powers of roots

Let us designate by $S_0, S_1, S_2, S_3, \ldots$ the sums of the n roots of equation (4) when raised respectively to the powers $0, 1, 2, 3, \ldots$. For example,

$$S_3 = \alpha_1{}^3 + \alpha_2{}^3 + \ldots + \alpha_n{}^3.$$

We shall provide a method whereby these sums may systematically be calculated, illustrating the method for the cubic equation

$$x^3 + ax^2 + bx + c = 0 \tag{10}$$

with roots α, β and γ.

S_0 obviously has the value 3, while S_1 has the value $-a$. To find S_2 we use the identity

$$(\alpha + \beta + \gamma)^2 = (\alpha^2 + \beta^2 + \gamma^2) + 2(\beta\gamma + \gamma\alpha + \alpha\beta),$$

giving $\qquad\qquad S_2 = a^2 - 2b,$

from equations (8).

To find S_3, we do *not* use further identities; rather we substitute the three roots into the cubic in turn, and add the three equations thus obtained, yielding

$$S_3 + aS_2 + bS_1 + cS_0 = 0.$$

Substituting the values for S_0, S_1 and S_2, we find that

$$S_3 = -a^3 + 3ab - 3c.$$

To find S_4, we first multiply the cubic equation (10) by x, and again substitute the three roots and add, obtaining

$$S_4 + aS_3 + bS_2 + cS_1 = 0.$$

Substituting the values of S_1, S_2, S_3 previously found, we obtain

$$S_4 = a^4 - 4a^2b + 2b^2 + 4ac.$$

Sums of higher powers may be found systematically by extending this method and substituting the sums of lower powers already found.

Example 3 If α, β, γ, δ are four numbers whose sum is zero, prove that

$$6(\alpha^5 + \beta^5 + \gamma^5 + \delta^5) = 5(\alpha^2 + \beta^2 + \gamma^2 + \delta^2)(\alpha^3 + \beta^3 + \gamma^3 + \delta^3).$$

Let the quartic equation whose roots are α, β, γ, δ be

$$x^4 + ax^2 + bx + c = 0,$$

the coefficient of x^3 being equal to zero since the sum of the roots vanishes.
From the identity

$$(\textstyle\sum \alpha)^2 = \sum \alpha^2 + 2 \sum \alpha\beta$$

we obtain

$$0 = S_2 + 2a,$$

so $S_2 = -2a$. Dividing the quartic by x, substituting the four roots in turn and adding, we obtain

$$S_3 = -aS_1 - 4b - c\left(\frac{1}{\alpha} + \frac{1}{\beta} + \frac{1}{\gamma} + \frac{1}{\delta}\right)$$

$$= -4b - c\left(\frac{\beta\gamma\delta + \alpha\gamma\delta + \alpha\beta\delta + \alpha\beta\gamma}{\alpha\beta\gamma\delta}\right)$$

$$= -4b - c(-b/c) = -3b.$$

Substituting the four roots in turn into the quartic equation and adding, we obtain

$$S_4 = -aS_2 - bS_1 - 4c$$
$$= 2a^2 - 4c.$$

Finally, multiplying the quartic by x, substituting the four roots and adding, we obtain

$$S_5 = -aS_3 - bS_2 - cS_1$$
$$= 5ab.$$

Then

$$5S_2S_3 = 5 . 2a . 3b = 6S_5.$$

Example 4 Find the four numbers whose sum is 2, the sum of their squares being 30, the sum of their cubes being 44, and the sum of their fourth powers being 354.
Let the four numbers be the roots of the quartic equation

$$x^4 + ax^3 + bc^2 + cx + d = 0.$$

Proceeding as before, we find that the values of S_1, S_2, S_3 and S_4 are given by

$$S_1 = -a = 2,$$
$$S_2 = a^2 - 2b = 30,$$
$$S_3 = -a^3 + 3ab - 3c = 44,$$
$$S_4 = a^4 - 4a^2b + 4ac + 2b^2 - 4d = 354.$$

Solving these successively for a, b, c and d, we find that

$$a = -2, b = -13, c = 14, d = 24,$$

so the quartic is

$$x^4 - 2x^3 - 13x^2 + 14x + 24 = 0,$$

or

$$(x + 1)(x - 2)(x + 3)(x - 4) = 0.$$

The four numbers are therefore $-1, 2, -3, 4$.

2.4 The formation of new equations

An equation of the nth degree is given. Without solving the equation, it is required to form a second equation whose roots are given functions of the roots of the original equation. To accomplish this systematically, each root of the new equation must be capable of being expressed in terms of the same function of each root respectively of the original equation.

If the given equation is $f(x) = 0$, with roots α_1, α_2, α_3, $\ldots \alpha_n$, let new roots be defined by

$$\beta_1 = g(\alpha_1), \quad \beta_2 = g(\alpha_2), \ldots, \quad \beta_n = g(\alpha_n),$$

where g is a function symbol.

To find the new equation possessing these roots, we change the variable from x to y, using the transformation $y = g(x)$. In any given example, this may be solved for x in terms of y in the form $x = h(y)$, and substituted into the polynomial equation $f(x) = 0$. Finally, we may rearrange the resulting equation to take the form of a polynomial equation of degree n.

The simplest and possibly the most important example of this is the reduction of the roots of an equation by a given amount h. Let α_1, $\alpha_2, \ldots, \alpha_n$ be the roots of the equation

$$x^n + c_1 x^{n-1} + c_2 x^{n-2} + \ldots + c_{n-1} x + c_n = 0.$$

It is required to find the equation with the roots

$$\beta_1 = \alpha_1 - h, \quad \beta_2 = \alpha_2 - h, \ldots, \quad \beta_n = \alpha_n - h.$$

To accomplish this, we change the variable from x to y, using

$$y = x - h,$$

or

$$x = y + h.$$

The equation becomes

$$(y + h)^n + c_1(y + h)^{n-1} + c_2(y + h)^{n-2} +$$
$$\ldots + c_{n-1}(y + h) + c_n = 0,$$

which may be expanded directly term by term using the binomial theorem for a positive integral index. Finally the various terms may be collected together to yield a polynomial of degree n in y.

In particular, the coefficient of y^{n-1} arises from the binomial expansion of the first two terms; the coefficient is obviously $nh + c_1$. In particular, if we choose $h = -c_1/n$, the coefficient of y^{n-1} vanishes.

For the cubic equation

$$x^3 + ax^2 + bx + c = 0$$

if we reduce the roots by $-a/3$ by the substitution $y = x + a/3$, we obtain a cubic equation in y that has the form

$$y^3 + py + q = 0$$

possessing no term involving y^2. This is known as the *standard form* of the cubic equation.

Similarly, the quartic equation

$$x^4 + ax^3 + bx^2 + cx + d = 0$$

is reduced to standard form by the substitution $y = x + \frac{1}{4}a$, yielding

$$y^4 + py^2 + qy + r = 0.$$

Further examples of this transformation technique are given in the following examples.

Example 5 Find the standard form of the quartic equation

$$x^4 - 8x^3 + 2x^2 - 5x + 2 = 0.$$

We make the substitution $y = x + (-8)/4$; that is $x = y + 2$. The equation becomes

$$(y + 2)^4 - 8(y + 2)^3 + 2(y + 2)^2 - 5(y + 2) + 2 = 0,$$

or, upon direct expansion of these brackets

$$y^4 - 22y^2 - 61y - 48 = 0.$$

Example 6 If α, β and γ are the roots of the cubic equation

$$x^3 + px + q = 0,$$

find the corresponding *equation of squared differences*, namely that cubic equation possessing the roots $(\beta - \gamma)^2$, $(\gamma - \alpha)^2$ and $(\alpha - \beta)^2$.

Each of the new roots must be expressed in terms of one root respectively of the original equation. For example,

$$\begin{aligned}
(\beta - \gamma)^2 &= (\beta + \gamma)^2 - 4\beta\gamma \\
&= \alpha^2 - 4\alpha\beta\gamma/\alpha \\
&= \alpha^2 + 4q/\alpha \\
&= (\alpha^3 + 4q)/\alpha \\
&= (-p\alpha - q + 4q)/\alpha \quad \text{(from the given cubic)} \\
&= -p + 3q/\alpha
\end{aligned}$$

We use therefore the transformation

$$y = -p + 3q/x,$$

or
$$x = 3q/(y + p),$$

yielding
$$27q^3/(y + p)^3 + 3pq/(y + p) + q = 0.$$

Rearranging this as a cubic equation by cross multiplication, we obtain

$$y^3 + 6py^2 + 9p^2y + 4p^3 + 27q^2 = 0.$$

From this equation, we may deduce that the product of the squared differences has the value

$$(\beta - \gamma)^2(\gamma - \alpha)^2(\alpha - \beta)^2 = -4p^3 - 27q^2.$$

Example 7   Find the quartic equation whose roots are the squares of the roots of the equation

$$x^4 + ax^3 + bx^2 + cx + d = 0.$$

We make the substitution $y = x^2$, or $x = \sqrt{y}$, yielding

$$y^2 + ay\sqrt{y} + by + c\sqrt{y} + d = 0,$$

or
$$y^2 + by + d = -(ay + c)\sqrt{y}.$$

Squaring yields

$$y^4 + 2by^3 + (b^2 + 2d)y^2 + 2bdy + d^2 = y(a^2y^2 + 2acy + c^2),$$

or $$y^4 + (2b - a^2)y^3 + (b^2 + 2d - 2ac)y^2 + (2bd - c^2)y + d^2 = 0.$$

Example 8   If α, β and γ are the roots of the cubic equation

$$x^3 - x + 1 = 0,$$

find the cubic equation with the roots

$$\frac{1}{\beta^2} + \frac{1}{\gamma^2}, \quad \frac{1}{\gamma^2} + \frac{1}{\alpha^2}, \quad \frac{1}{\alpha^2} + \frac{1}{\beta^2}.$$

Noting from section 2.3 that $\Sigma \alpha^2 = 2$, we have

$$\frac{1}{\beta^2} + \frac{1}{\gamma^2} = \frac{\beta^2 + \gamma^2}{\beta^2\gamma^2} = \frac{2 - \alpha^2}{\beta^2\gamma^2} = \frac{(2 - \alpha^2)\alpha^2}{\alpha^2\beta^2\gamma^2}$$

$$= (2 - \alpha^2)\alpha^2 = 2\alpha^2 - \alpha.\alpha^3$$

$$= 2\alpha^2 - \alpha(\alpha - 1) = \alpha^2 + \alpha,$$

so we make the substitution $y = x^2 + x$.

Multiplying this substitution by x, and eliminating x^3 from the given cubic, we obtain

$$x^2 = xy + 1 - x.$$

Elimination of x^2 from this result by the substitution gives

$$xy + 1 = y,$$

or
$$x = (y - 1)/y.$$

Finally, placing this value of x in the substitution, we obtain

$$y = (y - 1)^2/y^2 + (y - 1)/y$$

simplifying to
$$y^3 - 2y^2 + 3y - 1 = 0.$$

Example 9   If α, β, γ and δ are the roots of the quartic equation

$$x^4 + ax^3 + bx^2 + cx + d = 0,$$

form the cubic equation possessing the roots

$$r = \alpha\delta + \beta\gamma, \quad s = \beta\delta + \gamma\alpha, \quad t = \gamma\delta + \alpha\beta$$

In this example, we may form the elementary symmetric functions of the new roots r, s and t in terms of the elementary symmetric functions of the given roots:

$$\sum \alpha = -a, \quad \sum \alpha\beta = b, \quad \sum \alpha\beta\gamma = -c, \quad \alpha\beta\gamma\delta = d.$$

Obviously, $$r + s + t = \sum \alpha\beta = b.$$

By direct multiplication and rearrangement, we have

$$st + tr + rs = (\sum \alpha)(\sum \alpha\beta\gamma) - 4\alpha\beta\gamma\delta$$
$$= ac - 4d.$$

Finally, regrouping the product rst yields

$$rst = \alpha\beta\gamma\delta(\alpha^2 + \beta^2 + \gamma^2 + \delta^2)$$
$$+ (\beta^2\gamma^2\delta^2 + \alpha^2\gamma^2\delta^2 + \alpha^2\beta^2\delta^2 + \alpha^2\beta^2\gamma^2)$$
$$= d(\alpha^2 + \beta^2 + \gamma^2 + \delta^2) + d^2(\alpha^{-2} + \beta^{-2} + \gamma^{-2} + \delta^{-2}).$$

The identity $$(\sum \alpha)^2 = \sum \alpha^2 + 2 \sum \alpha\beta$$

yields $$\sum \alpha^2 = a^2 - 2b.$$

Moreover, if we place $y = 1/x$, we obtain the quartic equation possessing the roots α^{-1}, β^{-1}, γ^{-1} and δ^{-1}, namely

$$y^4 + (c/d)y^3 + (b/d)y^2 + (a/d)y + (1/d) = 0,$$

from which it follows that

$$\sum \alpha^{-2} = (c/d)^2 - 2(b/d).$$

Hence $$rst = d(a^2 - 2b) + d^2[(c/d)^2 - 2(b/d)]$$
$$= da^2 + c^2 - 4bd.$$

Using these elementary symmetric functions, we may write down the cubic equation possessing the roots r, s and t, namely

$$z^3 - bz^2 + (ac - 4d)z + 4bd - da^2 - c^2 = 0.$$

2.5   Special methods for the solution of polynomial equations

The following methods may all appear to be somewhat artificial; they are seldom of value in solving a general equation. These methods depend upon a hint being supplied, which is rather unusual in practice though perhaps common under examination conditions.

Method i.   The reduction of a quartic equation to a biquadratic.   If the coefficients in the given quartic equation in x are specially chosen, the reduction of this quartic to its standard form in y may produce a reduced equation that has neither a y^3 term nor a y term occurring in it. Such an equation is called a *biquadratic*, and may be solved as a quadratic equation in y^2.

Example 10   Reduce the quartic equation

$$x^4 - 8x^3 - x^2 + 68x + 60 = 0$$

to standard form, and hence solve the equation.

We make the substitution $x = y + 2$ to eliminate the y^3 term:

$$(y + 2)^4 - 8(y + 2)^3 - (y + 2)^2 + 68(y + 2) + 60 = 0,$$

simplifying to $y^4 - 25y^2 + 144 = 0,$

or $(y^2 - 9)(y^2 - 16) = 0.$

The solutions for y are -4, -3, $+3$, $+4$, so the solutions for x given by $x = y + 2$ are -2, -1, 5, 6.

Method ii.   Reciprocal equations.   We shall illustrate this method by considering a quartic equation supposed to be such that its coefficients read the same from left to right as from right to left namely

$$ax^4 + bx^3 + cx^2 + bx + a = 0.$$

We divide this equation by x^2, and make the substitution

$$y = x + x^{-1}, \tag{11}$$

from which it follows that

$$x^2 + x^{-2} \equiv (x + x^{-1})^2 - 2 = y^2 - 2.$$

The new equation is a quadratic in y. Having found the two values for y, we may solve equation (11) for x using these two values of y in turn.

Example 11   Solve the quartic equation

$$8x^4 - 54x^3 + 101x^2 - 54x + 8 = 0.$$

This is a reciprocal equation by inspection, so it may be rearranged as follows:

$$8(x^2 + x^{-2}) - 54(x + x^{-1}) + 101 = 0,$$

or $8(y^2 - 2) - 54y + 101 = 0,$

or $8y^2 - 54y + 85 = 0,$

where $y = x + x^{-1}$. Factorizing, we obtain

$$(2y - 5)(4y - 17) = 0,$$

possessing the solutions $y = \frac{5}{2}$ and $\frac{17}{4}$.

When $y = \frac{5}{2}$, the equation for x is

$$x + x^{-1} = \frac{5}{2},$$

or $x^2 - \frac{5}{2}x + 1 = 0,$

with the solutions $x = \frac{1}{2}$ and 2.

When $y = \frac{17}{4}$, the equation for x is

$$x^2 - \tfrac{17}{4}x + 1 = 0,$$

with the solutions $x = \frac{1}{4}$ and 4.

The four solutions for x are therefore $\frac{1}{4}$, $\frac{1}{2}$, 2, 4.

Method iii. The use of the symmetric functions of the roots. The relationships between the elementary symmetric functions of the roots of an equation and its coefficients were explained in section 2.2. The use of these relationships *by themselves* is of no value in solving the equation. But if one additional piece of information is supplied concerning the roots, this together with these relationships often enable the equation to be solved.

Example 12 Solve the quartic equation

$$x^4 + 6x^3 - 37x^2 - 138x + 504 = 0,$$

given that the sum of two of its roots equals the sum of the other two roots.

If α, β, γ and δ are the four roots, the four symmetric functions are related to the coefficients by the following equations:

$$\alpha + \beta + \gamma + \delta = -6, \tag{12}$$

$$\alpha\delta + \beta\delta + \gamma\delta + \beta\gamma + \gamma\alpha + \alpha\beta = -37, \tag{13}$$

$$\beta\gamma\delta + \alpha\gamma\delta + \alpha\beta\delta + \alpha\beta\gamma = 138, \tag{14}$$

$$\alpha\beta\gamma\delta = 504. \tag{15}$$

We have the additional equation

$$\alpha + \beta = \gamma + \delta.$$

Equations (12) and (16) give immediately

$$\alpha + \beta = \gamma + \delta = -3.$$

Equation (13) may be rearranged thus:

$$\alpha\beta + \gamma\delta + (\alpha + \beta)(\gamma + \delta) = -37,$$

so
$$\alpha\beta + \gamma\delta = -46.$$

This equation gives the sum of $\alpha\beta$ and $\gamma\delta$ while equation (15) gives their product; elementary algebra yields

$$\alpha\beta = -28, \quad \gamma\delta = -18.$$

Since $\alpha + \beta = -3$ and $\alpha\beta = -28$, it follows that $\alpha = 4$, $\beta = -7$, and since $\gamma + \delta = -3$ and $\gamma\delta = -18$, it follows that $\gamma = 3$, $\delta = -6$.

The four roots are therefore 4, -7, 3, -6.

Example 13 Find the condition satisfied by the coefficients of the equation

$$x^4 + ax^3 + bx^2 + cx - d^2 = 0$$

if the product of two of its roots equals minus the product of the other two roots.

If α, β, γ and δ are the four roots, we have the five equations

$$\alpha + \beta + \gamma + \delta = -a,$$
$$\alpha\beta + \gamma\delta + \alpha\gamma + \alpha\delta + \beta\gamma + \beta\delta = b,$$
$$\beta\gamma\delta + \alpha\gamma\delta + \alpha\beta\delta + \alpha\beta\gamma = -c,$$
$$\alpha\beta\gamma\delta = -d^2,$$
$$\alpha\beta = -\gamma\delta.$$

The last two equations yield

$$\alpha\beta = d, \quad \gamma\delta = -d.$$

The second equation yields

$$(\alpha + \beta)(\gamma + \delta) = b, \tag{17}$$

while the third equation gives, on eliminating $\alpha\beta$ and $\gamma\delta$,

$$-\beta - \alpha + \delta + \gamma = -c/d.$$

Taken with the first, this equation gives

$$\alpha + \beta = \tfrac{1}{2}(-a + c/d), \quad \gamma + \delta = -\tfrac{1}{2}(a + c/d).$$

Finally, substituting into equation (17), we obtain

$$\tfrac{1}{4}(a - c/d)(a + c/d) = b,$$

giving the required condition

$$a^2 d^2 - c^2 = 4bd^2.$$

2.6 Repeated roots of polynomial equations

If the polynomial equation $f_n(x) = 0$ of degree n has a root $x = \alpha$ repeated m times, then $(x - \alpha)^m$ is a factor of the ploynomial $f_n(x)$, and the remaining factor is a polynomial $q_{n-m}(x)$ of degree $n - m$. We say that α is an *m-fold root* of $f_n(x) = 0$. We have

$$f_n(x) \equiv (x - \alpha)^m q_{n-m}(x).$$

It is understood that α is not a root of $q_{n-m}(x)$.

Differentiating this identity with respect to x, we obtain

$$f_n'(x) \equiv m(x - \alpha)^{m-1} q_{n-m}(x) + (x - \alpha)^m q_{n-m}'(x);$$

this vanishes when $x = \alpha$, provided the integer m is greater than unity. In fact, $(x - \alpha)^{m-1}$ is a factor of $f_n'(x)$, so α is an $(m - 1)$-fold root of $f_n'(x)$. Successive differentiation yields the following results:

If α is an m-fold root of $f_n(x)$, then

α is an $(m - 1)$-fold root of $f_n'(x)$,

α is an $(m - 2)$-fold root of $f_n''(x)$,

α is an $(m - 3)$-fold root of $f_n'''(x)$,

. . . .

α is a single root of $f_n^{(m-1)}(x)$,

α is not a root of $f_n^{(m)}(x)$.

One important application of these results concerns the cubic equation. If the cubic

$$x^3 + ax^2 + bx + c = 0$$

has a repeated root, we can find this root explicitly in terms of a, b and c.

If this special root is denoted by α, then α is also a root of the equation formed by differentiating the given cubic. Hence we have

$$\alpha^3 + a\alpha^2 + b\alpha + c = 0$$

and
$$3\alpha^2 + 2a\alpha + b = 0. \tag{18}$$

On multiplying the first equation by 3 and the second by α and subtracting, we obtain

$$a\alpha^2 + 2b\alpha + 3c = 0.$$

We now eliminate α^2 by multiplying this equation by 3 and subtracting it from equation (18) multiplied by a, obtaining

$$(2a^2 - 6b)\alpha + ab - 9c = 0,$$

from which we deduce that

$$\alpha = (9c - ab)/(2a^2 - 6b).$$

It should be stressed *that this is only a root* of the given cubic equation provided the cubic has a repeated root, since otherwise equation (18) would not be valid.

Example 14 Solve the cubic equation

$$9x^3 + 33x^2 - 56x + 20 = 0,$$

suspecting the existence of a repeated root.

Dividing by 9 to make the coefficient of x^3 equal to unity, we have

$$a = \tfrac{33}{9} = \tfrac{11}{3}, \quad b = -\tfrac{56}{9}, \quad c = \tfrac{20}{9}.$$

Then *if* the equation has a repeated root, it must be

$$\alpha = (9c - ab)/(2a^2 - 6b)$$
$$= \tfrac{2}{3}$$

upon substitution. We must finally check that this root is really a root of the given cubic; it is found to be so. The third root is easily obtained, since the product of the three roots is $-\tfrac{20}{9}$. Dividing by the square of this repeated root, we obtain -5 for the third root.

2.7 The quadratic equation

The student should recall the simple algebraical method of completing the square to obtain the solution of the quadratic equation

$$ax^2 + bx + c = 0.$$

In terms of the coefficients, the roots are given by

$$x = [-b \pm \sqrt{(b^2 - 4ac)}]/2a.$$

The quantity $b^2 - 4ac$ is termed the *discriminant* of the quadratic, since it enables us to investigate the reality of the roots without directly evaluating them. If $b^2 - 4ac > 0$, the two roots are real and distinct; if $b^2 - 4ac = 0$, the roots are identical, while if $b^2 - 4ac < 0$, the roots are complex. In the first case, the graph of the function

$$y = ax^2 + bx + c$$

cuts the x-axis in two distinct points; in the second case, the x-axis is a tangent to the graph, while in the third case, the curve does not cut the x-axis in any real point.

The student should learn how to write down the roots of the quadratic equation when the coefficient of x is written in the form $2h$. The roots of

$$ax^2 + 2hx + c = 0$$

are given by $\qquad x = [-h \pm \sqrt{(h^2 - ac)}]/a.$

Sometimes the condition is required for the two quadratic equations

$$ax^2 + bx + c = 0,$$
$$Ax^2 + Bx + C = 0$$

to possess a common root α. If this is so, we have

$$a\alpha^2 + b\alpha + c = 0,$$
$$A\alpha^2 + B\alpha + C = 0.$$

Solving for α^2 and α we obtain

$$\frac{\alpha^2}{\begin{vmatrix} b & c \\ B & C \end{vmatrix}} = \frac{-\alpha}{\begin{vmatrix} a & c \\ A & C \end{vmatrix}} = \frac{1}{\begin{vmatrix} a & b \\ A & B \end{vmatrix}},$$

or $\qquad \alpha^2 = (bC - Bc)/(aB - Ab),$

$$\alpha = -(aC - Ac)/(aB - Ab).$$

Eliminating α, we obtain immediately

$$(bC - Bc)(aB - Ab) = (aC - Ac)^2.$$

This is also a sufficient condition, for if this condition is valid, the algebra is reversible, indicating that the two quadratic equations have a common root.

2.8 The cubic equation

We consider the cubic equation in its standard form

$$x^3 + px + q = 0,$$

and in order to discuss the reality or otherwise of its roots we consider the graph of the function

$$y = x^3 + px + q.$$

Clearly the cubic must possess at least one real root, for when x is large and positive so is y, the x^3 term dominating the expression for y; moreover, when x is large and negative so is y. Hence the continuous graph of y must cut the x-axis at least once. This argument applies to all equations of odd degree.

If the cubic has three real roots, the graph of y must possess two real stationary points, one a maximum and one a minimum, such that the value of y at the maximum is positive and at the minimum negative.

Stationary values of y exist at those values of x for which the derivative of y vanishes, namely where

$$3x^2 + p = 0,$$

so
$$x = \pm \sqrt{(-\tfrac{1}{3}p)}.$$

Evidently p must be negative in order that these two values of x should be real. Then

$$y = \pm(-\tfrac{1}{3}p)\sqrt{(-\tfrac{1}{3}p)} \pm p\sqrt{(-\tfrac{1}{3}p)} + q$$
$$= \pm\tfrac{2}{3}p\sqrt{(-\tfrac{1}{3}p)} + q.$$

If these two values have opposite signs, their product must be negative:

$$[q + \tfrac{2}{3}p\sqrt{(-\tfrac{1}{3}p)}][q - \tfrac{2}{3}p\sqrt{(-\tfrac{1}{3}p)}] < 0,$$

or
$$4p^3 + 27q^2 < 0.$$

This is the only condition for the existence of three real distinct roots of the cubic equation; it automatically implies that p is negative. The quantity $4p^3 + 27q^2$ is termed the *discriminant* of the cubic.

If $4p^3 + 27q^2 = 0$, two of the roots are identical, since one of the stationary values of y must then be zero. Finally, if $4p^3 + 27q^2 > 0$, two of the roots are complex; the two stationary values of y lie on the same side of the x-axis, so the graph cannot cut this axis between these stationary points.

There are various methods, some of historical interest only, by which the standard cubic equation can be solved. We shall give here the usual method for finding numerically the real roots of the equation.

Case i. If the equation has three real roots, we have

$$4p^3 + 27q^2 < 0.$$

We seek values of x and θ such that the three terms on the left hand side of the cubic

$$x^3 + px + q = 0$$

are respectively proportional to the terms on the left hand side of the trigonometrical identity

$$4 \cos^3 \theta - 3 \cos \theta - \cos 3\theta = 0.$$

It follows that x and θ must satisfy the ratios

$$\frac{x^3}{4 \cos^3 \theta} = -\frac{px}{3 \cos \theta} = -\frac{q}{\cos 3\theta}. \tag{19}$$

The first equality provides

$$x/\cos \theta = \sqrt{(-\tfrac{4}{3}p)},$$

so

$$x = \cos \theta \sqrt{(-\tfrac{4}{3}p)}, \tag{20}$$

where it is understood that p is negative. Substituting this value of $x/\cos \theta$ into the second equality (19), we obtain

$$-\tfrac{1}{3}p\sqrt{(-\tfrac{4}{3}p)} = -q/\cos 3\theta,$$

so

$$\cos 3\theta = 3q/[p\sqrt{(-\tfrac{4}{3}p)}]. \tag{21}$$

Since the discriminant is negative, $3q/[p\sqrt{(-\tfrac{4}{3}p)}]$ lies between -1 and $+1$, so cosine tables now provide the value of 3θ. If the value of 3θ lying between 0 and 180° is $\alpha°$, we may take three distinct solutions of equation (21), namely

$$3\theta = \alpha, \quad 360 \pm \alpha,$$

so

$$\theta = \tfrac{1}{3}\alpha, \quad 120 \pm \tfrac{1}{3}\alpha.$$

Equation (20) finally gives the required values of x:

$$x = \sqrt{(-\tfrac{4}{3}p)} \cos \tfrac{1}{3}\alpha, \quad \sqrt{(-\tfrac{4}{3}p)} \cos (120 \pm \tfrac{1}{3}\alpha).$$

The reader will see that most of the numerical work has in fact been accomplished by the compilers of the cosine tables.

Case ii. If the cubic equation has only one real root, the above trigonometrical solution fails to provide a real value for θ, so we use hyperbolic functions instead. If p is negative, we compare the given cubic with the identity

$$4 \cosh^3 \theta - 3 \cosh \theta - \cosh 3\theta = 0.$$

The steps are identical with case (i), with cos replaced by cosh throughout. Equation (21) becomes

$$\cosh 3\theta = 3q/[p\sqrt{(-\tfrac{4}{3}p)}],$$

where the sign of the square root $\sqrt{(-\tfrac{4}{3}p)}$ is chosen to be opposite to the sign of q. This ensures that $\cosh 3\theta$ is positive, and also greater than unity since $4p^3 + 27q^2 > 0$. Tables of the hyperbolic cosine yield one value of 3θ, and hence one value of θ. The one real solution for x is then given by the hyperbolic version of equation (20), namely

$$x = \cosh \theta \sqrt{(-\tfrac{4}{3}p)},$$

where the chosen sign of the square root is preserved throughout.

Case iii. If p is positive, we use the identity connecting the hyperbolic sine functions:

$$4 \sinh^3 \theta + 3 \sinh \theta - \sinh 3\theta = 0.$$

The analysis follows case (*i*) directly, except that cos is replaced by sinh, and $-p$ by $+p$. Again, only one real solution for x is obtained.

Example 15 Solve the cubic equation $x^3 - 3x + 1 = 0$.
We first must test the sign of the discriminant. Here, $p = -3, q = 1$, so

$$4p^3 + 27q^2 = -4.27 + 27 < 0,$$

so the equation has three real roots.
Comparing the terms in the cubic with those in the identity

$$4 \cos^3 \theta - 3 \cos \theta - \cos 3\theta = 0,$$

we obtain

$$\frac{x^3}{4 \cos^3 \theta} = \frac{x}{\cos \theta} = -\frac{1}{\cos 3\theta},$$

yielding

$$x = 2 \cos \theta,$$

and

$$\cos 3\theta = -\tfrac{1}{2}.$$

Hence

$$3\theta = 120°, 240°, 480°,$$

and

$$\theta = 40°, 80°, 160°.$$

The values of x are then given by

$$x = 2 \cos 40°, 2 \cos 80°, 2 \cos 160°$$
$$= 1·532, 0·347, -1·879.$$

Example 16 Find the real root of the cubic equation $x^3 - 3x + 3 = 0$.
Here $p = -3, q = 3$, and the discriminant $4p^3 + 27q^2 = 135$ is positive. Since p is negative, we compare the terms in the given cubic with those in the identity

$$4 \cosh^3 \theta - 3 \cosh \theta - \cosh 3\theta = 0,$$

yielding

$$\frac{x^3}{4 \cosh^3 \theta} = \frac{x}{\cosh \theta} = -\frac{1}{\cosh 3\theta},$$

from which we deduce that

$$x^2 = 4 \cosh^2 \theta,$$

or

$$x = -2 \cosh \theta,$$

where we have chosen the minus sign to be opposite to the positive sign of q. It follows that

$$\cosh 3\theta = 3/2,$$

whence $$3\theta = 0.9624,$$

and $$\theta = 0.3208.$$

Hence $$\cosh \theta = 1.052,$$

and $$x = -2.104.$$

Example 17 Solve for the real root of the cubic equation $x^3 + 3x + 3 = 0$.

Both p and the discriminant are obviously positive. We therefore compare the terms in the cubic with those in the identity

$$4 \sinh^3 \theta + 3 \sinh \theta - \sinh 3\theta = 0,$$

yielding the ratios $$\frac{x^3}{4 \sinh^3 \theta} = \frac{x}{\sinh \theta} = -\frac{3}{\sinh 3\theta},$$

from which we deduce that $$x = 2 \sinh \theta.$$

(Either sign for the square root may be chosen here). Then $\sinh 3\theta$ has the value

$$\sinh 3\theta = -3/2,$$

whence $$3\theta = -1.195,$$

and $$\theta = -0.398.$$

Finally, $$\sinh \theta = -0.409,$$

so $$x = -0.818.$$

2.9   The quartic equation

The following simple method for solving the quartic equation in standard form is worthy of note amongst various other methods.

The equation $$x^4 + px^2 + qx + r = 0$$

is given. We shall resolve this into two quadratic factors, which, since there is no x^3 term, must be of the form

$$(x^2 + ax + b)(x^2 - ax + c) = 0.$$

Comparing coefficients in these two expressions, we have

$$p = c + b - a^2, \quad q = ac - ab, \quad r = bc.$$

The first two of these equations give

$$b + c = p + a^2, \quad b - c = -q/a,$$

so $$b = \tfrac{1}{2}(p + a^2 - q/a), \quad c = \tfrac{1}{2}(p + a^2 + q/a).$$

The product of these is r, so

$$4r = (p + a^2)^2 - q^2/a^2,$$

this being a bicubic in a^2:

$$a^6 + 2pa^4 + (p^2 - 4r)a^2 - q^2 = 0.$$

One value at least of a^2 from this equation must be positive, so a real value of a results. The values of b and c then follow, all being real, thereby completing the factorization of the quartic equation into two quadratic factors.

Example 18 Solve the quartic equation

$$y^4 + 4y^3 - 5y^2 - 12y + 6 = 0.$$

To reduce this equation to standard form, we make the preliminary substitution $y = x - 1$, yielding

$$x^4 - 11x^2 + 6x + 10 = 0.$$

Assuming factors of the form $(x^2 + ax + b)(x^2 - ax + c)$, we obtain the equations

$$-11 = c + b - a^2, \quad 6 = ac - ab, \quad 10 = bc.$$

Following the theory just given, the cubic equation for a^2 becomes

$$a^6 - 22a^4 + 81a^2 - 36 = 0.$$

Generally, such a cubic equation would have to be solved by the methods given in section 2.8, but in this case, a simple root $a^2 = 4$ exists, as may be seen by inspection. Hence we may take $a = 2$, from which it follows that $b = -5, c = -2$.

The factors of the reduced quartic equation are now

$$(x^2 + 2x - 5)(x^2 - 2x - 2) = 0,$$

so the roots are given by the solutions of the two quadratic equations involved; these are

$$x = -1 \pm \sqrt{6}, \quad 1 \pm \sqrt{3}.$$

Finally, $y = x - 1$, so

$$y = -2 \pm \sqrt{6}, \quad \pm \sqrt{3}.$$

EXERCISES

(1). Use the remainder theorem to calculate the remainder when
   (i) $x^5 - x^4 + x^3 - x^2 + x - 1$ is divided by $x^2 - 5x + 6$,
   (ii) $x^5 + 2x^4 + 3x^3 + 4x^2 + 5x + 6$ is divided by $x^2 - 2x + 1$.

(2). Reduce the quartic equations to standard form, and hence solve them
   (i) $x^4 + 20x^3 + 145x^2 + 450x + 504 = 0$,
   (ii)* $x^4 - 4x^3 + x^2 + 6x + 2 = 0$.

(3). Solve the reciprocal equations:
   (i) $6x^4 + 5x^3 - 38x^2 + 5x + 6 = 0$,
   (ii)* $6x^4 - 25x^3 + 37x^2 - 25x + 6 = 0$.

(4). By putting $x - x^{-1} = y$, solve the equation

$$2x^4 + 3x^3 - 4x^2 - 3x + 2 = 0.$$

(5). Solve the cubic equations (i) $x^3 - 27x - 27 = 0$, (ii) $x^3 - 6x - 4 = 0$.
   (iii) $x^3 + 3x^2 - 9x - 3 = 0$, (iv)* $4x^3 + 3x = 3$.

(6). Using the method given in section 2.9, solve the quartic equation
$$x^4 + 12x^3 + 30x^2 + 76x + 21 = 0.$$

(7).* (i)   Find the condition for the roots of the equation
$$x^3 + px^2 + qx + r = 0$$
to be in geometric progression, and solve the equation
$$3x^3 - 26x^2 + 52x - 24 = 0.$$

(ii)   Show that the equation $x^3 + 3x^2 + 6x - 3 = 0$ has one real root.
Prove that this lies between 0 and 1, and find it to one place of decimals.

(8).* Solve the equation
$$x^4 - 11x^3 + 28x^2 + 36x - 144 = 0.$$
You are given that the four roots can be divided into two pairs in such a way that the product of the first pair of roots is minus the product of the second pair.

(9).* Solve the equation $x^4 - 2x^3 - x^2 + 6x - 6 = 0$, which has two roots whose product is -3.

(10).* Show that the cubic polynomial $x^3 + 3ax + b$ can be expressed in the form
$$\frac{p(x - q)^3 - q(x - p)^3}{p - q},$$
where p, q are given by the relations $p + q = -b/a, pq = -a$.
Deduce the real root of the equation $x^3 - 18x + 30 = 0$.

(11).* It is given that there is a real number p such that both p and $-p$ are roots of the equation
$$x^4 + 4x^3 - x^2 + kx - 6 = 0.$$
Find k and solve the equation.

(12).* It is given that the sum of two roots of the equation
$$x^4 - 8x^3 + 19x^2 + px + 2 = 0$$
is equal to the sum of the other two. Find the value of p, and all the roots of the equation.

(13).* If the equation $x^3 + 3ax^2 + 3bx + c = 0$ has a repeated root, show that this root has the value $\frac{1}{2}(c - ab)/(a^2 - b)$.
Solve the equation $4x^3 - 12x^2 - 15x - 4 = 0$.

(14).* Express the equation $\cos 4\theta = \cos 3\theta$ as an equation in $\cos \theta$.
Hence, or otherwise, find the value of
$$\cos^2 (2\pi/7) + \cos^2 (4\pi/7) + \cos^2 (6\pi/7).$$

(15).* Given that $\alpha + \beta + \gamma = 2$, $\alpha^2 + \beta^2 + \gamma^2 = 26$, $\alpha^3 + \beta^3 + \gamma^3 = 38$, find $\beta\gamma + \gamma\alpha + \alpha\beta$ and $\alpha\beta\gamma$; hence find α, β, γ.

(16).* Find the equation whose roots are the squares of those of
$$x^3 - 3x^2 - x + 2 = 0.$$

(17).* The equation in t
$$xt^3 - 3yt^2 + 3zt - 1 = 0 \qquad (x \neq 0)$$
has two roots whose sum is zero. Prove that $x = 9yz$.

(18).* The polynomial $x^4 - x^3 + 2x^2 - 2x + 7$ has roots a, b, c, d. Find a polynomial of degree four whose roots are $a + b + c, b + c + d, c + d + a, d + a + b$. Find also a polynomial of degree four whose roots are a^2, b^2, c^2, d^2.

(19).$\star$ If the reciprocals of the roots of the cubic equation

$$x^3 + 3px^2 + 3qx + r = 0$$

are in arithmetic progression, prove that $2q^3 = r(3pq - r)$.

(20).$\star$ Given that a, b, c are the roots of the equation

$$x^3 + px^2 + qx + r = 0,$$

express $a^3 + b^3 + c^3$ in terms of p, q, r, and show that

$$a^{-3} + b^{-3} + c^{-3} = (3pqr - q^3 - 3r^2)/r^3.$$

(21).$\star$ α, β, γ are the roots of the equation $x^3 + px^2 + qx + r = 0$. Find the equation whose roots are $\alpha^2 - \beta\gamma$, $\beta^2 - \gamma\alpha$, $\gamma^2 - \alpha\beta$ and deduce the condition for the roots of the original equation to be in geometric progression.

(22).$\star$ If the equation $x^4 - 4ax^3 + 6x^2 + 1 = 0$ has a repeated root q, show that $3a = (q^2 + 3)/q$.

Hence or otherwise, prove that there is only one positive a giving a repeated root, and that this value of a is $(\frac{4}{3})^{\frac{3}{4}}$.

(23). If α, β, γ are the roots of the equation $x^3 + px + q = 0$, find the equation whose roots are $\beta^3 + \gamma^3$, $\gamma^3 + \alpha^3$, $\alpha^3 + \beta^3$.

ANSWERS TO EXERCISES

(1). (i) $161x - 301$. (ii) $35x - 14$. (2) (i) $-3, -4, -6, -7$.

    (ii) $1 \pm \sqrt{2}, 1 \pm \sqrt{3}$.

(3). (i) $2, \frac{1}{2}, -3, -\frac{1}{3}$. (ii) $\frac{1}{2}, 2, \frac{1}{6}(5 \pm i\sqrt{11})$. (4). $1, -1, -2, \frac{1}{2}$.

(5). (i) $6 \cos \frac{1}{9}r\pi$, $(r = 1, 5, 7)$. (ii) $2\sqrt{2} \cos \frac{1}{12}r\pi$, $(r = 1, 7, 9)$.

    (iii) $-1 + 4 \cos \frac{2}{9}r\pi$, $(r = 1, 2, 4)$. (iv) $\frac{1}{2}[(3 + \sqrt{10})^{\frac{1}{3}} - (3 + \sqrt{10})^{-\frac{1}{3}}]$.

(6). $-5 \pm \sqrt{22}, -1 \pm i\sqrt{6}$. (7) (i) $rp^3 - q^3 = 0$; $\frac{2}{3}, 2, 6$. (ii) 0.4.

(8). $-2, 3, 4, 6$. (9) $\pm \sqrt{3}, 1 \pm i$. (10). $-\sqrt[3]{12} - \sqrt[3]{18}$.

(11). $k = 12$; $x = \pm \sqrt{3}, 2 \pm \sqrt{2}$. (12). $p = -12$; $x = 2 \pm \sqrt{2}, 2 \pm \sqrt{3}$.

(13). $-\frac{1}{2}, -\frac{1}{3}, 4$. (14). $5/4$. (15). $-11, -12$; $1, -3, 4$.

(16). $x^3 - 11x^2 + 13x - 4 = 0$. (18). $x^4 - 3x^3 + 5x^2 - 3x + 7$;

    $x^4 + 3x^3 + 14x^2 + 24x + 49$. (20). $3pq - p^3 - 3r$.

(21). $x^3 + (3q - p^2)x^2 + (3q^2 - p^2q)x + (q^3 - rp^3) = 0$; $rp^3 = q^3$.

(23). $y^3 + 6qy^2 + (p^3 + 12q^2)y + 3p^3q + 8q^3 = 0$.

CHAPTER 3

THE THEORY OF FINITE AND INFINITE SERIES

3.1 Methods for the summation of finite series

If u_r is an expression that depends on the positive integer r in a given manner, then the set of numbers

$$u_1, u_2, u_3, \ldots$$

is called a *sequence*. Our present problem is to consider the *series* formed by adding together the first n terms of this sequence; we shall denote this sum by the symbol S_n:

$$S_n = u_1 + u_2 + \ldots + u_n = \sum_{r=1}^{n} u_r.$$

Where possible, we seek a composite expression for this sum. The two simplest finite series are the *arithmetic series* and the *geometric series*. The arithmetic series is defined by

$$u_r = a + (r - 1)d,$$

where d is the *common difference*. Its sum to n terms, the student will recall, is

$$S_n = \tfrac{1}{2}n[2a + (n - 1)d].$$

In particular, if $d = a = 1$, the series represents the sum of the first n positive integers; S_n is then given by

$$S_n = \tfrac{1}{2}n(n + 1). \tag{1}$$

The geometric series is defined by the general term

$$u_r = ax^{r-1},$$

where x is the *common ratio*. Its sum S_n to n terms is

$$S_n = a(1 - x^n)/(1 - x). \tag{2}$$

No general method exists whereby finite series may be summed; each case must be treated on its own merits, and by using experience and the knowledge of various broad principles, as the following examples show.

Example 1 *Generalizations of the geometric series.* Find the sum of the series

$$S_n = 1 + 3x^2 + 5x^4 + \ldots + (2n - 1)x^{2(n-1)}.$$

We form the product $x^2 S_n$

$$x^2 S_n = x^2 + 3x^4 + 5x^6 + \ldots + (2n - 3)x^{2(n-1)} + (2n - 1)x^{2n},$$

and then subtract this from the given series, yielding

$$(1 - x^2)S_n = 1 + 2x^2 + 2x^4 + \ldots + 2x^{2(n-1)} - (2n - 1)x^{2n}$$
$$= 2(1 + x^2 + x^4 + \ldots x^{2(n-1)}) - 1 - (2n - 1)x^{2n}$$
$$= 2(1 - x^{2n})/(1 - x^2) - 1 - (2n - 1)x^{2n},$$

since the series in the brackets is merely a geometric series with common ratio x^2. Hence

$$S_n = \frac{2(1 - x^{2n})}{(1 - x^2)^2} - \frac{1 + (2n - 1)x^{2n}}{1 - x^2}.$$

Example 2 *Series containing the binomial coefficients.* If n is a positive integer the binomial coefficients appear in the identity

$$(1 + x)^n \equiv 1 + {}_nC_1 x + {}_nC_2 x^2 + \ldots + {}_nC_{n-1}x^{n-1} + {}_nC_n x^n. \tag{3}$$

If we put $x = 1$, we obtain

$$1 + {}_nC_1 + {}_nC_2 + \ldots + {}_nC_n = 2^n.$$

Now let us differentiate identity (3), obtaining

$$n(1 + x)^{n-1} = {}_nC_1 + 2{}_nC_2 x + 3{}_nC_3 x^2 + \ldots + n{}_nC_n x^{n-1}; \tag{4}$$

when $x = 1$, this yields the sum

$${}_nC_1 + 2{}_nC_2 + 3{}_nC_3 + \ldots + n{}_nC_n = n2^{n-1}.$$

Multiplying equation (4) by x

$$nx(1 + x)^{n-1} = {}_nC_1 x + 2{}_nC_2 x^2 + 3{}_nC_3 x^3 + \ldots + n{}_nC_n x^n,$$

and differentiating again, we obtain

$$n(1 + x)^{n-1} + n(n - 1)x(1 + x)^{n-2} = {}_nC_1 + 2^2 {}_nC_2 x + 3^2{}_nC_3 x^2 + \ldots + n^2{}_nC_n x^{n-1}.$$

When $x = 1$, this yields the sum

$${}_nC_1 + 2^2 {}_nC_2 + 3^2 {}_nC_3 + \ldots + n^2 {}_nC_n = n2^{n-1} + n(n - 1)2^{n-2}$$
$$= n(n + 1)2^{n-2}.$$

Another type of series may be formed by recalling that the coefficients in the binomial expansion (3) read the same from left to right as from right to left. Equation (3) may be written

$$(1 + x)^n \equiv {}_nC_n + {}_nC_{n-1}x + {}_nC_{n-2}x^2 + \ldots + {}_nC_1 x^{n-1} + x^n.$$

If this is multiplied by identity (3), the left hand side becomes $(1 + x)^{2n}$, while the right hand side is a polynomial of degree $2n$ in x. The coefficients of corresponding powers of x on each side of this new identity may be equated, yielding various results. In particular, the coefficient of x^n on the left hand side is $_{2n}C_n$, while on the right hand side, upon picking out the terms, it is found to be

$$1 + {_nC_1}^2 + {_nC_2}^2 + \ldots + {_nC_{n-1}^2} + {_nC_n}^2.$$

The sum of this series has the value $_{2n}C_n$.

Example 3 *The sum of the first n squared integers.* Find the value of

$$S_n = 1^2 + 2^2 + 3^2 + \ldots + n^2.$$

We sum the identity

$$(r + 1)^3 - r^3 \equiv 3r^2 + 3r + 1$$

for all values of r from 1 to n, obtaining

$$\sum [(r + 1)^3 - r^3] = 3S_n + 3 \sum r + n.$$

On the left, each term cancels with its neighbour, leaving only $(n + 1)^3 - 1$, while on the right we may substitute the known sum for the first n positive integers, yielding

$$(n + 1)^3 - 1 = 3S_n + \tfrac{3}{2}n(n + 1) + n.$$

Finally, algebraical simplification produces the standard result

$$S_n = \tfrac{1}{6}n(n + 1)(2n + 1). \tag{5}$$

Example 4 Find the sum S_n of the squares of the first n odd integers

We have $S_n = 1^2 + 3^2 + 5^2 + \ldots + (2n - 1)^2$

$$= \sum_1^{2n} r^2 - [2^2 + 4^2 + \ldots + (2n)^2]$$

$$= \sum_1^{2n} r^2 - 4 \sum_1^n r^2$$

$$= \tfrac{1}{6}2n(2n + 1)(4n + 1) - \tfrac{1}{6}4n(n + 1)(2n + 1)$$

$$= \tfrac{1}{3}n(4n^2 - 1).$$

Example 5 *The sum of the cubes of the first n integers.* Find the value of

$$S_n = 1^3 + 2^3 + 3^3 + \ldots + n^3.$$

We sum the identity

$$(r + 1)^4 - r^4 \equiv 4r^3 + 6r^2 + 4r + 1$$

for all values of r from 1 to n, obtaining

$$\sum [(r + 1)^4 - r^4] = 4S_n + 6\sum r^2 + 4\sum r + n.$$

Each term cancels with its neighbour on the left hand side except the two terms $(n + 1)^4 - 1$, while on the right hand side we may substitute the known values for the sums of the first n integers and their squares, obtaining

$$(n + 1)^4 - 1 = 4S_n + n(n + 1)(2n + 1) + 2n(n + 1) + n.$$

Finally, algebraical simplification yields the standard result

$$S_n = [\tfrac{1}{2}n(n + 1)]^2. \tag{6}$$

The student should note the interesting result that this sum is the square of the sum of the first n integers.

Using these standard results, we may sum other more complicated sequences. For example, sum the sequence whose general term is

$$u_r = r(r + 1)(r + 2).$$

We have
$$S_n = 1.2.3 + 2.3.4 + 3.4.5 + \ldots + n(n + 1)(n + 2)$$
$$= \sum (r^3 + 3r^2 + 2r)$$
$$= \sum r^3 + 3 \sum r^2 + 2 \sum r$$
$$= \tfrac{1}{4}n^2(n + 1)^2 + \tfrac{1}{2}n(n + 1)(2n + 1) + n(n + 1)$$
$$= \tfrac{1}{4}n(n + 1)(n + 2)(n + 3).$$

Example 6 *The method of induction.* This method may often be used to verify the value of the sum of a series if the sum to n terms is already given, or if it is suspected. The reader should seek to write out inductive proofs in a logical manner. As an example, we shall prove that

$$\sum_{r=1}^{n} \frac{2.4.6 \ldots (2r)}{3.5.7 \ldots (2r + 1)} = \frac{2.4.6 \ldots (2n)(2n + 2)}{3.5.7 \ldots (2n + 1)} - 2. \qquad (7)$$

For $n = 1$ at least, both sides of this suggested equality have the value $\tfrac{2}{3}$. Hence two and only two mutually distinct conclusions are possible, one of which must be true. Either the result (7) is valid for all values of n, or else, since it is valid for $n = 1$, there must exist a value $n = N$, up to which equation (7) is true, but beyond which it is not true. In particular, the formula would not be true for $n = N + 1$.

In the latter case,

$$\sum_{1}^{N+1} = \sum_{1}^{N} + \text{the } (N + 1)\text{th term}$$

$$= \frac{2.4.6 \ldots (2N)(2N + 2)}{3.5.7 \ldots (2N + 1)} - 2 + \frac{2.4.6 \ldots (2N + 2)}{3.5.7 \ldots (2N + 3)}$$

$$= \frac{2.4.6 \ldots (2N + 2)(2N + 4)}{3.5.7 \ldots (2N + 3)} - 2,$$

by algebraical rearrangement. This result is contrary to the hypothesis that formula (7) is not valid for $n = N + 1$, so the second of the two conclusions is false. Hence the first conclusion is valid, namely formula (7) is true for all n.

Example 7 *The use of partial fractions.* If the general term u_r of the series is the ratio of one polynomial in r to another polynomial in r, there may or may not exist an expression for the sum of the series to n terms. If there is an expression for the sum, partial fractions may be used to evaluate it. We consider the example:

Find the sum of the first n terms of the series whose general term is given by

$$u_r = \frac{r}{(2r - 1)(2r + 1)(2r + 3)}.$$

When this term is expressed in terms of partial fractions (see section 3.7), we obtain

$$u_r = \frac{\frac{1}{16}}{2r - 1} + \frac{\frac{1}{8}}{2r + 1} - \frac{\frac{3}{16}}{2r + 3}.$$

It will be observed that the sum of the three constants occurring in the numerators of these three partial fractions is zero. This is a necessary condition for the existence of a simple composite expression for the sum of the first n terms of the series.

We now place $r = 1, 2, 3, \ldots, n$ in turn in this expanded form of u_r, and collect together in vertical columns terms with identical denominators, namely

u_1: $\qquad \dfrac{\frac{1}{16}}{1} + \dfrac{\frac{1}{8}}{3} - \dfrac{\frac{3}{16}}{5}$

u_2: $\qquad\qquad \dfrac{\frac{1}{16}}{3} + \dfrac{\frac{1}{8}}{5} - \dfrac{\frac{3}{16}}{7}$

u_3: $\qquad\qquad\qquad \dfrac{\frac{1}{16}}{5} + \dfrac{\frac{1}{8}}{7} - \dfrac{\frac{3}{16}}{9}$

$$\cdots\cdots\cdots$$

u_{n-2}: $\qquad\qquad\qquad\qquad \dfrac{\frac{1}{16}}{2n-5} + \dfrac{\frac{1}{8}}{2n-3} - \dfrac{\frac{3}{16}}{2n-1}$

u_{n-1}: $\qquad\qquad\qquad\qquad\qquad \dfrac{\frac{1}{16}}{2n-3} + \dfrac{\frac{1}{8}}{2n-1} - \dfrac{\frac{3}{16}}{2n+1}$

u_n: $\qquad\qquad\qquad\qquad\qquad\qquad \dfrac{\frac{1}{16}}{2n-1} + \dfrac{\frac{1}{8}}{2n+1} - \dfrac{\frac{3}{16}}{2n+3}.$

Upon addition, every vertical column containing three terms vanishes, leaving only the three terms at the beginning and the three at the end:

$$S_n = \frac{\frac{1}{16}}{1} + \frac{\frac{3}{16}}{3} - \frac{\frac{1}{16}}{2n+1} - \frac{\frac{3}{16}}{2n+3}$$

$$= \frac{n(n+1)}{2(2n+1)(2n+3)}.$$

Example 8 *The introduction of a second sequence.* If we require the sum of the sequence u_r to n terms, let us suppose that a second sequence v_r can be found such that

$$u_r = v_{r+1} - v_r.$$

Upon addition, all the terms involving the second sequence disappear, except the first one and the last one, yielding

$$S_n = v_{n+1} - v_1.$$

Considerable ingenuity may be necessary to detect the form of the second sequence as the following example shows:

Sum the series whose rth term is cosec $(2^r\theta)$.

The following identity may easily be proved, or quoted if known:

$$\cot \tfrac{1}{2}\alpha - \cot \alpha = \operatorname{cosec} \alpha.$$

Hence $\qquad\qquad u_r = \operatorname{cosec}(2^r\theta) = \cot(2^{r-1}\theta) - \cot(2^r\theta).$

The second sequence may then be chosen to be

$$v_r = -\cot(2^{r-1}\theta).$$

It follows that the sum is given by

$$S_n = v_{n+1} - v_1 = \cot\theta - \cot(2^n\theta).$$

Example 9 *Trigonometrical series.* These series are usually summed by using *De Moivre's theorem* in the theory of complex numbers, but the following method of multiplying by sin $\frac{1}{2}\alpha$ is worthy of note.
Find the sum of the $2n$ terms

$$S = \sin \theta - \sin (\theta - \phi) + \sin (\theta - 2\phi) - \sin (\theta - 3\phi) + \ldots$$
$$+ \sin [\theta - (2n - 2)\phi] - \sin [\theta - (2n - 1)\phi].$$

We first of all arrange for each term to have a positive sign attached; this can be accomplished by inserting an appropriate multiple of π in the respective angles:

$$S = \sin \theta + \sin (\theta - \phi - \pi) + \sin (\theta - 2\phi - 2\pi) + \sin (\theta - 3\phi - 3\pi)$$
$$+ \ldots + \sin [\theta - (2n - 1)\phi - (2n - 1)\pi].$$

Placing $\phi + \pi = \alpha$ temporarily, and multiplying throughout by $2 \sin \frac{1}{2}\alpha$, we obtain

$$2S \sin \tfrac{1}{2}\alpha = 2 \sin \tfrac{1}{2}\alpha \sin \theta + 2 \sin \tfrac{1}{2}\alpha \sin (\theta - \alpha) + 2 \sin \tfrac{1}{2}\alpha \sin (\theta - 2\alpha)$$
$$+ \ldots + 2 \sin \tfrac{1}{2}\alpha \sin [\theta - (2n - 1)\alpha]$$
$$= \cos (\tfrac{1}{2}\alpha - \theta) - \cos (\tfrac{1}{2}\alpha + \theta) + \cos (\tfrac{3}{2}\alpha - \theta) - \cos (\theta - \tfrac{1}{2}\alpha)$$
$$+ \ldots + \cos [(2n - \tfrac{1}{2})\alpha - \theta] - \cos [\theta - (2n - \tfrac{3}{2})\alpha]$$

upon replacing each product of two sines by the difference of two cosines. These cosines cancel in pairs, leaving

$$2S \sin \tfrac{1}{2}\alpha = -\cos (\tfrac{1}{2}\alpha + \theta) + \cos [(2n - \tfrac{1}{2})\alpha - \theta]$$
$$= 2 \sin n\alpha \sin [\theta - (n - \tfrac{1}{2})\alpha].$$

Hence $$S = \sin n\alpha \operatorname{cosec} \tfrac{1}{2}\alpha \sin [\theta - (n - \tfrac{1}{2})\alpha].$$

Finally, replacing α by $\phi + \pi$, we obtain

$$S = (-1)^n \sin n\phi \sec \tfrac{1}{2}\phi (-1)^n \cos [\theta - (n - \tfrac{1}{2})\phi]$$
$$= \sin n\phi \sec \tfrac{1}{2}\phi \cos [\theta - (n - \tfrac{1}{2})\phi].$$

3.2   The convergence of infinite series

The reader should always draw a sharp distinction between *algebra* and *analysis*. The processes considered thus far in the text have been purely algebraical processes; the concept of a *limit* has been entirely absent from the theory. But as soon as limiting operations are introduced, the realm of analysis has been reached. In its more elementary stages, the idea behind limiting operations is essentially intuitive, and while this basis is usually sufficient to understand the simpler applications of the theory, yet to a mathematician intuition, although often opening up new pathways of investigation, is never a substitute for mathematical rigour. From an elementary point of view, a *verbal* discussion of limiting processes is often considered satisfactory, but from a mathematical point of view, it is necessary to provide definitions of limiting operations involving *symbols* only. Some texts often attempt a dovetailing of these two methods of approach, but with little success if carefully examined. Mathematical rigour cannot be watered down, and in the long run, the only correct and rigorous treatment of limiting operations is essentially difficult for the reader not specializing in mathematics. For this reason, the following approach to the convergence of infinite series is essentially intuitive in character; no attempt has been made to indulge in "half-hearted rigour", which is illogical in the extreme.

Limiting processes concern functions either of a continuous variable x or of a discrete variable n, where n may be a positive integer. If $y = f(x)$ or $y = u(n)$ are given, the method by which the value of y is found when x and n are given is merely to substitute the values of x or n into the defining functional definitions. If this substitution process yields a form for y which cannot be calculated owing to some arithmetical impasse, we say that the function remains undetermined at such values of x or n. For example, if

$$y = (x^2 - 1)/(x - 1),$$

the value of the function when $x = 2$ is merely 3/1 by direct substitution. On the other hand, when $x = 1$, direct substitution yields 0/0, which has no arithmetical meaning. This impasse means that the function is undetermined when $x = 1$. If the reader suggests that we cancel the common factor $(x - 1)$ to yield $y = x + 1$, we merely reply that this is now a different function, in no way at all indicating that the value of the given function should be 2 when $x = 1$ (see section 14.7).

Infinity is introduced into analysis as a *process* and not as a number, although once the basic process is understood the symbol ∞ for infinity may often be treated as a number in many formulae, though not in all.

As n becomes larger, the fact that $1/n$ tends to 0, that $(n + 1)/(n - 1)$ tends to 1 and that $n/\sqrt{(4n^2 + 5)}$ tends to $\frac{1}{2}$ are obvious statements from an intuitive point of view. These three cases all have a common feature incorporated in the following general definition. We say that a function $u(n)$ tends to a limit l as n tends to infinity if, for *all* n sufficiently large, $u(n)$ differs from its limit l by an arbitrarily small quantity. In other words, $u(n)$ and its limit l are as near together as we please for all values of n sufficiently large.

Mathematically speaking, these verbal statements should be reduced to an acceptable symbolic definition, and then the proof that $u(n)$ tends to a limit could be reduced to a formal verification that the definition is satisfied. Interested readers will find this definition given in more advanced texts.

If $u(n)$ has a limit l, we write

$$\lim_{n \to \infty} u(n) = l.$$

Thus, for example,

$$\lim_{n \to \infty} \frac{4n^3 - 6n}{\sqrt{(9n^6 + 5n^3)}} = \frac{4}{3}.$$

Obviously only the highest powers of n need be retained in the numerator and denominator of the ratio when n is large.

We may now consider the convergence of infinite series. Let

$$S_n = u_1 + u_2 + u_3 + \ldots + u_n.$$

As n becomes large, more terms of the sequence are included in the sum S_n. We are led to investigate the value of S_n as n tends to infinity. If an explicit formula exists for S_n, this may be examined directly, but usually either such a formula does not exist or cannot easily be found. To avoid these difficulties, various standard tests are devised in order to examine what happens to S_n as n tends to infinity.

If S_n tends to a limit S, we say that the infinite series is *convergent* and that its sum to infinity is S. If it does not tend to a limit we say that the series is *divergent*. Thus the sum of the simple arithmetic progression

$$S_n = 1 + 2 + 3 + \ldots + n = \tfrac{1}{2}n(n + 1)$$

becomes indefinitely large as n increases; hence the series is divergent. The series whose rth term is $(-1)^r$ has a sum, this being -1 and 0 alternately. Since no limit exists, the series is divergent, though in this case the sum does not become large; such a series is often called *oscillatory*.

Finally, the behaviour of the geometric series

$$S_n = 1 + x + x^2 + \ldots + x^{n-1} = (1 - x^n)/(1 - x)$$

depends on the value of x. If $x > 1$, x^n becomes large; hence the series diverges, this term being in the numerator of S_n. If $x < -1$, x^n becomes large in magnitude but alternates in sign. The series is therefore oscillatory, each oscillation being larger than the previous one. If $x = 1$, the sum S_n is merely n, so the series diverges, while if $x = -1$, the series oscillates finitely. Finally, if $|x| < 1$, $|x^n|$ tends to zero as n becomes large, so

$$S = \lim_{n \to \infty} S_n = 1/(1 - x).$$

The series is therefore convergent if $|x| < 1$, and its sum to infinity is $1/(1 - x)$.

There are three main problems, listed below, associated with infinite series; we shall consider these throughout the remaining sections of this chapter.

Problem i. If a sequence u_r is given, does its sum S_n to n terms converge? Certain special series require individual treatment, but various standard tests are developed and used to test the convergence of most series.

Problem ii. If a sequence u_r is given, such that its sum to infinity is known to be convergent, find an expression for this sum to infinity. This problem is usually soluble only for the more elementary sequences.

Problem iii. If $f(x)$ is a given function of x, find the convergent power series

$$\sum_{r=0}^{\infty} a_r x^r$$

such that its sum to infinity equals $f(x)$. This is a straightfoward problem if $f(x)$ is formed from the simpler functions of elementary mathematics.

3.3 Tests for some special series

The two standard tests of convergence that we shall develop in section 3.5 do not cover series of the *harmonic* type. Such series need independent investigation; we shall first consider the series formed by the sequence $u_r = 1/r$.

The sum may be grouped into various brackets thus

$$1 + \tfrac{1}{2} + (\tfrac{1}{3} + \tfrac{1}{4}) + (\tfrac{1}{5} + \tfrac{1}{6} + \tfrac{1}{7} + \tfrac{1}{8}) + (\tfrac{1}{9} + \ldots + \tfrac{1}{16}) + \ldots,$$

each bracket terminating in a term of the form 2^{-n}, n being an integer. Each term in any particular bracket is greater than the last term, so the given series is greater than

$$1 + \tfrac{1}{2} + (\tfrac{1}{4} + \tfrac{1}{4}) + (\tfrac{1}{8} + \tfrac{1}{8} + \tfrac{1}{8} + \tfrac{1}{8}) + (\tfrac{1}{16} + \ldots + \tfrac{1}{16}) + \ldots$$

$$= 1 + \tfrac{1}{2} + \tfrac{1}{2} + \tfrac{1}{2} + \ldots,$$

which obviously increases without limit; it therefore follows that the harmonic series diverges. The reader should note that this example shows that a series whose terms individually tend to zero as r becomes large nevertheless can be divergent.

The second series that we consider here is that for which $u_r = 1/r^s$, where s is a given constant. If $s < 1$, each term is obviously greater than the corresponding term $1/r$ in the harmonic series. Since each term is greater than the respective term of a divergent series, the series itself must be divergent.

If $s > 1$, we may group the terms in a different way thus:

$$1 + \left(\frac{1}{2^s} + \frac{1}{3^s}\right) + \left(\frac{1}{4^s} + \frac{1}{5^s} + \frac{1}{6^s} + \frac{1}{7^s}\right) + \left(\frac{1}{8^s} + \ldots + \frac{1}{15^s}\right) + \ldots$$

In any particular bracket, each term is less than the term at the beginning of the bracket, so the sum is less than

$$1 + \left(\frac{1}{2^s} + \frac{1}{2^s}\right) + \left(\frac{1}{4^s} + \frac{1}{4^s} + \frac{1}{4^s} + \frac{1}{4^s}\right) + \left(\frac{1}{8^s} + \ldots + \frac{1}{8^s}\right) + \ldots$$

$$= 1 + \frac{1}{2^{s-1}} + \frac{1}{2^{2(s-1)}} + \frac{1}{2^{3(s-1)}} + \ldots$$

which is the sum of a convergent geometric series with common ratio 2^{1-s}, being less than unity since $s > 1$. We conclude that the generalized harmonic series converges only if $s > 1$.

3.4 Remarks on convergent series

We shall now make various general remarks concerning infinite series, many of which appear obvious, but rigorous proofs would depend upon a careful symbolical definition of a limit.

Remark i. If $u_1 + u_2 + u_3 + \ldots$ converges to the sum S, then $au_1 + au_2 + au_3 + \ldots$ converges to the sum aS.

If $u_1 + u_2 + u_3 + \ldots$ converges, so does the series formed by adding or cutting off a finite number of terms at the beginning of the given series.

Remark ii. A sequence u_r is *bounded above* if there exists a fixed number U such that u_r is less than U for all values of r. We say that U is an *upper bound* of the sequence. Obviously, any number greater than U is also an upper bound of the sequence. For example, 5 is an upper bound of the sequence $u_r = 4 - r^{-1}$.

Similarly, a sequence u_r is *bounded below* if there exists a number L such that u_r is greater than L for all values of r. We say that a sequence u_r is *bounded* if it has both an upper bound U and a lower bound L.

A sequence is *strictly monotonic* if $u_{r+1} > u_r$ for every value of r, or if $u_{r+1} < u_r$ for every value of r. If the signs read $\geqslant$ or $\leqslant$, we merely say that the sequence is *monotonic*; that is, the terms either do not decrease or they do not increase. An example of a strictly increasing monotonic series is the geometric series with a positive common ratio greater than unity, while if the positive common ratio is less than unity the sequence is strictly decreasing. A series that is merely monotonic could for example be

$$1, 1, 2, 2, 3, 3, 4, 4, 5, 5, \ldots .$$

Remark iii. Theorem. If a sequence u_r is monotonically increasing and is bounded above, then the sequence has a limit U.

We shall not prove this theorem, but it is intuitively obvious in an elementary way. If U_1 is any upper bound of the sequence, all numbers greater than U_1 are also upper bounds, and many numbers less than U_1 may also be upper bounds. In particular, we may suppose that U is the *least upper bound* such that all numbers of the sequence are not greater than U. Then as r increases, u_r attains values as near to U as we please, and since the sequence is monotonic, as soon as u_r has approached very near to U, it certainly cannot escape again, for it cannot become less than a value already attained and it cannot become greater than U. The value U is therefore the limit of the sequence.

Similarly, if a sequence decreases monotonically, and is bounded below, then u_r tends to a limit, which is the *greatest lower bound* of the sequence.

For example, $u_r = 4 - r^{-1}$ has an upper bound 6. Similarly, 5 is an upper bound, as are $4\frac{1}{2}$, $4\frac{1}{4}$, etc. But obviously 4 is the least upper bound; u_r is always less than 4, but if any number slightly less than 4 is given, values of r can be found so u_r is greater. Moreover, u_r increases steadily. The conditions of the theorem are satisfied, so u_r tends to the limit 4.

Remark iv. The alternating sign test. If the terms of a sequence are alternately positive and negative, and if after a finite number of terms, the magnitude of these terms decreases steadily to zero, then the series converges. That is, if all the u's are positive, then the sum

$$u_1 - u_2 + u_3 - u_4 + \ldots$$

converges, where

$$u_1 > u_2 > u_3 > u_4 > \ldots \to 0.$$

The series may be grouped thus:

$$(u_1 - u_2) + (u_3 - u_4) + (u_5 - u_6) + \ldots ;$$

each bracket is positive, so the sum increases steadily in value. But the series may also be grouped thus:

$$u_1 - (u_2 - u_3) - (u_4 - u_5) - \ldots < u_1$$

since again every bracket is positive. Hence the sum increases steadily and is bounded above. In keeping with remark iii, the series therefore converges to a limit. For example, such a series is given by

$$1 - \tfrac{1}{2} + \tfrac{1}{3} - \tfrac{1}{4} + \tfrac{1}{5} - \tfrac{1}{6} + \ldots,$$

with a sum to infinity known to be $\log_e 2$.

Remark v. If $\Sigma \, u_r$ is a convergent series, then u_r tends to zero as r becomes large. For when n is large enough, S_n must be as near to its limit S as we please, and moreover it must remain as near to S as we please when n is still further increased. But this condition would be invalidated if the next term added, u_{n+1} say, were not sufficiently small. The term u_n must therefore tend to zero.

This condition is not *sufficient* for convergence. The series defined by $u_r = r^{-1}$ certainly has the property that $u_r \to 0$, but the series is divergent.

Remark vi. Definition of absolute convergence. We have already shown that the series $1 + \tfrac{1}{2} + \tfrac{1}{3} + \tfrac{1}{4} + \tfrac{1}{5} + \ldots$ is divergent, but that the series $1 - \tfrac{1}{2} + \tfrac{1}{3} - \tfrac{1}{4} + \tfrac{1}{5} - \ldots$ is convergent. The fact that the character of a series may be wholly altered when the signs of many of its terms are changed leads to the following definition:

The series $u_1 + u_2 + u_3 + \ldots$, where the individual terms are not necessarily positive, converges *absolutely* if the series of moduli

$$|u_1| + |u_2| + |u_3| + \ldots$$

converges.

Hence the series $1 - \tfrac{1}{2} + \tfrac{1}{3} - \tfrac{1}{4} + \ldots$ does not converge absolutely, since the series of moduli $1 + \tfrac{1}{2} + \tfrac{1}{3} + \tfrac{1}{4} + \ldots$ does not converge. But the series $1 - \tfrac{1}{2} + \tfrac{1}{4} - \tfrac{1}{8} + \tfrac{1}{16} - \ldots$ converges absolutely, since the series formed by the moduli $1 + \tfrac{1}{2} + \tfrac{1}{4} + \tfrac{1}{8} + \tfrac{1}{16} + \ldots$ converges, being a geometric series.

A series that converges but not absolutely is said to be *conditionally convergent*.

Remark vii. Theorem. The sequence $u_1, u_2, u_3, \ldots$ is given, where some of the terms may be positive and some negative. Then if the series

$$|u_1| + |u_2| + |u_3| + \ldots$$

converges, so does the series $u_1 + u_2 + u_3 + \ldots$. That is to say, an absolutely convergent series also converges.

If we agree that any series either diverges (that is, S_n is not bounded), or oscillates finitely, or converges, then this theorem may be proved as follows.

If the sum of the absolutely convergent series is S, then the sum of the series $u_1 + u_2 + u_3 + \ldots$ cannot be greater than S nor less than $-S$.

The sum of the series is therefore bounded. Moreover, since the series is absolutely convergent, $|u_r|$ and hence u_r both tend to zero. The series cannot therefore oscillate finitely. The only other possibility is that the series converges.

Remark viii.   Theorem.   If the series $u_1 + u_2 + u_3 + \ldots$ is absolutely convergent, then the terms in the series may be rearranged in any manner, and the rearranged series is still convergent possessing the same sum S as the original series. We shall not prove this theorem, but would stress that the reader should be on his guard about rearranging an infinite number of terms of a series.

Example 10   The geometric series $1 - \frac{1}{2} + \frac{1}{4} - \frac{1}{8} + \frac{1}{16} - \ldots$ is absolutely convergent to the sum $\frac{2}{3}$. If the negative terms are rearranged systematically to infinity to yield the new series

$$1 - \frac{1}{2} - \frac{1}{8} + \frac{1}{4} - \frac{1}{32} - \frac{1}{128} + \frac{1}{16} - \frac{1}{256} - \frac{1}{512} + \frac{1}{64} - \ldots$$

then this new series also converges, and its sum is $\frac{2}{3}$.

But the series $1 - \frac{1}{2} + \frac{1}{3} - \frac{1}{4} + \frac{1}{5} - \ldots$ is not absolutely convergent; it may not therefore be rearranged. The reader should recognize the sum of the series to be $\log_e 2$. If we rearrange its negative terms as follows, we obtain a new series with a different sum:

$$1 - \frac{1}{2} - \frac{1}{4} + \frac{1}{3} - \frac{1}{6} - \frac{1}{8} + \frac{1}{5} - \frac{1}{10} - \frac{1}{12} + \frac{1}{7} - \ldots$$
$$= (1 - \frac{1}{2}) - \frac{1}{4} + (\frac{1}{3} - \frac{1}{6}) - \frac{1}{8} + (\frac{1}{5} - \frac{1}{10}) - \frac{1}{16} \ldots$$
$$= \frac{1}{2} - \frac{1}{4} + \frac{1}{6} - \frac{1}{8} + \frac{1}{10} - \frac{1}{12} + \ldots$$
$$= \frac{1}{2}(1 - \frac{1}{2} + \frac{1}{3} - \frac{1}{4} + \frac{1}{5} - \frac{1}{6} + \ldots)$$
$$= \frac{1}{2} \log_e 2.$$

Remark ix.   Let two power series be given:

$$a_0 + a_1 x + a_2 x^2 + a_3 x^3 + \ldots, \quad b_0 + b_1 x + b_2 x^2 + b_3 x^3 + \ldots,$$

the first converging to the sum $f(x)$ and the second to $g(x)$. Formally, the two series may be multiplied together term by term, and the various powers of x collected together systematically, yielding the new series

$$h(x) = a_0 b_0 + (a_0 b_1 + a_1 b_0)x + (a_0 b_2 + a_1 b_1 + a_2 b_0)x^2 + \ldots.$$

It does *not* follow that this new series either is convergent or that its sum is $f(x)g(x)$.

We shall quote the following theorem without proof: If the two series for $f(x)$ and $g(x)$ are absolutely convergent, then their rearranged product $h(x)$ converges and has the value $f(x)g(x)$.

For example, the two series

$$(1 - x)^{-1} = 1 + x + x^2 + \ldots, \quad (1 - 2x)^{-1} = 1 + 2x + 4x^2 + \ldots$$

are absolutely convergent if $|x| < \frac{1}{2}$, so they may be multiplied together. We obtain

$$[(1 - x)(1 - 2x)]^{-1} = 1 + 3x + 7x^2 + 15x^3 + \ldots.$$

3.5   The ratio and comparison tests for convergence

The ratio test.   The series $u_1 + u_2 + u_3 + \ldots$ is given; we shall test this for absolute convergence.

If (after an irrelevant finite number of initial terms) the ratio of the modulus of each term to the modulus of the preceeding term is less than some number k, itself less than 1, then the given series is absolutely convergent, and hence it is also convergent (section 3.4, vii).

In symbols, we require the inequality

$$|u_{r+1}/u_r| < k < 1.$$

Ignoring the early terms, for which this condition may not apply, we have

$$|u_2/u_1| < k, \quad |u_3/u_2| < k, \quad |u_4/u_3| < k, \ldots,$$

so $|u_2| < k\,|u_1|, \quad |u_3| < k\,|u_2| < k^2\,|u_1|, \quad |u_4| < k^3\,|u_1|, \ldots.$

Hence $|u_1| + |u_2| + |u_3| + \ldots < |u_1|\,(1 + k + k^2 + \ldots)$

$$= |u_1|/(1 - k),$$

since $k < 1$.

Consisting of positive terms, the sum to n terms of the series

$$|u_1| + |u_2| + |u_3| + \ldots$$

increases monotonically, and moreover the sum is bounded by the value $|u_1|/(1 - k)$. Hence, by section 3.4, iii, the series converges.

The given series therefore converges absolutely, and hence it also converges.

In using this test, the ratio of the *general* terms $|u_{r+1}|$ and $|u_r|$ must be employed; using some particular value of r is not sufficient. The requirement may also be stated in a different way: if

$$\lim_{r \to \infty} |u_{r+1}/u_r| = l < 1,$$

then the series converges, for this limit implies the required inequality.

If the ratio $|u_{r+1}/u_r|$ tends to unity, the ratio test is inconclusive. The series may or may not converge; more delicate tests would be required to investigate this exceptional case. If the inequality

$$|u_{r+1}/u_r| > k > 1$$

holds for all large r, then the series diverges.

The comparison test for series with positive terms. If the series of positive terms $v_1 + v_2 + v_3 + \ldots$ is known to be convergent, and if

$$u_r/v_r < k,$$

where k is a fixed number for all large r, then the series

$$u_1 + u_2 + u_3 + \ldots$$

converges.

Since the u's are all positive, the sum to n terms is certainly monotonically increasing. Moreover, neglecting the first few terms for which the inequalities may not apply, we have

$$u_1 < kv_1, \quad u_2 < kv_2, \quad u_3 < kv_3, \ldots,$$

so $$u_1 + u_2 + u_3 + \ldots < k(v_1 + v_2 + v_3 + \ldots)$$

which is a definite finite number. Hence the sum of the u series is bounded. It follows that the u series must be convergent.

Otherwise expressed, if the ratio u_r/v_r tends to a finite limit as r tends to infinity, then the u series converges if the v series converges.

On the other hand, if the v series diverges and if $u_r/v_r > k$ or if $\lim (u_r/v_r)$ exists, then the u series diverges.

Example 11   Test the following series for convergence:

(i) $\dfrac{1}{1+a} - \dfrac{2}{2+a} + \dfrac{3}{3+a} - \dfrac{4}{4+a} + \ldots$ (a not a negative integer),

(ii) $\dfrac{1}{\log 2} - \dfrac{1}{\log 3} + \dfrac{1}{\log 4} - \dfrac{1}{\log 5} + \ldots,$

(iii) $\dfrac{\frac{1}{2}}{(2.1+3)^2} + \dfrac{(\frac{1}{2})^2}{(2.2+3)^2} + \dfrac{(\frac{1}{2})^3}{(2.3+3)^2} + \ldots.$

(iv) $\dfrac{x}{1.2.3} + \dfrac{x^2}{2.3.4} + \dfrac{x^3}{3.4.5} + \dfrac{x^4}{4.5.6} + \ldots,$

(v) $1 + \dfrac{3}{2.4} + \dfrac{7}{4.9} + \dfrac{15}{8.16} + \dfrac{31}{16.25} + \ldots,$

(vi) $\dfrac{1}{1^5-a^5} + \dfrac{1}{2^5-a^5} + \dfrac{1}{3^5-a^5} + \dfrac{1}{4^5-a^5} + \ldots$ (a not an integer).

The series are tested as follows.

(i) The general term is $(-1)^{r+1} r/(r+a)$, which tends to $(-1)^{r+1}$ as r tends to infinity. The terms do not tend to zero, so the series cannot converge (section 3.4, v); in fact, it oscillates finitely.

(ii) The general term is $(-1)^r/\log r$. These terms alternate in sign, and since $\log r$ increases steadily with r, $1/\log r$ decreases steadily to zero. The series therefore converges, by the alternating sign test.

(iii) The general term is $(\frac{1}{2})^r/(2r + 3)^2$. The ratio test provides

$$|u_{r+1}/u_r| = \frac{1}{2}(2r + 3)^2/(2r + 5)^2 \to \frac{1}{2} < 1;$$

hence the series converges.

(iv) The general term is $x^r/r(r + 1)(r + 2)$. The ratio test provides

$$|u_{r+1}/u_r| = |x| \, r/(r + 3) \to |x|.$$

Hence if $|x| < 1$, the series converges absolutely; if $|x| > 1$, the series diverges, while if $|x| = 1$, the ratio test provides no answer.

But if $x = -1$, the terms alternate in sign, and their magnitude decreases steadily to zero, so the series converges by the alternating sign test. If $x = +1$, the use of partial fractions shows that every term cancels with its near neighbours in the infinite sum, except the first few terms. The series is therefore convergent.

(v) The general term is $(2^r - 1)/2^{r-1} r^2$. The ratio test is inconclusive, so we use the comparison test. Let us choose the suitable series $v_r = r^{-2}$, known to be convergent (section 3.3). Then

$$u_r/v_r = (2^r - 1)/2^{r-1} \to 2,$$

a finite limit. Hence the given series converges.

(vi) The general term is $1/(r^5 - a^5)$. Again the ratio test is inconclusive, so we compare it with the known convergent series specified by $v_r = r^{-5}$. The ratio u_r/v_r tends to unity, so the series converges.

3.6   The binomial series

In this chapter, we shall assume the expansions for the binomial series, the exponential series and the logarithmic series, obtaining them in section 14.5. The object of the present sections is to consider the convergence of these series, to sum given series in terms of these standard series, and to expand given functions in terms of these series.

If n is a positive integer, the binomial expansion of $(1 + x)^n$ is given by

$$(1 + x)^n = 1 + {}_nC_1 x + {}_nC_2 x^2 + \ldots + {}_nC_r x^r + \ldots + x^n.$$

Here, the coefficient ${}_nC_r$ has its usual meaning, namely

$$ {}_nC_r = \frac{n(n - 1)(n - 2) \ldots (n - r + 1)}{1.2.3 \ldots r}.$$

The numerator and denominator each contain r factors, all being integers; in terms of factorials, this may be written as

$$ {}_nC_r = n!/r!(n - r)!\,.$$

It proves useful to generalize this notation in order to embrace values of n which are not positive integers. If n is now any positive or negative rational fraction (including integers), let n_r denote the ratio

$$n_r = \frac{n(n-1)(n-2)\ldots(n-r+1)}{1.2.3\ldots r}.$$

It can be seen that r factors, starting with n, occur in the numerator, each factor being less by unity than the preceeding one. Sometimes, the symbol $\binom{n}{r}$ is used to denote n_r.

With this notation, the general expansion of $(1+x)^n$ may be stated to be

$$(1+x)^n = 1 + n_1 x + n_2 x^2 + n_3 x^3 + \ldots + n_r x^r + \ldots$$

where the series extends to infinity, except when n is a positive integer in which case the series terminates. We are not concerned with the proof of this expansion here; all we shall do is to test its convergence properties and use it in various examples.

The general term in this expansion is $n_r x^r$; in the ratio test, we form the ratio of the following term to this term, namely

$$\left| \frac{n_{r+1} x^{r+1}}{n_r x^r} \right| = \left| \frac{n-r}{r+1} \right| |x| \to |x|,$$

as r becomes large for fixed n and x. Hence, if $|x| < 1$, the series converges absolutely, while if $|x| > 1$ the series diverges. If $|x| = 1$, the ratio test is inconclusive; more powerful tests must then be used the results of which we shall merely quote here. If $x = +1$, the series converges if $n > -1$, while if $x = -1$, the series converges if $n > 0$.

The sum of the series equals the value of the function $(1+x)^n$ only if $|x| < 1$, neglecting the subtle case $|x| = 1$. If $n = \frac{1}{2}$, for example, $(1+x)^{\frac{1}{2}}$, being a square root, has two values one positive and one negative. The infinite series is however a single-valued expression. In cases like this, the sum of the series is *always given by the positive value* of the square root and *not* by the negative value.

If $|x| > 1$, it is not possible to expand $(1+x)^n$ as a power series in ascending powers of x. However we may expand it in inverse powers of x, for, taking x^n out as a factor when possible, we have

$$(1+x)^n = x^n(1+x^{-1})^n$$
$$= x^n(1 + n_1 x^{-1} + n_2 x^{-2} + n_3 x^{-3} + \ldots)$$
$$= x^n + n_1 x^{n-1} + n_2 x^{n-2} + \ldots,$$

the expansion being valid when $|x^{-1}| < 1$, that is, when $|x| > 1$.

Three types of problem may now be considered.

Problem i. If $f(x)$ is the sum of the absolutely convergent power series

$$f(x) = c_0 + c_1 x + c_2 x^2 + \ldots ,$$

find the sum of the first $n + 1$ coefficients:

$$c_0 + c_1 + c_2 + \ldots + c_n.$$

We form the function $f(x)/(1 - x)$. The expansion of $(1 - x)^{-1}$ is given by the binomial expansion:

$$(1 - x)^{-1} = 1 + x + x^2 + x^3 + \ldots ,$$

being merely the geometric series, absolutely convergent if $|x| < 1$. The product $f(x)(1 - x)^{-1}$ may therefore be regarded as the product of two absolutely convergent series, valid in their common range of convergence. As a series, the product may be calculated by multiplying together each series term by term (see section 3.4, ix), yielding upon gathering up terms

$$f(x)(1 - x)^{-1} = c_0 + (c_0 + c_1)x + (c_0 + c_1 + c_2)x^2 + \ldots .$$

Hence we see that the sum of the coefficients that we require is merely the coefficient of x^n in the expansion of $f(x)(1 - x)^{-1}$ in ascending powers of x. It is evident that an explicit formula for this sum can only be obtained if this function can be expanded as a power series in a simple way.

In particular, let $f(x) = (1 - x)^{-p}$, p being any rational fraction. The sum of the first $n + 1$ coefficients in its expansion is the coefficient of x^n in the expansion of $(1 - x)^{-p}(1 - x)^{-1}$. But

$$(1 - x)^{-p-1} = 1 + (-p - 1)_1 x + (-p - 1)_2 x^2 + \ldots + (-p - 1)_n x^n + \ldots ,$$

so we obtain the equation

$$1 + (-p)_1 + (-p)_2 + \ldots + (-p)_n = (-p - 1)_n.$$

Problem ii. Summation of series of the binomial type. A given infinite series may be summed as a binomial expansion only if the coefficients of the powers of x (or of some numerical value) are of the correct type. Inspection will reveal whether this is so or not, and rearrangement of the terms will then provide the values of x and n required. The chief feature that distinguishes the binomial series from other series is that the coefficients contain an increasing number of factors both in their numerators and in their denominators. The process is illustrated by examples at the end of this section, but the steps to be followed in any suspected case are as follows:

(*a*) Arrange complete factorials to be present in the denominators of each term.
(*b*) Arrange that all the factors in each numerator should descend in steps of unity.
(*c*) Arrange for the numerators to have the same number of factors as the denominators.
(*d*) Arrange the power of x (or of some numerical factor) in any term to be the same as the number of factors in the numerator of that term.
(*e*) Arrange all coefficients to be positive by inserting necessary minus signs within the x values.
(*f*) The values of x and n may now be seen directly. Write down the expansion of $(1 + x)^n$, and compare it with the series just obtained, and note whether the first few terms are missing or not. The final sum can then be deduced.

Example 12   Sum the series

$$S = \frac{1}{2} \cdot \frac{1}{2^4} - \frac{1}{2.4} \cdot \frac{1}{2^8} + \frac{1.3}{2.4.6} \cdot \frac{1}{2^{12}} - \frac{1.3.5}{2.4.6.8} \cdot \frac{1}{2^{16}} + \dots$$

Since the number of factors in both numerator and denominator of each term increases by unity, the series may be a binomial series. Following the steps just given, we obtain

$$S = \frac{1}{1!} \cdot \frac{1}{2^5} - \frac{1}{2!} \cdot \frac{1}{2^{10}} + \frac{1.3}{3!} \cdot \frac{1}{2^{15}} - \frac{1.3.5}{4!} \cdot \frac{1}{2^{20}} + \dots$$

after arranging the factorials appropriately in the denominators. Multiplying each integer in each numerator by $-\frac{1}{2}$ so the factors decrease by unity, we have

$$S = \frac{1}{1!} \cdot \frac{1}{2^5} + \frac{(-\frac{1}{2})}{2!} \cdot \frac{1}{2^9} + \frac{(-\frac{1}{2}).(-\frac{3}{2})}{3!} \cdot \frac{1}{2^{13}} + \frac{(-\frac{1}{2}).(-\frac{3}{2}).(-\frac{5}{2})}{4!} \cdot \frac{1}{2^{17}} + \dots$$

The number of factors in each numerator must be the same as in the factorial in the denominator; an extra $\frac{1}{2}$ is therefore inserted *in front of* each numerator:

$$S = \frac{\frac{1}{2}}{1!} \cdot \frac{1}{2^4} + \frac{(\frac{1}{2}).(-\frac{1}{2})}{2!} \cdot \frac{1}{2^8} + \frac{(\frac{1}{2}).(-\frac{1}{2}).(-\frac{3}{2})}{3!} \cdot \frac{1}{2^{12}}$$

$$+ \frac{(\frac{1}{2}).(-\frac{1}{2}).(-\frac{3}{2}).(-\frac{5}{2})}{4!} \cdot \frac{1}{2^{16}} + \dots$$

Finally, the index of x must be identical with the number of factors in each numerator respectively:

$$S = \frac{\frac{1}{2}}{1!} (2^{-4}) + \frac{(\frac{1}{2}).(-\frac{1}{2})}{2!} (2^{-4})^2 + \frac{(\frac{1}{2}).(-\frac{1}{2}).(-\frac{3}{2})}{3!} (2^{-4})^3$$

$$+ \frac{(\frac{1}{2}).(-\frac{1}{2}).(-\frac{3}{2}).(-\frac{5}{2})}{4!} (2^{-4})^4 + \dots$$

Then x must evidently be 2^{-4}, while n must be the first numerical factor in each numerator, namely $\frac{1}{2}$. Consider

$$(1 + x)^n = (1 + 2^{-4})^{\frac{1}{2}}$$

$$= 1 + \frac{\frac{1}{2}}{1!} (2^{-4}) + \frac{(\frac{1}{2}).(-\frac{1}{2})}{2!} (2^{-4})^2 + \frac{(\frac{1}{2}).(-\frac{1}{2}).(-\frac{3}{2})}{3!} (2^{-4})^3 + \dots$$

S is then seen to be

$$S = (1 + x)^n - 1 = (1 + \tfrac{1}{16})^{\frac{1}{2}} - 1 = \tfrac{1}{4}(\sqrt{17} - 4).$$

Example 13   Sum the series

$$S = \frac{3}{2}\left(\frac{1}{3}\right) + \frac{3.5}{2.3}\left(\frac{1}{3}\right)^2 + \frac{3.5.7}{2.3.4}\left(\frac{1}{3}\right)^3 + \dots$$

Suspecting a binomial series, we proceed as before:

$$S = \frac{3}{2!}\left(\frac{1}{3}\right) + \frac{3.5}{3!}\left(\frac{1}{3}\right)^2 + \frac{3.5.7}{4!}\left(\frac{1}{3}\right)^3 + \ldots$$

$$= \frac{(-\frac{3}{2})}{2!}\left(-\frac{2}{3}\right) + \frac{(-\frac{3}{2}).(-\frac{5}{2})}{3!}\left(-\frac{2}{3}\right)^2 + \frac{(-\frac{3}{2}).(-\frac{5}{2}).(-\frac{7}{2})}{4!}\left(-\frac{2}{3}\right)^3 + \ldots,$$

giving, after multiplying through by $-\frac{1}{2}$:

$$-\tfrac{1}{2}S = \frac{(-\frac{1}{2}).(-\frac{3}{2})}{2!}\left(-\frac{2}{3}\right) + \frac{(-\frac{1}{2}).(-\frac{3}{2}).(-\frac{5}{2})}{3!}\left(-\frac{2}{3}\right)^3$$

$$+ \frac{(-\frac{1}{2}).(-\frac{3}{2}).(-\frac{5}{2}).(-\frac{7}{2})}{4!}\left(-\frac{2}{3}\right)^3 + \ldots$$

or

$$\tfrac{1}{3}S = \frac{(-\frac{1}{2}).(-\frac{3}{2})}{2!}\left(-\frac{2}{3}\right)^2 + \frac{(-\frac{1}{2}).(-\frac{3}{2}).(-\frac{5}{2})}{3!}\left(-\frac{2}{3}\right)^3$$

$$+ \frac{(-\frac{1}{2}).(-\frac{3}{2}).(-\frac{5}{2}).(-\frac{7}{2})}{4!}\left(-\frac{2}{3}\right)^4 + \ldots$$

$$= [1 + (-\tfrac{2}{3})]^{-\frac{1}{2}} - (1 + \tfrac{1}{2}.\tfrac{2}{3})$$

$$= \sqrt{3} - \tfrac{4}{3}.$$

Hence $\qquad S = 3\sqrt{3} - 4.$

Example 14 Sum the series

$$S = \tfrac{1}{2}x + \frac{1}{2.4}x^3 + \frac{1.3}{2.4.6}x^5 + \ldots,$$

where $x = 2t/(1 + t^2)$.

We have

$$xS = \frac{1}{1!}(\tfrac{1}{2}x^2) + \frac{1}{2!}(\tfrac{1}{2}x^2)^2 + \frac{1.3}{3!}(\tfrac{1}{2}x^2)^3 + \ldots$$

$$= \frac{\tfrac{1}{2}}{1!}(x^2) - \frac{(\frac{1}{2}).(-\frac{1}{2})}{2!}(x^2)^2 + \frac{(\frac{1}{2}).(-\frac{1}{2}).(-\frac{3}{2})(x^2)^3}{3!} - \ldots$$

Comparing this with

$$(1 - x^2)^{\frac{1}{2}} = 1 - \tfrac{1}{2}x^2 + \frac{(\frac{1}{2}).(-\frac{1}{2})}{2!}(x^2)^2 - \ldots,$$

we can see that $\qquad xS = 1 - \sqrt{(1 - x^2)},$

so $\qquad S = [1 - \sqrt{(1 - x^2)}]/x,$

where the *positive* root of $1 - x^2$ is taken, provided $x^2 < 1$.

If $x = 2t/(1 + t^2)$, we note that

$$0 < (t^2 - 1)^2 \quad \text{if} \quad t \neq \pm 1,$$

so

$$4t^2 < (t^2 + 1)^2,$$

or

$$x^2 = 4t^2/(1 + t^2)^2 < 1.$$

All values of t are therefore permitted except $t = \pm 1$. Then

$$S = \left[1 - \sqrt{\left(1 - \frac{4t^2}{(1 + t^2)^2} \right)} \right] \frac{1 + t^2}{2t}$$

$$= \left[1 - \frac{\sqrt{[(1 - t^2)^2]}}{1 + t^2} \right] \frac{1 + t^2}{2t}$$

$$= [1 + t^2 - \sqrt{\{(1 - t^2)^2\}}]/2t$$

where $\sqrt{\{(1 - t^2)^2\}}$ is positive. If $|t| > 1$ this root must be $t^2 - 1$, while if $|t| < 1$, it must be $1 - t^2$. Hence

$$S = [1 + t^2 - (t^2 - 1)]/2t = 1/t \quad \text{if} \quad |t| > 1,$$

and

$$S = [1 + t^2 - (1 - t^2)]/2t = t \quad \text{if} \quad |t| < 1.$$

Problem iii. The expansion of functions using the binomial series. This involves the use of partial fractions, so the next section is devoted to a discussion of this subject.

3.7 Partial fractions and the binomial expansion

If $f_m(x)$ is a polynomial of degree m in x and $g_n(x)$ is one of degree n, consider the ratio $f_m(x)/g_n(x)$. If $m \geqslant n$, long division is possible, yielding a quotient and a remainder whose degree is less than n. Without loss of generality then, we may take $m < n$ in the ratio $f_m(x)/g_n(x)$.

Under these circumstances, it is possible to resolve $f_m(x)/g_n(x)$ into *partial fractions*, the denominators of which are the factors of $g_n(x)$. The following choice of factors is made.

(i) If $g_n(x)$ has a non-repeated factor $(x - \alpha)$, the partial fraction chosen is $A/(x - \alpha)$, where A is a constant.

(ii) If $g_n(x)$ has a repeated factor $(x - \beta)^2$, we choose

$$\frac{B}{(x - \beta)} + \frac{C}{(x - \beta)^2} \; ;$$

for a factor $(x - \gamma)^3$, we choose

$$\frac{D}{(x - \gamma)} + \frac{E}{(x - \gamma)^2} + \frac{F}{(x - \gamma)^3} \, ,$$

and so on.

(iii) If $g_n(x)$ has a quadratic factor $x^2 + \mu x + \nu$ with no real linear factors, or if the real factors involve awkward square roots, we choose a partial fraction of the form

$$\frac{Gx + H}{x^2 + \mu x + \nu}.$$

Generally, the degree of the numerator in any partial fraction is taken to be one less than that occurring in its denominator.

The problem is to find the constants introduced into the partial fractions. The method for finding the constants for the non-repeated factors is shown in the following two examples, while the second pair of examples deals with repeated factors.

Example 15   Resolve $(2x + 1)/[(x - 1)(x - 2)(x - 3)]$ into partial fractions.

We assume the following identity, satisfied for all values of x:

$$\frac{2x + 1}{(x - 1)(x - 2)(x - 3)} \equiv \frac{A}{x - 1} + \frac{B}{x - 2} + \frac{C}{x - 3}.$$

We first cross-multiply in order to eliminate the denominators:

$$2x + 1 \equiv A(x - 2)(x - 3) + B(x - 1)(x - 3) + C(x - 1)(x - 2).$$

We now place $x = 1$, 2 and 3 in turn, yielding $A = \frac{3}{2}$, $B = -5$, $C = \frac{7}{2}$.

Example 16   Resolve $(x^2 + 6)/[(x^2 - 3x + 3)(x - 3)]$ into partial fractions.

Assume the following identity, satisfied for all values of x:

$$\frac{x^2 + 6}{(x^2 - 3x + 3)(x - 3)} \equiv \frac{Ax + B}{x^2 - 3x + 3} + \frac{C}{x - 3}.$$

Cross-multiplication yields

$$x^2 + 6 \equiv (Ax + B)(x - 3) + C(x^2 - 3x + 3).$$

When $x = 3$, we obtain $C = 5$.

Various methods may be used to obtain A and B; these will be discussed in example 17. Here, we insert $C = 5$, and take this term to the other side of the equation, yielding

$$(Ax + B)(x - 3) \equiv x^2 + 6 - 5(x^2 - 3x + 3) \equiv -4x^2 + 15x - 9$$

$$\equiv (x - 3)(-4x + 3).$$

Hence $Ax + B = -4x + 3,$

thereby completing the problem.

Example 17   Resolve $(3x + 1)/[(x + 1)^2(x - 2)]$ into partial fractions.

We assume $$\frac{3x + 1}{(x + 1)^2(x - 2)} \equiv \frac{A}{(x + 1)^2} + \frac{B}{x + 1} + \frac{C}{x - 2},$$

and cross-multiply to obtain

$$3x + 1 \equiv A(x - 2) + B(x + 1)(x - 2) + C(x + 1)^2. \tag{8}$$

Method i. We place $x = -1$ and 2 in turn, giving $A = \frac{2}{3}$ and $C = \frac{7}{9}$. We can choose no value of x that gives B directly, but we may put x equal to any suitable value, $x = 0$ say. Then

$$1 \equiv -2A - 2B + C,$$

yielding $B = -\frac{7}{9}$, using the known values of A and C.

Method ii. We first find A as before, namely the coefficient of that fraction containing the highest index in its denominator: $A = \frac{2}{3}$.

We insert this into the identity (8), and take $\frac{2}{3}(x - 2)$ to the left hand side:

$$3x + 1 - \tfrac{2}{3}(x - 2) \equiv \tfrac{7}{3}(x + 1) \equiv B(x + 1)(x - 2) + C(x + 1)^2$$

or, dividing by $x + 1$:

$$\tfrac{7}{3} \equiv B(x - 2) + C(x + 1).$$

Putting $x = -1$ and 2 in turn yields $B = -\frac{7}{9}$, $C = \frac{7}{9}$.

Method iii. Find $A = \frac{2}{3}$ as before, and substitute into (8); then differentiate the identity with respect to x to obtain

$$3 \equiv \tfrac{2}{3} + B[(x - 2) + (x + 1)] + 2C(x + 1),$$

or $\qquad\quad \tfrac{7}{3} \equiv B(2x - 1) + 2C(x + 1).$

Putting $x = -1$ and $\frac{1}{2}$ in turn yields $B = -\frac{7}{9}$, $C = \frac{7}{9}$.

Method iv. Having found A as before, equate coefficients of two suitable powers of x:

$$\text{coefficient of } x^2: \quad 0 = B + C,$$

$$\text{coefficient of } x: \quad 3 = \tfrac{2}{3} - B + 2C.$$

The solution of these equations is $B = -\frac{7}{9}$, $C = \frac{7}{9}$.

Example 18 Expand the function $9x^3/[(x - 1)^2(x + 2)(x - 2)^2]$ in ascending powers of x, stating the range of validity of the expansion.

The ratio is first resolved into partial fractions:

$$\frac{9x^3}{(x - 1)^2(x + 2)(x - 2)^2} \equiv \frac{A}{(x - 1)^2} + \frac{B}{x - 1} + \frac{C}{x + 2} + \frac{D}{(x - 2)^2} + \frac{E}{x - 2},$$

so $\quad 9x^3 \equiv A(x + 2)(x - 2)^2 + B(x - 1)(x + 2)(x - 2)^2 + C(x - 1)^2(x - 2)^2$
$$+ D(x - 1)^2(x + 2) + E(x - 1)^2(x + 2)(x - 2).$$

Placing x equal to 1, -2 and 2 in turn, we obtain $A = 3$, $C = -\frac{1}{2}$, $D = 18$. Equating coefficients of x^4 and of the constant term:

$$0 = B + C + E,$$

$$0 = 8A - 8B + 4C + 2D - 4E,$$

yielding $B = 14$, $E = -\frac{27}{2}$.

Using the binomial expansion, we therefore expand each of the five separate partial fractions occurring in the expression

$$\frac{3}{(x - 1)^2} + \frac{14}{x - 1} - \frac{\frac{1}{2}}{x + 2} + \frac{18}{(x - 2)^2} - \frac{\frac{27}{2}}{x - 2}.$$

Firstly we arrange each denominator to contain the term $+1$, and then expand:

$$\frac{3}{(1-x)^2} - \frac{14}{1-x} - \frac{\frac{1}{4}}{1+\frac{1}{2}x} + \frac{\frac{9}{2}}{(1-\frac{1}{2}x)^2} + \frac{\frac{27}{4}}{1-\frac{1}{2}x}$$

$$= 3[1 + 2x + 3x^2 + 4x^3 + \ldots + (r+1)x^r + \ldots]$$
$$- 14(1 + x + x^2 + x^3 + \ldots + x^r + \ldots)$$
$$- \tfrac{1}{4}[1 - \tfrac{1}{2}x + (\tfrac{1}{2}x)^2 - \ldots + (-1)^r(\tfrac{1}{2}x)^r + \ldots]$$
$$+ \tfrac{9}{2}[1 + 2(\tfrac{1}{2}x) + 3(\tfrac{1}{2}x)^2 + \ldots + (r+1)(\tfrac{1}{2}x)^r + \ldots]$$
$$+ \tfrac{27}{4}[1 + (\tfrac{1}{2}x) + (\tfrac{1}{2}x)^2 + \ldots + (\tfrac{1}{2}x)^r + \ldots]$$

valid if $|x| < 1$ and $|\tfrac{1}{2}x| < 1$. We must have $|x| < 1$ for both conditions jointly to be satisfied.

The coefficient of x^r in the expansion is

$$3(r+1) - 14 - \tfrac{1}{4}(-\tfrac{1}{2})^r + \tfrac{9}{2}(r+1)(\tfrac{1}{2})^r + \tfrac{27}{4}(\tfrac{1}{2})^r$$
$$= 3r - 11 + (\tfrac{1}{2})^r[\tfrac{9}{2}r + \tfrac{45}{4} - \tfrac{1}{4}(-1)^r].$$

3.8   The exponential and related series

In this section, we merely quote the standard series; they are derived in later sections of the text. We consider:

$$\exp x \equiv e^x = 1 + x + \frac{x^2}{2!} + \frac{x^3}{3!} + \ldots + \frac{x^r}{r!} + \ldots,$$

$$e^{-x} = 1 - x + \frac{x^2}{2!} - \frac{x^3}{3!} + \ldots + (-1)^r \frac{x^r}{r!} + \ldots,$$

$$\sinh x = x + \frac{x^3}{3!} + \frac{x^5}{5!} + \ldots + \frac{x^{2r+1}}{(2r+1)!} + \ldots,$$

$$\cosh x = 1 + \frac{x^2}{2!} + \frac{x^4}{4!} + \ldots + \frac{x^{2r}}{(2r)!} + \ldots,$$

$$\sin x = x - \frac{x^3}{3!} + \frac{x^5}{5!} - \ldots + (-1)^r \frac{x^{2r+1}}{(2r+1)!} + \ldots,$$

$$\cos x = 1 - \frac{x^2}{2!} + \frac{x^4}{4!} - \ldots + (-1)^r \frac{x^{2r}}{(2r)!} + \ldots.$$

The convergence of all these six series is demonstrated by the ratio test. For example, for e^x we have

$$\left| \frac{u_{r+1}}{u_r} \right| = \left| \frac{x^{r+1}/(r+1)!}{x^r/r!} \right| = \left| \frac{x}{r+1} \right| \to 0$$

as r becomes large for *any* fixed value of x. Hence the series converges for *all* values of x; moreover, the series is absolutely convergent, so it may be multiplied term by term by any other absolutely convergent series.

Recalling the identity $a = \exp(\log_e a)$, we may expand a^x in the form

$$a^x = \exp(x \log_e a)$$
$$= 1 + x \log_e a + \frac{(x \log_e a)^2}{2!} + \ldots + \frac{(x \log_e a)^r}{r!} + \ldots.$$

Series that can be summed in terms of these standard series are easily distinguished from the binomial series. In common with the binomial, such series consist of powers of x with factorials in the denominators, but exponential-type series do not have an increasing number of factors in the numerators.

The rth term of a typical series is given by

$$u_r = \frac{\text{polynomial of degree } n \text{ in } r}{r!} x^r.$$

The polynomial in the numerator is split up into various terms designed to cancel with the *highest* integers in the factorial. Thus we let:

polynomial of degree $2 \equiv A + Br + Cr(r-1)$,
polynomial of degree $3 \equiv A + Br + Cr(r-1) + Dr(r-1)(r-2)$,
polynomial of degree $4 \equiv A + Br + Cr(r-1) + Dr(r-1(r-2)$
$$+ Er(r-1)(r-2)(r-3).$$

If the polynomial is of degree n, $(n+1)$ constants are thereby introduced; these are found by comparing coefficients of powers of r. Several pure exponential series are thus produced, each being summed by inspection. The first $(n-1)$ terms in the given series require special care as the following examples show, but the right answer is obtained if factorials of negative integers are placed equal to infinity (in denominators).

Other exponential-type series are summed by a judicious examination of the terms involved.

Example 19   Sum the series whose rth term is $(3r-5)2^r/r!$.
Since the numerator is only linear in r, no rearrangement is necessary. Taking the $3r$ and the 5 separately, we have

$$u_r = \left(\frac{3}{(r-1)!} - \frac{5}{r!} \right) 2^r.$$

When $r = 0$, the first term u_0 needs special attention unless we interpret $(r-1)! = (-1)!$ to be infinity. Written explicitly, the sum equals

$$3\left(2 + \frac{2^2}{1!} + \frac{2^3}{2!} + \frac{2^4}{3!} + \ldots\right) - 5\left(1 + \frac{2}{1!} + \frac{2^2}{2!} + \ldots\right) = 6e^2 - 5e^2 = e^2.$$

Example 20 Sum the series given by $u_r = (1 - r - 3r^2 + 2r^3)x^r/r!$.

Firstly we rearrange the numerator thus:

$$1 - r - 3r^2 + 2r^3 \equiv A + Br + Cr(r - 1) + Dr(r - 1)(r - 2),$$

giving, upon equating coefficients

$$1 = A, \quad -1 = B - C + 2D, \quad -3 = C - 3D, \quad 2 = D.$$

or

$$A = 1, \quad B = -2, \quad C = 3, \quad D = 2.$$

Hence

$$u_r = \frac{1 - 2r + 3r(r - 1) + 2r(r - 1)(r - 2)}{r!} x^r$$

$$= \frac{x^r}{r!} - \frac{2x^r}{(r - 1)!} + \frac{3x^r}{(r - 2)!} + \frac{2x^r}{(r - 3)!}.$$

When $r = 0, 1, 2$, the negative factorials interpreted as infinity give the correct values for the first three terms. Hence the sum equals

$$\left(1 + x + \frac{x^2}{2!} + \ldots\right) - 2\left(x + \frac{x^2}{1!} + \frac{x^3}{2!} + \ldots\right) + 3\left(x^2 + \frac{x^3}{1!} + \frac{x^4}{2!} + \ldots\right)$$

$$+ 2\left(x^3 + \frac{x^4}{1!} + \frac{x^5}{2!} + \ldots\right)$$

$$= e^x - 2xe^x + 3x^2e^x + 2x^3e^x$$

$$= (1 - 2x + 3x^2 + 2x^3)e^x.$$

Example 21 Sum the series

$$4 + \frac{6x}{1!} + \frac{2x^2}{2!} + \frac{2x^3}{3!} + \frac{4x^4}{4!} + \frac{6x^5}{5!} + \frac{2x^6}{6!} + \frac{2x^7}{7!} + \frac{4x^8}{8!} + \frac{6x^9}{9!} + \frac{2x^{10}}{10!} + \ldots$$

As far as the numerators are concerned, it can be seen that the coefficients progress in groups of four, namely 4, 6, 2, 2. Exponential-type series are suggested, so we try an arbitrary combination of four such series:

$$A \cos x + B \sin x + C \cosh x + D \sinh x.$$

In such a series, the coefficients have numerators that progress in groups of four; it is therefore sufficient to equate coefficients of the first four terms:

$$4 = A + C, \quad 6 = B + D, \quad 2 = -A + C, \quad 2 = -B + D.$$

Hence $A = 1, B = 2, C = 3, D = 4$, so the sum is

$$\cos x + 2 \sin x + 3 \cosh x + 4 \sinh x.$$

Example 22 If the coefficients of x and x^2 vanish in the expansion of

$$\frac{1 - ax}{1 - bx} e^{cx} \quad (c \neq 0),$$

in terms of x, show that $a = -b = \frac{1}{2}c$, and find the coefficient of x^4.

If $|x|$ is small enough, $1/(1 - bx)$ may be expanded as an absolutely convergent series; term by term multiplication with the exponential series is then permitted, yielding

$$(1 - ax)(1 + bx + b^2x^2 + b^3x^3 + b^4x^4 + \ldots)$$
$$(1 + cx + \tfrac{1}{2}c^2x^2 + \tfrac{1}{6}c^3x^3 + \tfrac{1}{24}c^4x^4 + \ldots).$$

Collecting together the various coefficients:

the constant term $= 1$,

coefficient of $x = 0 = c - a + b$,

coefficient of $x^2 = 0 = \tfrac{1}{2}c^2 - ac + bc - ab + b^2$,

coefficient of $x^3 = \tfrac{1}{6}c^3 - \tfrac{1}{2}ac^2 + \tfrac{1}{2}bc^2 - abc + b^2c - ab^2 + b^3$,

coefficient of $x^4 = \tfrac{1}{24}c^4 - \tfrac{1}{6}ac^3 + \tfrac{1}{6}bc^3 - \tfrac{1}{2}abc^2 + \tfrac{1}{2}b^2c^2 - ab^2c + b^3c - ab^3 + b^4$.

Since $c - a + b$ vanishes, the last three terms in the coefficients of x^2, x^3 and x^4 also vanish, giving $c = 2a$ from the coefficient of x^2. Taken with $c - a + b = 0$, we obtain $a = -b = \tfrac{1}{2}c$. In terms of a, the coefficient of x^4 is then

$$a^4(\tfrac{16}{24} - \tfrac{8}{6} - \tfrac{8}{6} + \tfrac{4}{2} + \tfrac{4}{2} - 2) = 0.$$

3.9   The logarithmic series

Here we merely quote the expansion for $\log_e (1 + x)$, leaving the proof of its formal expansion until later. We have

$$\log_e (1 + x) = x - \frac{x^2}{2} + \frac{x^3}{3} - \ldots + (-1)^{r-1}\frac{x^r}{r} + \ldots.$$

We use the ratio test to examine the convergence of this series, obtaining

$$\left|\frac{u_{r+1}}{u_r}\right| = \left|\frac{xr}{r + 1}\right| \to |x|$$

as r tends to infinity. Hence the series converges if $|x| < 1$. Moreover, if $x = +1$, the series converges by the alternating sign test, but $x = -1$, the series is proportional to the harmonic series, so it is divergent. The series represents the functions only in the range $-1 < x \leqslant 1$. When x is replaced by $-x$, we have

$$\log_e (1 - x) = -x - \frac{x^2}{2} - \frac{x^3}{3} - \frac{x^4}{4} - \ldots - \frac{x^r}{r} - \ldots,$$

valid in the range $-1 \leqslant x < 1$.

Subtracting these two series, we obtain

$$\log_e (1 + x) - \log_e (1 - x) = \log_e \left(\frac{1 + x}{1 - x}\right)$$

$$= 2\left(x + \frac{x^3}{3} + \frac{x^5}{5} + \ldots\right) \qquad (9)$$

valid only in the open interval $-1 < x < 1$.

If we place $y = (1 + x)/(1 - x)$, then $x = (y - 1)/(y + 1)$, and whatever the positive value of y, x lies between -1 and $+1$ as can easily be ascertained. Hence

$$\log_e y = 2\left[\frac{y-1}{y+1} + \frac{1}{3}\left(\frac{y-1}{y+1}\right)^3 + \frac{1}{5}\left(\frac{y-1}{y+1}\right)^5 + \cdots\right] \qquad (10)$$

valid for all positive values of y.

Another important formula is obtained by putting

$$(1 + x)/(1 - x) = (n + 1)/n,$$

so $$x = (2n + 1)^{-1}.$$

Provided n does not lie in the range $-1 < n < 0$, x lies in the range $-1 < x < 1$, so

$$\tfrac{1}{2} \log \left[(n + 1)/n\right] = (2n + 1)^{-1} + \tfrac{1}{3}(2n + 1)^{-3} + \tfrac{1}{5}(2n + 1)^{-5} + \cdots.$$

Formula (10) may be used to calculate the numerical value of $\log_e y$. If only the first n terms are used in the calculation, the error equals

$$2\left[\frac{1}{2n+1}\left(\frac{y-1}{y+1}\right)^{2n+1} + \frac{1}{2n+3}\left(\frac{y-1}{y+1}\right)^{2n+3} + \cdots\right]$$

$$< \frac{2}{2n+1}\left[\left(\frac{y-1}{y+1}\right)^{2n+1} + \left(\frac{y-1}{y+1}\right)^{2n+3} + \cdots\right]$$

$$= \frac{2}{2n+1} \cdot \left(\frac{y-1}{y+1}\right)^{2n+1} \cdot \frac{1}{1 - [(y-1)/(y+1)]^2} \text{ since } \left|\frac{y-1}{y+1}\right| < 1$$

$$= (y - 1)^{2n+1}/[2y(2n + 1)(y + 1)^{2n-1}].$$

If $\log_e 2$ is calculated using only 4 terms, the error is less than

$$1/[4.9.3^7] = 0 \cdot 00001203.$$

The characteristic feature of a logarithmic series is that powers of x appear with only integers in the denominators. The use of partial fractions is often necessary to rearrange the general term of a given series; examples 23 and 24 demonstrate this.

Example 23 Sum the series with the general term

$$u_r = \frac{7r^2 + 11r + 2}{r(r + 1)(r + 2)}\left(\frac{1}{2}\right)^r.$$

Resolving into partial fractions, we obtain

$$u_r = \left[\frac{1}{r} + \frac{2}{r + 1} + \frac{4}{r + 2}\right]\left(\frac{1}{2}\right)^r.$$

Adjusting the index of $\frac{1}{2}$ in the various terms, we obtain for the sum

$$[\tfrac{1}{2} + \tfrac{1}{2}(\tfrac{1}{2})^2 + \tfrac{1}{3}(\tfrac{1}{2})^3 + \ldots] + 4[\tfrac{1}{2}(\tfrac{1}{2})^2 + \tfrac{1}{3}(\tfrac{1}{2})^3 + \tfrac{1}{4}(\tfrac{1}{2})^4 + \ldots]$$
$$+ 16[\tfrac{1}{3}(\tfrac{1}{2})^3 + \tfrac{1}{4}(\tfrac{1}{2})^4 + \tfrac{1}{5}(\tfrac{1}{2})^5 + \ldots]$$
$$= -\log(1 - \tfrac{1}{2}) + 4[-\log(1 - \tfrac{1}{2}) - \tfrac{1}{2}] + 16[-\log(1 - \tfrac{1}{2}) - \tfrac{1}{2} - \tfrac{1}{2}(\tfrac{1}{2})^2]$$
$$= 21 \log_e 2 - 12.$$

Example 24 Sum the series whose general term is

$$u_r = \frac{3r + 2}{(2r - 1)2r(2r + 1)}.$$

Resolved into partial fractions, u_r takes the form

$$u_r = \frac{\tfrac{7}{4}}{2r - 1} - \frac{2}{2r} + \frac{\tfrac{1}{4}}{2r + 1}.$$

Gathering together terms with similar denominators into vertical columns, the sum becomes

$$\frac{\tfrac{7}{4}}{1} - \frac{2}{2} + \frac{\tfrac{1}{4}}{3}$$
$$\frac{\tfrac{7}{4}}{3} - \frac{2}{4} + \frac{\tfrac{1}{4}}{5}$$
$$\frac{\tfrac{7}{4}}{5} - \frac{2}{6} + \frac{\tfrac{1}{4}}{7}$$

$$. \quad . \quad . \quad . \quad . \quad . \quad .$$

$$= \tfrac{7}{4} + 2(-\tfrac{1}{2} + \tfrac{1}{3} - \tfrac{1}{4} + \tfrac{1}{5} - , , ,)$$
$$= \tfrac{7}{4} + 2(\log 2 - 1) = 2\log 2 - \tfrac{1}{4}.$$

Example 25 Assuming that

$$\sin\theta = \theta\left(1 - \frac{\theta^2}{\pi^2}\right)\left(1 - \frac{\theta^2}{2^2\pi^2}\right)\left(1 - \frac{\theta^2}{3^2\pi^2}\right)\ldots$$

show that

$$\frac{1}{1^4} + \frac{1}{2^4} + \frac{1}{3^4} + \frac{1}{4^4} + \ldots = \frac{\pi^4}{90}.$$

Taking logarithms of the infinite product for $\sin\theta$, we obtain

$$\log\sin\theta = \log\theta + \log(1 - \theta^2/\pi^2) + \log(1 - \theta^2/2^2\pi^2) + \ldots$$
$$= \log\theta - [(\theta^2/\pi^2) + \tfrac{1}{2}(\theta^2/\pi^2)^2 + \ldots]$$
$$- [(\theta^2/2^2\pi^2) + \tfrac{1}{2}(\theta^2/2^2\pi^2)^2 + \ldots]$$
$$= \log\theta - (\theta^2/\pi^2)(1 + 2^{-2} + 3^{-2} + \ldots)$$
$$- (\theta^4/2\pi^4)(1 + 2^{-4} + 3^{-4} + \ldots)$$

expanding up to the term θ^4.

But expanding $\sin \theta$ and then its logarithm, we obtain

$$\log \sin \theta = \log \left(\theta - \frac{\theta^3}{3!} + \frac{\theta^5}{5!} - \ldots\right) = \log \theta + \log (1 - \tfrac{1}{6}\theta^2 + \tfrac{1}{120}\theta^4 - \ldots)$$

$$= \log \theta - (\tfrac{1}{6}\theta^2 - \tfrac{1}{120}\theta^4) - \tfrac{1}{2}(\tfrac{1}{6}\theta^2 - \tfrac{1}{120}\theta^4)^2$$

$$= \log \theta - \tfrac{1}{6}\theta^2 - \tfrac{1}{180}\theta^4$$

again up to the term θ^4. Equating the coefficient of θ^4 in these two methods of expansion, we obtain the required series.

EXERCISES

(1). Sum to n terms the series whose rth term is given by

(i)★ $(r^2 + 3r + 1)/[r^2(r + 1)^2]$,

(ii)★ $r/[(r + 4)(r + 5)(r + 6)]$,

(iii) $(r + 2)^2/[r(r + 1)(r + 2)(r + 3)]$,

(iv) $(n + r)^2$,

(v) $(2^r - 1)x^{r-1}$,

(vi)★ $(2r + 1)3^r$.

(vii)★ If $f(x) = x^2(ax^2 + bx + c)$, determine values of a, b, c such that

$$f[(n + 1)n] - f[n(n - 1)] = n^7$$

for all n. Hence find a formula for the sum of the seventh powers of the integers from 1 to N.

(viii)★ Prove that $8 \sin x \cos^3 x = 2 \sin 2x + \sin 4x$, and find the sum to n terms of the series whose rth term is $\sin rx$. Prove also that

$$\sum_{r=1}^{n} \sin rx \cos^3 rx = 0$$

for $x = \pi/n$ and for $x = \pi/(n + 1)$.

(2). Prove by induction that

(i) $$\sum_{r=1}^{n} \frac{2r}{1 + r^2 + r^4} = 1 - \frac{1}{1 + n + n^2},$$

(ii)★ $\sum_{r=1}^{n} \tan^{-1} (1/2r^2) = \tan^{-1} (2n + 1) - \tfrac{1}{4}\pi$.

(3)★. Sum the geometric progression $1 + x + \ldots + x^n$, and hence evaluate the sum $1 + 2x + \ldots + nx^{n-1}$, and the sum to infinity

$$1 + \frac{2}{3} + \frac{3}{3^2} + \frac{4}{3^3} + \ldots + \frac{n}{3^{n-1}} + \ldots.$$

(4). Test for convergence or otherwise the series whose general terms are given by:

(i) $(2r - 1)^{-2}$, (ii) $1/[r(r + 2)]$, (iii) $(2r + 4)/[r(r + 2)(r + 4)]$,

(iv) $(1 + 2 + \ldots + r)/r^3$, (v) $r^{\frac{1}{2}}/(r + 1)$, (vi) $(r^{\frac{1}{2}} - 1)/(r^2 + 1)$,

(vii) $1/(rx^r)$, (viii) r^2x^r, (ix) $1.3 \ldots (2r - 1)x^r/2.5 \ldots (3r - 1)$,

(x) $r^4x^r/r!$, (xi) $(-1)^r(r + 1)/r$, (xii) $(-1)^r(\sin rx)/r^{\frac{3}{2}}$,

(xiii) $(-1)^rx^r/r^{\frac{1}{2}}$, (xiv) $(r^2 - 1)x^r/(r^2 + 1)$, (xv) $(\cos rx)/r^2$.

(5). Resolve into partial fractions:

(i)★ $1/[x(x + 1)^2(1 - x)^3]$,   (ii)★ $1/[x(1 + x^2)^2]$,

(iii)★ $(x^3 + x^2 - x + 1)/(x + 1)^4$,   (iv)★ $x(x + 2)/[(2 - x)^3(1 - x)]$.

(6)★. By writing the expression $(1 + x)/[(1 - 2x)(1 - x)]$ in partial fractions show that, if x is numerically less than $\frac{1}{2}$, the coefficient of x^n in its expansion in ascending powers of x is $3.2^n - 2$.

(7)★. Express the function $1/[(x^2 + 1)(x - 2)]$ as a sum of partial fractions. For what range of values of x can the function be expanded as a series of ascending powers of x? Find the coefficients of x^{2n} and x^{2n+1}.

(8)★. Find coefficients a, b and c such that

$$27 + 32(1 - 4x)(1 - x)^2 = a(1 - x)^2 + b(1 - 4x)^2 + c(1 - x)(1 - 4x)^2.$$

Express $27/(1 - 5x + 4x^2)^2$ in terms of partial fractions and obtain its expansion in positive integral powers of x, stating the range of values of x for which the expansion is valid. Deduce that $4^{n+2}(3n + 1) + 3n + 11$ has 27 as a factor for all positive integral values of n.

(9)★. Express $(11x - 2)/[(x - 2)^2(x^2 + 1)]$ in terms of partial fractions. Show that the coefficient of x^{2n} in the expansion of this expression in positive powers of x is $(4n + 3)2^{-2n-1} + 2(-1)^{n-1}$, and find the coefficient of x^{2n+1}. State the range of values of x for which this expansion is valid.

(10)★. Express in partial fractions $f(x) = 25x/[(1 - x)^2(1 - 6x)]$, and find the coefficient of x^n in the expansion of $f(x)$ in a series of ascending powers of x. Deduce that an integer of the form $6^{n+1} - 5(n + 1) - 1$ is divisible by 25.

(11)★. Express $(2x^3 - 2x^2 + 3x + 1)/[(1 - x)(1 - 2x)(1 + x)^2]$ in terms of partial fractions. Deduce that if this expression is expanded as a power series in x the coefficient of x^n in the expansion is $2^{n+1} + (-1)^{n+1}n - 1$.

(12)★. Express $x(x^2 + 7)/[8x^3 + 1 - 3x^2(x^2 + 2)]$ in partial fractions. Hence expand it in a power series that converges for sufficiently small values of x. (The denominator has a repeated zero.)

(13)★. Show that the coefficients of x^{2k} and x^{2k+1} in the expansion of $25/[(1 - 2x)^2(1 + x^2)^2]$ as a series of ascending powers of x are respectively $(10k + 7)4^{k+1} - 3(-1)^k$ and $(5k + 6)4^{k+2} + 4(-1)^k$. Deduce that every integer of these forms is divisible by 25.

(14). Find the sum to infinity of the series

(i)★
$$\frac{5}{3.6} + \frac{5.7}{3.6.9} + \frac{5.7.9}{3.6.9.12} + \cdots,$$

(ii)
$$1 + \frac{1}{2}\left(\frac{3}{4}\right) + \frac{1.3}{2.4}\left(\frac{3}{4}\right)^2 + \frac{1.3.5}{2\,4\,6}\left(\frac{3}{4}\right)^3 + \cdots$$

(iii)
$$1 - \frac{1}{5} + \frac{1.4}{5.10} - \frac{1.4.7}{5.10.15} + \cdots.$$

(15)★. If $f(x) = (5x^2 - 4x^3)/[(1 + x)(2 - x)^2]$, where $|x| < 1$, show that the sum of the coefficients in its expansion in ascending integral powers of x, up to and including the coefficient of x^n, is equal to $(n - 1)2^{-n} + 1$ if n is even, and $(n - 1)2^{-n}$ if n is odd.

(16)★. Show that the sum of the first $(n + 1)$ coefficients in the expansion of

$(1 - x)^m$ in ascending powers of x is equal to the coefficient of x^n in the expansion of $(1 - x)^{m-1}$, whatever the value of m. Find the value of

$$1 + \tfrac{1}{2} + \frac{1.3}{2.4} + \ldots + \frac{1.3.5 \ldots (2n - 1)}{2.4.6 \ldots 2n}.$$

$(17)^{\star}$. Prove that when x is small $(x^2 + 6x + 12)/(x^2 - 6x + 12)$ differs from e^x by terms of the order of x^5.

By putting $x = \tfrac{1}{6}i\pi$, show that an approximate value of π is given by the positive root of the equation

$$z^2 + 36(2 + \sqrt{3})z - 432 = 0.$$

$(18)^{\star}$. Sum the infinite series whose general term is given below, starting with the value of r given in brackets.

(i) $(3r + 2)/(r + 1)!$: $(r = 1)$, (ii) $(r - 1)^2 x^r/r!$: $(r = 2)$,
(iii) $(-1)^r (r + 1)/r! (r + 2)$: $(r = 1)$, (iv) $r^3/r!$: $(r = 1)$,
(v) $(4r^2 - 1)/r!$: $(r = 1)$, (vi) $(r^2 - 2r + 3)/r!$: $(r = 1)$,
(vii) $(2r + 1)2^{2r}/(2r)!$: $(r = 0)$, (viii) $(3r^2 - 4r - 2)/r!$: $(r = 1)$,
(ix) $(2r - 1)(2r + 1)(2r + 3)/(2r)!$: $(r = 1)$, (x) $x^r/r(r - 2)!$: $(r = 4)$,
(xi) $r^2(r + 1)^2/r!$: $(r = 1)$, (xii) $x^r(x - r)^2/r!$: $(r = 0)$,
(xiii) $x^{4r}/(4r)!$: $(r = 0)$, (xiv) $x^{4r-3}/(4r - 3)!$: $(r = 1)$.

$(19)^{\star}$. A circular arc subtends an angle θ at the centre of the circle and a, b, c are the lengths of the chords of the arc, of two-thirds of the arc and of one-third of the arc respectively. Prove that numbers x, y, z can be found independent of θ, a, b, c such that the length of the arc is $ax + by + cz$ approximately, the approximation being correct to the order θ^6, and determine these values.

$(20)^{\star}$. Express as an infinite series the coefficient of x^n in the power series expansion of $\exp(e^x)$, and by summing this series for the case $n = 2$, find the coefficient of x^2 in the expansion.

$(21)^{\star}$. Sum the infinite series whose general term is given below, starting with the value $r = 1$.

(i) $(r + 2)/r(r + 1)3^r$ (ii) $x^r/r(r + 1)(r + 2)$,
(iii) $x^r/(r^2 + r)$,   (iv) $1/[r(r + 1)(n + 1)^r]$.

$(22)^{\star}$. Find the values of a and b if the expansion of

$$\frac{1 + ax}{1 + bx} \log_e (1 + x)$$

in powers of x contains no term in x^2 and no term in x^3, and show that the coefficient of x^4 is $-\tfrac{1}{36}$.

$(23)^{\star}$. If $1 + x = b/a$, show that

$$(b^2 - a^2)/2ab = x - \tfrac{1}{2}x^2 + \tfrac{1}{3}x^3 - \ldots.$$

Hence, show that if b is nearly equal to a, $(b^2 - a^2)/2ab$ exceeds $\log (b/a)$ by about $(b - a)^3/6a^3$.

$(24)^{\star}$. Using the expansion of $\log y$ in ascending powers of $(y - 1)/(y + 1)$, show that, if $-\pi/3 < \theta < \pi/3$, then $\log \cos \theta$ differs from $-2 \tan^2 \tfrac{1}{2}\theta$ by less than $\tfrac{1}{36}$.

$(25)^{\star}$. Show that, if $-1 < x < +1$,

$$(1 - x)^{-x} = 1 - x \log (1 - x) + \frac{x^2}{2!} [\log (1 - x)]^2 - \frac{x^3}{3!} [\log (1 - x)]^3 + \ldots$$

and hence expand $(1 - x)^{-x}$ in powers of x up to the term in x^6.

(26)*. Express $1 + \cos \theta$ in terms of $\cos \frac{1}{2}\theta$ and show that, if θ is small,

$$\log_e (1 + \cos \theta) = \log_e 2 - \tfrac{1}{4}\theta^2 - \tfrac{1}{96}\theta^4$$

approximately.

(27)*. If x is an acute angle, prove that

$$\tan x = x + \frac{x^3}{3} + \frac{2x^5}{15} + \dots .$$

Hence prove that

$$\log \sec x = \frac{x^2}{2} + \frac{x^4}{12} + \frac{x^6}{45} + \dots .$$

When $x = 0.1$, show that $1 + \log \sec x - \cosh x$ is approximately 4.2×10^{-6}.

(28)*. Find the first (non-vanishing) term in the expansion of

$$(1 - e^x)(1 + \tfrac{1}{3}x)^{-3} + \log_e (1 + x).$$

(29)*. Find the expansion of $[(\sinh x) \log (1 + x)]/x^2(1 + x)^3$ as a power series in x, up to and including the term in x^2.

(30)*. Show that numbers a, b, c can be found such that the difference between $e^x(1 - ax + bx^2 - cx^3)$ and $1 + ax + bx^2 + cx^3$ does not involve any power of x lower than x^7.

(31)*. Show that, for small values of x,

$$\sec^2 (\tfrac{1}{4}\pi + x) = 2 + 4x + ax^2 + bx^3 + cx^4 + \dots ,$$

and determine a, b, c. Expand $\sqrt{[2 + \sec^2 (\tfrac{1}{4}\pi + x)]}$ in ascending powers of x as far as the term involving x^3.

ANSWERS TO EXERCISES

(1). (i) $2 - (n + 2)/(n + 1)^2$. (ii) $\frac{1}{10} - (n + 3)/(n + 5)(n + 6)$.

    (iii) $\frac{29}{36} - (6n^2 + 27n + 29)/6(n + 1)(n + 3)$. (iv) $\frac{1}{6}n(2n + 1)(7n + 1)$.

    (v) $(2^{n+1}x^n - 2)/(2x - 1) - (x^n - 1)/(x - 1)$. (vi) $n3^{n+1}$.

    (vii) $a = \frac{1}{8}, b = -\frac{1}{6}, c = \frac{1}{12}, \frac{1}{24}n^2(n + 1)^2(3n^4 + 6n^3 - n^2 - 4n + 2)$.

(3). $(1 - x^{n+1})/(1 - x), [nx^{n+1} - (n + 1)x^n + 1]/(1 - x)^2, \frac{9}{4}$.

(4). (i) conv. (ii) conv. (iii) conv. (iv) div. (v) div. (vi) conv.

    (vii) $|x| < 1$ div., $|x| > 1$ conv., $x = 1$ div., $x = -1$ conv.

    (viii) $|x| < 1$ conv., $|x| \geqslant 1$ div. (ix) $|x| < \frac{3}{2}$ conv., $|x| > \frac{3}{2}$ div. (x) conv.

        (xi) osc. (xii) abs. conv.

    (xiii) $x \leqslant -1$ div., $|x| < 1$ conv., $x = 1$ conv., $x > 1$ osc.

    (xiv) $|x| < 1$ conv., $x \leqslant -1$ osc., $x \geqslant 1$ div. (xv) abs. conv.

(5). (i) $1/x - 5/16(x + 1) - 1/8(x + 1)^2 + 11/16(1 - x) + 1/2(1 - x)^2$
       $+ 1/4(1 - x)^3$.

    (ii) $1/x - x/(1 + x^2) - x/(1 + x^2)^2$.

    (iii) $1/(x + 1) - 2/(x + 1)^2 + 2/(x + 1)^4$.

    (iv) $-3/(2 - x) - 2/(2 - x)^2 - 8/(2 - x)^3 + 3/(1 - x)$.

(7). $1/5 (x - 2) - (x + 2)/5(1 + x^2), -1 < x < 1; - [2(-1)^n + 2^{-2n-1}]/5,$
      $-[(-1)^n + 2^{-2n-2}]/5.$

(8). $a = 48, b = 3, c = 8$; $48/(1 - 4x)^2 + 3/(1 - x)^2 + 8/(1 - x)$
      $- 32/(1 - 4x); \Sigma [4^{n+2}(3n + 1) + 3n + 11]x^n; |x| < \frac{1}{4}.$

(9). $1/(2 - x) + 4/(2 - x)^2 + (x - 2)/(x^2 + 1); (4n + 5)2^{-2n-2} + (-1)^n;$
      $-1 < x < 1.$

(10). $-1/(1 - x) - 5/(1 - x)^2 + 6/(1 - 6x), 6^{n+1} - 5(n + 1) - 1$.

(11). $-1/(1 - x) + 2/(1 - 2x) + 1/(1 + x) - 1/(1 + x)^2$.

(12). $-1/(1 - x)^2 + 2/(1 - x)^3 - 1/(1 + 3x)$;

$$7x + \sum_{n=2}^{\infty} [(n + 1)(2n + 3) - (-1)^n 3^n] x^n.$$

(14). (i) $\sqrt{3} - \frac{2}{3}$. (ii) 2. (iii) $\frac{1}{2}\sqrt[3]{5}$.

(16). $3 . 5 . 7 \ldots (2n + 1)/2 . 4 . 6 \ldots (2n)$.

(18). (i) $2e - 1$. (ii) $e^x(1 - x + x^2) - 1$. (iii) $3/e - \frac{3}{2}$. (iv) $5e$. (v) $7e + 1$.
  (vi) $3(e - 1)$. (vii) $(3e^4 - 1)/2e^2$. (viii) 0. (ix) $3 + \frac{1}{2}(7e - 1/e)$.
  (x) $(x - 1)e^x + 1 - \frac{1}{2}x^2 - \frac{1}{3}x^3$. (xi) $27e$. (xii) xe^x. (xiii) $\frac{1}{2}(\cosh x + \cos x)$.
  (xiv) $\frac{1}{2}(\sinh x - \sin x)$.

(19). $x = \frac{1}{10}, y = -\frac{9}{10}, z = \frac{243}{10}$.

(20). $1 + 1/n! + 2^n/2! \, n! + 3^n/3! \, n! + \ldots, e + 1$.

(21). (i) $1 + \log_e \frac{2}{3}$. (ii) $\frac{3}{4} - \frac{1}{2}/x - [(1 - x)^2/2x^2] \log_e (1 - x)$.
  (iii) $1 + [(1 - x)/x] \log_e (1 - x)$. (iv) $1 - n \log (1 + 1/n)$.

(22). $a = \frac{2}{3}, b = \frac{1}{6}$.

(25). $1 + x^2 + \frac{1}{2}x^3 + \frac{5}{6}x^4 + \frac{3}{4}x^5 + \frac{33}{40}x^6$.

(28). $-19x^4/216$.

(29). $1 - \frac{7}{2}x + 8x^2$.

(30). $a = \frac{1}{2}, b = \frac{1}{10}, c = \frac{1}{120}$.

(31). $a = 8, b = \frac{40}{3}, c = \frac{64}{3}; \ 2 + x + \frac{7}{4}x^2 + \frac{59}{24}x^3$.

CHAPTER 4

INEQUALITIES

4.1 Elementary observations

This chapter will not be restricted merely to algebraical inequalities and algebraical methods; the differential and integral calculus may also be used to prove inequalities of various forms.

The elementary basis of the subject, although almost self-evident, is nevertheless fraught with danger to the unwary, for in some respects inequalities may be manipulated according to the same rules as equations, while in other respects they are quite distinct. Throughout the chapter, we are concerned only with real numbers.

If it is given that $a > b$, then any positive or negative number c may be added to each side of the inequality, at the same time preserving the inequality

$$a + c > b + c.$$

In particular, if $c = -a - b$, the result is $-b > -a$.

If each side is multiplied or divided by a *positive* number c, the inequality is preserved:

$$ac > bc \quad \text{or} \quad a/c > b/c.$$

But if c is negative, the sign of the inequality is reversed:

$$ac < bc \quad \text{or} \quad a/c < b/c.$$

If both a and b are positive, the inequality $a > b$ may be divided by ab, yielding

$$1/b > 1/a.$$

4.2 Algebraical inequalities

Inequalities may be proved by a variety of methods; certain standard methods exist, while other inequalities need individual treatment each on its own merit. The following examples use the devices:

(*a*) If a quadratic equation has real roots, its discriminant is positive.

(*b*) The method whereby all terms of an inequality are brought to its left hand side, which is then rearranged or factorized.

(*c*) Inequalities containing ratios, whose numerators and denominators are linear functions of x, require cross-multiplication, special regard being paid to sign.

(*d*) Special methods.

Example 1 If x, y, z are three variables restricted by the conditions

$$x + y + z = 15, \quad yz + zx + xy = 72,$$

prove that $3 \leqslant x \leqslant 7$.

We may eliminate one variable, say z, from the two given equations. Then

$$z = 15 - x - y$$

and

$$z(x + y) + x y = 72,$$

so

$$(x + y)(15 - x - y) + xy = 72.$$

Arranged as a quadratic in y, this is

$$y^2 + y(x - 15) + x^2 - 15x + 72 = 0.$$

In order that y should be real, the discriminant of this equation must not be negative, so

$$(x - 15)^2 - 4(x^2 - 15x + 72) \geqslant 0,$$

or

$$(x - 7)(x - 3) \leqslant 0.$$

It follows that $3 \leqslant x \leqslant 7$.

Example 2 If a, b, c are positive numbers with $a + b > c$, show

$$a/(1 + a) + b/(1 + b) > c/(1 + c).$$

We take all terms to the left hand side and rearrange thus:

$$\frac{a}{1 + a} + \frac{b}{1 + b} - \frac{c}{1 + c} = \frac{a(1 + b)(1 + c) + b(1 + a)(1 + c) - c(1 + a)(1 + b)}{(1 + a)(1 + b)(1 + c)}$$

$$= \frac{(a + b - c) + ab(c + 2)}{(1 + a)(1 + b)(1 + c)} > 0,$$

since both terms in the numerator are positive.

Example 3 (i) If a and b are distinct positive numbers, prove

$$a^3b^5 + a^5b^3 < a^8 + b^8.$$

(ii) If $0 < a < b < c$, prove

$$\frac{a - c}{b} > \frac{b - c}{a} + \frac{a - b}{c}.$$

Proof of (i). Taking all terms to the left hand side, we have

$$a^3b^5 + a^5b^3 - a^8 - b^8 \equiv (a^3 - b^3)(b^5 - a^5) < 0,$$

since one bracket must be positive and the other negative.

Proof of (ii). Taking all terms to the left hand side, we have

$$\frac{a - c}{b} - \frac{b - c}{a} - \frac{a - b}{c} \equiv \frac{ac(a - c) + bc(c - b) + ab(b - a)}{abc}$$

$$\equiv \frac{(a - b)(b - c)(c - a)}{abc} > 0$$

since $a - b < 0$, $b - c < 0$, $c - a > 0$.

Example 4   Find the ranges of x such that

$$\frac{2x - 1}{x - 2} + \frac{3x - 2}{x - 4} > 1.$$

If $(x - 2)(x - 4) > 0$, that is either if $x < 2$ or $x > 4$, we may cross-multiply by $(x - 2)(x - 4)$, obtaining

$$(2x - 1)(x - 4) + (x - 2)(3x - 2) - (x - 2)(x - 4) > 0,$$

reducing to $(4x - 11)x > 0.$

This implies either $x < 0$ or $x > \frac{11}{4}$. The ranges common to both these requirements are $x < 0$, $x > 4$.

On the other hand, if $2 < x < 4$, then $(x - 2)(x - 4)$ is negative, so cross-multiplication requires the inequality to be reversed:

$$(2x - 1)(x - 4) + (x - 2)(3x - 2) - (x - 2)(x - 4) < 0,$$

reducing to $x(4x - 11) < 0,$

implying that $0 < x < \frac{11}{4}$. The common range of these two requirements is $2 < x < \frac{11}{4}$.

The complete set of ranges for x is then $x < 0$, $2 < x < \frac{11}{4}$, $x > 4$.

Example 5   If $x > 0$, but not equal to unity, and if p, q are positive integers such that $p > q$, show that

$$\frac{x^p - 1}{p} > \frac{x^q - 1}{q}.$$

Extend this inequality to include the case when p and q are positive rational fractions. If $m > 1$, deduce

$$x^m - 1 > m(x - 1).$$

First of all, we consider the special case $q = p - 1$. Then

$$\frac{x^p - 1}{p} - \frac{x^{p-1} - 1}{p - 1} \equiv \frac{(x - 1)px^{p-1} - (x^p - 1)}{p(p - 1)}$$

$$\equiv (x - 1)(px^{p-1} - x^{p-1} - x^{p-2} - \ldots - x - 1)/p(p - 1)$$

where we have factorized $x^p - 1$. Now if $x > 1$, each of the two brackets in the numerator is positive. The second bracket is positive since

$$x^{p-1} > x^{p-2} > x^{p-3} > \ldots > x > 1,$$

so $px^{p-1} >$ the sum of these p values.

Similarly, if $x < 1$, each bracket is negative. In both cases, the product is positive, so

$$\frac{x^p - 1}{p} > \frac{x^{p-1} - 1}{p - 1}.$$

Hence, upon diminishing the index of x and the denominator successively in steps of unity until q is attained, we conclude that

$$\frac{x^p - 1}{p} > \frac{x^q - 1}{q}.$$

Consider now the rational fractions $r/s > t/u$. This implies that $ru > st$, where both ru and st are integers. Let $x^{1/su} = y$. Then

$$\frac{x^{r/s} - 1}{r/s} = su\left(\frac{y^{ru} - 1}{ru}\right) > su\left(\frac{y^{st} - 1}{st}\right) = \frac{x^{t/u} - 1}{t/u},$$

demonstrating that the inequality is valid for positive rational fractions.

In particular, let $p = m$ and $q = 1$, where $m > 1$. Then

$$(x^m - 1)/m > (x - 1),$$

or

$$x^m - 1 > m(x - 1).$$

4.3 Quadratic forms

The expression

$$S \equiv ax^2 + 2hxy + by^2,$$

where a, b, h are real numbers, is known as a *quadratic form* in the two real variables x and y. We seek conditions under which the value of S is positive for all real values of x and y, excluding the special pair of values $x = y = 0$.

We may rearrange S by completing the square:

$$
\begin{aligned}
S &\equiv (a^2x^2 + 2haxy + aby^2)/a \\
&= [a^2x^2 + 2haxy + h^2y^2 + (ab - h^2)y^2]/a \\
&= [(ax + hy)^2 + (ab - h^2)y^2]/a.
\end{aligned}
$$

If $y = 0$, in order that $S = ax^2$ should be positive, we require a to be positive. Moreover, when $ax + hy = 0$, we require $ab - h^2$ to be positive. A moment's reflexion shows that these two conditions are both necessary and sufficient conditions for S always to be positive; they may be written as

$$a > 0, \quad \begin{vmatrix} a & h \\ h & b \end{vmatrix} > 0. \tag{1}$$

Such a quadratic form S is called *positive definite*. If the determinant vanishes, S is evidently a perfect square.

The theory may be extended to embrace quadratic forms in three variables x, y, z:

$$S \equiv ax^2 + by^2 + cz^2 + 2fyz + 2gzx + 2hxy.$$

We seek necessary and sufficient conditions under which S is positive for all real values of x, y, z, neglecting the triplet $x = y = z = 0$.

We rearrange this form S, first by completing the square for all terms containing x, and then again for all terms containing y in the remainder:

$$\begin{aligned}
aS &\equiv a^2x^2 + 2ax(hy + gz) + aby^2 + 2afyz + acz^2 \\
&= (ax + hy + gz)^2 - (hy + gz)^2 + aby^2 + 2afyz + acz^2 \\
&= (ax + hy + gz)^2 + (ab - h^2)y^2 + 2(af - gh)yz + (ac - g^2)z^2.
\end{aligned}$$
(2)

Once again we require a to be positive, in order that S should be positive when $y = z = 0$. The first term on the right of (2) is always positive, being a perfect square. The remaining terms form a quadratic form in y and z; this must be positive definite for all values of y and z, the condition being

$$ab - h^2 > 0, \quad \begin{vmatrix} ab - h^2 & af - gh \\ af - gh & ac - g^2 \end{vmatrix} > 0.$$

When expanded, this determinant is

$$a(abc + 2fgh - af^2 - bg^2 - ch^2) > 0,$$

which may be rearranged into a 3×3 determinant:

$$\begin{vmatrix} a & h & g \\ h & b & f \\ g & f & c \end{vmatrix} > 0.$$

Hence the three conditions under which S is positive definite are

$$a > 0, \quad \begin{vmatrix} a & h \\ h & b \end{vmatrix} > 0, \quad \begin{vmatrix} a & h & g \\ h & b & f \\ g & f & c \end{vmatrix} > 0. \tag{3}$$

If this 3×3 determinant vanishes, the quadratic form in y and z on the right hand side of (2) is a perfect square. Hence aS is either the sum or the difference of two squared linear expressions; it may therefore be factorized into two linear factors, these being either real or complex. If this 3×3 determinant does not vanish, the expression S cannot be resolved into linear factors.

Example 6 Two quadratic forms are given:

$$S_1 = 6x^2 + 2y^2 + 3z^2 + 8zx - 4xy, \quad S_2 = 5x^2 + y^2 + 5z^2 + 8zx - 2xy.$$

Find the range of values of k such that $S_1 + kS_2$ is positive definite.

The combined quadratic form is

$$(6 + 5k)x^2 + (2 + k)y^2 + (3 + 5k)z^2 + (8 + 8k)zx - (4 + 2k)xy.$$

This is positive definite if the following three conditions are satisfied:

$$6 + 5k > 0, \quad \begin{vmatrix} 6 + 5k & -2 - k \\ -2 - k & 2 + k \end{vmatrix} > 0, \quad \begin{vmatrix} 6 + 5k & -2 - k & 4 + 4k \\ -2 - k & 2 + k & 0 \\ 4 + 4k & 0 & 3 + 5k \end{vmatrix} > 0;$$

these simplify to

$$6 + 5k > 0, \quad 4(k + 1)(k + 2) > 0, \quad 4(k + 1)(k + 2)(k - 1) > 0.$$

The first inequality implies $k > -\frac{6}{5}$.
The second inequality implies $k < -2$ or $k > -1$.
The third inequality implies $-2 < k < -1$ or $k > 1$.
The common range of validity for all three inequalities is $k > 1$.

4.4 Application to rational algebraical functions

The quotient $y = (ax^2 + 2hx + b)/(Ax^2 + 2Hx + B)$ is given; every real value of x may be substituted except the real roots of the denominator. Two types of problem arise.

Problem i. The symbols a, h, b, A, H, B have given numerical values, but one or more may involve an arbitrary parameter k. We seek that range of values for the parameter k such that all real values of y are produced.

The equation is equivalent to

$$(a - Ay)x^2 + 2(h - Hy)x + (b - By) = 0.$$

Since x is always real, the discriminant must be positive; that is

$$(h - Hy)^2 - (a - Ay)(b - By) > 0,$$

or $\quad (H^2 - AB)y^2 + (bA + aB - 2hH)y + (h^2 - ab) > 0$

for all values of y. This form must be positive definite, so we require

$$H^2 - AB > 0, \quad \begin{vmatrix} H^2 - AB & \frac{1}{2}(bA + aB - 2hH) \\ \frac{1}{2}(bA + aB - 2hH) & h^2 - ab \end{vmatrix} > 0.$$

An examination of these inequalities containing the parameter k enables the required range of k to be found.

Problem ii. The symbols a, h, b, A, H, B have given numerical values; we seek the range of values of x for which y is greater than a given value p.

For the range r_1 of values of x for which $Ax^2 + Bx + C$ is positive, we may cross-multiply to obtain

$$(a - pA)x^2 + 2(h - pH)x + (b - pB) > 0. \tag{4}$$

Let r_2 be the range of values of x for which this inequality is satisfied (deduced from the roots of the quadratic polynomial in x). Then the range common to r_1 and r_2 is part of the range that we require.

Let r_3 be the range of values of x for which $Ax^2 + 2Hx + B$ is negative. Cross-multiplication now reverses the inequality (4). If r_4 is the range of values of x for which this new inequality is satisfied, then the range common to r_3 and r_4 also satisfies the requirements.

Example 7★   Show that the expression $y = (x^2 - 3ax + 2a^2)/(x^2 - 3x + 2)$, where a is not equal to 1, can assume any real value for real values of x only if $\frac{1}{2} < a < 2$.

Show that if $a = 0$ there will be two extreme values between which the expression cannot lie and determine these values.

After cross-multiplication, the given equation becomes

$$x^2(1 - y) - 3(a - y)x + 2(a^2 - y) = 0.$$

Since x is real, the discriminant of this equation is positive:

$$9(a - y)^2 - 8(1 - y)(a^2 - y) \geqslant 0,$$

or $$y^2 + 2y(4a^2 - 9a + 4) + a^2 \geqslant 0.$$

The discriminant of this quadratic form must be negative, so

$$(4a^2 - 9a + 4)^2 - a^2 \leqslant 0,$$

or $$8(a - 1)^2(2a - 1)(a - 2) \leqslant 0.$$

This implies $\frac{1}{2} < a < 2$.

If $a = 0$, the given equation becomes

$$(y - 1)x^2 - 3yx + 2y = 0.$$

Since x is real, we require

$$9y^2 - 8y(y - 1) \geqslant 0,$$

or $$y(y + 8) \geqslant 0.$$

This is not possible for the range $-8 < y < 0$.

Example 8★   Prove that, when x is real, the function $y = (7 - 4x)/(x^2 - 2x + 2)$ assumes only values lying between -1 and 4 inclusive.

Find the ranges of values of x for which the value of the function is positive and less than 3.

Arranged as a quadratic equation in x, the given equation is

$$yx^2 + 2x(2 - y) + 2y - 7 = 0.$$

Since x is always real, we require

$$(2 - y)^2 - y(2y - 7) \geqslant 0,$$

or $$(-y + 4)(y + 1) \geqslant 0.$$

This implies that $-1 \leqslant y \leqslant 4$.

If y is less than 3, we may cross-multiply the inequality by the denominator, since this is positive definite. We obtain

$$7 - 4x < 3x^2 - 6x + 6,$$

or $$(3x + 1)(x - 1) > 0.$$

This implies that either $x < -\frac{1}{3}$ or $x > 1$.

But y is also given to be positive; hence $7 - 4x > 0$, or $x < \frac{7}{4}$. The ranges common to these results are $x < -\frac{1}{3}$, $1 < x < \frac{7}{4}$.

4.5   Application of the calculus to inequalities

The use of the calculus is often necessary in the proof of inequalities involving different types of functions of x. The basis of the method is obvious graphically, but a careful analytical proof depends on analysis more detailed than that undertaken in this text.

The use of differentiation.   If $y = f(x)$ and $y = g(x)$ are two given functions, such that when $x = a$, $f(a) = g(a)$, and such that for all $x > a$, $df(x)/dx > dg(x)/dx$, then for all $x > a$ we conclude that $f(x) > g(x)$. This follows since $f(x)$ is increasing more rapidly than $g(x)$, so the graph of $y = f(x)$ must always be above that of $y = g(x)$.

This argument may be modified to apply to the left of $x = a$. If $f(a) = g(a)$, and if for $x < a$, $df(x)/dx < dg(x)/dx$, then $f(x) > g(x)$.

The use of integration.   If $f(x) > g(x)$ for $x > a$, then

$$\int_a^t f(x)\, dx > \int_a^t g(x)\, dx,$$

where $t > a$. This result is equivalent to the fact that the area under the graph $y = f(x)$ is greater than the area under the graph $y = g(x)$.

Example 9   Prove

(i) $\cos x > 1 - \frac{1}{2}x^2$ for $0 < x < \frac{1}{2}\pi$.

(ii) $x^m - 1 > m(x - 1)$ for $x > 0$, $x \neq 1$, $m > 1$.

(i) When $x = 0$, $\cos x = 1 - \frac{1}{2}x^2 = 1$; both functions therefore have the same value at the left hand end of the range considered. The derivatives of the two functions are $-\sin x$ and $-x$ respectively. Now $x > \sin x$ in the given range, so $-\sin x > -x$.

Since the derivatives of the given functions satisfy the required inequality, it follows that the functions themselves satisfy the inequality.

(ii) Consider the two functions $f(x) = x^m - 1$ and $g(x) = m(x - 1)$. When $x = 1$, we have $f(1) = g(1) = 0$. The derivatives are given by

$$f'(x) = mx^{m-1}, \quad g'(x) = m.$$

When $x > 1$,

$$f'(x) = mx^{m-1} > m = g'(x),$$

so we conclude that $f(x) > g(x)$.

When $x < 1$,

$$0 < f'(x) < m = g'(x),$$

so again we conclude that $f(x) > g(x)$.

4

Example 10 If $x > 1$, prove

$$\text{(i)} \quad x - 1 > \log x > 1 - x^{-1}.$$
$$\text{(ii)} \quad x^2 - 1 > 2x \log x > 4(x - 1) - 2 \log x.$$

(i) If $t > 1$, we have the inequalities

$$1 > t^{-1} > t^{-2}.$$

Integration yields

$$\int_1^x dt > \int_1^x t^{-1} dt > \int_1^x t^{-2} dt$$

provided $x > 1$; that is

$$x - 1 > \log x > 1 - x^{-1}.$$

(ii) Integrating a second time, we obtain

$$\int_1^x (t - 1) dt > \int_1^x \log t \, dt > \int_1^x (1 - t^{-1}) dt$$

provided $x > 1$. The integrals yield

$$\tfrac{1}{2}x^2 - x + \tfrac{1}{2} > x \log x - x + 1 > x - \log x - 1,$$
or $\qquad\qquad x^2 - 1 > 2x \log x > 4(x - 1) - 2 \log x.$

4.6 Arithmetic and geometric means

If a and b are two positive numbers, we have $(\sqrt{a} - \sqrt{b})^2 \geqslant 0$; hence

$$a - 2\sqrt{(ab)} + b \geqslant 0,$$
or $\qquad\qquad \tfrac{1}{2}(a + b) \geqslant \sqrt{(ab)}$

the equality sign being valid only if $a = b$. $\tfrac{1}{2}(a + b)$ is defined to be the arithmetic mean of the two numbers a and b, while $\sqrt{(ab)}$ is their geometric mean.

This result may be generalized to embrace the n positive numbers $a, b, c, \ldots, k$.

Their arithmetic mean is defined to be

$$A = (a + b + c + \ldots + k)/n,$$

and their geometric mean by

$$G = (abc \ldots k)^{1/n}.$$

Theorem. The arithmetic mean of n positive numbers is not less than their geometric mean.

In symbols, we shall prove that $A \geqslant G$ where $A = G$ only if the n numbers are identical.

Various purely algebraical proofs may be provided for this theorem, but for brevity we shall give a proof based on analysis.

We note first that

$$\log x \leqslant x - 1$$

for all positive values of x, the equality sign being valid only if $x = 1$. Graphically this is so because the graph $y = \log x$ lies wholly below its tangent at $x = 1$, namely $y = x - 1$.

Let us place x equal to $a/A, b/A, \ldots, k/A$ in turn in this inequality, yielding

$$\log (a/A) \leqslant a/A - 1, \ldots, \log (k/A) \leqslant (k/A) - 1,$$

with equality only if $x = 1$ in any case. Adding, we obtain

$$\log \left(\frac{abc \ldots k}{A^n}\right) \leqslant \frac{a + b + c + \ldots + k}{A} - n = 0$$

with equality only if all the n numbers are equal to A. Hence

$$(abc \ldots k)/A^n \leqslant 1,$$

this being equivalent to $A \geqslant G$, with equality only if

$$a = b = c = \ldots = k = A = G.$$

Example 11   If a, b, c are three positive numbers, prove

$$(b + c)(c + a)(a + b) \geqslant 8abc.$$

If x, y, z are the lengths of the three sides of a triangle, prove

$$(y + z - x)(z + x - y)(x + y - z) \leqslant xyz.$$

We have

$$b + c \geqslant 2\sqrt{(bc)}, \quad c + a \geqslant 2\sqrt{(ca)}, \quad a + b \geqslant 2\sqrt{(ab)}.$$

Multiplication yields the result

$$(b + c)(c + a)(a + b) \geqslant 8abc.$$

Since x, y, z are the lengths of the sides of a triangle, the sum of any two is greater than the third, so we may take

$$a = y + z - x, \quad b = z + x - y, \quad c = x + y - z.$$

Substitution into the first result yields

$$2x.2y.2z \geqslant 8(y + z - x)(z + x - y)(x + y - z);$$

the given result follows.

Example 12   If the sum of n positive numbers is less than M, prove that the sum of their reciprocals is greater than n^2/M.

The arithmetic and geometric means are related by

$$(a + b + \ldots + k)/n \geqslant (abc \ldots k)^{1/n}.$$

Applied to the n reciprocals, the theorem gives

$$\frac{1}{n}\left(\frac{1}{a} + \frac{1}{b} + \ldots + \frac{1}{k}\right) \geqslant \left(\frac{1}{a} \cdot \frac{1}{b} \ldots \frac{1}{k}\right)^{1/n}.$$

Hence
$$\frac{1}{a} + \frac{1}{b} + \ldots + \frac{1}{k} \geqslant \frac{n}{(ab \ldots k)^{1/n}}$$

$$\geqslant \frac{n}{(a + b + \ldots + k)/n}$$

$$> n^2/M,$$

where twice in succession we have increased the value of the denominator, thereby decreasing the value of the fraction.

Example 13   If the sum of the three numbers x, y, z is 4, show that xyz^2 cannot be greater than $\frac{125}{64}$.

Treating x, y, z^2 as three positive numbers, we have

$$\tfrac{1}{3}(x + y + z^2) \geqslant (xyz^2)^{\frac{1}{3}},$$

or
$$[\tfrac{1}{3}(z^2 - z + 4)]^3 \geqslant xyz^2.$$

Hence
$$xyz^2 \leqslant \tfrac{1}{27} \text{ minimum } (z^2 - z + 4)^3$$

where z is restricted to the range $0 < z < 4$. The minimum value occurs where $z = \tfrac{1}{2}$; hence $xyz^2 \leqslant \tfrac{1}{27}(\tfrac{1}{4} - \tfrac{1}{2} + 4)^3 = \tfrac{125}{64}$.

EXERCISES

(1). If a and b are unequal positive numbers, prove the inequalities:
  (i) $(a^4 + b^4)(a + b) > (a^3 + b^3)(a^2 + b^2)$.
  (ii) $2(a^5 + b^5) > (a^3 + b^3)(a^2 + b^2)$.
  (iii) $2(a^5 + b^5) > (a + b)(a^4 + b^4)$.
  (iv) $a^3b + ab^3 < a^4 + b^4$.
  (v) $(a^4 + b^4)(a^5 + b^5) < 2(a^9 + b^9)$.
  (vi) $a^3 - a^2 > a^{-2} - a^{-3}$, $(a \neq 1)$.
  (vii) $a^{m+n} + b^{m+n} > a^m b^n + a^n b^m$, $(m, n \text{ positive integers})$.

(2)*. If a, b, c, d are any real numbers, prove that

$$a^4 + b^4 \geqslant 2a^2b^2, \quad a^4 + b^4 + c^4 + d^4 \geqslant 4abcd.$$

Prove also that

$$(a^2 + b^2)^2 + (c^2 + d^2)^2 \geqslant 2(ab + cd)^2.$$

If $a^4 + b^4 + c^4 + d^4 \leqslant 1$, show that

$$a^{-4} + b^{-4} + c^{-4} + d^{-4} \geqslant 16.$$

(3). Prove that if x_i, y_i and z_i are three sets of real numbers ($i = 1, 2, \ldots, n$)

$$\sqrt{\sum_1^n (x_i - y_i)^2} + \sqrt{\sum_1^n (y_i - z_i)^2} \geqslant \sqrt{\sum_1^n (x_i - z_i)^2}.$$

(4). Prove the following inequalities for positive numbers:

(i) $\frac{1}{2}(n + 1) > (n!)^{1/n}$.

(ii) $(a + b + c)^3 \geqslant 27(b + c - a)(c + a - b)(a + b - c)$.

(iii) $(bc + ca + ab)(a^4 + b^4 + c^4) \geqslant 9a^2b^2c^2$.

(iv) $\left(\dfrac{a}{e} + \dfrac{b}{f} + \dfrac{c}{g}\right)\left(\dfrac{e}{a} + \dfrac{f}{b} + \dfrac{g}{c}\right) \geqslant 9$.

(5). Prove the following inequalities:

(i) $2 \leqslant x + x^{-1} \leqslant x^3 + x^{-3}$, $\quad (x > 0)$.

(ii) $\cos x - 1 + \frac{1}{2}x^2 - \frac{1}{24}x^4 < 0$, $\quad (0 < x < \frac{1}{2}\pi)$.

(iii) $\sin x - x + \frac{1}{6}x^3 > 0$, $\quad (0 < x < \frac{1}{2}\pi)$.

(iv)* If $f(x) = e^x(x^2 - 6x + 12) - (x^2 + 6x + 12)$, show that $f'''(x) > 0$ when $x \neq 0$. Deduce that $f(x) > 0$ when $x > 0$ and that when $x > 0$, $\tanh x > 3x/(x^2 + 3)$.

(6)*. Use the expression $(a - b)^2 + (b - c)^2 + (c - a)^2$ to show that for all real unequal values of a, b, c,

$$a^2 + b^2 + c^2 > bc + ca + ab.$$

Prove that the quadratic equation

$$(x - b)(x - c) + (x - c)(x - a) + (x - a)(x - b) = 0$$

always has real roots.

(7)*. Prove that the expression $2x^2 - 5x + 4$ is positive for all real values of x, and find for what ranges of values of x it lies between 1 and 2. Find also for what values of k the expression

$$2x^2 - 5x + 4 - k(x - 1)^2$$

will be positive for all real values of x.

(8)*. By expressing the polynomial $x^4 - 8x^3 + 32x^2 - 64x + 48$ in the form $(x^2 + px + q)^2 - r$, or otherwise, show that it is not negative for any real value of x.

(9)*. If $y = x(x + 2)/(x - 2)(x - d)$, show that y can assume all real values for all real values of x if d lies between -2 and 0.
If $d = -1\frac{1}{2}$, find the range of values of x for which $y \geqslant 1$.

(10)*. Show that the expression $(2x - 7)/(x - 2)(x - 4)$ assumes every real value for real values of x. Prove also that if the value of the expression exceeds 1, x lies between 2 and 3 or between 4 and 5. Illustrate by sketching a graph of the expression.

(11)*. Show that for all real values of x the value of the function

$$\frac{2a(x - 1)\sin^2 \theta}{x^2 - \sin^2 \theta}$$

cannot lie between $a(1 - \cos \theta)$ and $a(1 + \cos \theta)$. Sketch the graph of this function, assuming that θ is a positive acute angle.

(12)*. Show that the function $y = (x^2 + 2ax + b)/(x + c)^2$, where x is a real variable and a, b, c are real constants, can assume all values which are either not less than or not greater than a certain number; and distinguish between the two cases. Illustrate by sketching the graphs of

(i) $y = (x^2 + 1)/(x - 1)^2$,   (ii) $y = (x^2 - 4)/(x - 1)^2$.

(13)*. Show that $y = (x^2 + 2x + k)/(x^2 - 2x + k)$ assumes all real values for real x if $k \leqslant 0$, but not otherwise.

Give a rough sketch of the graph of y for $k = -1$.

(14)*. If $y = (x^2 + x \sin \theta + 1)/(x^2 + x \cos \theta + 1)$, show that, for all real values of x and θ, y lies between $\frac{1}{8}(4 - \sqrt{7})$ and $\frac{1}{8}(4 + \sqrt{7})$.

(15)*. Find, by non-graphical methods, the values of x such that

(i) $\frac{1}{6}(x^3 - x^2) > x^2 + 9x + 12$,
(ii) $(2 - x)^{-1} < (x - 3)^{-1}$,
(iii) $x(x^2 + 5x - 4) > (x + 2)(7 - x)$,
(iv) $-2 < (2x + 1)/(x - 2) < 1$.

ANSWERS TO EXERCISES

(7). $\frac{1}{2} < x < 1, \frac{3}{2} < x < 2;\ k < \frac{7}{4}$. (9). $-\frac{3}{2} < x < -\frac{6}{5}, x > 2$.
(15). (i) $-3 < x < -2, x > 12$. (ii) $2 < x < 2\frac{1}{2}, x > 3$.
(iii) $-7 < x < -1, x > 2$. (iv) $-3 < x < \frac{3}{4}$.

CHAPTER 5

HYPERBOLIC FUNCTIONS

5.1 Definitions

An *even function* of x is one for which $f(-x) = f(x)$; the graph of such a function for $x > 0$ is identical with the mirror image in the y-axis of the graph for $x < 0$. Simple examples are $y = 1 + x^2$, $y = \cos x$. An *odd function* of x is one for which $f(-x) = -f(x)$; the graph of such a function for $x > 0$ is identical with the reflection of the graph for $x < 0$ firstly in the x-axis and then in the y-axis. Simple examples are $y = x + x^3$, $y = \sin x$. An even function must of necessity contain only even powers of x in its power-series expansion, while an odd function contains only odd powers.

The more general functions are neither odd nor even, but from a theoretical and numerical point of view it is often convenient to define odd and even functions that are intimately connected with more general functions.

If $y = g(x)$ is a general function, we consider the two functions

$$y_1 = \tfrac{1}{2}[g(x) + g(-x)], \quad y_2 = \tfrac{1}{2}[g(x) - g(-x)].$$

The first function is evidently even, since a change in the sign of x does not change the sign of the function, while the second function is odd, since if x is changed in sign the function as a whole is also changed in sign. Moreover, the sum of these two functions is $g(x)$. We call y_1 the *even part* of $g(x)$, and y_2 the *odd part*.

Similar considerations may be applied to the exponential function e^x. The even part is defined to be $\cosh x$, and the odd part to be $\sinh x$, namely
$$\cosh x = \tfrac{1}{2}(e^x + e^{-x}), \quad \sinh x = \tfrac{1}{2}(e^x - e^{-x}).$$

Replacing the exponential functions by their power series, we obtain the expansions of $\sinh x$ and $\cosh x$ in the form

$$\sinh x = x + x^3/3! + x^5/5! + \ldots + x^{2r+1}/(2r+1)! + \ldots,$$
$$\cosh x = 1 + x^2/2! + x^4/4! + \ldots + x^{2r}/(2r)! + \ldots.$$

These series are absolutely convergent for all values of x.

The remaining hyperbolic functions are defined by analogy with the trigonometric functions:

$$\tanh x = \sinh x/\cosh x, \quad \coth x = 1/\tanh x, \quad \operatorname{sech} x = 1/\cosh x,$$
$$\operatorname{cosech} x = 1/\sinh x.$$

In Fig. 1, graph (a) represents $\frac{1}{2}e^x$, (b) sinh x, (c) cosh x, (d) tanh x, (e) sech x. It should be noticed that cosh x is always greater than unity except at $x = 0$, and that cosh x and sinh x are both approximately

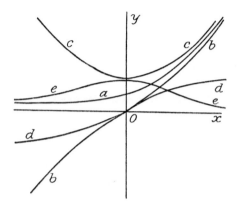

FIG. 1

equal to $\frac{1}{2}e^x$ when x is large and positive. The function tanh x lies between the bounds -1 and $+1$. None of the hyperbolic functions is periodic.

Example 1   Find the first four terms in the expansion of tanh x in powers of x.
    Since tanh x is the quotient of an odd and even function, tanh x must be an odd function; its power series must therefore consist only of odd powers of x. Let

$$\text{tanh } x = ax + bx^3 + cx^5 + dx^7 + \ldots.$$

Multiplying by cosh x, and inserting the series for sinh x and cosh x, we obtain

$$x + \tfrac{1}{6}x^3 + \tfrac{1}{120}x^5 + \tfrac{1}{5040}x^7 = (ax + bx^3 + cx^5 + dx^7)(1 + \tfrac{1}{2}x^2 + \tfrac{1}{24}x^4 + \tfrac{1}{720}x^6),$$

including all terms up to x^7. We now equate the coefficients of the corresponding powers of x, obtaining

coefficient of x: $1 = a$,

coefficient of x^3: $\tfrac{1}{6} = \tfrac{1}{2}a + b$,

coefficient of x^5: $\tfrac{1}{120} = \tfrac{1}{24}a + \tfrac{1}{2}b + c$,

coefficient of x^7: $\tfrac{1}{5040} = \tfrac{1}{720}a + \tfrac{1}{24}b + \tfrac{1}{2}c + d$.

The solution of these equations is $a = 1$, $b = -\tfrac{1}{3}$, $c = \tfrac{2}{15}$, $d = -\tfrac{17}{315}$.

    The inverse hyperbolic functions are defined by analogy with the trigonometric functions.

The statement $y = \sinh^{-1} x$ implies $x = \sinh y$. We may express $\sinh^{-1} x$ in terms of logarithms as follows. Since

$$x = \sinh y = \tfrac{1}{2}(e^y - e^{-y}),$$

cross-multiplication by $2e^y$ yields the quadratic equation in e^y

$$e^{2y} - 2xe^y - 1 = 0,$$

possessing the two roots $e^y = x \pm \sqrt{(x^2 + 1)}$. The negative sign is rejected if real numbers only are considered, so

$$y = \sinh^{-1} x = \log_e [x + \sqrt{(x^2 + 1)}]. \tag{1}$$

A similar calculation may be carried out for $y = \cosh^{-1} x$. This implies that

$$x = \tfrac{1}{2}(e^y + e^{-y}),$$

or
$$e^{2y} - 2xe^y + 1 = 0,$$

possessing the roots $e^y = x \pm \sqrt{(x^2 - 1)}$. Both signs are permitted here, since either sign yields a positive value for e^y. Hence

$$y = \cosh^{-1} x = \log_e [x \pm \sqrt{(x^2 - 1)}]. \tag{2}$$

A glance at the graph of the hyperbolic cosine shows that $\cosh^{-1} x$ must have two values, equal but opposite in sign. The two values of the logarithm (2) are equal but opposite in sign.

The corresponding calculation for $y = \tanh^{-1} x$ does not involve a quadratic equation. The definition

$$x = \tanh y = (e^y - e^{-y})/(e^y + e^{-y})$$

yields
$$e^{2y} = (1 + x)/(1 - x).$$

Hence
$$y = \tanh^{-1} x = \tfrac{1}{2} \log_e [(1 + x)/(1 - x)]. \tag{3}$$

5.2 Various identities

By adding and subtracting in turn the definitions of $\sinh x$ and $\cosh x$, we obtain

$$\cosh x + \sinh x = e^x, \tag{4}$$
$$\cosh x - \sinh x = e^{-x}. \tag{5}$$

If these two equations are multiplied together, we obtain the result

$$\cosh^2 x - \sinh^2 x = 1. \tag{6}$$

We now raise equations (4) and (5) to the nth power,

$$(\cosh x + \sinh x)^n = e^{nx} = \cosh nx + \sinh nx,$$
$$(\cosh x - \sinh x)^n = e^{-nx} = \cosh nx - \sinh nx.$$

The expansion of these two expressions on the left hand side by the binomial theorem for a positive integral index yields

$$\cosh nx + \sinh nx = \cosh^n x + {}_nC_1 \cosh^{n-1} x \sinh x$$
$$+ {}_nC_2 \cosh^{n-2} x \sinh^2 x + \ldots,$$

$$\cosh nx - \sinh nx = \cosh^n x - {}_nC_1 \cosh^{n-1} x \sinh x$$
$$+ {}_nC_2 \cosh^{n-2} x \sinh^2 x - \ldots.$$

Addition yields

$$\cosh nx = \cosh^n x + {}_nC_2 \cosh^{n-2} x \sinh^2 x$$
$$+ {}_nC_4 \cosh^{n-4} x \sinh^4 x + \ldots$$

and subtraction yields

$$\sinh nx = {}_nC_1 \cosh^{n-1} x \sinh x + {}_nC_3 \cosh^{n-3} x \sinh^3 x + \ldots.$$

In other words, we have derived formulae that express the hyperbolic functions of the multiple values nx in terms of hyperbolic functions of x itself.

If this formula for $\sinh nx$ is divided by $\cosh nx$, and then if the numerator and denominator are divided by $\cosh^n x$, we obtain

$$\tanh nx = \frac{{}_nC_1 \tanh x + {}_nC_3 \tanh^3 x + {}_nC_5 \tanh^5 x + \ldots}{1 + {}_nC_2 \tanh^2 x + {}_nC_4 \tanh^4 x + {}_nC_6 \tanh^6 x + \ldots}.$$

When $n = 2$ and 3, we obtain the standard results

$$\cosh 2x = \cosh^2 x + \sinh^2 x = 2 \cosh^2 x - 1 = 1 + 2 \sinh^2 x,$$
$$\sinh 2x = 2 \sinh x \cosh x,$$
$$\tanh 2x = 2 \tanh x/(1 + \tanh^2 x),$$
$$\cosh 3x = \cosh^3 x + 3 \cosh x \sinh^2 x = 4 \cosh^2 x - 3 \cosh x,$$
$$\sinh 3x = 3 \cosh^2 x \sinh x + \sinh^3 x = 3 \sinh x + 4 \sinh^3 x,$$
$$\tanh 3x = (3 \tanh x + \tanh^3 x)/(1 + 3 \tanh^2 x).$$

These formulae may of course be derived directly from the original definitions, but this general theory demonstrates a complete similarity with the complex-number theory of the trigonometrical ratios. The student should notice how the above identities compare and contrast with the corresponding trigonometrical formulae.

Let us now multiply equation (4) by the similar equation obtained by replacing x by y:

$$e^x e^y = \cosh x \cosh y + \sinh x \sinh y + \cosh x \sinh y + \sinh x \cosh y.$$

In this formula we now replace x and y by $-x$ and $-y$ respectively, obtaining

$$e^{-x} e^{-y} = \cosh x \cosh y + \sinh x \sinh y - \cosh x \sinh y - \sinh x \cosh y.$$

Adding these two results, and dividing by 2, we produce the result

$$\cosh (x + y) = \cosh x \cosh y + \sinh x \sinh y,$$

while subtraction yields

$$\sinh (x + y) = \sinh x \cosh y + \cosh x \sinh y.$$

If the sign of y is changed, we have

$$\cosh (x - y) = \cosh x \cosh y - \sinh x \sinh y,$$

$$\sinh (x - y) = \sinh x \cosh y - \cosh x \sinh y.$$

When $\sinh (x + y)$ is divided by $\cosh (x + y)$, we find

$$\tanh (x + y) = (\tanh x + \tanh y)/(1 + \tanh x \tanh y).$$

5.3 Problems concerning hyperbolic functions

Hyperbolic functions enter mathematical theory usually through the solution of differential and difference equations and through certain types of definite and indefinite integrals; many of these topics are considered later in the text. Here we shall consider a few problems relating only to the definitions and properties of the functions.

Example 2 If $\tan x = \tanh y$, prove that $2 \tan^{-1} (\sin 2x) = \tan^{-1} (\sinh 4y)$.

If $2 \tan^{-1} (\sin 2x) = \alpha$, we have

$$\tan \alpha = \tan [2 \tan^{-1} (\sin 2x)]$$

$$= \frac{2 \sin 2x}{1 - \sin^2 2x} = \frac{2 \sin 2x}{\cos^2 2x} = \frac{4 \sin x \cos x}{(2 \cos^2 x - 1)^2}$$

$$= \frac{4 \tan x \sec^{-2} x}{(2 \sec^{-2} x - 1)^2} = \frac{4 \tan x(1 + \tan^2 x)^{-1}}{[2(1 + \tan^2 x)^{-1} - 1]^2}$$

$$= \frac{4 \tan x(1 + \tan^2 x)}{(1 - \tan^2 x)^2} = \frac{4 \tanh y(1 + \tanh^2 y)}{(1 - \tanh^2 y)^2}$$

$$= \frac{4 \tanh y(\cosh^2 y + \sinh^2 y) \cosh^2 y}{(\cosh^2 y - \sinh^2 y)^2}$$

$$= 4 \sinh y \cosh y \cosh 2y = 2 \sinh 2y \cosh 2y = \sinh 4y;$$

hence $\qquad\qquad \alpha = \tan^{-1} (\sinh 4y).$

Example 3 Find the sum of the finite series

$$S_n = \sinh x + \sinh 2x + \sinh 3x + \ldots + \sinh nx.$$

In terms of exponentials, the sum is given by

$$S_n = \tfrac{1}{2}(e^x + e^{2x} + \ldots + e^{nx}) - \tfrac{1}{2}(e^{-x} + e^{-2x} + \ldots + e^{-nx})$$

$$= \tfrac{1}{2}e^x \frac{e^{nx} - 1}{e^x - 1} - \tfrac{1}{2}e^{-x} \frac{e^{-nx} - 1}{e^{-x} - 1},$$

since each bracket is a finite geometric progression. The quickest method of simplifying each numerator and denominator is to notice that

$$e^\theta - 1 = e^{\frac{1}{2}\theta}(e^{\frac{1}{2}\theta} - e^{-\frac{1}{2}\theta}) = 2e^{\frac{1}{2}\theta} \sinh \tfrac{1}{2}\theta;$$

hence
$$S_n = \tfrac{1}{2}e^x \frac{e^{\frac{1}{2}nx} \sinh \tfrac{1}{2}nx}{e^{\frac{1}{2}x} \sinh \tfrac{1}{2}x} - \tfrac{1}{2}e^{-x} \frac{e^{-\frac{1}{2}nx} \sinh \tfrac{1}{2}nx}{e^{-\frac{1}{2}x} \sinh \tfrac{1}{2}x}$$

$$= \frac{\sinh \tfrac{1}{2}nx}{2 \sinh \tfrac{1}{2}x} (e^{\frac{1}{2}(n+1)x} - e^{-\frac{1}{2}(n+1)x})$$

$$= \sinh \tfrac{1}{2}nx \sinh \tfrac{1}{2}(n + 1) x \operatorname{cosech} \tfrac{1}{2}x.$$

Example 4 Solve the equation $a \cosh x + b \sinh x = c$.

Case i. If $|b| > |a|$, we arrange the signs so that b is positive; we then divide by $\sqrt{(b^2 - a^2)}$, and let

$$\sinh \theta = a/\sqrt{(b^2 - a^2)}, \quad \cosh \theta = b/\sqrt{(b^2 - a^2)}.$$

This implies that $\tanh \theta = a/b$, so θ may be found uniquely from suitable tables. Then

$$\sinh \theta \cosh x + \cosh \theta \sinh x = c/\sqrt{(b^2 - a^2)},$$

or
$$\sinh (x + \theta) = c/\sqrt{(b^2 - a^2)}.$$

Hence
$$x + \theta = \sinh^{-1} [c/\sqrt{(b^2 - a^2)}],$$

or
$$x = \sinh^{-1} [c/\sqrt{(b^2 - a^2)}] - \tanh^{-1} (a/b).$$

This answer may be expressed in terms of logarithms if required.

Case ii. If $|b| = |a|$, the equation takes the form

$$\cosh x \pm \sinh x = c/a,$$

or $e^{\pm x} = c/a$. For real solutions, we require $c/a > 0$, yielding

$$x = \pm \log_e (c/a).$$

Case iii. If $|b| < |a|$, we arrange the sign of a to be positive, divide by $\sqrt{(a^2 - b^2)}$, and let

$$\cosh \theta = a/\sqrt{(a^2 - b^2)}, \quad \sinh \theta = b/\sqrt{(a^2 - b^2)},$$

implying that $\tanh \theta = b/a$. The equation becomes

$$\cosh \theta \cosh x + \sinh \theta \sinh x = c/\sqrt{(a^2 - b^2)},$$

or
$$\cosh (x + \theta) = c/\sqrt{(a^2 - b^2)}.$$

A solution exists only if $c/\sqrt{(a^2 - b^2)}$ is greater than unity, in which case

$$x = \cosh^{-1} [c/\sqrt{(a^2 - b^2)}] - \tanh^{-1} (b/a).$$

EXERCISES

*Some of these exercises require techniques introduced
later in the text.*

(1). Prove the following identities:
   (i) $\cosh^2 (A + B) - \cosh^2 (A - B) = \sinh 2A \sinh 2B$.
   (ii) $\sin^2 A \cosh^2 B + \cos^2 A \sinh^2 B = \frac{1}{2}(\cosh 2B - \cos 2A)$.
   (iii) $\cosh^6 A - \sinh^6 A = 1 + \frac{3}{4} \sinh^2 2A$.
   (iv) $\cosh^{-1} (\sec^2 A + \tan^2 A) = 2 \cosh^{-1} (\sec A)$.

(2)*. Prove that in the range $0 < \theta < \frac{1}{2}\pi$, the equation
$$\cosh^{-1} (\sec \theta) + \log (\sin 2\theta) = 0$$
has just one solution, namely $\theta = \sin^{-1} [\frac{1}{2}\sqrt{(3 - 1)}]$.

(3)*. From the definition of $\tanh x$ in terms of e^x, prove that
$$\tanh (A + B) = \frac{\tanh A + \tanh B}{1 + \tanh A \tanh B}.$$
If $A + B + C = 0$, prove that
   (i) $\tanh A + \tanh B + \tanh C + \tanh A \tanh B \tanh C = 0$,
   (ii) $1 + \cosh A + \cosh B + \cosh C = 4 \cosh \frac{1}{2}A \cosh \frac{1}{2}B \cosh \frac{1}{2}C$.

(4)*. Prove that $\tanh^2 \frac{1}{2}a = (\cosh a - 1)/(\cosh a + 1)$.
If
$$\sinh x = \frac{\sinh u \sinh v}{\cosh u - \cosh v}, \quad \text{and} \quad \sinh y = \frac{\sinh u \sinh v}{\cosh u + \cosh v},$$
where u and v are positive and u is greater than v, prove that
$$\cosh x = \frac{\cosh u \cosh v - 1}{\cosh u - \cosh v}, \quad \text{and} \quad \tanh \frac{1}{2}(x - y) = \frac{\sinh v}{\sinh u}.$$

(5). Prove that
$$\frac{1 + \tanh (x + y + z)}{1 - \tanh (x + y + z)} = \frac{(1 + \tanh x)(1 + \tanh y)(1 + \tanh z)}{(1 - \tanh x)(1 - \tanh y)(1 - \tanh z)}.$$

(6). Prove that
$$1 + \cosh \theta + \frac{\cosh 2\theta}{2!} + \frac{\cosh 3\theta}{3!} + \ldots = e^{\cosh \theta} \cosh (\sinh \theta).$$

(7)*. From the definitions of $\sinh x$ and $\cosh x$ prove that
$$2 \sinh A \cosh B = \sinh (A + B) - \sinh (B - A).$$
   (i) Prove that if $\theta \neq 0$,
$$\cosh \theta + \cosh 3\theta + \ldots + \cosh (2n - 1)\theta = \frac{1}{2}\sinh 2n\theta \operatorname{cosech} \theta.$$
   (ii) Prove by induction or otherwise that if $\theta \neq 0$,
$$\sum_{r=1}^{n} \operatorname{sech} (r - 1)\theta \operatorname{sech} r\theta = \tanh n\theta \operatorname{cosech} \theta,$$
and show that the sum to infinity of the series is $\operatorname{cosech} |\theta|$.

(8). Solve the equations
   (i) $5 \cosh x - 3 \sinh x = 5$,   (ii) $5 \sinh x + 3 \cosh x = -3$.

(9)*. Given that

$$\tfrac{1}{6}\sinh x = \tfrac{1}{9}\sinh y = \tfrac{1}{28}\sinh (x + y)$$

show that either $\sinh x = 0$ or $5\cosh y = 28 - 9\cosh x$. Hence eliminate y and prove that either $x = 0$, $y = 0$, or $x = \log_e 3$, $y = \log_e 5$ or $x = -\log_e 3$, $y = -\log_e 5$.

(10)*. Sketch the graph of the function $\cosh x + a \sinh x$ $(a > 0)$ for the range $-\infty < x < \infty$, distinguishing between the cases $a > 1$, $a = 1$, $a < 1$. Hence or otherwise show that the equation $\cosh x + a \sinh x = 0$ has one real root if $a > 1$. If $0 < a < 1$, for what real values of b does the equation

$$\cosh x + a \sinh x = b$$

have a real root?

(11)*. Prove that the real finite value of x which satisfies the equations

$$2\cosh x - \sinh x = \sinh y,$$
$$3\cosh x - 4\sinh x = \cosh y$$

is given by $\tanh x = \tfrac{1}{4}$. Express the values of x and y which satisfy the above equations as logarithms to base e.

(12). (i)* Sketch the graph of $\tanh x$, and show that, for $x > 0$, the function $(\cosh x)/x$ has a minimum value. (You are not asked to find this value.)

(ii) As x tends to 0, prove that

$$(\tan x - \tanh x)/x^3 \to \tfrac{2}{3}, \quad (\sinh x - \sin x)/x^3 \to \tfrac{1}{3}.$$

(13). (i) Using the substitution $\sinh x = \tan \theta$, prove that

$$\int_0^\infty \operatorname{sech} x \, dx = \tfrac{1}{2}\pi.$$

(ii)* Find the area contained between the lines $x = 0$, $x = 4$ and the two branches of the curve $y^2 = x^2 - 4x + 8$.

(14)*. Show graphically that $\sin x - \tanh x$ has an infinity of real roots; find the smallest positive root correct to two places of decimals.

Show also that, if n is any large positive integer, a pair of roots lie in the neighbourhood of $x = (2n + \tfrac{1}{2})\pi$, and that the second approximation to these roots is given by

$$x = (2n + \tfrac{1}{2})\pi \pm 2e^{-(2n+\frac{1}{2})\pi}.$$

(15)*. Sketch, in the same diagram, the graphs of $y = \tan x$ and $y = \tanh x$, and show that every interval of the form $(n - \tfrac{1}{2})\pi < x < (n + \tfrac{1}{2})\pi$ includes a real root of the equation $\tan x = \tanh x$, n being any integer.

Show further that the numerically large roots of the equation are given approximately by $x = \pm(k + \tfrac{1}{4})\pi$, where k is a positive integer.

(16)*. Sketch the curve $y = c \cosh (x/c)$, where c is constant. If ψ is the inclination to the x-axis of the tangent at a point P of this curve, s is the arc length from the lowest point of the curve to P and ρ is the radius of curvature at P, prove the following results:

(i) $y = c \sec \psi$, $x = c \log (\sec \psi + \tan \psi)$,
(ii) $s = c \tan \psi = c \sinh (x/c)$, (iii) $c\rho = y^2$.

(17)*. Sketch the graph of $\coth x$. Hence show that the equation $\coth x = ax + b$, where a and b are any real constants different from zero, has two real roots or none. Show that, if a has any positive value, the equation has two real roots, and that, if a is negative, the equation has no real roots when b lies between -1 and $+1$.

ANSWERS TO EXERCISES

(8). (i) $2 \sinh^{-1} \frac{3}{4} = \log_e 4$. (ii) $-\log_e 4$.

(10). $b \geqslant \min (\cosh x + a \sinh x) = \sqrt{(1 - a^2)}$.

(11). $x = \frac{1}{2} \log \frac{5}{3}$, $y = \frac{1}{2} \log 15$. (13). (ii) $8\sqrt{2} + 8 \log (1 + \sqrt{2})$.

CHAPTER 6

THE ARGAND DIAGRAM

6.1 Complex numbers

The student may already have employed in elementary work the symbol i (or j) used to represent the square root $\sqrt{(-1)}$. It must be appreciated however that this does *not* define the symbol i. Any new quantity introduced into algebra or analysis *must* be defined in terms of more elementary quantities and concepts previously defined. To say that i represents $\sqrt{(-1)}$ is no true definition, for $\sqrt{(-1)}$ is not defined in elementary algebra. All that can be said with certainty is that the symbol i^2 is defined to be -1, but this provides no information about i itself. A strict definition of the symbol i requires new concepts, yet based on the processes of elementary algebra. Various methods for accomplishing this may be formulated, but the idea of an *ordered number pair* appears to be the most popular. We shall not concern ourselves here with these abstractions in spite of their importance in more formal theory, but though we do not provide a strict definition of the symbol i, the student should rapidly acquire a "feel" for the symbol when it is put into use.

We assume the symbol i has the following properties:

(i) i behaves exactly like an ordinary algebraic symbol.

(ii) i^2 is defined to be -1 and may always be replaced by -1.

(iii) If a, b, c, d are positive or negative rational or irrational numbers, the equation

$$a + ib = c + id$$

implies that $a = c, b = d$.

A *complex number* z is defined in terms of two rational or irrational numbers x and y, by compounding them together with the symbol i thus:

$$z = x + iy.$$

The number x (that does not multiply the i) is called the *real part* of the complex number, so we write $x = \mathrm{Rl}\, z$. The number y (that multiplies the i) is called the *imaginary part* of the complex number, and we write $y = \mathrm{Im}\, z$.

Thus if $z = 6 - 4i$, we have $6 = \mathrm{Rl}\, z$, $-4 = \mathrm{Im}\, z$.

102

6.2   Representation of complex numbers

The complex number $z = x + iy$ is *represented* on a plane by a point P with coordinates (x, y) with respect to a set of perpendicular right-handed axes Ox, Oy. The point P itself may often be somewhat loosely spoken of as *being* the complex number z rather than the *representation* of z.

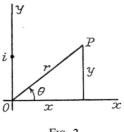

FIG. 2

Ox and Oy are called the *real axis* and the *imaginary axis* respectively. Such a figure is called the *Argand diagram*, or in more advanced work, the *complex z-plane*. The complex number (or merely number) i is represented by the point with Cartesian coordinates $(0, 1)$.

The *modulus* of z is defined to be the positive length OP, and we write

$$r = |z| = +\sqrt{(x^2 + y^2)}.$$

The angle θ, the angle in radians between Ox and OP (anticlockwise from Ox being the positive sense), is called the argument of z; we write

$$\theta = \arg z.$$

Numerically speaking, θ must be calculated carefully; it is not merely $\tan^{-1}(y/x)$, since the quadrant must be taken into consideration.

It can be seen that r and θ are the polar coordinates of the point P, with the distinction that r is always positive; in the theory of polar coordinates, r may sometimes be negative.

The modulus of i is 1, and its argument is $\frac{1}{2}\pi$; the modulus of $-i$ is 1, and its argument is $-\frac{1}{2}\pi$.

If $z = 1 + i$, the Cartesian coordinates of P are $(1, 1)$; the modulus of z is $\sqrt{2}$, and its argument is $\frac{1}{4}\pi$. The complex number $z = -1 - i$ is represented by the point $(-1, -1)$; its modulus is $\sqrt{2}$, and its argument $\frac{5}{4}\pi$. In this latter case, it would be wrong to assert that

$$\arg z = \tan^{-1}(-1/-1) = \tan^{-1} 1 = \tfrac{1}{4}\pi,$$

since the point is in the third quadrant.

The argument of z is not unique; an arbitrary integral multiple of 2π may be added, but the actual point P remains undisturbed. The *principal value* of the argument is chosen to lie in the range $-\pi < \arg z \leqslant \pi$. For example, if $z = -\sqrt{3} + i$, $|z| = 2$, and $\arg z$ may be $\frac{5}{6}\pi$, $\frac{17}{6}\pi$, $-\frac{7}{6}\pi$, etc., but the principal value of $\arg z$ is $\frac{5}{6}\pi$.

If two complex numbers possess the same modulus, and if their two arguments either are equal or differ by an integral multiple of 2π, the two numbers are equal, in the sense that the real parts and imaginary parts are respectively equal.

From Fig. 1, we note that $x = r\cos\theta$, $y = r\sin\theta$, so

$$z = x + iy = r(\cos\theta + i\sin\theta).$$

It will be seen later that the complex number $\cos\theta + i\sin\theta$ has properties of exceptional importance. Its modulus is 1 and its argument is θ.

All points satisfying the equation $|z| = 1$ lie on what is termed the *unit circle*; its centre is the origin and its radius unity.

Two complex numbers may be added and subtracted as follows. If

$$z_1 = x_1 + iy_1, \quad z_2 = x_2 + iy_2,$$

then

$$z_1 \pm z_2 = (x_1 \pm x_2) + i(y_1 \pm y_2);$$

$x_1 \pm x_2$ is the real part of the sum or difference, while $y_1 \pm y_2$ is the imaginary part.

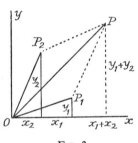

FIG. 3

In the Argand diagram, addition is accomplished by completing the parallelogram defined by the two sides OP_1, OP_2. Subtraction may be reduced to the addition of the two numbers z_1 and $(-z_2)$.

In $\triangle OP_1P$, we have the inequality

$$OP \leqslant OP_1 + P_1P = OP_1 + OP_2;$$

hence

$$|z_1 + z_2| \leqslant |z_1| + |z_2|.$$

Replacing z_2 by $-z_2$, and noting that $|-z_2| = |z_2|$, we conclude that

$$|z_1 - z_2| \leqslant |z_1| + |z_2|.$$

Inequalities are not defined for complex numbers themselves; inequalities occur only in real algebra, of which these moduli are examples.

A new complex number may be formed from $z = x + iy$ by changing the sign of the imaginary part y; this new number is denoted by $z^\star$, and is called the *complex conjugate* of z. We have

$$z^\star = x - iy.$$

In the Argand diagram, the point $z^\star$ is the image of the point z in the real axis Ox. It is evident that $|z| = |z^\star|$ and $\arg z = -\arg z^\star$.

6.3 Multiplication and division of complex numbers

Two complex numbers $z_1 = x_1 + iy_1$ and $z_2 = x_2 + iy_2$ may be multiplied together either in their Cartesian form or in their polar form. The methods of ordinary algebra yield

$$z_1 z_2 = (x_1 + iy_1)(x_2 + iy_2)$$
$$= x_1 x_2 + ix_1 y_2 + iy_1 x_2 + i^2 y_1 y_2$$
$$= (x_1 x_2 - y_1 y_2) + i(x_1 y_2 + x_2 y_1)$$

upon separating the terms of the product into real and imaginary parts.

The geometrical significance of this result is not obvious, but the use of polar coordinates clarifies the process:

$$z_1 z_2 = r_1(\cos \theta_1 + i \sin \theta_1) r_2(\cos \theta_2 + i \sin \theta_2)$$
$$= r_1 r_2 [\cos \theta_1 \cos \theta_2 - \sin \theta_1 \sin \theta_2$$
$$+ i(\cos \theta_1 \sin \theta_2 + \sin \theta_1 \cos \theta_2)]$$
$$= r_1 r_2 [\cos (\theta_1 + \theta_2) + i \sin (\theta_1 + \theta_2)].$$

Hence

$$|z_1 z_2| = r_1 r_2 = |z_1|\,|z_2|, \arg (z_1 z_2) = \theta_1 + \theta_2 = \arg z_1 + \arg z_2.$$

That is to say, the modulus of a product equals the product of the moduli, and the argument of a product equals the sum of the arguments.

Example 1 Multiply $\sqrt{3} + i$ by $-3 + 3i$ using both the Cartesian and the polar form.

The Cartesian form is obtained directly:

$$z_1 z_2 = (\sqrt{3} + i)(-3 + 3i) = (-3\sqrt{3} - 3) + i(3\sqrt{3} - 3).$$

In polar form, we have

$$|z_1| = 2, \arg z_1 = \tfrac{1}{6}\pi; \quad |z_2| = 3\sqrt{2}, \arg z_2 = \tfrac{3}{4}\pi.$$

Hence $\qquad z_1 z_2 = 2(\cos \tfrac{1}{6}\pi + i \sin \tfrac{1}{6}\pi).3\sqrt{2}(\cos \tfrac{3}{4}\pi + i \sin \tfrac{3}{4}\pi)$

$$= 6\sqrt{2}(\cos \tfrac{11}{12}\pi + i \sin \tfrac{11}{12}\pi).$$

The modulus of the product is $6\sqrt{2}$, and its argument is $\tfrac{11}{12}\pi$.

The product $z_1 z_2$ may be represented by a point in the Argand diagram, and this point may easily be constructed from the points representing z_1 and z_2.

Let P_1, P_2, U, P represent z_1, z_2, 1, $z = z_1 z_2$ respectively. Construct the triangle OUP_1, and then on OP_2 as base construct triangle OP_2P similar to OUP_1. Then $\angle UOP_1 = \angle P_2OP = \theta_1$, so

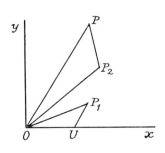

$$\arg z = \angle POU =$$
$$\angle POP_2 + \angle P_2OU = \theta_1 + \theta_2.$$

Moreover,

$$OP/OP_2 = OP_1/OU = OP_1,$$

FIG. 4

since $OU = 1$. Hence $OP = OP_1.OP_2$, or $|z| = |z_1|\,|z_2|$. It follows that the complex number z represented by P is the complex number $z_1 z_2$.

The product of a complex number z and its complex conjugate $z^\star$ is of importance. We have

$$zz^\star = (x + iy)(x - iy) = x^2 + y^2,$$

so $zz^\star = |z|^2$, This relationship shows how the sum of two squares $x^2 + y^2$ may be factorized into two linear complex factors.

If the complex number $z_1 = x + iy$ is multiplied by i, we obtain the product $i(x + iy) = -y + ix$. Interpreted in polar form, the line OP_1, where P_1 represents z, is merely rotated anticlockwise by an angle $\frac{1}{2}\pi$ to its new position OP.

Division by a complex number may be considered firstly by considering the reciprocal of z. We have, upon multiplying numerator and denominator by the conjugate $z^\star$:

$$\frac{1}{z} = \frac{z^\star}{zz^\star} = \frac{x - iy}{x^2 + y^2}.$$

By this means, the symbol i is removed from the denominator and placed in the numerator. Hence

$$\mathrm{Rl}(1/z) = x/(x^2 + y^2), \quad \mathrm{Im}(1/z) = -y/(x^2 + y^2).$$

In particular,

$$1/(\cos\theta + i\sin\theta) = \cos\theta - i\sin\theta.$$

To simplify the general quotient z_1/z_2, we multiply numerator and denominator by $z_2^\star$ obtaining

$$\frac{z_1}{z_2} = \frac{x_1 + iy_1}{x_2 + iy_2} = \frac{(x_1 + iy_1)(x_2 - iy_2)}{(x_2 + iy_2)(x_2 - iy_2)}$$
$$= \frac{(x_1 x_2 + y_1 y_2) + i(x_2 y_1 - y_2 x_1)}{x_2^{\,2} + y_2^{\,2}}.$$

In polar form, we have

$$\frac{z_1}{z_2} = \frac{r_1(\cos \theta_1 + i \sin \theta_1)}{r_2(\cos \theta_2 + i \sin \theta_2)} = \frac{r_1}{r_2}(\cos \theta_1 + i \sin \theta_1)(\cos \theta_2 - i \sin \theta_2)$$

$$= (r_1/r_2)[\cos \theta_1 \cos \theta_2 + \sin \theta_1 \sin \theta_2 + i(\sin \theta_1 \cos \theta_2 - \cos \theta_1 \sin \theta_2)]$$

$$= (r_1/r_2)[\cos (\theta_1 - \theta_2) + i \sin (\theta_1 - \theta_2)] .$$

Hence

$$|(z_1/z_2)| = |z_1|/|z_2|, \quad \arg (z_1/z_2) = \arg z_1 - \arg z_2.$$

In other words, the modulus of the quotient equals the quotient of the moduli, and the argument of the quotient equals the difference of the arguments.

Example 2 Find the modulus and argument of

$$z = \frac{1 + i}{1 + \cos \theta + i \sin \theta} .$$

It is always useful to express combinations as $1 + \cos \theta + i \sin \theta$ in terms of half-angles. Then

$$z = \frac{1 + i}{2 \cos^2 \tfrac{1}{2}\theta + 2i \sin \tfrac{1}{2}\theta \cos \tfrac{1}{2}\theta}$$

$$= \frac{1 + i}{2 \cos \tfrac{1}{2}\theta(\cos \tfrac{1}{2}\theta + i \sin \tfrac{1}{2}\theta)}$$

$$= \frac{(1 + i)(\cos \tfrac{1}{2}\theta - i \sin \tfrac{1}{2}\theta)}{2 \cos \tfrac{1}{2}\theta} .$$

The modulus of $1 + i$ is $\sqrt{2}$ and its argument is $\tfrac{1}{4}\pi$; hence

$$|z| = \tfrac{1}{2}\sqrt{2} \, |\sec \tfrac{1}{2}\theta|,$$

and

$$\arg z = \tfrac{1}{4}\pi - \tfrac{1}{2}\theta - \arg (\sec \tfrac{1}{2}\theta).$$

If $\sec \tfrac{1}{2}\theta$ is positive, its argument is 0, but if $\sec \tfrac{1}{2}\theta$ is negative, its argument may be taken to be π.

Example 3 By using the extension of the inequality

$$|z_1 + z_2| \leqslant |z_1| + |z_2|,$$

prove that all values of z satisfying

$$z \cos \theta + z^2 \cos 2\theta + z^3 \cos 3\theta + \ldots + z^6 \cos 6\theta = 1$$

(with θ real) also satisfy the condition $|z| > \tfrac{1}{2}$.

We have

$$1 = |z \cos \theta + z^2 \cos 2\theta + \ldots + z^6 \cos 6\theta|$$

$$\leqslant |z \cos \theta| + |z^2 \cos 2\theta| + \ldots + |z^6 \cos 6\theta|$$

$$= |z| \, |\cos \theta| + |z|^2 \, |\cos 2\theta| + \ldots + |z|^6 \, |\cos 6\theta|$$

$$\leqslant |z| + |z|^2 + \ldots + |z|^6 \quad \text{since } |\cos r\theta| \leqslant 1$$

$$= |z| \, (1 - |z|^6)/(1 - |z|).$$

Consider the suggestion $|z| \leqslant \frac{1}{2}$. Then we may multiply the inequality through by the positive quantity $1 - |z|$, obtaining

$$1 - |z| \leqslant |z| - |z|^7,$$

or
$$2|z| - |z|^7 \geqslant 1.$$

But a graph shows that $2|z| - |z|^7$ is less than 1 for $|z| \leqslant \frac{1}{2}$. Hence the suggestion that $|z| \leqslant \frac{1}{2}$ is impossible, so we conclude that $|z| > \frac{1}{2}$.

6.4 Geometrical problems in the Argand diagram

Since the moduli and the arguments of complex numbers are associated with certain lengths and angles in the Argand diagram, various geometrical problems can be solved with the aid of complex numbers. First of all, various standard constructions must be interpreted.

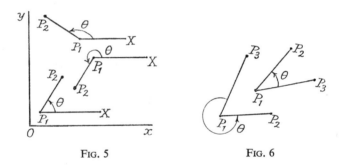

FIG. 5   FIG. 6

If P_1 represents $z_1 = x_1 + iy_1$ and P_2 represents $z_2 = x_2 + iy_2$, consider the difference $z_2 - z_1$. This complex number has $x_2 - x_1$ as its real part and $y_2 - y_1$ as its imaginary part. Hence its modulus is

$$|z_2 - z_1| = \sqrt{[(x_2 - x_1)^2 + (y_2 - y_1)^2]} = P_1P_2,$$

that is, the length of the segment P_1P_2. $\mathrm{Arg}(z_2 - z_1) = \theta$ is given by

$$\theta = \tan^{-1}[(y_2 - y_1)/(x_2 - x_1)],$$

regard being paid to the requisite quadrant, as Fig. 5 shows.

The positive angle θ is always given by the following construction. From P_1, draw a line P_1X parallel to $+Ox$. Then the positive angle from P_1X to P_1P_2 is the positive angle θ. Note that the line drawn parallel to Ox is *not* drawn through P_2. The construction merely changes the origin from O to P_1, namely to the point representing the *number being subtracted*.

The quotient $z = (z_2 - z_1)/(z_3 - z_1)$ may now be interpreted geometrically. If z_1, z_2, z_3 are represented respectively by P_1, P_2, P_3, then the modulus of z is P_2P_1/P_3P_1. The argument of z is given by

$$\arg(z_2 - z_1) - \arg(z_3 - z_1) = \angle P_2P_1X - \angle P_3P_1X = \angle P_2P_1P_3,$$

where the angle is measured positively from P_1P_3 (representing the denominator) to P_1P_2 (representing the numerator) in the anticlockwise sense.

The mid-point of the segment P_1P_2 is given by P, representing the complex number $z = \frac{1}{2}(z_1 + z_2)$, for the directed segment P_1P is given by $z - z_1 = \frac{1}{2}(z_2 - z_1)$, and PP_2 by $z_2 - z = \frac{1}{2}(z_2 - z_1)$; the two directed segments P_1P and PP_2 are therefore equal as far as length and direction are concerned.

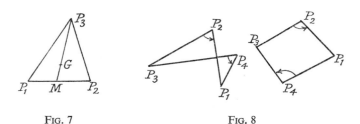

FIG. 7   FIG. 8

The complex number represented by the centroid of the triangle $P_1P_2P_3$ may be found from the known fact that the three medians of the triangle intersect in the centroid G, where G trisects each median.

The complex number $z = \frac{1}{2}(z_1 + z_2)$ represents M, the mid-point of P_1P_2. Since the directed segment MP_3 is represented by $z_3 - z$, the segment MG is represented by $\frac{1}{3}(z_3 - z)$. Hence G represents the number given by the sum of the two complex numbers representing P_1M and MG, namely

$$z + \tfrac{1}{3}(z_3 - z) = \tfrac{1}{3}z_3 + \tfrac{2}{3}z = \tfrac{1}{3}(z_1 + z_2 + z_3).$$

Considerations of this nature enable us to find the condition for the representations P_1, P_2, P_3, P_4 of four given numbers z_1, z_2, z_3, z_4 to be concyclic.

In the first figure, $\angle P_1P_2P_3 = \angle P_1P_4P_3$, so

$$\arg \frac{z_1 - z_2}{z_3 - z_2} = \arg \frac{z_1 - z_4}{z_3 - z_4},$$

$$\arg \frac{z_1 - z_2}{z_3 - z_2} . \frac{z_3 - z_4}{z_1 - z_4} = 0.$$

This means that $(z_1 - z_2)(z_3 - z_4)/(z_3 - z_2)(z_1 - z_4)$ is a positive real quantity.

In the second figure, $\angle P_1P_2P_3 + \angle P_3P_4P_1 = \pi$, so

$$\arg \frac{z_1 - z_2}{z_3 - z_2} . \frac{z_3 - z_4}{z_1 - z_4} = \pi,$$

indicating that $(z_1 - z_2)(z_3 - z_4)/(z_3 - z_2)(z_1 - z_4)$ is a negative real quantity.

These two results may be combined into one, namely that

$$\text{Im} \frac{(z_1 - z_2)(z_3 - z_4)}{(z_3 - z_2)(z_1 - z_4)} = 0.$$

Since the algebra is reversible, this necessary condition is also sufficient.

Example 4 *ABCDEFGH* is a regular octagon inscribed in the circle $|z| = \sqrt{2}$, with *A* on the positive real axis. If *P* is any point z on this circle, prove that the product of the 8 complex numbers represented by the directed segments *AP*, *BP*, *CP*, ..., *HP* is $z^8 - 16$, and prove that the product of the lengths of these 8 segments is less than 32.

The 8 points *A*, *B*, ..., *H* represent the complex numbers $\sqrt{2}$, $1 + i$, $\sqrt{2}i$, $-1 + i$, $-\sqrt{2}$, $-1 - i$, $-\sqrt{2}i$, $1 - i$, so the 8 segments represent the complex numbers $z - \sqrt{2}$, $z - (1 + i)$, $z - \sqrt{2}i$, $z - (-1 + i)$, $z + \sqrt{2}$, $z + (1 + i)$, $z + \sqrt{2}i$, $z + (-1 + i)$. With suitable rearrangement of factors, their product is

$$(z - \sqrt{2})(z + \sqrt{2})[z - (1 + i)][z + (1 + i)](z - \sqrt{2}i)(z + \sqrt{2}i)$$
$$[z - (-1 + i)][z + (-1 + i)]$$
$$= (z^2 - 2)[z^2 - (1 + i)^2](z^2 + 2)[z^2 - (-1 + i)^2]$$
$$= (z^2 - 2)(z^2 + 2)(z^2 - 2i)(z^2 + 2i)$$
$$= (z^4 - 4)(z^4 + 4) = z^8 - 16.$$

The lengths of the 8 segments are given by the moduli of these complex numbers:

$$AP.BP.CP \ldots HP = |z - 2| \, |z + 2| \ldots |z + (-1 + i)|$$
$$= |z^8 - 16|$$
$$\leqslant |z^8| + |16| = 32, \qquad \text{since } |z| = \sqrt{2}.$$

Example 5 *ABC* is an isosceles triangle, with $\angle B = \angle C = \theta$. If *A*, *B*, *C* represent the complex numbers z_1, z_2, z_3 respectively, prove the identity

$$(z_3 - z_2)^2 = 4(z_3 - z_1)(z_1 - z_2) \cos^2 \theta.$$

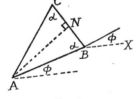

Two complex numbers are equal if their moduli and arguments are respectively equal.

As far as their moduli are concerned, if *N* is the foot of the perpendicular from *A* to *BC*, we have

$$|(z_3 - z_2)^2| = BC^2 = 4CN^2 = 4CN.NB$$
$$= 4AC \cos \theta \, AB \cos \theta$$
$$= 4 |z_3 - z_1| \, |z_1 - z_2| \cos^2 \theta.$$

FIG. 9

As far as their arguments are concerned, let ϕ be the angle between *AB* and the positive real axis. Then

$$\arg (z_3 - z_2) = \angle CBX = \pi + \phi - \theta,$$
$$\arg (z_3 - z_1) = \phi + \angle BAC = \pi - 2\theta + \phi,$$
$$\arg (z_1 - z_2) = \text{reflex } \angle XBA = \pi + \phi.$$

It follows immediately that

$$2 \arg (z_3 - z_2) = \arg (z_3 - z_1) + \arg (z_1 - z_2) = 2\pi + 2\phi - 2\theta,$$

thereby proving the given identity.

6.5 Interpretation of loci in the Argand diagram

Various elementary curves and constructions in a plane can be expressed in terms of complex numbers. Throughout we use z as the general point on the locus.

(i) The line commencing at the point $z_0 = x_0 + iy_0$ and making an angle θ with the positive real axis is given by

$$\arg (z - z_0) = \theta.$$

(ii) If a line segment is defined by its two end points z_1 and z_2, any point on the complete line containing the segment is given parametrically in the form $z_1 + \alpha(z_2 - z_1)$, where α is a real parameter.

(iii) The perpendicular bisector of the segment defined by the two end points z_1 and z_2 is given by

$$|z - z_1| = |z - z_2|.$$

(iv) The circle with centre z_0 and radius r is given by

$$|z - z_0| = r.$$

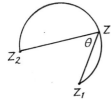

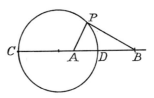

FIG. 10   FIG. 11

(v) The arc of the circle standing on the chord with end points z_1 and z_2, such that an angle θ is subtended by the chord at points on the arc, is given by

$$\arg \frac{z - z_1}{z - z_2} = \theta.$$

(vi) If A and B are the two points representing z_1 and z_2, the locus of a point P, such that the ratio AP/BP is constant, is a circle known as Apollonius' circle; its equation is

$$\left| \frac{z - z_1}{z - z_2} \right| = c.$$

The proof of this theorem is found in elementary geometrical texts.

If this circle cuts the line AB in the points C and D, let C and D be given by $z_1 + \alpha(z_2 - z_1)$, from (ii). Hence

$$\left| \frac{\alpha(z_2 - z_1)}{z_1 + \alpha(z_2 - z_1) - z_2} \right| = c,$$

or

$$\left| \frac{\alpha}{\alpha - 1} \right| = c.$$

Squaring, we obtain

$$\alpha^2 = c^2(\alpha^2 - 2\alpha + 1)$$

or

$$\alpha^2(c^2 - 1) - 2\alpha c^2 + c^2 = 0,$$

with the two real roots $\alpha = (c^2 \pm c)/(c^2 - 1) = c/(c \pm 1)$.

The points C and D are then given by

$$z = z_1 + c(z_2 - z_1)/(c \pm 1)$$

$$= (cz_2 \pm z_1)/(c \pm 1).$$

The centre of the circle is given by the average of these two complex numbers, namely by

$$\frac{1}{2}\left(\frac{cz_2 + z_1}{c + 1} + \frac{cz_2 - z_1}{c - 1}\right) = \frac{c^2 z_2 - z_1}{c^2 - 1},$$

and the radius is given by half the modulus of the difference of these two complex numbers, namely by

$$\frac{1}{2}\left|\frac{cz_2 + z_1}{c + 1} - \frac{cz_2 - z_1}{c - 1}\right| = \left|\frac{c(z_2 - z_1)}{c^2 - 1}\right|.$$

(vii) If z_1 and z_2 are the two foci of an ellipse, its equation is given by

$$|z - z_1| + |z - z_2| = c.$$

(viii) One branch of a hyperbola, possessing z_1 and z_2 as foci, is given by

$$|z - z_1| - |z - z_2| = c.$$

EXERCISES

(1). Simplify (i) $(2 + i)(3 - 2i)$, (ii) $(1 - i)^3$, (iii) $(1 - 2i)/(1 + i)$, (iv) $(2 + 3i)/(1 - 2i)$, (v) $(5 + 3i)^{-1} - (5 - 3i)^{-1}$.

(2). Express in modulus argument form: (i) $1 + i\sqrt{3}$, (ii) $i - \sqrt{3}$, (iii) $2 - i\sqrt{2}$, (iv) $-4 - 3i$.

(3). If $z_1 = \cos\theta + i\sin\theta$ and $z_2 = \cos\phi + i\sin\phi$, prove
(i) $(1 + z)/(1 - z) = i\cot\frac{1}{2}\theta$,
(ii) $\cos(\theta + \phi) = \frac{1}{2}(z_1 z_2 + z_1^{-1} z_2^{-1})$.

(4). Simplify

$$\left(\frac{a + ib}{a - ib}\right)^2 - \left(\frac{a - ib}{a + ib}\right)^2.$$

(5). If z_1, z_2, a, b are complex numbers, prove that
(i) $|z_1 - z_2|^2 + |z_1 + z_2|^2 = 2|z_1|^2 + 2|z_2|^2$,
(ii) $|a + \sqrt{(a^2 - b^2)}| + |a - \sqrt{(a^2 - b^2)}| = |a + b| + |a - b|$.

(6). Solve the equation $x^2 + x + 1 = 0$, and show that each root is the square of the other.

(7). Show that the equation with the four roots $x = \frac{1}{2}(\pm\sqrt{3} \pm i)$ is

$$x^4 + x^2 + 1 = 0.$$

(8)*. If the points P and Q in an Argand diagram represent the complex numbers z_1 and z_2 respectively and O is the origin, show that if the triangle OPQ is isosceles and right-angled at O, then $z_1^2 + z_2^2 = 0$.
Find the complex numbers represented by the vertices of a square if one vertex represents $3 + 3i$ and the centre of the square represents $1 + 2i$.

(9)*. A point $z = x + iy$ in the Argand diagram is such that $|z| = 2$, $x = 1$ and $y > 0$. Determine the point and find the distance between z and the point $z^2/2$.

Show also that the points 2, z, $z^2/2$, $z^3/4$, $z^4/8$ and $z^5/16$ are the vertices of a regular hexagon.

(10)*. If $z = 1 + i$, mark in an Argand diagram the four points A, B, C and D representing z, z^2, z^3 and z^4 respectively. Find, by calculation or from your diagram, the moduli and arguments of the complex numbers $z^3 - 1$ and $z + z^4$.

Show that arg $(z^3 - z^4)/(z^2 - z^4)$ is given by the angle BDC and hence, or otherwise, show that the angles BDC and ACB are equal.

(11)*. If $z_1 = 2 + i$, $z_2 = -2 + 4i$, and $z_3^{-1} = z_1^{-1} + z_2^{-1}$, find z_3.

If z_1, z_2, z_3 are represented on an Argand diagram by the points P_1, P_2, P_3, show that $\overrightarrow{OP_2} = 2i\,\overrightarrow{OP_1}$ and $\overrightarrow{OP_3} = \frac{2}{5}i\,\overrightarrow{P_2P_1}$. Hence prove that P_3 is the foot of the perpendicular from O on the line P_1P_2.

(12)*. A regular pentagon $ABCDE$ is inscribed in the circle $x^2 + y^2 = 1$, the vertex A being the point $(1, 0)$. Obtain the complex numbers $x + iy$ of which the points A, B, C, D, E form a representation in an Argand diagram.

(13)*. By means of an Argand diagram, or otherwise, show that if $|z| = 1$, the real part of $(1 + z)/(1 - z)$ is zero.

(14)*. Mark on an Argand diagram the points $\sqrt{3} + i$, $2 + 2\sqrt{3}i$, and their product. What is the general relation between the positions of the points $a + ib$ and $(\sqrt{3} + i)(a + ib)$?

A triangle ABC has its vertices at the points 0, $2 + 2\sqrt{3}i$ and $-1 + \sqrt{3}i$ respectively. A similar triangle $A'B'C'$ has its vertices A' and B' at the points 0 and $8i$ respectively. Find the position of C'.

(15)*. Indicate in the Argand diagram the points P, Q, R corresponding to the complex numbers $p = z + w$, $q = z - w$, $r = z/z^\star$ respectively, where z and w are given complex numbers different from zero, and $z^\star$ is the conjugate of z.

Show that (i) if $\angle POQ = \frac{1}{2}\pi$, then z and w have the same modulus; (ii) if $OP = OQ$, then w^2/z^2 is real and negative, where O denotes the point corresponding to zero.

(16)*. $ABCDEF$ is a regular hexagon inscribed in the circle $|z| = a$ in the Argand diagram, A being the point $(a, 0)$. If P, representing the complex number z, is any point on the circle, write down the complex numbers represented by the six points obtained by drawing lines from the origin equal and parallel to the directed lines $\overrightarrow{AP}$, $\overrightarrow{BP}$, $\overrightarrow{CP}$, $\overrightarrow{DP}$, $\overrightarrow{EP}$, $\overrightarrow{FP}$, and prove that their product is $z^6 - a^6$. Hence prove that

$$AP.BP.CP.DP.EP.FP \leqslant 2a^6.$$

(17)*. Triangles BCX, CAY, ABZ are described on the sides of a triangle ABC. If the points A, B, C, X, Y, Z in the Argand diagram represent the complex numbers a, b, c, x, y, z respectively, and

$$\frac{x - c}{b - c} = \frac{y - a}{c - a} = \frac{z - b}{a - b},$$

show that the triangles BCX, CAY, ABZ are similar.

Prove also that the centroids of ABC, XYZ are coincident.

(18)*. In the Argand diagram, PQR is an equilateral triangle of which the circumcentre is at the origin. If P represents the number $2 + i$, find the numbers represented by Q and R.

(19)*. (i) Find the modulus and argument of $1 + \cos\theta + i\sin\theta$.

(ii) A square $ABCD$ has for its sides the lines $x = \pm a$, $y = \pm a$. If P is any point on the circumcircle of $ABCD$, prove that $PA.PB.PC.PD$ cannot exceed $8a^4$. At what points on the circle does the above product equal $8a^4$?

(20)*. Show that a necessary and sufficient condition that the points denoted by z_1, z_2 and the origin should form an equilateral triangle is

$$z_1{}^2 - z_1 z_2 + z_2{}^2 = 0.$$

(21)*. If the argument of the complex number $(z - 1)/(z + 1)$ is $\frac{1}{4}\pi$, show that z lies upon a fixed circle whose centre is at the point which represents i.

(22*). If $z = x + iy$, find x and y when

$$\frac{2z}{1 + i} - \frac{2z}{i} = \frac{5}{2 + i}.$$

(23)*. Describe the following loci in the Argand diagram:

(i) $\arg[(z - z_1)/(z - z_2)] = \frac{1}{6}\pi$,

(ii) $|z - z_1| - |z - z_2| = 1$,

(iii) $\arg[(z - 2)/(z + 1)] = \frac{1}{2}\pi$.

(iv) $|z + 3i|^2 - |z - 3i|^2 = 12$,

(v) $|z + ik|^2 + |z - ik|^2 = 10k^2$, $(k > 0)$.

ANSWERS TO EXERCISES

(1). (i) $8 - i$. (ii) $-2 - 2i$. (iii) $-\frac{1}{2} - \frac{3}{2}i$. (iv) $-\frac{4}{5} + \frac{7}{5}i$. (v) $-\frac{3}{17}i$.

(2). (i) 2, $\frac{1}{3}\pi$. (ii) 2, $\frac{5}{6}\pi$. (iii) 2, $315°$. (iv) 5, $216°52'$.

(4). $4iab/(a^2 + b^2)^2$.   (6). $\frac{1}{2}(-1 \pm \sqrt{3}i)$.   (8). $4i$, $-1 + i$, 2.

(9). $z = 1 + i\sqrt{3}$; 2.   (10). $\sqrt{13}$, $146°19'$; $\sqrt{10}$, $161°34'$.

(11). $(6 + 8i)/5$.   (12). $\cos\left(\frac{2}{5}\pi r\right) + i\sin\left(\frac{2}{5}\pi r\right)$, $r = 0, 1, 2, 3, 4$.

(14). $-2\sqrt{3} + 2i$.   (18). $\frac{1}{2}[\sqrt{3} - 2 - i(1 + 2\sqrt{3})]$, $\frac{1}{2}[-2 - \sqrt{3} + i(2\sqrt{3} - 1)]$.

(19). (i) $|2\cos\frac{1}{2}\theta|$, $\frac{1}{2}\theta$ or $\frac{1}{2}\theta + \pi$. (ii) $\pm a\sqrt{2}$, $\pm ia\sqrt{2}$.

(22). $\frac{1}{2}(1 - 3i)$.   (23). (iv) $y = 1$. (v) $x^2 + y^2 = 4k^2$.

CHAPTER 7

DE MOIVRE'S THEOREM AND APPLICATIONS

7.1 De Moivre's theorem

We consider a complex number with unit modulus in polar form, namely $z = \cos \theta + i \sin \theta$, a combination often abbreviated to $z = \operatorname{cis} \theta$.

Theorem: If n is any positive or negative integer or rational fraction, one value of $(\cos \theta + i \sin \theta)^n$ is $\cos n\theta + i \sin n\theta$.

Case i. The simplest case occurs when n is a positive integer. Since

$$(\cos \theta + i \sin \theta)(\cos \phi + i \sin \phi) = \cos (\theta + \phi) + i \sin (\theta + \phi) \quad (1)$$

we obtain, when $\theta = \phi$,

$$(\cos \theta + i \sin \theta)^2 = \cos 2\theta + i \sin 2\theta.$$

Since the theorem is certainly valid when $n = 2$, the general case for a positive integral index may be verified by induction. If

$$(\cos \theta + i \sin \theta)^n = \cos n\theta + i \sin n\theta,$$

then

$$\begin{aligned}
(\cos \theta + i \sin \theta)^{n+1} &= (\cos \theta + i \sin \theta)^n(\cos \theta + i \sin \theta) \\
&= (\cos n\theta + i \sin n\theta)(\cos \theta + i \sin \theta) \\
&= \cos [(n + 1)\theta] + i \sin [(n + 1)\theta],
\end{aligned}$$

where we have put $\phi = n\theta$ in equation (1). This verifies the theorem for all positive integers n.

Case ii. If n is a negative integer, $-m$ say, where m is positive, we have

$$\begin{aligned}
(\cos \theta + i \sin \theta)^{-m} &= 1/(\cos \theta + i \sin \theta)^m \\
&= 1/(\cos m\theta + i \sin m\theta) \\
&= \cos m\theta - i \sin m\theta \\
&= \cos (-m\theta) + i \sin (-m\theta).
\end{aligned}$$

Case iii. If n has the form $1/q$, where q is a positive integer, let $(\cos \theta + i \sin \theta)^{1/q}$ expressed in polar form be $r(\cos \psi + i \sin \psi)$. Then

$$\begin{aligned}
\cos \theta + i \sin \theta &= r^q(\cos \psi + i \sin \psi)^q \\
&= r^q(\cos q\psi + i \sin q\psi).
\end{aligned}$$

Equating moduli and arguments, we obtain $1 = r^q$, $\theta = q\psi$, where we have equated θ to just one value of the argument of the right hand side; other values will be considered later. Hence $r = 1$ and $\psi = \theta/q$, giving

$$(\cos\theta + i\sin\theta)^{1/q} = \cos(\theta/q) + i\sin(\theta/q).$$

Case iv. If $n = -1/q$, result (iii) may be modified by taking its reciprocal.

Case v. If $n = \pm p/q$, results (iii) and (iv) may be modified by raising them to the pth power by result (i).

Example 1   Find the 10*th* power of the complex number $z = \sqrt{3} + i$.

Firstly we express z in polar form. Noting that $|z| = 2$ and that arg z has the value $\tan^{-1} 1/\sqrt{3} = \frac{1}{6}\pi$, we have $z = 2\operatorname{cis}\frac{1}{6}\pi$. Hence

$$z^{10} = 2^{10}(\cos\tfrac{10}{6}\pi + i\sin\tfrac{10}{6}\pi)$$
$$= 1024(\tfrac{1}{2} - i\tfrac{1}{2}\sqrt{3}) = 512(1 - i\sqrt{3}).$$

Example 2   By considering $(1 + i)^n$ when n is a positive integer, show that

$$_nC_0 - {}_nC_2 + {}_nC_4 - \ldots = 2^{\frac{1}{2}n}\cos\tfrac{1}{4}n\pi,$$
$$_nC_1 - {}_nC_3 + {}_nC_5 - \ldots = 2^{\frac{1}{2}n}\sin\tfrac{1}{4}n\pi.$$

We have

$$(1 + i) = \sqrt{2}(\cos\tfrac{1}{4}\pi + i\sin\tfrac{1}{4}\pi);$$

hence

$$(1 + i)^n = 2^{\frac{1}{2}n}(\cos\tfrac{1}{4}n\pi + i\sin\tfrac{1}{4}n\pi).$$

Also, using the binomial theorem, we have

$$(1 + i)^n = {}_nC_0 + {}_nC_1(i) + {}_nC_2(i)^2 + {}_nC_3(i)^3 + {}_nC_4(i)^4 + \ldots$$
$$= ({}_nC_0 - {}_nC_2 + {}_nC_4 - \ldots) + i({}_nC_1 - {}_nC_3 + {}_nC_5 - \ldots).$$

On equating real and imaginary parts of these two distinct expressions for $(1 + i)^n$, we obtain the required results.

7.2   Roots of complex numbers

Let us consider in more detail the qth roots of $(\cos\theta + i\sin\theta)$. From case (iii) above, its value is $\cos\psi + i\sin\psi$, where

$$\cos\theta + i\sin\theta = \cos q\psi + i\sin q\psi;$$

hence

$$\cos\theta = \cos q\psi, \quad \sin\theta = \sin q\psi.$$

The general solution of these equations is

$$q\psi = \theta + 2r\pi,$$

where r is any integer, so

$$\psi = (\theta + 2r\pi)/q.$$

The various roots are then given by

$$\cos[(\theta + 2r\pi)/q] + i\sin[(\theta + 2r\pi)/q],$$

and are known as the *branches* of the multi-valued function $z^{1/q}$.

If we let the values of r commence at some integer r_0, and run consecutively through the integers to $r_0 + q - 1$, then q distinct roots are produced. However, the root produced when r attains the value $r_0 + q$ repeats the root when $r = r_0$ (since 2π is merely added to this latter root's argument), so no further distinct roots are produced beyond $r = r_0 + q - 1$.

Hence we have q and only q distinct qth roots given by

$$(\cos \theta + i \sin \theta)^{1/q} = \cos [(\theta + 2r\pi)/q] + i \sin [(\theta + 2r\pi)/q]$$
$$(r = 0, 1, 2, \ldots, q - 1),$$

or any other suitable set of q consecutive integers. If q is odd, of the form $2n + 1$, it is sometimes useful to take

$$r = -n, -(n - 1), \ldots, -2, -1, 0, 1, 2, \ldots, (n - 1), n;$$

while if q is even of the form $2n$, we may take

$$r = -n, -(n - 1), \ldots, -2, -1, 0, 1, 2, \ldots, (n - 2), (n - 1).$$

It is obvious that these q qth roots are all spaced evenly round the unit circle in the Argand diagram, commencing with argument θ/q, and separated in argument from each other by the angle $2\pi/q$.

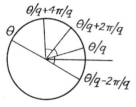

FIG. 12

Example 3 Find the three cube roots of 1 and i, and the four fourth roots of -1.

In polar form, $1 = \cos 0 + i \sin 0$, so

$$1 = \cos \tfrac{2}{3}r\pi + i \sin \tfrac{2}{3}r\pi, \quad (r = 0, 1, 2)$$
$$= 1, (r = 0); \quad -\tfrac{1}{2} + \tfrac{1}{2}i\sqrt{3}, (r = 1); \quad -\tfrac{1}{2} - \tfrac{1}{2}i\sqrt{3}, (r = 2).$$

The student should plot these points round the unit circle in the Argand diagram.

In polar form, $i = \cos \tfrac{1}{2}\pi + i \sin \tfrac{1}{2}\pi$, so

$$i^{\frac{1}{3}} = \cos (\tfrac{1}{6}\pi + \tfrac{2}{3}r\pi) + i \sin (\tfrac{1}{6}\pi + \tfrac{2}{3}r\pi) \quad (r = 0, 1, 2)$$
$$= \tfrac{1}{2}\sqrt{3} + \tfrac{1}{2}i, (r = 0); \quad -\tfrac{1}{2}\sqrt{3} + \tfrac{1}{2}i, (r = 1); \quad -i, (r = 2).$$

In polar form, $-1 = \cos \pi + i \sin \pi$, so

$$(-1)^{\frac{1}{4}} = \cos (\tfrac{1}{4}\pi + \tfrac{1}{2}r\pi) + i \sin (\tfrac{1}{4}\pi + \tfrac{1}{2}r\pi) \quad (r = 0, 1, 2, 3)$$
$$= (1 + i)/\sqrt{2}, (-1 + i)/\sqrt{2}, (-1 - i)/\sqrt{2}, (1 - i)/\sqrt{2}.$$

Example 4 Evaluate (i) $\sqrt{(5 - 12i)}$, (ii) $(2i - 2)^{\frac{1}{4}}$.

The modulus of $5 - 12i$ is 13, and its argument is $-\tan^{-1} \tfrac{12}{5} = \theta$, say, in the fourth quadrant. Then

$$\sqrt{(5 - 12i)} = \sqrt{13}[\cos (\tfrac{1}{2}\theta + r\pi) + i \sin (\tfrac{1}{2}\theta + r\pi)] \quad (r = 0, 1)$$
$$= \pm\sqrt{13}(\cos \tfrac{1}{2}\theta + i \sin \tfrac{1}{2}\theta).$$

Now $\cos \theta = \tfrac{5}{13} = 2 \cos^2 \tfrac{1}{2}\theta - 1$, so $\cos^2 \tfrac{1}{2}\theta = \tfrac{9}{13}$. We choose

$$\cos \tfrac{1}{2}\theta = 3/\sqrt{13}, \sin \tfrac{1}{2}\theta = -2/\sqrt{13},$$

the signs referring to the fourth quadrant. Hence

$$\sqrt{(5 - 12i)} = \pm(3 - 2i).$$

The modulus of $(2i - 2)$ is $2\sqrt{2}$, and its argument $\frac{3}{4}\pi$. Hence

$$(2i - 2)^{\frac{1}{3}} = \sqrt{2}(\cos \tfrac{3}{4}\pi + i \sin \tfrac{3}{4}\pi)^{\frac{1}{3}} \cdot (1)^{\frac{1}{3}},$$

where for convenience of calculation the multi-valued nature of the cube root has been transferred from the complex number itself to unity. We have

$$(2i - 2)^{\frac{1}{3}} = \sqrt{2}(\cos \tfrac{1}{4}\pi + i \sin \tfrac{1}{4}\pi) \cdot (1)^{\frac{1}{3}}$$
$$= (1 + i) \cdot (1)^{\frac{1}{3}}.$$

Using the three cube roots of unity found in example 3, we find

$$(2i - 2)^{\frac{1}{3}} = (1 + i) \times (1; \ -\tfrac{1}{2} \pm \tfrac{1}{2}i\sqrt{3})$$
$$= 1 + i; \ (-\tfrac{1}{2} \mp \tfrac{1}{2}\sqrt{3}) + i(-\tfrac{1}{2} \pm \tfrac{1}{2}\sqrt{3}).$$

Example 5 Solve the equation $(2x - 1)^5 = 32x^5$.

This is an equation of the fourth degree, since the terms in x^5 disappear; we expect therefore four solutions. Taking the fifth root of each side, introducing the five fifth roots of unity in the process, we obtain

$$2x - 1 = 2x \cdot (1)^{\frac{1}{5}}$$
$$= 2x(\cos \tfrac{2}{5}r\pi + i \sin \tfrac{2}{5}r\pi), \quad (r = 1, 2, 3, 4).$$

The case $r = 0$ is excluded, since this gives rise to the inconsistent equation $2x - 1 = 2x$. The solution for x is

$$x = 1/2(1 - \cos \tfrac{2}{5}r\pi - i \sin \tfrac{2}{5}r\pi)$$
$$= 1/4(\sin^2 \tfrac{1}{5}r\pi - i \sin \tfrac{1}{5}r\pi \cos \tfrac{1}{5}r\pi)$$
$$= 1/[-4i \sin \tfrac{1}{5}r\pi(\cos \tfrac{1}{5}r\pi + i \sin \tfrac{1}{5}r\pi)]$$
$$= \tfrac{1}{4}i \ \mathrm{cosec} \ \tfrac{1}{5}r\pi(\cos \tfrac{1}{5}r\pi - i \sin \tfrac{1}{5}r\pi)$$
$$= \tfrac{1}{4} + \tfrac{1}{4}i \cot \tfrac{1}{5}r\pi, \quad (r = 1, 2, 3, 4).$$

7.3 Roots of polynomials

Let

$$a_0 + a_1z + a_2z^2 + \ldots + a_nz^n \equiv \sum_{s=0}^{n} a_sz^s = 0$$

be a polynomial equation of degree n in z, where the $(n + 1)$ coefficients are real numbers. The *fundamental theorem of algebra* states that this equation possesses n roots either real or complex, due allowance being made for repeated roots.

In other words, in order to solve such an equation completely, it is not necessary to introduce any other type of number apart from complex numbers. This result is obvious for a quadratic equation, for which an explicit solution exists in terms of its coefficients, but a careful proof is necessary for equations of higher degree; such a proof may be found in more specialized texts.

Let us assume, then, that $z = r(\cos \theta + i \sin \theta)$ is a root expressed in polar form of the given equation. Then

$$\sum a_s r^s (\cos \theta + i \sin \theta)^s = 0,$$

or
$$\sum a_s r^s (\cos s\theta + i \sin s\theta) = 0.$$

Equating real and imaginary parts to zero, we obtain

$$\sum a_s r^s \cos s\theta = 0, \quad \sum a_s r^s \sin s\theta = 0.$$

We now multiply the second equation by i, and subtract from the first, obtaining

$$\sum a_s r^s (\cos s\theta - i \sin s\theta) = 0,$$

or
$$\sum a_s r^s (\cos \theta - i \sin \theta)^s = 0.$$

Hence the conjugate quantity $z^\star = r (\cos \theta - i \sin \theta)$ is also a root of the given equation. It follows that complex roots of such an equation are grouped together into conjugate pairs.

A polynomial with real coefficients may have a number of real roots α, yielding real factors of the form $(z - \alpha)$, and complex roots of the form $\gamma \pm i\delta$. The factors associated with such a pair of roots are

$$(z - \gamma - i\delta)(z - \gamma + i\delta) = (z - \gamma)^2 + \delta^2,$$

a real quadratic factor. Hence any polynomial with real coefficients may be resolved into real factors, these being either linear or quadratic. These factors are found from the solution of the equation, which, apart from simple analytical cases, often requires a lengthy numerical calculation.

The reader should recognize the following factors:

$$x^3 - 1 = (x - 1)(x^2 + x + 1), \quad x^3 + 1 = (x + 1)(x^2 - x + 1),$$
$$x^4 + 1 = (x^2 + x\sqrt{2} + 1)(x^2 - x\sqrt{2} + 1).$$

The following examples show how the roots may be found in special cases, how they may be grouped to form real quadratic factors when possible, and how deductions may be drawn both from the roots and from the factors.

Example 6 Factorize the expression $f(x) \equiv x^{2n} - 2x^n \cos 2n\theta + 1$ into real factors. Examine various consequences of this factorization by giving to x and θ certain values.

To find the roots, we consider the equation $f(x) = 0$. Using the standard formula to solve this as a quadratic in x^n, we obtain

$$x^n = \cos 2n\theta \pm \sqrt{(\cos^2 2n\theta - 1)}$$
$$= \cos 2n\theta \pm i \sin 2n\theta.$$

Taking the nth root, we find for the $2n$ values of x:

$$x = \cos(2\theta + 2\pi r/n) \pm i \sin(2\theta + 2\pi r/n), \quad r = 0, 1, 2, \ldots, (n-1).$$

Each value of r provides a pair of conjugate roots, so the general quadratic factor is

$$[x - \cos(2\theta + 2\pi r/n) - i \sin(2\theta + 2\pi r/n)]$$
$$\times [x - \cos(2\theta + 2\pi r/n) + i \sin(2\theta + 2\pi r/n)]$$
$$= x^2 - 2x \cos(2\theta + 2\pi r/n) + 1.$$

Hence we conclude that

$$x^{2n} - 2x^n \cos 2\theta + 1 \equiv \prod_{r=0}^{n-1} [x^2 - 2x \cos(2\theta + 2\pi r/n) + 1], \qquad (2)$$

where no constant factor is required, since the coefficient of x^{2n} on the right-hand side is obviously unity.

When $x = 1$, the identity (2) yields

$$2(1 - \cos 2n\theta) \equiv 2^n \prod_{r=0}^{n-1} [1 - \cos(2\theta + 2\pi r/n)],$$

or, in terms of half-angles,

$$4 \sin^2 n\theta \equiv 2^{2n} \prod_{r=0}^{n-1} \sin^2(\theta + \pi r/n).$$

The square root then yields the identity

$$\sin n\theta \equiv 2^{n-1} \prod_{r=0}^{n-1} \sin(\theta + \pi r/n).$$

For example, when $n = 4$,

$$\sin 4\theta \equiv 8 \sin \theta \sin(\theta + \tfrac{1}{4}\pi) \sin(\theta + \tfrac{1}{2}\pi) \sin(\theta + \tfrac{3}{4}\pi).$$

We shall now place $\theta = \pi/4n$ in the identity (2); since $\cos 2n\theta = 0$, we have

$$x^{2n} + 1 = \prod_{r=0}^{n-1} \{x^2 - 2x \cos[(\tfrac{1}{2}\pi + 2\pi r)/n] + 1\},$$

or

$$x^n + x^{-n} = \prod_{r=0}^{n-1} \{x - 2\cos[(\tfrac{1}{2}\pi + 2\pi r)/n] + x^{-1}\}.$$

Finally, let $x = e^{i\phi}$ (see section 7.4), yielding

$$\cos n\phi = 2^{n-1} \prod_{r=0}^{n-1} \{\cos \phi - \cos[(\tfrac{1}{2}\pi + 2\pi r)/n]\}.$$

Example 7 Solve the equation

$$(x + ia)^{2n} + (x - ia)^{2n} = (x^2 + a^2)^n.$$

If the left hand side is expanded, the i's evidently disappear, so the equation is of the $2n$th degree with real coefficients.

If we place $p = x + ia$, $q = x - ia$, the given equation becomes

$$p^{2n} + q^{2n} = p^n q^n.$$

This is a quadratic equation in p^n; the solution is

$$p^n = \tfrac{1}{2}[q^n \pm \sqrt{(q^{2n} - 4q^{2n})}]$$
$$= q^n(\tfrac{1}{2} \pm \tfrac{1}{2}i\sqrt{3})$$
$$= q^n(\cos \tfrac{1}{3}\pi \pm i \sin \tfrac{1}{3}\pi).$$

Taking the nth root, we obtain

$$p = q\{\cos [(\tfrac{1}{3}\pi + 2\pi r)/n] \pm i \sin [(\tfrac{1}{3}\pi + 2\pi r)/n]\}, \quad r = 0, 1, 2, \ldots, n - 1,$$
$$= q(\cos \alpha \pm i \sin \alpha),$$

say. It follows that

$$x + ia = (x - ia)(\cos \alpha \pm i \sin \alpha),$$

from which we obtain the solution for x:

$$x = \frac{ia(1 + \cos \alpha \pm i \sin \alpha)}{\cos \alpha - 1 \pm i \sin \alpha}.$$

Expressions of this character may always be simplified by the use of half angles:

$$x = \frac{ia(2 \cos^2 \tfrac{1}{2}\alpha \pm 2i \sin \tfrac{1}{2}\alpha \cos \tfrac{1}{2}\alpha)}{- 2 \sin^2 \tfrac{1}{2}\alpha \pm 2i \sin \tfrac{1}{2}\alpha \cos \tfrac{1}{2}\alpha}$$

$$= \pm a \cot \tfrac{1}{2}\alpha$$
$$= \pm a \cot [(\tfrac{1}{6}\pi + \pi r)/n], \quad r = 0, 1, 2, \ldots, n - 1.$$

The product of the $2n$ roots is given by the constant term in the given equation, namely by $[2(-1)^n - 1]a^{2n}$. Hence

$$(-1)^n \prod_{r=0}^{n-1} a^2 \cot^2 [(\tfrac{1}{6}\pi + \pi r)/n] = [2(-1)^n - 1]a^{2n},$$

or

$$\prod_{r=0}^{n-1} \cot^2 [(\tfrac{1}{6}\pi + \pi r)/n] = 2 - (-1)^n.$$

For example, when $n = 3$,

$$\cot^2 \tfrac{1}{18}\pi \, \cot^2 \tfrac{7}{18}\pi \, \cot^2 \tfrac{13}{18}\pi = 3.$$

7.4   The exponential form

If $z = \cos \theta + i \sin \theta$, where θ is expressed in radians, differentiation with respect to θ yields

$$\frac{dz}{d\theta} = -\sin \theta + i \cos \theta = i(\cos \theta + i \sin \theta) = iz.$$

Integration then yields $z = Ae^{i\theta}$, where A is the constant of integration. In particular, when $\theta = 0$, $z = 1$; this shows that $A = 1$, giving the result

$$\cos \theta + i \sin \theta = e^{i\theta}.$$

This new expression for $\cos \theta + i \sin \theta$ is important in all further developments of the theory.

The reciprocal of this result is

$$\cos \theta - i \sin \theta = e^{-i\theta}.$$

Addition and subtraction respectively give

$$\cos \theta = (e^{i\theta} + e^{-i\theta})/2, \quad \sin \theta = (e^{i\theta} - e^{-i\theta})/2i.$$

Inserting the series for $e^{\pm i\theta}$:

$$e^{\pm i\theta} = 1 \pm i\theta - \frac{\theta^2}{2!} \mp \frac{i\theta^3}{3!} + \frac{\theta^4}{4!} \pm \cdots,$$

we obtain the standard series for $\cos \theta$ and $\sin \theta$:

$$\cos \theta = 1 - \frac{\theta^2}{2!} + \frac{\theta^4}{4!} - \frac{\theta^6}{6!} + \cdots,$$

$$\sin \theta = \theta - \frac{\theta^3}{3!} + \frac{\theta^5}{5!} - \frac{\theta^7}{7!} + \cdots,$$

where θ is in radians. Each series is absolutely convergent for all values of θ.

A general complex number z may now be written in the form

$$z = x + iy = r(\cos \theta + i \sin \theta) = re^{i\theta}.$$

The following identities should be learnt, since they are in constant use:

$$e^0 = e^{2\pi i} = e^{4\pi i} = \ldots = e^{2\pi n i} = 1,$$

$$e^{\frac{1}{2}i\pi} = \cos \tfrac{1}{2}\pi + i \sin \tfrac{1}{2}\pi = i,$$

$$e^{-\frac{1}{2}i\pi} = \cos \tfrac{1}{2}\pi - i \sin \tfrac{1}{2}\pi = -i,$$

$$e^{-i\pi} = \cos \pi + i \sin \pi = -1.$$

The function $e^{i\theta}$ is evidently periodic in θ with period 2π.

De Moivre's theorem is consistent with this new functional form. For

$$(\cos \theta + i \sin \theta)^n = (e^{i\theta})^n = e^{in\theta} = \cos n\theta + i \sin n\theta.$$

If n is the complex number $a + ib$, we define $(\cos \theta + i \sin \theta)^{a+ib}$ to be

$$(\cos \theta + i \sin \theta)^{a+ib} = (e^{i\theta})^{a+ib} = e^{i(a+ib)\theta}$$

$$= e^{-b\theta} e^{ia\theta}$$

$$= e^{-b\theta}(\cos a\theta + i \sin a\theta).$$

The real part is $e^{-b\theta} \cos a\theta$ and the imaginary part $e^{-b\theta} \sin a\theta$.

Various interesting identities may now be produced. For example, when $\theta = \frac{1}{2}\pi$, $a = 0$, $b = 1$, we have $\cos \theta + i \sin \theta = i$, and $a + ib = i$, so

$$i^i = e^{-\frac{1}{2}\pi},$$

a real quantity, exhibiting a remarkable relationship between the three fundamental numbers i, e, π.

It is often necessary to simplify expressions of the type $\pm 1 \pm e^{\pm i\theta}$, where any combination of signs is permitted. Simplification is effected by taking out a factor $e^{\pm \frac{1}{2}i\theta}$; for example

$$1 + e^{i\theta} = e^{\frac{1}{2}i\theta}(e^{-\frac{1}{2}i\theta} + e^{\frac{1}{2}i\theta}) = 2 \cos \tfrac{1}{2}\theta \; e^{\frac{1}{2}i\theta},$$
$$1 - e^{-i\theta} = e^{-\frac{1}{2}i\theta}(e^{\frac{1}{2}i\theta} - e^{-\frac{1}{2}i\theta}) = 2i \sin \tfrac{1}{2}\theta \; e^{-\frac{1}{2}i\theta}.$$

Example 8   If $z = e^{i\theta}$, find the real and imaginary parts of

$$w = \sqrt{[(1 + z)/(1 - z)]}.$$

We have

$$w = \sqrt{\frac{1 + e^{i\theta}}{1 - e^{i\theta}}} = \sqrt{\frac{e^{-\frac{1}{2}i\theta} + e^{\frac{1}{2}i\theta}}{e^{-\frac{1}{2}i\theta} - e^{\frac{1}{2}i\theta}}} = \sqrt{\frac{\cos \frac{1}{2}\theta}{-i \sin \frac{1}{2}\theta}} = \sqrt{(i \cot \tfrac{1}{2}\theta)}.$$

If $\cot \frac{1}{2}\theta$ is positive, that is if $2n\pi < \theta < (2n + 1)\pi$ where n is any integer,

$$w = \sqrt{(e^{\frac{1}{2}i\pi} \cot \theta)} = \pm e^{\frac{1}{4}i\pi}\sqrt{(\cot \tfrac{1}{2}\theta)} = \pm(1 + i)\sqrt{(\tfrac{1}{2} \cot \tfrac{1}{2}\theta)}.$$

The real part is $\pm \sqrt{(\frac{1}{2} \cot \frac{1}{2}\theta)}$ and the imaginary part $\pm \sqrt{(\frac{1}{2} \cot \frac{1}{2}\theta)}$.

If $\cot \frac{1}{2}\theta$ is negative, that is if $(2n - 1)\pi < \theta < 2n\pi$, we have

$$w = \sqrt{[e^{-\frac{1}{2}i\pi}(-\cot \tfrac{1}{2}\theta)]} = \pm e^{-\frac{1}{4}i\pi}\sqrt{(-\cot \tfrac{1}{2}\theta)} = \pm(1 - i)\sqrt{(-\tfrac{1}{2} \cot \tfrac{1}{2}\theta)}.$$

The real part is $\pm \sqrt{(-\frac{1}{2} \cot \frac{1}{2}\theta)}$ and the imaginary part $\mp \sqrt{(-\frac{1}{2} \cot \frac{1}{2}\theta)}$.

Example 9   Evaluate the integral of $e^{ax} \cos bx$.

Instead of $\cos bx$, we consider the modified integrand $e^{ax}(\cos bx + i \sin bx)$:

$$\int e^{ax}(\cos bx + i \sin bx) \, dx = \int e^{ax+ibx} \, dx$$

$$= \frac{e^{ax+ibx}}{a + ib}$$

$$= \frac{e^{ax}(\cos bx + i \sin bx)(a - ib)}{a^2 + b^2}$$

$$= \frac{e^{ax}[(a \cos bx + b \sin bx) + i(a \sin bx - b \cos bx)]}{a^2 + b^2}.$$

The required integral is obviously given by the real part of this expression, while the corresponding integral containing $\sin bx$ is given by the imaginary part.

7.5 Summation of trigonometrical series

Let us suppose that the sum of the finite or infinite real series

$$a_0 + a_1 p + a_2 p^2 + \ldots + a_r p^r + \ldots$$

may be found by elementary methods to be the function $A(p)$.

Consider the two trigonometrical series

$$C = a_0 + a_1 \cos \theta + a_2 \cos 2\theta + \ldots + a_r \cos r\theta + \ldots$$
$$S = \qquad a_1 \sin \theta + a_2 \sin 2\theta + \ldots + a_r \sin r\theta + \ldots.$$

It follows that

$$C + iS = a_0 + a_1(\cos \theta + i \sin \theta) + a_2(\cos 2\theta + i \sin 2\theta) + \ldots$$
$$= a_0 + a_1 e^{i\theta} + a_2 e^{2i\theta} + \ldots$$
$$= A(e^{i\theta}).$$

Hence $$C = \mathrm{Rl}\, A(e^{i\theta}), \quad S = \mathrm{Im}\, A(e^{i\theta}).$$

This method, available for the summation of various trigonometrical series, is illustrated by the following examples. Further examples occur in section 7.6.

Example 10 If

$$C = 1 + \cos \theta + \cos 2\theta + \ldots + \cos n\theta,$$
$$S = \qquad \sin \theta + \sin 2\theta + \ldots + \sin n\theta,$$

then $$C + iS = 1 + e^{i\theta} + e^{2i\theta} + \ldots + e^{ni\theta},$$

a geometrical progression in $e^{i\theta}$. Its sum is given by

$$C + iS = \frac{e^{(n+1)i\theta} - 1}{e^{i\theta} - 1} = \frac{e^{\frac{1}{2}(n+1)i\theta} \sin [\frac{1}{2}(n + 1)\theta]}{e^{\frac{1}{2}i\theta} \sin \frac{1}{2}\theta}$$

$$= (\cos \tfrac{1}{2}n\theta + i \sin \tfrac{1}{2}n\theta) \sin [\tfrac{1}{2}(n + 1)\theta]\, \mathrm{cosec}\, \tfrac{1}{2}\theta.$$

Hence $$C = \cos \tfrac{1}{2}n\theta \sin [\tfrac{1}{2}(n + 1)\theta]\, \mathrm{cosec}\, \tfrac{1}{2}\theta,$$
$$S = \sin \tfrac{1}{2}n\theta \sin [\tfrac{1}{2}(n + 1)\theta]\, \mathrm{cosec}\, \tfrac{1}{2}\theta.$$

Example 11 If

$$C = 1 + {}_nC_1 \cos \theta + {}_nC_2 \cos 2\theta + \ldots + \cos n\theta,$$
$$S = \qquad {}_nC_1 \sin \theta + {}_nC_2 \sin 2\theta + \ldots + \sin n\theta,$$

then $$C + iS = 1 + {}_nC_1 e^{i\theta} + {}_nC_2 e^{2i\theta} + \ldots + e^{ni\theta}$$
$$= (1 + e^{i\theta})^n \quad \text{(a binomial series)}$$
$$= (e^{\frac{1}{2}i\theta}.\, 2 \cos \tfrac{1}{2}\theta)^n$$
$$= 2^n \cos^n \tfrac{1}{2}\theta(\cos \tfrac{1}{2}n\theta + i \sin \tfrac{1}{2}n\theta).$$

Hence $$C = 2^n \cos^n \tfrac{1}{2}\theta \cos \tfrac{1}{2}n\theta, \quad S = 2^n \sin^n \tfrac{1}{2}\theta \sin \tfrac{1}{2}n\theta.$$

Example 12 The sum of the series containing n terms

$$1 + 2p + 3p^2 + \ldots np^{n-1}$$

is given to be $$\frac{(p-1)[(n+1)p^n - 1] - (p^{n+1} - p)}{(p-1)^2},$$

obtained by differentiating the sum to n terms of the series $p + p^2 + \ldots + p^n$.
If $\theta = 2\pi/n$, let

$$C = 1 + 2\cos\theta + 3\cos 2\theta + \ldots + n\cos(n-1)\theta,$$
$$S = \quad 2\sin\theta + 3\sin 2\theta + \ldots + n\sin(n-1)\theta.$$

Then $C + iS = 1 + 2e^{i\theta} + 3e^{2i\theta} + \ldots + ne^{(n-1)\theta}$

$$= \frac{(n+1) - 1}{e^{i\theta} - 1} \quad (\text{since } p^n = e^{ni\theta} = 1 \text{ when } \theta = 2\pi/n)$$

$$= \frac{n}{e^{\frac{1}{2}i\theta}.2i\sin\frac{1}{2}\theta} = \tfrac{1}{2}n\operatorname{cosec}\tfrac{1}{2}\theta\,(-i\cos\tfrac{1}{2}\theta - \sin\tfrac{1}{2}\theta).$$

Hence $C = -\tfrac{1}{2}n, \quad S = -\tfrac{1}{2}n\cot\tfrac{1}{2}\theta.$

7.6 Functions of a complex variable

If $z = x + iy$, the function $f(z) \equiv f(x + iy)$ may be separated into
its real and imaginary parts.

If the given function is e^z, we have

$$e^z = e^{x+iy} = e^x(\cos y + i\sin y);$$

its real part is $e^x\cos y$ and its imaginary part $e^x\sin y$.

In order to treat the trigonometrical and hyperbolic functions, we
note first that

$$\sin i\theta = (e^{ii\theta} - e^{-ii\theta})/2i = (e^{-\theta} - e^{+\theta})/2i = i\sinh\theta.$$

Similarly,

$$\cos i\theta = \cosh\theta, \quad \sinh i\theta = i\sin\theta, \quad \cosh i\theta = \cos\theta.$$

Hence

$$\sin z = \sin(x + iy) = \sin x\cos iy + \sin iy\cos x$$
$$= \sin x\cosh y + i\sinh y\cos x,$$

and $\cos z = \cos(x + iy) = \cos x\cos iy - \sin iy\sin x$

$$= \cos x\cosh y - i\sinh y\sin x.$$

Similarly, $\sinh(x + iy) = \sinh x\cos y + i\sin y\cosh x,$

$$\cosh(x + iy) = \cosh x\cos y + i\sin y\sinh x.$$

Various deductions may be drawn from these results:

(i) When $y = 2\pi$, we have $\cosh(x + 2\pi i) = \cosh x$, showing that $\cosh x$ is
periodic with the imaginary period $2\pi i$.

(ii) The function tan z may be simplified as follows:

$$\tan z = \frac{\sin z}{\cos z} = \frac{\sin x \cosh y + i \sinh y \cos x}{\cos x \cosh y - i \sinh y \sin x}$$

$$= \frac{\tan x + i \tanh y}{1 - i \tan x \tanh y}$$

$$= \frac{\tan x - \tan x \tanh^2 y + i(\tanh y + \tan^2 x \tanh y)}{1 + \tan^2 x \tanh^2 y}$$

$$= \frac{\tan x \operatorname{sech}^2 y + i \tanh y \sec^2 x}{1 + \tan^2 x \tanh^2 y}.$$

(iii) The modulus of sinh z may be found as follows:

$$|\sinh z|^2 = \sinh^2 x \cos^2 y + \cosh^2 x \sin^2 y$$
$$= (\cosh^2 x - 1) \cos^2 y + \cosh^2 x (1 - \cos^2 y)$$
$$= \cosh^2 x - \cos^2 y$$
$$= \tfrac{1}{2}(\cosh 2x - \cos 2y).$$

Similarly, $|\cosh z|^2 = \tfrac{1}{2}(\cosh 2x + \cos 2y),$

$$|\sin z|^2 = \tfrac{1}{2}(\cosh 2y - \cos 2x),$$
$$|\cos z|^2 = \tfrac{1}{2}(\cosh 2y + \cos 2x).$$

The value of log z may be evaluated by expressing $z = x + iy$ in the multi-valued polar form $re^{i\theta + 2\pi in}$, where n is any integer. Then

$$\operatorname{Log} z = \operatorname{Log}(re^{i\theta + 2\pi in}) = \log_e r + i(\theta + 2\pi n),$$

the capital L denoting a multi-valued expression. Whatever the value of θ, if n is chosen so that $-\pi < \theta + 2\pi n \leqslant \pi$, we obtain the *principal value* of the logarithm, and to avoid confusion, we write it as $\log_e z$. If $z = x > 0$, a real quantity, we have

$$\operatorname{Log}_e x = \log_e x + 2\pi in.$$

If $z = -x$, where $x > 0$, we have $\theta = \pi$, so

$$\operatorname{Log}_e(-x) = \log_e x + \pi i(2n + 1).$$

If the function is a^z, where a is a general complex number with $|a| = r$, arg $a = \theta + 2\pi n$, we have

$$a^z = e^{z \operatorname{Log} a} = e^{(x+iy)}[\log r + i(\theta + 2\pi n)]$$
$$= e^{x \log r - y(\theta + 2\pi n)} \operatorname{cis}[x(\theta + 2\pi n) + y \log r].$$

Finally, the various inverse functions may be considered by examining, for example, the function $\sin^{-1} z$.

If $w = \sin^{-1} z$, then

$$z = \sin w = (e^{iw} - e^{-iw})/2i,$$

so
$$e^{2iw} - 2ize^{iw} - 1 = 0.$$

Hence
$$e^{iw} = iz \pm \sqrt{(1 - z^2)},$$

yielding
$$\sin^{-1} z = w = -i\{\log [iz \pm \sqrt{(1 - z^2)}]\}.$$

In particular, if $z = x$, being real, positive and greater than unity, we have

$$\sin^{-1} x = -i\{\log [ix \pm i\sqrt{(x^2 - 1)}]\}$$
$$= -i\{i(\tfrac{1}{2}\pi + 2n\pi) + \log_e [x \pm \sqrt{(x^2 - 1)}]\}$$
$$= \tfrac{1}{2}\pi + 2n\pi - i\log_e [x \pm \sqrt{(x^2 - 1)}].$$

But if x is positive and less than unity, then $ix \pm \sqrt{(1 - x^2)}$ is of modulus unity and of argument

$$\tan^{-1} [x/\sqrt{(1 - x^2)}] \quad \text{or} \quad \pi - \tan^{-1} [x/\sqrt{(1 - x^2)}].$$

Then
$$\sin^{-1} x = -i[\log_e 1 + i\{2\pi n + \tan^{-1} [x/\sqrt{(1 - x^2)}]\}]$$
$$= 2\pi n + \tan^{-1} [x/\sqrt{(1 - x^2)}]$$

on the one hand, and on the other

$$\sin^{-1} x = 2\pi n + \pi - \tan^{-1} [x/\sqrt{(1 - x^2)}],$$

in keeping of course with the elementary formulae of real trigonometry.

Example 13 Find the real and imaginary parts of the complex number

$$z = (1 + i)^{\log(1+i)},$$

using principal values only.

We have, in polar form, $1 + i = \sqrt{2}e^{\frac{1}{4}i\pi}$, so

$$\log_e (1 + i) = \log (\sqrt{2}e^{\frac{1}{4}i\pi}) = \tfrac{1}{2}\log 2 + \tfrac{1}{4}i\pi.$$

Hence
$$z = (\sqrt{2}e^{\frac{1}{4}i\pi})^{\frac{1}{2}\log 2 + \frac{1}{4}i\pi}$$
$$= e^{(\frac{1}{2}\log 2)(\frac{1}{2}\log 2 + \frac{1}{4}i\pi)}e^{\frac{1}{4}i\pi(\frac{1}{2}\log 2 + \frac{1}{4}i\pi)}$$
$$= 2^{\frac{1}{4}\log 2}e^{-\pi^2/16}e^{\frac{1}{4}i\pi\log 2}$$
$$= 2^{\frac{1}{4}\log 2}e^{-\pi^2/16}[\cos (\tfrac{1}{4}\pi \log 2) + i \sin (\tfrac{1}{4}\pi \log 2)].$$

Example 14 Find the sum of the infinite series

$$C = 1 - \tan^2 \theta \frac{\cos 2\theta}{2!} + \tan^4 \theta \frac{\cos 4\theta}{4!} - \dots.$$

Form the series S by replacing the cosines of the multiple angles by the sines:

$$S = -\tan^2 \theta \frac{\sin 2\theta}{2!} + \tan^4 \theta \frac{\sin 4\theta}{4!} - \dots.$$

Then

$$C + iS = 1 - \frac{\tan^2 \theta \, e^{2i\theta}}{2!} + \frac{\tan^4 \theta \, e^{4i\theta}}{4!} - \cdots$$

$$= \cos (\tan \theta \, e^{i\theta})$$

$$= \cos (\sin \theta + i \sin \theta \tan \theta)$$

$$= \cos (\sin \theta) \cosh (\sin \theta \tan \theta) - i \sin (\sin \theta) \sinh (\sin \theta \tan \theta).$$

Hence $C = \cos (\sin \theta) \cosh (\sin \theta \tan \theta), \quad S = - \sin (\sin \theta) \sinh (\sin \theta \tan \theta).$

Example 15 Solve the equation

$$\tan z = \tfrac{1}{2} + \tfrac{1}{2}i\sqrt{3}.$$

In terms of exponentials, this equation is

$$\frac{e^{iz} - e^{-iz}}{i(e^{iz} + e^{-iz})} = e^{\frac{1}{3}\pi i},$$

or

$$e^{iz} - e^{-iz} = e^{\frac{5}{6}} \, (e^{iz} + e^{-iz});$$

hence

$$e^{2iz} = \frac{1 + e^{\frac{5}{6}\pi i}}{1 - e^{\frac{5}{6}\pi i}} = -i \cot \tfrac{5}{12}\pi = e^{-\frac{1}{2}i\pi + 2\pi i n} \cot \tfrac{5}{12}\pi.$$

Taking logarithms, we obtain

$$2iz = -\tfrac{1}{2}i\pi + 2\pi i n + \log \cot \tfrac{5}{12}\pi,$$

or

$$z = -\tfrac{1}{4}\pi + \pi n - \tfrac{1}{2}i \log \cot \tfrac{5}{12}\pi.$$

Example 16 Sum the infinite series

$$C = \cos \theta - \frac{\cos 2\theta}{2} + \frac{\cos 3\theta}{3} - \cdots, \quad (0 \leqslant \theta < \pi).$$

We introduce the companion series

$$S = \sin \theta - \frac{\sin 2\theta}{2} + \frac{\sin 3\theta}{3} - \cdots;$$

hence

$$C + iS = e^{i\theta} - \frac{e^{2i\theta}}{2} + \frac{e^{3i\theta}}{3} - \cdots$$

$$= \log (1 + e^{i\theta}) \quad \text{(since } |e^{i\theta}| = 1 \text{ but } e^{i\theta} \neq -1\text{)}$$

$$= \log [e^{\frac{1}{2}i\theta}(e^{-\frac{1}{2}i\theta} + e^{\frac{1}{2}i\theta})]$$

$$= \log [e^{\frac{1}{2}i\theta} . 2 \cos \tfrac{1}{2}\theta]$$

$$= \log (2 \cos \tfrac{1}{2}\theta) + \tfrac{1}{2}i\theta,$$

where no integral multiple of 2π need be added since $C + iS$ obviously has the value $\log 2$ when $\theta = 0$. Hence

$$C = \log (2 \cos \tfrac{1}{2}\theta), \quad S = \tfrac{1}{2}\theta.$$

Example 17★ If $u + iv = \log [(x + iy + a)/(x + iy - a)]$, prove

(i) $x^2 + y^2 - 2ax \coth u + a^2 = 0$,

(ii) $x = \dfrac{a \sinh u}{\cosh u - \cos v}$,

(iii) $|x + iy|^2 = \dfrac{a^2(\cosh u + \cos v)}{\cosh u - \cos v}.$

In (i), the imaginary part v is eliminated. We have

$$u = \text{Rl} \log \frac{x + iy + a}{x + iy - a} = \log \left| \frac{x + iy + a}{x + iy - a} \right| = \tfrac{1}{2} \log \frac{(x + a)^2 + y^2}{(x - a)^2 + y^2}.$$

Hence

$$e^{2u} = \frac{x^2 + y^2 + a^2 + 2ax}{x^2 + y^2 + a^2 - 2ax},$$

or

$$[(x^2 + y^2 + a^2) - 2ax]e^{2u} = (x^2 + y^2 + a^2) + 2ax.$$

It follows that

$$x^2 + y^2 + a^2 = 2ax(e^{2u} + 1)/(e^{2u} - 1) = 2ax \coth u.$$

In (ii), y is eliminated. Taking the exponential of the given equation, we have

$$\frac{x + iy + a}{x + iy - a} = e^{u + iv},$$

yielding

$$x + iy = a \frac{e^{u + iv} + 1}{e^{u + iv} - 1}. \tag{3}$$

Hence

$$x = a \, \text{Rl} \frac{e^{u + iv} + 1}{e^{u + iv} - 1} = a \, \text{Rl} \frac{(e^{u + iv} + 1)(e^{u - iv} - 1)}{(e^{u + iv} - 1)(e^{u - iv} - 1)}$$

$$= a \, \text{Rl} \frac{e^{2u} - e^{u + iv} + e^{u - iv} - 1}{e^{2u} - e^{u + iv} - e^{u - iv} + 1} = \frac{a(e^u - e^{-u})}{e^u + e^{-u} - 2 \cos v}$$

$$= \frac{a \sinh u}{\cosh u - \cos v}.$$

In (iii), the modulus of $x + iy$ is required. From equation (3), we have

$$|x + iy|^2 = a^2 \frac{e^{u + iv} + 1}{e^{u + iv} - 1} \cdot \frac{e^{u - iv} + 1}{e^{u - iv} - 1} = a^2 \frac{e^{2u} + e^{u + iv} + e^{u - iv} + 1}{e^{2u} - e^{u + iv} - e^{u - iv} + 1}$$

$$= a^2 \frac{e^u + e^{-u} + e^{iv} + e^{-iv}}{e^u + e^{-u} - e^{iv} - e^{-iv}} = a^2 \frac{\cosh u + \cos v}{\cosh u - \cos v}.$$

7.7   Trigonometrical functions of multiple angles

If n is a positive integer, we have the standard result

$$\cos n\theta + i \sin n\theta = (\cos \theta + i \sin \theta)^n.$$

We now expand the right hand side by the binomial theorem, taking care of the powers of i that occur, obtaining

$$\cos n\theta + i \sin n\theta = \cos^n \theta + {}_nC_1 i \cos^{n-1} \theta \sin \theta - {}_nC_2 \cos^{n-2} \theta \sin^2 \theta$$
$$- {}_nC_3 i \cos^{n-3} \theta \sin^3 \theta + {}_nC_4 \cos^{n-4} \theta \sin^4 \theta + \dots.$$

Equating real and imaginary parts, we obtain

$$\cos n\theta = \cos^n \theta - {}_nC_2 \cos^{n-2} \theta \sin^2 \theta + {}_nC_4 \cos^{n-4} \theta \sin^4 \theta - \dots, \tag{4}$$

$$\sin n\theta = {}_nC_1 \cos^{n-1} \theta \sin \theta - {}_nC_3 \cos^{n-3} \theta \sin^3 \theta + \dots. \tag{5}$$

Since $\sin^2\theta$, $\sin^4\theta$, ... can all be expressed in terms of $\cos^2\theta$, it follows from result (4) that $\cos n\theta$ can always be expressed as a polynomial of degree n in $\cos\theta$. For example,

$$\cos 5\theta = \cos^5\theta - {}_5C_2\cos^3\theta\sin^2\theta + {}_5C_4\cos\theta\sin^4\theta$$
$$= \cos^5\theta - 10\cos^3\theta\,(1 - \cos^2\theta)$$
$$+ 5\cos\theta\,(1 - 2\cos^2\theta + \cos^4\theta)$$
$$= 16\cos^5\theta - 20\cos^3\theta + 5\cos\theta.$$

If result (4) is divided by $\cos^n\theta$, it follows that

$$\cos n\theta/\cos^n\theta = 1 - {}_nC_2\tan^2\theta + {}_nC_4\tan^4\theta - \dots$$

If result (5) is divided by $\sin\theta$, it follows that

$$\sin n\theta/\sin\theta = {}_nC_1\cos^{n-1}\theta - {}_nC_3\cos^{n-3}\theta\sin^2\theta + \dots \qquad (6)$$

This can always be expressed as a polynomial of degree $n - 1$ in $\cos\theta$. If n is odd, all the cosines raised to even powers on the right hand side can be expressed as polynomials in $\sin^2\theta$; hence $\sin n\theta/\sin\theta$ can be expressed as a polynomial in $\sin^2\theta$, of degree $\frac{1}{2}(n - 1)$.

To find the expanded form of $\tan n\theta$, we form the quotient $\sin n\theta/\cos n\theta$ and divide numerator and denominator by $\cos^n\theta$, obtaining

$$\tan n\theta = \frac{{}_nC_1\tan\theta - {}_nC_3\tan^3\theta + {}_nC_5\tan^5\theta - \dots}{1 - {}_nC_2\tan^2\theta + {}_nC_4\tan^4\theta - \dots}. \qquad (7)$$

For example,

$$\tan 5\theta = \frac{5\tan\theta - 10\tan^3\theta + \tan^5\theta}{1 - 10\tan^2\theta + 5\tan^4\theta}.$$

Example 18 If n is odd, factorize $\sin n\theta/\sin\theta$.

From equation (6), we have just shown that $\sin n\theta/\sin\theta$ is a polynomial of degree $\frac{1}{2}(n - 1)$ in $\sin^2\theta$. In order to factorize this expression, we first of all find $\frac{1}{2}(n - 1)$ roots. It vanishes when $\sin n\theta = 0$, that is at the $\frac{1}{2}(n - 1)$ values of θ given by

$$n\theta = \pi, 2\pi, 3\pi, \dots, \tfrac{1}{2}(n - 1)\pi,$$

so $$\sin^2\theta = \sin^2\pi/n, \sin^2 2\pi/n, \dots, \sin^2[\tfrac{1}{2}(n - 1)\pi/n].$$

Hence the factors may be written in the form

$$1 - \frac{\sin^2\theta}{\sin^2\pi/n}, 1 - \frac{\sin^2\theta}{\sin^2 2\pi/n}, \dots, 1 - \frac{\sin^2\theta}{\sin^2[\tfrac{1}{2}(n - 1)\pi/n]}.$$

Introducing a constant factor, we have the product

$$\frac{\sin n\theta}{\sin\theta} \equiv A\left(1 - \frac{\sin^2\theta}{\sin^2\pi/n}\right)\left(1 - \frac{\sin^2\theta}{\sin^2 2\pi/n}\right)\dots\left(1 - \frac{\sin^2\theta}{\sin^2[\tfrac{1}{2}(n - 1)\pi/n]}\right).$$

To find A, let $\theta \to 0$. The left hand side tends to n, while the right hand side tends to A. Hence

$$\frac{\sin n\theta}{\sin \theta} \equiv n \prod_{r=1}^{\frac{1}{2}(n-1)} \left(1 - \frac{\sin^2 \theta}{\sin^2 r\pi/n}\right).$$

Example 19 Express $\tan 7\theta$ in terms of $\tan \theta$. Examine the roots and various implications of the equation

$$t^6 - 21t^4 + 35t^2 - 7 = 0.$$

Equation (7) shows that

$$\tan 7\theta = \frac{7 \tan \theta - 35 \tan^3 \theta + 21 \tan^5 \theta - \tan^7 \theta}{1 - 21 \tan^2 \theta + 35 \tan^4 \theta - 7 \tan^6 \theta}.$$

If θ is chosen so that $\tan 7\theta = 0$, then the equation

$$7 \tan \theta - 35 \tan^3 \theta + 21 \tan^5 \theta - \tan^7 \theta = 0$$

implies $7\theta = r\pi$, or $\theta = \frac{1}{7}r\pi$.

The roots of the equation

$$t^7 - 21t^5 + 35t^3 - 7t = 0$$

are then given by $\quad t = \tan\left(\frac{1}{7}r\pi\right), \quad (r = 0, 1, \ldots, 6)$.

The zero root may be removed, leaving the equation

$$t^6 - 21t^4 + 35t^2 - 7 = 0$$

with the six roots $\quad t = \tan\left(\frac{1}{7}r\pi\right), \quad (r = 1, 2, \ldots, 6)$.

If we now let $s = t^2$, the three roots of the cubic equation

$$s^3 - 21s^2 + 35s - 7 = 0$$

are given by $\quad s = t^2 = \tan^2\left(\frac{1}{7}r\pi\right), \quad (r = 1, 2, 3)$.

The product of these three roots is given in terms of the constant coefficient occurring in the cubic, namely

$$\tan^2 \tfrac{1}{7}\pi \, \tan^2 \tfrac{2}{7}\pi \, \tan^2 \tfrac{3}{7}\pi = 7,$$

or $\qquad\qquad \tan \tfrac{1}{7}\pi \, \tan \tfrac{2}{7}\pi \, \tan \tfrac{3}{7}\pi = \sqrt{7}.$

If α, β, γ are the three roots, we have

$$\sec^4 \tfrac{1}{7}\pi + \sec^4 \tfrac{2}{7}\pi + \sec^4 \tfrac{3}{7}\pi = \sum (1 + \tan^2 \tfrac{1}{7}r\pi)^2$$
$$= \sum (1 + 2\alpha + \alpha^2)$$
$$= 3 + 2.21 + \sum \alpha^2.$$

But $\qquad\qquad \left(\sum \alpha\right)^2 = \sum \alpha^2 + 2\sum \alpha\beta,$

so $\qquad\qquad\qquad 21^2 = \sum \alpha^2 + 2.35,$

or $\qquad\qquad\qquad \sum \alpha^2 = 21^2 - 2.35 = 371.$

Hence $\qquad \sec^4 \tfrac{1}{7}\pi + \sec^4 \tfrac{2}{7}\pi + \sec^4 \tfrac{3}{7}\pi = 3 + 42 + 371 = 416.$

Example 20 If n is odd, show that $(1 + \cos n\theta)/(1 + \cos \theta)$ is the square of a polynomial of degree $\frac{1}{2}(n - 1)$ in $\cos \theta$. Find this polynomial if $n = 7$.

We express $\cos n\theta$ and $\cos \theta$ respectively in terms of half-angles thus:

$$\frac{1 + \cos n\theta}{1 + \cos \theta} = \frac{2 \cos^2 \frac{1}{2}n\theta}{2 \cos^2 \frac{1}{2}\theta} = \left(\frac{\cos \frac{1}{2}n\theta}{\cos \frac{1}{2}\theta}\right)^2.$$

Using equation (4), we have

$$\frac{\cos \tfrac{1}{2}n\theta}{\cos \tfrac{1}{2}\theta} = \cos^{n-1} \tfrac{1}{2}\theta - {}_nC_2 \cos^{n-3} \tfrac{1}{2}\theta \sin^2 \tfrac{1}{2}\theta + \ldots,$$

which, since n is odd, is a polynomial of degree $n - 1$ in $\cos \tfrac{1}{2}\theta$ such that only even powers of $\cos \tfrac{1}{2}\theta$ occur. Hence it is a polynomial of degree $\tfrac{1}{2}(n - 1)$ in $\cos^2 \tfrac{1}{2}\theta$; this implies it must be a polynomial of degree $\tfrac{1}{2}(n - 1)$ in $\cos \theta$, since $\cos^2 \tfrac{1}{2}\theta = \tfrac{1}{2}(\cos \theta + 1)$.

When $n = 7$, the expression is given by

$$\frac{\cos\tfrac{7}{2}\theta}{\cos\tfrac{1}{2}\theta} = \cos^6 \tfrac{1}{2}\theta - {}_7C_2 \cos^4 \tfrac{1}{2}\theta \sin^2 \tfrac{1}{2}\theta + {}_7C_4 \cos^2 \tfrac{1}{2}\theta \sin^4 \tfrac{1}{2}\theta - {}_7C_6 \sin^6 \tfrac{1}{2}\theta$$

$$= [\tfrac{1}{2}(\cos \theta + 1)]^3 - 21[\tfrac{1}{2}(\cos \theta + 1)]^2[\tfrac{1}{2}(1 - \cos \theta)]$$
$$+ 35[\tfrac{1}{2}(\cos \theta + 1)][\tfrac{1}{2}(1 - \cos \theta)]^2 - 7[\tfrac{1}{2}(1 - \cos \theta)]^3$$
$$= 8 \cos^3 \theta - 4 \cos^2 \theta - 4 \cos \theta + 1.$$

7.8   Expansion in terms of functions of multiple angles

If we wish to express, say, $\cos^n \theta$ in terms of trigonometrical functions of multiple angles, we use its exponential representation thus:

$$\cos^n \theta = [\tfrac{1}{2}(e^{i\theta} + e^{-i\theta})]^n$$
$$= 2^{-n}[e^{ni\theta} + {}_nC_1 e^{(n-2)i\theta} + {}_nC_2 e^{(n-4)i\theta} + \ldots$$
$$+ {}_nC_{n-2} e^{-(n-4)i\theta} + {}_nC_{n-1} e^{-(n-2)i\theta} + e^{-ni\theta}$$
$$= (\cos n\theta + {}_nC_1 \cos (n - 2)\theta + {}_nC_2 \cos (n - 4)\theta + \ldots)/2^{n-1},$$

upon gathering up respective terms. If n is even, this series terminates with the constant term ${}_nC_{\tfrac{1}{2}n}$, while if n is odd, it ends with the term ${}_nC_{\tfrac{1}{2}(n+1)} \cos \theta$.

As an explicit example,

$$64 \sin^7 \theta = 64[(e^{i\theta} - e^{-i\theta})/2i]^7 = \tfrac{1}{2}i(e^{i\theta} - e^{-i\theta})^7$$
$$= \tfrac{1}{2}i(e^{7i\theta} - 7e^{5i\theta} + 21e^{3i\theta} - 35e^{i\theta} + 35e^{-i\theta} - 21e^{-3i\theta}$$
$$+ 7e^{-5i\theta} - e^{-7i\theta})$$
$$= -\sin 7\theta + 7 \sin 5\theta - 21 \sin 3\theta + 35 \sin \theta.$$

Example 21   Find all the roots of the equation
$$16 \sin^5 \theta = \sin 5\theta.$$

We have
$$16 \sin^5 \theta = 16[(e^{i\theta} - e^{-i\theta})/2i]^5$$
$$= (e^{5i\theta} - 5e^{3i\theta} + 10e^{i\theta} - 10e^{-i\theta} + 5e^{-3i\theta} - e^{-5i\theta})/2i$$
$$= \sin 5\theta - 5 \sin 3\theta + 10 \sin \theta.$$

The given equation becomes
$$5 \sin 3\theta = 10 \sin \theta,$$
or
$$3 \sin \theta - 4 \sin^3 \theta = 2 \sin \theta.$$
Hence
$$\sin \theta = 0, \quad \text{or} \quad \sin^2 \theta = \tfrac{1}{4},$$
that is,
$$\sin \theta = 0, \tfrac{1}{2}, -\tfrac{1}{2}.$$

All solutions are then given by

$$\theta = r\pi, \quad \tfrac{1}{6}\pi + 2r\pi, \quad \tfrac{5}{6}\pi + 2r\pi, \quad -\tfrac{1}{6}\pi + 2r\pi, \quad -\tfrac{5}{6}\pi + 2r\pi.$$

7.9 Simple transformations

If z is the complex number $x + iy$, then any function of z, $w = f(x + iy)$ say, is itself a complex number; it may be resolved into real and imaginary parts, where the real part u and the imaginary part v are functions of x and y. We write

$$w = f(x + iy) = u(x, y) + iv(x, y).$$

In section 7.6, we considered various simple functions such as e^z, $\sin z$ and $\cosh z$, but more complicated combinations of these elementary functions may also be resolved into their real and imaginary parts.

We now consider two planes: the complex z-plane with axes Ox, Oy, and the complex w-plane, with axes Ou, Ov. Any point $P(x, y)$ in the z-plane provides values of $u(x, y)$ and $v(x, y)$ yielding the co-ordinates of one or more points $Q(u, v)$ in the w-plane. Conversely, a point Q in the w-plane gives rise to one or more points P in the z-plane. Moreover, if P traces out a locus in the z-plane, then Q will trace out a locus in the w-plane, and conversely. The z-plane is said to be *mapped* on the w-plane.

The equations $u = u(x, y)$, $v = v(x, y)$ may formally be solved for x, y in terms of u, v, giving $x = x(u, v)$, $y = y(u, v)$. If P then traces out the locus $g(x, y) = 0$ in the z-plane, then Q traces out the locus $g[x(u, v), y(u, v)] = 0$ in the w-plane. Conversely, if Q traces out the locus $h(u, v) = 0$ in the w-plane, then P traces out the locus $h[u(x, y), v(x, y)] = 0$ in the z-plane. A system of curves in one plane is mapped into a system of curves in the other plane.

Theorem. If two curves in the z-plane intersect in P at an angle ϕ, such that $dw/dz \neq 0$ at P, then the corresponding two curves in the w-plane intersect in Q at the same angle ϕ.

We employ the elements of the theory of partial differentiation to differentiate the function w with respect to x and y, obtaining

$$\frac{\partial w}{\partial x} = \frac{df}{dz}\frac{\partial z}{\partial x} = \frac{\partial u}{\partial x} + i\frac{\partial v}{\partial x}, \tag{8}$$

and

$$\frac{\partial w}{\partial y} = \frac{df}{dz}\frac{\partial z}{\partial y} = \frac{\partial u}{\partial y} + i\frac{\partial v}{\partial y},$$

or

$$\frac{df}{dz} = \frac{\partial u}{\partial x} + i\frac{\partial v}{\partial x}, \quad i\frac{df}{dz} = \frac{\partial u}{\partial y} + i\frac{\partial v}{\partial y},$$

since $\partial z/\partial x = 1$ and $\partial z/\partial y = i$.

When df/dz is eliminated, we obtain

$$i\left(\frac{\partial u}{\partial x} + i\frac{\partial v}{\partial x}\right) = \frac{\partial u}{\partial y} + i\frac{\partial v}{\partial y},$$

or, upon equating real and imaginary parts,

$$\frac{\partial u}{\partial x} = \frac{\partial v}{\partial y}, \quad \frac{\partial u}{\partial y} = -\frac{\partial v}{\partial x},$$

important equations known as the *Riemann-Cauchy conditions*. They are valid at points where $w = f(z)$ possesses a differential coefficient with respect to z.

If $P(x, y)$ and $P'(x + \delta x, y + \delta y)$ are two nearby points defining a small line-segment PP' in the z-plane, the corresponding points in the w-plane are $Q[u(x, y), v(x, y)]$ and

$$Q'[u(x + \delta x, y + \delta y), v(x + \delta x, y + \delta y)]$$

$$\equiv \left[u(x,y) + \frac{\partial u}{\partial x}\delta x + \frac{\partial u}{\partial y}\delta y, v(x, y) + \frac{\partial v}{\partial x}\delta x + \frac{\partial v}{\partial y}\delta y\right]$$

$$= \left[u(x,y) + \frac{\partial u}{\partial x}\delta x - \frac{\partial v}{\partial x}\delta y, v(x, y) + \frac{\partial v}{\partial x}\delta x + \frac{\partial u}{\partial x}\delta y\right],$$

using the Riemann-Cauchy conditions. PP' is then represented by the coordinate differentials $\delta x, \delta y$, and QQ' by the differentials

$$\frac{\partial u}{\partial x}\delta x - \frac{\partial v}{\partial x}\delta y, \quad \frac{\partial v}{\partial x}\delta x + \frac{\partial u}{\partial x}\delta y.$$

Then

$$QQ'^2 = \left(\frac{\partial u}{\partial x}\delta x - \frac{\partial v}{\partial x}\delta y\right)^2 + \left(\frac{\partial v}{\partial x}\delta x + \frac{\partial u}{\partial x}\delta y\right)^2$$

$$= \left[\left(\frac{\partial u}{\partial x}\right)^2 + \left(\frac{\partial v}{\partial x}\right)^2\right](\delta x^2 + \delta y^2)$$

$$= |dw/dz|^2\, PP'^2,$$

from equation (8); hence

$$QQ' = |dw/dz|\, PP'.$$

Under the transformation, the length of the given segment PP' undergoes a magnification by the factor $|dw/dz|$. All line segments radiating from the point P are magnified by the same factor; the factor is independent of the direction of the segment.

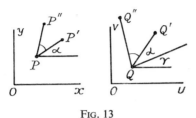

FIG. 13

If the segment PP' makes an angle α with Ox, if QQ' makes an angle β with Ou and if $\arg(dw/dz) = \gamma$, so that

$$\tan \gamma = (\partial v/\partial x)/(\partial u/\partial x)$$

from equation (8), it follows that

$$\tan \beta = \frac{\dfrac{\partial v}{\partial x}\,\delta x + \dfrac{\partial u}{\partial x}\,\delta y}{\dfrac{\partial u}{\partial x}\,\delta x - \dfrac{\partial v}{\partial x}\,\delta y} = \frac{\dfrac{\partial v/\partial x}{\partial u/\partial x} + \dfrac{\delta y}{\delta x}}{1 - \dfrac{\delta y}{\delta x}\cdot\dfrac{\partial v/\partial x}{\partial u/\partial x}}$$

$$= \frac{\tan \gamma + \tan \alpha}{1 - \tan \alpha \tan \gamma} = \tan(\alpha + \gamma).$$

We conclude that the direction of the segment PP' is rotated through an angle $\gamma = \arg(dw/dz)$ to give the direction of the segment QQ'. This angle γ depends only on the point P and is independent of the direction of the segment PP'.

In particular, if PP' and PP'' are two segments through P, mapping into the two segments QQ' and QQ'' through Q, then QQ' and QQ'' are obtained from PP' and PP'' respectively by rotation through the angle γ and by magnification by the factor $|dw/dz|$. Hence $\angle Q''QQ' = \angle P''PP'$. Angles are therefore conserved under the transformation, which is consequently designated as *conformal*. In particular, orthogonal curves in the z-plane transform into orthogonal curves in the w-plane.

Example 22 Examine the transformation $w = 1/z$.

We have

$$u + iv = \frac{1}{x + iy} = \frac{x - iy}{x^2 + y^2},$$

giving

$$u = x/(x^2 + y^2), \quad v = -y/(x^2 + y^2).$$

Moreover, $z = 1/w$, so we see immediately that

$$x = u/(u^2 + v^2), \quad y = -v/(u^2 + v^2).$$

In the z-plane, lines parallel to Ox have equations of the form $y = c$, a constant. The corresponding locus in the w-plane is given by

$$y = c = -v/(u^2 + v^2),$$

or $$u^2 + v^2 + v/c = 0,$$

a circle with its centre at the point $(0, -1/2c)$ passing through the origin.

In the z-plane, all points above the line $y = c$ satisfy $y > c$. In the w-plane, the corresponding points satisfy

$$-v/(u^2 + v^2) > c$$

or $$c(u^2 + v^2) + v < 0.$$

Such points must all lie inside the circle if $c > 0$ but outside the circle if $c < 0$. (This deduction is made by noting whether the inequality is satisfied for large values of u and v.) It follows that points below the line $y = c$ map into points lying outside the circle if $c > 0$ but inside the circle if $c < 0$.

More complicated regions in the z-plane may be chosen. Let z lie in the region defined by the common interior of the two circles $|z - 2| = 1$, $|z - 3| = 1$. The first circle transforms to

$$|w^{-1} - 2| = 1,$$

or $$|1 - 2w| = |w|.$$

Taking the square of the modulus of each side, we obtain

$$(1 - 2u)^2 + 4v^2 = u^2 + v^2,$$

or $$3u^2 + 3v^2 - 4u + 1 = 0.$$

This is a circle of radius $\frac{1}{3}$ and centre $u = \frac{2}{3}$, $v = 0$; its equation may be written in the form $|w - \frac{2}{3}| = \frac{1}{3}$.

The second circle transforms to the circle in the w-plane

$$8u^2 + 8v^2 - 6u + 1 = 0,$$

which may be expressed in the form $|w - \frac{3}{8}| = \frac{1}{8}$.

We need only examine one point in order to ascertain whether the given interior maps into the common interior or exterior of the two circles in the w-plane. The point $z = 0$ is obviously an exterior point in the z-plane; in the w-plane, this corresponds to $w = \infty$, also an exterior point. We conclude that the common interior of the two circles $|z - 2| = 1$, $|z - 3| = 1$ in the z-plane transforms into the common interior of the two circles $|w - \frac{2}{3}| = \frac{1}{3}$, $|w - \frac{3}{8}| = \frac{1}{8}$ in the w-plane.

Example 23   Examine the transformation $w = z^2$.

Resolving w into its real and imaginary parts, we obtain

$$u + iv = (x + iy)^2 = x^2 - y^2 + 2ixy,$$

so $$u = x^2 - y^2, \quad v = 2xy.$$

The solutions for x and y in terms of u and v are not of course single-valued.

The perpendicular lines $u = c$, $v = d$ in the w-plane transform to the loci

$$x^2 - y^2 = c, \quad 2xy = d$$

in the z-plane. They form two families of rectangular hyperbolae; any member of the first family intersects any member of the second family orthogonally.

In the z-plane, consider the boundary of the triangle defined by the vertices $0, 2 + i, 2 - i$. The three sides are given respectively by the lines $2y = x$, $x = 2$, $2y = -x$ respectively. In the w-plane, the corresponding points traces out what may be termed a *curvilinear triangle*.

For the first side, we eliminate x and y from

$$u = x^2 - y^2, \quad v = 2xy, \quad 2y = x,$$

obtaining $4u = 3v$. The second side $x = 2$ yields the parabola

$$16u = 64 - v^2,$$

and the third side $2y = -x$ yields the line $4u = -3v$.

Example 24 Examine the transformation $w = z + z^{-1}$, and find how the circle $|z| = r$ maps from the z-plane onto the w-plane.

Any point $z = re^{i\theta}$ (θ real) lies on the given circle, so

$$w = re^{i\theta} + r^{-1}e^{-i\theta};$$

hence $\qquad u = r\cos\theta + r^{-1}\cos\theta, \quad v = r\sin\theta - r^{-1}\sin\theta.$

Eliminating θ, we have

$$\frac{u^2}{(r + r^{-1})^2} + \frac{v^2}{(r - r^{-1})^2} = \cos^2\theta + \sin^2\theta = 1,$$

an ellipse in the w-plane. Its semi-axes are $r + r^{-1}$ and $|r - r^{-1}|$, its major axis being directed along Ou.

Its eccentricity e is given by

$$(r - r^{-1})^2 = (r + r^{-1})^2(1 - e^2),$$

yielding $e = 2/(r + r^{-1})$.

The foci of the ellipse are the points on the major axis Ou given by

$$u = \pm(r + r^{-1})e = \pm 2,$$

so all ellipses in the w-plane for all values of r have the same foci. In other words, concentric circles in the z-plane, with the origin as their common centre, map into confocal ellipses in the w-plane.

If $R > 1$, consider the two circles $|z| = R$ and $|z| = R^{-1}$ in the z-plane. The two corresponding ellipses in the w-plane are identical with semi-axes $R + R^{-1}$ and $R - R^{-1}$.

The interior of the circle $|z| = R^{-1}$, containing the particular point $z = 0$, obviously maps into the exterior of the ellipse, since this exterior contains the corresponding particular point $w = \infty$. The annular region between the two circles in the z-plane, containing the point $z = 1$, which maps into the focus $w = 2$ in the w-plane, maps into the interior of the ellipse. The exterior of the circle $|z| = R$, containing the point $z = \infty$, maps into the exterior of the ellipse, containing the corresponding point $w = \infty$.

Example 25 Examine the *bilinear transformation* $w = (z - 1)/(z + 1)$.

Note. Transformations of the form $w = (az + b)/(cz + d)$ are the only transformations under which w is a single-valued function of z and z is a single-valued function of w.

We have

$$u + iv = \frac{(x - 1) + iy}{(x + 1) + iy} = \frac{[(x - 1) + iy][(x + 1) - iy]}{(x + 1)^2 + y^2},$$

showing that

$$u = \frac{x^2 - 1 + y^2}{(x + 1)^2 + y^2}, \quad v = \frac{y(x + 1) - y(x - 1)}{(x + 1)^2 + y^2}.$$

The circle $|w| = c$ in the w-plane may be mapped onto the z-plane by considering the expression $u^2 + v^2 = c^2$ in terms of x and y, or by the following simpler device. We have

$$c^2 = |w|^2 = ww\star,$$

where $w\star$ is the conjugate of w. Substituting the value of w in terms of z we obtain

$$c^2(z + 1)(z\star + 1) = (z - 1)(z\star - 1),$$

or $\qquad c^2(zz\star + z + z\star + 1) = zz\star - (z + z\star) + 1.$

In terms of x and y, this is

$$(c^2 - 1)(x^2 + y^2) + (c^2 + 1) \cdot 2x + (c^2 - 1) = 0.$$

This locus is a circle in the z-plane; its centre is at the point $[-(c^2 + 1)/(c^2 - 1), 0]$ and its radius is $2c^2/|c^2 - 1|$.

The circle $|w| = 1$ in the w-plane maps into the line $x = 0$ in the z-plane.

Example 26 Examine the transformation $w = \log \sin z$.

We have

$$u + iv = \log \sin (x + iy) = \log (\sin x \cosh y + i \cos x \sinh y).$$

Hence $\quad u = \log |\sin x \cosh y + i \cos x \sinh y| = \tfrac{1}{2} \log [\tfrac{1}{2}(\cosh 2y - \cos 2x)],$

(see section 7.6), and

$$v = \arg (\sin x \cosh y + i \cos x \sinh y) + 2n\pi.$$

The line $y = 0$ in the z-plane transforms into

$$u = \tfrac{1}{2} \log [\tfrac{1}{2}(1 - \cos 2x)] = \log |\sin x|,$$

and $\qquad v = \arg (\sin x) + 2n\pi.$

As x varies from 0 to $\tfrac{1}{2}\pi$, u varies from $-\infty$ to 0 along any line $v = 2n\pi$; as x varies from $\tfrac{1}{2}\pi$ to π, u varies from 0 to $-\infty$ along any line $v = 2n\pi$; as x varies from π to $\tfrac{3}{2}\pi$, u varies from $-\infty$ to 0 along any line $v = \pi + 2n\pi$; as x varies from $\tfrac{3}{2}\pi$ to 2π, u varies from 0 to $-\infty$ along any line $v = \pi + 2n\pi$.

7.10 The complex representation of harmonically varying quantities

The real quantity $x = a \cos (pt + \alpha)$ is a typical physical quantity that varies harmonically with time; a is the *amplitude*, $pt + \alpha$ is the *phase*, and α is the *phase constant*, its value depending on the origin chosen for the measurement of the time t. The *period* is $2\pi/p$ and the *frequency* is $p/2\pi$.

It proves convenient mathematically to *represent* this real physical quantity by the *complex representation*

$$X = ae^{i(pt+\alpha)} = a\cos(pt + \alpha) + i\sin(pt + \alpha).$$

The physical quantity under consideration is given by Rl X; that is, by the real part of the representation. In the Argand diagram, X is represented by a point moving round a circle centre O radius a, with constant angular velocity p. Engineers usually represent X by the vector OX, thereby using in effect a *representation of a representation*, without however a very clear appreciation of the basis for such a procedure.

It is usual to write $X = Ae^{ipt}$, where $A = ae^{i\alpha}$ is the *complex amplitude*.

In applications, the same symbol is employed generally for the real physical quantity as for the complex amplitude; no confusion arises in so doing.

Let $y = b\cos(pt + \beta)$ be a second physical quantity with the same period as x. It is represented by $Y = Be^{ipt}$, where B is the complex amplitude $be^{i\beta}$.

By means of this device, the addition of two physical quantities x and y is simplified. We have

$$x + y = \text{Rl}(X + Y) = \text{Rl}(A + B)e^{ipt}.$$

The representation of $x + y$ is then $(A + B)e^{ipt}$, whose complex amplitude $A + B$ is the sum of the two individual complex amplitudes A and B. It is *not* true that the resultant real amplitude equals the sum of a and b. In most problems, it is usual to drop the time factor e^{ipt}, and to work solely with the complex amplitudes.

Let us now consider the operation of differentiation. Physically we have

$$x = a\cos(pt + \alpha),$$

so
$$dx/dt = -pa\sin(pt + \alpha)$$
$$= pa\cos(pt + \alpha + \tfrac{1}{2}\pi)$$
$$= \text{Rl } pae^{i(pt+\alpha+\frac{1}{2}\pi)}$$
$$= \text{Rl } ipAe^{ipt}.$$

Hence the representation of dx/dt is given by $ipAe^{ipt}$, which obviously has the value dX/dt. In other words, the representation of the differential coefficient of the physical quantity is the differential coefficient of the representation of that quantity. In fact, to differentiate, we merely multiply the representation by ip, at the same time consistently omitting the factor e^{ipt}.

In most physical problems where these ideas are used, the equations that occur are linear in the variables as x and y; hence the operations of addition, differentiation and their equivalents only are required. The advantage of the method is that the time factor disappears from the mathematics, and need only be introduced when a real part is required.

The student should notice carefully that representations cannot be multiplied together. The product xy is not represented by XY, since

$$xy = (\text{Rl } X)(\text{Rl } Y) \neq \text{Rl } (XY).$$

If $x = \text{Rl } ae^{i(pt+\alpha)}$ and $y = \text{Rl } be^{i(pt+\beta)}$, we usually require the *average* of the product xy over a period, rather than xy itself at any particular time. We have

$$\text{Average } xy = \frac{ab}{2\pi/p} \int_0^{2\pi/p} \cos(pt+\alpha)\cos(pt+\beta)\, dt$$

$$= \frac{pab}{2\pi} \int_0^{2\pi/p} \tfrac{1}{2}[\cos(2pt+\alpha+\beta) + \cos(\alpha-\beta)]\, dt$$

$$= \frac{pab}{4\pi}\cos(\alpha-\beta) \cdot \frac{2\pi}{p}$$

$$= \tfrac{1}{2}ab\cos(\alpha-\beta)$$

$$= \text{Rl } \tfrac{1}{2}abe^{i(\alpha-\beta)}$$

$$= \text{Rl } \tfrac{1}{2}ae^{i(pt+\alpha)}be^{-i(pt+\beta)}$$

$$= \text{Rl } (\tfrac{1}{2}XY^\star).$$

Hence the real part of the product of $\tfrac{1}{2}X$ and $Y^\star$ immediately produces the time average of x and y. In particular,

$$\text{Average } x^2 = \text{Rl } (\tfrac{1}{2}XX^\star) = \tfrac{1}{2}\,|X|^2.$$

These ideas may be illustrated by considering a series circuit containing an inductance L, a capacitance C and a resistance R.

If j is the current in the circuit at time t, and q the charge on that plate of the condenser into which the current flows, then the voltage in the circuit (in the direction of j) is $-L\, dj/dt - q/C$. This voltage across the resistance R is related to the current by Ohm's law, namely by

$$-L\frac{dj}{dt} - \frac{q}{C} = jR.$$

We now consider currents having the time variation e^{ipt}. Noting that $j = dq/dt$, we replace j and q by their complex amplitudes J and Q, the differential coefficients dj/dt and d^2j/dt^2 being replaced by ipJ and $-p^2J$ respectively. The equation for J becomes

$$-p^2LJ + RipJ + J/C = 0,$$

or

$$p^2L - ipR - 1/C = 0.$$

The solution for p is

$$p = [iR \pm \sqrt{(4L/C - R^2)}]/2L,$$

which may pictorially be regarded as a complex angular velocity.

If we choose the phase constant α to be zero, J is then real, so

$$j = J \operatorname{Rl} \exp \left(\frac{i[iR \pm \sqrt{(4L/C - R^2)}]t}{2L} \right)$$

$$= Je^{-Rt/2L} \cos [\sqrt{(4L/C - R^2)}\, t/2L].$$

If $R \neq 0$, the factor $e^{-Rt/2L}$ denotes *attenuation*. If $4LC - R^2 > 0$ (as just assumed) the circuit is *oscillatory*, while if $4LC - R^2 < 0$, the real part is then given by

$$j = Je^{-Rt/2L} \exp [-\sqrt{(R^2 - 4L/C)}\, t/2L],$$

an *evanescent* current with no oscillations. Finally, when $R = 0$, we have

$$j = J \cos [t/\sqrt{(LC)}],$$

representing undamped oscillations with period $2\pi\sqrt{(LC)}$.

EXERCISES

(1). Evaluate (i) $(\operatorname{cis} 2\theta)^{\frac{1}{2}}$, (ii) $(-i)^{\frac{1}{3}}$, (iii) $(1 - i\sqrt{3})^{\frac{2}{3}}$, (iv) $(1 + i)^{\frac{1}{4}}$,
(v) $(5 - 12i)^{\frac{1}{2}}$, (vi) $(2i - 2)^{\frac{1}{3}}$, (vii) $[(\sqrt{3} - 1) + i(\sqrt{3} + 1)]^{\frac{1}{3}}$,
(viii) $(3 + 4i)^{30}/(1 + 2i)^{50}$.

(2)★. If $w = 3z - 6 - 4/z$, express the modulus of w in terms of θ, when $z = e^{i\theta}$; hence find the greatest and least values of this modulus.

Solve the equation for z in terms of w and find the real and imaginary parts of z when $w = 5i - 5$.

(3)★. Show that, if $\tan \theta = m$ and $\tan \theta' = m'$, then

$$\frac{m - i}{m' - i} \div \frac{m + i}{m' + i} = e^{2i(\theta - \theta')}.$$

Deduce that, if $\theta - \theta' = \frac{1}{2}\pi$, then $mm' = -1$.

(4)★. Prove that one of the values of

$$\left(\frac{1 + \sin \theta + i \cos \theta}{1 + \sin \theta - i \cos \theta} \right)^n$$

is equal to $\operatorname{cis} [n(\frac{1}{2}\pi - \theta)]$. Obtain all the values of

$$\left(\frac{\sqrt{2} + 1 + i}{\sqrt{2} + 1 - i} \right)^{\frac{1}{4}}$$

in the form $a + ib$.

(5)★. Find a complex number z whose argument is $\frac{1}{6}\pi$ such that

$$|z - \sqrt{3} + i| = |z - 2\sqrt{3} - 2i|.$$

(6). Solve the equations

(i) $(1 - x)^5 = x^5$,

(ii) $(z + 1)^6 = 64(z - 1)^6$,

(iii) $(5 + z)^5 - (5 - z)^5 = 0$,

(iv) $(z - \sqrt{3} + 2i)^6 + 64 = 0$,

(v) $z^6 + z^4 + z^2 + 1 = 0$.

(7)⋆. By first solving the equation $\cos 3\theta + \sin 3\theta = 0$, show that the roots of the equation $t^2 + 4t + 1 = 0$ are

$$t = -\tan(\pi/12) \quad \text{and} \quad t = -\tan(5\pi/12).$$

(8)⋆. Show that $x^4 - 2x^2 - 36x + k = 0$ has not more than two real zeros. If their sum is 2, find k and all the zeros.

(9)⋆. Prove that the locus of z in the Argand diagram such that $|(z - a)/(z - b)|$ is constant is a circle.

Show that the roots of the equation $(z - 1)^5 = 32(z + 1)^5$ are points on a circle of radius $\frac{4}{3}$, having the values

$$(-3 + 4i \sin \tfrac{2}{5}r\pi)/(5 - 4 \cos \tfrac{2}{5}r\pi) \qquad (r = 0, 1, \ldots, 4).$$

Deduce that

$$\prod_{r=1}^{5} (-3 + 4i \sin \tfrac{2}{5}r\pi) = -\frac{33}{31} \prod_{r=1}^{5} (5 - 4 \cos \tfrac{2}{5}r\pi).$$

(10)⋆. Show that every root of the equation $(z + 1)^{2n} + (z - 1)^{2n} = 0$ where n is a positive integer, is purely imaginary.

If the roots are represented in an Argand diagram by points $P_1, P_2, \ldots, P_{2n}$, prove that, if O is the origin,

$$OP_1{}^2 + OP_2{}^2 + \ldots + OP_{2n}^2 = 2n(2n - 1).$$

(11)⋆. Show that all the roots of the equation $(1 + x)^{2n+1} = (1 - x)^{2n+1}$ are given by $\pm i \tan [r\pi/(2n + 1)]$ where $r = 0, 1, \ldots, n$.

By putting $n = 2$, show that $\tan^2 \tfrac{1}{5}\pi \tan^2 \tfrac{2}{5}\pi = 5$.

(12)⋆. If n is a positive integer, prove that

$$x^{2n} - 1 = (x^2 - 1) \prod_{k=1}^{n-1} [x^2 - 2x \cos(k\pi/n) + 1].$$

Deduce that

(i) $\dfrac{\sin n\theta}{\sin \theta} = 2^{n-1} \prod_{k=1}^{n-1} [\cos \theta - \cos(k\pi/n)]$,

(ii) $\sqrt{n} = 2^{n-1} \prod_{k=1}^{n-1} \sin(k\pi/2n)$.

(13)⋆. If n is a positive integer, prove that

$$a^{2n} + b^{2n} = \prod_{k=1}^{n} \{a^2 - 2ab \cos [(2r - 1)\pi/2n] + b^2\}.$$

Deduce that

(i) $\cos n\theta = 2^{n-1} \prod_{r=1}^{n} \{\cos \theta - \cos [(2r - 1)\pi/2n]\}$,

(ii) $\cos 2n\theta = 2^{2n-1} \prod_{r=1}^{n} \{\cos^2 \theta - \cos^2 [(2r - 1)\pi/4n]\}$,

(iii) $\prod_{r=1}^{n} \sin [(2r - 1)\pi/4n] = 2^{\frac{1}{2}-n}$.

(14)★. By finding the real quadratic factors of $x^{2n} + x^{2n-1} + \ldots + x + 1$, show that

$$2^n \sin\frac{\pi}{2n+1} \sin\frac{2\pi}{2n+1} \ldots \sin\frac{n\pi}{2n+1} = \sqrt{(2n+1)}.$$

(15)★. Resolve $x^6 - x^3 + 1$ into real quadratic factors and deduce that
   (i) $\cos\frac{1}{9}\pi + \cos\frac{5}{9}\pi + \cos\frac{7}{9}\pi = 0$,
   (ii) $\cos\frac{1}{9}\pi \cos\frac{5}{9}\pi \cos\frac{7}{9}\pi = \frac{1}{8}$,
   (iii) $\sin\frac{1}{9}\pi \sin\frac{5}{9}\pi \sin\frac{7}{9}\pi = \frac{1}{8}\sqrt{3}$.

(16)★. If n is a positive integer, prove that

$$x^{2n} + a^{2n} = \prod_{r=1}^{n} \{x^2 - 2xa\cos[(2r-1)\pi/2n] + a^2\}.$$

Hence show that

$$(1+x)^{2n} + (1-x)^{2n} = 2\prod_{r=1}^{n} \{x^2 + \tan^2[(2r-1)\pi/4n]\}.$$

(17)★. Show that, provided $|r| < 1$, the sum to infinity of the series

$$r\sin\theta + r^2\sin 2\theta + r^3\sin 3\theta + \ldots$$

is $r\sin\theta/(1 - 2r\cos\theta + r^2)$.

(18)★. (i) Sum the infinite series in which x and θ are real:

$$x\sin\theta + \frac{x^3\sin 3\theta}{3!} + \frac{x^5\sin 5\theta}{5!} + \ldots.$$

   (ii) In the triangle ABC, show that, with the usual notation, if $b < c$,

$$\frac{a^n}{c^n}\left[\sin A + n\frac{b}{c}\sin 2A + \frac{n(n+1)}{2!}\frac{b^2}{c^2}\sin 3A + \ldots\right] = \sin(A + nB).$$

(19). Prove that

$$\sum_{r=1}^{n} {}_nC_r\sin 2r\theta = 2^n\cos^n\theta\sin n\theta.$$

(20)★. Prove that

$$\sin\alpha - \sin(\alpha+\beta) + \sin(\alpha+2\beta) - \ldots - \sin[\alpha + (2n-1)\beta]$$
$$= -\sin n\beta\cos[\alpha + (n - \tfrac{1}{2})\beta]\sec\tfrac{1}{2}\beta,$$

where α and β are real numbers.
$A_1, A_2, \ldots, A_{2n}$ are the vertices of a regular polygon of $2n$ sides. Prove that the sum of the lengths $A_1A_3, A_1A_5, \ldots, A_1A_{2n-1}$ differs from the sum of $A_1A_2, A_1A_4, \ldots, A_1A_{2n}$ by $a\sec^2(\pi/4n)$, where $2a$ is the length of one side.

(21)★. Sum the series $x\sin\theta + x^2\sin 2\theta + \ldots + x^n\sin n\theta$. With the usual notation for the triangle ABC show that, if $b < c$,

$$\frac{a^2b}{c}\left(\sin A + \frac{b}{c}\sin 2A + \frac{b^2}{c^2}\sin 3A + \ldots\right) = 2\Delta.$$

(22)★. If α is real and lies within a certain range which should be stated, show that

$$\sum_{n=0}^{\infty}\tan^n\alpha\cos nx = \text{Rl}[1/(1 - e^{ix}\tan\alpha)].$$

Hence evaluate the sum of the infinite series.

(23)★. Sum to n terms the series whose rth term is $(2r - 1)x^{r-1}$.
If $\alpha = 2\pi/n$, where n is a positive integer, show that

$$1 + 3\cos\alpha + 5\cos 2\alpha + \ldots + (2n - 1)\cos(n - 1)\alpha = -n,$$
$$3\sin\alpha + 5\sin 2\alpha + \ldots + (2n - 1)\sin(n - 1)\alpha = -n\cot\tfrac{1}{2}\alpha.$$

(24)★. Express the left-hand side of the equation

$$\cos 6\theta + 6\cos 4\theta - 9\cos 3\theta + 15\cos 2\theta - 27\cos\theta + 14 = 0$$

as a polynomial in $\cos\theta$, and hence find all angles θ between $0°$ and $360°$ inclusive satisfying the equation.

(25)★. By writing $z = \cos\theta + i\sin\theta$, $z^{-1} = \cos\theta - i\sin\theta$, express $32i\sin\theta\cos^4\theta$ in terms of z, and hence prove that

$$16\cos^4\theta\sin\theta = \sin 5\theta + 3\sin 3\theta + 2\sin\theta.$$

(26)★. Express $2^{10}\cos^{11}\theta$ in the form $\Sigma\, a_r\cos(2r + 1)\theta$.

(27)★. By writing $2\cos\theta = z + z^{-1}$ and $2i\sin\theta = z - z^{-1}$, where $z = \operatorname{cis}\theta$, prove that

$$2^6\sin^5\theta\cos^2\theta = \sin 7\theta - 3\sin 5\theta + \sin 3\theta + 5\sin\theta.$$

(28)★. Find all the values of z for which (a) $\sinh z = 2$, (b) $\sin z = 2$.

(29)★. Prove that $\cos 5\theta = 16\cos^5\theta - 20\cos^3\theta + 5\cos\theta$ and hence show that the roots of the equation

$$16x^5 - 20x^3 + 5x = 1$$

are 1, $\cos\tfrac{2}{5}\pi$, $\cos\tfrac{4}{5}\pi$, the last two being double roots.

(30)★. Prove that $\cos 6\theta = 32\cos^6\theta - 48\cos^4\theta + 18\cos^2\theta - 1$. By putting $x = \cos^2\theta$, show that the roots of the equation

$$64x^3 - 96x^2 + 36x - 3 = 0$$

are $\cos^2\pi/18$, $\cos^2 5\pi/18$, $\cos^2 7\pi/18$, and deduce that

$$\sec^2\pi/18 + \sec^2 5\pi/18 + \sec^2 7\pi/18 = 12.$$

(31)★. Establish the formulae

$$16\sin^5\theta = \sin 5\theta - 5\sin 3\theta + 10\sin\theta,$$
$$32\cos^6\theta = \cos 6\theta + 6\cos 4\theta + 15\cos 2\theta + 10.$$

Solve completely the equation

$$\cos 5\theta + 5\cos 3\theta + 10\cos\theta = \tfrac{1}{2}$$

where θ is real.

(32)★. Show that the expression $2(1 - x)\cos\theta/(1 - 2x\cos 2\theta + x^2)$ can be written in the form $A(1 - xe^{2i\theta})^{-1} + B(1 - xe^{-2i\theta})^{-1}$, where A and B are independent of x, and find the values of A, B.

Deduce that, if $1 > x > -1$, $(1 - x)\cos\theta/(1 - 2x\cos 2\theta + x^2)$ has the value

$$\cos\theta + x\cos 3\theta + x^2\cos 5\theta + \ldots + x^{n-1}\cos(2n - 1)\theta + \ldots.$$

Hence express $\cos 7\theta\sec\theta$ in terms of $\cos 2\theta$.

(33)★. Find the real and imaginary parts of $\cos z$, where $z = x + iy$. Solve completely the equation

$$\cos z = [e(1 - i) + e^{-1}(1 + i)]/2\sqrt{2}.$$

(34)★. Show that $\cosh^{-1} i$ has the value

$$\log[(-1)^{n-1} + \sqrt{2}] + \tfrac{1}{2}i(2n - 1)\pi,$$

n being a positive integer.

(35)$\star$. If $\sinh(p + iq) = a + ib$, prove
$$\cos^4 q + (a^2 + b^2 - 1)\cos^2 q - a^2 = 0.$$
Hence find $\sinh^{-1}(\tfrac{3}{8}\sqrt{3} + \tfrac{5}{8}i)$.

(36)$\star$. Prove that $\cos^{-1} 2 = 2n\pi \pm i\log(2 + \sqrt{3})$, where n is any integer.
If $\tan z = \operatorname{cis}\alpha$ where α is real and acute, prove that
$$z = (n + \tfrac{1}{4})\pi + \tfrac{1}{2}i\log\tan(\tfrac{1}{4}\pi + \tfrac{1}{2}\alpha).$$

(37)$\star$. Express $\tan(x + iy)$ in the form $u + iv$, where x, y, u, v are real.
If $\tan(x + iy) = \sin(p + iq)$, where x, y, p, q are real, prove that
$$\tan p \sinh 2y = \tanh q \sin 2x.$$

(38)$\star$. If $w = \log[(z + a)/(z - a)]$, where $z = x + iy$, $w = u + iv$, and x, y, u, v, a are all real, prove that
$$\tanh u = \frac{2ax}{x^2 + y^2 + a^2}, \quad \tan v = -\frac{2ay}{x^2 + y^2 - a^2}.$$

(39)$\star$. If $e^w = (z - i)/(z + i)$. where $w = u + iv$, $z = x + iy$, prove that
$$u = \tfrac{1}{2}\log\frac{x^2 + y^2 - 2y + 1}{x^2 + y^2 + 2y + 1}, \quad v = \tan^{-1}\frac{2x}{1 - x^2 - y^2}.$$

(40)$\star$. If $u + iv = \cot(x + iy)$ where u, v, x and y are real, show that
$$u = \sin 2x/(\cosh 2y - \cos 2x).$$
Show that all the values of z satisfying the equation $\cos z = \tfrac{5}{4}$ are given by $z = 2n\pi \pm i\log 2$, where n is zero or any integer.

(41)$\star$. If w is a complex number and $w\star$ is its conjugate, show that
$$|w|^2 = ww\star, \quad \arg w = \tan^{-1}\{(w - w\star)/[i(w + w\star)]\}.$$
If $w = \tan \tfrac{1}{2}z$, where $w = u + iv$ and $z = x + iy$, prove that
$$\frac{1 + u^2 + v^2}{1 - u^2 - v^2} = \frac{\cosh y}{\cos x} \quad\text{and}\quad \frac{v}{u} = \frac{\sinh y}{\sin x}.$$

(42)$\star$. If $\sin^{-1}(\operatorname{cis} x) = u + iv$, where x, u, v are real and $0 < x < \tfrac{1}{2}\pi$ whilst v is positive, prove that
$$u = \sin^{-1}\sqrt{(1 - \sin x)}, \quad v = \log[\sqrt{(\sin x)} + \sqrt{(1 + \sin x)}].$$

(43)$\star$. Prove that $\tanh^{-1} x = \tfrac{1}{2}\log[(1 + x)/(1 - x)]$.
If P is the point in an Argand diagram representing the complex number $x + iy$, and if A and B represent ± 1 respectively, prove that the real part of $\tanh^{-1}(x + iy)$ is $\tfrac{1}{2}\log PB/PA$.

(44)$\star$. (i) Find the general solution of the equation $\sin z = 3i\cos z$.
(ii) If $u + iv = \coth(x + iy)$, show that
$$v = -\sin 2y/(\cosh 2x - \cos 2y).$$
Hence show that
$$iv = (1 - e^{2(x-iy)})^{-1} - (1 - e^{2(x+iy)})^{-1},$$
and deduce that, if $x < 0$, v can be expressed as the infinite series
$$-2\sum_{r=1}^{\infty} e^{2rx}\sin 2ry.$$

(45)$\star$. On an Argand diagram z is a representative point and $w = (z - 2)/(z - i)$. Show that, when the point represented by w moves along the real axis, z traces the line through 2 and i.
Find the locus of z when w moves along the imaginary axis.

(46)$\star$. The complex number z is given by $z = \cos w$, where $w = u + iv$. What are the loci in the z-plane corresponding to

(i) $v = \sinh^{-1} \tfrac{1}{2}\sqrt{2}$, u variable, (ii) $u = \tfrac{1}{3}\pi$, v variable?

(47)$\star$. If $zz_1 = k^2$, where z and z_1 are complex and k is real and if the point which represents z in the Argand diagram describes a circle of radius c whose centre is at (a, b), show that the point which represents z_1 describes a circle of radius $k^2 c/(a^2 + b^2 - c^2)$.

(48)$\star$. If $w = u + iv = e^{\pi z/a}$, where $z = x + iy$, and a is real and positive, find the loci in the w-plane corresponding to the lines $y = 0$ and $y = a$ in the z-plane.

(49)$\star$. The vertices O, A, B, C of a square in the Argand diagram represent the numbers 0, 1, $1 + i$, i respectively. Show that, when the point z describes the perimeter of the square, the point z^2 describes a closed contour consisting of part of the real axis and arcs of two parabolae. Sketch this contour.

(50)$\star$. Two complex variables z and w are connected by the relation $zw + z - w + 1 = 0$. If $z = 2 + e^{i\theta}$, prove that $w = -2 + i\tan\tfrac{1}{2}\theta$, and describe the loci of the points z and w as θ varies from $-\pi$ to π.

(51)$\star$. If x, y, u, v are real numbers such that $u + iv = e^{x+iy}$, prove that $u^2 + v^2 = e^{2x}$ and $v/u = \tan y$.

Indicate in an Argand diagram the path of the point (u, v) when the point (x, y) moves in a positive sense round the boundary of the rectangle formed by the co-ordinate axes and the lines $x = 1$, $y = \tfrac{1}{4}\pi$.

(52)$\star$. If the complex variables $w = u + iv$, $z = x + iy$ are related by $w = \sin z$, find the loci in the w-plane corresponding to (i) the line $x = \tfrac{1}{4}\pi$, (ii) that part of the line $y = \log 2$ for which $0 \leqslant x \leqslant 2\pi$ in the z-plane. Illustrate by sketches.

(53)$\star$. If P represents the number $z = x + iy$ in an Argand diagram and if Q represents $w = 1/(1 + z)$, trace the locus of Q as P describes a circle of unit radius with its centre at the origin.

(54)$\star$. If $w = (z - 1)/(z + 1)$, where $w = u + iv$ and $z = x + iy$, express u and v in terms of x and y. Show that the straight line $u = k$ (where k is a real constant) in the w-plane transforms into a circle through the point -1 in the z-plane, and find its centre and radius. Sketch the circles given by $k = 0$, $k = \tfrac{1}{2}$, and examine the case when $k = 1$.

(55)$\star$. Show that by the relation $w = z^2$, where $z = x + iy$, $w = u + iv$, lines through the origin in the z-plane are transformed into lines through the origin in the w-plane.

Show also that the line $x = \lambda$ (where λ is a positive constant) is transformed into a parabola in the w-plane with its focus at the origin, and indicate by a figure the sense in which the point w describes this parabola as y varies from $-\infty$ to $+\infty$ on the line $x = \lambda$.

Sketch the area in the w-plane which corresponds to the interior of the triangle in the z-plane formed by the lines $y = 0$, $x = 1$, $y = x$.

ANSWERS TO EXERCISES

(1). (i) $\pm\operatorname{cis}\theta$. (ii) i, $\tfrac{1}{2}(\pm\sqrt{3} - i)$. (iii) $\sqrt[5]{4}\operatorname{cis}[\tfrac{2}{15}\pi(3r - 1)]$, $r = 0, 1, 2, 3, 4$.
   (iv) $2^{\frac{1}{3}}\operatorname{cis}[\tfrac{1}{18}\pi(1 + 8r)]$, $r = 0, 1, 2, 3$. (v) $\pm(3 - 2i)$.
   (vi) $1 + i$, $\tfrac{1}{2}[-1 \mp \sqrt{3} \pm i(\sqrt{3} \mp 1)]$. (vii) $2\operatorname{cis}25°$, $2\operatorname{cis}145°$, $2\operatorname{cis}265°$.
   (viii) $5^5(\cos 138° - i\sin 138°)$.

(2). $\sqrt{(61 + 12\cos\theta - 24\cos 2\theta)}$, $85\frac{3}{4}$, 25; $1 + i$, $\frac{2}{3}(-1 + i)$.

(4). $(\text{cis } \frac{1}{16}\pi)(\pm 1; \pm i)$. (5). $\sqrt{3} + i$.

(6). (i) $\frac{1}{2} - \frac{1}{2}i \tan \frac{1}{5}r\pi$, $r = 0, 1, 2, 3, 4$.

  (ii) $(3 - 4i\sin\frac{1}{8}r\pi)/(5 - 4\cos\frac{1}{8}r\pi)$, $r = 0, 1, \ldots, 5$.

  (iii) $5i\tan\frac{1}{8}r\pi$, $r = 0, \pm 1, \pm 2$.

  (iv) $2\sqrt{3} - i, 2\sqrt{3} - 3i, \sqrt{3}, \sqrt{3} - 4i, -3i, -i$.

  (v) $\pm i$, cis $[\frac{1}{4}i(2r + 1)]$, $r = 0, 1, 2, 3$.

(8). $k = -80$; $x = -2, 4, 1 \pm 3i$.   (18). (i) $\cosh(x\cos\theta)\sin(x\sin\theta)$.

(22). $|\alpha| < \frac{1}{4}\pi$, $(1 - \tan\alpha\cos x)/(\sec^2\alpha - 2\tan\alpha\cos x)$.

(23). $[1 + x - x^n(2n + 1) + x^{n+1}(2n - 1)]/(1 - x)^2$.

(24). $32\cos^6\theta - 36\cos^3\theta + 4$; $0°, 60°, 300°, 360°$.

(26). $_{11}C_5\cos\theta + _{11}C_4\cos 3\theta + _{11}C_3\cos 5\theta + _{11}C_2\cos 7\theta + _{11}C_1\cos 9\theta + \cos 11\theta$.

(28). (a) $\log(2 + 2\sqrt{2}) + 2\pi in$, $\log(2\sqrt{2} - 2) + (2n + 1)\pi i$.

  (b) $i\log(2 \pm \sqrt{3}) + (2n + \frac{1}{2})\pi$.   (31). $(n + \frac{1}{2})\pi$, $(2n \pm \frac{1}{3})\pi$.

(32). $A = e^{i\theta}, B = e^{-i\theta}$; $\cos 7\theta \sec\theta = $ (coefficient of x^3) $\sec\theta = $ $8\cos^3 2\theta - 4\cos^2 2\theta - 4\cos 2\theta + 1$.   (33). $x = -\frac{1}{4}\pi + 2n\pi, y = 1$.

(35). $\log 2 + \frac{1}{6}i\pi$ or $-\log 2 + \frac{5}{6}i\pi$.   (44). (i) $\frac{1}{2}i\log 2 + \frac{1}{2}\pi + n\pi$.

(45). $x^2 + y^2 = 2x + y$.   (46). (i) $2x^2 + 6y^2 = 3$, (ii) $12x^2 - 4y^2 = 3$.

(48). Real u-axis from 0 to $+\infty$; real u-axis from 0 to $-\infty$.

(52). (i) $2u^2 - 2v^2 = 1$; (ii) $\frac{16}{25}u^2 + \frac{16}{9}v^2 = 1$.   (53) $u = \frac{1}{2}$.

(54). Centre $x = k/(1 - k), y = 0$; radius $= 1/|k - 1|$.

CHAPTER 8

THE COORDINATE GEOMETRY OF THE STRAIGHT LINE AND THE CIRCLE

Both two and three dimensional coordinate geometry represent geometrical constructs and constructions by algebraic equations and operations. Each elementary construction in geometry is associated with its own individual algebraic counterpart. In any geometrical problem, the given features must first of all be translated into their algebraic equivalents. The algebra must then be manipulated by operations that correspond to constructions given in the problem. Finally, the answer obtained in algebraic form must be translated back into geometrical form.

Our method of approach to the theory of straight lines is first to derive all the algebraic representations that we judge necessary, and then to apply them to various problems.

8.1 Elementary results and revision

Points in a plane are designated by their coordinates (x, y) with respect to a suitably chosen set of right-handed Cartesian axes Ox, Oy previously established in the plane.

The distance of the point $P(x, y)$ from the origin O is $\sqrt{(x^2 + y^2)}$, while the distance between $Q(x_1, y_1)$ and $R(x_2, y_2)$ is $\sqrt{[x_1 - x_2)^2 + (y_1 - y_2)^2]}$.

A *locus* in the plane is represented by an equation $f(x, y) = 0$. In particular, a linear equation $ax + by + c = 0$ represents a *straight line*, and an equation containing quadratic terms

$$ax^2 + 2hxy + by^2 + 2fy + 2gx + c = 0$$

represents a *conic*.

If O' is a new origin, with coordinates (x_0, y_0) with respect to axes Ox, Oy, and if new axes $O'X$, $O'Y$ are chosen respectively parallel to Ox, Oy, the old and the new coordinates of a point P are related by

$$x = X + x_0, \quad y = Y + y_0.$$

The locus $f(x, y) = 0$ in the original system transforms, in the new system, to $f(X + x_0, \ Y + y_0) = 0$.

A straight line is represented by various forms of linear equation in keeping with its given geometrical construction:

(i) If a straight line passes through the point $(0, c)$ making an angle θ with Ox, then its equation is $y = mx + c$, where $m = \tan \theta$ is the gradient of the line.

(ii) If a straight line passes through the point (x_0, y_0) with given gradient m, its equation is $y - y_0 = m(x - x_0)$.

(iii) If the straight line makes signed intercepts a and b on the axes Ox and Oy respectively, its equation is $x/a + y/b = 1$.

(iv) If the line is defined by two points (x_1, y_1), (x_2, y_2) lying on it, then its equation is

$$\frac{y - y_1}{y_2 - y_1} = \frac{x - x_1}{x_2 - x_1}.$$

(v) If the perpendicular distance from the origin to the line is p, and if $\tan \alpha$ is the gradient of this perpendicular, then the equation of the line is $x \cos \alpha + y \sin \alpha = p$.

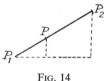
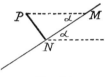

F<small>IG</small>. 14   F<small>IG</small>. 15

A parametric representation may easily be established on the line joining the points $P_1(x_1, y_1)$ and $P_2(x_2, y_2)$. Let P be the point on this line such that the ratio P_1P/PP_2 equals λ, having regard to the sense of the segments P_1P, PP_2. From the figure, it can be seen that the x and y coordinate differences of the points also satisfy the same ratios, so we have

$$\frac{x - x_1}{x_2 - x} = \lambda = \frac{y - y_1}{y_2 - y},$$

or

$$x = \frac{x_1 + \lambda x_2}{1 + \lambda}, \qquad y = \frac{y_1 + \lambda y_2}{1 + \lambda}.$$

The point P_1 is given by $\lambda = 0$, and P_2 by $\lambda = \infty$. If λ is negative, P lies outside the segment P_1P_2, lying to the right if $-\infty < \lambda < -1$, and to the left if $-1 < \lambda < 0$.

8.2 The perpendicular distance from a point to a line

Let P be the given point (x_0, y_0) and PN the perpendicular from P to the line $ax + by + c = 0$. Let PM be the line through P parallel to Ox, so $\angle PMN = \alpha$, where $\tan \alpha = -a/b$.

At M, $y = y_0$, so from the equation of the line the value of x at P is given by

$$x = -(by_0 + c)/a.$$

Hence

$$PM = -(by_0 + c)/a - x_0 = -(ax_0 + by_0 + c)/a.$$

Finally,

$$PN = PM \sin \alpha = -\frac{ax_0 + by_0 + c}{a} \cdot \frac{-a}{\sqrt{(a^2 + b^2)}} = \frac{ax_0 + by_0 + c}{\sqrt{(a^2 + b^2)}}.$$

Sometimes the sign of this expression is positive, sometimes negative. The line divides the whole plane into two infinite regions; if P is in one region, PN is always positive, while if P is in the other region, PN is negative.

8.3   Rotation of rectangular axes

The point P has coordinates (x, y) with respect to the axes Ox, Oy.

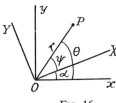

FIG. 16

These axes are rotated through an angle α, in which position they are denoted by OX, OY. Polar coordinates (r, θ) are established in the system Oxy, with Ox as initial line; similarly, polar coordinates (r, ψ) are established in the system OXY, with OX as initial line.

We have the relationships:

$$x = r \cos \theta, \quad y = r \sin \theta, \quad X = r \cos \psi, \quad Y = r \sin \psi.$$

To express X, Y in terms of x, y we have

$$X = r \cos \psi = r \cos (\theta - \alpha)$$
$$= r (\cos \theta \cos \alpha + \sin \theta \sin \alpha) = x \cos \alpha + y \sin \alpha,$$
$$Y = r \sin \psi = r \sin (\theta - \alpha)$$
$$= r (\sin \theta \cos \alpha - \cos \theta \sin \alpha) = y \cos \alpha - x \sin \alpha.$$

Similarly,

$$x = X \cos \alpha - Y \sin \alpha, \quad y = X \sin \alpha + Y \cos \alpha.$$

These four formulae need not be memorized; they may be written down immediately by observing that X, say, consists of the sum of the resolved parts of x and y along OX, and similarly for the other three quantities.

8.4 The intersection of two lines

If $y = m_1x + c_1$, $y = m_2x + c_2$ are two given lines, making angles α_1, α_2 with Ox respectively, then the tangent of the angle between the lines is

$$\tan(\alpha_2 - \alpha_1) = \frac{\tan\alpha_2 - \tan\alpha_1}{1 + \tan\alpha_2\tan\alpha_1} = \frac{m_2 - m_1}{1 + m_2m_1}.$$

In particular, if the two lines are perpendicular, $\tan(\alpha_2 - \alpha_1) = \infty$, so $1 + m_1m_2 = 0$. In other words, the gradient perpendicular to m is $-1/m$.

If two lines are given in the general form

$$a_1x + b_1y + c_1 = 0, \quad a_2x + b_2y + c_2 = 0,$$

the point in which they intersect may be considered by formally solving the equations thus:

$$\frac{x}{\begin{vmatrix} b_1 & c_1 \\ b_2 & c_2 \end{vmatrix}} = \frac{-y}{\begin{vmatrix} a_1 & c_1 \\ a_2 & c_2 \end{vmatrix}} = \frac{1}{\begin{vmatrix} a_1 & b_1 \\ a_2 & b_2 \end{vmatrix}}.$$

If $(a_1b_2 - a_2b_1) \neq 0$, a unique solution exists, indicating that the two lines meet in a point. If $(a_1b_2 - a_2b_1) = 0$, but at least one of $(b_1c_2 - b_2c_1)$, $(a_1c_2 - a_2c_1)$ does not vanish, then there is no finite solution; geometrically the lines are parallel. Finally, if all the three determinants vanish, the two lines are identical; every point on the line is a solution.

If these two lines intersect in the unique point P, we often require the equation of a general line passing through P. To this end, we do *not* find the coordinates of P, rather we consider the equation

$$(a_1x + b_1y + c_1) + \lambda(a_2x + b_2y + c_2) = 0, \tag{1}$$

where λ is any constant. Certainly this equation represents a line, since it is linear; moreover, the point P satisfies the equation, since at P, both brackets individually, and hence the combined expression, vanish. Equation (1) is therefore the required equation.

As λ is varied, thereby producing different lines, line (1) rotates about P. In particular, λ can be chosen to satisfy one given condition.

(i) If the line is to have a definite gradient m, we have

$$m = -(a_1 + \lambda a_2)/(b_1 + \lambda b_2),$$

yielding

$$\lambda = -(mb_1 + a_1)/(mb_2 + a_2).$$

(ii) If the line is to pass through the definite point (x_0, y_0), we require

$$(a_1x_0 + b_1y_0 + c_1) + \lambda(a_2x_0 + b_2y_0 + c_2) = 0,$$

yielding $\lambda = -(a_1x_0 + b_1y_0 + c_1)/(a_2x_0 + b_2y_0 + c_2).$

8.5 The area of a triangle

A triangle may be defined in terms of its three vertices $A(x_1, y_1)$, $B(x_2, y_2)$, $C(x_3, y_3)$. If the three points A, B, C are labelled anticlockwise, the area of the triangle ABC is given by

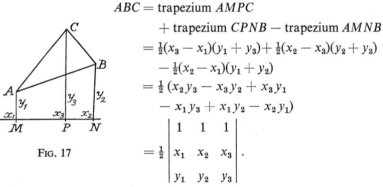

FIG. 17

$$
\begin{aligned}
ABC &= \text{trapezium } AMPC \\
&\quad + \text{trapezium } CPNB - \text{trapezium } AMNB \\
&= \tfrac{1}{2}(x_3 - x_1)(y_1 + y_3) + \tfrac{1}{2}(x_2 - x_3)(y_2 + y_3) \\
&\quad - \tfrac{1}{2}(x_2 - x_1)(y_1 + y_2) \\
&= \tfrac{1}{2}\,(x_2 y_3 - x_3 y_2 + x_3 y_1 \\
&\quad\quad - x_1 y_3 + x_1 y_2 - x_2 y_1) \\
&= \tfrac{1}{2}\begin{vmatrix} 1 & 1 & 1 \\ x_1 & x_2 & x_3 \\ y_1 & y_2 & y_3 \end{vmatrix}.
\end{aligned}
$$

This result should be memorized. The determinant has a positive value only if the three points A, B, C are arranged in the anticlockwise sense.

The area of a plane figure defined by four or more vertices may be found by splitting it up into triangles. A careful figure should be drawn to ensure that the correct triangles are used in the calculation. This is especially important if the polygon contains internal reflex angles, since some triangles may have to be subtracted rather than added to yield the required area.

8.6 The combined representation of two lines

If $a_1x + b_1y + c_1 = 0$ and $a_2x + b_2y + c_2 = 0$ are the equations of two lines, the product

$$(a_1x + b_1y + c_1)(a_2x + b_2y + c_2) = 0$$

represents the pair of lines. If this is multiplied out, we obtain the equation

$$
a_1a_2x^2 + (a_1b_2 + a_2b_1)xy + b_1b_2y^2 + (b_1c_2 + c_2b_1)y \\
+ (a_1c_2 + a_2c_1)x + c_1c_2 = 0,
$$

which is of the general form

$$ax^2 + 2hxy + by^2 + 2fy + 2gx + c = 0. \qquad (2)$$

Conversely, an equation of this general form need not necessarily represent two lines; only if it factorizes into two linear factors can it represent two straight lines. If no factors exist, the equation represents a *non-degenerate* conic.

If both lines pass through the origin, we require $c_1 = c_2 = 0$; the general equation then takes the homogeneous form

$$ax^2 + 2hxy + by^2 = 0.$$

To find the condition for equation (2) to represent two lines intersecting in the point (x_0, y_0), we choose axes through this point parallel to Ox, Oy, using the transformation

$$x = X + x_0, \quad y = Y + y_0.$$

We obtain

$$a(X + x_0)^2 + 2h(X + x_0)(Y + y_0) + b(Y + y_0)^2$$
$$+ 2f(Y + y_0) + 2g(X + x_0) + c = 0,$$

or

$$aX^2 + 2hXY + bY^2 + 2(ax_0 + hy_0 + g)X + 2(hx_0 + by_0 + f)Y$$
$$+ (ax_0^2 + 2hx_0y_0 + by_0^2 + 2fy_0 + 2gx_0 + c) = 0.$$

Since this equation must represent two lines through the new origin, we require

$$ax_0 + hy_0 + g = 0, \tag{3}$$

$$hx_0 + by_0 + f = 0, \tag{4}$$

$$ax_0^2 + 2hx_0y_0 + by_0^2 + 2fy_0 + 2gx_0 + c = 0. \tag{5}$$

To simplify equation (5), we subtract from it x_0 times equation (3) and y_0 times equation (4), yielding

$$gx_0 + fy_0 + c = 0. \tag{6}$$

Equations (3), (4), (6) are consistent only if

$$\begin{vmatrix} a & h & g \\ h & b & f \\ g & f & c \end{vmatrix} = 0. \tag{7}$$

This is the necessary condition for the general equation (2) to represent two straight lines. It is also a sufficient condition since the algebra is reversible. The two linear factors of equation (2) may be found by inspection, by first factorizing the quadratic terms and then fitting in the remaining terms.

The new equation for this pair of lines is then

$$aX^2 + 2hXY + bY^2 = 0.$$

If two straight lines are given in the combined form (2), the gradients of the two lines are contained in the quadratic terms only. If we write the two lines in the form $y = m_1 x + c_1$, $y = m_2 x + c_2$, their product takes the form

$$y^2 - (m_1 + m_2)xy + m_1 m_2 x^2 + \ldots = 0.$$

On comparing coefficients in this equation with those in equation (2), we obtain the relations:

$$m_1 + m_2 = -2h/b, \quad m_1 m_2 = a/b.$$

If θ is the angle between the two lines (2), we have

$$
\begin{aligned}
\tan \theta &= (m_2 - m_1)/(1 + m_1 m_2) \\
&= \sqrt{[(m_1 + m_2)^2 - 4m_1 m_2]}/(1 + m_1 m_2) \\
&= \frac{2\sqrt{(h^2 - ab)}}{a + b}.
\end{aligned}
$$

If the condition (7) is satisfied, and if $a + b = 0$, $\tan \theta = \infty$, so the two lines are perpendicular.

If the condition (7) is satisfied, and if $h^2 - ab = 0$, the two lines are either parallel or identical. Expansion along the third row of determinant (7) yields

$$g(hf - bg) - f(af - hg) + c(ab - h^2) = 0,$$

which becomes, when the lines are parallel

$$2fgh - af^2 - bg^2 = 0.$$

Multiplication by a (provided $a \neq 0$) yields, upon replacing ab by h^2,

$$(af - gh)^2 = 0.$$

Hence the conditions for (2) to represent two parallel lines are $h^2 - ab = af - gh = 0$.
The perpendicular distance between two such parallel lines may be found as follows: We multiply equation (2) by a, obtaining

$$a^2 x^2 + 2ahxy + aby^2 + 2agx + 2afy + ac = 0,$$

or $$a^2 x^2 + 2ahxy + h^2 y^2 + 2agx + 2ghy + ac = 0.$$

Factorization yields

$$(ax + hy + c_1)(ax + hy + c_2) = 0,$$

where $c_1 + c_2 = 2g$, $c_1 c_2 = ac$. If (X, Y) is a point outside the region between the two lines, the two perpendicular distances from (X, Y) to the two lines are given by

$$\frac{aX + hY + c_1}{\sqrt{(a^2 + h^2)}} \quad \text{and} \quad \frac{aX + hY + c_2}{\sqrt{(a^2 + h^2)}}.$$

The required distance is given by the difference between these two quantities, namely by

$$\frac{|c_1 - c_2|}{\sqrt{(a^2 + h^2)}} = \frac{\sqrt{[(c_1 + c_2)^2 - 4c_1 c_2]}}{\sqrt{(a^2 + h^2)}} = \frac{2\sqrt{(g^2 - ac)}}{\sqrt{(a^2 + h^2)}}.$$

The combined equation of the two lines that bisect the angles formed by the line pair

$$ax^2 + 2hxy + by^2 = 0$$

may easily be found

If the line OA, given by $y = m_2 x$, and the line OB, given by $y = m_1 x$, form the angle AOB bisected by the line OC, given by $y = mx$, we have $\tan \sqrt{AOC} = \tan \sqrt{COB}$. In terms of gradients,

$$\frac{m_2 - y/x}{1 + m_2 y/x} = \frac{y/x - m_1}{1 + m_1 y/x}.$$

We now cross-multiply and collect up terms, obtaining

$$(y^2 - x^2)(m_1 + m_2) = 2xy(m_1 m_2 - 1),$$

or, in terms of a, b, c,

$$(y^2 - x^2)(-2h/b) = 2xy(a/b - 1),$$

simplifying to

$$\frac{x^2 - y^2}{a - b} = \frac{xy}{h}.$$

An important result concerning the equation of a line pair (or a conic) is as follows: If a line cuts a given line pair (or a conic) in the points A and B, find the combined equation of the line pair OA, OB, where O is the origin.

If the given line is $lx + my + n = 0$, and if the line pair (or conic) is given by equation (2), consider the homogeneous equation

$$ax^2 + 2hxy + by^2 + (2gx + 2fy)\left(-\frac{lx + my}{n}\right)$$
$$+ c\left(-\frac{lx + my}{n}\right)^2 = 0. \quad (8)$$

Certainly this homogeneous equation represents two lines through the origin O. Moreover, at A, $-(lx + my)/n = 1$, since A lies on the given line. The left hand side of equation (8) then vanishes, since A also lies on the line pair (or conic). Hence the point A must lie on the locus (8); similarly, B lies on it. Equation (8) is therefore the required equation.

Example 1 The perpendiculars from a point P to the two lines $ax^2 + 2hxy + by^2 = 0$ are such that the product of their lengths is a constant c^2. Find the equation of the locus of P.

Let the two lines have the individual equations $y = mx$, $y = nx$, where $m + n = -2h/b$, $mn = a/b$. If (X, Y) is a typical point P, the two perpendicular distances are given by

$$(Y - mX)/\sqrt{(1 + m^2)},\ (Y - nX)/\sqrt{(1 + n^2)}.$$

Hence $\quad c^2 = (Y - mX)(Y - nX)/\sqrt{(1 + m^2 + n^2 + m^2n^2)}$

$$= [Y^2 + mnX^2 - (m + n)XY]/\sqrt{[1 + m^2n^2 + (m + n)^2 - 2mn]}$$

$$= \left(Y^2 + \frac{a}{b}X^2 + \frac{2h}{b}XY\right)\Big/\sqrt{\left(1 + \frac{4h^2}{b^2} + \frac{a^2}{b^2} - 2\frac{a}{b}\right)}$$

$$= (aX^2 + 2hXY + bY^2)/\sqrt{(a^2 + b^2 + 4h^2 - 2ab)}.$$

This equation represents a hyperbola, with the given lines as its asymptotes.

Example 2   The constant c is chosen so that the equation

$$y^2 - 6xy + 8x^2 - 10x + 4y + c = 0$$

represents two straight lines through a point P. Find the equation of the two lines through P, parallel to the bisectors of the lines formed by joining the origin to the intersections of the given two lines and the line $y + x - 1 = 0$.

The condition that the given equation should represent two lines is

$$\begin{vmatrix} 8 & -3 & -5 \\ -3 & 1 & 2 \\ -5 & 2 & c \end{vmatrix} = 0,$$

yielding $c = 3$. The factors are then given by

$$(y - 2x + 1)(y - 4x + 3) = 0,$$

where the quadratic terms should be factorized first, and then the factors of 3 inserted and adjusted to yield the linear terms $-10x + 4y$. The point of intersection of the two lines is obviously $P(1, 1)$.

To find the equation of the lines joining the origin to the two points in which the line $y + x - 1 = 0$ cuts the given lines, we make the given equation homogeneous by means of the factor $(x + y)$:

$$y^2 - 6xy + 8x^2 + (4y - 10x)(x + y) + 3(x + y)^2 = 0,$$

or $\qquad\qquad\qquad\qquad 8y^2 - 6xy + x^2 = 0.$

The equation of the bisectors of these two lines is given by

$$(y^2 - x^2)/(8 - 1) = xy/(-3),$$

or $\qquad\qquad\qquad\qquad 3y^2 + 7xy - 3x^2 = 0.$

The equation of the lines through $P(1, 1)$ parallel to these is found by replacing y by $Y - 1$, x by $X - 1$, namely by

$$3(Y - 1)^2 + 7(X - 1)(Y - 1) - 3(X - 1)^2 = 0,$$

or $\qquad\qquad\qquad 3Y^2 + 7XY - 3X^2 - 13Y - X + 7 = 0.$

Example 3 If the three sides of a triangle $V_1V_2V_3$ are given by the three lines $l_i \equiv a_ix + b_iy + c_i = 0$, $(i = 1, 2, 3)$, find equations giving the orthocentre of the triangle.

The orthocentre H lies on the line through V_1 perpendicular to V_2V_3. Any line through V_1 is of the form $l_2 + \lambda l_3 = 0$. The gradient of this line is $-(a_2 + \lambda a_3)/(b_2 + \lambda b_3)$, while that of V_2V_3 is $-a_1/b_1$. The product of these two gradients must be -1, yielding

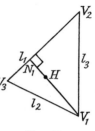

$$\lambda = -(a_1a_2 + b_1b_2)/(a_1a_3 + b_1b_3).$$

The line V_1H is then given by

$$(a_1a_3 + b_1b_3)(a_2x + b_2y + c_2)$$
$$- (a_1a_2 + b_1b_2)(a_3x + b_3y + c_3) = 0.$$

FIG. 18

The orthocentre also lies on the two lines V_2H and V_3H, given by

$$(a_1a_2 + b_1b_2)(a_3x + b_3y + c_3) - (a_2a_3 + b_2b_3)(a_1x + b_1y + c_1) = 0,$$
$$(a_2a_3 + b_2b_3)(a_1x + b_1y + c_1) - (a_1a_3 + b_1b_3)(a_2x + b_2y + c_2) = 0.$$

8.7 The representation of a circle

The student should recall the following elementary results. A *circle* of *radius* r and centre $(0, 0)$ is represented by the equation $x^2 + y^2 = r^2$.

If the radius vector OP to any point on the circle makes a positive angle θ with the axis Ox, the *parametric* representation of points on the circle is given by $x = r \cos \theta$, $y = r \sin \theta$.

If the centre of the circle is the point (x_0, y_0), the equation of the circle is

$$x^2 + y^2 - 2xx_0 - 2yy_0 + x_0{}^2 + y_0{}^2 - r^2 = 0.$$

The characteristic features of this equation are that the coefficients of x^2 and y^2 are equal, and that the coefficient of xy vanishes. Hence the general equation

$$ax^2 + 2hxy + by^2 + 2gx + 2fy + c = 0$$

represents a circle provided $a = b$, $h = 0$.

In particular, the equation

$$x^2 + y^2 + 2gx + 2fy + c = 0 \tag{9}$$

may be expressed in the form

$$(x + g)^2 + (y + f)^2 = f^2 + g^2 - c,$$

from which we deduce that the centre is the point $(-g, -f)$, and that its radius r is given by $\sqrt{(f^2 + g^2 - c)}$ provided $f^2 + g^2 > c$. If $f^2 + g^2 = c$, equation (9) represents a *point circle* $(-g, -f)$ of zero radius.

8.8 Tangent properties

(i) The gradient of the tangent at a point (x_1, y_1) on the circle (9) may be found by differentiation. Generally,

$$2x + 2y \frac{dy}{dx} + 2g + 2f \frac{dy}{dx} = 0,$$

so at the point (x_1, y_1) we have $dy/dx = -(x_1 + g)/(y_1 + f)$. Hence the equation of the tangent is

$$y - y_1 = - \frac{x_1 + g}{y_1 + f} (x - x_1),$$

or $\qquad (x - x_1)(x_1 + g) + (y - y_1)(y_1 + f) = 0.$

But $\qquad (x_1 + g)^2 + (y_1 + f)^2 = f^2 + g^2 - c,$

since the point (x_1, y_1) lies on the circle. Addition yields

$$(x + g)(x_1 + g) + (y + f)(y_1 + f) = f^2 + g^2 - c,$$

or $\qquad xx_1 + yy_1 + g(x + x_1) + f(y + y_1) + c = 0.$

That is, x^2 is replaced by xx_1, $2x$ by $x + x_1$, and so on.

If the circle has the equation $x^2 + y^2 = r^2$, the tangent at the point (x_1, y_1) has the equation $xx_1 + yy_1 = r^2$.

(ii) A given line $y = mx + d$ cuts the circle (9) only if the magnitude of the perpendicular distance from its centre to the line is less than the radius; that is if

$$\left| \frac{-f + gm - d}{\sqrt{(1 + m^2)}} \right| < \sqrt{(f^2 + g^2 - c)}.$$

If this condition is satisfied, the two points of intersection may be found by solving the equations of the line and circle simultaneously.

On the other hand, if we have an equality sign rather than an inequality sign, the given line touches the circle. Squaring this condition we obtain,

$$(-f + gm - d)^2 = (1 + m^2)(f^2 + g^2 - c),$$

yielding $\qquad d = -f + mg \pm \sqrt{(f^2 + g^2 - c)}\sqrt{(1 + m^2)}.$

Hence the lines

$$y = mx - f + mg \pm \sqrt{(f^2 + g^2 - c)}\sqrt{(1 + m^2)}$$

touch the circle for all values of the gradient m.

(iii) If P (x_1, y_1) is a point external to the circle (9), let PT, PT' be the two tangents drawn from P to the circle centre C. Then the square of the length of these tangents is given by

$$PT^2 = PT'^2 = CP^2 - CT^2$$
$$= (x_1 + g)^2 + (y_1 + f)^2 - (f^2 + g^2 - c)$$
$$= x_1^2 + y_1^2 + 2gx_1 + 2fy_1 + c,$$

a result obtained merely by substituting the coordinates of P into the equation of the circle.

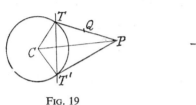

FIG. 19   FIG. 20

(iv) We may easily find the combined equation of the pair of tangents PT, PT'. Let the circle be given by $x^2 + y^2 = r^2$. If $Q(X, Y)$ is any point on either tangent from P, any other point on this tangent may be expressed parametrically in the form

$$\left(\frac{x_1 + \lambda X}{1 + \lambda}, \ \frac{y_1 + \lambda Y}{1 + \lambda} \right).$$

This line intersects the circle where

$$(x_1 + \lambda X)^2 + (y_1 + \lambda Y)^2 = r^2(1 + \lambda)^2,$$

or

$$\lambda^2(X^2 + Y^2 - r^2) + 2\lambda(Xx_1 + Yy_1 - r^2) + (x_1^2 + y_1^2 - r^2) = 0.$$

This quadratic in λ must have equal roots, since PT only touches the circle, so

$$(Xx_1 + Yy_1 - r^2)^2 = (X^2 + Y^2 - r^2)(x_1^2 + y_1^2 - r^2).$$

(v) Two circles intersect in two real points if the distance between their centres is less than the sum of their radii but greater than the positive difference between their radii. The two circles touch each other if the distance between their centres equals either the sum of their radii or the positive difference between their radii.

Two circles intersect *orthogonally* at P and Q if the two tangents at P (and also at Q) are perpendicular. If the two circles are given by

$$x^2 + y^2 + 2gx + 2fy + c = 0, \quad x^2 + y^2 + 2Gx + 2Fy + C = 0,$$

their two centres are $C(-g, -f)$ and $C'(-G, -F)$ and their radii are given by $CP^2 = f^2 + g^2 - c$ and $C'P^2 = F^2 + G^2 - C$ respectively.

The two circles are orthogonal if $\angle CPC' = 90°$, so

$$CP^2 + C'P^2 = CC'^2;$$

that is, provided

$$f^2 + g^2 - c + F^2 + G^2 - C = (g - G)^2 + (f - F)^2,$$

or

$$2fF + 2gG = c + C.$$

(vi) If $P(x_1, y_1)$ is an external point to the circle

$$x^2 + y^2 + 2gx + 2fy + c = 0,$$

and if the two tangents drawn from P to the circle touch the circle at T and T', then the line TT' is called the *polar line* of the *pole P* with respect to the circle (see Fig. 19). If P is inside the circle, a polar line may also be defined, but we leave this more general case until the pole and polar properties of a conic are discussed.

Let T be the point (x_2, y_2) and T' the point (x_3, y_3). The tangent at T passes through P, so

$$x_2 x_1 + y_2 y_1 + g(x_2 + x_1) + f(y_2 + y_1) + c = 0.$$

Similarly,

$$x_3 x_1 + y_3 y_1 + g(x_3 + x_1) + f(y_3 + y_1) + c = 0.$$

We now consider the linear equation

$$xx_1 + yy_1 + g(x + x_1) + f(y + y_1) + c = 0.$$

Certainly it represents a straight line; moreover the points T and T' satisfy it, by the relations just noted. Hence it must be the equation of the polar line TT'; possessing a form similar to that of the tangent.

(vii) If $ax + by + c = 0$ is the polar line of a point P with respect to the circle $x^2 + y^2 = r^2$, we may find the coordinates of P.

If P is the point (x_1, y_1), its polar line is $xx_1 + yy_1 = r^2$. Comparing these coefficients with those in the given line, we obtain

$$x_1/a = y_1/b = -r^2/c,$$

so the point P is $(-ar^2/c, -br^2/c)$.

A similar calculation may be carried out for the general circle.

8.9　The circumcircle of a triangle

If the triangle ABC is specified by means of its three vertices (x_1, y_1), (x_2, y_2), (x_3, y_3), and if its circumcircle is assumed to have the form

$$x^2 + y^2 + 2gx + 2fy + c = 0,$$

substituting the coordinates of the three vertices into this equation, and eliminating $2f$, $2g$ and c, we obtain the required equation

$$\begin{vmatrix} x^2 + y^2 & x & y & 1 \\ x_1^2 + y_1^2 & x_1 & y_1 & 1 \\ x_2^2 + y_2^2 & x_2 & y_2 & 1 \\ x_3^2 + y_3^2 & x_3 & y_3 & 1 \end{vmatrix} = 0.$$

If the triangle ABC is specified by means of the equations of its three sides BC, CA, AB, we proceed in a different manner. Let the three sides be

$$ax + by + c = 0, \ \alpha x + \beta y + \gamma = 0, \ Ax + By + C = 0.$$

Consider the locus given by the equation

$$(\alpha x + \beta y + \gamma)(Ax + By + C) + \lambda(Ax + By + C)(ax + by + c)$$
$$+ \mu(ax + by + c)(\alpha x + \beta y + \gamma) = 0,$$

where λ and μ are arbitrary constants. Certainly it represents a conic, being of the second degree in x and y. Moreover, it passes through A, B and C. For example, at A, two of the brackets vanish, so the whole of the left hand side of the equation vanishes.

We now choose λ and μ so that the locus represents a circle, namely we equate the coefficients of x^2 and y^2, and place the coefficient of xy equal to zero. This yields

$$\alpha A + \lambda Aa + \mu \alpha a = \beta B + \lambda Bb + \mu b \beta,$$
$$\alpha B + \beta A + \lambda(Ab + Ba) + \mu(a\beta + b\alpha) = 0.$$

These two simultaneous equations are now solved for λ and μ, yielding a unique circle passing through A, B, C.

8.10 Systems of coaxal circles

Consider the two point circles consisting of the two general points $A(-g, -f)$ and $B(-G, -F)$. Their equations are

$$A(x, y) \equiv (x + g)^2 + (y + f)^2 = 0, \quad B(x, y) \equiv (x + G)^2 + (y + F)^2 = 0 \quad (10)$$

respectively. If λ is an arbitrary parameter, we define the family of curves

$$A(x, y) + \lambda B(x, y) \equiv S_\lambda(x, y) \equiv (x + g)^2 + (y + f)^2 + \lambda[(x + G)^2 + (y + F)^2] = 0$$
$$(10)$$

to be a system of *coaxal circles*, with A and B as the *limiting points*. Certainly every curve of the family is a circle, for the coefficients of x^2 and y^2 are both equal to $(1 + \lambda)$, and the coefficient of xy vanishes.

In particular, the value $\lambda = -1$ provides the one straight line in the family, called the *radical axis*. Its equation is

$$A(x, y) - B(x, y) \equiv R(x, y) \equiv 2x(g - G) + 2y(f - F) + f^2 + g^2 - F^2 - G^2 = 0.$$

The centre of the general circle in the family is the point

$$\left(-\frac{g + \lambda G}{1 + \lambda}, \ -\frac{f + \lambda F}{1 + \lambda} \right),$$

evidently lying on the line AB.

The coaxal system may also be specified in terms of any two circles in the family, namely by equations of the form

$$S_\alpha + \mu S_\beta = 0 \quad \text{or} \quad S_\alpha + \nu R = 0.$$

In such a specification, the two limiting points are found by choosing the values of μ or ν that cause the radii to vanish.

This family is a non-intersecting system of circles. For if we make the hypothesis that the two circles of the system given by $\lambda = \alpha$, $\lambda = \beta$ intersect in the two points K, L, then all members would pass through the points K, L, since the general equation $S_\alpha + \mu S_\beta = 0$ is satisfied at K, L for all values of μ. But the two point circles clearly cannot pass through both K and L, so the hypothesis is false.

If $P(x_1, y_1)$ is any point on the radical axis, we have

$$A(x_1, y_1) - B(x_1, y_1) \equiv R(x_1, y_1) = 0. \tag{11}$$

The square of the length of the tangent from P to the general circle (10) is given by

$$\frac{A(x_1, y_1) + \lambda B(x_1, y_1)}{1 + \lambda} = \frac{A(x_1, y_1) + \lambda A(x_1, y_1)}{1 + \lambda} \quad \text{(from section 8.8, iii)}$$

$$= A(x_1, y_1),$$

or $B(x_1, y_1)$. Here, we have divided equation (10) of the general circle by $1 + \lambda$

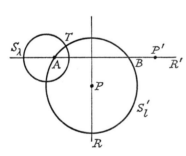

FIG. 21

in order to render the coefficients of x^2 and y^2 equal to unity. We conclude that the lengths of tangents from P to all circles of the system are equal; this is the special property enjoyed by the radical axis. Moreover, the radical axis is obviously the perpendicular bisector of the segment AB, since $PA = PB$.

We shall now form a second system of coaxal circles, with properties distinct from those of the first system. Consider all circles that pass through the two points A, B. The equation of the circle S' on AB as diameter is

$$S' \equiv [x + \tfrac{1}{2}(g + G)]^2 + [y + \tfrac{1}{2}(f + F)]^2 - \tfrac{1}{4}[(g - G)^2 + (f - F)^2] = 0,$$

since its centre lies at the mid-point of AB and its radius is $\tfrac{1}{2}AB$. Expressed otherwise, the equation is

$$S' \equiv x^2 + y^2 + x(g + G) + y(f + F) + gG + fF = 0.$$

The line AB has the equation

$$R'(x, y) \equiv (y + f)(G - g) - (x + g)(F - f) = 0.$$

Hence any circle through the points A and B is of the form

$$S_l(x, y) \equiv S'(x, y) + lR'(x, y) = 0,$$

since this is certainly a circle and it automatically passes through A and B for all values of l. It is a coaxial system, but with no real limiting points or point circles, for the circle on AB as diameter is clearly the smallest circle in the system.

The line AB with the equation $R'(x, y) = 0$ is the radical axis of the system. If $P'(x_2, y_2)$ is any point on this axis, the square of lengths of tangents from P' to any circle of the system is given by

$$S_l(x_2, y_2) \equiv S'(x_2, y_2) + lR'(x_2, y_2) = S'(x_2, y_2),$$

a constant independent of l.

Finally, any circle S_λ of the first system of coaxal circles is orthogonal to any circle S_l' of the second system of coaxal circles. For if P is the centre of S_l', and if S_λ and S_l' intersect in T, then $PA = PT = PB$, being radii of the circle S_l'. But since P is on the radical axis of the first system, PT is the tangent to S_λ at T, so PT is perpendicular to the radius of S_λ through T. This proves the theorem.

We shall now choose the coordinate axes in such a way that the equations of the two systems of circles are simplified.

Let the first system of coaxal circles be defined in terms of the two point circles $(\pm a, 0)$. Their equations are

$$(x - a)^2 + y^2 = 0, \quad (x + a)^2 + y^2 = 0,$$

so the system is given by

$$(x - a)^2 + y^2 + \lambda[(x + a)^2 + y^2] = 0.$$

Upon dividing by $1 + \lambda$, and replacing $2a(\lambda - 1)/(\lambda + 1)$ by μ, we obtain

$$S_\mu(x, y) \equiv x^2 + y^2 + \mu x + a^2 = 0. \tag{12}$$

The radical axis is given by the line $x = 0$, namely the y-axis. If $P(0, y_1)$ is any point on this axis, the square of the length of tangents from P to every circle of the system is given by $y_1^2 + a^2$, independent of the parameter μ.

The second system of coaxal circles consists of all circles passing through the two points $(\pm a, 0)$. The line joining these points is $y = 0$, while the circle with these points at the ends of a diameter has the equation $x^2 + y^2 - a^2 = 0$. The family is then given by

$$S_\nu(x, y) \equiv x^2 + y^2 + \nu y - a^2 = 0. \tag{13}$$

The radical axis is the line $y = 0$. If $(x_1, 0)$ is any point P' on this axis, then the square of the length of tangents from P' to every circle of the system is given by $x_1^2 - a^2$, independent of the parameter ν.

Moreover, any circle of the first system (12) is orthogonal to any circle of the second system (13), for the value of "$2fF + 2gG - c - C$" (see v, section 8.8) is obviously zero.

Theorem. The limiting points of a coaxal system (when they exist) are *inverse points* with respect to every circle of the system.

Inverse points with respect to a circle are defined as follows. If a circle centre C and radius r is given, the two points P and Q are inverse points with respect to this circle if (i) C, P, Q are collinear, with P and Q both on the same side of C, (ii) $CP.CQ = r^2$.

For the general circle (12), the centre C is the point $(-\tfrac{1}{2}\mu, 0)$ and the radius is given by $\sqrt{(\tfrac{1}{4}\mu^2 - a^2)}$. The limiting points A and B being the points $(\pm a, 0)$, we have

$$CA.CB = (-\tfrac{1}{2}\mu - a)(-\tfrac{1}{2}\mu + a) = \tfrac{1}{4}\mu^2 - a^2 = r^2,$$

thereby proving the theorem.

Example 4* Find the coordinates of the pole of the line $lx + my + n = 0$ with respect to the circle $x^2 + y^2 + 2gx + 2fy + c = 0$. Show that the poles of an arbitrary fixed line through the point $(a, 0)$ with respect to all circles through the points $(a, 0)$ and $(-a, 0)$ lie on a hyperbola also passing through the point $(a, 0)$.

If the pole is (X, Y), its polar is given by

$$xX + yY + g(x + X) + f(y + Y) + c = 0.$$

Upon comparing the coefficients in this equation with those in the given line, we obtain

$$\frac{X + g}{l} = \frac{Y + f}{m} = \frac{gX + fY + c}{n}$$

$$= \frac{gX + fY + c - gX - g^2 - fY - f^2}{n \quad -gl \quad -fm}$$

$$= \frac{c - g^2 - f^2}{n - gl - fm}.$$

(The student should note this algebraic step, since it eliminates unnecessary manipulation.) Hence

$$X = (lc + fgm - lf^2 - ng)/(n - gl - fm),$$
$$Y = (mc + fgl - mg^2 - nf)/(n - gl - fm).$$

The equation of any circle through the two points $(\pm a, 0)$ has the form (13):

$$x^2 + y^2 + 2vy - a^2 = 0.$$

Any line through $(a, 0)$ has the form $y = p(x - a)$, or $px - y - pa = 0$. The pole of this line is therefore given by substituting $l = p$, $m = -1$, $n = -pa$, $f = v$, $g = 0$, $c = -a^2$, namely

$$X = (-pa^2 - pv^2)/(v - ap),$$
$$Y = (a^2 + apv)/(v - ap).$$

To eliminate v, we divide X by p, and add to Y, obtaining

$$Y + X/p = -v.$$

(This particular method of simplification was not directly obvious, careful inspection and experiment is sometimes necessary to find the best method.) Substituting this value of v into the value of Y, we obtain

$$Y(-Y - X/p - ap) = a^2 - ap(Y + X/p),$$

or
$$Y^2 + XY/p - aX + a^2 = 0.$$

This locus is a hyperbola (see section 10.1), passing through $(a, 0)$.

Example 5   The circle $x^2 + y^2 = 1$ and the radical axis $y = 2$ define a coaxal system. P is the point $(X, 0)$ on the x-axis such that the chord of contact of the tangents drawn from P to a particular circle of the system subtends a right-angle at the origin. Show that the y-coordinate y_1 of the centre of this circle cannot lie in the range

$$4 - \sqrt{14} < y_1 < 4 + \sqrt{14}.$$

When $y_1 = 9$, show that $X = \sqrt{11}$.

The general circle of the system has the equation

$$x^2 + y^2 - 1 + \lambda(y - 2) = 0.$$

The chord of contact UV of tangents drawn from $(X, 0)$ to this circle is the polar of this point; its equation is

$$xX - 1 + \tfrac{1}{2}\lambda y - 2\lambda = 0.$$

To find the equation of the lines OU, OV we render the equation of the circle homogeneous by using the factor $(xX + \tfrac{1}{2}\lambda y)/(1 + 2\lambda)$, yielding

$$x^2 + y^2 + \lambda y \left(\frac{xX + \tfrac{1}{2}\lambda y}{1 + 2\lambda}\right) - (1 + 2\lambda)\left(\frac{xX + \tfrac{1}{4}\lambda y}{1 + 2\lambda}\right)^2 = 0.$$

These two lines are perpendicular, so the sum of the coefficients of x^2 and y^2 must vanish, giving

$$2 + \frac{\tfrac{1}{2}\lambda^2}{1 + 2\lambda} - \frac{X^2 + \tfrac{1}{4}\lambda^2}{1 + 2\lambda} = 0,$$

or
$$X^2 = \tfrac{1}{4}\lambda^2 + 4\lambda + 2.$$

Since X^2 must be positive, λ must lie outside the range given by the two roots of the quadratic equation $\tfrac{1}{4}\lambda^2 + 4\lambda + 2 = 0$; that is,

$$\lambda < -8 - 2\sqrt{14}, \; \lambda > -8 + 2\sqrt{14}.$$

Now the centre of the circle is given by $y_1 = -\tfrac{1}{2}\lambda$, or $\lambda = -2y_1$. Hence

$$-2y_1 < -8 - 2\sqrt{14}, \quad \text{or} \quad -2y_1 > -8 + 2\sqrt{14},$$

which is the same thing as stating that y_1 must not lie in the range

$$4 - \sqrt{14} < y_1 < 4 + \sqrt{14}.$$

Finally, when $y_1 = 9$, $\lambda = -18$. X^2 is then given by

$$X^2 = \tfrac{1}{4}\lambda^2 + 4\lambda + 2 = 81 - 72 + 2 = 11,$$

yielding $X = \sqrt{11}$.

Example 6★ Find the equations of all the common tangents to the circles
$$x^2 + y^2 - 1 = 0, \quad x^2 + y^2 - 8x + 12 = 0.$$

The general line $lx + my + n = 0$ touches the general circle
$$x^2 + y^2 + 2gx + 2fy + c = 0$$

provided the perpendicular distance from the centre to the line equals the radius, namely if
$$\left| \frac{lg + mf - n}{\sqrt{(l^2 + m^2)}} \right| = \sqrt{(f^2 + g^2 - c)},$$

or
$$(lg + mf - n)^2 = (l^2 + m^2)(f^2 + g^2 - c).$$

Applied to the given circles, this equation yields
$$n^2 = (l^2 + m^2),$$
$$(4l + n)^2 = (l^2 + m^2)(16 - 12) = 4(l^2 + m^2).$$

To solve these equations, we eliminate $l^2 + m^2$, obtaining
$$(4l + n)^2 = 4n^2,$$

or
$$4l + n = \pm 2n.$$

Since n, say, is arbitrary, we may place its value equal to 4, yielding $l = 1$ or -3. Finally,
$$m = \pm\sqrt{(n^2 - l^2)} = \pm 15 \text{ when } l = 1,$$
$$\text{or } \pm\sqrt{7} \quad \text{when } l = -3.$$

The four common tangents are therefore
$$x \pm \sqrt{15}y + 4 = 0, \; 3x \pm \sqrt{7}y - 4 = 0.$$

EXERCISES

(1)★. The equations of the sides AB, AC of a triangle ABC, referred to rectangular axes, are $3x - 4y = -1$, $5x + 6y = 1$ respectively. Find the equation of the side BC if the orthocentre of the triangle is the origin.

(2)★. Find the coordinates of the points which divide the line joining two given points (x_1, y_1) and (x_2, y_2), internally and externally in the ratio $l:m$. The vertices of the quadrilateral $ABCD$ are, in order $(2, 3)$, $(-4, 3)$, $(-8, -2)$, $(4, -5)$; in what ratios do the diagonals AC and BD divide one another?

(3)★. Find the area enclosed by the pentagon $ABCDE$ whose vertices are respectively $(1, 3)$, $(4, 1)$, $(5, 3)$, $(3, 2)$, $(2, 4)$.

(4)★. O, A, B, C, D, E, F are the points $(0, 0)$, $(1, 3)$, $(6, -2)$, $(8, 5)$, $(5, 9)$, $(4, 2)$, $(-1, 10)$ respectively; find the area of the heptagon $OABCDEF$.

(5)★. Show that the condition that the triangle formed by the lines $ax^2 + 2hxy + by^2 = 0$, $lx + my - 1 = 0$ may be right-angled is
$$(a + b)(al^2 + 2hlm + bm^2) = 0.$$

(6)★. Find the equation of the pair of lines obtained by rotating the lines represented by $ax^2 + 2hxy + by^2 = 0$ about the origin through a positive angle of $60°$. Write down the equation which corresponds to the case $a = 0$, $b = 1$, $2h = \sqrt{3}$, and sketch the two pairs of lines in this case.

(7)★. From a point $P(p,q)$ perpendiculars PM, PN are drawn to the straight lines given by the equation $ax^2 + 2hxy + by^2 = 0$. Show that if O is the origin, the area of the triangle OMN is

$$\frac{(aq^2 - 2hpq + bp^2)\sqrt{(h^2 - ab)}}{(a - b)^2 + 4h^2}.$$

(8)★. Show that the pair of straight lines joining the origin O to the intersections A and B of the line $lx + my = 1$ with the conic $ax^2 + by^2 = 1$ has the equation

$$(a - l^2)x^2 - 2lmxy + (b - m^2)y^2 = 0.$$

Deduce that if AOB is a right-angle, then the line AB touches the circle

$$(a + b)(x^2 + y^2) = 1.$$

(9)★. The line $y = l - kx$ cuts the lines $ax^2 + 2hxy + by^2 = 0$ in A and B and the lines through A and B perpendicular to OA and OB respectively meet in P. Show that, as l is varied, the locus of P is the straight line

$$(a - b)(x + ky) = 2h(kx - y).$$

(10)★. If the lines $ax^2 + 2hxy + by^2 = 0$ meet the line $qx + py = pq$ in points which are equidistant from the origin, prove that

$$h(p^2 - q^2) = pq(b - a).$$

(11)★. Prove that the equation

$$x^2 - y^2 + 2xy \sinh \theta + 2ax \cosh \theta + a^2 = 0$$

represents a pair of straight lines for all values of θ, and show that the locus of their point of intersection is $x^2 + y^2 = a^2$.

(12)★. Show that $x^2 + 4xy - 2y^2 + 6x - 12y - 15 = 0$ represents a pair of straight lines, and that these lines together with the pair $x^2 + 4xy - 2y^2 = 0$ form a rhombus.

---

(13)★. Find the value of k if the equation

$$2x^2 - 5xy + 2y^2 - 7x + 11y + k = 0$$

represents two straight lines. For this value of k show that the two lines intersect at a point on the circle

$$x^2 + y^2 - 12x + 6y + 20 = 0,$$

and find the equation of the tangent to the circle at this point.

(14)★. Find the equations of the two circles each of which cuts each of the circles $x^2 + y^2 - 2x + 2y - 7 = 0$ and $x^2 + y^2 = 3$ at right-angles and touches the line $y = 1$.

(15). The circle $x^2 + y^2 = a^2$ cuts the positive x-axis in A. If P is a general point on this circle, find the locus of M, the mid-point of the chord AP. If the negative x-axis cuts the first circle in B, and if Q is a general point on the locus of M, find the locus of N, the mid-point of the line BQ.

(16)★. The chord of contact of the tangents drawn from a point P on the x-axis to the circle $x^2 + y^2 - 2ay + 2a - 1 = 0$ subtends a right-angle at the origin. Prove that $a \geqslant 2 + \sqrt{2}$, and show that, when $a = 4$, $OP = \sqrt{2}$.

(17)★. Find the equation of the pair of lines joining the origin to the points in which the pair of lines

$$4x^2 - 15xy - 4y^2 + 39x + 65y - 169 = 0$$

are met by the line $x + 2y - 5 = 0$. Show that the quadrilateral having the first pair, and also the second pair, as adjacent sides is cyclic, and find the equation of its circumcircle.

(18)*. The pair of lines $ax^2 + 2hxy + by^2 = 0$ is met by the line $lx + my = 1$ at A and B. Prove that the circle on AB as diameter has the equation

$$(x^2 + y^2)(am^2 - 2hml + bl^2) + 2x(hm - bl) + 2y(hl - am) + a + b = 0.$$

(19)*. A circle touches each of the circles $x^2 + y^2 = 2ax$ and $x^2 + y^2 = 6ax$, one internally and the other externally. Show that it cuts orthogonally the circle $x^2 + y^2 = 3ax$.

(20)*. Show that the circles

$$x^2 + y^2 - 4x + 2y + 1 = 0, \quad x^2 + y^2 + 2x - 6y + 1 = 0$$

touch externally, and find the coordinates of the point of contact.

Find also the equation of the circle which touches both these circles at the same point and which passes through the point $(3, 2)$.

(21)*. Find the limiting points for the coaxal system

$$(x - 1)^2 + (y - 2)^2 + \lambda(x^2 + y^2 + 2x + 5) = 0.$$

(22)*. A coaxal system of circles contains the circle

$$x^2 + y^2 + 2gx + 2fy + c = 0,$$

and one of its limiting points is $(-g, 0)$; find the equation of the radical axis and the coordinates of the other limiting point. Show that the system of circles orthogonal to this system is

$$f(x^2 + y^2) + 2fgx - (g^2 - c)y + fg^2 + \mu(x + g) = 0.$$

(23)*. The limiting points of a family of coaxal circles are the points $(\pm 2, 0)$ and l is the line whose equation is $2x + 3y = 2$. Find the equation of that circle of the family which cuts from l a chord subtending a right-angle at the origin.

Find the equation of that circle of the orthogonal coaxal system which also cuts from l a chord subtending a right-angle at the origin.

ANSWERS TO EXERCISES

(1). $36y = 9x + 19$.   (2). $\frac{1}{4}, \frac{3}{5}$.   (3). Area $(ABD + BCD + DEA) = 3\frac{1}{2}$.

(4). Area $(OAF + AEF + ABE + EBC + ECD) = 44\frac{1}{2}$.

(6). $(a - 2h\sqrt{3} + 3b)x^2 + 2(a\sqrt{3} - 2h - b\sqrt{3})xy + (3a + 2h\sqrt{3} + b)y^2 = 0$, $y(y - x\sqrt{3}) = 0$.   (13). $k = 5, (3, 1), 4y - 3x + 5 = 0$.

(14). $x^2 + y^2 + 4x + 3 = 0, x^2 + y^2 - 4y + 3 = 0$.

(15). $(x - \frac{1}{4}a)^2 + y^2 = \frac{1}{4}a^2; \ (x + \frac{1}{4}a)^2 + y^2 = \frac{1}{16}a^2$.

(17). $3x^2 - 8xy - 3y^2 = 0, x^2 + y^2 - 2x - 4y = 0$.

(20). $(\frac{4}{5}, \frac{3}{5}), x^2 + y^2 - 22x + 26y + 1 = 0$.

(21). $\lambda = 0, (1, 2); \ \lambda = -3, (-2, -1)$.

(22). $y = (g^2 - c)/2f, \ [-g, (g^2 - c)/f]$.

(23). $x^2 + y^2 - \frac{19}{2}x + 4 = 0, x^2 + y^2 + \frac{22}{3}y - 4 = 0$.

CHAPTER 9

THE THEORY OF CONICS

9.1 The intersection of a line and a conic

From an algebraic point of view, a *conic* is defined to be any locus represented by an equation containing terms up to degree *two* in x and y. Its most general equation is therefore

$$S \equiv ax^2 + 2hxy + by^2 + 2fy + 2gx + c = 0. \tag{1}$$

In section 8.6, we have proved that, provided

$$\begin{vmatrix} a & h & g \\ h & b & f \\ g & f & c \end{vmatrix} = 0,$$

the equation can be factorized and that it represents two straight lines, thereby forming a *degenerate conic*.

If $f = g = 0$, the centre of the conic is the origin, since if the point (x_0, y_0) lies on the conic, so does the point $(-x_0, -y_0)$. If $h = 0$, we shall see later that the axes of the conic are parallel to the axes of coordinates.

If the line $y = mx + d$ is given, the points in which this line intersects a conic may be found by eliminating y, and by solving the resulting quadratic equation for x. Theoretically however, it is simpler to use the straight line in parametric form.

If $A(x_1, y_1)$, $B(x_2, y_2)$ are any two points, the equation of the line joining them is

FIG. 22

$$\frac{y - y_1}{y_2 - y_1} = \frac{x - x_1}{x_2 - x_1} = \lambda,$$

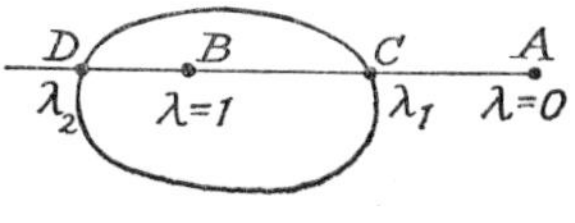

where λ is proportional to the *signed* distance of the point (x, y) from A. Hence

$$x = \lambda(x_2 - x_1) + x_1, \quad y = \lambda(y_2 - y_1) + y_1.$$

This line cuts conic (1) in points C and D, whose values of λ satisfy the equation

$$a[\lambda(x_2 - x_1) + x_1]^2 + 2h[\lambda(x_2 - x_1) + x_1][\lambda(y_2 - y_1) + y_1]$$
$$+ b[\lambda(y_2 - y_1) + y_1]^2 + 2f[\lambda(y_2 - y_1) + y_1]$$
$$+ 2g[\lambda(x_2 - x_1) + x_1] + c = 0.$$

169

We now introduce the standard abbreviations:

$$S_1 \equiv axx_1 + h(xy_1 + x_1y) + byy_1 + f(y + y_1) + g(x + x_1) + c,$$
$$S_{11} \equiv ax_1{}^2 + 2hx_1y_1 + by_1{}^2 + 2fy_1 + 2gx_1 + c,$$
$$S_{12} \equiv ax_1x_2 + h(x_1y_2 + x_2y_1) + by_1y_2 + g(x_1 + x_2)$$
$$+ f(y_1 + y_2) + c,$$

and similarly for S_2 and S_{22}. The equation for λ may now be rearranged to take the form

$$\lambda^2(S_{22} - 2S_{12} + S_{11}) + 2\lambda(S_{12} - S_{11}) + S_{11} = 0. \qquad (2)$$

This quadratic equation provides two values of λ, say λ_1 and λ_2; they may be either real, identical or complex.

We may now make the following deductions from equation (2).

(i) *The tangent at A.* Let $A(x_1, y_1)$ lie on the conic, so $\lambda_1 = 0$ and $S_{11} = 0$. For arbitrary B, the remaining point of intersection of AB and the conic is given by

$$\lambda_2 = -2S_{12}/(S_{22} - 2S_{12}).$$

In particular, if $B(x_2, y_2)$ is chosen so that the line AB touches the conic at A, this second point of intersection must also be given by $\lambda_2 = 0$. Hence B, the general point on the tangent at A, satisfies $S_{12} = 0$. In current coordinates, the equation of the tangent at A is $S_1 = 0$, where S_1 is given by the above definition.

(ii) *The polar of A.* If A is a given internal or external point, let the line AB rotate about A. The *polar* of A is defined to be the locus of the point B, when the signed distances AC, BD, AD, BC satisfy the equation

$$AC.BD = -AD.BC.$$

Four such points are said to form a *harmonic range*. These signed distances are proportional to the differences between the values of λ at the end points of the four segments, so

$$(\lambda_1 - 0)(\lambda_2 - 1) = -(\lambda_2 - 0)(\lambda_1 - 1),$$

simplifying to $\qquad 2\lambda_1\lambda_2 = \lambda_1 + \lambda_2.$

Extracting the product and the sum of the roots from the coefficients of equation (2), we find that

$$2S_{11} = -2(S_{12} - S_{11}),$$

or $S_{12} = 0$. Changing to current coordinates, we find that the polar of the *pole* A is the line $S_1 = 0$. This line clearly passes through the points of contact of the tangents drawn from A to the conic when A is an external point; this is in keeping with the more elementary definition of the polar line given for the circle.

(*iii*) *The combined equation of the two tangents from A.* If the line AB is to touch the conic, equation (2) for λ must have repeated roots, so

$$(S_{12} - S_{11})^2 = S_{11}(S_{22} - 2S_{12} + S_{11}),$$

or, upon simplification,

$$S_{12}{}^2 = S_{11}S_{22}.$$

In current coordinates, the general point B on either tangent from A satisfies the equation

$$S_1{}^2 = SS_{11}.$$

9.2   The central conic in its simplest form

If the centre of the conic is chosen to be the origin, and if its axes are parallel to Ox and Oy, the equation of the conic takes the simple form

$$S \equiv ax^2 + by^2 + c = 0.$$

If the conic (either a parabola or two parallel lines) has no centre, its equation cannot be arranged in this form.

The tangent at the point (x_1, y_1), the gradient of which may also be found by differentiation, is given by

$$S_1 \equiv axx_1 + byy_1 + c = 0.$$

Its gradient is $-ax_1/by_1$, so the equation of the normal at the point (x_1, y_1) must be

$$y - y_1 = \frac{by_1}{ax_1}(x - x_1),$$

or

$$ax_1 y - by_1 x = ax_1 y_1 - bx_1 y_1.$$

The equation of the tangents from $A(x_1, y_1)$ to the conic is given by

$$(axx_1 + byy_1 + c)^2 = (ax_1{}^2 + by_1{}^2 + c)(ax^2 + by^2 + c).$$

In particular, if A is chosen so that these two lines are perpendicular, the sum of the coefficients of x^2 and y^2 must vanish, yielding

$$a^2 x_1{}^2 + b^2 y_1{}^2 = (a + b)(ax_1{}^2 + by_1{}^2 + c),$$

or

$$x_1{}^2 + y_1{}^2 = -c(a + b)/ab,$$

showing that A lies on a circle, known as the *director circle* of the conic.

Polar theory.   The polar of the pole (x_1, y_1) is the line

$$S_1 \equiv axx_1 + byy_1 + c = 0;$$

this line may also be defined by the simpler argument used for the circle (see section 8.8).

Conversely, if the polar line is given by $lx + my + n = 0$, we require to find the pole (x_1, y_1). Its polar line is $axx_1 + byy_1 + c = 0$, so, upon comparing coefficients,

$$ax_1/l = by_1/m = c/n,$$

showing that the pole is the point $(cl/an, cm/bn)$. If the pole lies on the conic, the polar touches the conic at that point, being the tangent there. Hence the line $lx + my + n = 0$ touches the given conic if

$$a\left(\frac{cl}{an}\right)^2 + b\left(\frac{cm}{bn}\right)^2 + c = 0,$$

or
$$l^2/a + m^2/b + n^2/c = 0.$$

If the pole $P(x_1, y_1)$ varies along the straight line joining the points $A(x_2, y_2)$ and $B(x_3, y_3)$, the general position of P is given parametrically by

$$\frac{x_2 + \lambda x_3}{1 + \lambda}, \quad \frac{y_2 + \lambda y_3}{1 + \lambda}.$$

Its polar is given by

$$ax\left(\frac{x_2 + \lambda x_3}{1 + \lambda}\right) + by\left(\frac{y_2 + \lambda y_3}{1 + \lambda}\right) + c = 0,$$

or
$$(axx_2 + byy_2 + c) + \lambda(axx_3 + byy_3 + c) = 0.$$

This is a line that rotates about a fixed point, namely the point of intersection of the two polar lines of A and B.

An important *theorem* is the following. If the polar of the point $P_1(x_1, y_1)$ passes through the point $P_2(x_2, y_2)$, then the polar of the point P_2 passes through the point P_1. The condition for the polar of P_1 to pass through P_2 is

$$S_{12} \equiv ax_1x_2 + by_1y_2 + c = 0;$$

this is the same condition for the polar of P_2 to pass through P_1. Such pairs of points P_1 and P_2 are called *conjugate points*, and such pairs of lines are called *conjugate lines*.

The theory of conjugate diameters. Let $y = mx$ be any diameter of the conic, and let $P(x_1, mx_1)$ be a typical point on this diameter. The polar of P is given by $axx_1 + bymx_1 + c = 0$, or

$$y = -ax/bm - c/bmx_1.$$

The gradient of all such polar lines is the same for all points P on the given diameter. In particular, as P approaches infinity (that is, as $x_1 \to \infty$), the polar line takes the simpler form

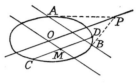

$$y = -ax/bm,$$

FIG. 23

a diameter of the conic, *conjugate* to the given diameter. Hence the two diameters $y = mx$ and $y = m'x$ are conjugate if

$$m' = -a/bm, \quad \text{or} \quad mm' = -a/b. \tag{3}$$

A more elementary definition of conjugate diameters may be given. The diameter $y = mx$ is given; $y = mx + d$ is any parallel chord, cutting the conic in C and D. We shall find the locus of M, the mid-point of CD. Eliminating y between the equations of the chord and conic, we obtain for x:

$$ax^2 + b(mx + d)^2 + c = 0,$$

or
$$(a + bm^2)x^2 + 2bmdx + bd^2 + c = 0.$$

But the value of x at M is the average of the two values of x at C and D, namely

$$x = -bmd/(a + bm^2),$$

upon picking out the sum of the roots from the quadratic equation in x. Then at M,

$$y = mx + d = ad/(a + bm^2).$$

The locus of M is then found by eliminating d; division yields

$$y/x = -a/bm.$$

The locus of M is then the diameter conjugate to $y = mx$, namely $y = -ax/bm$.

If two conics are given:

$$ax^2 + 2hxy + by^2 = 1, \quad Ax^2 + 2Hxy + By^2 = 1,$$

in general, there exist two pairs of conjugate diameters, mutually conjugate with respect to both conics.

Let $y = mx$ be one diameter, where m is to be found. The polars of any point (x_1, mx_1) on it are given by

$$axx_1 + h(xmx_1 + yx_1) + bymx_1 = 1,$$
$$Axx_1 + H(xmx_1 + yx_1) + Bymx_1 = 1.$$

As $x_1 \to \infty$, these two lines assume the form of the conjugate diameters, namely

$$ax + h(xm + y) + bym = 0, \quad Ax + H(xm + y) + Bym = 0.$$

We require these two lines to be identical, so upon comparing their gradients we have

$$\frac{bm + h}{a + hm} = \frac{Bm + H}{A + Hm},$$

or $m^2(hB - Hb) + m(aB - Ab) + aH - Ah = 0.$

This is a quadratic equation, yielding in general two values of m; hence there are two pairs of mutually conjugate diameters.

9.3   The ellipse and the hyperbola

We now place $c = -1$ in the standard form of the central conic, obtaining $ax^2 + by^2 = 1$. If $a > 0$ and $b > 0$, the locus is called an *ellipse*, while if $a > 0$ and $b < 0$ (or vice versa) the locus is a *hyperbola*. The standard equations for the ellipse and hyperbola are expressed in the forms

$$\frac{x^2}{a^2} + \frac{y^2}{b^2} = 1, \qquad \frac{x^2}{a^2} - \frac{y^2}{b^2} = 1;$$

it is expected that their shapes are well-known to the student. The ellipse cuts the coordinate axes in the points $(\pm a, 0)$ and $(0, \pm b)$; while the hyperbola cuts the x-axis only in the points $(\pm a, 0)$. $2a$ and $2b$ are the lengths of the axes of the ellipse, the longer one being the *major axis* and the smaller one the *minor axis*. The major axis for the hyperbola is the x-axis. The two foci of either conic are situated on the major axis.

Parametrically, $x = a \cos \theta$, $y = b \sin \theta$ for an ellipse; $x = a \cosh \theta$, $y = b \sinh \theta$ for the right-hand branch of the hyperbola and $x = -a \cosh \theta$, $y = b \sinh \theta$ for the left-hand branch. The form $x = a \sec \theta$, $y = b \tan \theta$ may also be used for the complete hyperbola.

For a hyperbola, if $a = b$, we obtain the equation of a *rectangular hyperbola*, namely $x^2 - y^2 = a^2$. A parametric form for this locus is given by $x = a(1 + t^2)/(1 - t^2)$, $y = 2at/(1 - t^2)$. If the coordinate axes are rotated through an angle of $45°$ clockwise by the transformation

$$x = X/\sqrt{2} + Y/\sqrt{2}, y = Y/\sqrt{2} - X/\sqrt{2},$$

the equation of the rectangular hyperbola assumes its simplest form

$XY = \frac{1}{2}a^2 = c^2$, say. The asymptotes of the hyperbola are the Ox and Oy axes. A suitable parametric representation for this locus is given by $X = ct$, $Y = c/t$, or vice versa.

The gradient of the tangent at a point on a conic given parametrically may be found by differentiation. For the ellipse,

$$\frac{dy}{dx} = \frac{d(b \sin \theta)/d\theta}{d(a \cos \theta)/d\theta} = -\frac{b}{a} \cot \theta,$$

so the equation of the tangent at the point $(a \cos \theta, b \sin \theta)$ is

$$y - b \sin \theta = -b \cot \theta \, (x - a \cos \theta)/a,$$

or $\qquad\qquad ay \sin \theta + bx \cos \theta = ab.$

The equation of the normal at this point is

$$y - b \sin \theta = a \tan \theta \, (x - a \cos \theta)/b.$$

For the rectangular hyperbola $xy = c^2$,

$$\frac{dy}{dx} = \frac{d(c/t)}{d(ct)} = -\frac{1}{t^2},$$

yielding the equation of the tangent

$$yt^2 + x = 2ct,$$

and the equation of the normal

$$y - c/t = t^2(x - ct).$$

The *eccentricity* e of the ellipse $x^2/a^2 + y^2/b^2 = 1$ is defined by $e^2 = 1 - b^2/a^2$ provided $b < a$. The two internal points $(\pm ae, 0)$ are called the *foci* of the ellipse, and the two lines $x = \pm a/e$ are respectively the corresponding *directrices*.

If P is any point on the ellipse, S the focus $(ae, 0)$ and N the foot of the perpendicular from P to the corresponding directrix $x = a/e$, then we have the relation $PS = ePN$, this often being used as the definition of an ellipse. If P is the point $(a \cos \theta, b \sin \theta)$, we have

$$
\begin{aligned}
PS^2 &= (a \cos \theta - ae)^2 + (b \sin \theta)^2 \\
&= a^2 \cos^2 \theta - 2a^2 e \cos \theta + a^2 e^2 \\
&\quad + a^2(1 - e^2)(1 - \cos^2 \theta) \\
&= a^2 - 2a^2 e \cos \theta + a^2 e^2 \cos^2 \theta \\
&= e^2(a/e - a \cos \theta)^2 \\
&= e^2 PN^2.
\end{aligned}
$$

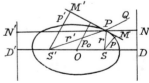

Fig. 24

For the hyperbola $x^2/a^2 - y^2/b^2 = 1$, the eccentricity e is defined by the equation $e^2 = 1 + b^2/a^2$; here, $e > 1$. The points $(\pm ae, 0)$ are again the foci of the conic, while the lines $x = \pm a/e$ are the directrices. The relation $PS = ePN$ is valid for all points on the hyperbola.

Either chord through a focus perpendicular to the major axis is called a *latus rectum* of the conic. The length of the *semi-latus rectum* is the value of y when $x = ae$; its value is b^2/a for both the ellipse and hyperbola.

9.4 Some properties of the ellipse

Referring to Fig. 24, we have
$$r = SP = ePN, \quad r' = S'P = ePN'.$$
Hence $\quad r + r' = e(PN + PN') = 2ODe = 2e(a/e) = 2a.$

Also $\qquad\qquad r^2 = (x - ae)^2 + y^2,$

and $\qquad\qquad r'^2 = (x + ae)^2 + y^2,$

where P is the general point (x, y). Subtraction yields
$$r'^2 - r^2 = 4aex;$$
hence $\qquad\qquad r' - r = 4aex/(r + r')$
$$= 2ex,$$
since $r + r' = 2a$. Combining these two expressions, we obtain
$$r = a - ex, \quad r' = a + ex.$$
Their product is $\qquad rr' = a^2(1 - e^2 \cos^2 \theta).$ $\hfill (4)$

Angles and tangents. Referring to Fig. 24, we shall prove that $\angle MPS = \angle M'PS'$, namely that the tangent at P is equally inclined to the two lines joining P to the foci.

The gradient of the line $S'PQ$ is $y/(x + ae)$, where (x, y) is the point P. The gradient of the tangent at P, PM, is given by $-xb^2/a^2y$, and the gradient of the line PS is given by $y/(x - ae)$. Hence

$$\tan \angle QPM = \dfrac{\dfrac{y}{x + ae} + \dfrac{xb^2}{a^2y}}{1 - \dfrac{yxb^2}{(x + ae)a^2y}}$$

$$= \frac{a^2y^2 + xb^2(x + ae)}{a^2xy + a^3ey - yxb^2}$$

$$= \frac{a^2b^2 + aeb^2x}{a^2e^2xy + a^3ey}$$

$$= \frac{ab^2(a + ex)}{a^2ey(ex + a)}$$

$$= b^2/aey.$$

$$\tan \angle MPS = \dfrac{-\dfrac{xb^2}{a^2y} - \dfrac{y}{x - ae}}{1 - \dfrac{xb^2y}{a^2y(x - ae)}}$$

$$= \frac{-xb^2(x - ae) - a^2y^2}{a^2yx - a^3ye - xb^2y}$$

$$= \frac{-a^2b^2 + aeb^2x}{a^2e^2xy - a^3ye}$$

$$= \frac{ab^2(-a + ex)}{a^2ey(ex - a)}$$

$$= b^2/aey.$$

We conclude that $\angle MPS = \angle M'PS'$. $\hfill (5)$

The director and auxiliary circles.   The line $y = mx + c$ cuts the ellipse $x^2/a^2 + y^2/b^2 = 1$ where

$$b^2x^2 + a^2(mx + c)^2 = a^2b^2,$$

or $\qquad x^2(a^2m^2 + b^2) + 2a^2\,mcx + a^2c^2 - a^2b^2 = 0.$

The line is a tangent to the ellipse if this quadratic equation has equal roots, namely if

$$m^2c^2a^4 = (a^2m^2 + b^2)(a^2c^2 - a^2b^2),$$

or $\qquad c = \pm\sqrt{(a^2m^2 + b^2)}.$

Hence the lines $y = mx \pm \sqrt{(a^2m^2 + b^2)}$ touch the ellipse for all m.
The lines

$$y = -\frac{x}{m} \pm \sqrt{\left(\frac{a^2}{m^2} + b^2\right)}$$

are the perpendicular tangents; they may be written in the form

$$ym + x = \pm\sqrt{(a^2 + b^2m^2)}.$$

We may now find the locus of the point of intersection of perpendicular tangents by eliminating m. We have

$$(y - mx)^2 + (ym + x)^2 = (a^2m^2 + b^2) + (a^2 + b^2m^2)$$

or $\qquad x^2 + y^2 = a^2 + b^2.$

This is the *director circle* of the ellipse.

The line $y = -(x - ae)/m$ is the line through the focus S perpendicular to the tangents to the ellipse of gradient m. To find the locus of the feet of the perpendiculars from the focus S to the tangents of the ellipse, we now eliminate m:

$$(y - mx)^2 + (ym + x)^2 = (a^2m^2 + b^2) + a^2e^2,$$

or $\qquad (x^2 + y^2)(1 + m^2) = a^2(1 + m^2).$

The locus $x^2 + y^2 = a^2$ is known as the *auxiliary circle* of the ellipse; it stands on the major axis as diameter.

Conjugate diameters.   The two diameters $y = mx$ and $y = m'x$ are conjugate provided $mm' = -b^2/a^2$ (see section 9.2). If $P(a\cos\theta, b\sin\theta)$ and $Q(a\cos\phi, b\sin\phi)$ are points at the ends of these two conjugate diameters respectively, such that POQ is an acute angle, then $m = (b/a)\tan\theta$ and $m' = (b/a)\tan\phi$, giving $\tan\theta\tan\phi = -1$. Hence

$$\tan(\theta - \phi) = \frac{\tan\theta - \tan\phi}{1 + \tan\theta\tan\phi} = \infty,$$

so $|\theta - \phi| = \frac{1}{2}\pi$.

The p-r equation with respect to a focus.   Referring to Fig. 24, let p be the length of the perpendicular SM from S to the tangent at P, where $SP = r$. We require to find the relationship between p and r.

If P is the point $(a \cos \theta, b \sin \theta)$, the tangent at P is given by

$$\frac{x \cos \theta}{a} + \frac{y \sin \theta}{b} - 1 = 0;$$

it follows that the length p_0 of the perpendicular from the origin to this tangent is given by

$$p_0{}^2 = \frac{1}{\dfrac{\cos^2 \theta}{a^2} + \dfrac{\sin^2 \theta}{b^2}}.$$

Hence

$$\frac{1}{p_0{}^2} = \frac{\cos^2 \theta}{a^2} + \frac{\sin^2 \theta}{b^2} = \frac{1}{b^2} - \cos^2 \theta \left(\frac{1}{b^2} - \frac{1}{a^2} \right)$$

$$= \frac{1}{b^2} - \frac{e^2 \cos^2 \theta}{b^2} = \frac{rr'}{b^2}, \qquad (6)$$

from equation (4).   Now $p/r = p'/r'$, since $\angle SPM = \angle S'PM'$, from equation (5).   Hence

$$\frac{p}{r} = \frac{p + p'}{r + r'} = \frac{2p_0}{2a}.$$

It follows that

$$\frac{1}{p^2} = \frac{a^2}{r^2 p_0{}^2} = \frac{r'}{b^2 r} \text{ (from 6)} = \frac{2a - r}{b^2 r} = \frac{2a}{b^2 r} - \frac{1}{b^2}. \qquad (7)$$

This result will be of importance in the theory of central orbits.

Example 1★   Prove that the equation of the normal at the point $P(a \cos \theta, b \sin \theta)$ on the ellipse $x^2/a^2 + y^2/b^2 = 1$ is

$$ax/\cos \theta - by/\sin \theta = a^2 - b^2.$$

If PP' is a chord of the ellipse drawn parallel to the y-axis, and the normal at P meets the diameter through P' in Q, prove that the locus of the mid-point of PQ is the ellipse

$$x^2/a^6 + y^2/b^6 = 1/(a^2 + b^2)^2.$$

The gradient of the tangent at P is $-(b/a) \cot \theta$, so the gradient of the normal at P is $(a/b) \tan \theta$.   Its equation is

$$y - b \sin \theta = a \tan \theta(x - a \cos \theta)/b,$$

reducing to the given equation.

Let the chord parallel to Oy have the equation $x = a \cos \theta$. P is the point already considered, while P' is the point $(a \cos \theta, -b \sin \theta)$.   The diameter OP' has the equation

$$y = -xb \tan \theta/a.$$

This diameter intersects the normal at P in Q; eliminating y, we obtain

$$\frac{ax}{\cos\theta} + \frac{b}{\sin\theta}\cdot\frac{bx\tan\theta}{a} = a^2 - b^2,$$

or
$$x = a(a^2 - b^2)\cos\theta/(a^2 + b^2).$$

Then
$$y = -b(a^2 - b^2)\sin\theta/(a^2 + b^2).$$

The coordinates of M are given by the averages of the coordinates of P and Q, namely

$$x = \frac{a(a^2 - b^2)\cos\theta}{2(a^2 + b^2)} + \tfrac{1}{2}a\cos\theta = \frac{a^3\cos\theta}{a^2 + b^2},$$

$$y = -\frac{b(a^2 - b^2)\sin\theta}{2(a^2 + b^2)} + \tfrac{1}{2}b\sin\theta = \frac{b^3\sin\theta}{a^2 + b^2}.$$

Eliminating θ, by using $\cos^2\theta + \sin^2\theta = 1$, we obtain the ellipse

$$x^2/a^6 + y^2/b^6 = 1/(a^2 + b^2)^2.$$

Example 2★ Prove that the line $lx + my + n = 0$ touches the ellipse $x^2/a^2 + y^2/b^2 = 1$ if $a^2l^2 + b^2m^2 = n^2$.

Lines are drawn through the origin O perpendicular to the tangents from a point P to the ellipse. If the lines are conjugate diameters of the ellipse prove that P lies on the ellipse $a^2x^2 + b^2y^2 = a^4 + b^4$.

We eliminate y between the equations of the line and ellipse, obtaining

$$\frac{x^2}{a^2} + \frac{(lx + n)^2}{m^2b^2} = 1,$$

or
$$(m^2b^2 + l^2a^2)x^2 + 2a^2lnx + a^2n^2 - a^2m^2b^2 = 0.$$

The line touches the ellipse if this quadratic equation in x has equal roots, namely if

$$(a^2ln)^2 = (m^2b^2 + l^2a^2)(a^2n^2 - a^2m^2b^2),$$

reducing to the given equation.

Let the line $lx + my + n = 0$ be one tangent from $P(X, Y)$ to the ellipse, so $lX + mY + n = 0$. The line through O perpendicular to this line has the gradient $-m/l$.

Now eliminate n, obtaining

$$a^2l^2 + b^2m^2 = (lX + mY)^2,$$

or
$$(b^2 - Y^2)(m/l)^2 - 2XY(m/l) + a^2 - X^2 = 0,$$

possessing two values of the root m/l. These two values are the gradients of two conjugate diameters, so their product must be $-b^2/a^2$. Hence

$$\frac{a^2 - X^2}{b^2 - Y^2} = -\frac{b^2}{a^2},$$

or
$$a^2X^2 + b^2Y^2 = a^4 + b^4.$$

Example 3★ Show that the equation of the chord joining the points on the ellipse $x^2/a^2 + y^2/b^2 = 1$, whose eccentric angles are θ and ϕ, is

$$bx\cos\tfrac{1}{2}(\theta + \phi) + ay\sin\tfrac{1}{2}(\theta + \phi) = ab\cos\tfrac{1}{2}(\theta - \phi).$$

If the chord touches the circle on the minor axis of the ellipse as diameter, prove that its length is $a \sin (\theta \sim \phi)$.

If P and Q are the points $(a \cos \theta, b \sin \theta)$ and $(a \cos \phi, b \sin \phi)$ respectively, the chord AB is given by

$$\frac{x - a \cos \theta}{a \cos \phi - a \cos \theta} = \frac{y - b \sin \theta}{b \sin \phi - b \sin \theta},$$

or $bx(\sin \phi - \sin \theta) - ay(\cos \phi - \cos \theta) = ab(\cos \theta \sin \phi - \cos \phi \sin \theta)$

$$= -ab \sin (\theta - \phi).$$

Expressing this equation in terms of half-angles, we obtain

$$2bx \cos \tfrac{1}{2}(\phi + \theta) \sin \tfrac{1}{2}(\phi - \theta) - 2ay \sin \tfrac{1}{2}(\phi + \theta) \sin \tfrac{1}{2}(\theta - \phi)$$
$$= -2ab \sin \tfrac{1}{2}(\theta - \phi) \cos \tfrac{1}{2}(\theta - \phi),$$

yielding the required answer upon division by $2 \sin \tfrac{1}{2}(\phi - \theta)$.

The circle on the minor axis as diameter has the equation $x^2 + y^2 = b^2$. The line touches this circle if the perpendicular distance from its centre O to the line equals the radius, namely if

$$\frac{a^2 b^2 \cos^2 \tfrac{1}{2}(\theta - \phi)}{b^2 \cos^2 \tfrac{1}{2}(\theta + \phi) + a^2 \sin^2 \tfrac{1}{2}(\theta + \phi)} = b^2,$$

or $a^2 \cos^2 \tfrac{1}{2}(\theta - \phi) = b^2 \cos^2 \tfrac{1}{2}(\theta + \phi) + a^2 \sin^2 \tfrac{1}{2}(\theta + \phi).$

The length of the chord PQ is given by

$$PQ^2 = a^2(\cos \phi - \cos \theta)^2 + b^2(\sin \phi - \sin \theta)^2$$

$$= a^2[2 \sin \tfrac{1}{2}(\phi + \theta) \sin \tfrac{1}{2}(\theta - \phi)]^2 + b^2[2 \cos \tfrac{1}{2}(\phi + \theta) \sin \tfrac{1}{2}(\phi - \theta)]^2$$

$$= 4 \sin^2 \tfrac{1}{2}(\theta - \phi)[a^2 \sin^2 \tfrac{1}{2}(\phi + \theta) + b^2 \cos^2 \tfrac{1}{2}(\phi + \theta)]$$

$$= 4 \sin^2 \tfrac{1}{2}(\theta - \phi). a^2 \cos^2 \tfrac{1}{2}(\theta - \phi)$$

$$= a^2 \sin^2 (\theta - \phi).$$

Hence $PQ = a \sin (\theta \sim \phi)$, where $\theta \sim \phi$ implies the positive difference between θ and ϕ.

9.5   Some properties of the hyperbola

Many properties of the hyperbola are proved by the same methods as used for the ellipse. If S and S' are the right- and left-hand foci respectively, then $S'P - SP = 2a$ if P lies on the right-hand branch of the hyperbola, while $SP - S'P = 2a$ if P lies on the left-hand branch.

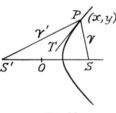

If P is on the right-hand branch, $r' - r = 2a$, and

$$r^2 = (x - ae)^2 + y^2,$$
$$r'^2 = (x + ae)^2 + y^2.$$

FIG. 25

Subtraction yields

$$r'^2 - r^2 = 4aex,$$

so

$$r' + r = 2ex.$$

For the left-hand branch, for which $x < 0$, we have

$$r' + r = -2ex.$$

If PT is the tangent at P, we have the theorem $\angle TPS = \angle TPS'$.
The line $y = mx \pm \sqrt{(m^2a^2 - b^2)}$ touches the hyperbola for all values
of the gradient m, provided $m^2a^2 \geqslant b^2$.

The director circle has the equation

$$x^2 + y^2 = a^2 - b^2, \qquad (a^2 \geqslant b^2)$$

being the locus of the points of intersection of perpendicular tangents.
The auxiliary circle has the equation $x^2 + y^2 = a^2$, being the locus of
the feet of the perpendiculars from S to the tangents of the hyperbola.

The p-r equation may be found by the same method as used for the
ellipse, but two different results emerge. If the tangents are drawn at
points on that branch of the hyperbola containing the focus S on its
concave side, the relationship is

$$\frac{1}{p^2} = \frac{2a}{b^2r} + \frac{1}{b^2}, \qquad (8)$$

while if the tangents are drawn at points on that branch for which S
is on its convex side, the result is

$$\frac{1}{p^2} = \frac{1}{b^2} - \frac{2a}{b^2r}. \qquad (9)$$

The tangent at the point P on the hyperbola, as P tends to infinity
along the curve, assumes a definite limiting position in the finite part
of the Oxy plane. Such tangents are called the *asymptotes* of the curve.
If P is the point $(\pm a \cosh \theta, b \sinh \theta)$, the tangent is

$$\pm (x/a) \cosh \theta - (y/b) \sinh \theta = 1,$$

where the two signs refer respectively to the two branches. We divide
by $\cosh \theta$, and let $\theta \to \infty$. In the process, $1/\cosh \theta \to 0$ and $\tanh \theta \to 1$,
so the tangents assume the simple forms

$$x/a \pm y/b = 0.$$

Written in the form of one equation, this is

$$\frac{x^2}{a^2} - \frac{y^2}{b^2} = 0.$$

This pair of lines intersects in the centre of the hyperbola.

Example 4 The tangent at a point P on the rectangular hyperbola $xy = c^2$ meets the x-axis in T. The line through T perpendicular to this tangent cuts the hyperbola again in the points U and V. Prove that the locus of the mid-point of UV is the curve $x^3 + c^2 y = 0$.

The tangent at the point P $(ct, c/t)$ is given by

$$y - c/t = -(x - ct)/t^2;$$

its gradient is $-1/t^2$ and it cuts the x-axis in the point $T(2ct, 0)$. The line through T perpendicular to this tangent is therefore

$$y = t^2(x - 2ct).$$

If this tangent cuts the hyperbola in points whose parameter is given by v, then

$$c/v = t^2(cv - 2ct),$$

or
$$t^2v^2 - 2t^3v - 1 = 0.$$

The mid-point of UV is given in terms of the two parameters v_1 and v_2 of U and V by

$$x = \tfrac{1}{2}(cv_1 + cv_2),$$
$$y = \tfrac{1}{2}(c/v_1 + c/v_2) = \tfrac{1}{2}c(v_1 + v_2)/v_1v_2.$$

Picking out the sum and product of the two roots of the quadratic equation in v, we obtain

$$v_1 + v_2 = 2t, \quad v_1v_2 = -1/t^2.$$

Hence
$$x = ct, \quad y = -ct^3.$$

The locus of this mid-point is then obtained by eliminating t, yielding $x^3 = -c^2y$.

Example 5 $P'OP$ is a diameter of the hyperbola $x^2/a^2 - y^2/b^2 = 1$. Its conjugate diameter cuts the conjugate hyperbola $x^2/a^2 - y^2/b^2 = -1$ in Q and Q'. Prove
 (i) $OP^2 - OQ^2 = a^2 - b^2$,
 (ii) The tangents at P, P', Q, Q' form a parallelogram of constant area.
If the line POP' is given by $y = mx$, its conjugate diameter is $y = b^2x/a^2m$. Let P be the point (x_1, mx_1) and Q the point $(x_2, b^2x_2/a^2m)$.

It follows that

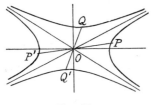

FIG. 26

$$OP^2 = x_1^2(1 + m^2),$$
$$OQ^2 = x_2^2(a^4m^2 + b^4)/a^4m^2.$$

Now x_1 is given by $x_1^2/a^2 - m^2x_1^2/b^2 = 1$, so

$$x_1^2 = a^2b^2/(b^2 - a^2m^2).$$

Moreover, x_2 is given by

$$x_2^2/a^2 - (b^2x_2/a^2m)^2/b^2 = -1,$$

so
$$x_2^2 = a^4m^2/(b^2 - a^2m^2).$$

Hence
$$OP^2 - OQ^2 = \frac{a^2b^2(1 + m^2)}{b^2 - a^2m^2} - \frac{a^4m^2(a^4m^2 + b^4)}{(b^2 - a^2m^2)a^4m^2} = a^2 - b^2,$$

upon simplification.

The area of the parallelogram is eight times the area of triangle OPQ; hence the area equals

$$4 \begin{vmatrix} 0 & 0 & 1 \\ x_1 & y_1 & 1 \\ x_2 & y_2 & 1 \end{vmatrix} = 4(x_1y_2 - x_2y_1) = 4x_1x_2(b^2/a^2m - m)$$

$$= 4 \frac{ab.a^2m}{b^2 - a^2m^2} \cdot \frac{b^2 - a^2m^2}{a^2m} = 4ab.$$

Example 6★ The rectangular hyperbola $xy = c^2$ is cut by any circle in four points. Prove that the sum of the squares of the distances of these four points from the centre of the hyperbola is equal to the square on the diameter of the circle.

Let the general circle $x^2 + y^2 + 2gx + 2fy + d = 0$ cut the hyperbola in A, B, C, D. The square of the diameter of this circle is $4(f^2 + g^2 - d)$.

The parameter t of a typical point of intersection A is given by

$$c^2t^2 + c^2/t^2 + 2gct + 2fc/t + d = 0,$$

or

$$c^2t^4 + 2gct^3 + dt^2 + 2fct + c^2 = 0.$$

Now $OA^2 = c^2t^2 + c^2/t^2$, so

$$\sum OA^2 = c^2 \sum t^2 + c^2 \sum t^{-2}.$$

But

$$\left(\sum t_1\right)^2 = \sum t_1^2 + 2\sum t_1 t_2,$$

so, upon choosing the appropriate coefficients from the quartic equation in t, we obtain

$$\sum t_1^2 = (-2gc/c^2)^2 - 2d/c^2 = (4g^2 - 2d)/c^2.$$

The quartic in $s = 1/t$ is given by

$$c^2s^4 + 2fcs^3 + ds^2 + 2gcs + c^2 = 0,$$

so

$$\sum t^{-2} = \sum s^2 = (4f^2 - 2d)/c^2.$$

Hence

$$\sum OA^2 = (4g^2 - 2d) + (4f^2 - 2d) = 4(f^2 + g^2 - d),$$

thereby proving the result.

9.6 The parabola

Definition. The general equation (1) of the conic does not always possess a centre. The condition for this is investigated in section 10.1; it is sufficient here to state that the equation under such circumstances may be reduced to the simple form $y^2 = 4ax$. The point $S(a, 0)$ is the *focus* of the conic and the line $x = -a$ the *directrix*. The length of the semi-latus rectum is the value of y at the focus; evidently $y = 2a$ when $x = a$.

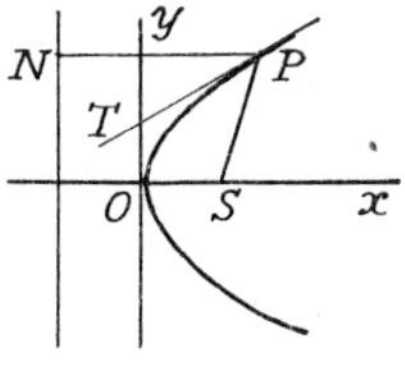

FIG. 27

Parametrically, we may write $x = at^2, y = 2at$.

If N is the foot of the perpendicular from the general point P to the directrix, then $PN = a + at^2$, and

$$PS = \sqrt{[(x - a)^2 + y^2]} = \sqrt{[(at^2 - a)^2 + 4a^2t^2]} = at^2 + a = PN.$$

7

This result is often used as the definition of a parabola; the eccentricity PS/PN is equal to unity.

Tangents. The equation of the tangent at $P(x_1, y_1)$ follows from the general theory of section 9.1, namely

$$yy_1 = 2a(x + x_1).$$

Parametrically, $dy/dx = (dy/dt)/(dx/dt) = 1/t$, so the tangent is

$$y - 2at = (x - at^2)/t,$$

or
$$ty - x - at^2 = 0. \tag{10}$$

It may easily be proved that $\angle NPT = \angle TPS$ by considering the gradients of the lines PN, PT, PS; these are 0, $1/t$, $2t/(t^2 - 1)$ respectively.

The tangent at $Q(au^2, 2au)$ is perpendicular to the tangent at $P(at^2, 2at)$ if $1/ut = -1$, namely is $u = -1/t$. The tangent at Q is then

$$-y/t - x - a/t^2 = 0$$

from equation (10), or

$$yt + xt^2 + a = 0. \tag{11}$$

The locus of the point of intersection of perpendicular tangents is found by eliminating t between equations (10) and (11). Subtraction yields $x = -a$, the directrix, being the degenerate form of the director circle for the central conic.

The line $y = mx + c$ cuts the parabola $y^2 = 4ax$ where $(mx + c)^2 = 4ac$, namely

$$m^2x^2 + 2mcx - 4ax + c^2 = 0.$$

In particular, the line touches the parabola provided $(mc - 2a)^2 = m^2c^2$, or $c = a/m$. Hence the line $y = mx + a/m$ is a tangent to the parabola for all values of the gradient m.

Normals. Since the gradient of the tangent at P is $1/t$, that of the normal at P is $-t$. The normal at $P(at^2, 2at)$ has the equation

$$y - 2at = -t(x - at^2),$$

or
$$y + tx - 2at - at^3 = 0.$$

If we require all the normals that pass through the point (h, k), we need

$$k + th - 2at - at^3 = 0 \tag{12}$$

yielding three values of t: t_1, t_2, t_3. The three normals that pass through a given point (h, k) satisfy the conditions:

$$t_1 + t_2 + t_3 = 0, \quad t_2t_3 + t_3t_1 + t_1t_2 = 2 - h/a, \quad t_1t_2t_3 = k/a,$$

since there is no term in t^2 in the cubic equation for t.

Let the equation of the circle through the three feet of these normals be

$$x^2 + y^2 + 2gx + 2fy + c = 0.$$

This circle cuts the parabola in four points whose parameters t_1, t_2, t_3, t_4 are given by

$$a^2t^4 + 4a^2t^2 + 2gat^2 + 4fat + c = 0.$$

Evidently $t_1 + t_2 + t_3 + t_4 = 0$, from which it follows that $t_4 = 0$. We conclude that the circumcircle of the feet of the three normals drawn through any point passes through the origin.

Since $c = 0$, the quartic equation reduces to the cubic equation

$$at^3 + (4a + 2g)t + 4f = 0.$$

Comparing this equation with equation (12) we see that

$$4a + 2g = 2a - h, \quad 4f = -k.$$

The centre of this circumcircle is then $(-g, -f) \equiv (a + \tfrac{1}{2}h, \tfrac{1}{4}k)$.

Confocal parabolae. The equation of the parabola with vertex O and axes Ox', Oy' is $y'^2 = 4ax'$. If the focus S is a new origin, let

$$y = y', \quad x = x' - a,$$

so the transformed equation of the parabola is

$$y^2 = 4a(x + a).$$

Different values of a yield different parabolae, but their common focus is at the origin S. To find those members of the confocal system that pass through the point (h, k), we have

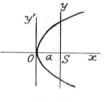

FIG. 28

$$k^2 = 4a(h + a),$$

yielding two values of a: a_1, a_2 say, whose product a_1a_2 equals $-k^2/4$. The equations of the two parabolae are

$$y^2 = 4a_1x + 4a_1{}^2, \quad y^2 = 4a_2x + 4a_2{}^2.$$

The gradients respectively are $2a_1/y$ and $2a_2/y$, having the values $2a_1/k$ and $2a_2/k$ at the common point (h, k). The product of these gradients is $4a_1a_2/k^2 = -1$, demonstrating that the two confocal parabolae through any point are orthogonal.

The p-r equation. The length p of the perpendicular from the focus S to the tangent (10) at $P(at^2, 2at)$ is given by

$$p^2 = (a + at^2)^2/(1 + t^2) = a^2(1 + t^2).$$

But the length r of the segment SP is given by $a(t^2 + 1)$. Hence

$$p^2 = ar. \tag{13}$$

Example 7 P_1 and P_2 are the parabolae $y^2 = 4ax$, $y^2 = -4ax$ respectively; S_1 and S_2 are their two foci. A tangent from S_2 to P_1 cuts P_2 in P and Q. Prove that the tangents to S_2 at P and Q intersect at R, one end of the latus rectum of P_1, and that S_2R touches P_1.

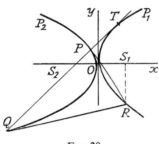

Fig. 29

The tangent at any point $T(at^2, 2at)$ of P_1 is $yt - x - at^2 = 0$; to pass through the point $S_2(-a, 0)$, we require $t = \pm 1$. Choosing $t = +1$, we find that the line PS_2Q is given by $y - x - a = 0$.

The point R is the pole of the line PQ with respect to P_2. If R is (x_1, y_1), its polar is $yy_1 = -2a(x + x_1)$, so, on comparing coefficients in the equations of these two identical lines, we find

$$y_1/1 = -2a/1 = -2ax_1/a.$$

Hence R is the point $(a, -2a)$, which is one end of the latus rectum through S_1. Finally, the tangent at this point has the equation

$$y(-2a) = 2a(x + a),$$

obviously passing through the point $S_2(-a, 0)$.

Example 8★   The tangents drawn to the parabola $y^2 = 4ax$ from a point P are equidistant from a fixed point $Q(h, 0)$ on its axis. Prove that the locus of P is a circle passing through Q and find the position of its centre.

Let the two tangents through P have the equations.

$$yt - x - at^2 = 0, \quad yu - x - au^2 = 0, \quad (t \neq u).$$

The lengths of the perpendiculars from Q to these tangents are given by

$$\left| \frac{h + at^2}{\sqrt{(1 + t^2)}} \right| = \left| \frac{h + au^2}{\sqrt{(1 + u^2)}} \right|,$$

or, upon squaring and cross-multiplying

$$(h + at^2)^2(1 + t^2) = (h + au^2)^2(1 + u^2).$$

Division by $t^2 - u^2$ yields

$$2ah + a^2(t^2 + u^2) - h^2 + a^2u^2t^2 = 0.$$

The expressions $t^2 + u^2$ and t^2u^2 must be eliminated using the equations of the two tangents. Multiplying these respectively by u and t, and subtracting, we obtain $aut = x$. If the equations of the two tangents are subtracted, we obtain $y = a(t + u)$. It follows that

$$a^2(t^2 + u^2) = a^2[(t + u)^2 - 2ut] = y^2 - 2ax.$$

Hence the locus of P becomes

$$2ah + y^2 - 2ax - h^2 + x^2 = 0,$$

obviously a circle passing through the point $Q(h, 0)$. The centre of the circle is the focus of the parabola $(a, 0)$.

EXERCISES

The parabola

(1)★. Show that the equation of the tangent at the point $P(ap^2, 2ap)$ on the parabola $y^2 = 4ax$ is $py = x + ap^2$, and that this tangent meets the tangent at $Q(aq^2, 2aq)$ at the point $(apq, ap + aq)$.

If P, Q, R are three points on the parabola $y^2 = 4ax$ such that the tangents at P and Q meet on the hyperbola $xy = c^2$ and the tangents at P and R meet on the hyperbola, prove that the tangents at Q and R also meet on the hyperbola.

(2)★. Find the equation of the chord joining the two points $P(at^2, 2at)$, $Q(au^2, 2au)$ on the parabola $y^2 = 4ax$, and prove that $u = -1/t$ if the chord passes through the focus. PSQ is a focal chord of a parabola whose focus is S and whose vertex is A. PA and QA are produced to meet the directrix in R and T respectively. Prove that RST is a right-angle.

(3)★. Find the equation of the tangent and of the normal to the parabola $y^2 = 4ax$ at the point $P(at^2, 2at)$. The normal at P bisects the angle between a line PQ and the line PS which joins P to the focus S. Prove that PQ is parallel to the axis of the parabola.

(4)★. Find the equations of the tangent and normal to the parabola $y^2 = 4ax$ at the point $(at^2, 2at)$. If the normal to a parabola at a point P meets the curve again in Q, and the tangents at P and Q intersect in T, prove that PT is bisected by the directrix.

(5)★. Find the equation of the tangent to the parabola $y^2 = 4ax$ at the point $(at^2, 2at)$. Show that the tangents drawn to this parabola from a point on the line $x = c$ meet the line $x = -c$ in points which are equidistant from the axis of the parabola.

(6)★. Obtain the equation of the chord QR of the parabola $y^2 = 4ax$ whose mid-point is $P(h, k)$. Find the locus of P when the tangents to the parabola at Q and R are perpendicular; find also, in this case, the locus of the point of intersection of the normals to the parabola at Q and R.

(7)★. Show that the equation of the normal to the parabola $y^2 = 4ax$ at the point $(at^2, 2at)$ is $y + tx = 2at + at^3$.

Two of the normals to the parabola from the point $P(X, Y)$ are perpendicular. Show that P lies on the parabola $y^2 = a(x - 3a)$ and that the length of the chord joining the feet of the perpendicular normals is $X + a$.

(8)★. Obtain the equations of the tangent and normal to the parabola $y^2 = 4ax$ at the point $(at^2, 2at)$. Two triangles are formed respectively by the tangents and normals to the parabola at any three of its points; prove that the line joining their orthocentres is parallel to the x-axis.

(9)★. Find, in its simplest form, the equation of the chord which joins the points $(at^2, 2at)$ and $(au^2, 2au)$ of the parabola $y^2 = 4ax$. Two variable points P, Q on this parabola subtend a right-angle at the vertex. Show that PQ meets the x-axis in a fixed point. Show also that the mid-point of PQ moves on a fixed parabola and find the coordinates of its vertex and focus.

(10)★. Show that the locus of the mid-points of all parallel chords of the parabola $y^2 = 4ax$, which have gradient m, is the line $my = 2a$.

P is a fixed point $(aT^2, 2aT)$ and Q is a variable point $(at^2, 2at)$ on $y^2 = 4ax$. A line through the mid-point of PQ parallel to the x-axis meets the ordinate of Q in R. Show that the locus of R is a parabola.

(11)★. Find the equation of the tangent to the parabola $y^2 = 4ax$ parallel to the line $ty - x = 0$ and the coordinates of its point of contact.

Prove that the equation of the locus of the point of intersection of tangents to the parabola $y^2 = 4ax$, which intercept a constant length c on the directrix is

$$(y^2 - 4ax)(x + a)^2 = c^2x^2.$$

(12)★. A is the point $(4a, 4a)$ and P is a variable point on the parabola $y^2 = 4ax$; the chord AQ is drawn parallel to the normal at P. If the tangents at P and Q intersect at R, prove that the locus of R is the hyperbola

$$x^2 + 2xy + 8ax + 4ay + 4a^2 = 0.$$

(13)★. A variable straight line, whose direction is fixed, cuts a parabola in P and Q. Prove that the locus of points of intersection of the normals at P and Q to the parabola is a straight line which is itself normal to the parabola.

(14)★. If the tangents at two points on the parabola $y^2 = 4ax$ intersect at Q and the normals at the same points intersect at P, express the coordinates of P in terms of X and Y, where Q is the point (X, Y). Hence show that, (i) if the locus of P is a line parallel to the x-axis, the locus of Q is a hyperbola; (ii) if the locus of P is a line parallel to the y-axis, the locus of Q is a parabola.

(15)★. Prove that the normals at the ends of a focal chord of the parabola $y^2 = 4ax$ intersect on the parabola $y^2 = ax - 3a^2$.

The ellipse

(16)★. Define conjugate diameters of an ellipse and prove that $y = mx$ and $y = m'x$ are conjugate diameters of the ellipse $x^2/a^2 + y^2/b^2 = 1$ if $mm' = -b^2/a^2$. Prove that the perpendicular from a focus $S(ae, 0)$ to a diameter meets the conjugate diameter on the directrix corresponding to S.

(17)★. Find the equation of the two lines joining the origin O to the points of intersection P, Q of the line $lx + my = 1$ and the ellipse $x^2 - xy + y^2 = 1$. Prove that, if $\angle POQ$ is a right-angle, the line PQ touches the circle $x^2 + y^2 = \frac{1}{2}$.

(18)★. Find the coordinates of the foci S, S' of the ellipse whose equation is $16x^2 + 25y^2 = 100$. Obtain the equation of the tangent to this ellipse at the point $P(2, 1\cdot2)$ and also the equation of the line SZ through S perpendicular to SP. Show that the tangent at P meets SZ at a point on the directrix corresponding to the focus S.

(19)★. Prove that any two conjugate diameters of an ellipse form with either directrix a triangle whose orthocentre is at the corresponding focus.

(20)★. Find the equation of the chord of the ellipse $x^2/a^2 + y^2/b^2 = 1$ whose mid-point is (h, k). Prove that the equation of the chord of this ellipse which is bisected at right-angles by the line $lx + my + n = 0$ is

$$m(a^2 - b^2)(mx - ly) + n(a^2m^2 + b^2l^2) = 0.$$

(21)★. Find the equations of the tangents to the ellipse $x^2/a^2 + y^2/b^2 = 1$ which are parallel to the line $y = mx$. Prove that any point from which tangents drawn to this ellipse are equally inclined to the line $y = x \tan \theta$ lies on the hyperbola

$$x^2 - 2xy \cot 2\theta - y^2 = a^2 - b^2.$$

(22)★. D_1 and D_2 are two points on the ellipse $x^2/a^2 + y^2/b^2 = 1$, and the tangents at these points meet at P. If P is the point (h, k), obtain the combined equation of the diameters CD_1 and CD_2. Find the locus of P (i) when the diameters are perpendicular; (ii) when they are conjugate. Show that the two loci meet in four points, which are the vertices of a rectangle.

(23)★. Show that the line $lx + my + n = 0$ touches the parabola $y^2 = 4ax$ if $am^2 = nl$. If the polar of a point P with respect to the ellipse $(x + a)^2/a^2 + y^2/b^2 = 1$ touches the parabola $y^2 = 4ax$, show that the locus of P is the hyperbola

$$x(x + a)/a^4 - y^2/b^4 = 0.$$

Find the asymptotes of this hyperbola and show that they intercept on the y-axis a length equal to the semi-latus rectum of the ellipse.

(24)★. Obtain the equation of the normal to the ellipse $x^2/a^2 + y^2/b^2 = 1$, $(a > b > 0)$, at the point $(a \cos \theta, b \sin \theta)$.

Express $\cos \theta$ and $\sin \theta$ in terms of $t = \tan \frac{1}{2}\theta$, and deduce that, in general, four normals can be drawn to an ellipse from a given point.

If the given point is $(0, k)$ and four real normals can be drawn, prove that the two normals, which do not lie along the minor axis, cut the ellipse at points on the line

$$(a^2 - b^2)y + b^2k = 0.$$

(25)★. Tangents are drawn to an ellipse of eccentricity e from a point on a concentric circle. Prove that the chord of contact of the tangents touches a concentric coaxial ellipse of eccentricity $e\sqrt{(2 - e^2)}$.

(26)★. P is a point on the ellipse $x^2/a^2 + y^2/b^2 = 1$ and A, A' are the points $(-a, 0)$, $(a, 0)$. If AP, $A'P$ meet a directrix at Q, Q', and if S is the corresponding focus, prove that SQ, SQ' are at right-angles. If PS meets the ellipse again at P', prove that AP', $A'P'$ meet the same directrix at Q', Q.

(27)★. Prove that the equation of the normal to the ellipse $x^2/a^2 + y^2/b^2 = 1$ at the point $(a \cos \theta, b \sin \theta)$ is $ax \sec \theta - by \csc \theta = a^2 - b^2$.

If P is the pole of this normal with respect to the ellipse, find the coordinates of P. Show that the locus of P is the curve

$$a^6/x^2 + b^6/y^2 = (a^2 - b^2)^2.$$

(28)★. Find all the points A which have the same polar line with respect to the two conics $x^2 + 2y^2 = 1$ and $x^2 + 2y^2 - 1 + (x - \frac{1}{2})^2 = 0$.

(29)★. Obtain the equations of the tangent and normal to the ellipse $x^2/a^2 + y^2/b^2 = 1$ at the point P $(a \cos \theta, b \sin \theta)$. The normal meets the x-axis at G and the tangent meets the y-axis at T. Find the coordinates of G and T and show that the locus of the circumcentre of the triangle OGT is

$$16a^2x^2y^2 - 4(a^2 - b^2)^2y^2 + b^2(a^2 - b^2)^2 = 0.$$

(30)★. Prove that the equation of the normal at the point $(a \cos \theta, b \sin \theta)$ of the ellipse $x^2/a^2 + y^2/b^2 = 1$ is

$$ax \sin \theta - by \cos \theta = (a^2 - b^2) \sin \theta \cos \theta.$$

If PSQ and $PS'R$ are focal chords of an ellipse with foci S, S', prove that the tangents at Q and R intersect on the normal at P.

(31)★. Find the equation of the polar of the point $P(X, Y)$ with respect to the ellipse $x^2/a^2 + y^2/b^2 = 1$. If this ellipse be denoted by S, and the ellipse $x^2/a^4 + y^2/b^4 = 1/c^2$ be denoted by S', show that the polars of points on S' with respect to S

touch the circle $x^2 + y^2 = c^2$, and also that the polars of points on this circle with respect to S touch the ellipse S'.

The hyperbola

(32)*. A chord PQ of the rectangular hyperbola $xy = c^2$ meets the asymptotes at R and S; prove that $PR = SQ$. A variable tangent to the parabola $y^2 = 4ax$ meets the hyperbola $xy = c^2$ in two points P, Q. Prove that the locus of the mid-point of PQ is a parabola.

(33). A is the point in the third quadrant on the rectangular hyperbola $xy = c^2$ that is nearest to the origin. If P is a general point on the hyperbola, prove that the locus of the mid-point of the chord AP is the rectangular hyperbola

$$2xy + c(x + y) = 0.$$

(34)*. Prove that the equation of the normal at the point $(ct, c/t)$ on the rectangular hyperbola $xy = c^2$ is $xt^3 - yt + c(1 - t^4) = 0$. Prove also that this normal meets the hyperbola again at the point with parameter $-1/t^3$.

Hence show that the locus of the mid-points of normal chords of the hyperbola is given by the equation $c^2(x^2 - y^2)^2 + 4x^3y^3 = 0$.

(35)*. If $P(x, y)$ and $Q(X, Y)$ are inverse points for the circle $x^2 + y^2 = 1$, prove that $x = X/(X^2 + Y^2)$, $y = Y/(X^2 + Y^2)$.

Show that the inverse of the curve $(x - y)(x^2 + y^2) + xy = 0$ with respect to the circle $x^2 + y^2 = 1$ is a hyperbola, and find the equations of the asymptotes of the hyperbola.

(36)*. P_i $(i = 1, 2, 3)$ are the points $(kt_i, k/t_i)$ on the rectangular hyperbola $xy = k^2$. Show that the circumcircle of the triangle $P_1P_2P_3$ cuts the hyperbola at a fourth point P_4 with parameter $t_4 = 1/t_1t_2t_3$.

Q_i $(i = 1, 2, 3, 4)$ are the other points at which the circles of curvature at the points P_i cut the hyperbola. Show that $Q_1Q_2Q_3Q_4$ is a cyclic quadrilateral.

(37)*. Prove that the straight line $lx + my + n = 0$ touches the hyperbola $b^2x^2 - a^2y^2 = a^2b^2$ if $a^2l^2 - b^2m^2 = n^2$.

The circle $x^2 + y^2 - 2\alpha y + \beta = 0$ cuts one asymptote of the hyperbola in the distinct points P, P'; and the other in Q, Q'; where P and Q are on the same side of the y-axis. If PQ is a tangent to the hyperbola, prove that the circle must pass through the foci of the hyperbola.

(38)*. The tangent to the hyperbola $xy = c^2$ at the point $(ct, c/t)$ intersects the hyperbola $xy = -c^2$ at the points M and N. Show that the tangents at M and N to the hyperbola $xy = -c^2$ intersect on the hyperbola $xy = c^2$.

(39)*. Find the equation of the tangent and the normal to the hyperbola $xy = c^2$ at the point $(ct, c/t)$. The chord LM of this hyperbola subtends a right-angle at a third point N on the hyperbola. Show that the tangent at N is perpendicular to LM.

(40)*. Sketch the hyperbolae $x^2/a^2 - y^2/b^2 = 1$, $y^2/b^2 - x^2/a^2 = 1$, showing their asymptotes. State the eccentricity of each curve.

If S, S' are the foci of the first hyperbola, e is its eccentricity, P is any point $x_1 = a \cosh \theta$, $y_1 = b \sinh \theta$, on this hyperbola and the tangent at P meets the other hyperbola in Q and R, show that

    (i) $SP = ex_1 - a$,   (ii) $PQ = PR$,   (iii) $PQ^2 = 2SP.S'P$.

(41)*. The equation of the asymptotes of a hyperbola is $y^2 = m^2x^2$ and the hyperbola passes through the points $(a, 0)$ and $(-a, 0)$. Find the equation of the hyperbola. A point P on this hyperbola is equidistant from one of its asymptotes and the x-axis. Prove that, for all values of m, P lies on the curve

$$(x^2 - y^2)^2 = 4x^2(x^2 - a^2).$$

(42)*. Find the equation of the tangent to the rectangular hyperbola $xy = c^2$ at the point $P(ct, c/t)$. If this tangent meets the axes Ox, Oy at Q and R, show that P bisects QR and that the area of the triangle OQR is independent of t. Deduce that, if p is the perpendicular distance of the tangent from O and if $OP = r$, then pr is constant.

(43)*. Find the equation of the chord of the hyperbola $x^2/a^2 - y^2/b^2 = 1$ whose mid-point is (h, k). Show that the locus of the mid-points of the chords of the above hyperbola which are tangents to the ellipse $x^2/a^2 + y^2/b^2 = 1$ is

$$a^2b^2(b^2x^2 + a^2y^2) = (a^2y^2 - b^2x^2)^2.$$

(44)*. Find the equation of the polar of the point (X, Y) with respect to the rectangular hyperbola $xy = c^2$. Show that the locus of the poles of chords of this hyperbola which touch $x^2 - y^2 = c^2$ is $y^2 - x^2 = 4c^2$.

(45)*. Prove that the equation of the chord joining the points $(ct, c/t)$ and $(cu, c/u)$ on the rectangular hyperbola $xy = c^2$ is $ytu + x = c(t + u)$.

P, Q, R, S are four points on a rectangular hyperbola such that the chords PQ and RS are perpendicular. Show that the remaining pairs of chords PR, QS and PS, QR are also perpendicular. Deduce that if a chord of a rectangular hyperbola subtends a right-angle at some point A of it, the chord is parallel to the normal at A.

(46)*. Prove that the equation of the tangent to the hyperbola $x^2/a^2 - y^2/b^2 = 1$ at the point $[\frac{1}{2}a(t + t^{-1}), \frac{1}{2}b(t - t^{-1})]$ is

$$bx(t^2 + 1) - ay(t^2 - 1) = 2abt.$$

A variable tangent to the above hyperbola cuts the asymptotes in points L and M. Prove that the locus of the centre of the circle OLM, where O is the origin, is given by the equation $4(a^2x^2 - b^2y^2) = (a^2 + b^2)^2$.

ANSWERS TO EXERCISES

(6). $ky - 2ax = k^2 - 2ah$, $2ax - y^2 = 2a^2$, $ax - y^2 = 3a^2$.

(9). $y^2 = 2ax - 8a^2$; vertex: $(4a, 0)$; focus: $(-a, 0)$.

(14). $x = 2a - X + Y^2/a$, $y = -XY/a$. (17). $x^2 - xy + y^2 = (lx + my)^2$.

(18). $x = \pm \frac{3}{2}$, $16x + 15y = 50$, $24y + 10x = 15$.

(22). $\dfrac{x^2}{a^2} + \dfrac{y^2}{b^2} = \left(\dfrac{hx}{a^2} + \dfrac{ky}{b^2}\right)^2$; (i) $\dfrac{x^2}{a^4} + \dfrac{y^2}{b^4} = \dfrac{1}{a^2} + \dfrac{1}{b^2}$, (ii) $\dfrac{x^2}{a^2} + \dfrac{y^2}{b^2} = 2$.

(23). $b^2(x + \frac{1}{2}a) \pm a^2y = 0$. (27) $P[a^3 \sec \theta/(a^2 - b^2), b^3 \csc \theta/(b^2 - a^2)]$.

(28). All points on $x = \frac{1}{2}$. (29). $G:[(a - b^2/a) \cos \theta, 0]$; $T:(0, b \csc \theta)$.

(35). $y + 1 = 0$, $x - 1 = 0$. (40). $\sqrt{(1 + b^2/a^2)}$, $\sqrt{(1 + a^2/b^2)}$.

(41). $y^2 = m^2(x^2 - a^2)$.

CHAPTER 10

THE GENERAL AND POLAR EQUATIONS
OF THE CONIC

10.1 Preliminary examination of the general equation

The general equation

$$S \equiv ax^2 + 2hxy + by^2 + 2fy + 2gx + c = 0$$

of a conic is given. If

$$D \equiv \begin{vmatrix} a & h & g \\ h & b & f \\ g & f & c \end{vmatrix} = 0,$$

the locus degenerates to two straight lines. If $D > 0$ and $(ab - h^2) > 0$, the equation represents no real locus, since the quadratic form

$$ax^2 + by^2 + cz^2 + 2fyz + 2gzx + 2hxy$$

is of fixed sign for all real values of x, y, z, where in the present case $z = 1$ (see section 4.3).

If the values of x and y are numerically large, the locus is given approximately by the quadratic terms, namely by

$$ax^2 + 2hxy + by^2 \doteq 0,$$

so $$y \doteq [-h \pm \sqrt{(h^2 - ab)}]/b.$$

An ellipse, being a closed finite shape, requires y to be complex for large x; hence $h^2 - ab < 0$. A hyperbola however is of infinite extent, so we require y to be real for large x; hence $h^2 - ab > 0$. If exceptionally $h^2 = ab$, the locus is a parabola; the terms of the second degree form a perfect square.

10.2 The centre of a conic

If the conic possesses a centre, let the axes be transformed to parallel axes CX, CY through the centre $C(j, k)$, using the equations $x = X + j$, $y = Y + k$. The new equation of the conic is

$$a(X + j)^2 + 2h(X + j)(Y + k) + b(Y + k)^2$$
$$+ 2f(Y + k) + 2g(X + j) + c = 0.$$

192

Since C is the centre, the coefficients of X and of Y must vanish, leaving only quadratic terms variable. This ensures that if (X, Y) lies on the locus, so does the point $(-X, -Y)$. Picking out these coefficients, we have

$$aj + hk + g = 0, \quad hj + bk + f = 0,$$

from which we conclude that

$$\frac{j}{hf - bg} = \frac{-k}{af - hg} = \frac{1}{ab - h^2}.$$

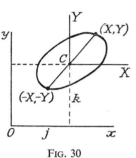

A unique centre $C(j, k)$ exists provided $ab - h^2 \neq 0$, that is provided the curve is not a parabola. The equation of the central conic may then be expressed in the form

$$aX^2 + 2hXY + bY^2 = \text{constant}.$$

FIG. 30

As an aid to memory, the student should notice that the two equations giving the centre (j, k) are also given by $\partial S/\partial x = 0$, $\partial S/\partial y = 0$.

10.3 The axes of a conic

We shall consider the equation of a central conic with its centre at the origin in the form

$$ax^2 + 2hxy + by^2 + c = 0.$$

Let new axes OX, OY be chosen, obtained respectively from Ox, Oy by rotation through an angle θ in the positive sense. We have

$$x = X \cos \theta - Y \sin \theta, \quad y = X \sin \theta + Y \cos \theta,$$

yielding the new equation for the conic

$$a(X \cos \theta - Y \sin \theta)^2 + 2h(X \cos \theta - Y \sin \theta)(X \sin \theta + Y \cos \theta)$$
$$+ b(X \sin \theta + Y \cos \theta)^2 + c = 0.$$

These new axes OX, OY are directed along the *principal axes* of the conic if the coefficient of XY vanishes. This yields

$$(b - a) \sin \theta \cos \theta + h(\cos^2 \theta - \sin^2 \theta) = 0,$$

or
$$\tan 2\theta = 2h/(a - b).$$

If $\tan \theta = m$, we have

$$\frac{2m}{1 - m^2} = \frac{2h}{a - b},$$

or
$$hm^2 + m(a - b) - h = 0,$$

yielding two values of m whose product is -1. This shows that there are two principal perpendicular axes.

The combined equation of these two axes may be expressed in the form

$$(y - m_1 x)(y - m_2 x) = 0,$$

or

$$y^2 - (m_1 + m_2)xy + m_1 m_2 x^2 = 0.$$

Hence

$$y^2 + (a - b)xy/h - x^2 = 0,$$

or

$$\frac{x^2 - y^2}{a - b} = \frac{xy}{h}.$$

These two lines are the bisectors of the line pair $ax^2 + 2hxy + by^2 = 0$, which, as we shall see later, is the combined equation of the two asymptotes of the conic, provided they exist.

10.4   The lengths of the axes

Let the equation of the central conic be written in the form

$$ax^2 + 2hxy + by^2 = 1,$$

where the centre of the conic is at the origin, and where unity stands on the right hand side of the equation.

Consider the points in which this conic is cut by the concentric circle $x^2 + y^2 = r^2$, or

$$x^2/r^2 + y^2/r^2 = 1,$$

where r is an arbitrary radius.   The points of intersection also satisfy the equation formed by subtracting the equation of this circle from that of the conic, namely

$$(a - r^{-2})x^2 + 2hxy + (b - r^{-2})y^2 = 0. \tag{1}$$

But this is obviously the combined equation of the two straight lines joining the origin to the points of intersection. If m stands for the gradient y/x of either line, then m is given by

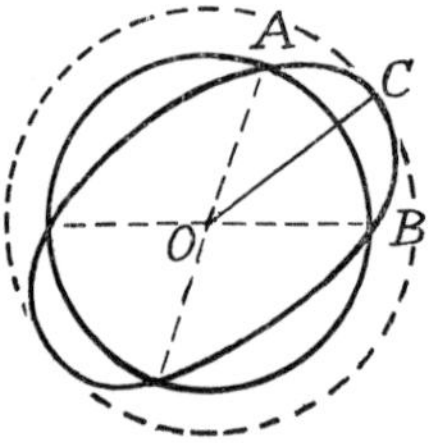

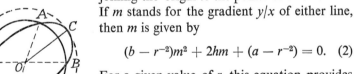

$$(b - r^{-2})m^2 + 2hm + (a - r^{-2}) = 0. \tag{2}$$

For a given value of r, this equation provides two values of m, namely two lines OA, OB. But if r should equal the length of one of the semiprincipal axes (as OC in Fig. 31), these two values of m are identical.   The

FIG. 31

quadratic equation (2) then has equal roots, so

$$h^2 = (b - r^{-2})(a - r^{-2}),$$

or

$$r^4(ab - h^2) - (a + b)r^2 + 1 = 0.$$

This is a biquadratic equation giving two values of r^2: $r_1{}^2$ and $r_2{}^2$ say. If both are positive, the conic is an ellipse; if one is negative, the conic is a hyperbola.

If the conic is an ellipse, its area is given by

$$\pi r_1 r_2 = \pi/\sqrt{(ab - h^2)},$$

upon picking out the product $r_1{}^2 r_2{}^2$ from the coefficients of the biquadratic equation.

The eccentricity of the conic may be found once the values of $r_1{}^2$ and $r_2{}^2$ are known. In terms of a standard notation, $b^2 = \pm a^2(1 - e^2)$ for an ellipse and a hyperbola respectively.

The gradients of the principal axes may be calculated by the method of this present section rather than by the method of section 10.3. If equation (2) has equal roots, then

$$m = -h/(b - r^{-2}),$$

where r^{-2} has either the value $r_1{}^{-2}$ or $r_2{}^{-2}$. This method shows the particular value of the gradient associated with r_1 and r_2 respectively.

10.5   The asymptotes of a hyperbola

The *asymptotes* of a hyperbola are the finite limiting forms of the tangents at points on the hyperbola as these points tend to infinity along the branches. Their equation may be found by the following reasoning.

For the standard equation $x^2/a^2 - y^2/b^2 = 1$, we have seen in section 9.5 that the equation of the asymptotes is given jointly by

$$x^2/a^2 - y^2/b^2 = 0.$$

That is, the equation of the hyperbola is adjusted by modifying the constant term only, in order that the resulting equation should represent two straight lines through the centre. In this adjustment, the quadratic terms must remain unaltered, otherwise the directions of the lines would differ completely from the directions of the hyperbolic branches at infinity. Moreover, the linear terms must also remain unaltered, otherwise the point of intersection of the lines would differ from the centre of the hyperbola.

Hence, for the general equation of the hyperbola, the constant term alone is modified in such a way that the new equation represents two straight lines. Let the asymptotes of the hyperbola

$$ax^2 + 2hxy + by^2 + 2fy + 2gx + c = 0$$

be represented by the equation

$$ax^2 + 2hxy + by^2 + 2fy + 2gx + c + \lambda = 0.$$

Since this represents two straight lines, we have

$$\begin{vmatrix} a & h & g \\ h & b & f \\ g & f & c+\lambda \end{vmatrix} = 0,$$

or $\qquad \lambda = - \begin{vmatrix} a & h & g \\ h & b & f \\ g & f & c \end{vmatrix} /(ab - h^2).$

In some cases, the value of λ required may be noted immediately by inspection. In other cases, the method used at the end of example 2 below may simplify the arithmetic involved.

If the two asymptotes are perpendicular, the hyperbola is *rectangular*; the condition for this is $a + b = 0$.

10.6   The parabola

The general equation of the conic represents a parabola if the terms of the second degree in x and y form a perfect square. Let us write the equation in the form

$$(ax + by)^2 + 2fy + 2gx + c = 0.$$

There are two methods whereby this general equation may be simplified.

Method i. In this method, we seek to rearrange the equation to take the form $Y^2 = 4AX$, where the line $Y = 0$ (being the *axis* of the parabola) is perpendicular to the line $X = 0$ (being the *tangent at the vertex*). Moreover, the values of X and Y must be the signed lengths of the perpendiculars from a point on the parabola to the Y and X axes respectively.

As they stand, the two lines $ax + by = 0$ and $2fy + 2gx + c = 0$ are not in general perpendicular; we therefore introduce a constant d thus:

$$(ax + by + d)^2 + 2(f - bd)y$$
$$+ 2(g - ad)x + c - d^2 = 0 \quad (3)$$

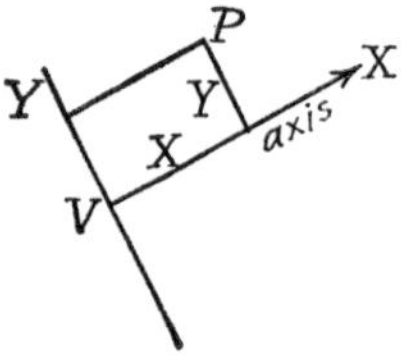

FIG. 32

the equation as a whole being unaltered by this rearrangement. The two lines

$$ax + by + d = 0 \qquad (4)$$
$$2(f - bd)y + 2(g - ad)x + c - d^2 = 0 \qquad (5)$$

are perpendicular if $\quad \dfrac{a}{b} \cdot \dfrac{(g - ad)}{(f - bd)} = -1,$

yielding $\qquad d = (ag + bf)/(a^2 + b^2).$

With this value of d, equation (4) represents the axis and equation (5) the tangent at the vertex of the parabola (3). These two lines intersect at the vertex V.

Let equation (3) then reduce to

$$(ax + by + d)^2 = Fy + Gx + C. \qquad (6)$$

Let the two new coordinate axes VX, VY be directed along the axis of the parabola and along the tangent at V respectively. Moreover, let Y be the perpendicular distance from $P(x, y)$ to VX, and let X be the perpendicular distance from $P(x, y)$ to VY. Then

$$Y = (ax + by + d)/\sqrt{(a^2 + b^2)}, \quad X = (Fy + Gx + C)/\sqrt{(F^2 + G^2)}.$$

Hence equation (6) becomes

$$Y^2(a^2 + b^2) = X\sqrt{(F^2 + G^2)},$$

or
$$Y^2 = \frac{\sqrt{(F^2 + G^2)}}{a^2 + b^2} X,$$

being the transformed equation of the parabola.

The length of the latus rectum is $(F^2 + G^2)^{\frac{1}{2}}/(a^2 + b^2)$.

When the parabola is sketched in the original Oxy-plane, it should be ascertained whether the curve lies to the right or to the left of the line VY. This may be decided by plotting one or two of the points in which the given equation is cut by the axes $x = y = 0$.

Method ii. Let the focus S be the point (X, Y), and let the directrix have the equation $lx + my + n = 0$. Then the perpendicular distance from $P(x, y)$ to the directrix is $(lx + my + n)/\sqrt{(l^2 + m^2)}$ and the distance SP is given by

$$\sqrt{[(X - x)^2 + (Y - y)^2]}.$$

Since the eccentricity of the parabola is unity, we have

$$(lx + my + n)^2 = (l^2 + m^2)[(X - x)^2 + (Y - y)^2],$$

or
$$(mx - ly)^2 - 2x[(l^2 + m^2)X + ln] - 2y[(l^2 + m^2)Y + mn]$$
$$+ (l^2 + m^2)(X^2 + Y^2) - n^2 = 0.$$

Comparing the coefficients in this equation with those in the given equation, we find

$$\frac{m^2}{a^2} = \frac{-lm}{ab} = \frac{l^2}{b^2}$$

$$= \frac{mn + (l^2 + m^2)Y}{-f} = \frac{ln + (l^2 + m^2)X}{-g} = \frac{(l^2 + m^2)(X^2 + Y^2) - n^2}{c}.$$

We may choose $m = a$, $l = -b$, thereby satisfying the first three ratios; the other ratios yield

$$an + (a^2 + b^2)Y = -f,$$
$$-bn + (a^2 + b^2)X = -g,$$
$$(a^2 + b^2)(X^2 + Y^2) - n = c,$$

being three equations for n, X, Y.

The length of the semi-latus rectum is given by the perpendicular distance from focus S to the directrix.

It should be pointed out that this method may be used for any conic, upon the introduction of another unknown, namely the eccentricity e.

Example 1   Investigate the conic

$$7x^2 + 2xy + 7y^2 + 30x + 18y + 15 = 0.$$

Here, $a = 7$, $b = 7$, $c = 15$, $f = 9$, $g = 15$, $h = 1$.

Character.   We have $h^2 - ab = -48 < 0$, so the conic is an ellipse.

Centre.   The equations yielding the centre are

$$aj + hk + g \equiv 7j + k + 15 = 0,$$
$$hj + bk + f \equiv j + 7k + 9 = 0.$$

Their solution is $j = -2$, $k = -1$, so the centre is the point $(-2, -1)$.

Direction of the axes.   We have $\tan 2\theta = 2h/(a - b) = 2/0 = \infty$; hence $2\theta = \frac{1}{2}\pi$ or $\frac{3}{2}\pi$. It follows that $\theta = \frac{1}{4}\pi$ or $\frac{3}{4}\pi$, and that the gradients of the two axes are $+1$ and -1. The equations of these two axes through the centre are then given by

$$y + 1 = +1.(x + 2) \quad \text{and} \quad y + 1 = -(x + 2),$$

or $\qquad\qquad y = x + 1 \qquad\qquad \text{and} \qquad y = -x - 3.$

Length of axes.   Referred to the centre as origin, the equation of the ellipse is

$$7x^2 + 2xy + 7y^2 = 24. \tag{7}$$

The biquadratic equation for the lengths of the semi-principal axes is

$$r^4(ab - h^2) - (a + b)r^2 + 1 = 0,$$

or $\qquad\qquad 48r^4 - 24.14r^2 + 24^2 = 0,$

where the value 24 on the right hand side of (7) has been taken into consideration. Factorization yields

$$(r^2 - 3)(r^2 - 4) = 0,$$

from which we conclude that $r = 2$ or $\sqrt{3}$. It may be shown that the axis with semi-length 2 is directed along that line through the centre with gradient -1.

Area.   We have $\pi r_1 r_2 = 2\pi\sqrt{3}$.

Eccentricity.   Using the formula $r_2^2 = r_1^2(1 - e^2)$, where r_1 is greater than r_2, we find that $3 = 4(1 - e^2)$, so $e = \frac{1}{2}$.

Director circle.   Its centre is $(-2, -1)$ and its radius is given by $\sqrt{(r_1^2 + r_2^2)} = \sqrt{7}$; its equation is

$$(x + 2)^2 + (y + 1)^2 = 7,$$

or $\qquad\qquad x^2 + y^2 + 4x + 2y - 2 = 0.$

Foci.   These are situated at a distance 'ae' $= 1$ from the centre $(-2, -1)$ along the major axis $y = -x - 3$. Their coordinates are

$$x = -2 \pm \cos 45° = -2 \pm 1/\sqrt{2},$$
$$y = -1 \mp \cos 45° = -1 \mp 1/\sqrt{2}.$$

Directrices.   The gradient of these lines must be $+1$, and they must pass through the points on the major axis $y = -x - 3$ at a distance 'a/e' $= 4$ from the centre. These points are

$$x = -2 \pm 4\cos 45° = -2 \pm 2\sqrt{2},$$
$$y = -1 \mp 4\cos 45° = -1 \mp 2\sqrt{2}.$$

The directrices are then given by

$$y = x + 1 - 4\sqrt{2}, \quad y = x + 1 + 4\sqrt{2}.$$

Example 2 Investigate the conic

$$108x^2 - 312xy + 17y^2 + 96x + 278y + 713 = 0.$$

Here, $a = 108$, $b = 17$, $c = 713$, $f = 139$, $g = 48$, $h = -156$.
Character. We have $h^2 - ab = 156^2 - 108.17 > 0$, so the conic is a hyperbola.
Centre. The equations yielding the centre are

$$aj + hk + g \equiv 108j - 156k + 48 = 0,$$
$$hj + bk + f \equiv -156j + 17k + 139 = 0,$$

with the solution $j = 1$, $k = 1$; the centre is therefore $(1, 1)$. Referred to this centre as origin, the equation of the conic is

$$108x^2 - 312xy + 17y^2 = -900. \tag{8}$$

Direction of axes. The equation for $\tan \theta = m$ is

$$hm^2 + m(a - b) - h = 0,$$

or
$$156m^2 - 91m - 156 = 0.$$

Dividing by 13, and factorizing, we obtain

$$(3m - 4)(4m + 3) = 0,$$

with the roots $\frac{4}{3}$, $-\frac{3}{4}$. The equations of the axes with respect to the original coordinate axes are

$$y - 1 = \tfrac{4}{3}(x - 1), \quad y - 1 = -\tfrac{3}{4}(x - 1).$$

The first line cuts the conic in real points, so it is the major axis. This may be seen easily by finding where the line $y = \frac{4}{3}x$ cuts conic (8).
Length of axes. The biquadratic for r^2 is

$$r^4(ab - h^2) - (a + b)r^2 + 1 = 0$$

where unity is required on the right hand side of equation (8). The equation is

$$r^4(108.17 - 156^2) + 125.900r^2 + 900^2 = 0,$$

simplifying to
$$(r^2 + 4)(r^2 - 9) = 0.$$

The length of the real semi-major axis is therefore $r_1 = 3$. Also $r_2^2 = -4$.
Eccentricity. Using the formula $|r_2^2| = r_1^2(e^2 - 1)$, we find $e = \frac{1}{3}\sqrt{13}$.
Asymptotes. We add the constant λ to the equation of the hyperbola, where

$$\begin{vmatrix} 108 & -156 & 48 \\ -156 & 17 & 139 \\ 48 & 139 & 713 + \lambda \end{vmatrix} = 0.$$

To avoid the evaluation of this determinant, we may proceed as follows. We drop the constant -900 occurring in equation (8), obtaining for the asymptotes

$$108x^2 - 312xy + 17y^2 = 0,$$

or

$$(6x - 17y)(18x - y) = 0,$$

referred to axes through the point $(1, 1)$ in the original coordinate system. In this original system, the asymptotes will be given by

$$(6x - 17y + 11)(18x - y - 17) = 0,$$

where each factor vanishes at the centre $(1, 1)$. This method shows that the constant $713 + \lambda$ must equal -11.17, so $\lambda = -900$.

Example 3   Investigate the conic

$$x^2 - 2xy + y^2 - 10x - 14y + 49 = 0.$$

The second degree terms form a perfect square, so the conic is a parabola; its equation is

$$(x - y)^2 - 10x - 14y + 49 = 0.$$

Introducing the constant d, we have

$$(x - y + d)^2 - 2(5 + d)x - 2(7 - d)y + 49 - d^2 = 0.$$

We require the two lines with gradients $+1$ and $-(5 + d)/(7 - d)$ to be perpendicular. This implies $(5 + d)/(7 - d) = 1$, so $d = 1$. The equation of the parabola then becomes

$$(x - y + 1)^2 = 12x + 12y - 48.$$

We conclude that the line $x - y + 1 = 0$ is the axis of the parabola, and that the line $x + y - 4 = 0$ is the equation of the tangent at the vertex V. The vertex is given by the coordinates of the point of intersection of these two lines, namely $(\tfrac{3}{2}, \tfrac{5}{2})$.

Finally, let $X = (x + y - 4)/\sqrt{2}$ and $Y = (x - y + 1)/\sqrt{2}$, yielding

$$Y^2 = (6\sqrt{2})X.$$

The length of the latus rectum is therefore $6\sqrt{2}$.

It may be checked that the given parabola intersects neither the x-axis nor the y-axis in real points. The parabola is therefore wholly restricted to one quadrant, obviously that quadrant in which the vertex lies, namely the first quadrant.

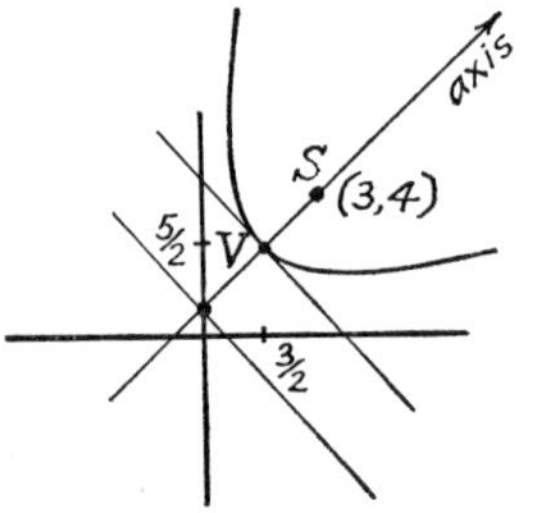

FIG. 33

If S is the focus, the length SV equals one quarter of the length of the latus rectum, namely $\tfrac{3}{2}\sqrt{2}$. The coordinates of S are found from those of V by a displacement of length $\tfrac{3}{2}\sqrt{2}$ along the axis $x - y + 1 = 0$ in the direction of the first quadrant, namely

$$x - \tfrac{3}{2} + \tfrac{3}{2}\sqrt{2}\cos 45^\circ = 3, \quad y = \tfrac{5}{2} + \tfrac{3}{2}\sqrt{2}\cos 45^\circ = 4.$$

The directrix, parallel to the tangent at the vertex, has gradient -1; it passes through the point on the axis with coordinates

$$x = \tfrac{3}{2} - \tfrac{3}{2}\sqrt{2}\cos 45^\circ = 0, \quad y = \tfrac{5}{2} - \tfrac{3}{2}\sqrt{2}\cos 45^\circ = 1.$$

Its equation is therefore $x + y = 1$.

10.7 The straight line in polar coordinates

The point O is the *origin* or *pole*, and Ox is the arbitrary *initial line*. A point P in the plane is specified by the positive length $OP = r$ and by the angle $\angle POx = \theta$ (positive when measured in the anticlockwise sense). More generally, r may be negative, $-s$ say, for a given value of θ; this is interpreted as the point $(s, \theta + \pi)$. Thus the point given by $r = -4$, $\theta = 30°$ is the same point as that specified by $r = 4$, $\theta = 210°$.

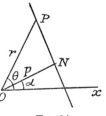

FIG. 34

A straight line in the plane is uniquely specified by the length p of the perpendicular ON from the origin to the line, and by $\angle NOx = \alpha$. If $P(r, \theta)$ is a general point on the line, we have

$$p = r \cos \angle PON = r \cos (\theta - \alpha).$$

Generally, then, an equation of the form

$$Ar \cos \theta + Br \sin \theta + C = 0$$

represents a straight line. To standardize this, we divide by $\sqrt{(A^2 + B^2)}$, obtaining

$$\frac{Ar \cos \theta + Br \sin \theta}{\sqrt{(A^2 + B^2)}} = \frac{-C}{\sqrt{(A^2 + B^2)}}.$$

Finally, let $-A/\sqrt{(A^2 + B^2)} = \cos \alpha$, $\quad -B/\sqrt{(A^2 + B^2)} = \sin \alpha$, $C/\sqrt{(A^2 + B^2)} = p$, yielding

$$r(\cos \theta \cos \alpha + \sin \theta \sin \alpha) = p,$$

in standard form.

The use of the calculus in problems involving polar coordinates is dealt with in section 14.11.

10.8 The equation of the conic in polar coordinates

Let one focus S be situated at the origin and let Ox be perpendicular to and directed towards the corresponding directrix NR. When $\theta = \frac{1}{2}\pi$, r will equal l, the length of the semi-latus rectum. Now

$$r = OP = ePN = e(OR - OM) = eOR - er \cos \theta,$$

so

$$r(1 + e \cos \theta) = eOR = l,$$

since the point $r = l$, $\theta = \frac{1}{2}\pi$ satisfies the equation. Hence

$$l/r = 1 + e \cos \theta \tag{9}$$

is the standard equation of the conic in polar coordinates, where l and e are the parameters taken to define the curve.

Asymptotes exist if points may be found at which $r = \infty$; this implies $\cos \theta = -1/e$, so $e > 1$ for asymptotes to exist.

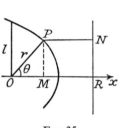

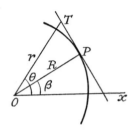

Fig. 35   Fig. 36

The polar equation of the tangent at the point $P(R, \beta)$ of the conic may be found as follows.

The equation of the tangent PT must be of the general form

$$l/r = A \cos \theta + B \sin \theta,$$

where l is inserted for convenience. The point $P(R, \beta)$ lies on it, so

$$l/R = A \cos \beta + B \sin \beta = 1 + e \cos \beta,$$

since P also lies on the conic.

Moreover, $dr/d\theta$ must have the same value at P both for the line and for the conic, so that the line and the conic are locally identical near P; hence

$$-A \sin \beta + B \cos \beta = -e \sin \beta.$$

Solving for A and B, we have

$$A = e + \cos \beta, \quad B = \sin \beta.$$

Hence

$$l/r = (e + \cos \beta) \cos \theta + \sin \beta \sin \theta,$$

or $$l/r = \cos (\theta - \beta) + e \cos \theta. \qquad (10)$$

Example 4 PT, PU are the two distinct tangents from a point P to a conic. If S is a focus, prove $\angle PSU = \angle PST$.

Let P be the point (ρ, α). If the tangents from P touch the conic $l/r = 1 + e \cos \theta$ at the points $T(R_1, \beta_1)$ and $U(R_2, \beta_2)$, then the equation of the tangent TP is

$$l/r = \cos (\theta - \beta_1) + \theta \cos \theta.$$

Since P lies on this tangent,

$$l/\rho = \cos (\alpha - \beta_1) + e \cos \alpha.$$

Similarly, $$l/\rho = \cos (\alpha - \beta_2) + e \cos \alpha,$$

since P lies on the tangent at U.

Hence $\cos (\alpha - \beta_1) = \cos (\alpha - \beta_2)$, so

$$\alpha - \beta_1 = 2n\pi \pm (\alpha - \beta_2).$$

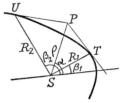

If $n = 0$, the positive sign yields $\beta_1 = \beta_2$, which is inadmissible since the two tangents PT, PU are distinct. The minus sign yields

$$\alpha - \beta_1 = \beta_2 - \alpha,$$

namely $\angle PSU = \angle PST$.

FIG. 37

Example 5★ State the conditions under which two curves whose polar equations are $r = f(\theta)$, $r = F(\theta)$ touch at the point $\theta = \alpha$.

Show that the equation to the circle which touches the conic $l/r = 1 + e \cos \theta$ at the point $\theta = \alpha$ and passes through the focus is

FIG. 38

$$r(1 + e \cos \alpha)^2 = l \cos (\theta - \alpha) + el \cos (\theta - 2\alpha).$$

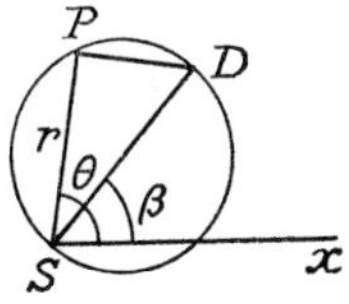

The required conditions are $f(\alpha) = F(\alpha)$, $df(\alpha)/d\theta = dF(\alpha)/d\theta$.

In Fig. 38, $SD = 2a$ is a diameter of a circle through the pole S, such that $\angle DSx = \beta$. If $P(r, \theta)$ is a general point on the circle, $SP/SD = \cos \angle PSD$; hence

$$r = 2a \cos (\theta - \beta) = 2a \cos \beta \cos \theta + 2a \sin \beta \sin \theta.$$

The general circle through S has the equation

$$r = f(\theta) = A \cos \theta + B \sin \theta.$$

Moreover, the equation of the conic is given by

$$r = F(\theta) = l/(1 + e \cos \theta).$$

It is given that these two loci touch at the point $\theta = \alpha$, hence

$$A \cos \alpha + B \sin \alpha = l/(1 + e \cos \alpha),$$
$$-A \sin \alpha + B \cos \alpha = le \sin \alpha/(1 + e \cos \alpha)^2.$$

Eliminating A and B from the general equation of the circle and from these two conditions, we obtain

$$\begin{vmatrix} r & -\cos \theta & -\sin \theta \\ l/(1 + e \cos \alpha) & -\cos \alpha & -\sin \alpha \\ le \sin \alpha/(1 + e \cos \alpha)^2 & \sin \alpha & -\cos \alpha \end{vmatrix} = 0.$$

This simplifies to the given equation.

EXERCISES

(1)★. Find the lengths and directions of the axes of the conic
$$19x^2 - 16xy + 49y^2 = 85.$$

(2)★. Find the equations and the lengths of the principal axes of the conic $73x^2 - 72xy + 52y^2 = 100$. What is value of the eccentricity?

(3) ★. Find the equations and lengths of the axes of the conic
$$14x^2 - 4xy + 11y^2 = 25.$$

(4) ★. Find the lengths of the principal axes of the ellipse $5x^2 + 4xy + 8y^2 = 36a^2$. The rectangle is drawn whose sides touch the ellipse and are parallel to Ox, Oy. Prove that its area is $8a^2\sqrt{10}$.

(5) ★. Find the equations of each asymptote and each principal axis of the hyperbola $32x^2 + 60xy + 7y^2 = 52$. Determine which of the axes meets the curve in real points.

(6) ★. Show that the area enclosed by the ellipse $13x^2 - 32xy + 37y^2 = 4$ is $4\pi/15$, and determine the eccentricity.

(7) ★. Show that the conic $x^2 + y^2 - 4xy - 2x - 20y - 11 = 0$ is a hyperbola. Find the coordinates of the centre, and show that the distance between the vertices of the two branches of the hyperbola is 12.

(8) ★. Find the centre and the lengths of the principal axes of the conic whose equation is $13x^2 - 12xy + 4y^2 - 16x = 0$. Show that the axes are inclined at an angle $\tan^{-1} 2$ to the coordinate axes; sketch the curve.

(9) ★. Show that the principal axes of the conic
$$11x^2 + 6xy + 19y^2 - 2x - 26y + 3 = 0$$
are $3x - y + 1 = 0$, $x + 3y - 2 = 0$. Show that the equation of the curve referred to its principal axes is $5x^2 + 10y^2 = 3$.

(10) ★. Show that the conic $(2x + y - 3)^2 - (2x - 4y + 2)^2 = 3$ is a hyperbola and find the equations of its asymptotes and axes.

Obtain the equation of the hyperbola having the same asymptotes and passing through the origin, and show that this hyperbola meets the parabola $y^2 = 2(y - 2x)$ in three coincident points at the origin.

(11) ★. Show that the conic $(2x + 3y - 5)^2 - 9(2x + y - 3)^2 = 30$ is a hyperbola; find the equations of its asymptotes and principal axes.

(12) ★. The equation of an ellipse is $8x^2 + 12xy + 17y^2 + 2gx + 2fy - 27 = 0$. Determine g and f so that the centre is the point $(2, 1)$. Further, show that in this case the major axis is parallel to the line $x + 2y = 0$ and that the lengths of the axes are $4\sqrt{5}$ and $2\sqrt{5}$.

(13) ★. Find the centre of the conic $9x^2 - 4xy + 6y^2 - 14x - 8y + 1 = 0$. Show that this conic is an ellipse; find its eccentricity and its area.

(14) ★. Show that the conic $x^2 - 6xy - 7y^2 - 2x + 4y - 1 = 0$ is a hyperbola; find its centre and the equation of each axis and each asymptote.

(15) ★. Find the centre of the conic
$$41x^2 - 24xy + 34y^2 + 82x - 24y + 16 = 0.$$
Show that the conic is an ellipse; find its eccentricity and its area.

(16) ★. Find the coordinates of the centre and the equations of the axes of the conic $2x^2 + 3xy - 2y^2 - 24x + 7y + 12 = 0$. Show that the conic is a rectangular hyperbola and that the length of its transverse axis is 4.

(17) ★. Find the separate equations of the asymptotes of the hyperbola $4x^2 - 20xy - 11y^2 + 4x + 62y - 36 = 0$. Draw a rough sketch of the curve and find the equation of its transverse (focal) axis. Prove that the hyperbola has eccentricity $\tfrac{5}{4}$.

(18)⋆. The asymptotes of a hyperbola which passes through the origin are parallel to the lines $x = 0$, $x + y = 0$, and the line $3x - y - 5 = 0$ touches it at the point $(2, 1)$. Find the equations of the hyperbola and its asymptotes.

(19)⋆. Show that the locus of a point whose rectangular coordinates are $x = (2t + 1)/(t - 1)$, $y = (1 - 2t)/(t + 1)$, is a rectangular hyperbola. Find the coordinates of its vertices and of its foci.

(20)⋆. Prove that the latus rectum of the parabola

$$9x^2 + 6xy + y^2 + 2x + 3y + 4 = 0$$

is $7\sqrt{10}/100$, and sketch the curve.

(21)⋆. Find the coordinates of the vertex, and of the length of the latus rectum, of the parabola $3x^2 - 5x + 3 = 2y$. Find also the equations of the tangents from the origin to the curve.

---

(22)⋆. Show that the equation of the tangent at the point where $\theta = \alpha$ on the parabola $l/r = 1 + \cos\theta$ is $l/r = \cos(\theta - \alpha) + \cos\theta$. If the tangents at $P(r_1, \alpha)$ and $Q(r_2, \beta)$ intersect at $T(r_3, \gamma)$, prove that $\alpha + \beta = 2\gamma$. If the point T is on the latus rectum, $\gamma = \frac{1}{2}\pi$, prove that $1/r_1 + 1/r_2 = 2/l$.

(23)⋆. The vectorial angles of the points A and B on the conic $l/r = 1 + e\cos\theta$ are $\alpha - \beta$ and $\alpha + \beta$ respectively. Prove that the equation of the chord AB is

$$l/r = \sec\beta\cos(\theta - \alpha) + e\cos\theta.$$

Find the points of intersection of the straight line $l/r = 2\cos\theta + \tan\alpha\sin\theta$ and the conic $l/r = 1 + \cos\theta$, and show that the tangents at these points intersect at an angle α.

(24)⋆. Prove that for the conic $l/r = 1 + e\cos\theta$ the equation of the chord joining the points whose vectorial angles are $\alpha - \beta$ and $\alpha + \beta$ is

$$l/r = \sec\beta\cos(\theta - \alpha) + e\cos\theta.$$

Variable points P and Q on one branch of a rectangular hyperbola are such that PQ subtends a right-angle at a focus S. Show that the locus of the foot of the perpendicular from S on PQ is a straight line parallel to the directrix.

(25)⋆. If ϕ is the eccentric angle of the point $P(r, \theta)$ on the ellipse $l/r = 1 + e\cos\theta$, where $e < 1$, prove that $r = a(1 - e\cos\phi)$.

Show that if there is a diameter PQ of the ellipse that subtends a right-angle at a focus, then $e \geqslant 1/\sqrt{2}$.

(26)⋆. Find the polar equation of a conic referred to a focus as pole, and prove that, if PSP' is a focal chord of the conic, $1/SP + 1/SP' = 2/l$, where l is the length of the semi-latus rectum.

If the tangents at P and P' meet in T, prove that $\tan PTP' = 2a/ST$, where $2a$ is the length of the axis of the conic through the focus S.

ANSWERS TO EXERCISES

(1). $y = \frac{1}{4}x, y = -4x$; semi-axes: $\sqrt{5}, \sqrt{\frac{5}{4}}$.   (2), $y = -\frac{3}{4}x, y = \frac{4}{3}x$; semi-axes: 1, 2; $e = \frac{1}{2}\sqrt{3}$.   (3). $y = 2x, y = -\frac{1}{2}x$; semi-axes: $\sqrt{\frac{5}{3}}, \sqrt{\frac{5}{2}}$.

(4). Semi-axes: $2a, 3a$.   (5). $7y + 4x = 0, y + 8x = 0$; $2y + 3x = 0$, $3y - 2x = 0$; the axis $3y - 2x = 0$.   (6). $\frac{2}{3}\sqrt{2}$.   (7). $(-7, -4)$.

(8). (2, 3), semi-axes: 4, 1.   (10). Asymptotes: $4x - 3y - 1 = 0$, $y - 1 = 0$; axes: $y = 2x - 1$, $2y = -x + 3$; $(2x + y - 3)^2 - (2x - 4y + 2)^2 = 5$.

(11). $x - 1 = 0$, $4x + 3y - 7 = 0$; $y + 3x - 4 = 0$, $3y - x - 2 = 0$.

(12). $f = -29$, $g = -22$.   (13). (1, 1); $e = 1/\sqrt{2}$, $\pi\sqrt{2}$.   (14). $(\frac{13}{16}, -\frac{1}{16})$; $y - 3x + \frac{5}{2} = 0$, $3y + x - \frac{5}{8} = 0$, $x + y - \frac{3}{4} = 0$, $x - 7y - \frac{5}{4} = 0$.

(15). $(-1, 0)$; $\pi/\sqrt{2}$, $1/\sqrt{2}$.   (16). (3, 4); $y + 3x - 13 = 0$, $3y - x - 9 = 0$.

(17). $2x + y - 5 = 0$, $2x - 11y + 7 = 0$, $y = 2x - 3$.   (18). $5x^2 + 5xy - 7x - 16y = 0$; $5x - 16 = 0$, $5x + 5y + 9 = 0$.   (19). $(-1, 1)$, $(2, -2)$; $(\frac{1}{2} \pm \frac{3}{2}\sqrt{2}, -\frac{1}{2} \pm \frac{3}{2}\sqrt{2})$.   (21). $(\frac{5}{6}, \frac{11}{24})$; $\frac{2}{3}$; $2y + 11x = 0$, $2y - x = 0$.

(23). $r = \frac{1}{2}l$, $\theta = 0$; $r = \frac{1}{2}l \sec^2 \alpha$, $\theta = 2\alpha$.

CHAPTER 11

THE PLANE AND THE STRAIGHT LINE

11.1 Direction cosines

A three dimensional coordinate system $Oxyz$ is defined by three mutually perpendicular axes Ox, Oy, Oz; the system is right-handed if the positive direction Oz is related to the sense of rotation through $90°$ from Ox to Oy by the right-handed cork screw rule.

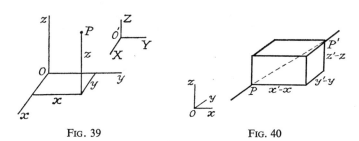

FIG. 39   FIG. 40

A point $P(x, y, z)$ is specified by the three signed perpendicular distances x, y, z from P to the planes Oyz, Ozy, Oxy respectively.

The length OP is given by an application of Pythagoras' theorem, namely

$$OP = \sqrt{(x^2 + y^2 + z^2)}. \tag{1}$$

If P' is the point (x', y', z'), the coordinates of P' relative to P are $(x' - x, y' - y, z' - z)$, so PP' is given by

$$PP' = \sqrt{[(x' - x)^2 + (y' - y)^2 + (z' - z)^2]}. \tag{2}$$

If $O'(\alpha, \beta, \gamma)$ is a new origin, and if axes $O'X$, $O'Y$, $O'Z$ are drawn parallel respectively to Ox, Oy, Oz, the coordinates of $P(x, y, z)$ in the original system are related to the coordinates of $P(X, Y, Z)$ in the new system by the equations

$$x = X + \alpha, \quad y = Y + \beta, \quad z = Z + \gamma.$$

The *direction* and *sense* of a line PP' (from P to P') in space are specified by means of three *direction cosines* (l, m, n). Through P, draw lines PX, PY, PZ parallel to the three axes; then l, m, n are defined by

$$l = \cos P'PX, \quad m = \cos P'PY, \quad n = \cos P'PZ.$$

From the rectangular box in Fig. 40 built around the diagonal PP', we note that

$$l = (x' - x)/PP', \quad m = (y' - y)/PP', \quad n = (z' - z)/PP'. \quad (3)$$

Substitution into formula (2) yields the identity

$$l^2 + m^2 + n^2 = 1. \quad (4)$$

Note further that

$$x' - x = lPP', \quad y' - y = mPP', \quad z' - z = nPP'. \quad (5)$$

If the sense of the line is reversed, the direction cosines of the line $P'P$ are evidently $-l, -m, -n$, for the angles concerned are now the supplements of those in the first case.

If two lines are parallel, their direction cosines are respectively identical (but one set may be reversed in sign).

In particular, the direction cosines of the three axes Ox, Oy, Oz are evidently $(1, 0, 0)$, $(0, 1, 0)$, $(0, 0, 1)$, respectively.

If the line passes through the origin, and if $P(x, y, z)$ is a point on line such that $OP = 1$, then

$$l = x, m = y, \quad n = z.$$

The *direction ratios* of a line are three numbers α, β, γ proportional to l, m, n. To convert direction ratios into direction cosines, we must divide by $\sqrt{(\alpha^2 + \beta^2 + \gamma^2)}$, in order that the sum of squares of the three new values should be unity.

If a line is defined by the two points $P(x, y, z)$ and $P'(x', y', z')$, then equations (3) show that the direction ratios of the line may be taken to be $x' - x$, $y' - y$, $z' - z$. To convert these to direction cosines, we divide by the length PP'.

Theorem.   If two lines have direction cosines (l, m, n) and (l', m', n'), then the cosine of the angle between the lines is given by

$$\cos \theta = ll' + mm' + nn'. \quad (6)$$

Let lines OP and OP' be drawn through the origin parallel to the given lines, such that $OP = OP' = 1$. Then the coordinates of P and P' are (l, m, n) and (l', m', n') respectively. Applying the cosine formula to $\triangle OPP'$, we have

$$PP'^2 = OP^2 + OP'^2 - 2OP \cdot OP' \cos \theta.$$

Hence

$$(l - l')^2 + (m - m')^2 + (n - n')^2 = 2 - 2 \cos \theta,$$

or

$$2 - 2(ll' + mm' + nn') = 2 - 2 \cos \theta$$

using equation (4) for both sets of direction cosines It follows that

$$\cos \theta = ll' + mm' + nn'.$$

In particular, the two lines are perpendicular if

$$ll' + mm' + nn' = 0.$$

Under these circumstances, direction ratios may be used rather than direction cosines. For example, if the line PQ is perpendicular to RS, where P, Q, R, S are the points (x_1, y_1, z_1), (x_2, y_2, z_2), (x_3, y_3, z_3), (x_4, y_4, z_4) respectively, then the direction ratios of PQ are $x_2 - x_1$, $y_2 - y_1$, $z_2 - z_1$ and of RS, $x_4 - x_3$, $y_4 - y_3$, $z_4 - z_3$; hence

$$(x_2 - x_1)(x_4 - x_3) + (y_2 - y_1)(y_4 - y_3) + (z_2 - z_1)(z_4 - z_3) = 0.$$

11.2 The plane

Definition i. A plane is uniquely specified by one point $Q(x_1, y_1, z_1)$ lying on it and by the direction cosines (l, m, n) of its *normal*, where the normal implies that direction perpendicular to the plane.

Let $P(x, y, z)$ be the general point of the plane. We use the fact that the line PQ is perpendicular to the normal for all points P in the plane. Since the direction ratios of PQ are $x - x_1, y - y_1, z - z_1$, we have

$$l(x - x_1) + m(y - y_1) + n(z - z_1) = 0,$$

or $lx + my + nz = \text{constant}.$

A linear equation, then, defines a plane. In standard notation, we shall write

$$ax + by + cz + d = 0$$

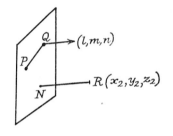

Fig. 41

to be the equation of a general plane. The coefficients a, b, c are usually the direction ratios of the normal.

It should be pointed out that the angle between two planes is taken to refer to the angle between their normals.

Definition ii. Three non-collinear points $P(x_1, y_1, z_1)$, $Q(x_2, y_2, z_2)$, $R(x_3, y_3, z_3)$ define a plane. Its equation is

$$\begin{vmatrix} x & y & z & 1 \\ x_1 & y_1 & z_1 & 1 \\ x_2 & y_2 & z_2 & 1 \\ x_3 & y_3 & z_3 & 1 \end{vmatrix} = 0;$$

this equation clearly is linear in x, y and z, and the coordinates of P, Q and R individually satisfy the equation (two rows of the determinant being equal).

It follows that the four points P, Q, R, $S(x_4, y_4, z_4)$ are coplanar if

$$\begin{vmatrix} x_1 & y_1 & z_1 & 1 \\ x_2 & y_2 & z_2 & 1 \\ x_3 & y_3 & z_3 & 1 \\ x_4 & y_4 & z_4 & 1 \end{vmatrix} = 0.$$

If the plane cuts off signed intercepts a, b, c from the three coordinate axes, its equation is

$$\frac{x}{a} + \frac{y}{b} + \frac{z}{c} = 1;$$

the three points $(a, 0, 0)$, $(0, b, 0)$, $(0, 0, c)$ obviously satisfy this equation.

The perpendicular from a point to a plane. In Fig. 41, let $R(x_2, y_2, z_2)$ be a given point, and $ax + by + cz + d = 0$ the given plane. Let $N(X, Y, Z)$ be the foot of the perpendicular from R to the plane. The direction ratios of RN are given by (a, b, c) and also by $(X - x_2,$ $Y - y_2, Z - z_2)$; these two sets of ratios, being proportional, yield

$$\frac{X - x_2}{a} = \frac{Y - y_2}{b} = \frac{Z - z_2}{c} = \lambda,$$

say. But (X, Y, Z) lies on the plane; hence

$$a(a\lambda + x_2) + b(b\lambda + y_2) + c(c\lambda + z_2) + d = 0,$$

giving

$$\lambda = -(ax_2 + by_2 + cz_2 + d)/(a^2 + b^2 + c^2).$$

Two results may now be deduced:

(i) The foot N of the perpendicular from R has the coordinates

$$X = a\lambda + x_2, \quad Y = b\lambda + y_2, \quad Z = c\lambda + z_2,$$

where this value of λ is substituted.

(ii) The length of the perpendicular RN is given by

$$\begin{aligned} RN &= \sqrt{[(X - x_2)^2 + (Y - y_2)^2 + (Z - z_2)^2]} \\ &= \sqrt{(a^2\lambda^2 + b^2\lambda^2 + c^2\lambda^2)} \\ &= \frac{ax_2 + by_2 + cz_2 + d}{\sqrt{(a^2 + b^2 + c^2)}} \end{aligned}$$

upon substituting one value of the square root of λ^2. The modulus of this result is taken if the positive distance RN is required. Otherwise, the expression $ax + by + cz + d$ divides all space into two regions; for points R lying in one region this expression is positive, and for the other region it is negative. The expression is zero for points lying on the plane only.

The plane through the intersection of two planes. Let

$$ax + by + cz + d = 0, \quad Ax + By + Cz + D = 0$$

be two distinct non-parallel planes. Geometrically, these two planes intersect in a line. Consider the equation

$$(ax + by + cz + d) + \lambda(Ax + By + Cz + D) = 0,$$

where λ is a parameter. Certainly it represents a plane, being linear in x, y, z; moreover, any point on the line of intersection of the two given planes satisfies the equation, since at such points both brackets vanish separately. Hence the equation represents a plane passing through the line of intersection of the two given planes. As λ varies, the plane rotates about this line.

If this plane is required to pass through a given point (x_1, y_1, z_1), λ may be found by substituting the coordinates of this point into the equation of the plane.

Example 1   Plane P_1 contains the point (7,2,6) and passes through the line of intersection of the two planes $x + y - 2z - 1 = 0$ and $2x + 2y - 3z - 2 = 0$. Plane P_2 contains the three points $(1, 1, 1), (-3, 1, 0), (1, 4, 2)$. Find the cosine of the angle between P_1 and P_2.

The plane P_1 must be of the form

$$(x + y - 2z - 1) + \lambda(2x + 2y - 3z - 2) = 0.$$

Since the point (7, 2, 6) lies on it, we have

$$(7 + 2 - 12 - 1) + \lambda(14 + 4 - 18 - 2) = 0$$

yielding $\lambda = -2$. The plane is therefore

$$3x + 3y - 4z - 3 = 0.$$

The plane P_2 is given by the equation

$$\begin{vmatrix} x & y & z & 1 \\ 1 & 1 & 1 & 1 \\ -3 & 1 & 0 & 1 \\ 1 & 4 & 2 & 1 \end{vmatrix} = 0,$$

or, upon expansion, by $3x + 4y - 12z + 5 = 0$.

The direction cosines of the normals to the two planes are given by $(3, 3, -4)/\sqrt{34}$ and $(3, 4, -12)/13$ respectively. Hence

$$\cos \theta = \frac{3.3 + 3.4 + 4.12}{13\sqrt{34}} = \frac{69}{13\sqrt{34}}.$$

Example 2 The point N is the foot of the perpendicular from the point $P(5, -6, 13)$ to the plane $2x - 4y + 5z - 9 = 0$. Find the length of the perpendicular from N to the plane $12x - 3y + 4z + 8 = 0$.

If N is the point (X, Y, Z) satisfying

$$2X - 4Y + 5Z - 9 = 0,$$

then the direction ratios of PN are given by both $(2, -4, 5)$ and by $(X - 5, Y + 6, Z - 13)$. Hence

$$(X - 5)/2 = (Y + 6)/(-4) = (Z - 13)/5 = \lambda$$

say, so $X = 2\lambda + 5$, $Y = -4\lambda - 6$, $Z = 5\lambda + 13$. Substituting into (7), we obtain

$$2(2\lambda + 5) - 4(-4\lambda - 6) + 5(5\lambda + 13) = 9,$$

with the solution $\lambda = -2$. Hence N is the point $(1, 2, 3)$.

The perpendicular distance from N to the second plane is then given by

$$\frac{12.1 - 3.2 + 4.3 + 8}{\sqrt{(12^2 + 3^2 + 4^2)}} = \frac{26}{\sqrt{169}} = 2.$$

11.3   The intersection of three planes

Let the three planes have the equations

$$P_1: a_1x + b_1y + c_1z + d_1 = 0,$$
$$P_2: a_2x + b_2y + c_2z + d_2 = 0,$$
$$P_3: a_3x + b_3y + c_3z + d_3 = 0.$$

If we solve these three equations simultaneously, the theory given in section 1.7 shows that a unique point (x, y, z) exists satisfying all three equations, provided

$$\begin{vmatrix} a_1 & b_1 & c_1 \\ a_2 & b_2 & c_2 \\ a_3 & b_3 & c_3 \end{vmatrix} \neq 0.$$

Generally, then, three planes intersect in a unique point.

On the other hand, the vanishing of this determinant is the condition for the three simultaneous homogeneous equations

$$a_1l + b_1m + c_1n = 0,$$
$$a_2l + b_2m + c_2n = 0,$$
$$a_3l + b_3m + c_3n = 0.$$

to possess a non-zero solution (l, m, n). In other words, a direction (l, m, n) exists perpendicular to the three directions (a_1, b_1, c_1), (a_2, b_2, c_2), (a_3, b_3, c_3), namely to the three normals of the given planes. If this direction (l, m, n) is regarded as perpendicular to the page, then the three normals to the three planes will lie in the page. The lines of intersection of the three planes with the page may then exhibit the various possibilities shown in Fig. 42.

(i) Generally a triangle is formed; in three dimensions, the three planes form a prism with three parallel edges with no common finite point.

(ii) The three lines may pass through a point. In three dimensions, the three planes pass through a common line; the coordinates of every point on this line satisfy the three given equations.

(iii) One line is parallel to a second line but not to the third. In three dimensions, two planes are parallel, but the third plane intersects the other two; there is no finite solution.

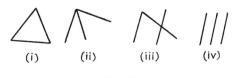

(i)   (ii)   (iii)   (iv)

FIG. 42

(iv) All the three lines are parallel; no finite solution exists since all the three planes are parallel to each other, unless the three planes are identical.

The condition for case (ii) is that all the four 3×3 determinants formed from the coefficients of the given equations should vanish. Any one of the three equations is merely a linear combination of the other two.

11.4 The straight line

Definition i. A straight line is specified uniquely by one definite point $F(x_1, y_1, z_1)$ on it and by the direction cosines of the line. If $P(x, y, z)$ is any point on the line, and if the length FP is the signed distance s, then the values of l, m and n are given by

$$(x - x_1)/s = l, \quad (y - y_1)/s = m, \quad (z - z_1)/s = n,$$

or

$$\frac{x - x_1}{l} = \frac{y - y_1}{m} = \frac{z - z_1}{n} (= s). \tag{8}$$

Equations (8) provide the equations of the line; in fact, two equations are necessary to specify a line, namely the equations of any two planes through the line. Form (8) constitutes the standard form of the equation of a line.

If instead we use the direction ratios (a, b, c) of the line, we have

$$\frac{x - x_1}{a} = \frac{y - y_1}{b} = \frac{z - z_1}{c} = \lambda, \qquad (9)$$

where λ is now proportional to the signed distance FP. To convert into the actual distance s, we multiply by $\sqrt{(a^2 + b^2 + c^2)}$, since this factor converts the direction ratios into direction cosines.

Parametrically, we may write

$$x = a\lambda + x_1, \quad y = b\lambda + y_1, \quad z = c\lambda + z_1. \qquad (10)$$

Definition ii. A line may also be defined by two definite points $F(x_1, y_1, z_1)$ and $G(x_2, y_2, z_2)$ on it. If $P(x, y, z)$ is the general point on the line, the direction ratios of the segment FP must be proportional to those of the segment FG; that is

$$\frac{x - x_1}{x_2 - x_1} = \frac{y - y_1}{y_2 - y_1} = \frac{z - z_1}{z_2 - z_1} = \lambda$$

where λ is a parameter, evidently proportional to the signed distance FP. The value $\lambda = 0$ gives F and $\lambda = 1$ gives G.

The mid-point of FG is given by $\lambda = \frac{1}{2}$, or

$$x = \tfrac{1}{2}(x_1 + x_2), \quad y = \tfrac{1}{2}(y_1 + y_2), \quad z = \tfrac{1}{2}(z_1 + z_2).$$

Let P divide the segment FG in such a way that the signed distances FP and PG satisfy the ratio $FP/PG = \mu$. Then FP is proportional to λ and $PG = FG - FP$ to $1 - \lambda$. Hence $\lambda/(1 - \lambda) = \mu$, or $\mu = \lambda/(1 + \lambda)$
Then

$$x = \lambda(x_2 - x_1) + x_1 = \lambda x_2 + (1 - \lambda)x_1 = (x_1 + \mu x_2)/(1 + \mu).$$

Similarly,

$$y = (y_1 + \mu y_2)/(1 + \mu), \quad z = (z_1 + \mu z_2)/(1 + \mu).$$

The point in which a line cuts a plane. The line

$$(x - x_1)/a = (y - y_1)/b = (z - z_1)/c = \lambda$$

cuts the plane $Ax + By + Cz + D = 0$ in a point whose parameter is found by substituting the parametric form of points on the line into the equation of the plane. This yields

$$A(a\lambda + x_1) + B(b\lambda + y_1) + C(c\lambda + z_1) + D = 0,$$

or $\lambda = -(Ax_1 + By_1 + Cz_1 + D)/(Aa + Bb + Cc)$. The values of x, y and z may now be determined.

The line defined by two general planes. A line may be defined as the line of intersection of the two planes $ax + by + cz + d = 0$, $Ax + By + Cz + D = 0$. The direction ratios (α, β, γ) of this line of intersection are perpendicular to the direction ratios (a, b, c) and (A, B, C) of the normals to the two planes; hence

$$a\alpha + b\beta + c\gamma = 0, \quad A\alpha + B\beta + C\gamma = 0.$$

It follows that

$$\frac{\alpha}{bC - Bc} = \frac{\beta}{cA - Ca} = \frac{\gamma}{aB - Ab};$$

so we may take the three direction ratios to be $bC - Bc$, $cA - Ca$, $aB - Ab$.

To express the equations of the line in standard form, we must also find the coordinates of any point on the line. For example, we may let $x = 0$, and solve for y and z. If this point is denoted by (x_1, y_1, z_1), the equations of the line may be expressed in the form

$$\frac{x - x_1}{bC - Bc} = \frac{y - y_1}{cA - Ca} = \frac{z - z_1}{aB - Ab}.$$

The perpendicular from a point to a line. Let N be the foot of the perpendicular from $P(x_2, y_2, z_2)$ to the line

$$(x - x_1)/a = (y - y_1)/b = (z - z_1)/c = \lambda.$$

If N is specified by the parameter λ, then the direction ratios of PN:

$$\lambda a + x_1 - x_2, \quad \lambda b + y_1 - y_2, \quad \lambda c + z_1 - z_2$$

are perpendicular to those for the line. Hence

$$a(\lambda a + x_1 - x_2) + b(\lambda b + y_1 - y_2) + c(\lambda c + z_1 - z_2) = 0,$$

so

$$\lambda = [a(x_2 - x_1) + b(y_2 - y_1) + c(z_2 - z_1)]/(a^2 + b^2 + c^2).$$

Using this value of λ, the coordinates of N and also the length PN may be found.

Two coplanar lines. The two lines

$$(x - x_1)/a = (y - y_1)/b = (z - z_1)/c = \lambda, \tag{11}$$

$$(x - x_2)/A = (z - z_2)/B = (z - z_2)/C = \mu \tag{12}$$

are *coplanar* if they intersect. Values of λ and μ must exist that satisfy the three equations:

$$x = a\lambda + x_1 = A\mu + x_2,$$
$$y = b\lambda + y_1 = B\mu + y_2,$$
$$z = c\lambda + z_1 = C\mu + z_2.$$

8

The condition for these three equations to be consistent in λ and μ is

$$\begin{vmatrix} a & A & x_1 - x_2 \\ b & B & y_1 - y_2 \\ c & C & z_1 - z_2 \end{vmatrix} = 0.$$

The values of λ and μ may then be found, and the point of intersection calculated.

The normal to the plane defined by these two intersecting lines is of course perpendicular to the two directions (a, b, c) and (A, B, C).

The common perpendicular to two skew lines. Two lines in space are called *skew* if they are non-parallel and non-intersecting. If equations (11) and (12) represent two skew lines, let P, with parameter λ, and Q, with parameter μ, be points one on each line respectively. The segment PQ has direction ratios

$$a\lambda + x_1 - A\mu - x_2, \quad b\lambda + y_1 - B\mu - y_2, \quad c\lambda + z_1 - C\mu - z_2.$$

We may choose λ and μ so that PQ is perpendicular to both lines; that is,

$$a(a\lambda + x_1 - A\mu - x_2) + b(b\lambda + y_1 - B\mu - y_2)$$
$$+ c(c\lambda + z_1 - C\mu - z_2) = 0,$$

$$A(a\lambda + x_1 - A\mu - x_2) + B(b\lambda + y_1 - B\mu - y_2)$$
$$+ C(c\lambda + z_1 - C\mu - z_2) = 0.$$

These two equations may be solved for λ and μ; these yield the coordinates of P and Q, and hence the length and equations of the common perpendicular PQ.

This length PQ is also the shortest distance between the two skew lines. Generally,

$$PQ^2 = (a\lambda + x_1 - A\mu - x_2)^2 + (b\lambda + y_1 - B\mu - y_2)^2$$
$$+ (c\lambda + z_1 - C\mu - z_2)^2.$$

The values of the parameters yielding the minimum value of PQ^2 are given by the equations $\partial PQ^2/\partial\lambda = 0$, $\partial PQ^2/\partial\mu = 0$. These two equations are obviously identical with those we have just used in finding the common perpendicular.

The standard form for the equations of two skew lines. Let PQ, of length $2c$, be the unique common perpendicular to the two lines L_1 and L_2. O is the mid-point of PQ, and OP is taken to be the Oz axis. Through O let the line l_1 be drawn parallel to L_1, and l_2 parallel to L_2.

Then L_1 is at the constant height c above the plane l_1Ol_2, and L_2 is at a depth c below this plane. Let the axis Ox bisect $\angle l_1Ol_2$; finally choose Oy to complete the right-handed system $Oxyz$.

If $\angle l_1Ox = \alpha$ and $\tan \alpha = m$, the equation of the line l_1 in the Oxy plane is $y = x \tan \alpha = mx$; hence the line L_1 has the equations

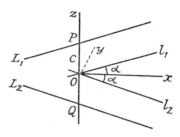

$$y = x \tan \alpha, \quad z = c,$$

or $\quad y = mx, \quad z = c.$

Similarly, the equations of the line L_2 are

$$y = -x \tan \alpha, \quad z = -c,$$

Fig. 43

or $\quad y = -mx, \quad z = -c.$

Parametrically, the general point on L_1 may be taken to be $(\lambda, m\lambda, c)$, and on L_2 the general point is given by $(\mu, -m\mu, -c)$.

Sometimes these two sets of equations are written in the form

$$\frac{x}{\cos \alpha} = \frac{y}{\sin \alpha} = \frac{z - c}{0}, \qquad \frac{x}{\cos \alpha} = \frac{-y}{\sin \alpha} = \frac{z + c}{0}.$$

Their direction cosines are given by $(\cos \alpha, \sin \alpha, 0)$ and $(\cos \alpha, -\sin \alpha, 0)$ respectively; their direction ratios are $(1, m, 0)$, $(1, -m, 0)$.

The solution of problems. When confronted with a problem involving lines and planes, the student should survey the problem from a purely constructional point of view. By what *elementary* constructions can we pass from the given facts to the required results? These elementary constructions may then (and only then) be translated into symbols and equations, by using the various methods and results just produced in these sections. No equation should be written down blindly, without first knowing the trend of the argument from a constructional point of view.

Example 3 Show that the two lines

$$(x - 18)/(-7) = (y - 9)/3 = (z - 1)/5, \quad (x + 6)/3 = (y - 5)/13 = (z - 11)/5$$

intersect; find the equation of their common plane and of the normal through their point of intersection.

Parametrically, the first line is given by: $x = -7\lambda + 18, y = 3\lambda + 9, z = 5\lambda + 1$; the second line is given by $x = 3\mu - 6$, $y = 13\mu + 5, z = 5\mu + 11$. The two lines intersect if the three equations

$$x = -7\lambda + 18 = 3\mu - 6,$$
$$y = 3\lambda + 9 = 13\mu + 5,$$
$$z = 5\lambda + 1 = 5\mu + 11$$

are consistent. The solution of the first two equations is $\lambda = 3$, $\mu = 1$, obviously satisfying the third equation. The common point is then $P(-3, 18, 16)$.

The normal (l, m, n) to the plane is perpendicular to the two lines, so

$$-7l + 3m + 5n = 0, \quad 3l + 13m + 5n = 0,$$

yielding $l:m:n = 1:-1:2$.

The plane defined by the two lines has this normal and it passes through P; its equation is

$$(x + 3) - (y - 18) + 2(z - 16) = 0,$$

or
$$x - y + 2z = 11.$$

The equations of the normal through P are given by

$$(x + 3)/1 = (y - 18)/(-1) = (z - 16)/2.$$

Example 4 Find the equations of (i) the projection of (ii) the image of the line $\frac{1}{2}x = y - 1 = -(z - 1) = \lambda$ in the plane $x + y + z = 4$, and find the cosine of the angle between the line and its image.

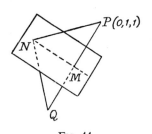

The parametric form of the general point on the given line is $(2\lambda, \lambda + 1, 1 - \lambda)$. The line intersects the plane in N, whose parameter is given by the equation

$$2\lambda + (\lambda + 1) + (1 - \lambda) = 4,$$

or $\lambda = 1$. Hence N is the point $(2, 2, 0)$.

From $P(0, 1, 1)$, a point on the given line, drop the perpendicular PM to the plane. The line NM is the projection of NP on the plane, and if PM is extended to Q, where $PM = MQ$, then NQ is the image line required.

Fig. 44

The direction ratios of PMQ are $(1, 1, 1)$, being the normal to the plane; the line PMQ through $P(0, 1, 1)$ has the equations

$$x = y - 1 = z - 1 = \mu.$$

The parameter of the point P on this line is $\mu = 0$; the parameter of M is given by the equation

$$\mu + (\mu + 1) + (\mu + 1) = 4,$$

or $\mu = \frac{2}{3}$. Since Q is determined by the condition $PM = MQ$ along this line, it follows that the parameter of Q is double that at P, namely $\mu = \frac{4}{3}$. Hence M is $(\frac{2}{3}, \frac{5}{3}, \frac{5}{3})$ and Q is $(\frac{4}{3}, \frac{7}{3}, \frac{7}{3})$.

The equations of the projection NM are given by

$$\frac{x - 2}{\frac{2}{3} - 2} = \frac{y - 2}{\frac{5}{3} - 2} = \frac{z - 0}{\frac{5}{3} - 0},$$

or
$$(x - 2)/4 = (y - 2) = -z/5.$$

The image line NQ is given by

$$\frac{x - 2}{\frac{4}{3} - 2} = \frac{y - 2}{\frac{7}{3} - 2} = \frac{z - 0}{\frac{7}{3} - 0},$$

or
$$(x - 2)/2 = (y - 2)/(-1) = -z/7.$$

The direction of the given line is specified by the direction cosines $(2, 1, -1)/\sqrt{6}$, and that of the image line by $(2, -1, -7)/\sqrt{54}$. Hence

$$\cos \theta = \frac{2 \cdot 2 - 1 \cdot 1 + 1 \cdot 7}{\sqrt{6}\sqrt{54}} = \frac{5}{9}.$$

Example 5* Find the length and equations of the shortest distance between the two lines

$$(x - 6)/2 = (y + 4)/5 = z - 2, \quad (x + 1)/(-4) = (y - 9)/5 = (z - 5)/7.$$

The general point P on the first line is given by $(2\lambda + 6, 5\lambda - 4, \lambda + 2)$ and Q on the second line by $(-4\mu - 1, 5\mu + 9, 7\mu + 5)$. Then

$$PQ^2 = (2\lambda + 6 + 4\mu + 1)^2 + (5\lambda - 4 - 5\mu - 9)^2 + (\lambda + 2 - 7\mu - 5)^2$$
$$= (2\lambda + 4\mu + 7)^2 + (5\lambda - 5\mu - 13)^2 + (\lambda - 7\mu - 3)^2.$$

Now PQ is a minimum when $\partial PQ^2/\partial \lambda = \partial PQ^2/\partial \mu = 0$, namely when

$$2(2\lambda + 4\mu + 7) + 5(5\lambda - 5\mu - 13) + (\lambda - 7\mu - 3) = 0,$$
$$4(2\lambda + 4\mu + 7) - 5(5\lambda - 5\mu - 13) - 7(\lambda - 7\mu - 3) = 0,$$

or

$$5\lambda - 4\mu - 9 = 0, \quad 4\lambda - 15\mu - 19 = 0.$$

The solution of these two equations is $\lambda = 1$, $\mu = -1$, so P and Q are the points $(8, 1, 3)$ and $(3, 4, -2)$ respectively. Hence

$$PQ = \sqrt{(5^2 + 3^2 + 5^2)} = \sqrt{59},$$

and the equations of the line PQ are

$$(x - 3)/5 = (y - 4)/(-3) = (z + 2)/5.$$

Example 6 The two skew lines $y = mx$, $z = c$ and $y = -mx$, $z = -c$ are given, where $m \neq 1$. The point A lies on the first line and B on the second, such that the lines OA and OB are perpendicular. Prove that M, the mid-point of AB, lies on a hyperbola of eccentricity $\sqrt{(1 + m^2)}$, whose asymptotes are parallel to the two given lines.

Parametrically, let A and B be the points $(\lambda, m\lambda, c)$ and $(\mu, -m\mu, -c)$ respectively. Then M is the point

$$x = \tfrac{1}{2}(\lambda + \mu), \quad y = \tfrac{1}{2}m(\lambda - \mu), \quad z = 0. \tag{13}$$

The direction ratios of the lines OA and OB may be taken to be the coordinates of A and B respectively. Since OA is perpendicular to OB, we have

$$\lambda\mu - m^2\lambda\mu - c^2 = 0,$$

or

$$\lambda\mu(1 - m^2) = c^2. \tag{14}$$

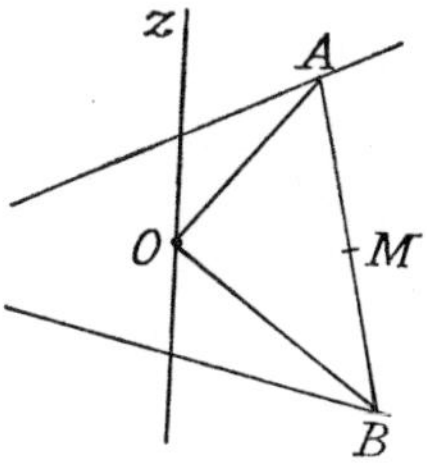

From equation (13), the locus of M lies in the plane $z = 0$; to find its equation we eliminate λ and μ from equations (13) and (14):

$$x^2 - y^2/m^2 = \tfrac{1}{4}[(\lambda + \mu)^2 - (\lambda - \mu)^2]$$
$$= \lambda\mu = c^2/(1 - m^2),$$

FIG. 45

a hyperbola. Its asymptotes are given by $x^2 - y^2/m^2 = 0$, parallel to the two skew lines. Its eccentricity is given by $m^2 = (e^2 - 1)$, or by $e = \sqrt{(1 + m^2)}$.

EXERCISES

(1)★. Find the equation of the plane which contains the line
$$(x - 1)/2 = (y + 1)/3 = (z - 2)/(-1)$$
and is perpendicular to the plane $3x - y + 4z = 5$. Hence find the direction cosines of the projection of the line on the given plane.

(2)★. Show that the two lines
$$(x - 1)/2 = y + 2 = z/3 \quad \text{and} \quad (x - 2)/3 = (y - 2)/(-2) = (z - 4)/2$$
have a common point. Find the perpendicular distance between the first line and the parallel line
$$(x - 1)/2 = (y - 7)/1 = (z - 1)/3.$$

(3)★. Show that the line whose equations are
$$(x + 1)/3 = (y - 2)/6 = (z - 3)/4$$
is parallel to the plane $2x + 3y - 6z + 7 = 0$. Find the distance of the line from the plane and the equations of the projection of the line on the plane.

(4)★. Find the equation of the plane parallel to and equidistant from the two lines
$$(x + 27)/4 = (y - 32)/3 = (z - 2)/2,$$
$$(x - 31)/2 = (y + 25)/2 = (z + 14)/(-7).$$

(5)★. Show that, in general, one and only one straight line can be drawn through a given point $P_1(x_1, y_1, z_1)$ to meet both the lines $z = a, y = 0$ and $x = 0, z = -a$. Find the direction ratios of this line, and obtain the locus of P_1 for which the line is parallel to the plane $Ax + By + Cz = 0$.

(6)★. If O is the origin of coordinates, A is the point $(-1, 1, -4)$, N is a point on the line $x = \frac{1}{2}y = -\frac{1}{2}z$ such that AN is perpendicular to this line, and B is a point such that $NB = NA$ and NB is perpendicular to the plane ONA, find the co-ordinates of N and of the two positions of B.

(7)★. Find the equations of all the lines through the origin which make equal angles with the three lines
$$x - y = x - z = 0, \quad x + y = x - z = 0, \quad x + y = x + z = 0.$$

(8)★. Points A, B, C are chosen, one on each of the coordinate axes of a rectangular Cartesian system, in such a way that the lines joining them to a given point $P(a, b, c)$, not on any of the coordinate planes, are mutually perpendicular. Find the coordinates of the points A, B, C and prove that the plane ABC bisects at right-angles the line joining P to the origin.

(9)★. Find equations of the line through the point $(2, 3, 4)$ which is parallel to the line of intersection of the planes $x + y - 2z = 1, 2x - 3y + z = -3$. Find the perpendicular distance between these lines.

(10)★. A plane is drawn through the line $x + y = 1, z = 0$ to make an angle $\sin^{-1}(\frac{1}{3})$ with the plane $x + y + z = 0$. Prove that two such planes can be drawn and find their equations. Prove also that the angle between the planes is $\cos^{-1}(\frac{7}{9})$.

(11)★. The equations of two straight lines are
$$x - 4 = 3 - y = z + 4 \quad \text{and} \quad (x - 14)/4 = y - 3 = (z - 2)/2.$$
Prove that the lines intersect and find the equations of the common perpendicular, p, through the point of intersection. Calculate the length of the perpendicular from the origin to the line p.

(12)★. Find the equations of the line which meets the two lines

$$(x - 4)/3 = y - 2 = (z - 7)/5, \quad x + 3 = 4 - y = (z + 3)/3,$$

and is perpendicular to both of them. What is the shortest distance between the two given lines?

(13)★. Two lines are given by the equations

$$x = 2, \quad y - z = 1 \quad \text{and} \quad 6x = 3(y - 1) = 2(z - 2).$$

Find the length of their common perpendicular and the coordinates of its feet.

(14)★. Find the coordinates of the point in which the line of shortest distance between

$$x + 1 = (y - 1)/2 = 2 - z \quad \text{and} \quad (x - 1)/2 = y = (z + 1)/(-3)$$

cuts the plane $y = 0$.

(15)★. Find the length and the coordinates of the feet of the common perpendicular to the two lines given by the equations

$$(x + 1)/2 = (y + 1)/2 = 2 - z \quad \text{and} \quad x + 2y + z - 13 = 2x + y - z + 1 = 0.$$

(16)★. (i) Find the perpendicular distance from the point $(2, 2, 1)$ to the line of intersection of the two planes

$$2x - y - z = 3, \quad 3x - y - 3z = 4.$$

(ii) The coordinates of the four points A, B, C, D are respectively $(1, 2, 1)$, $(-1, 0, 2)$, $(2, 1, 3)$ and $(3, -1, 1)$. Find the shortest distance between the lines AB and CD.

(17)★. P and P' are the feet of the common perpendicular to the two skew lines $y - mx = 0$, $z = c$ and $y + mx = 0$, $z = -c$. Q and Q' are two other points on the respective lines and R is the mid-point of QQ'. If $PQ^2 + P'Q'^2$ is constant, show that the locus of R is an ellipse.

(18)★. If points P and P' are taken on the two skew lines $y = mx$, $z = c$ and $y = -mx$, $z = -c$, such that $OP = k . OP'$, where O is the origin and k is a positive constant different from 1, prove that the locus of intersection of the line PP' with the plane $z = 0$ is a hyperbola.

(19)★. If P and Q are points on the lines $y = mx$, $z = c$ and $y = -mx$, $z = -c$ respectively such that PQ subtends a right-angle at the origin and R is a point of trisection of PQ, prove that the locus of R is, in general, a hyperbola.

(20)★. Points P and Q are taken on the lines $y = 2x$, $z = c$ and $y = -2x$, $z = -c$ respectively such that $OP = 2OQ$, where O is the origin. Prove that the locus of intersection of the line PQ with the plane $z = 0$ is the hyperbola

$$60x^2 - 100xy + 15y^2 + 12c^2 = 0.$$

(21)★. Find the equation of the plane through the point $(1, -1, 2)$, parallel to the x-axis and also parallel to the line

$$x + 2y - 3z = 0 = 2x - 3y + z.$$

(22)★. Find the ratio in which N, the foot of the perpendicular from the origin, divides the line joining the points $A(4, 6, 0)$ and $B(1, 2, -1)$ and prove that N does not lie between A and B.

(23)★. If (a, b, c) are the rectangular Cartesian coordinates of a point P, and if X, Y, Z are the feet of the perpendiculars from P to the axes, find the equation of the plane XYZ.

If the line l through P perpendicular to the plane XYZ meets this plane at D and the coordinate planes at A, B, C, prove that

$$PA^{-1} + PB^{-1} + PC^{-1} = 2PD^{-1}.$$

Prove that the shortest distance between l and Ox is $|b^2 - c^2|/\sqrt{(b^2 + c^2)}$.

(24)*. If A, B, C, D are four points such that $AB^2 + CD^2 = AC^2 + BD^2$, prove that BC is perpendicular to AD.

(25)*. (i) Find the equation of the plane which contains the point $(2, 1, 0)$ and the line $4x - 3y + z = 2$, $x + 2y + 3z = 1$.

(ii) If the plane $z = 0$ is horizontal, find the direction cosines of a line of greatest slope of the plane $3x - 4y + 2z = 8$.

(26)*. Show that the planes

$$2x + y - 3z + 5 = 0, \quad 5x - 7y + 2z + 3 = 0, \quad x + 10y - 11z + 12 = 0$$

have a common line p which is equally inclined to the axes.

Find the equations of the line q through the origin, parallel to the first of the given planes and perpendicular to the line p. Find also the shortest distance between the lines p and q.

(27)*. Show that, for all values of λ, the point $(3 + \lambda, 5 + 2\lambda, 2 + 3\lambda)$ is on the line through $A(3, 5, 2)$ perpendicular to the plane $x + 2y + 3z - 5 = 0$.

Perpendiculars AP and BQ are drawn through the points $A(3, 5, 2)$ and $B(-7, -1, 0)$ to the given plane. Find the coordinates of P and Q. If M is the midpoint of PQ find the equations of the line in the plane, passing through M and perpendicular to PQ.

Find also the equations of the reflexion of AB in the plane.

(28)*. Find the equation of the plane through the line of intersection of the planes $2x - y + 3z = 1$, $x + 2y + z = 2$ which contains the point $A(1, 2, -1)$. A line drawn through A at right-angles to this plane meets the first two planes in PQ respectively. Show that the length PQ is $\frac{5}{3}\sqrt{2}$.

(29)*. Obtain the standard form of the equations of the following two lines:
(i) The line L through $(1, 0, -2)$ perpendicular to the plane $3x + 2y + z = 0$,
(ii) the line M of intersection of the planes $x - 4y + z = 1$, $2x + y - z = 2$.
Hence find the equations of the line through the point $(0, 0, 7)$ meeting both L and M.

(30)*. Light from a point-source at $A(7, 0, 0)$ strikes a small mirror at the origin O, the normal to which has direction ratios $2:1:2$. Show that the actual direction cosines of the reflected ray are $-\frac{1}{9}, \frac{4}{9}, \frac{8}{9}$.

If the reflected ray strikes another mirror at a point B distant 9 units from O, find the direction cosines of the normal to this mirror if after further reflexion the light returns to the source A.

ANSWERS TO EXERCISES

(1). $x - y - z = 0$, $(5, 7, -2)/3\sqrt{26}$.   (2). $(5, 0, 6)$; $\sqrt{(502/7)}$.

(3). 1; $(x + \frac{4}{5})/3 = (y - \frac{17}{7})/6 = (z - \frac{16}{7})/4$.   (4). $25x - 32y - 2z + 50 = 0$.

(5). $[x_1(z_1 - a), y_1(z_1 + a), z_1^2 - a^2]$; $Ax_1(z_1 - a) + By_1(z_1 + a) + C(z_1^2 - a^2) = 0$.

(6). $N(1, 2, -2)$; $B: (3, 0, -3)$, $(-1, 4, -1)$.

(7). x-axis, y-axis, z-axis, $x = y = -z$.

(8). $A: x = (a^2 + b^2 + c^2)/2a$; $B: y = (a^2 + b^2 + c^2)/2b$; $C: z = (a^2 + b^2 + c^2)/2c$.

(9). $x - 2 = y - 3 = z - 4$; $2\sqrt{\frac{2}{3}}$.

(10). $x + y + 2z = 1$, $x + y + \frac{2}{5}z = 1$.

(11). $(x - 6)/3 = (1 - y)/2 = (z + 2)/(-5)$; $31/\sqrt{19}$.

(12). $-\frac{1}{2}(x - 1) = y - 1 = z - 2$; $\sqrt{6}$.   (13). $4/\sqrt{3}$; $(2, \frac{11}{3}, \frac{8}{3})$, $(\frac{4}{3}, \frac{7}{3}, 4)$.

(14). $x = -46/5, z = -1$.   (15). $\sqrt{26}$; $(1, 1, 1), (0, 4, 5)$.   (16). (i) $\sqrt{\frac{5}{7}}$; (ii) $\frac{7}{5}$.

(21). $y - z + 3 = 0$.   (22). $AN/NB = 18/5$.

(25). (i) $3x - 5y - 2z - 1 = 0$;   (ii) $(-6, 8, 25)/5\sqrt{29}$.

(26). p: $x + 1 = y = z - 1$; q: $x/4 = -y/5 = z$; $5/\sqrt{14}$.   (27). $P(2, 3, -1)$;
    $Q(-6, 1, 3)$; $x + 2 = -\frac{1}{2}(y - 2) = z - 1$; $(1 - x)/3 = y - 1 = (z + 4)/5$.

(28). $4x + 3y + 5z - 5 = 0$.

(29). (i) $(x - 1)/3 = \frac{1}{2}y = z + 2$.
    (ii) $x - 1 = y = z/3$; $2x = 4y = 7 - z$.   (30). $(5, 1, 2)$.

CHAPTER 12

THE SPHERE AND THE QUADRIC

12.1 The sphere

If the centre of the sphere is the origin O, then any point $P(x, y, z)$ on the sphere is at a constant distance r from O. The equation of the sphere must be

$$x^2 + y^2 + z^2 = r^2.$$

If the centre C of the sphere is the point (a, b, c), the coordinate differences of the radial segment CP are $x - a$, $y - b$, $z - c$, so the equation of the sphere must be

$$(x - a)^2 + (y - b)^2 + (z - c)^2 = r^2. \tag{1}$$

This equation of the most general sphere has the expanded form

$$x^2 + y^2 + z^2 - 2ax - 2by - 2cz + a^2 + b^2 + c^2 - r^2 = 0.$$

The characteristic features of this equation are (i) the coefficients of x^2, y^2, z^2 are equal, (ii) there are no terms involving yz, zx, xy.

If the general equation is given in the form

$$x^2 + y^2 + z^2 + 2ux + 2vy + 2wz + d = 0, \tag{2}$$

its centre is $(-u, -v, -w)$ and its radius is $\sqrt{(u^2 + v^2 + w^2 - d)}$, results found by completing the squares for the terms in x, y, z respectively.

Tangent planes. Let $P(x_1, y_1, z_1)$ be a general point on sphere (1), so

$$(x_1 - a)^2 + (y_1 - b)^2 + (z_1 - c)^2 = r^2. \tag{3}$$

The normal at P is directed along the radius CP; its direction ratios are $x_1 - a$, $y_1 - b$, $z_1 - c$. The normal at P has the equations

$$\frac{x - a}{x_1 - a} = \frac{y - b}{y_1 - b} = \frac{z - c}{z_1 - c}.$$

The *tangent plane* at P is the plane through P that touches the surface at P; its normal is directed along the radius CP, so its equation is

$$(x - x_1)(x_1 - a) + (y - y_1)(y_1 - b) + (z - z_1)(z_1 - c) = 0.$$

224

To simplify this equation, we add equation (3) to it, obtaining

$$(x - a)(x_1 - a) + (y - b)(y_1 - b) + (z - c)(z_1 - c) = r^2.$$

In other words, to derive the equation of the tangent plane from the equation of the sphere, we replace x^2, y^2, z^2 by xx_1, yy_1, zz_1 respectively, and $2x$, $2y$, $2z$ by $(x + x_1)$, $(y + y_1)$, $(z + z_1)$ respectively.

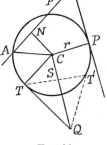

If equation (2) is used for the sphere, the tangent plane at (x_1, y_1, z_1) is given by

$$xx_1 + yy_1 + zz_1 + u(x + x_1)$$
$$+ v(y + y_1) + w(z + z_1) + d = 0.$$

Tangent lines. If $Q(x_2, y_2, z_2)$ is an external point, let QT be any line that touches the sphere at T; such a line is called a *tangent line* to the sphere. The length QT is given by

FIG. 46

$$QT^2 = CQ^2 - CT^2 = (x_2 - a)^2 + (y_2 - b)^2 + (z_2 - c)^2 - r^2.$$

If the sphere is expressed in the form (2), the length of the tangent QT is given merely by substituting the coordinates of Q into the equation of the sphere:

$$QT^2 = x_2{}^2 + y_2{}^2 + z_2{}^2 + 2ux_2 + 2vy_2 + 2wz_2 + d.$$

This expression must of course be positive for external points, but for internal points it will be negative.

Condition for a plane to touch a sphere. If the magnitude of the perpendicular distance from the centre $C(a, b, c)$ to the plane

$$p \equiv lx + my + nz + c' = 0$$

is equal to the radius, then the plane touches the sphere. Algebraically,

$$(la + mb + nc + c')^2/(l^2 + m^2 + n^2) = r^2.$$

If the magnitude of the perpendicular distance is less than r, the plane cuts the sphere in a circle. In Fig. 46, the line CN perpendicular to the plane p cuts this plane in the centre N of the circle. If the perpendicular distance CN is calculated, the radius of the circle is given by $AN = \sqrt{(r^2 - CN^2)}$. The coordinates of N may be calculated by finding the point of intersection of the line CN and the plane p.

Condition for a line to touch a sphere. The line

$$(x - \alpha)/l = (y - \beta)/m = (z - \gamma)/n = \lambda$$

intersects the sphere (2) in points whose parameters are given by

$$(l\lambda + \alpha)^2 + (m\lambda + \beta)^2 + (n\lambda + \gamma)^2 + 2u(l\lambda + \alpha)$$
$$+ 2v(m\lambda + \beta) + 2w(n\lambda + \gamma) + d = 0,$$

that is, by

$$\lambda^2(l^2 + m^2 + n^2) + 2\lambda(l\alpha + m\beta + n\gamma + ul + vm + wn)$$
$$+ \alpha^2 + \beta^2 + \gamma^2 + 2u\alpha + 2v\beta + 2w\gamma + d = 0.$$

If the discriminant of this quadratic equation is positive, the line intersects the sphere in two real points; if it vanishes, the line is a tangent line to the sphere, the repeated value of λ giving the coordinates of the point of contact.

The polar plane. The tangent plane at $T(x_3, y_3, z_3)$ on the sphere $x^2 + y^2 + z^2 = r^2$ has the equation

$$xx_3 + yy_3 + zz_3 = r^2.$$

If the point $Q(x_2, y_2, z_2)$ lies on this plane (see Fig. 46), we have

$$x_2x_3 + y_2y_3 + z_2z_3 = r^2 \qquad (4)$$

We now consider the plane

$$xx_2 + yy_2 + zz_2 = r^2.$$

If T is *any* point on the circle defined by this plane and the sphere, then equation (4) shows that the tangent plane at T passes through Q. This plane is called the *polar plane* of the *pole* Q.

Evidently if the polar plane of $Q(x_2, y_2, z_2)$ passes through the point $R(x_4, y_4, z_4)$, then the polar plane of R passes through Q, for the necessary condition in both cases is

$$x_2x_4 + y_2y_4 + z_2z_4 = r^2.$$

Such pairs of points Q and R are called *conjugate points*.

The complete theory of the polar plane is considered in sections 12.5 and 12.6 in relation to quadrics.

If the line CQ $x/x_2 = y/y_2 = z/z_2 = \lambda$ cuts the polar plane of Q in S, then the parameter of S is given by

$$\lambda(x_2^2 + y_2^2 + z_2^2) = r^2,$$

so $\lambda = r^2/CQ^2$. Hence S is the point $(x_2r^2/CQ^2, y_2r^2/CQ^2, z_2r^2/CQ^2)$. Evidently

$$CS^2 = (x_2^2 + y_2^2 + z_2^2)r^4/CQ^4 = r^4/CQ^2,$$

so $CS.CQ = r^2$. This result shows that S and Q are inverse points with respect to the sphere.

12.2 Two spheres

A moment's reflexion shows that two spheres intersect in a circle provided the distance between their centres is less than the sum of their radii and greater than the positive difference between their radii. The two spheres touch externally if the distance between the centres equals the sum of the radii, while they touch internally if the distance between the centres equals the positive difference between the radii.

Let the first sphere be of radius r with its centre at the point (a, b, c); let r' and (a', b', c') refer to the second sphere. Their two equations are

$$S \equiv (x - a)^2 + (y - b)^2 + (z - c)^2 - r^2 = 0,$$
$$S' \equiv (x - a')^2 + (y - b')^2 + (z - c')^2 - R^2 = 0.$$

Evidently the equation $S + \lambda S' = 0$ represents a sphere since the three quadratic terms present, x^2, y^2 and z^2, all have the same coefficient $(1 + \lambda)$. Moreover this sphere must contain all the common points of the given spheres S and S'. Hence this general sphere stands on the circle of intersection of S and S'. The parameter λ may be chosen so that the general sphere satisfies some given condition, for example that it should pass through a given point, or that it should touch a given plane.

In particular, if $\lambda = -1$, the equation $S - S' = 0$ represents a plane, since the quadratic terms disappear; it must be the plane containing the circle of intersection of S and S', providing they intersect. Whether the two spheres intersect or not, this plane is called their *radical plane*.

To find the coordinates of the centre N of the circle of intersection of the spheres S and S', we write down the equations of the line of centres CD, and find where it cuts the radical plane $S - S' = 0$. Also, if the perpendicular distance CN from the centre C to the

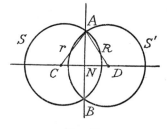

FIG. 47

radical plane is found, the radius AN of the circle of intersection is given by $\sqrt{(r^2 - CN^2)}$. Evidently these calculations can easily be carried out in any numerical example.

Orthogonal spheres. Two spheres intersect *orthogonally* if $\angle CAD = 90°$. The required condition is

$$R^2 + r^2 = CD^2 = (a - a')^2 + (b - b')^2 + (c - c')^2.$$

If the two spheres are given in the form

$$x^2 + y^2 + z^2 + 2ux + 2vy + 2wz + d = 0,$$
$$x^2 + y^2 + z^2 + 2u'x + 2v'y + 2w'z + d' = 0,$$

this condition is equivalent to

$$(u^2 + v^2 + w^2 - d) + (u'^2 + v'^2 + w'^2 - d')$$
$$= (u - u')^2 + (v - v')^2 + (w - w')^2,$$

simplifying to $2(uu' + vv' + ww') = d + d'.$

Radical planes, lines and points. If $P(x_1, y_1, z_1)$ is a point on the radical plane $S - S' = 0$ of the two spheres $S = 0$, $S' = 0$, let PT, PT' be tangent lines from P to the two spheres respectively. The lengths of these tangents are given by

$$PT^2 = (x_1 - a)^2 + (y_1 - b)^2 + (z_1 - c)^2 - r^2,$$
$$PT'^2 = (x_1 - a')^2 + (y_1 - b')^2 + (z_1 - c')^2 - R^2.$$

But $P(x_1, y_1, z_1)$ lies on the radical plane, so

$$S - S' = (x_1 - a)^2 + (y_1 - b)^2 + (z_1 - c)^2 - r^2 - (x_1 - a')^2$$
$$- (y_1 - b')^2 - (z_1 - c')^2 + R^2 = 0,$$

showing that $PT = PT'$. Hence all tangent lines from P to both spheres are of equal length.

Moreover, if PT_λ is a tangent line from P to the general sphere $S + \lambda S' = 0$, it follows that $PT_\lambda = PT = PT'$, a constant for every sphere.

If $S = 0$, $S' = 0$, $S'' = 0$ are three general spheres, there are three radical planes given by

$$S' - S'' = 0, \quad S'' - S = 0, \quad S - S' = 0.$$

Evidently these planes are not independent, since the equation of the third plane is obtained by adding the equations of the first two planes. The three planes pass through a definite line, called the *radical line* of the three spheres. If P is any point on this line, the tangents from P to all three spheres are of equal length.

Finally, if $S''' = 0$ is the equation of a fourth sphere the four radical lines of the four groups of three spheres

$$S' - S'' = S'' - S''' = 0, \quad S - S'' = S'' - S''' = 0,$$
$$S - S' = S' - S''' = 0, \quad S - S' = S' - S'' = 0$$

all pass through a common point, namely the common point of the three planes (say)

$$S' - S'' = S'' - S''' = S - S'' = 0.$$

This point is known as the *radical point* of the four spheres. From this point (and only from this point) tangents drawn to the four spheres are of equal length.

Example 1 Find the equation of the sphere that passes through the four points $(-2, 0, 3)$, $(1, -1, -1)$, $(2, 3, 2)$, $(-2, 3, 4)$. Find the centre and radius of the circular section cut on this sphere by the plane $y - z = 0$, and also the equation of the curve formed by projecting this circle on the plane $y = 0$.

Let the equation of the sphere be

$$x^2 + y^2 + z^2 + 2ux + 2vy + 2wz + d = 0.$$

Inserting the coordinates of the four given points into this equation, we obtain the four equations in u, v, w, d:

$$13 - 4u \qquad + 6w + d = 0,$$
$$3 + 2u - 2v - 2w + d = 0,$$
$$17 + 4u + 6v + 4w + d = 0,$$
$$29 - 4u + 6v + 8w + d = 0.$$

If the first three equations are subtracted in turn from the fourth equation. we obtain the three equations in u, v, w:

$$16 \qquad + 6v + 2w = 0,$$
$$26 - 6u + 8v + 10w = 0,$$
$$12 - 8u \qquad + 4w = 0;$$

these possess the solution $u = 2$, $v = -3$, $w = 1$, together with $d = -11$.

The equation of the sphere becomes

$$x^2 + y^2 + z^2 + 4x - 6y + 2z - 11 = 0,$$

or
$$(x + 2)^2 + (y - 3)^2 + (z + 1)^2 = 25.$$

Its centre is the point $(-2, 3, -1)$, and its radius is 5.

The perpendicular (see Fig. 46) CN from the centre C to the plane $y - z = 0$ is of length $(3 + 1)/\sqrt{2} = 2\sqrt{2}$; hence

$$AN^2 = AC^2 - AN^2 = 25 - 8 = 17,$$

so the radius of the circle is $AN = \sqrt{17}$.

The equations of the perpendicular CN are

$$(x + 2)/0 = (y - 3)/1 = (z + 1)/(-1);$$

this line evidently cuts the plane $y = z$ in the point $N(-2, 1, 1)$.

Finally, the x and z coordinates of every point on this circle are transformed unchanged by orthognal projection to the plane $y = 0$. The locus in the Oxz plane of this projection is found by eliminating y from the defining equations

$$(x + 2)^2 + (y - 3)^2 + (z + 1)^2 = 25 \quad \text{and} \quad y = z.$$

Hence
$$(x + 2)^2 + (z - 3)^2 + (z + 1)^2 = 25,$$

or
$$(x + 2)^2 + 2(z - 1)^2 = 17,$$

an ellipse with centre $(-2, 0, 1)$.

Example 2★ Prove that the two circles

$$x^2 + y^2 + z^2 - 2x + 3y + 4z - 5 = 0, \quad 5y + 6z + 1 = 0;$$
$$x^2 + y^2 + z^2 - 3x - 4y + 5z - 6 = 0, \quad x + 2y - 7z = 0$$

lie on the same sphere, and find its equation.

Any sphere containing the first circle has the form

$$x^2 + y^2 + z^2 - 2x + 3y + 4z - 5 + \lambda(5y + 6z + 1) = 0,$$

and any sphere containing the second circle has the form

$$x^2 + y^2 + z^2 - 3x - 4y + 5z - 6 + \mu(x + 2y - 7z) = 0.$$

If both circles lie on the same sphere, it must be possible to choose λ and μ so these two spheres are identical. Equating the coefficients of x, y, z respectively and the constant terms, we obtain

$$-2 \quad\quad = -3 + \mu,$$
$$3 + 5\lambda = -4 + 2\mu,$$
$$4 + 6\lambda = \quad 5 - 7\mu,$$
$$-5 + \quad \lambda = -6.$$

The first and last equations yield $\lambda = -1$, $\mu = 1$. These values satisfy the remaining two equations, verifying that the two circles lie on one definite sphere; its equation is

$$x^2 + y^2 + z^2 - 2x - 2y - 2z - 6 = 0.$$

Example 3 Show that the two spheres

$$x^2 + y^2 + z^2 + 2x + 8y + 4z + 20 = 0,$$
$$x^2 + y^2 + z^2 + 2x + 2y - 2 = 0$$

do not intersect. Prove that all tangent planes common to both spheres pass through one or other of two points, each collinear with the centres of the two spheres.

The first sphere has centre $(-1, -4, -2)$ and radius 1, while the second sphere has centre $(-1, -1, 0)$ and radius 2. The distance between the centres is $\sqrt{13}$, greater than 3, the sum of the radii. The two spheres do not therefore intersect.

Let any common tangent plane have the equation $lx + my + nz + p = 0$, where $l^2 + m^2 + n^2 = 1$. Using the fact that the perpendicular distances to the plane from the centres must respectively equal the radii, we have

$$(-l - 4m - 2n + p)^2 = 1,$$
$$(-l - m + p)^2 = 4.$$

Hence $\quad\quad -l - 4m - 2n + p = \pm 1, \quad -l - m + p = \pm 2,$

where any combination of signs is permitted. Expressing m and n in terms of l and p, we find that

$$m = \pm 2 - l + p$$

and $\quad\quad 2n = \pm 1 - l - 4m + p = \pm 1 - 4(\pm 2) + 3l - 3p.$

Hence the plane is

$$lx + (\pm 2 - l + p)y + \tfrac{1}{2}[\pm 1 - 4(\pm 2) + 3l - 3p]z + p = 0,$$

or $\quad l(x - y + \tfrac{3}{2}z) + p(y - \tfrac{3}{2}z + 1) + (\pm 2y \pm \tfrac{1}{2}z - 2(\pm 2)z) = 0,$

where in the last bracket either $+2$ is used or -2 in both places.

For all permitted values of l and p, this variable plane obviously passes through the intersection of the three planes

$$x - y + \tfrac{3}{2}z = 0, \quad y - \tfrac{3}{2}z + 1 = 0, \quad \pm 2y \pm \tfrac{1}{2}z - 2(\pm 2)z = 0.$$

Taking $+2$ and $+\tfrac{1}{2}$ (or -2 and $-\tfrac{1}{2}$), these planes intersect in the point $(-1, -7, -4)$; taking $+2$ and $-\tfrac{1}{2}$ (or -2 and $+\tfrac{1}{2}$), they intersect in the point $(-1, -3, -\tfrac{4}{3})$.

The equations of the line joining the two centres are given by

$$(x + 1)/0 = (y + 1)/3 = z/2 = \lambda.$$

$\lambda = -2$ gives the first point and $\lambda = -\tfrac{2}{3}$ the second point; the two fixed points are therefore collinear with the two centres.

12.3 Spherical trigonometry

Although spherical trigonometry is not a branch of coordinate geometry, we shall consider the subject here, since it is concerned with the surface geometry of a sphere.

A *great circle* is cut on the surface of a sphere by a plane passing through its centre. Any other plane, not passing through the centre, intersects the sphere in a circle known as a *small circle*. Geographically, lines of *latitude* form small circles, while lines of *longitude* and the *equator* form great circles.

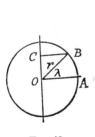

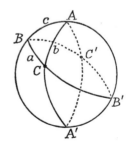

Fig. 48   Fig. 49

One unique great circle passes through two *general* points P and Q on the surface, namely that given by the intersection of the sphere and the plane OPQ, where O is the centre. If PQ is the shorter arc of this circle, then PQ is the shortest distance between P and Q on the surface.

If the radius of the sphere equals r, and if CB is the radius of a small circle at latitude λ, then $CB = r \cos \lambda$. The length of arc along this small circle intercepted between two lines of longitude differing by ω radians is given by $\omega r \cos \lambda$.

A *spherical triangle* is formed by three *great* circles on the surface intersecting in the vertices A, B, C. Clearly these three great circles intersect again on the far side of the sphere in A', B', C', where the lines AA', BB', CC' pass through the centre O. Various other triangles are produced on the surface such as ABC'.

At a vertex A, two tangent lines may be drawn to the sphere that are also tangents to the two great circles intersecting in A. The angle between these two tangents at A is regarded as the angle at A in the spherical triangle; this angle is designated by A. Any side AB of the triangle is measured by the *angle AOB* subtended at O by the great circle arc AB; we denote this angle by c. The length of the great circle arc AB is evidently cr, where c is measured in radians.

The area of the spherical triangle ABC may be found by the following reasoning. The line AOA' is a diameter of the sphere. The two great circle arcs ABA' and ACA' enclose a *lune* on the surface. The ratio of the area of this lune to the total area of the sphere equals the ratio of the angle in radians at A between the two great circles to the complete angle 2π around the point A. That is,

$$\frac{\text{Area of lune } AA'}{4\pi r^2} = \frac{A}{2\pi},$$

yielding

$$\text{Area of lune } AA' = 2Ar^2,$$

provided A is measured in radians.

The area of the triangle ABC may now be found as follows:

$$2\pi r^2 = \text{Area of the top hemispherical face of the sphere}$$

$$= \triangle ABC + \triangle CA'B' + \triangle ACB' + \triangle BA'C$$

$$= \text{lune } C + (\text{lune } B - \triangle ABC) + (\text{lune } A - \triangle ABC)$$

$$= 2(A + B + C)r^2 - 2\triangle ABC.$$

Hence

$$\triangle ABC = (A + B + C - \pi)r^2,$$

where A, B and C are measured in radians. The quantity $A + B + C - \pi$ is termed the *spherical excess* of the triangle. The area being positive, this result shows that $A + B + C > \pi$, unlike the corresponding result for a plane triangle.

12.4 Solution of spherical triangles

We shall now prove the *cosine* and *sine formulae* for a spherical triangle ABC, restricting ourselves to the case in which the angles a, b, c, A, B, C are less than π radians or $180°$.

Let OA be the z-axis of a three dimensional system of coordinates, and let the axis Ox lie in the plane OAB. If the plane OAC intersects the plane Oxy in the line OP, then $\angle POx = A$; also $\angle AOC = b$, $\angle AOB = c$.

If the radius of the sphere is unity, the direction cosines of the radii OB and OC are respectively the coordinates of the points B and C. Now B is the point $(\sin c, 0, \cos c)$ and C is

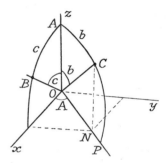

$$(ON \cos A,\ ON \sin A,\ OC \cos b)$$
$$= (\sin b \cos A,\ \sin b \sin A,\ \cos b).$$

The cosine of the angle between OB and OC, namely $\cos a$, is now deduced from the direction cosines of these lines, namely

FIG. 50

$$\cos a = \cos b \cos c + \sin b \sin c \cos A.$$

Similarly,

$$\cos b = \cos c \cos a + \sin c \sin a \cos B,$$
$$\cos c = \cos a \cos b + \sin a \sin b \cos C.$$

These cosine formulae enable one side of the triangle to be calculated if the other two sides and the included angle are known.

If $A = 90°$, then $\cos a = \cos b \cos c$, and if $b = 90°$, we have

$$\cos a = \sin c \cos A.$$

If the radius r is large, and the angles a, b, c small, the cosine formula reduces to that for a plane triangle. If a' is the length of the arc BC, then $a = a'/r$, yielding to the second order

$$\cos a = 1 - a'^2/2r^2, \quad \text{and} \quad \sin a = a'/r.$$

The cosine formula becomes

$$\left(1 - \frac{a'^2}{2r^2}\right) = \left(1 - \frac{b'^2}{2r^2}\right)\left(1 - \frac{c'^2}{2r^2}\right) + \frac{b'}{r}\cdot\frac{c'}{r}\cos A,$$

reducing upon simplification to

$$a'^2 = b'^2 + c'^2 - 2b'c' \cos A.$$

The sine formula for a spherical triangle may be deduced from the cosine formula. We have

$$\frac{\sin^2 A}{\sin^2 a} = \frac{1 - \cos^2 A}{\sin^2 a}$$

$$= \frac{1 - \left(\dfrac{\cos a - \cos b \cos c}{\sin b \sin c}\right)^2}{\sin^2 a}$$

$$= \frac{(1 - \cos^2 b)(1 - \cos^2 c) - (\cos a - \cos b \cos c)^2}{\sin^2 a \sin^2 b \sin^2 c}$$

$$= \frac{1 - \cos^2 a - \cos^2 b - \cos^2 c + 2 \cos a \cos b \cos c}{\sin^2 a \sin^2 b \sin^2 c},$$

symmetrical in a, b, c. We conclude that

$$\frac{\sin A}{\sin a} = \frac{\sin B}{\sin b} = \frac{\sin C}{\sin c}.$$

The arithmetic manipulation occurring in the solution of a spherical triangle is very similar to that for a plane triangle. The following formulae, useful when logarithms are employed, may also be proved, though we shall not provide their proofs here. The close analogy with the formulae of plane trigonometry should be noticed.

If $s = \frac{1}{2}(a + b + c)$ and $S = \frac{1}{2}(A + B + C)$, then

$$\cos \tfrac{1}{2}A = \sqrt{\left(\frac{\sin s \sin (s - a)}{\sin b \sin c}\right)},$$

$$\cos \tfrac{1}{2}a = \sqrt{\left(\frac{\cos (S - B) \cos (S - C)}{\sin B \sin C}\right)},$$

$$\sin \tfrac{1}{2}A = \sqrt{\left(\frac{\sin (s - b) \sin (s - c)}{\sin b \sin c}\right)},$$

$$\sin \tfrac{1}{2}a = \sqrt{\left(\frac{-\cos S \cos (S - A)}{\sin B \sin C}\right)},$$

$$\tan \tfrac{1}{2}A = \sqrt{\left(\frac{\sin (s - b) \sin (s - c)}{\sin s \sin (s - a)}\right)},$$

$$\tan \tfrac{1}{2}a = \sqrt{\left(\frac{-\cos S \cos (S - A)}{\cos (S - B) \cos (S - C)}\right)},$$

$$\tan \tfrac{1}{2}(B - C) = \frac{\sin \tfrac{1}{2}(b - c)}{\sin \tfrac{1}{2}(b + c)} \cot \tfrac{1}{2}A.$$

Example 4   The sides of a spherical triangle are $a = \frac{1}{6}\pi$, $b = \frac{1}{3}\pi$, $c = \frac{1}{4}\pi$. Find the area of the triangle if the sphere is of unit radius.

In terms of the sides, we have

$$\cos A = \frac{\cos a - \cos b \cos c}{\sin b \sin c} = \left(\frac{\sqrt{3}}{2} - \frac{1}{2}\cdot\frac{1}{\sqrt{2}}\right)\Big/\frac{\sqrt{3}}{2}\cdot\frac{1}{\sqrt{2}} =$$

$$\sqrt{2} - \frac{1}{\sqrt{3}} = 0\cdot8369,$$

$$\cos B = \frac{\cos b - \cos c \cos a}{\sin c \sin a} = \left(\frac{1}{2} - \frac{1}{\sqrt{2}}\cdot\frac{\sqrt{3}}{2}\right)\Big/\frac{1}{\sqrt{2}}\cdot\frac{1}{2} =$$

$$\sqrt{2} - \sqrt{3} = -0\cdot3178,$$

$$\cos C = \frac{\cos c - \cos a \cos b}{\sin a \sin b} = \left(\frac{1}{\sqrt{2}} - \frac{\sqrt{3}}{2}\cdot\frac{1}{2}\right)\Big/\frac{1}{2}\cdot\frac{\sqrt{3}}{2} =$$

$$\frac{2\sqrt{6}}{3} - 1 = 0\cdot6330,$$

yielding

$$A = 33°12', \quad B = 108°32', \quad C = 50°44'.$$

Hence,

$$\triangle ABC = (A° + B° + C°)\pi/180 - \pi$$
$$= 192°28'\pi/180 - \pi$$
$$= 192\cdot5\pi/180 - \pi = 0\cdot218.$$

Example 5★   Find the saving of the great circle route over that which follows the parallel between two points of the same latitude λ, differing by 90° in longitude. Show the saving is greatest and amounts to about 265 miles for the 52nd parallel, approximately.

Let the angle A at the North pole be 90°; let B and C be points on the two great circles through A at the same latitude λ. Then $b = c = 90° - \lambda°$.

The radius of the circle of latitude containing B and C is $r \cos \lambda$, so the length of the arc BC along this circle of latitude is $\frac{1}{2}\pi r \cos \lambda$.

Moreover, along the great circle between B and C, we have

$$\cos a = \cos b \cos c + \sin b \sin c \cos A = \sin^2 \lambda,$$

so

$$\text{arc } BC = ar = r \cos^{-1}(\sin^2 \lambda).$$

The saving is therefore $\frac{1}{2}\pi r \cos \lambda - r \cos^{-1}(\sin^2 \lambda)$.

This is a maximum when its derivative with respect to λ vanishes, namely

$$-\tfrac{1}{2}\pi r \sin \lambda + \frac{2r \sin \lambda \cos \lambda}{\sqrt{(1 - \sin^4 \lambda)}} = 0.$$

Cancelling $r \sin \lambda$, and noting that $\sqrt{(1 - \sin^4 \lambda)} = \cos \lambda \sqrt{(1 + \sin^2 \lambda)}$ we have

$$2/\sqrt{(1 + \sin^2 \lambda)} = \tfrac{1}{2}\pi,$$

yielding $\sin^2 \lambda = 0\cdot6211$ and $\lambda = 52°$ approximately.

If $r = 4000$ miles, the saving is

$$4000[\tfrac{1}{2}\pi \cos 52 - \cos^{-1}(0\cdot6211)]$$
$$= 4000(\tfrac{1}{2}\pi 0\cdot6157 - 51\cdot6°\pi/180) \fallingdotseq 265 \text{ miles.}$$

12.5   The general quadric

The general equation in x, y, z containing all terms up to the second degree represents a *quadric*; we write

$$S \equiv ax^2 + by^2 + cz^2 + 2fyz + 2gzx + 2hxy$$
$$+ 2ux + 2vy + 2wz + d = 0.$$

If $u = v = w = 0$, the origin is the centre of the quadric, for if (x_0, y_0, z_0) satisfies the equation, so does the point $(-x_0, -y_0, -z_0)$. If $f = g = h = 0$, the axes of the quadric are parallel to the coordinate axes. Most quadrics may be reduced to the simple form

$$ax^2 + by^2 + cz^2 + d = 0,$$

or, more simply, $ax^2 + by^2 + cz^2 = 1.$

For some special quadrics however, as for conics, this reduction is not possible.

The following general theory, similar to that given in section 9.1, may be omitted if desired, the reader passing over to section 12.6.

Let P be a general point on the line joining $A(x_1, y_1, z_1)$ to $B(x_2, y_2, z_2)$. Parametrically, P may be taken to be

$$x = x_1(1 - \lambda) + \lambda x_2, \quad y = y_1(1 - \lambda) + \lambda y_2, \quad z = z_1(1 - \lambda) + \lambda z_2,$$

where λ is proportional to the signed distance AP. The point A is given by $\lambda = 0$, and B by $\lambda = 1$.

This line cuts the quadric in C and D; the parameters λ_1 and λ_2 of these points are obtained by substituting the coordinates of P into the equation $S = 0$, and by rearranging this equation to be a quadratic in λ. We obtain

$$a[x_1(1 - \lambda) + \lambda x_2]^2 + \ldots + 2f[y_1(1 - \lambda) + \lambda y_2][z_1(1 - \lambda) + \lambda z_2] + \ldots$$
$$+ 2u[x_1(1 - \lambda) + \lambda x_2] + \ldots + d = 0,$$

or $$\lambda^2(S_{11} - 2S_{12} + S_{22}) + 2\lambda(S_{12} - S_{11}) + S_{11} = 0, \tag{5}$$

using the extended form of the notation introduced in section 9.1. There are three cases to be considered.

Case i. Let A be on the quadric, so $S_{11} = 0$. We seek all points B such that the line AB touches the quadric at A, implying that the two points C and D must coincide in A. The quadratic equation (5) must have equal roots $\lambda = 0$, so the coefficient of λ must vanish. This is evidently equivalent to $S_{12} = 0$. The locus of B is therefore the plane $S_1 = 0$, a plane that is called the *tangent plane* at A.

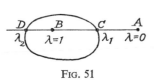

FIG. 51

Case ii. If A is a point from which tangent lines may be drawn to the quadric, we may find the equation of the *cone* formed by all such tangent lines from A. The points C and D must coincide if AB is a tangent. The quadratic equation (5) has identical roots, so

$$(S_{12} - S_{11})^2 = S_{11}(S_{11} - 2S_{12} + S_{22}),$$

or $$S_{12}^2 = S_{11}S_{22}.$$

The locus of B is therefore given by the equation

$$S_1{}^2 = SS_{11}.$$

Case iii. For an arbitrary point A, we seek the locus of B such that the signed lengths AC, BD, AD, BC satisfy the condition

$$AC.BD/AD.BC = -1.$$

The point B is stated to be the *harmonic conjugate* of A with respect to C and D. The parameters of points being proportional to their signed distance from A, this condition is equivalent to

$$(0 - \lambda_1)(1 - \lambda_2)/(0 - \lambda_2)(1 - \lambda_1) = -1,$$

or
$$\lambda_1 + \lambda_2 = 2\lambda_1\lambda_2.$$

Choosing the sum and product of the roots from the coefficients of the quadratic equation (5), we find

$$-2(S_{12} - S_{11}) = 2S_{11},$$

or $S_{12} = 0$. The locus of B is therefore the plane $S_1 = 0$, known as the *polar plane* of the *pole A*.

12.6   The simpler equation of the quadric

Tangent planes.   Let us consider the equation of the quadric in the form

$$S \equiv ax^2 + by^2 + cz^2 + d = 0.$$

If $P(x_1, y_1, z_1)$ is a point on this quadric, the direction ratios of the normal to the surface at P are given by

$$\partial S/\partial x, \quad \partial S/\partial y, \quad \partial S/\partial z$$

evaluated at P (see section 15.8). These are proportional to ax_1, by_1, cz_1 respectively.

The tangent plane passes through P, its normal coinciding with the normal to the surface at P; its equation is

$$(x - x_1)ax_1 + (y - y_1)by_1 + (z - z_1)cz_1 = 0,$$

or
$$axx_1 + byy_1 + czz_1 + d = 0, \tag{6}$$

equivalent to the equation $S_1 = 0$ found in section 12.5.

The equations of the normal at P are given by

$$(x - x_1)/ax_1 = (y - y_1)/by_1 = (z - z_1)/cz_1.$$

Let a given plane have the equation

$$lx + my + nx + p = 0.$$

This will be a tangent plane to the quadric if it is of the form (6), where (x_1, y_1, z_1) satisfies the equation of the quadric. Comparing coefficients, we have

$$ax_1/l = by_1/m = cz_1/n = d/p,$$

so the point $(x_1, y_1, z_1) \equiv (ld/ap, md/bp, nd/cp)$ must lie on the quadric. Substituting into its equation, we obtain

$$a(ld/ap)^2 + b(md/bp)^2 + c(nd/cp)^2 + d = 0,$$

or

$$l^2/a + m^2/b + n^2/c + p^2/d = 0.$$

This is the condition for a given plane to touch a given quadric.

Polar theory. Let $P(x_1, y_1, z_1)$ be the *pole*, namely a point from which tangents can be drawn to the quadric. Then the points of contact of all tangent lines through P to the quadric lie on a plane, called the *polar plane* of the pole P. Its equation is

$$axx_1 + byy_1 + czz_1 + d = 0;$$

this may be proved by the same method as that given for the sphere in section 12.1.

If the polar plane is given in the form

$$lx + my + nz + p = 0,$$

its pole is found by comparing coefficients in these two equations, namely

$$ax_1/l = by_1/m = cz_1/n = d/p;$$

we conclude that the pole is the point $(ld/ap, md/bp, nd/cp)$.

If the polar plane of $P(x_1, y_1, z_1)$ passes through $Q(x_2, y_2, z_2)$, we have

$$ax_1x_2 + by_1y_2 + cz_1z_2 + d = 0.$$

This is the condition that the polar plane of Q should pass through P. Two such points are called *conjugate points*.

If the pole P varies along line L_1 defined by two of its points $A(x_3, y_3, z_3)$ and $B(x_4, y_4, z_4)$, then the polar plane of P rotates about a line L_2. For P satisfies the line whose equations are

$$(x - x_3)/(x_4 - x_3) = (y - y_3)/(y_4 - y_3) = (z - z_3)/(z_4 - z_3) = \lambda,$$

so parametrically, P may be taken to be the point given by

$$x = \lambda x_4 + (1 - \lambda)x_3, \quad y = \lambda y_4 + (1 - \lambda)y_3, \quad z = \lambda z_4 + (1 - \lambda)z_3.$$

Its polar plane has the equation

$$ax[\lambda x_4 + (1 - \lambda)x_3] + by[\lambda y_4 + (1 - \lambda)y_3]$$
$$+ cz[\lambda z_4 + (1 - \lambda)z_3] + d = 0,$$

or $(1 - \lambda)(axx_3 + byy_3 + czz_3 + d)$
$$+ \lambda(axx_4 + byy_4 + czz_4 + d) = 0.$$

This variable plane therefore contains the fixed line L_2 defined by the polar planes of A and B.

Conversely, if Q is any point on L_2, then A and Q are conjugate points; so also are B and Q. Hence the polar plane of Q passes through A and B; it therefore contains the line L_1. Two such lines L_1 and L_2 with this property are called *polar lines*.

If the line L_2 cuts the quadric in points C and D (whose coordinates can be found), the two tangent planes at C and D evidently contain the line L_1.

Planes and quadrics. We first observe that a straight line cuts a quadric in two points, whose coordinates may either be real, coincident or imaginary. Such points are obviously found by substituting the parametric form of a point on the line into the equation of the quadric.

FIG. 52

A plane cuts a quadric in a plane curve. But any line in this plane cuts the quadric and hence this plane curve in two points, which may be either real, coincident or imaginary. But a conic is the only plane curve such that any line in its plane cuts it in two such points. It follows that a plane cuts a quadric in a conic.

If $P(x_1, y_1, z_1)$ is a given point, we may find the equation of the plane through P such that P is the centre of the conic intercepted on the quadric.

The equation

$$(x - x_1)/l = (y - y_1)/m = (z - z_1)/n = \lambda$$

represents any chord through P. It cuts the quadric

$$ax^2 + by^2 + cz^2 + d = 0$$

in points A and B given by

$$a(l\lambda + x_1)^2 + b(m\lambda + y_1)^2 + c(n\lambda + z_1)^2 + d = 0. \qquad (7)$$

If this chord AB lies in the required plane, P must be the centre of the segment AB. The sum of the values of λ at A and B therefore vanishes, so

$$alx_1 + bmy_1 + cnz_1 = 0,$$

being proportional to the coefficient of λ in equation (7). This result may be reinterpreted to show that the direction PN with direction ratios (ax_1, by_1, cz_1) is perpendicular to AB with direction ratios (l, m, n). PN must therefore be the normal to the required plane, whose equation then becomes

$$(x - x_1)ax_1 + (y - y_1)by_1 + (z - z_1)cz_1 = 0. \qquad (8)$$

Conversely, if

$$lx + my + nz + p = 0 \qquad (9)$$

is a given plane, we may find the coordinates (x_1, y_1, z_1) of the centre of the conic so formed by comparing coefficients in equations (8) and (9), obtaining

$$ax_1/l = by_1/m = cz_1/n = -(ax_1{}^2 + by_1{}^2 + cz_1{}^2)/p.$$

This set of equations may be solved for x_1, y_1, z_1 by equating these ratios to λ, and inserting the values $x_1 = l\lambda/a$, $y_1 = m\lambda/b$, $z_1 = n\lambda/c$ into equation (9) of the plane in which $P(x_1, y_1, z_1)$ lies, thereby determining λ.

12.7 The standard equations of the quadric

Thus far, we have considered the quadric $ax^2 + by^2 + cz^2 + d = 0$ without any examination of the general shape of the surface. Three standard equations produce real surfaces.

The ellipsoid. This has an equation of the form

$$x^2/a^2 + y^2/b^2 + z^2/c^2 = 1.$$

The surface is evidently finite in extent; any point $P(x, y, z)$ on this surface satisfies the inequalities

$$|x| \leqslant a, \quad |y| \leqslant b, \quad |z| \leqslant c.$$

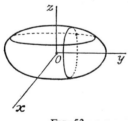

Fig. 53

Any plane section must therefore be a conic of finite extent, namely an ellipse or a circle. In particular, if $b = c$, the quadric is a *quadric of revolution* about the x-axis. In Figure 53, we have illustrated sections parallel to the planes Oxy, Oxz.

The hyperboloid of one sheet. This has an equation of the form

$$x^2/a^2 + y^2/b^2 - z^2/c^2 = 1.$$

Any plane $z = $ constant, k say, cuts the surface in an ellipse, for the x and y coordinates satisfy

$$x^2/a^2 + y^2/b^2 = 1 + k^2/c^2 > 0.$$

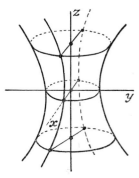

But if the plane is of the form $y = $ constant, K say, the x and z coordinates of the conic intercepted on the quadric satisfy

$$x^2/a^2 - z^2/c^2 = 1 - K^2/b^2.$$

If $|K| < b$, this equation represents a hyperbola, its major axis parallel to Ox, but if $|K| > b$, the major axis of the hyperbola is parallel to Oz.

Similar results are valid for planes of the form $x = $ constant.

FIG. 54

Some of these features are illustrated in Figure 54. The whole surface forms a continuous whole, so it is designated as being of "*one sheet*".

The hyperboloid of two sheets. This has an equation of the form

$$x^2/a^2 - y^2/b^2 - z^2/c^2 = 1.$$

A plane $x = k$ cuts the quadric in an ellipse with the equation

$$y^2/b^2 + z^2/c^2 = k^2/a^2 - 1$$

provided $|k| > a$. If $|k| < a$, the plane does not intersect the quadric. Planes parallel to Oxz and Oxy cut the surface in hyperbolae.

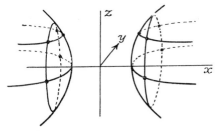

FIG. 55

Such a surface is designated as being of "*two sheets*", since it consists of two distinct parts, namely for $x < -a$ and $x > a$.

The paraboloids. In the reduction of the general equation of the quadric, it is not always possible to remove the linear terms. Under these circumstances, the standard form is taken to be

$$x^2/a^2 \pm y^2/b^2 = z/c,$$

where $c > 0$. Such surfaces are called *paraboloids*. The plane $z = k$ intersects the surface in an ellipse or hyperbola depending on the sign chosen in the equation, while planes of the form $x = K$, $y = K$ yield parabolae. Fig. 56 illustrates the surface with a positive sign; z must be positive for real values of x and y. Fig. 57 illustrates the surface with the negative sign: a *saddle-point* exists at the origin.

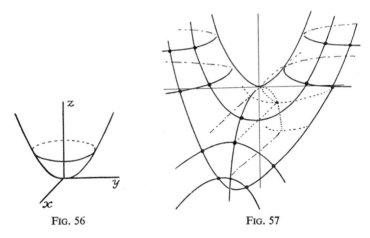

FIG. 56   FIG. 57

The hyperboloids of one sheet and the hyperbolic-paraboloids enjoy the common property of possessing generators. A *generator* is a straight line, infinite in extent, that lies wholly in the surface. Consider the equation

$$x^2/a^2 + y^2/b^2 - z^2/c^2 = 1,$$

or $$x^2/a^2 - z^2/c^2 = 1 - y^2/b^2.$$

Factorization yields

$$\left(\frac{x}{a} + \frac{z}{c}\right)\left(\frac{x}{a} - \frac{z}{c}\right) = \left(1 + \frac{y}{b}\right)\left(1 - \frac{y}{b}\right).$$

Consider the two lines

$$\frac{x}{a} + \frac{z}{c} = \lambda\left(1 - \frac{y}{b}\right), \qquad \frac{x}{a} - \frac{z}{c} = \frac{1}{\lambda}\left(1 + \frac{y}{b}\right), \tag{10}$$

$$\frac{x}{a} + \frac{z}{c} = \mu\left(1 + \frac{y}{b}\right), \qquad \frac{x}{a} - \frac{z}{c} = \frac{1}{\mu}\left(1 - \frac{y}{b}\right), \tag{11}$$

where λ and μ are parameters.

By multiplication, it can be seen that any point on line (10) for any value of λ satisfies the equation of the quadric; likewise any point on line (11) satisfies the equation of the quadric.

Two families of generators exist, namely family (10) given by all values of λ and family (11) for all values of μ.

System (10) forms a set of mutually non-intersecting family of lines. The two lines given by $\lambda = h, k$ intersect only if the determinant of the coefficients

$$\begin{vmatrix} 1/a & h/b & 1/c & -h \\ 1/a & -1/hb & -1/c & -1/h \\ 1/a & k/b & 1/c & -k \\ 1/a & -1/kb & -1/c & -1/k \end{vmatrix}$$

vanishes. Its value is however $4(h - k)^2/abchk$, which cannot vanish if $h \neq k$. The two lines do not therefore intersect.

Similarly, family (11) forms a non-intersecting system of lines.

But each line in family (10) intersects each line in family (11). The determinant of the coefficients

$$\begin{vmatrix} 1/a & h/b & 1/c & -h \\ 1/a & -1/hb & -1/c & -1/h \\ 1/a & -k/b & 1/c & -k \\ 1/a & 1/kb & -1/c & -1/k \end{vmatrix}$$

FIG. 58

vanishes, since (row 1 − row 3) is proportional to (row 2 − row 4).

If three generators from one family are given, the whole of the hyperboloid is traced out by all the common transversals; these form the generators of the second family.

Example 6* Show that the plane $3x + 2y + z = p$ touches the ellipsoid

$$3x^2 + 4y^2 + z^2 = 20 \text{ if } p = \pm 10,$$

and find the length of the chord of contact between the two tangent planes. What is the angle between this chord and the common normal to the planes?

If one point of contact is (x_1, y_1, z_1), the tangent plane there is

$$3xx_1 + 4yy_1 + zz_1 = 20.$$

Comparing coefficients in this and the given plane we have

$$3x_1/3 = 4y_1/2 = z_1/1 = 20/p,$$

yielding $x_1 = 20/p$, $y_1 = 10/p$, $z_1 = 20/p$. This point lies on the quadric, so

$$3(20/p)^2 + 4(10/p)^2 + (20/p)^2 = 20,$$

yielding $p = \pm 10$.

The two points of contact are then $(2, 1, 2)$ and $(-2, -1, -2)$. The length of the chord between them is $\sqrt{(16 + 4 + 16)} = 6$.

The direction ratios of this chord may be taken to be (4, 2, 4), so the direction cosines are ($\frac{2}{3}$, $\frac{1}{3}$, $\frac{2}{3}$). The direction cosines of the normal to the tangent planes are (3, 2, 1)/$\sqrt{14}$. Hence the angle between these two directions is

$$\cos^{-1}[(2 \cdot 3 + 2 + 2)/3\sqrt{14}] = \cos^{-1}(10/3\sqrt{14}).$$

Example 7★ Prove that the mid-points of a set of parallel chords of an ellipsoid are coplanar. If the equation of the ellipsoid is $6x^2 + 3y^2 + 4z^2 = 1$ and the direction cosines of the chords are given by $l:m:n = 2:5:4$, find the inclination of the chords to the normal of the plane which bisects them.

Let $M(X, Y, Z)$ be the mid-point of the chord with fixed direction cosines (l, m, n). Then the line

$$(x - X)/l = (y - Y)/m = (z - Z)/n = \lambda$$

cuts the ellipsoid $ax^2 + by^2 + cz^2 = 1$ in points whose parameters are given by

$$a(l\lambda + X)^2 + b(m\lambda + Y)^2 + c(n\lambda + Z)^2 = 1.$$

The mid-point is given by $\lambda = 0$, so the values of λ satisfying this equation must be equal but opposite in sign. The sum of the roots vanishes, so

$$alX + bmY + cnZ = 0,$$

showing that M lies on the plane $alx + bmy + cnz = 0$.

Inserting the given values $a = 6$, $b = 3$, $c = 4$, $l:m:n = 2:5:4$, we obtain the equation of the plane

$$12x + 15y + 16z = 0.$$

The direction cosines of the chords are $(2:5:4)/\sqrt{45}$, and those for the normal to the plane are (12, 15, 16)/25. Hence the required angle is

$$\cos^{-1}[(2 \cdot 12 + 5 \cdot 15 + 4 \cdot 16)/25\sqrt{45}] = \cos^{-1}(163/75\sqrt{5}).$$

Example 8★ Find the equations of the tangent plane and of the normal at the point (X, Y, Z) of the ellipsoid $2x^2 + 3y^2 + z^2 = 1$.

Show that the equation $x^2 + y^2 = 3z^2$ represents a right circular cone of semi-vertical angle $60°$. If normals are drawn to the above ellipsoid at the points of intersection with the cone, prove that these normals meet the plane $z = 0$ in points lying on the ellipse $14x^2 + 5y^2 = 6$, $z = 0$.

The direction ratios of the normal at the point (X, Y, Z) on the ellipsoid are given by $(2X, 3Y, Z)$. The equation of the tangent plane is

$$2X(x - X) + 3Y(y - Y) + Z(z - Z) = 0,$$

or
$$2Xx + 3Yy + Zz = 1$$

since $2X^2 + 3Y^2 + Z^2 = 1$. The equations of the normal are

$$(x - X)/2X = (y - Y)/3Y = (z - Z)/Z.$$

If the point $P(x_1, y_1, z_1)$ lies on the surface $x^2 + y^2 = 3z^2$, so does the point $(\lambda x_1, \lambda y_1, \lambda z_1)$, since the equation is homogeneous of degree two. The line therefore joining the origin O to P lies wholly on the surface. Moreover, the surface is one of revolution about the z-axis, on account of the combination $(x^2 + y^2)$. The direction cosines of this axis are $(0, 0, 1)$, and those of OP are $(x_1, y_1, z_1)/\sqrt{(x_1{}^2 + y_1{}^2 + z_1{}^2)}$. Hence

$$\cos \angle POz = z_1/\sqrt{(x_1{}^2 + y_1{}^2 + z_1{}^2)} = z_1/\sqrt{(4z_1{}^2)} = \tfrac{1}{2},$$

showing that $\angle POz = 60°$.

Let the point (X, Y, Z) be common to both the ellipsoid and the cone:

$$2X^2 + 3Y^2 + Z^2 = 1, \quad X^2 + Y^2 = 3Z^2. \qquad (12)$$

The normal to the ellipsoid at (X, Y, Z) cuts the plane $z = 0$ where

$$(x - X)/2X = (y - Y)/3Y = -1,$$

namely $x = -X, y = -2Y$. To find the x,y-equation of this locus, we eliminate Z from equations (12), and substitute $X = -x$, $Y = -\tfrac{1}{2}y$; we obtain

$$X^2 + Y^2 = 3(1 - 2X^2 - 3Y^2),$$
or
$$7X^2 + 10Y^2 = 3.$$

In terms of x and y this equation becomes

$$14x^2 + 5y^2 = 6.$$

Example 9 Planes passing through the line $x = y - 2 = z$ meet the ellipsoid $x^2 + 4y^2 + 3z^2 = 1$ in an ellipse. Prove (i) the centres of these ellipses all lie on a (plane) conic, (ii) the centre of this conic is the point $(-\tfrac{1}{2}, \tfrac{1}{2}, -\tfrac{1}{2})$.

(i) Any plane through the given line may be written in the form

$$(y - 2 - z) + \lambda(z - x) = 0.$$

To find the centre (A, B, C) of the ellipse intercepted on the quadric by this plane we use the method and equation deduced at the end of section 12.6. This equation takes the form

$$A/(-\lambda) = 4B/1 = 3C/(\lambda - 1) = (A^2 + 4B^2 + 3C^2)/2.$$

Eliminating λ from the first three ratios, we obtain the equation

$$A + 4B + 3C = 0,$$

showing that the centres lie on the plane $x + 4y + 3z = 0$.

The second and fourth ratios yield the equation

$$A^2 + 4B^2 + 3C^2 = 8B,$$

showing that the locus of the centres is the conic intercepted on the quadric $x^2 + 4y^2 + 3z^2 = 8y$ by the plane $x + 4y + 3z = 0$.

(ii) To find the centre of this conic, we make the substitutions $x = X, y = Y + 1$, $z = Z$, in order to reduce the equation of the quadric to standard form. We obtain:

$$X + 4Y + 3Z + 4 = 0, \quad X^2 + 4Y^2 + 3Z^2 + 4 = 0.$$

The centre (p, q, r) of this conic is found by reapplying the method just used; we obtain the equations

$$p/1 = q/1 = r/1 = -(p^2 + 4q^2 + 3r^2/4,$$

yielding $p = q = r = -\tfrac{1}{2}$. In the original coordinate system, the centre is the point $(-\tfrac{1}{2}, \tfrac{1}{2}, -\tfrac{1}{2})$.

Example 10 All tangent lines to the sphere $x^2 + y^2 + z^2 = 1$ are drawn, having direction ratios $(2, 1, 1)$; these lines are intercepted by the quadric $x^2 + y^2 + 2z^2 = 4$. Show that the mid-points of these intercepts form an ellipse; find the lengths of its semi-axes.

The line $\frac{1}{2}(x - X) = y - Y = z - Z = \lambda$, where (X, Y, Z) lies on the sphere, touches the sphere if its direction ratios $(2, 1, 1)$ are such that the line is perpendicular to the normal at (X, Y, Z) with direction ratios (X, Y, Z). We have the equations

$$X^2 + Y^2 + Z^2 = 1, \quad 2X + Y + Z = 0. \tag{13}$$

This line intercepts the quadric in points whose parameters are given by

$$(2\lambda + X)^2 + (\lambda + Y)^2 + 2(\lambda + Z)^2 = 4.$$

The value of λ giving the mid-point of this intercept is provided by the average of the roots of this quadratic equation, namely by

$$\lambda = -(2X + Y + 2Z)/7 = -Z/7$$

from the second equation (13). The mid-point is therefore

$$x = X + 2\lambda = X - \tfrac{2}{7}Z, \quad y = Y + \lambda = Y - \tfrac{1}{7}Z, \quad z = Z + \lambda = \tfrac{6}{7}Z,$$

so $$Z = \tfrac{7}{6}z, \quad X = x + \tfrac{1}{3}z, \quad Y = y + \tfrac{1}{6}z.$$

To eliminate X, Y, Z, we substitute these values into equations (13), thereby obtaining relationships between the x, y, z coordinates of the mid-points:

$$(x + \tfrac{1}{3}z)^2 + (y + \tfrac{1}{6}z)^2 + (\tfrac{7}{6}z)^2 = 1,$$
$$2(x + \tfrac{1}{3}z) + (y + \tfrac{1}{6}z) + \tfrac{7}{6}z = 0.$$

Rearranged, the mid-points lie on the plane

$$2x + y + 2x = 0 \tag{14}$$

and on the quadric

$$x^2 + y^2 + \tfrac{3}{2}z^2 + \tfrac{1}{3}z(2x + y) = 1$$

or on the ellipsoid

$$x^2 + y^2 + \tfrac{1}{6}z^2 = 1, \tag{15}$$

using $2x + y = -2z$ from (14). Hence the locus of the mid-points lies on the ellipse intercepted on the ellipsoid (15) by the plane (14).

The origin must be the centre of this ellipse, since the plane (14) passes through O. To find the lengths of the semi-axes, we require the maximum and minimum values of $r^2 = x^2 + y^2 + z^2$ subject to conditions (14) and (15), that is, of $r^2 = 1 + \tfrac{1}{6}z^2$ from equation (15).

The minimum value of z^2 is zero, so the minimum value of r^2 is 1, yielding 1 as the length of the semi-minor axis.

To find the maximum value of z^2 we eliminate y between equations (14) and (15), obtaining

$$5x^2 + 8xz + \tfrac{29}{6}z^2 = 1.$$

The solution for x in terms of z contains the discriminant

$$64z^2 - 20(\tfrac{29}{6}z^2 - 1).$$

The largest permissible value of z^2 makes this discriminant vanish, giving $z^2 = \tfrac{30}{49}$. Hence the maximum value of $r^2 = 1 + \tfrac{5}{49} = \tfrac{54}{49}$, showing that the length of the semi-major axis is $\tfrac{3}{7}\sqrt{6}$.

THE SPHERE AND THE QUADRIC

Example 11   A variable line passes through the point (a, pa, pa) with direction ratios $(2, p - p^{-1}, p + p^{-1})$, where p is a parameter. Find the equation of the surface generated by the line. Find also the equations of the two sets of generators on the surface, and the locus of the points of intersection of perpendicular generators.

A typical line has the equations

$$\frac{x - a}{2} = \frac{y - pa}{p - p^{-1}} = \frac{z - pa}{p + p^{-1}}.$$

Rearranging, we obtain the equations

$$(x - a)(p - p^{-1}) = 2(y - pa), \quad (x - a)(p + p^{-1}) = 2(z - pa).$$

The successive addition and subtraction of these two equations yield

$$(x - a)p = (y + z - 2pa), \quad (x - a)(-p^{-1}) = (y - z).$$

Solving each equation for p, we obtain

$$p = \frac{y + z}{x + a} = \frac{a - x}{y - z},$$

giving the equation of the surface in the form

$$x^2 + y^2 - z^2 = a^2.$$

We now factorize the rearranged form of the equation

$$y^2 - z^2 = a^2 - x^2,$$

obtaining $$(y - z)(y + z) = (a - x)(a + x).$$

The two families of generators are then given by

$$\left.\begin{array}{l} y - z = q(a - x) \\ y + z = (a + x)/q \end{array}\right\}, \quad \left.\begin{array}{l} y - z = r(a + x) \\ y + z = (a - x)/r \end{array}\right\},$$

or

$$\left.\begin{array}{l} qx + y - z = qa \\ x - qy - qz = -a \end{array}\right\}, \quad \left.\begin{array}{l} rx - y + z = -ra \\ x + ry + rz = a \end{array}\right\}.$$

The direction ratios of these two lines are given by

$$-2q, \quad q^2 - 1, \quad -q^2 - 1 \quad \text{and} \quad -2r, \quad 1 - r^2, \quad 1 + r^2.$$

The lines are perpendicular if

$$4qr + (q^2 - 1)(1 - r^2) - (1 + q^2)(1 + r^2) = 0,$$

simplifying to $r = 1/q$.

The point of intersection is then given by

$$\frac{y - z}{a - x} = \frac{a + x}{y + z} = q = \frac{1}{r} = \frac{a + x}{y - z} = \frac{y + z}{a - x}.$$

The second and third ratios imply that $z = 0$; while the first and second ratios imply that $x^2 + y^2 = a^2$. The locus of the point of intersection of perpendicular generators is therefore the circle $x^2 + y^2 = a^2$ in the plane $z = 0$.

9

EXERCISES

The sphere

(1) $\star$. Find the equation of each of the spheres which passes through the circle $x^2 + y^2 + z^2 - 2x - 6y = 0, 2x - 4y + 2z - 5 = 0$, and touches the plane $z = 0$. Prove that the distance between the centres of these spheres is $\sqrt{6}$ and that the distance between their points of contact with the plane $z = 0$ is $\sqrt{5}$.

(2) $\star$. Show that if the plane $px + qy + z = 5$ touches the sphere $x^2 + y^2 + z^2 = 16$, then $16(p^2 + q^2) = 9$. Find the condition for this plane to touch the sphere $(x + 5)^2 + y^2 + z^2 = 25$. Hence find the equations of the real common tangent planes of these two spheres which pass through the point $(0, 0, 5)$.

(3) $\star$. If the plane $ax + by + cz + d = 0$ touches the sphere

$$(x - 1)^2 + y^2 + (z - 1)^2 = 1,$$

prove that $a^2 + b^2 + c^2 = (a + c + d)^2$. If this plane also passes through the point $(0, 0, 2)$, show that it cuts the plane $z = 0$ in a line which touches the parabola $y^2 = 4x, z = 0$.

(4) $\star$. Find the equation of the sphere with centre $(3, 0, 8)$ which cuts off a chord of length 16 on the line of intersection of the planes

$$2x + y - z = 7, \quad 4x - 4y - 5z = 29.$$

(5) $\star$. Find the equation of the sphere whose centre is the origin, and whose radius is 5 units. Find the range of values of λ for which the plane $3x + 4y + 12z = \lambda$ cuts the sphere, and find the radius of the circle of intersection in the case $\lambda = 39$.

(6) $\star$. Find the equation of the sphere whose centre is the point $(1, 2, 3)$ and which touches the plane $3x + 2y + z + 4 = 0$. Find also the radius of the circle in which the sphere is cut by the plane given by the equation $x + y + z = 0$.

(7) $\star$. Find the values of c for which the sphere

$$x^2 + y^2 + z^2 + 18x - 6y + 2z + c = 0$$

touches the sphere $x^2 + y^2 + z^2 - 6x + 2y - 4z + 13 = 0$, and obtain the co-ordinates of the points of contact.

(8) $\star$. Find the equation of the sphere whose centre is at the point $A(5, -10, 5)$ and which touches the plane $9x + 12y + 20z = 0$.

A sphere is drawn with its centre at the origin and passing through A. Prove that the circle in which it cuts the first sphere lies in the plane $10x - 20y + 10z = 299$.

(9) $\star$. Find the centre and radius of the circle in which the spheres

$$x^2 + y^2 + z^2 - 8x - 10y - 4z - 15 = 0,$$
$$x^2 + y^2 + z^2 + 2x + 10y + 6z + 5 = 0$$

intersect, and obtain the equation of the sphere on which this circle is a great circle.

(10) $\star$. Find the coordinates of the centre and the radius of the sphere $x^2 + y^2 + z^2 - 2x - 4y + 6z = 2$. Show that the intersection of this sphere and the sphere $x^2 + y^2 + z^2 - 4x - 6y + 4z + 4 = 0$ is a circle lying in the plane $x + y + z = 3$. Find the coordinates of the centre and the radius of this circle.

(11) $\star$. Find the condition that the plane $lx + my + nz + p = 0$ should touch the sphere $x^2 + y^2 + z^2 + 2ux + 2vy + 2wz + d = 0$.

Find the equations of the tangent planes to the sphere
$$x^2 + y^2 + z^2 - 2x - 4y + 2z - 219 = 0$$
which intersect in the line $3(x - 10) = -4(y - 14) = -6(z - 2)$.

(12)★. A line with direction ratios $l:m:n$ is drawn through the fixed point $(0, 0, a)$ to touch the sphere $x^2 + y^2 + z^2 - 2ax = 0$. Prove that $m^2 + 2nl = 0$. Find the coordinates of the point P in which this line meets the plane $z = 0$ and prove that, as the line varies, P traces out the parabola $y^2 = 2ax$, $z = 0$.

(13)★. Find the centre and radius of the circle of intersection of the sphere $x^2 + y^2 + z^2 + 12x - 12y - 16z + 111 = 0$ and the plane $2x + 2y + z - 17 = 0$. Show that there exist two planes through the origin which meet this plane at right-angles and touch the sphere.

(14)★. Show that the line $(x - 6)/3 = (y - 7)/4 = (z - 3)/5$ touches the sphere $x^2 + y^2 + z^2 = 2x + 4y + 4$ and find the coordinates of the point of contact. Find the equations of the two tangent planes to this sphere which contain the line $(x - 7)/5 = (y - 11)/6 = (3 - z)/2$.

(15)★. Find the equation of the sphere whose centre is at the origin and which touches the line $x = y - a = z - 2a$. Find the point of contact and the equation of the tangent plane to the sphere at that point.
Find also the equations of the two planes which pass through the given line and touch the sphere $x^2 + y^2 + z^2 = a^2$.

(16)★. A sphere is drawn to touch the three coordinate planes and to pass through the point $(5, 1, 2)$. Find the equations of the two spheres which satisfy these conditions.
Find also the equation of the tangent plane to each sphere at the point $(5, 1, 2)$ and determine the angle between these tangent planes.

(17)★. Three spheres have centres $(0, 0, 0)$, $(3a, 0, 0)$, $(0, 4a, 0)$ and radii $a, 2a, 3a$ respectively, and two planes, making an acute angle θ with each other, are such that every one of the spheres touches the two planes. Show that $\cos \theta = \frac{5}{18}$.

(18)★. Find the condition that the spheres
$$x^2 + y^2 + z^2 + 2ax + 2by + 2cz + d = 0,$$
$$x^2 + y^2 + z^2 + 2a'x + 2b'y + 2c'z + d' = 0$$
should be orthogonal. Prove that there exist eight spheres, of radius 5 units, which are orthogonal to the sphere $x^2 + y^2 + z^2 = 16$, touch the x-axis, and cut off a segment of length 2 units from the y-axis.

(19)★. Find the equations of the two spheres which touch the plane $z = 4a$ and which intersect the plane $x + y + z = 3a$ in a circle of radius a and centre (a, a, a).

(20)★. Find the condition that the plane $lx + my + nz + p = 0$ should touch the sphere $(x - a)^2 + (y - b)^2 + (z - c)^2 = r^2$. Three spheres S_1, S_2, S_3 have centres $(0, 0, 0)$, $(3, 0, 0)$, $(0, 30, 0)$ and radii $1, 1, 19$ respectively. Find the equations of all common tangent planes π of the three spheres such that S_1 and S_3 lie on opposite sides, S_2 and S_3 on the same side of π. Show that there are two such planes and that the acute angle between them is θ, where $\cos \theta = \frac{7}{9}$.

Spherical trigonometry

(21)★. In the spherical triangle ABC the angle C is $90°$ and $a = 30°$, $b = 90°$. Find the side c and the area of the triangle.

(22)*. Two ships sail from (35°S., 110°W.) to (35°S., 175°E.). One ship steams along the minor arc of the great circle passing between these points, while the other ship follows the minor arc of the circle of latitude through these points. Taking the radius of the Earth as 4000 miles, compare the distances steamed by the two ships.

(23)*. In a spherical triangle ABC, $A = \frac{1}{4}\pi$, $b = c = \frac{1}{2}\pi$, and D is the mid-point of the side AC. If $BDC = \alpha$, show that $\cos \alpha = 1/\sqrt{3}$ and show that the areas of the triangles ABD and ABC are in the ratio $(3\pi - 8\alpha):\pi$.

(24)*. If B and C are points on the equator whose longitudes differ by 90° and A is a point in latitude λ on the meridian through C, prove that in the triangle ABC the side AB and the angle A are both right-angles. If M, the mid-point of the side AB, has latitude α and the difference of the longitudes of M and B is β, show that $\sqrt{2} \sin \alpha = \sin \lambda$, $\tan \beta = \cos \lambda$.

(25)*. What is the area of the triangle on the surface of the earth formed by the North pole and the points 30°N., 10°W. and 30°N., 80°E.?

(26)*. ABC are three points on the surface of the earth of radius 4000 miles, $AB = AC = 10$ miles and $\angle BAC = 90°$. Show that the spherical excess of the triangle ABC is approximately 0·6 of a second.

(27)*. The sides a, b, c of triangle ABC are $\frac{1}{2}\pi$, $\frac{1}{3}\pi$, $\frac{1}{4}\pi$ respectively. Prove that, if P is the mid-point of BC, then $\cos AP = \frac{1}{4}(2 + \sqrt{2})$.

(28)*. Find in square miles (correct to three significant figures) the area of an equilateral triangle whose sides are 1500 miles long, drawn on the surface of a sphere of radius 4000 miles.

(29)*. In an isosceles spherical triangle ABC, $AB = AC = \cos^{-1}(1/\sqrt{3})$ and $BC = 90°$. Show that the angles of the triangle are 45°, 45° and 120°.

If P is the mid-point of BC, calculate AP. Show that the area of the triangle exceeds $\frac{1}{2}$ (arc BC) (arc AP) by approximately $0·013\pi R^2$, where R is the radius of the sphere.

(30)*. If ABC is a spherical triangle and D is the mid-point of the side BC, prove that $2 \cos AD \cos BD = \cos AB + \cos AC$. Hence show that the latitude and longitude of the mid-point of the great circle arc from the point latitude 0, longitude 0 to the point latitude λ, longitude 90°, has latitude $\sin^{-1}(\sin \lambda/\sqrt{2})$ and longitude $\tan^{-1}(\cos \lambda)$.

The quadric

(31)*. Find the equations of the tangent planes to the ellipsoid $x^2 + 2y^2 + 3z^2 = 6$ which intersect in the line $x = 3 - y = 3z$, and the coordinates of their points of contact.

(32)*. Show that the polar planes of points on the line
$$3(x - 1) = 6(y + 1) = 2(z - 2)$$
with respect to the ellipsoid $x^2 + 3y^2 + 2z^2 = 1$ all pass through the line given by $3(x + 3) = -45y = -10(z - 1)$.

(33)*. Show that the three quadrics
$$x^2/2 + y^2/5 + z^2/10 = 1, \quad -x^2/2 + y^2 + z^2/6 = 1, \quad -x^2/6 - y^2/3 + z^2/2 = 1$$
are mutually orthogonal at their common point $(1, 1, \sqrt{3})$.

(34)*. The normal at $P(1, 1, 1)$ to the ellipsoid $x^2 + 2y^2 + 3z^2 = 6$ meets the plane $z = 0$ at A. Find the pole of the plane which bisects AP at right-angles and show that it is on the line joining P to the origin.

(35) ★. If the polar plane of P with respect to the ellipsoid $ax^2 + by^2 + cz^2 = 1$ touches the sphere with unit radius and centre the origin, prove that P lies on the ellipsoid $a^2x^2 + b^2y^2 + c^2z^2 = 1$.

(36) ★. If the normal at P to the ellipsoid $ax^2 + by^2 + cz^2 = 1$ meets the co-ordinate planes in E, F and G, show that $PE:PF:PG = 1/a:1/b:1/c$.

If further, $PE^2 + PF^2 + PG^2 = k^2$, where k is constant, show that P also lies on the ellipsoid

$$a^2x^2 + b^2y^2 + c^2z^2 = a^2b^2c^2k^2/(b^2c^2 + c^2a^2 + a^2b^2).$$

(37) ★. Write down the equations of the tangent plane and of the normal at the point (x_1, y_1, z_1) to the surface $x^2 + 2yz = 2$. Find the equations of the tangent planes to this surface which are parallel to the plane $4x + y - 7z = 0$. Find also the coordinates of the point in which the normal at $(2, 1, -1)$ meets the surface again.

(38) ★. A tangent plane to the ellipsoid $x^2 + 2y^2 + 3z^2 = \frac{4}{9}$ at a point in the positive octant where this surface is cut by the plane $y = z$ touches the sphere $x^2 + y^2 + z^2 = \frac{4}{17}$. Find the equations of the plane and of the normals at the points of contact on the ellipsoid and the sphere.

(39) ★. Prove that any plane section of the surface $ax^2 + by^2 + cz^2 = 1$ $(0 < a < b < c)$ is either an ellipse or a circle.

Show that there are two, and only two, real planes through the origin which cut the surface in ellipses whose orthogonal projections on the x,y-plane are circles, and that the angle between these planes is

$$\cos^{-1}[(a - b + c)/(b + c - a)].$$

(40) ★. The point $P(p, q, r)$ lies on the ellipsoid E whose equation is $ax^2 + by^2 + cz^2 = 1$. Find the condition that the straight line through P with direction ratios $l:m:n$ should touch E. If P also lies on two other ellipsoids with the equations $a^2x^2 + b^2y^2 + c^2z^2 = 1$ and $a^3x^2 + b^3y^2 + c^3z^2 = 1$, and the normal to E at P meets E again at Q, prove that PQ has length 2. If PQ is also normal to E at Q, prove that E is a sphere, provided that P does not lie in any coordinate plane.

(41) ★. Prove that, if the normal at the point (α, β, γ) on the quadric $ax^2 + by^2 + cz^2 = 1$ touches the sphere $x^2 + y^2 + z^2 = r^2$, the point (α, β, γ) must also lie on the surface

$$(x^2 + y^2 + z^2 - r^2)(a^2x^2 + b^2y^2 + c^2z^2) = 1.$$

(42) ★. Find the locus of the centres of the ellipses in which the ellipsoid $x^2 + 2y^2 + 3z^2 = 16$ is cut by the tangent planes to the sphere $x^2 + y^2 + z^2 = 1$.

(43) ★. Write down the equation of a plane which makes intercepts a, a and c on the x-, y- and z-axes respectively. If this plane touches the ellipsoid $x^2 + 4y^2 + 4z^2 = 16$, show that $c = \pm 2a/\sqrt{(a^2 - 20)}$, and prove that the coordinates (x_1, y_1, z_1) of the point of contact P are given by $ax_1 = 4ay_1 = 4cz_1 = 16$. Show that as a varies the locus of the foot of the perpendicular from P upon the plane Oyz is the ellipse $5y^2 + z^2 = 4$.

(44) ★. If the normal at any point P on the ellipsoid

$$x^2/a^2 + y^2/b^2 + z^2/c^2 = 1$$

meets the plane $z = 0$ at G and GP is produced to Q so that $PQ = GP$, show that the locus of Q is

$$a^2x^2/(a^2 + c^2)^2 + b^2y^2/(b^2 + c^2)^2 + z^2/4c^2 = 1.$$

(45) ★. Describe the geometrical character of the intersections of the surface $x^2 + y^2 - z^2 = 1$ by planes parallel to the coordinate planes.

Prove that the tangent plane to the surface at any one of its points (X, Y, Z)

cuts the surface in a locus whose orthogonal projection on to the plane $z = 0$ has the equation

$$x^2(Y^2 - 1) + y^2(X^2 - 1) - 2xyXY + 2xX + 2yY - X^2 - Y^2 = 0.$$

What is the geometrical nature of this projection?

(46)*. Find the equations of the two planes containing the line $x + y = 0 = 3 - z$ which touch the ellipsoid $3x^2 + 4y^2 + 6z^2 = 12$.

Show that the equations of the line joining the points at which these planes touch the ellipsoid may be expressed in the form $3x - 4y = 0 = 3z - 2$.

(47)*. Show that the distance between the points of contact of the two tangent planes to the quadric $x^2 + y^2 - 2z^2 = 1$ passing through the line $(x + 1)/4 = (y + 1)/12 = (z + 1)/9$ is $5\sqrt{2}$ units.

(48)*. Prove that the line $(x - x_0)/l = (y - y_0)/m = (z - z_0)/n$ touches the ellipsoid $x^2/a^2 + y^2/b^2 + z^2/c^2 = 1$ if

$$c^2(x_0m - y_0l)^2 + a^2(y_0n - z_0m)^2 + b^2(z_0l - x_0n)^2 = l^2b^2c^2 + m^2a^2c^2 + n^2a^2b^2,$$

and find the coordinates of the point of contact.

Prove that the points of contact of the tangents to the ellipsoid from the point $(0, 0, kc)$, where $k > 1$, lie in the plane $z = c/k$.

ANSWERS TO EXERCISES

(1). $x^2 + y^2 + z^2 - 4x - 2y - 2z + 5 = 0,$ $\quad x^2 + y^2 + z^2 - 6x + 2y - 4z + 10 = 0.$

(2). $2p = q^2; x \pm 2\sqrt{2}y + 4z = 20.$ (4). $x^2 + y^2 + z^2 - 6x - 16z = 48.$

(5). $x^2 + y^2 + z^2 = 25; |\lambda| < 65; 4.$ (6). $(x - 1)^2 + (y - 2)^2 + (z - 3)^2 = 14;$ $\sqrt{2}.$

(7). $c = -53, (27, -9, 23)/13; c = -105, (51, -17, 29)/13.$

(8). $(x - 5)^2 + (y + 10)^2 + (z - 5)^2 = 1.$ (9). $(1, -1, -1), \sqrt{6};$ $x^2 + y^2 + z^2 - 2x + 2y + 2z - 3 = 0.$ (10). $(1, 2, -3), 4; (2, 3, -2),$ $\sqrt{13}.$

(11). $(lu + mv + nw - p)^2 = (l^2 + m^2 + n^2)(u^2 + v^2 + w^2 - d); 3x + 4y - 86 = 0,$ $2x + 2y + z - 50 = 0.$

(12). $(-al/n, -am/n).$ (13). $(-4, 8, 9), 4.$ (14). $(3, 3, -2);$ $2x - y + 2z - 9 = 0, 2x - 2y - z + 11 = 0.$ (15). $x^2 + y^2 + z^2 = 2a^2;$ $(-a, 0, a), x - z + 2a = 0, x(1 + \lambda) - y - \lambda z + a(1 + 2\lambda) = 0$ where $\lambda = -\frac{1}{2} \pm \frac{1}{2}\sqrt{3}.$

(16). $x^2 + y^2 + z^2 - 6(x + y + z) + 18 = 0, x^2 + y^2 + z^2 - 10(x + y + z) + 50 = 0; 2x - 2y - z = 6, 4y + 3z = 10; \cos^{-1}(\frac{11}{15}).$

(19). $(x - 2a)^2 + (y - 2a)^2 + (z - 2a)^2 = 4a^2, (x + 3a)^2 + (y + 3a)^2 + (z + 3a)^2 = 49a^2.$ (20). $2x + 2y \pm z - 3 = 0.$

(21). $c = 90°, R^2\pi/6.$ (22). $4289 - 4176 = 113$ miles.

(25). $R^2[2 \sin^{-1}(2/\sqrt{5}) - \frac{1}{2}\pi] = 0.6434R^2.$ (28). 0.977×10^6 sq. miles $= R^2(3\varepsilon - \pi)$ where $\varepsilon = \cos^{-1}[(\cos\alpha - \cos^2\alpha)\operatorname{cosec}^2\alpha], \alpha = \frac{3}{8}$ radians.

(29). $\cos^{-1}\sqrt{(\frac{2}{3})}.$ (31). $x + y - 3 = 0, (2, 1, 0); x + 2y + 3z - 6 = 0, (1, 1, 1).$

(34). $(\frac{18}{11}, \frac{18}{11}, \frac{18}{11}).$ (37). $xx_1 + yz_1 + zy_1 = 2; (x - x_1)/x_1 = (y - y_1)/z_1 = (z - z_1)/y_1; 4x + y - 7z = \pm 2; (-10, 7, -7).$

(38). $2x + 2y + 3z = 2; 9x - 4 = 9y - 2 = -(9z - 2); x = y = -z.$

(40). $apl + bqm + crn = 0.$ (42). $(x^2 + 2y^2 + 3z^2)^2 = (x^2 + 4y^2 + 9z^2).$

(46). $x + y \pm (z - 3) = 0.$

CHAPTER 13

THE THEORY OF VECTORS

13.1 Definition of a vector

The theory of vectors may be developed along two distinct lines of argument. (i) Vectors may be defined without the use of a coordinate system, this being introduced later in order to facilitate calculations. (ii) Vectors may be defined using a coordinate system from the beginning. We shall adopt the second method in the treatment given here, though perhaps the first is more fundamental if more abstract. The first method would correspond to the development of pure geometry, while the second to coordinate geometry.

A *vector* is a geometrical or physical entity possessing magnitude and direction such that it is compounded (added) to another similar entity by a defined law of addition (given later).

Let v be the *magnitude* of the vector, and let its direction cosines be specified with respect to a given three-dimensional set of axes by (l, m, n). We use the single symbol $\mathbf{v}$ to denote both the magnitude v and the direction cosines (l, m, n). Sometimes we write $v = |\mathbf{v}|$.

The vector $\mathbf{v}$ is specified uniquely by the quantities v, (l, m, n); it may be represented by a line of length v and direction cosines (l, m, n).

The three *components* of the vector $\mathbf{v}$ in the directions of the axes Ox, Oy, Oz are defined to be

$$v_x = lv, \quad v_y = mv, \quad v_z = nv.$$

Evidently the three components are merely the signed magnitudes of the projections of the representation of $\mathbf{v}$ on the three axes. The three components also define the vector uniquely, for

$$v_x^2 + v_y^2 + v_z^2 = v^2(l^2 + m^2 + n^2) = v^2,$$

so the magnitude of the vector is given by $\sqrt{(v_x^2 + v_y^2 + v_z^2)}$, and its direction ratios are given by (v_x, v_y, v_z), which may be converted into direction cosines by division by v.

The vector with components (l, m, n), denoted by $\mathbf{u}$, is termed a dimensionless *unit vector*; we have $\mathbf{v} = v\mathbf{u}$. Generally, the vector $p\mathbf{v}$, where p is a positive scalar multiplier, has the same direction as $\mathbf{v}$, but is of magnitude pv; its three components are merely pv_x, pv_y, pv_z.

The vector $-\mathbf{v}$ is equal in magnitude to the vector $\mathbf{v}$ but opposite in direction; its components are $-v_x$, $-v_y$, $-v_z$ and its direction cosines are $-l$, $-m$, $-n$.

The sum of two vectors $\mathbf{v}$ and $\mathbf{w}$ with components (v_x, v_y, v_z) and (w_x, w_y, w_z) respectively is defined to be a new vector $\mathbf{s}$, with components (s_x, s_y, s_z) defined by

$$s_x = v_x + w_x, \quad s_y = v_y + w_y, \quad s_z = v_z + w_z;$$

we write this method of composition in the symbolical form

$$\mathbf{s} = \mathbf{v} + \mathbf{w}.$$

Similarly the difference $\mathbf{d} = \mathbf{v} - \mathbf{w}$ is defined to be

$$d_x = v_x - w_x, \quad d_y = v_y - w_y, \quad d_z = v_z - w_z.$$

These definitions are of course merely analytical statements of the well-known *parallelogram law* of addition of vectors. A *force*, for example, is taken to be a vector because it is demonstrated experimentally that two such force vectors satisfy this law of addition.

Let (l, m, n), (l', m', n') be the direction cosines of $\mathbf{v}$ and $\mathbf{w}$. Then the magnitude of their sum $\mathbf{s}$ is given by

$$\begin{aligned}
s^2 &= (v_x + w_x)^2 + (v_y + w_y)^2 + (v_z + w_z)^2 \\
&= (v_x^2 + v_y^2 + v_z^2) + (w_x^2 + w_y^2 + w_z^2) + 2(v_x w_x + v_y w_y + v_z w_z) \\
&= v^2 + w^2 + 2vw(ll' + mm' + nn') \\
&= v^2 + w^2 + 2vw \cos \theta,
\end{aligned}$$

where θ is the angle between $\mathbf{v}$ and $\mathbf{w}$. This is merely the square of the length of the diagonal drawn for the parallelogram formed by the representations of $\mathbf{v}$ and $\mathbf{w}$.

Sometimes it is convenient to express a vector in pure vector notation, but exhibiting its components at the same time. By itself, the symbol $\mathbf{v}$ does not have this desirable property. Let $\mathbf{i}, \mathbf{j}, \mathbf{k}$ denote unit vectors along the three coordinate axes; they are of magnitude unity and their direction cosines are $(1, 0, 0)$, $(0, 1, 0)$, $(0, 0, 1)$ respectively. Then

$$\mathbf{v} = v_x \mathbf{i} + v_y \mathbf{j} + v_z \mathbf{k};$$

that is, $\mathbf{v}$ consists of vectors of magnitudes v_x, v_y, v_z directed respectively parallel to Ox, Oy, Oz. The vector $\mathbf{v} \pm \mathbf{w}$ may then be written as

$$\mathbf{v} \pm \mathbf{w} = (v_x \pm w_x)\mathbf{i} + (v_y \pm w_y)\mathbf{j} + (v_z \pm w_z)\mathbf{k}.$$

The position of a point P in a three dimensional coordinate system is specified by the *position vector* $\mathbf{r}$, with the components (x, y, z). If A and B are two points with position vectors $\mathbf{a}$ and $\mathbf{b}$, then the position of B relative to A is a vector generally written as $\overrightarrow{AB}$. In vector notation, we may write this vector as $\mathbf{b} - \mathbf{a}$. The components of this vector may be taken to be the direction ratios of the line AB.

The vector equation of a straight line. A straight line is specified by an arbitrary point A on it and by its direction cosines (l, m, n). If A has the position vector $\mathbf{a}$, and if $\mathbf{u}$ denotes the unit vector (l, m, n), then the position vector $\mathbf{r}$ of any point P on the line is given by

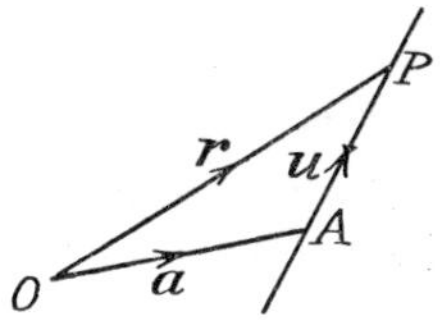

$$\mathbf{r} = \overrightarrow{OP} = \overrightarrow{OA} + \overrightarrow{AP} = \mathbf{a} + s\mathbf{u},$$

FIG. 59

where s is the signed length of the segment AP. If on the other hand the line is specified by two points A and B lying on it,

$$\mathbf{r} = \overrightarrow{OA} + \lambda\overrightarrow{AB} = \mathbf{a} + \lambda(\mathbf{b} - \mathbf{a}),$$

where λ is a parameter on the line.

Example 1 Show that the diagonals of a parallelogram $ABCD$ bisect each other at a point P.

Let the vertices A and B be denoted by the position vectors $\mathbf{a}$ and $\mathbf{b}$. Let the vertices C and D be obtained from B and A respectively by the common displacement $\mathbf{b}$; the position vectors of C and D are therefore $\mathbf{b} + \mathbf{c}$ and $\mathbf{a} + \mathbf{c}$.

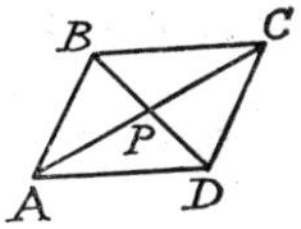

Then any point on the diagonal AC is of the form

$$\mathbf{r} = \mathbf{a} + \lambda(\mathbf{b} + \mathbf{c} - \mathbf{a}),$$

and any point on the diagonal BD is of the form

$$\mathbf{r} = \mathbf{b} + \mu(\mathbf{a} + \mathbf{c} - \mathbf{b}).$$

FIG. 60

If we choose $\lambda = \mu = \frac{1}{2}$, the common point of these two diagonals P is given by $\mathbf{r}_1 = \frac{1}{2}(\mathbf{a} + \mathbf{b} + \mathbf{c})$. This is the mid-point of AC, for $\overrightarrow{AP} = \mathbf{r}_1 - \mathbf{a}$ and $\overrightarrow{PC} = \mathbf{b} + \mathbf{c} - \mathbf{r}_1$ have the common value $\frac{1}{2}(\mathbf{b} + \mathbf{c} - \mathbf{a})$; similarly P is the mid-point of BD, since $\overrightarrow{BP} = \overrightarrow{PD} = \frac{1}{2}(\mathbf{a} + \mathbf{c} - \mathbf{b})$.

Example 2 Show that the lines joining the four vertices of the tetrahedron $OABC$ to the centroids of the opposite faces are concurrent.

Let the position vectors of A, B, C be $\mathbf{a}$, $\mathbf{b}$, $\mathbf{c}$ respectively, where O is the origin. The centroid G of triangle ABC stands one third of the way up the median $\overrightarrow{MA}$, where M bisects BC. The position vector of M is $\frac{1}{2}(\mathbf{b} + \mathbf{c})$, so the vector $\overrightarrow{MA}$ is

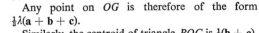

given by $\overrightarrow{OA} - \overrightarrow{OM} = \mathbf{a} - \frac{1}{2}(\mathbf{b} + \mathbf{c})$. Hence $\overrightarrow{OG} = \overrightarrow{OM} + \overrightarrow{MG} = \overrightarrow{OM} + \frac{1}{3}\overrightarrow{MA} = \frac{1}{2}(\mathbf{b} + \mathbf{c}) + \frac{1}{3}[\mathbf{a} - \frac{1}{2}(\mathbf{b} + \mathbf{c})] = \frac{1}{3}(\mathbf{a} + \mathbf{b} + \mathbf{c})$.

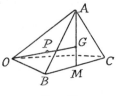

Any point on OG is therefore of the form $\frac{1}{3}\lambda(\mathbf{a} + \mathbf{b} + \mathbf{c})$.

Similarly, the centroid of triangle BOC is $\frac{1}{3}(\mathbf{b} + \mathbf{c})$, so any point on the line joining A to this centroid is $\mathbf{a} + \mu[\frac{1}{3}(\mathbf{b} + \mathbf{c}) - \mathbf{a}]$.

Similarly on the lines from B and C, we have the points

FIG. 61

$$\mathbf{b} + \nu[\tfrac{1}{3}(\mathbf{c} + \mathbf{a}) - \mathbf{b}], \quad \mathbf{c} + \rho[\tfrac{1}{3}(\mathbf{a} + \mathbf{b} - \mathbf{c}].$$

Now if we choose $\lambda = \mu = \nu = \rho = \frac{3}{4}$, we find that the point with position vector $\frac{1}{4}(\mathbf{a} + \mathbf{b} + \mathbf{c})$ lies on all four lines; the four lines therefore intersect in this point P. Moreover, $\overrightarrow{OP} = \frac{1}{4}(\mathbf{a} + \mathbf{b} + \mathbf{c})$ and $\overrightarrow{OG} = \frac{1}{3}(\mathbf{a} + \mathbf{b} + \mathbf{c})$. Hence the lengths of the vectors $\overrightarrow{OP}$ and $\overrightarrow{OG}$ satisfy the ratio $OP/OG = \frac{1}{4}/\frac{1}{3} = \frac{3}{4}$. A similar ratio holds for all the four lines joining the vertices to P.

13.2   The scalar product

If two vectors $\mathbf{v}$ and $\mathbf{w}$ are given, defined as before, their *scalar product* $\mathbf{v}.\mathbf{w}$ is defined, in terms of their components, to be

$$\mathbf{v}.\mathbf{w} = v_x w_x + v_y w_y + v_z w_z.$$

Sometimes the rather old fashioned notation $(\mathbf{vw})$ is still used to denote this product. The implications of this definition may be seen by expressing the vector components in terms of their direction cosines:

$$\mathbf{v}.\mathbf{w} = vlwl' + vmwm' + vnwn' = vw(ll' + mm' + nn') = vw\cos\theta;$$

that is, the scalar product is the product of the magnitudes of the two vectors and the cosine of the angle between their two directions.

Evidently $\mathbf{v}.\mathbf{w} = \mathbf{w}.\mathbf{v}$ directly from the definition, so multiplication is *commutative*.

In particular, if $\mathbf{v}$ is perpendicular to $\mathbf{w}$, $\cos\theta = 0$ implying $\mathbf{v}.\mathbf{w} = 0$.

A well-known example occurs in dynamics. If $\mathbf{F}$, with components (F_x, F_y, F_z), is a force whose point of application moves through a displacement $\mathbf{r}$, with components (x, y, z), the work done by the force is defined to be $Fr\cos\theta$, namely the scalar product $\mathbf{F}.\mathbf{r}$.

The component of a vector $\mathbf{v}$ in a given direction specified by the unit vector $\mathbf{u}$ is defined to be the signed magnitude of the projection of $\mathbf{v}$ on to the direction $\mathbf{u}$. Its value is $v\cos\theta$, which equals $\mathbf{v}.\mathbf{u}$ since $|\mathbf{u}| = u = 1$.

The distance of a point from the origin. If the point P, denoted by the position vector **r** with components (x, y, z), is at a distance r from the origin O, the length OP is given by

$$OP^2 = r^2 = x^2 + y^2 + z^2 = \mathbf{r}.\mathbf{r} = \mathbf{r}^2,$$

FIG. 62

where $\mathbf{r}^2$ is conventionally used instead of $\mathbf{r}.\mathbf{r}$.

The length of the perpendicular from a point to a line. Let the point Q have the position vector **b**, and let the given line AN be represented by the vector equation $\mathbf{r} = \mathbf{a} + s\mathbf{u}$. The vector $\overrightarrow{AQ}$ is $(\mathbf{b} - \mathbf{a})$, so the length AQ is given by $AQ^2 = (\mathbf{b} - \mathbf{a}).(\mathbf{b} - \mathbf{a}) = (\mathbf{b} - \mathbf{a})^2$. The length AN is the projection of the vector $\overrightarrow{AQ}$ on to the direction **u**, namely $(\mathbf{b} - \mathbf{a}).\mathbf{u}$. Hence

$$QN^2 = AQ^2 - AN^2 = (\mathbf{b} - \mathbf{a})^2 - [(\mathbf{b} - \mathbf{a}).\mathbf{u}]^2.$$

The actual vector NQ is given by

$$\overrightarrow{NQ} = \overrightarrow{NA} + \overrightarrow{AQ} = \overrightarrow{AQ} - \overrightarrow{AN} = \mathbf{b} - \mathbf{a} - [(\mathbf{b} - \mathbf{a}).\mathbf{u}]\mathbf{u},$$

where multiplying the magnitude $(\mathbf{b} - \mathbf{a}).\mathbf{u}$ by **u** yields the vector $\overrightarrow{AN}$.

The equation of a plane. Let A be a given point on the plane with position vector **a**; let **u** denote the unit normal to the plane. If P is any point on the plane, $\overrightarrow{AP} = \mathbf{r} - \mathbf{a}$ is perpendicular to **u**. Hence

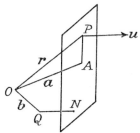

FIG. 63

$$(\mathbf{r} - \mathbf{a}).\mathbf{u} = 0,$$

or $\mathbf{r}.\mathbf{u} = \text{constant} = d,$

say. It is obvious that **u** need not be the *unit* normal: its components may consist of the direction ratios of the normal rather than the direction cosines.

The length p of the perpendicular from a point to a plane. If Q is the point with position vector **b**, and N the foot of the perpendicular from Q to the plane $\mathbf{r}.\mathbf{u} = d$, where **u** is a unit vector, then

$$\overrightarrow{ON} + \overrightarrow{NQ} = \overrightarrow{OQ},$$

so $$\overrightarrow{NQ} = p\mathbf{u} = \mathbf{b} - \mathbf{r},$$

where p is the signed length of $\overrightarrow{NQ}$ and **r** is the position vector of N. Scalar multiplication by **u** yields

$$p = \mathbf{b}.\mathbf{a} - \mathbf{r}.\mathbf{u} = \mathbf{b}.\mathbf{u} - d;$$

that is, the coordinates of Q are merely substituted into the equation of the plane. If **u** is not a unit vector, evidently

$$p = (\mathbf{b} \cdot \mathbf{u} - d)/\sqrt{(\mathbf{u}^2)}.$$

Example 3   If two pairs of opposite sides of a tetrahedron are perpendicular, prove that the two lines forming the third pair are perpendicular.

Let the sides OA, OB, OC of the tetrahedron $OABC$ be denoted by the vectors **a**, **b**, **c**. Then the sides BC, CA, AB are given by $(\mathbf{c} - \mathbf{b})$, $(\mathbf{a} - \mathbf{c})$, $(\mathbf{b} - \mathbf{a})$. Since OA is perpendicular to BC and OB to CA, we have

$$\mathbf{a} \cdot (\mathbf{c} - \mathbf{b}) = 0, \quad \mathbf{b}(\mathbf{a} - \mathbf{c}) = 0.$$

Addition yields

$$\mathbf{c} \cdot (\mathbf{a} - \mathbf{b}) = 0,$$

implying that OC is perpendicular to AB.

13.3   The vector product

It is convenient to define a third vector that is perpendicular to the plane specified by two vectors **v** and **w** intersecting in a point P. The direction ratios of the normal to the two directions (l, m, n) and (l', m', n') of **v** and **w** respectively may be taken to be

$$mn' - m'n, \quad nl' - n'l, \quad lm' - l'm. \tag{1}$$

The squared magnitude of this vector is

$$(mn' - m'n)^2 + (nl' - n'l)^2 + (lm' - l'm)^2$$
$$= l^2(m'^2 + n'^2) + m^2(n'^2 + l'^2) + n^2(l'^2 + m'^2)$$
$$\qquad\qquad - 2(mm'nn' + nn'll' + ll'nn')$$
$$= l^2(1 - n'^2) + m^2(1 - m'^2) + n^2(1 - n'^2)$$
$$\qquad\qquad - 2(mm'nn' + nn'll' + ll'nn')$$
$$= 1 - (ll' + mm' + nn')^2 = \sin^2 \theta.$$

The positive length of the vector is $\sin \theta$, where θ is restricted to lie in the range $0 < \theta < \pi$.

We define the *vector product* $\mathbf{v} \wedge \mathbf{w}$ (or sometimes $\mathbf{v} \times \mathbf{w}$ or $[\mathbf{vw}]$) to be the vector with components

$$v_y w_z - v_z w_y, \quad v_z w_x - v_x w_z, \quad v_x w_y - v_y w_x, \tag{2}$$

or $$vw(mn' - m'n), \quad vw(nl' - n'l), \quad vw(lm' - l'm).$$

Its magnitude is $vw \sin \theta$, directed along the normal to **v** and **w**. We must however decide the sense of the vector along the normal in relation to the sense of rotation from **v** to **w** through the angle θ ($0 < \theta < \pi$).

Let us denote the three directed lines along **v**, **w** and $\mathbf{v} \wedge \mathbf{w}$ by PX, PW and PZ. Consider continuous slow rotation of the system $PXWZ$

in an arbitrary manner. The direction cosines of the lines PX, PW and PZ vary continuously, but the magnitude $\sin \theta$ of the vector along PZ is constant, and this vector must always have the same sense along the normal PZ relative to $\mathbf{v}$ and $\mathbf{w}$.

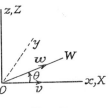

FIG. 64

In particular, let PX now point along Ox and PZ along Oz; then PW must lie in the plane Oxy. We have the values $l = 1$, $m = n = 0$, $l' = \cos \theta$, $m' = \sin \theta$, $n' = 0$. Substituting these values, we find that vector (2) takes the form $(0, 0, \sin \theta)$. If θ is positive in the permitted range, $\sin \theta$ is positive, so the vector product is directed along the positive sense of Oz. Hence, generally, the sense of the normal vector $\mathbf{v} \wedge \mathbf{w}$ is related to the sense of rotation from $\mathbf{v}$ to $\mathbf{w}$ through an angle θ $(0 < \theta < \pi)$ by the right-handed cork screw rule.

If $\theta = 0$ or π, the vector product is zero, so the ambiguity in its sense does not require examination.

From the definition (2), we note that $\mathbf{v} \wedge \mathbf{w} = -\mathbf{w} \wedge \mathbf{v}$; multiplication is not therefore commutative.

Since we may write

$$\mathbf{v} \wedge \mathbf{w} = (v_y w_z - v_z w_y)\mathbf{i} + (v_z w_x - v_x w_z)\mathbf{j} + (v_x w_y - v_y w_x)\mathbf{k},$$

we may express the vector product in the determinantal form

$$\mathbf{v} \wedge \mathbf{w} = \begin{vmatrix} \mathbf{i} & \mathbf{j} & \mathbf{k} \\ v_x & v_y & v_z \\ w_x & w_y & w_z \end{vmatrix}.$$

The student should use this form in numerical calculations, until he is able to write the cofactors down without having the determinant explicitly before him.

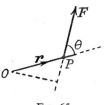

FIG. 65

A simple application of this concept concerns the definition of a *couple*. A force $\mathbf{F}$ acts at a point P, whose position vector relative to an origin O is $\mathbf{r}$. In elementary statics, the numerical value of the couple is $Fr \sin \theta$, taken in the anticlockwise sense in Fig. 65. In vector theory, the couple $\mathbf{G}$ is a vector, with magnitude $Fr \sin \theta$ and direction perpendicular to the plane of $\mathbf{F}$ and $\mathbf{r}$, and related to the sense of rotation by the right-handed cork screw rule. Hence $\mathbf{G} = \mathbf{r} \wedge \mathbf{F}$, since this vector has the correct magnitude, direction and sense.

The area of a triangle. The triangle ABC in space is given; its vertices A, B, C are specified by the position vectors **a**, **b**, **c** respectively. The scalar area of the triangle is $\frac{1}{2}AB.AC \sin \theta$. This is the magnitude of the vector product $\frac{1}{2}\overrightarrow{AB} \wedge \overrightarrow{AC}$, a vector directed normally to the plane ABC. But $\overrightarrow{AB} = \mathbf{b} - \mathbf{a}$ and $\overrightarrow{AC} = \mathbf{c} - \mathbf{a}$, so

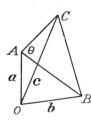

FIG. 66

$$\text{area vector} = \tfrac{1}{2}(\mathbf{b} - \mathbf{a}) \wedge (\mathbf{c} - \mathbf{a})$$
$$= \tfrac{1}{2}(\mathbf{b} \wedge \mathbf{c} + \mathbf{c} \wedge \mathbf{a} + \mathbf{a} \wedge \mathbf{b}),$$

since $\mathbf{a} \wedge \mathbf{a} = 0$. If A is the origin, the area vector is $\frac{1}{2}\mathbf{b} \wedge \mathbf{c}$.

Example 4* A vector **v** makes an angle $\cos^{-1} \frac{1}{3}$ with the vector $(1, -1, 1)$ and $\mathbf{v} \wedge \mathbf{a}$ has components $(-2, 1, 1)$ where **a** is the vector $(1, 2, 0)$. Show that there are two such vectors **v** and show also that the angle between them is $\cos^{-1}(-\frac{5}{7})$.

The scalar product of **v** and $(1, -1, 1)$ yields

$$v_x - v_y + v_z = \sqrt{(v_x{}^2 + v_y{}^2 + v_z{}^2)}\sqrt{3} \cos \theta$$
$$= \sqrt{(v_x{}^2 + v_y{}^2 + v_z{}^2)}/\sqrt{3}$$

so
$$3(v_x - v_y + v_z)^2 = v_x{}^2 + v_y{}^2 + v_z{}^2.$$

The three components of the vector product of **v** and **a** yield

$$-2v_z = -2, \quad v_z = 1, \quad 2v_x - v_y = 1.$$

Hence $v_z = 1$ and $v_y = 2v_x - 1$. Eliminating v_y from the scalar product and simplifying, we obtain the quadratic equation in v_x:

$$v_x{}^2 + 4v_x - 5 = 0,$$

with the roots $v_x = 1, -5$. Hence $v_y = 1, -11$ respectively.

The two vectors **v** are therefore $(1, 1, 1)$ and $(-5, -11, 1)$. If θ is the angle between them, we have

$$\cos \theta = \frac{-5 - 11 + 1}{\sqrt{3}\sqrt{147}} = -\frac{5}{7},$$

yielding $\theta = \cos^{-1}(-\frac{5}{7})$.

13.4   The triple products

The triple scalar product. If **u**, **v**, **w** are three vectors, the scalar product of **u** with the vector $\mathbf{v} \wedge \mathbf{w}$ is known as the *triple scalar product*. We write this as $\mathbf{u}.\mathbf{v} \wedge \mathbf{w}$, or perhaps more clearly $\mathbf{u}.(\mathbf{v} \wedge \mathbf{w})$. There is however no ambiguity in the notation $\mathbf{u}.\mathbf{v} \wedge \mathbf{w}$; it is *not* possible first to find the scalar product of the vectors **u** and **v**, and then to find the vector product of the *scalar* $\mathbf{u}.\mathbf{v}$ and the *vector* **w**.

In terms of components, we have

$$\mathbf{u} \cdot \mathbf{v} \wedge \mathbf{w} = u_x(v_y w_z - v_z w_y) + u_y(v_z w_x - v_x w_z) + u_z(v_x w_y - v_y w_x)$$

$$= \begin{vmatrix} u_x & u_y & u_z \\ v_x & v_y & v_z \\ w_x & w_y & w_z \end{vmatrix}.$$

The interchange of two pairs of rows in this determinant preserves its value; hence

$$\mathbf{u} \cdot \mathbf{v} \wedge \mathbf{w} = \mathbf{v} \cdot \mathbf{w} \wedge \mathbf{u} = \mathbf{w} \cdot \mathbf{u} \wedge \mathbf{v}. \tag{3}$$

Cyclic order of the three vectors is maintained, and the product symbols . and ∧ are written in the same order.

Since scalar multiplication is commutative, we have also

$$\mathbf{v} \wedge \mathbf{w} \cdot \mathbf{u} = \mathbf{w} \wedge \mathbf{u} \cdot \mathbf{v} = \mathbf{u} \wedge \mathbf{v} \cdot \mathbf{w}.$$

If the vector products in (3) are taken in the reverse order, we have

$$\mathbf{u} \cdot \mathbf{v} \wedge \mathbf{w} = -\mathbf{u} \cdot \mathbf{w} \wedge \mathbf{v}$$
$$= -\mathbf{v} \cdot \mathbf{u} \wedge \mathbf{w} = -\mathbf{w} \cdot \mathbf{v} \wedge \mathbf{u}.$$

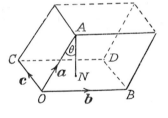

FIG. 67

If $\mathbf{u} = \mathbf{v}$, say, the determinant vanishes, so the triple scalar product vanishes if any two of the vectors occurring in it are identical or proportional. The geometrical significance of this result is obvious; $\mathbf{u}$ is perpendicular to $\mathbf{u} \wedge \mathbf{v}$ by its definition.

Volume of a parallelepiped. The three edges through the vertex O are specified by the vectors $\mathbf{a}$, $\mathbf{b}$, $\mathbf{c}$. The magnitude of the area of the base $OBDC$ is given by

$$\text{area } OBDC = 2 \triangle OBC = |\mathbf{b} \wedge \mathbf{c}|.$$

Then the volume of the parallelepiped has the value:

$$\text{volume} = \text{height } AN \times \text{area } OBDC$$
$$= OA \cos \theta \, |\mathbf{b} \wedge \mathbf{c}|$$
$$= |\mathbf{a}| \, |\mathbf{b} \wedge \mathbf{c}| \cos \theta$$
$$= \mathbf{a} \cdot \mathbf{b} \wedge \mathbf{c},$$

since θ is the angle between the vector $\mathbf{a}$ and the normal to the base.

Volume of a tetrahedron. The edges through one vertex O are given by the vectors $\mathbf{a}, \mathbf{b}, \mathbf{c}$. Then the volume has the value

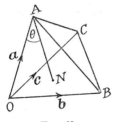

FIG. 68

$$\text{volume} = \tfrac{1}{3} \text{ base } OBC \times \text{ height } AN$$

$$= \tfrac{1}{3} \left| \tfrac{1}{2} \mathbf{b} \wedge \mathbf{c} \right| \times OA \cos \theta$$

$$= \tfrac{1}{6} |\mathbf{a}| |\mathbf{b} \wedge \mathbf{c}| \cos \theta$$

$$= \tfrac{1}{6} \mathbf{a} . \mathbf{b} \wedge \mathbf{c},$$

since θ is the angle between the vector $\mathbf{a}$ and the normal to the base. Explicitly, we have

$$\text{volume} = \tfrac{1}{6} \begin{vmatrix} a_x & a_y & a_z \\ b_x & b_y & b_z \\ c_x & c_y & c_z \end{vmatrix} .$$

Example 5 Find the condition that the two lines $\mathbf{r} = \mathbf{a} + h\mathbf{u}$ and $\mathbf{r} = \mathbf{b} + k\mathbf{v}$ should intersect. Under these conditions, find the position vector of the point of intersection.

The lines intersect if the three vectors $\mathbf{a} - \mathbf{b}, \mathbf{u}, \mathbf{v}$ all lie in a plane. This is so if $\mathbf{u}$, for example, is perpendicular to the normal of the plane defined by $\mathbf{a} - \mathbf{b}$ and $\mathbf{v}$, namely to the vector $\mathbf{v} \wedge (\mathbf{a} - \mathbf{b})$. The condition is therefore

$$\mathbf{u} . \mathbf{v} \wedge (\mathbf{a} - \mathbf{b}) = 0,$$

or

$$\mathbf{u} . \mathbf{v} \wedge \mathbf{a} = \mathbf{u} . \mathbf{v} \wedge \mathbf{b}.$$

Under these circumstances, we have

$$\mathbf{r} = \mathbf{a} + h\mathbf{u} = \mathbf{b} + k\mathbf{v}.$$

The vector product with $\mathbf{v}$ yields

$$\mathbf{v} \wedge \mathbf{a} + h\mathbf{v} \wedge \mathbf{u} = \mathbf{v} \wedge \mathbf{b};$$

and scalar multiplication by $\mathbf{b}$ produces

$$\mathbf{b} . \mathbf{v} \wedge \mathbf{a} + h\mathbf{b} . \mathbf{v} \wedge \mathbf{u} = 0,$$

or

$$h = -(\mathbf{b} . \mathbf{v} \wedge \mathbf{a})/(\mathbf{b} . \mathbf{v} \wedge \mathbf{u}).$$

Hence

$$\mathbf{r} = \mathbf{a} - \mathbf{u}(\mathbf{b} . \mathbf{v} \wedge \mathbf{a})/(\mathbf{b} . \mathbf{v} \wedge \mathbf{u}).$$

The triple vector product. If $\mathbf{u}, \mathbf{v}, \mathbf{w}$ are three given vectors, the *triple vector product* is defined to be the vector product of $\mathbf{u}$ with $\mathbf{v} \wedge \mathbf{w}$, namely $\mathbf{u} \wedge (\mathbf{v} \wedge \mathbf{w})$. It would be wrong to omit the brackets in this expression, for $\mathbf{u} \wedge \mathbf{v} \wedge \mathbf{w}$ is ambiguous, since $(\mathbf{u} \wedge \mathbf{v}) \wedge \mathbf{w}$ is another distinct possibility.

The x-component of $\mathbf{u} \wedge (\mathbf{v} \wedge \mathbf{w})$ is given by

$$u_y(v_x w_y - v_y w_x) - u_z(v_z w_x - v_x w_z)$$
$$= v_x(u_y w_y + u_z v_z) - w_x(u_y v_y + u_z v_z)$$
$$= (\mathbf{u}.\mathbf{w})v_x - (\mathbf{u}.\mathbf{v})w_x,$$

where we have added and subtracted again the term $u_x v_x w_x$ in order to complete the two scalar products. Similarly, the y and z-components are given by replacing v_x, w_x by v_y, w_y and v_z, w_z respectively. Hence

$$\mathbf{u} \wedge (\mathbf{v} \wedge \mathbf{w}) = (\mathbf{u}.\mathbf{w})\mathbf{v} - (\mathbf{u}.\mathbf{v})\mathbf{w}. \tag{4}$$

It should be noted that the scalar products occurring in brackets are merely scalar multipliers of the two vectors $\mathbf{v}$ and $\mathbf{w}$. The triple vector product is in fact a vector in the plane defined by $\mathbf{v}$ and $\mathbf{w}$.

Example 6 (i) Coupled with the identity (4), we have

$$\mathbf{v} \wedge (\mathbf{w} \wedge \mathbf{u}) = (\mathbf{v}.\mathbf{u})\mathbf{w} - (\mathbf{v}.\mathbf{w})\mathbf{u},$$
$$\mathbf{w} \wedge (\mathbf{u} \wedge \mathbf{v}) = (\mathbf{w}.\mathbf{v})\mathbf{u} - (\mathbf{w}.\mathbf{u})\mathbf{v}.$$

Adding these three identities, we obtain

$$\mathbf{u} \wedge (\mathbf{v} \wedge \mathbf{w}) + \mathbf{v} \wedge (\mathbf{w} \wedge \mathbf{u}) + \mathbf{w} \wedge (\mathbf{u} \wedge \mathbf{v}) = 0.$$

(ii) The product $(\mathbf{a} \wedge \mathbf{b}).(\mathbf{c} \wedge \mathbf{d})$ may be simplified. Writing $\mathbf{f} = \mathbf{a} \wedge \mathbf{b}$, we have

$$(\mathbf{a} \wedge \mathbf{b}).(\mathbf{c} \wedge \mathbf{d}) = \mathbf{f}.\mathbf{c} \wedge \mathbf{d} = \mathbf{c}.\mathbf{d} \wedge \mathbf{f}$$
$$= \mathbf{c}.[\mathbf{d} \wedge (\mathbf{a} \wedge \mathbf{b})]$$
$$= \mathbf{c}.[(\mathbf{d}.\mathbf{b})\mathbf{a} - (\mathbf{d}.\mathbf{a})\mathbf{b}]$$
$$= (\mathbf{a}.\mathbf{c})(\mathbf{b}.\mathbf{d}) - (\mathbf{a}.\mathbf{d})(\mathbf{b}.\mathbf{c}). \tag{5}$$

Example 7 Solve the equation $\mathbf{x} \wedge \mathbf{a} = \mathbf{b} - \mathbf{x}$ for $\mathbf{x}$.
Scalar and vector multiplication of this equation by suitable vectors are necessary to simplify the equation.
Scalar multiplication by $\mathbf{a}$ gives

$$\mathbf{a}.\mathbf{x} \wedge \mathbf{a} = 0 = \mathbf{a}.\mathbf{b} - \mathbf{a}.\mathbf{x}. \tag{6}$$

Vector multiplication by $\mathbf{a}$ yields

$$\mathbf{a} \wedge (\mathbf{x} \wedge \mathbf{a}) = \mathbf{a} \wedge \mathbf{b} - \mathbf{a} \wedge \mathbf{x}$$
$$= \mathbf{a} \wedge \mathbf{b} + \mathbf{b} - \mathbf{x}$$

from the given equation. Expanding the triple vector product, we obtain

$$(\mathbf{a}.\mathbf{a})\mathbf{x} - (\mathbf{a}.\mathbf{x})\mathbf{a} = \mathbf{a} \wedge \mathbf{b} + \mathbf{b} - \mathbf{x},$$

or

$$(\mathbf{a}.\mathbf{a})\mathbf{x} - (\mathbf{a}.\mathbf{b})\mathbf{a} = \mathbf{a} \wedge \mathbf{b} + \mathbf{b} - \mathbf{x}$$

from equation (6). The vector $\mathbf{x}$ is now multiplied by scalar factors only; hence

$$\mathbf{x} = [\mathbf{a} \wedge \mathbf{b} + \mathbf{b} + (\mathbf{a}.\mathbf{b})\mathbf{a}]/(1 + \mathbf{a}^2).$$

The reader should notice that it is only possible to divide by a scalar, never by a vector.

Example 8   Find the point of intersection of the three planes

$$\mathbf{r}.\mathbf{a} = p, \quad \mathbf{r}.\mathbf{b} = q, \quad \mathbf{r}.\mathbf{c} = s.$$

To find the vector $\mathbf{r}$, we must manufacture a vector equation from these three scalar equations. Consider

$$\mathbf{r} \wedge (\mathbf{b} \wedge \mathbf{c}) = (\mathbf{r}.\mathbf{c})\mathbf{b} - (\mathbf{r}.\mathbf{b})\mathbf{c} = s\mathbf{b} - q\mathbf{c}.$$

The vector product with $\mathbf{a}$ yields

$$\mathbf{a} \wedge [\mathbf{r} \wedge (\mathbf{b} \wedge \mathbf{c})] = s\mathbf{a} \wedge \mathbf{b} - q\mathbf{a} \wedge \mathbf{c},$$

or
$$(\mathbf{a}.\mathbf{b} \wedge \mathbf{c})\mathbf{r} - (\mathbf{a}.\mathbf{r})(\mathbf{b} \wedge \mathbf{c}) = q\mathbf{c} \wedge \mathbf{a} + s\mathbf{a} \wedge \mathbf{b}.$$

But $(\mathbf{a}.\mathbf{r}) = p$; hence

$$(\mathbf{a}.\mathbf{b} \wedge \mathbf{c})\mathbf{r} = p\mathbf{b} \wedge \mathbf{c} + q\mathbf{c} \wedge \mathbf{a} + s\mathbf{a} \wedge \mathbf{b},$$

yielding for $\mathbf{r}$ the solution

$$\mathbf{r} = (p\mathbf{b} \wedge \mathbf{c} + q\mathbf{c} \wedge \mathbf{a} + s\mathbf{a} \wedge \mathbf{b})/(\mathbf{a}.\mathbf{b} \wedge \mathbf{c}).$$

A unique solution exists provided $\mathbf{a}.\mathbf{b} \wedge \mathbf{c} \neq 0$, that is, provided the vectors $\mathbf{a}$, $\mathbf{b}$, $\mathbf{c}$ are not coplanar.

Example 9   Find the angle between the faces of a regular tetrahedron.

Let O be one vertex, with unit vectors $\mathbf{a}$, $\mathbf{b}$, $\mathbf{c}$ directed along the three edges through O. Each edge is inclined at $60°$ to the others, since each face of a regular tetrahedron is an equilateral triangle. This implies that

$$\mathbf{b}.\mathbf{c} = \mathbf{c}.\mathbf{a} = \mathbf{a}.\mathbf{b} = \cos 60° = \tfrac{1}{2}.$$

The normal to the face defined by the vectors $\mathbf{a}$ and $\mathbf{b}$ is directed along the vector $\mathbf{a} \wedge \mathbf{b}$; the unit normal is $\mathbf{a} \wedge \mathbf{b}/|\mathbf{a} \wedge \mathbf{b}|$. Similarly the unit normal to the face defined by $\mathbf{a}$ and $\mathbf{c}$ is $\mathbf{a} \wedge \mathbf{c}/|\mathbf{a} \wedge \mathbf{c}|$.

If θ is the angle between these normals, we have

$$\cos \theta = (\mathbf{a} \wedge \mathbf{b}).(\mathbf{a} \wedge \mathbf{c})/|\mathbf{a} \wedge \mathbf{b}| \, |\mathbf{a} \wedge \mathbf{c}|.$$

Now $|\mathbf{a} \wedge \mathbf{b}| = |\mathbf{a} \wedge \mathbf{c}| = \sin 60° = \tfrac{1}{2}\sqrt{3}$, and

$$(\mathbf{a} \wedge \mathbf{b}).(\mathbf{a} \wedge \mathbf{c}) = (\mathbf{a}.\mathbf{a})(\mathbf{b}.\mathbf{c}) - (\mathbf{a}.\mathbf{c})(\mathbf{b}.\mathbf{c})$$

from equation (5). Inserting the values of these scalar products, we obtain

$$(\mathbf{a} \wedge \mathbf{b}).(\mathbf{a} \wedge \mathbf{c}) = 1.\tfrac{1}{2} - \tfrac{1}{2}.\tfrac{1}{2} = \tfrac{1}{4}.$$

Hence
$$\cos \theta = \tfrac{1}{4}/\tfrac{3}{4} = \tfrac{1}{3}.$$

13.5   The motion of a charged particle in constant electric and magnetic fields

The *velocity* vector of a particle with components $(\dot{x}, \dot{y}, \dot{z})$ is denoted by $\dot{\mathbf{r}}$, and the *acceleration* vector $(\ddot{x}, \ddot{y}, \ddot{z})$ by $\ddot{\mathbf{r}}$. If $\mathbf{F}$ is the total force vector acting on this particle of mass m, the equations of motion may be written as the single vector equation

$$\mathbf{F} = m\ddot{\mathbf{r}}.$$

In particular, let the particle possess an electric charge e E.S.U.; if a constant electric field $\mathbf{E}$, with components (E_x, E_y, E_z) E.S.U., pervades the region, the contribution to the force is given by $e\mathbf{E}$. If the constant magnetic field is $\mathbf{H}$ E.M.U., the action of this field $\mathbf{H}$ on the effective current $e\dot{\mathbf{r}}$ is to produce a force on the particle perpendicular to both $\mathbf{H}$ and $\dot{\mathbf{r}}$, namely $e\dot{\mathbf{r}} \wedge \mathbf{H}/c$, where the constant c converts E.M. units into E.S. units. Finally, if $\mathbf{G}$ is the force per unit mass produced by other causes, weight for example, the equation of motion is

$$m\ddot{\mathbf{r}} = e\mathbf{E} + m\mathbf{G} + e\dot{\mathbf{r}} \wedge \mathbf{H}/c.$$

Initially, let us suppose that the particle is at rest at the origin at time $t = 0$; that is, $\mathbf{r} = \dot{\mathbf{r}} = 0$ at $t = 0$. This vector differential equation may be solved entirely in the spirit of vector theory without the use of the individual components; here, however, we shall illustrate the theory by a particular example using the components of the vectors concerned.

Example 10 Solve the equation given that $\mathbf{E} = (0, E, 0)$, $\mathbf{H} = (0, 0, H)$ and that gravity is inoperative. It is given that $\mathbf{r}$ and $\dot{\mathbf{r}}$ vanish at $t = 0$.

The three components of the vector equation of motion simplify to

$$m\ddot{x} = e\dot{y}H/c,$$
$$m\ddot{y} = eE - e\dot{x}H/c,$$
$$m\ddot{z} = 0.$$

The third equation has the obvious solution $z = \dot{z} = 0$.

The simplest method to solve the first two equations is to multiply the second by i and add to the first. If $z = x + iy$, we obtain

$$m\ddot{z} = ieE - eiH\dot{z}/c.$$

or
$$\ddot{z} + ip\dot{z} = ieE/m,$$

where $p = eH/cm$. The complementary function* for this differential equation is

$$z = A + Be^{-ipt},$$

and the particular integral takes the form

$$z = eEt/mp.$$

The general solution of the equation is therefore

$$z = A + Be^{-ipt} + eEt/mp.$$

At time $t = 0$, we have

$$x + iy = z = 0 = A + B,$$
$$\dot{x} + i\dot{y} = \dot{z} = 0 = -ipB + eE/mp,$$

yielding
$$A = ieE/mp^2, \quad B = -ieE/mp^2.$$

* The symbols e for the electric charge and for the exponential are of course quite distinct; so likewise are the coordinate z and the complex number $z = x + iy$.

We conclude that

$$z = (ieE/mp^2)(1 - e^{-ipt}) + eEt/mp.$$

Finally,

$$x = \text{Rl } z = eEt/mp - (eE/mp^2) \sin pt,$$
$$y = \text{Im } z = (eE/mp^2)(1 - \cos pt).$$

The solution for x may also be arranged in the form

$$x = (eE/mp^2)(pt - \sin pt),$$

showing that the path of the particle is a cycloid in the x, y-plane (see section 14.12).

EXERCISES

(1). Prove the following vector identities:

(i) $(a + b) \wedge (a - b) = -2a \wedge b$.

(ii) $(a \wedge b)^2 = a^2 b^2 - (a.b)^2$.

(iii) $(a \wedge b) \wedge (a \wedge c).d = (a.d)a \wedge b.c$.

(iv) $(b \wedge c).(a \wedge d) + (c \wedge a).(b \wedge d) + (a \wedge b).(c \wedge d) = 0$.

(v) $(a \wedge b) \wedge (c \wedge d) = (a \wedge b.d)c - (a \wedge b.c)d$.

(vi) $[a \wedge (b \wedge c)] \wedge c = (a.c)b \wedge c$.

(2). If $a + b + c = 0$, prove that $a \wedge b = b \wedge c = c \wedge a$, and interpret this geometrically.

(3). A and B are specified by the position vectors a and b. Prove that the equation of the plane bisecting the segment AB perpendicularly is

$$r.(a - b) = \tfrac{1}{2}(a^2 - b^2).$$

(4). A is an arbitrary vector and u is a unit vector. Prove that

$$A = (A.u)u + u \wedge (A \wedge u),$$

and show that this represents the decomposition of A into two components, one parallel to u and the other perpendicular to u.

(5)$\star$. If i, j, k are mutually perpendicular unit vectors, find the unit vectors which are perpendicular to both the vectors

$$3i + 5j - 7k, \quad 4i - j - 2k.$$

Find also the sine of the angle between these two given vectors.

(6)$\star$. (i) If A and B are vectors given by $A = 8i + 2j - 3k$, $B = 3i - 6j + 4k$, calculate $A.B$, and show that A and B are perpendicular.

(ii) If $A = 2i + 3j - k$, $B = i - 2j + 2k$, $C = 3i + j + k$, show that $A.B \wedge C = 0$ and $(A - B) \wedge C = 2A \wedge B$.

(iii) If $A = 2i + 3j + 4k$ and $B = 4i + 5j + 6k$, find the magnitude and direction cosines of $A \wedge B$.

(7)$\star$. The sides of a triangle are the vectors A, B, C where $A = B - C$.

(i) By scalar multiplication, square both sides of this equation and deduce the cosine rule for the solution of a triangle.

(ii) Show that the area of the triangle is $\tfrac{1}{2}\sqrt{[(A \wedge B).(A \wedge B)]}$.

Calculate the area when $A = i + j + k$, $B = 2i + 3k$.

(8)$\star$. If $\overrightarrow{OA} = 2j + k$ and $\overrightarrow{OB} = 2i + 3j$, find (i) $\cos \angle AOB$, (ii) the area of the triangle AOB, (iii) the area of the projection of the triangle AOB on to a plane normal to the unit vector k.

(9) *. The edges OP, OQ, OR of a tetrahedron $OPQR$ are the vectors **A**, **B**, **C** respectively, where $\mathbf{A} = 2\mathbf{i} + 4\mathbf{j}$, $\mathbf{B} = 2\mathbf{i} - \mathbf{j} + 3\mathbf{k}$, $\mathbf{C} = 4\mathbf{i} - 2\mathbf{j} + 5\mathbf{k}$. Evaluate $\mathbf{B} \wedge \mathbf{C}$ and deduce that OP is perpendicular to the plane OQR. Write down the length of OP and the area of the triangle OQR and hence the volume of the tetrahedron. Verify your result by evaluating $\mathbf{A} . \mathbf{B} \wedge \mathbf{C}$.

(10) *. The edges OA, OB, OC of a tetrahedron are mutually perpendicular and are represented by $a\mathbf{i}$, $b\mathbf{j}$, $c\mathbf{k}$, where $\mathbf{i}$, $\mathbf{j}$, $\mathbf{k}$ are unit vectors along these edges. The mid-points of AB, OC, AC, OB are P, Q, R, S respectively. Write down expressions for the vectors $\overrightarrow{PQ}$, $\overrightarrow{RS}$ and show that the angle between these vectors is $\cos^{-1}[(a^2 - b^2 - c^2)/(a^2 + b^2 + c^2)]$.

By considering the vector product $\overrightarrow{BA} \wedge \overrightarrow{BC}$ show that the area of the triangle ABC is $\frac{1}{2}\sqrt{(b^2c^2 + c^2a^2 + a^2b^2)}$.

(11) *. A tetrahedron has its vertices at the points O $(0, 0, 0)$, A $(1, 1, 2)$, B $(-1, 2, -1)$ and C $(0, -1, 3)$. By consideration of the vector product $\overrightarrow{AC} \wedge \overrightarrow{AB}$, or otherwise, determine (i) the area of the face ABC and (ii) the unit vector normal to the face ABC. Hence, or otherwise, determine the volume of the tetrahedron.

(12) *. A, B, C are three points with position vectors **a**, **b**, **c** relative to an origin O. Show that the vector $\frac{1}{2}[\mathbf{a} \wedge \mathbf{b} + \mathbf{b} \wedge \mathbf{c} + \mathbf{c} \wedge \mathbf{a}]$ has magnitude equal to the area of the triangle ABC and has direction perpendicular to the plane of the triangle. Show further that if D has position vector **d** the volume of the tetrahedron $ABCD$ is

$$\tfrac{1}{6}[\mathbf{a} \wedge \mathbf{b}.\mathbf{c} - \mathbf{b} \wedge \mathbf{c}.\mathbf{d} + \mathbf{c} \wedge \mathbf{d}.\mathbf{a} - \mathbf{d} \wedge \mathbf{a}.\mathbf{b}].$$

(13) *. The direction of a straight line AB is determined by the unit vector **n** and $\overrightarrow{AP}$ is the position vector relative to A of any point P. Prove that the perpendicular distance from P to AB is given by the magnitude of $\overrightarrow{AP} \wedge \mathbf{n}$. Hence, or otherwise, find the perpendicular distance of the point $(3, 1, 2)$ from the straight line

$$(x - 2)/3 = (y - 3)/2 = (z - 1)/2.$$

(14) *. A point P has position vector **r**, relative to an origin O, and two lines through O are specified in position by the unit vectors **u**, **v**. Lines PL, PM are drawn perpendicular to **u**, **v** respectively, and lines LM', ML' are drawn perpendicular to **v**, **u** respectively. Show that the position vector of L is $(\mathbf{r}.\mathbf{u})\mathbf{u}$ and obtain conditions (in terms of **r**, **u**, **v**) for the lengths OL', OM' to be equal. Interpret your result geometrically.

(15) *. The normals to three planes are in the directions of unit vectors $\mathbf{n}_1$, $\mathbf{n}_2$, $\mathbf{n}_3$. State the condition that there should be a unique point of intersection. Find an expression for its position vector in terms of the three perpendicular distances p_1, p_2, p_3 of the planes from the origin, the three vectors $\mathbf{n}_2 \wedge \mathbf{n}_3$, $\mathbf{n}_3 \wedge \mathbf{n}_1$, $\mathbf{n}_1 \wedge \mathbf{n}_2$ and the triple product $\mathbf{n}_1.\mathbf{n}_2 \wedge \mathbf{n}_3$.

(16) *. P is the foot of the perpendicular from a point B, with position vector **b**, to the line $\mathbf{r} = \mathbf{a} + \lambda\mathbf{t}$. Show that the equation of the line BP is

$$\mathbf{r} = \mathbf{b} + \mu\mathbf{t} \wedge [(\mathbf{a} - \mathbf{b}) \wedge \mathbf{t}],$$

and find the position vector of P.

(17) *. The points P and Q have position vectors **p** and **q** respectively and the plane Ω passes through the origin, having its normal along the vector **n**. Find the position

vectors $\mathbf{p}'$ and $\mathbf{q}'$ of the feet of the perpendiculars from P and Q to Ω. Express the angle subtended by the feet in terms of $\mathbf{p}, \mathbf{q}$ and $\mathbf{n}$. Apply your formulae to the case: $\mathbf{p} = (1, 2, -2)$, $\mathbf{q} = (5, 2, 2)$, $\mathbf{n} = (2, 1, -1)$ and show that the angle is $\cos^{-1}(-\tfrac{8}{7})$.

(18)*. The unit vectors $\mathbf{p}, \mathbf{q}$ make respective angles α, β with a unit vector $\mathbf{k}$, and the angle between the plane containing $\mathbf{p}, \mathbf{k}$ and that containing $\mathbf{q}, \mathbf{k}$ is θ. If $\mathbf{u} = \mathbf{k} \wedge \mathbf{p}$ and $\mathbf{v} = \mathbf{k} \wedge \mathbf{q}$ prove that $\mathbf{u}.\mathbf{v} = \sin \alpha \sin \beta \cos \theta$. Show also that $\mathbf{u} \wedge \mathbf{v}$ is parallel to $\mathbf{k}$ and of magnitude $\sin \alpha \sin \beta \sin \theta$.

(19)*. Find the vector $\mathbf{x}$ and the scalar λ which satisfy the equations $\mathbf{a} \wedge \mathbf{x} = \mathbf{b} + \lambda\mathbf{a}$, $\mathbf{a}.\mathbf{x} = 1$, where $\mathbf{a}$ and $\mathbf{b}$ have components $(1, 1, 1)$ and $(1, -1, 2)$ respectively.

(20)*. X is an unknown vector which satisfies the equations (i) $\mathbf{A} \wedge \mathbf{X} = \mathbf{B}$, (ii) $\mathbf{A}.\mathbf{X} = a$, where $\mathbf{A}$ and $\mathbf{B}$ are known vectors and a is a known scalar. By multiplying (i) vectorially by $\mathbf{A}$, prove that

$$\mathbf{X} = (\mathbf{B} \wedge \mathbf{A} + a\mathbf{A})/A^2.$$

(21)*. (i) If $\mathbf{A}, \mathbf{B}$ are given vectors, $\mathbf{B}$ being perpendicular to $\mathbf{A}$, and a is a given scalar, show that the solution of the equations $\mathbf{A}.\mathbf{X} = a$, $\mathbf{A} \wedge \mathbf{X} = \mathbf{B}$ for an unknown vector $\mathbf{X}$ is unique, and find it. Examine whether the solution is valid if $\mathbf{B}$ is not perpendicular to $\mathbf{A}$.

(ii) If $\mathbf{n}$ is a unit vector, show that the condition that the plane $\mathbf{n}.\mathbf{r} = p$ should touch the sphere $(\mathbf{r} - \mathbf{c})^2 = a^2$ is $(p - \mathbf{n}.\mathbf{c})^2 = a^2$.

(22)*. A and B are fixed points and $\mathbf{w}$ is a given vector perpendicular to AB. Describe in geometrical terms the loci defined by the following vector equations in three dimensional space:

$$\text{(i) } \overrightarrow{AP}.\overrightarrow{BP} = 0, \quad \text{(ii) } \overrightarrow{AP} \wedge \overrightarrow{PB} = \mathbf{w}.$$

(23)*. $\mathbf{i}, \mathbf{j}, \mathbf{k}$ are three mutually perpendicular unit vectors, and $\mathbf{a} = \mathbf{j} - \mathbf{k}$, $\mathbf{b} = \mathbf{i} - \mathbf{j} + 2\mathbf{k}$, $\mathbf{c} = \mathbf{i} + \mathbf{j}$. Calculate $\mathbf{a}.\mathbf{b}$, $\mathbf{a}.\mathbf{c}$, $\mathbf{b} \wedge \mathbf{c}$ and $\mathbf{a} \wedge (\mathbf{b} \wedge \mathbf{c})$, and verify that $\mathbf{a} \wedge (\mathbf{b} \wedge \mathbf{c}) = (\mathbf{a}.\mathbf{c})\mathbf{b} - (\mathbf{a}.\mathbf{b})\mathbf{c}$.

(24)*. (i) Show that $\mathbf{A}.\mathbf{A} - \mathbf{B}.\mathbf{B} = (\mathbf{A} + \mathbf{B}).(\mathbf{A} - \mathbf{B})$. If $(\mathbf{C} - \mathbf{A}).\mathbf{A} = (\mathbf{C} - \mathbf{B}).\mathbf{B}$ prove that $\mathbf{A} - \mathbf{B}$ and $\mathbf{C} - \mathbf{A} - \mathbf{B}$ are perpendicular.

(ii) Given that $\overrightarrow{OA} = \mathbf{A} = 2\mathbf{i} - 3\mathbf{j} + \mathbf{k}$, $\overrightarrow{OB} = \mathbf{B} = \mathbf{i} + \mathbf{j} + \mathbf{k}$, $\overrightarrow{OC} = \mathbf{C} = 4\mathbf{i} + 2\mathbf{j} - 2\mathbf{k}$, where $\mathbf{i}, \mathbf{j}, \mathbf{k}$ are mutually perpendicular unit vectors show that OA is perpendicular to OB and also to OC. Calculate the vector product $\mathbf{B} \wedge \mathbf{C}$ and the volume of the tetrahedron $OABC$.

(25)*. If $\mathbf{a}, \mathbf{b}, \mathbf{c}$ are the position vectors of three non-collinear points in space, show that (i) the vector equation of the plane joining them is $\mathbf{r}.(\mathbf{b} \wedge \mathbf{c} + \mathbf{c} \wedge \mathbf{a} + \mathbf{a} \wedge \mathbf{b}) = \mathbf{a}.\mathbf{b} \wedge \mathbf{c}$, and (ii) the volume V of the tetrahedron with vertices at the three points and at the origin is given by $6V = \pm\mathbf{a}.\mathbf{b} \wedge \mathbf{c}$. Establish also the formula

$$(\mathbf{b} \wedge \mathbf{c}).[(\mathbf{c} \wedge \mathbf{a}) \wedge (\mathbf{a} \wedge \mathbf{b})] = (\mathbf{a}.\mathbf{b} \wedge \mathbf{c})^2.$$

ANSWERS TO EXERCISES

(5). $\pm(17, 22, 23)/\sqrt{(1302)}$; $\sqrt{(62/83)}$.   (6). (i) 0. (iii). $2\sqrt{6}, (-1, 2, -1)/\sqrt{6}$.

(7). $\tfrac{1}{2}\sqrt{14}$.   (8). (i) $6/\sqrt{65}$, (ii) $\tfrac{1}{2}\sqrt{29}$, (iii) 2.   (9). $\mathbf{i} + 2\mathbf{j}, 2\sqrt{5}, \tfrac{5}{3}$.

(10). $\tfrac{1}{2}(-ai - bj + ck)$, $\tfrac{1}{2}(-ai + bj - ck)$.

(11). (i) $\tfrac{5}{2}\sqrt{3}$, (ii) $(1, -1, -1)/\sqrt{3}, \tfrac{5}{3}$.   (13). $\sqrt{(101/17)}$.

(14). $\mathbf{r}.\mathbf{u} = \mathbf{r}.\mathbf{v}$.   (15). $\mathbf{n}_1.\mathbf{n}_2 \wedge \mathbf{n}_3 \neq 0$, $\mathbf{x} = (p_1\mathbf{n}_3 \wedge \mathbf{n}_2 + p_2\mathbf{n}_1 \wedge \mathbf{n}_3 + p_3\mathbf{n}_2 \wedge \mathbf{n}_1)/(\mathbf{n}_1.\mathbf{n}_2 \wedge \mathbf{n}_3)$.   (16). $\mathbf{a} + t(t.\mathbf{b} - t.\mathbf{a})/t^2$.

(17). $\mathbf{p}' = \mathbf{p} - \mathbf{n}(\mathbf{p}.\mathbf{n})/\mathbf{n}^2$, $\mathbf{q}' = \mathbf{q} - \mathbf{n}(\mathbf{q}.\mathbf{n})/\mathbf{n}^2$,

$\quad \cos\theta = [(\mathbf{p}.\mathbf{q})\mathbf{n}^2 - (\mathbf{p}.\mathbf{n})(\mathbf{q}.\mathbf{n})]/\sqrt{\{[\mathbf{p}^2\mathbf{n}^2 - (\mathbf{p}.\mathbf{n})^2][\mathbf{q}^2\mathbf{n}^2 - (\mathbf{q}.\mathbf{n})^2]\}}$.

(19). $\lambda = -\frac{2}{3}$, $\mathbf{x} = (-\frac{2}{3}, \frac{2}{3}, 1)$.   (21). (i) $\mathbf{X} = (a\mathbf{A} - \mathbf{A} \wedge \mathbf{B})/\mathbf{A}^2$.

(22). (i) Sphere on AB as diameter; (ii) a straight line l parallel to AB, so the plane lAB is perpendicular to $\mathbf{w}$.   (23). $-3, 1, (-2, 2, 2), (4, 2, 2)$.

(24). $(-4, 6, -2), 14/3$.

CHAPTER 14

DIFFERENTIATION AND ITS APPLICATIONS

14.1 Theorems on differentiation

A function y of the independent variable x is given in the form $y = f(x)$; sometimes we write $y = y(x)$, where the y on the left denotes the value of the function for a particular value of x, and where the y on the right denotes the functional form. Graphically, this function defines a curve in the Oxy-plane, but the analysis that follows may be developed independently of geometrical interpretations. However it proves useful to use the geometrical terms, such as point and curve, even in non-geometrical contexts.

Attention is centred upon the definite point x_0, $y_0 = f(x_0)$. Nearby points of the curve are next considered, at which $x = x_0 + \delta x$, where δx is a small *finite increment*. The increment in y, denoted by δy, is then given by

$$\delta y = f(x_0 + \delta x) - f(x_0).$$

We say that the curve is *continuous* at the point (x_0, y_0) provided the increment δy can be made as small as we please by making the increment δx as small as we please. A more precise mathematical definition of continuity would avoid the rather vague notion of 'as small as we please'.

We may also form the ratio $\delta y/\delta x$:

$$\delta y/\delta x = [f(x_0 + \delta x) - f(x_0)]/\delta x.$$

If the limit of this ratio exists as δx tends to zero, and if the limit has the same value as δx tends to zero through either positive or negative values, then this limit is defined to be the *differential coefficient* or *derived function* of y at the point (x_0, y_0). This limit is written as dy/dx:

$$\frac{dy}{dx} = \lim_{\delta x \to 0} \frac{f(x_0 - \delta x) - f(x_0)}{\delta x}. \tag{1}$$

It should be stressed that the symbols dy and dx have no individual meaning in the quantity dy/dx. Oftentimes, we write $dy/dx = y'$ for brevity, or even as Dy, where D, denoting d/dx, stands for the operation of differentiation.

If this limit exists as $\delta x \to 0$, clearly δy must also tend to zero, otherwise $\delta y/\delta x$ would become infinite. The function is therefore continuous at the point (x_0, y_0). A function continuous at (x_0, y_0) need not, however, be differentiable at that point.

The precise meaning of a *limit* can be made clear only by more comprehensive analysis. For our purposes it is sufficient to state that a function $g(t)$ tends to a limit L as $t \to a$ if the difference $g(t) - L$ becomes indefinitely small as the difference $t - a$ becomes indefinitely small. A symbolical definition would avoid the use of the phrase "indefinitely small", since the meaning of a limit may be made precise without such a concept. Strictly speaking, the calculus does not deal with infinitely small quantities or *infinitesimals*; we shall make no mention of such concepts throughout our text.

If the limit dy/dx exists at all points in the range $a \leqslant x \leqslant b$, then the function is said to be *differentiable* throughout the range.

Geometrically, the derivative is the gradient of the tangent drawn to the curve $y = f(x)$ at the point (x_0, y_0).

The following theorems should be known by the student:

(i) If $y = f(x) \pm g(x)$, $y' = f' \pm g'$.
(ii) If $y = f(x)g(x)$, $y' = fg' + f'g$.
(iii) If $y = f(x)/g(x)$, $y' = (f'g - fg')/g^2$.

Function of a function. If y is a function of x, $y = y(x)$, and if x is a function of t, $x = x(t)$, then y is defined as a function of t when x is eliminated. We seek the value of dy/dt in terms of the derivatives of the two given functions. Evidently

$$\frac{\delta y}{\delta t} = \frac{\delta y}{\delta x} \cdot \frac{\delta x}{\delta t} ,$$

since, being finite quantities, δx may be cancelled. In the limit (but making the assumption that the limit of a product equals the product of the limits) we have

$$\frac{dy}{dt} = \frac{dy}{dx} \cdot \frac{dx}{dt} , \qquad (2)$$

a result known as the *chain rule*; this process may be extended to as many factors as required.

Inverse functions. If $y = y(x)$, this equation giving y in terms of x may formally be solved for x in terms of y, yielding $x = x(y)$. We seek the value of dx/dy in terms of the derivative of the given function. Evidently, in finite terms,

$$\frac{\delta x}{\delta y} = 1 \left/ \frac{\delta y}{\delta x} \right. ,$$

so in the limit we have

$$\frac{dx}{dy} = 1 \bigg/ \frac{dy}{dx} . \tag{3}$$

Functions defined parametrically. If $y = y(t)$, $x = x(t)$ are two given functions of t, t may be eliminated yielding y as a function of x. We seek the value of dy/dx in terms of the derivatives of the given functions. Evidently, in finite terms,

$$\frac{\delta y}{\delta x} = \frac{\delta y}{\delta t} \bigg/ \frac{\delta x}{\delta t} ,$$

so in the limit we have

$$\frac{dy}{dx} = \frac{dy}{dt} \bigg/ \frac{dx}{dt} . \tag{4}$$

Second differential coefficients. If $y = y(x)$ is given, its differential coefficient dy/dx, being itself a function of x, may again be differentiated, yielding the *second differential coefficient d^2y/dx^2*.

It can easily be shown that this second derivative may be expressed in the form

$$\frac{d^2y}{dx^2} = \lim_{\delta x \to 0} \frac{y(x_0 + 2\delta x) - 2y(x_0 + \delta x) + y(x_0)}{\delta x^2} ;$$

this result will be apparent after section 14.4 has been read.

Differentiating equation (2) with respect to t, we obtain

$$\frac{d^2y}{dt^2} = \frac{dy}{dx} \cdot \frac{d^2x}{dt^2} + \frac{d^2y}{dx^2} \left(\frac{dx}{dt}\right)^2. \tag{5}$$

We have treated the right hand side of (2) as a product, and the derivative of dy/dx *with respect to t* has been written as $d^2y/dx^2 . dx/dt$, by another application of the chain rule.

The differentiation of equation (3) with respect to y demands that the right hand side, being a function of x, be differentiated *with respect to x*, and then completed by the factor dx/dy according to the chain rule:

$$\frac{d^2x}{dy^2} = \frac{d}{dx}\left(1 \bigg/ \frac{dy}{dx}\right) \cdot \frac{dx}{dy}$$

$$= -\frac{\dfrac{d^2y}{dx^2}}{\left(\dfrac{dy}{dx}\right)^2} \cdot \frac{1}{\dfrac{dy}{dx}}$$

$$= -\frac{d^2y}{dx^2} \bigg/ \left(\frac{dy}{dx}\right)^3,$$

where we have differentiated $1/(dy/dx)$ as a quotient.

The differentiation of equation (4) with respect to x demands that the right hand side, being a function of t alone, be differentiated *with respect to t*, and then multiplied by $dt/dx = 1/(dx/dt)$ by the chain rule:

$$\frac{d^2y}{dx^2} = \frac{\dfrac{d}{dt}\left(\dfrac{dy}{dt} \middle/ \dfrac{dx}{dt}\right)}{\dfrac{dx}{dt}} = \frac{\dfrac{d^2y}{dt^2}\cdot\dfrac{dx}{dt} - \dfrac{dy}{dt}\cdot\dfrac{d^2x}{dt^2}}{\left(\dfrac{dx}{dt}\right)^3}. \tag{6}$$

14.2 The differential coefficients of the elementary functions

Algebraic functions. If $y = x^n$, where n is a positive integer, the use of the binomial series for a positive integral index yields

$$\delta y = (x + \delta x)^n - x^n = x^n + nx^{n-1}\,\delta x + \tfrac{1}{2}n(n-1)x^{n-2}\,\delta x^2 + \ldots - x^n,$$

so $\qquad\qquad \delta y/\delta x = nx^{n-1} + \tfrac{1}{2}n(n-1)x^{n-2}\,\delta x + \ldots.$

Hence, in the limit as $\delta x \to 0$,

$$dy/dx = nx^{n-1}. \tag{7}$$

If $y = x^{p/q}$, where p and q are positive integers, we take the qth power of each side, obtaining $y^q = x^p$. Differentiating, using result (7), where y is a function of x, we obtain

$$qy^{q-1}\frac{dy}{dx} = px^{p-1},$$

so $\qquad\qquad \dfrac{dy}{dx} = \dfrac{p}{q}\cdot\dfrac{x^{p-1}}{y^{q-1}} = (p/q)x^{p/q-1}$

upon simplification.

If r is a positive rational fraction, and if $y = x^{-r} = 1/x^r$, the use of the quotient rule provides

$$\frac{dy}{dx} = -rx^{r-1}/(x^r)^2 = -rx^{-r-1}.$$

It therefore appears that result (7) is applicable to all *rational* indices. We assume that (7) is valid if n is *irrational*, on the grounds of continuity. An exact discussion of this point and of the nature of irrational numbers would be beyond the immediate object of our text.

Trigonometrical functions. If $y = \sin x$, δy is given by

$$\delta y = \sin(x + \delta x) - \sin x = 2\cos(x + \tfrac{1}{2}\delta x)\sin\tfrac{1}{2}\delta x,$$

yielding

$$\frac{\delta y}{\delta x} = \frac{\cos(x + \tfrac{1}{2}\delta x)\sin\tfrac{1}{2}\delta x}{\tfrac{1}{2}\delta x}.$$

We now use the fact that $(\sin \theta)/\theta$ tends to unity as θ tends to zero, provided the angle θ is measured in *radians*; hence

$$dy/dx = \cos x.$$

If x is measured in degrees, we have

$$dy/dx = (\pi/180) \cos x.$$

The student should recognize that the proof of the limit $(\sin \theta)/\theta \to 1$ demands the use of *intuitive geometry*, since certain lengths occurring in a diagram are compared with each other. If such a method is to be avoided, as indeed it must in pure analysis, the function $y = \sin x$ must be defined by analytical means, distinct from geometrical means using a right-angled triangle. The integrals of the derivatives of the inverse trigonometrical functions may be used to define the trigonometrical functions analytically; the derivative of $y = \sin x$ then appears without geometrical intuition.

Similarly, we have

$$D \cos x = -\sin x, \quad D \tan x = \sec^2 x, \quad D \cot x = -\operatorname{cosec}^2 x,$$

$$D \sec x = \sec x \tan x, \quad D \operatorname{cosec} x = -\operatorname{cosec} x \cot x.$$

The inverse trigonometrical functions. The equation $y = \sin^{-1} x$ is regarded as the solution of the equation $x = \sin y$; the function is *multi-valued*. Differentiating x with respect to y, we obtain

$$dx/dy = \cos y = \sqrt{(1 - x^2)},$$

yielding $\qquad\qquad dy/dx = 1/\sqrt{(1 - x^2)}.$

Numerically, the sign of the square root requires careful attention since it depends on the value of y, this being a multi-valued function. The positive root is required if $-\tfrac{1}{2}\pi < y < \tfrac{1}{2}\pi$, or any similar interval separated from this by an integral multiple of 2π; the negative root is required elsewhere.

Similarly, we have

$$D \cos^{-1} x = -1/\sqrt{(1 - x^2)}, \quad D \tan^{-1} x = 1/(1 + x^2),$$

$$D \cot^{-1} x = -1/(1 + x^2), \quad D \sec^{-1} x = 1/[x\sqrt{(x^2 - 1)}],$$

$$D \operatorname{cosec}^{-1} x = -1/[x\sqrt{(x^2 - 1)}].$$

These formulae are correct at least in the interval $0 < y < \tfrac{1}{2}\pi$; the signs required for further intervals may be ascertained from a graph.

The exponential function. The method by which the differential coefficient of this function is determined depends upon the original definition of the function. The most artificial definition appears to the author to be

$$e^x = \lim_{n \to \infty} (1 + n^{-1})^{nx},$$

though this definition is in common use.

The simplest, and least artificial definition, is to define the function $y = \exp x$ as that function whose rate of change equals itself, namely

$$dy/dx = y, \tag{8}$$

such that $\exp 0 = 1$.

Firstly, we must make sure that no other function satisfies equation (8). Let us suppose that $y = \exp x$ and $y = v(x) \exp x$ both satisfy the equation, where $v(x)$ is a function to be found. Using the prime to denote differentiation, we have

$$\begin{aligned} v \exp x &= d(v \exp x)/dx \\ &= v' \exp x + v\, d(\exp x)/dx \\ &= v' \exp x + v \exp x, \end{aligned}$$

showing that $v' \exp x = 0$. Hence $v' = 0$ and $v = $ constant. The most general function satisfying equation (8) is therefore

$$y = k \exp x. \tag{9}$$

Consider now the function $y = \exp(x + a)$, where a is a constant. Evidently

$$\frac{dy}{dx} = \frac{d \exp(x + a)}{d(x + a)} = \exp(x + a).$$

The function $\exp(x + a)$ also satisfies equation (8), so it must be expressible in the form (9):

$$\exp(x + a) = k \exp x.$$

When $x = 0$, we obtain $\exp a = k$, yielding

$$\exp(x + a) = \exp x \exp a.$$

If now we place $x = a = v$, we obtain

$$\exp 2v = (\exp v)^2.$$

Generally, if n is a positive integer,

$$\exp nv = (\exp x)^n.$$

If we place $x = 2v, a = -v$, we obtain

$$\begin{aligned} \exp v &= \exp 2v \exp(-v) \\ &= (\exp v)^2 \exp(-v), \end{aligned}$$

yielding $$\exp(-v) = (\exp v)^{-1}.$$

Generally, if n is a positive integer,

$$\exp(-nv) = (\exp v)^{-n}.$$

Finally, if exp (v/n) is given, where n is an integer, let $v/n = u$. Then

$$\exp(v/n) = \exp u.$$

Taking the nth power of each side, we obtain

$$\exp v = (\exp u)^n,$$

so $$\exp(v/n) = \exp u = (\exp v)^{1/n}.$$

The case of exp (pv/q), embracing any rational fraction, is a combination of these previous cases.

The general result is that

$$\exp(rv) = (\exp v)^r$$

where r is any rational fraction. If $v = 1$, we have

$$\exp r = (\exp 1)^r.$$

The number exp 1 is denoted by e, having the value $2 \cdot 7182818 \dots$. We may therefore write

$$\exp r = e^r.$$

Irrational numbers may be introduced on the ground of continuity; generally then

$$\exp x = e^x, \quad \exp(x + y) = e^x e^y.$$

Moreover, by the definition,

$$de^x / dx = e^x.$$

The numerical value of e^x may be calculated from its power series, derived later in section 14.5.

The logarithmic function. This is the function inverse to the exponential function. The statement $y = \log_e x$ implies that $x = e^y$. Hence

$$\frac{dy}{dx} = 1 \Big/ \frac{dx}{dy} = 1/e^y = 1/x.$$

Evidently, $x = \exp(\log_e x)$ is an identity. To differentiate $y = a^x$, we first express a in the form $a = e^{\log_e a}$, yielding

$$y = e^{x \log_e a};$$

hence $$\frac{dy}{dx} = \log_e a \; e^{x \log_e a} = a^x \log_e a.$$

To differentiate a logarithm to another base a:

$$y = \log_a x,$$

we note that this implies $x = a^y$. Hence

$$\frac{dy}{dx} = 1 \Big/ \frac{dx}{dy} = \frac{1}{a^y \log_e a} = \frac{1}{x \log_e a}.$$

The formula for the *change of base* of logarithms should be recalled. If $y = \log_a x$, what is the value of $\log_b x$? Evidently $x = a^y$, so

$$\log_b x = \log_b (a^y) = y \log_b a = \log_b a \log_a x.$$

In particular, if we place $b = x$, we obtain

$$\log_x a \log_a x = 1,$$

or $\qquad\qquad \log_x a = 1/\log_a x.$

We may therefore differentiate a logarithm with respect to its base:

$$\frac{d}{dx} \log_x a = - \frac{1}{(\log_a x)^2} \cdot \frac{1}{x \log_e a} .$$

The logarithmic function is commonly given an independent definition, namely the area under the graph $1/t$. We write

$$\log_e x = \int_1^x \frac{dt}{t} ,$$

the limits being chosen so that $\log_e 1 = 0$. The differential coefficient of this function is obviously $1/x$, in keeping with the previous definition. More generally we should write

$$\int \frac{dt}{t} = \log |t|$$

if $t < 0$; this result differs from $\log t$ merely by a complex constant. Then if $a > b > 0$,

$$\int_{-a}^{-b} \frac{dt}{t} = \left[\log |t| \right]_{-a}^{-b} = \log (b/a),$$

a negative answer; we have however only used real quantities in its evaluation.

Logarithmic differentiation. The use of logarithms provides a suitable method for differentiating functions of the following type:

$$\text{(i)} \ y = u(x)v(x)w(x) \ldots, \quad \text{(ii)} \ y = [f(x)]^{g(x)}.$$

For case (i), we have

$$\log y = \log u + \log v + \log w + \ldots,$$

so, upon differentiating and using a prime to denote differentiation, we obtain

$$y'/y = u'/u + v'/v + w'/w + \ldots,$$

yielding $\qquad y' = y(u'/u + v'/v + w'/w + \ldots).$

For case (ii), we have

$$\log_e y = g(x) \log_e f(x);$$

hence $\qquad\qquad y'/y = g' \log_e f + gf'/f,$

or $\qquad\qquad y' = f^g(g' \log_e f + gf'/f).$

Hyperbolic functions. In chapter 5, we defined the functions

$$\sinh x = \tfrac{1}{2}(e^x - e^{-x}), \quad \cosh x = \tfrac{1}{2}(e^x + e^{-x}),$$

and so on. Differentiating the exponential functions occurring in these definitions, we obtain

$$D \sinh x = \cosh x, \quad D \cosh x = \sinh x.$$

The remaining functions have the differential coefficients:

$$D \tanh x = \operatorname{sech}^2 x, \quad D \coth x = -\operatorname{cosech}^2 x,$$
$$D \operatorname{sech} x = -\operatorname{sech} x \tanh x, \quad D \operatorname{cosech} x = -\operatorname{cosech} x \coth x.$$

The inverse hyperbolic functions. We write $y = \sinh^{-1} x$ as inverse of the function $x = \sinh y$. Differentiating this, we obtain

$$\frac{dy}{dx} = 1 \Big/ \frac{dx}{dy} = \frac{1}{\cosh y} = \frac{1}{\sqrt{(x^2 + 1)}}.$$

Similarly,

$$D \cosh^{-1} x = 1/\sqrt{(x^2 - 1)}, \quad D \tanh^{-1} x = 1/(1 - x^2),$$
$$D \coth^{-1} x = -1/(x^2 - 1), \quad D \operatorname{sech}^{-1} x = 1/[x\sqrt{(1 - x^2)}],$$
$$D \operatorname{cosech}^{-1} x = 1/[x\sqrt{(1 + x^2)}].$$

A graph should be used in the case of double-valued functions to ascertain the sign required for the square root.

Example 1   Differentiate the two functions

(i)$\star$ $y = \sin^{-1} [2x\sqrt{(1 - x^2)}]$, (ii)$\star$ $y = \log_e \left[e^x \left(\dfrac{x - 2}{x + 2}\right)^{\frac{3}{4}} \right]$.

(i) Differentiating by the chain rule, we obtain

$$Dy = \frac{1}{\sqrt{[1 - 4x^2(1 - x^2)]}} \cdot \left[2\sqrt{(1 - x^2)} - \frac{2x.x}{\sqrt{(1 - x^2)}} \right]$$

$$= \pm \frac{1}{1 - 2x^2} \cdot \frac{2(1 - 2x^2)}{\sqrt{(1 - x^2)}}$$

$$= \pm \frac{2}{\sqrt{(1 - x^2)}}.$$

(ii) We first simplify the logarithm, by writing

$$y = \log_e (e^x) + \tfrac{3}{4} \log (x - 2) - \tfrac{3}{4} \log (x + 2)$$
$$= x + \tfrac{3}{4} \log (x - 2) - \tfrac{3}{4} \log (x + 2);$$

hence $\quad Dy = 1 + \tfrac{3}{4}/(x - 2) - \tfrac{3}{4}/(x + 2)$
$$= (x^2 - 1)/(x^2 - 4)$$

upon simplification.

Example 2 (i) If $y = x^5 + x$, find d^2x/dy^2.

(ii) If $x = a \cos^3 t$, $y = a \sin^3 t$, find d^2y/dx^2.

(i) Since $dy/dx = 5x^4 + 1$, it follows that $dx/dy = 1/(5x^4 + 1)$.

Then
$$\frac{d^2x}{dy^2} = \frac{d}{dx}\left(\frac{1}{5x^4 + 1}\right)\frac{dx}{dy}$$

$$= -\frac{20x^3}{(5x^4 + 1)^3}.$$

(ii) The first derivative is given by

$$\frac{dy}{dx} = \frac{dy/dt}{dx/dt} = -\frac{3a \sin^2 t \cos t}{3a \cos^2 t \sin t} = -\tan t.$$

Hence $\quad \dfrac{d^2y}{dx^2} = \dfrac{d}{dt}(-\tan t) \cdot \dfrac{dt}{dx} = \dfrac{\sec^2 t}{3a \cos^2 t \sin t} = \dfrac{1}{3a \cos^4 t \sin t}$

14.3 Differential coefficients of the nth order.

Some elementary functions permit their nth differential coefficients to be written down immediately. If $y = x^r$, successive differentiation yields

$$d^ny/dx^n = r(r - 1) \ldots (r - n + 1)x^{r-n}.$$

If r is an integer, and $n \leqslant r$, we may write

$$\frac{d^ny}{dx^n} = \frac{r!}{(r - n)!} x^{r-n}.$$

If $y = \log_e x$, $dy/dx = 1/x$, and generally,

$$d^ny/dx^n = (-1)^{n-1}(n - 1)! \, x^{-n}.$$

If $y = e^{ax}$, we have generally $d^ny/dx^n = a^n e^{ax}$.
If $y = \sinh x$, we have

$$\frac{d^ny}{dx^n} = \frac{d^n}{dx^n} \tfrac{1}{2}(e^x - e^{-x})$$

$$= \tfrac{1}{2}[e^x - (-1)^n e^{-x}]$$

$$= \tfrac{1}{2}[1 - (-1)^n] \cosh x + \tfrac{1}{2}[1 + (-1)^n] \sinh x.$$

10

Similarly, if $y = \cosh x$, we have

$$d^n y/dx^n = \tfrac{1}{2}[1 + (-1)^n] \cosh x + \tfrac{1}{2}[1 - (-1)^n] \sinh x.$$

If $y = \sin x$, we have in terms of complex exponential functions:

$$\frac{d^n y}{dx^n} = \frac{d^n}{dx^n} (e^{ix} - e^{-ix})/2i$$

$$= [i^n e^{ix} - (-i)^n e^{-ix}]/2i$$

$$= (e^{\frac{1}{2}\pi n i} e^{ix} - e^{-\frac{1}{2}\pi n i} e^{-ix})/2i$$

$$= \sin (x + \tfrac{1}{2}\pi n).$$

Similarly, if $y = \cos x$, we have

$$d^n y/dx^n = \cos (x + \tfrac{1}{2}\pi n).$$

Other functions such as $y = \tan x$ do not possess simple forms for their nth differential coefficients, but it should be noticed that the formula

$$\frac{d^n}{dx^n} \frac{1}{(x - a)^r} = \frac{(-1)^n r(r + 1) \ldots (r + n - 1)}{(x - a)^{r+n}}$$

permits us to write down the nth derivatives of a rational function of x expressed as a sum of elementary partial fractions.

Example 3   Find the nth derivative of $y = 4x/[(x + 2)(x - 1)^2]$.

In terms of partial fractions, we have

$$y = \tfrac{8}{9}(x - 1)^{-1} + \tfrac{4}{3}(x - 1)^{-2} - \tfrac{8}{9}(x + 2)^{-1}.$$

The nth derivative is then given by

$$\frac{d^n y}{dx^n} = \frac{\tfrac{8}{9}(-1)^n n!}{(x - 1)^{n+1}} + \frac{(\tfrac{4}{3} - 1)^n (n + 1)!}{(x - 1)^{n+2}} - \frac{\tfrac{8}{9}(-1)^n n!}{(x + 2)^{n+1}}.$$

We shall now derive the expansion known as *Leibnitz's theorem*, namely the expanded form of the nth derivative of the product $u(x)v(x)$. To simplify the notation, we shall denote the operation d^n/dx^n by D^n. This symbol D^n is an *operator*, and it is regarded as operating on whatever function stands on its *right*. Hence we may write

$$D(uv) = (Du)v + uDv$$

using the elementary product rule. Differentiating again, we obtain

$$D^2(uv) = (D^2u)v + 2Du \cdot Dv + uD^2v.$$

It should be noticed that brackets or dots may be used to indicate the limits of any particular *operand* in cases of ambiguity.

These two results agree with the general expansion

$$D^n(uv) = D^nu.v + {}_nC_1D^{n-1}u.Dv + {}_nC_2D^{n-2}u.D^2v + \ldots$$
$$+ {}_nC_rD^{n-r}u.D^rv + {}_nC_{r+1}D^{n-r-1}u.D^{r+1}v + \ldots + uD^nv,$$

which we shall prove by induction. This theorem, known as Leibnitz's theorem, employs the binomial coefficients throughout.

Differentiating this equation, we obtain

$$D^{n+1}(uv) = (D^{n+1}u.v + D^nu.Dv) + {}_nC_1(D^nu.Dv + D^{n-1}u.D^2v) + \ldots$$
$$+ {}_nC_r(D^{n-r+1}u.D^rv + D^{n-r}u.D^{r+1}v)$$
$$+ {}_nC_{r+1}(D^{n-r}u.D^{r+1}v + D^{n-r-1}u.D^{r+2}v) + \ldots$$
$$+ (Du.D^nv + uD^{n+1}v).$$

But

$$1 + {}_nC_1 = {}_{n+1}C_1, \quad {}_nC_1 + {}_nC_2 = {}_{n+1}C_2, \ldots, {}_nC_r + {}_nC_{r+1} = {}_{n+1}C_{r+1},$$

yielding

$$D^{n+1}(uv) = D^{n+1}u.v + {}_{n+1}C_1D^nu.Dv + \ldots$$
$$+ {}_{n+1}C_{r+1}D^{n-r}u.D^{r+1}v + \ldots + uD^{n+1}v,$$

thereby verifying the theorem.

Example 4 Find the 10th derivative of $y = x^5 \cos x$.

Let $u = \cos x$, $v = x^5$, $n = 10$. Noting that $D^{10} \cos x = -\cos x$, $D^9 \cos x = -\sin x$, and so on, we have

$$D^{10}(x^5 \cos x) = -x^5 \cos x - 10.5x^4 \sin x + 45.20x^3 \cos x$$
$$+120.60x^2 \sin x - 210.120x \cos x - 252.120 \sin x$$
$$= \cos x(-x^5 + 45.20x^3 - 210.120x)$$
$$+ \sin x(-10.5x^4 + 120.60x^2 - 252.120).$$

Example 5 If $y = \exp(a \sin^{-1} x)$, find the value of $D^n y$ when $x = 0$.

In this context, it is usual to denote $D^n y$ by $y^{(n)}(x)$, its value at $x = 0$ being written as $y^{(n)}(0)$. The method is first to find a relation connecting y, y' and y'', then to differentiate this $(n - 2)$ times by Leibnitz's theorem, and finally to place $x = 0$. Differentiating y, we obtain

$$y' = a \exp(a \sin^{-1} x)/\sqrt{(1 - x^2)}.$$

The general rule is now to simplify this by eliminating all denominators and square roots, namely

$$(1 - x^2)(y')^2 = a^2y^2.$$

Note that Leibnitz's theorem cannot be applied to this equation, since the left-hand side consists of a product of three functions. We differentiate again, obtaining

$$(1 - x^2)2y'y'' - 2x(y')^2 = 2a^2yy',$$

or, on dividing by $2y'$,

$$(1 - x^2)y'' - xy' - a^2y = 0.$$

Leibnitz's theorem may now be applied. Differentiating $(n - 2)$ times, we obtain

$$(1 - x^2)y^{(n)} + (n - 2)(-2x)y^{(n-1)} + \tfrac{1}{2}(n - 2)(n - 3)(-2)y^{(n-2)}$$
$$-xy^{(n-1)} - (n - 2)y^{(n-2)} - a^2y^{(n-2)} = 0$$

simplifying to

$$(1 - x^2)y^{(n)} - (2n - 3)xy^{(n-1)} - [(n - 2)^2 + a^2]y^{(n-2)} = 0.$$

Now let $x = 0$, yielding

$$y^{(n)}(0) = [(n - 2)^2 + a^2]y^{(n-2)}(0).$$

Evidently $y(0) = 1$, $y'(0) = a$ from the original equations. Successive substitution then gives

$$y^{(n)}(0) = [(n - 2)^2 + a^2][(n - 4)^2 + a^2]y^{(n-4)}(0)$$
$$= [(n - 2)^2 + a^2][(n - 4)^2 + a^2] \dots (2^2 + a^2)a^2y(0)$$
$$= \prod_{r=1}^{\frac{1}{2}n} [(n - 2r)^2 + a^2]$$

if n is even; while if n is odd, we have

$$y^{(n)}(0) = [(n - 2)^2 + a^2][(n - 4)^2 + a^2] \dots (3^2 + a^2)(1^2 + a^2)y'(0)$$
$$= a \prod_{r=1}^{\frac{1}{2}(n-1)} [(n - 2r)^2 + a^2].$$

14.4   Taylor's and Maclaurin's power series

The complete investigation of the theory of these power series together with the most restricted conditions under which they are valid is beyond the intended scope of this text. We shall concern ourselves with the *simplest and least restricted form* of the theory, relying upon a graphical argument for the basis of the investigations. The following discussion in small type may be omitted if desired.

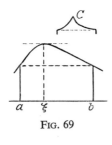

FIG. 69

Rolle's theorem. If a function $y = f(x)$, continuous in the range $a \leqslant x \leqslant b$, is such that it possesses a differential coefficient $f'(x)$ at all points in the range $a \leqslant x \leqslant b$, and such that $f(a) = f(b)$, then a point $x = \xi$ exists in the range $a < x < b$ such that $f'(\xi) = 0$. This is obvious graphically, for the function must possess at least either a maximum or a minimum in the given interval; the value of x at one of these stationary points is designated ξ. A graph with a cusp, such as the point C, is excluded from this theorem, since $f'(x)$ does not exist at such a point.

The mean value theorem. If a function $y = f(x)$, continuous in the range $a \leqslant x \leqslant b$, is such that it possesses a differential coefficient $f'(x)$ at all points in the range $a \leqslant x \leqslant b$, then a point ξ exists in the range $a < x < b$ such that

$$f(b) = f(a) + (b - a)f'(\xi);$$

that is, $[f(b) - f(a)]/(b - a) = f'(\xi).$

Geometrically, a point P exists between the end points A and B, such that the tangent at P is parallel to the chord AB. We assert the equality of the gradient of the chord $[f(b) - f(a)]/(b - a)$ and the gradient of this particular tangent $f'(\xi)$.

This result may be proved analytically by considering the function

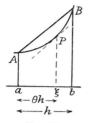

FIG. 70

$$f(b) - f(x) - (b - x)[f(b) - f(a)]/(b - a).$$

This function is differentiable throughout the range, and its value is zero when $x = a$ and b. The conditions for Rolle's theorem are therefore satisfied, so a point $x = \xi$ exists in the range $a < x < b$ at which its derivative

$$-f'(x) + [f(b) - f(a)]/(b - a)$$

vanishes, thereby proving the theorem.

In particular, it is usual to write $b = a + h$, and $\xi = a + \theta h$, where $0 < \theta < 1$, yielding

$$f(a + h) = f(a) + hf'(a + \theta h).$$

Taylor's series. If a function $y = f(x)$, continuous in the range $a \leqslant x \leqslant b$, is such that it possesses all differential coefficients up to the nth order at all points in the range $a \leqslant x \leqslant b$, then a point $x = \xi$ exists in the range $a < x < b$ such that

$$f(b) = f(a) + (b - a)f'(a) + (b - a)^2 f''(a)/2! + \ldots$$
$$+ (b - a)^{n-1} f^{(n-1)}(a)/(n - 1)! + (b - a)^n f^{(n)}(\xi)/n!$$

This is obviously a generalization of the mean value theorem. Consider the function

$$f(b) - f(x) - (b - x)f'(x) - \ldots - (b - x)^{n-1} f^{(n-1)}(x)/(n - 1)!$$

$$- \left(\frac{b - x}{b - a}\right)^n [f(b) - f(a) - (b - a)f'(a) - \ldots - (b - a)^{n-1} f^{(n-1)}(a)/(n - 1)!].$$

This function vanishes when $x = a$ and b. Hence, by Rolle's theorem, a value $x = \xi$ exists in the range $a < x < b$ at which its derivative

$$-\left(\frac{(b - x)^{n-1}}{(n - 1)!}\right) f^{(n)}(x) + \frac{n(b - x)^{n-1}}{(b - a)^n}$$

$$\times \left[f(b) - f(a) - (b - a)f'(a) - \ldots - \frac{(b - a)^{n-1}}{(n - 1)!} f^{(n-1)}(a)\right]$$

vanishes. Division by $n(b - x)^{n-1}/(b - a)^n$ concludes the proof of the theorem. If we let $b = a + h$ and $\xi = a + \theta h$, where $0 < \theta < 1$, we have

$$f(a + h) = f(a) + hf'(a) + \ldots + \frac{h^{n-1}}{(n - 1)!} f^{(n-1)}(a) + \frac{h^n}{n!} f^{(n)}(a + \theta h).$$

It should be noticed that this is not an infinite series. To convert it into an infinite series, we must let $n \to \infty$, and the resultant expression is only valid if the *remainder* term $h^n f^{(n)}(a + \theta h)/n!$ tends to zero. Strictly speaking, this condition always requires investigation, but this is sometimes difficult owing to the fact that the value of θ is not known. In simple applications however, we write

$$f(a + h) = \sum_{r=0}^{\infty} h^r f^{(r)}(a)/r!,$$

being satisfied if this is a convergent series. The series merely expresses the value of the function at $x = a + h$ in terms of the function and its derivatives at $x = a$.

Maclaurin's power series. In particular, we place $a = 0$ and $h = x$, yielding

$$f(x) = f(0) + xf'(0) + x^2 f''(0)/2! + \ldots + x^n f^{(n)}(0)/n! + \ldots$$

$$= \sum_{r=0}^{\infty} x^r f^{(r)}(0)/r!. \tag{10}$$

The convergence of this series should always be examined by the ratio test. Strictly speaking, the vanishing or otherwise of the remainder term $x^n f^{(n)}(\theta x)/n!$ should be examined as $n \to \infty$.

Simple independent proofs of these series, but void of rigour, may easily be supplied. If we assume series of the form

$$f(a + h) = c_0 + c_1 h + c_2 h^2 + c_3 h^3 + \ldots,$$
$$f(x) = d_0 + d_1 x + d_2 x^2 + d_3 x^3 + \ldots,$$

then successive differentiation with respect to h and x respectively yields the equations

$$f'(a + h) = c_1 + 2c_2 h + 3c_3 h^2 + \ldots,$$
$$f''(a + h) = \qquad 2c_2 + 3.2c_3 h + \ldots,$$
$$f'''(a + h) = \qquad\qquad 3.2c_3 + \ldots,$$
$$f'(x) = d_1 + 2d_2 x + 3d_3 x^2 + \ldots,$$
$$f''(x) = \qquad 2d_2 + 3.2d_3 x + \ldots,$$
$$f'''(x) = \qquad\qquad 3.2d_3 + \ldots.$$

Finally, let $h = x = 0$, giving

$$c_1 = f'(a), \quad c_2 = f''(a)/2!, \quad c_3 = f'''(a)/3!, \ldots,$$
$$d_1 = f'(0), \quad d_2 = f''(0)/2!, \quad d_3 = f'''(0)/3!, \ldots.$$

Taken with $c_0 = f(a)$, $d_0 = f(0)$, these are the coefficients of Taylor's power series and Maclaurin's power series respectively.

14.5   Application to series expansions

The exponential function. We have defined $y = \exp x$ as that unique function satisfying $dy/dx = y$, with $\exp 0 = 1$; moreover, we have shown that $y = e^x$. It follows that $d^n y/dx^n = e^x$, its value being unity when $x = 0$. Hence, using equation (10):

$$e^x = 1 + x + \frac{x^2}{2!} + \frac{x^3}{3!} + \ldots + \frac{x^n}{n!} + \ldots = \sum_{n=0}^{\infty} \frac{x^n}{n!}.$$

When $x = 1$, the numerical value of $e = 1 + 1 + 1/2! + 1/3! + \ldots$ may easily be calculated to be $2 \cdot 7182818 \ldots$ The series for e^x is convergent for all values of x, a result verified by the ratio test.

The logarithmic series. If $y = \log_e (1 + x)$, we have

$$y' = 1/(1 + x), \quad d^n y/dx^n = (-1)^{n-1}(n - 1)!/(1 + x).^n$$

When $x = 0$, $y'(0) = 1$ and $y^{(n)}(0) = (-1)^{n-1}(n - 1)!$; hence

$$\log_e (1 + x) = x - \frac{x^2}{2} + \frac{x^3}{3} - \ldots = \sum_{n=1}^{\infty} \frac{(-1)^{n-1} x^n}{n}.$$

This series converges if $-1 < x < 1$ by the ratio test, and when $x = 1$ by the alternating sign test.

The trigonometrical series. If $y = \sin x$, it and its successive derivatives $\cos x$, $-\sin x$, $-\cos x$, $\sin x, \ldots$, have the values $0, 1, 0, -1, 0, \ldots$ when $x = 0$. Hence

$$\sin x = x - \frac{x^3}{3!} + \frac{x^5}{5!} - \ldots,$$

provided x is in radians. Similarly,

$$\cos x = 1 - \frac{x^2}{2!} + \frac{x^4}{4!} - \ldots,$$

both series being convergent for all values of x.

The first few terms of the series for $\tan x$ may best be found by other methods, rather than by calculating its derivatives at $x = 0$. Since $\tan (-x) = -\tan x$, we conclude that its power series consists only of odd powers. Let

$$\tan x = \frac{\sin x}{\cos x} = ax + bx^3 + cx^5 + \ldots;$$

hence

$$x - \frac{x^3}{3!} + \frac{x^5}{5!} - \ldots = (ax + bx^3 + cx^5 + \ldots)\left(1 - \frac{x^2}{2!} + \frac{x^4}{4!} - \ldots\right).$$

Equating coefficients of x, x^3, $x^5, \ldots$, we obtain

$$1 = a, \; -\frac{1}{3!} = -\frac{1}{2!} + b, \; \frac{1}{5!} = \frac{a}{4!} - \frac{b}{2!} + c, \ldots,$$

yielding $a = 1$, $b = \frac{1}{3}$, $c = \frac{2}{15}$, ... Hence

$$\tan x = x + \tfrac{1}{3}x^3 + \tfrac{2}{15}x^5 + \dots.$$

The series for sec x may likewise be found.

The binomial series. If $y = (1 + x)^n$, where n is any positive or negative rational fraction, we conclude from section 14.2 that

$$y^{(r)}(x) = n(n - 1)(n - 2)\dots(n - r + 1)(1 + x)^{n-r},$$

yielding $y^{(r)}(0) = n(n - 1)(n - 2)\dots(n - r + 1),$

where that branch of $(1 + x)^{n-r}$ is chosen which is unity when $x = 0$. The Maclaurin series for the function is then

$$(1 + x)^n = 1 + nx + \frac{n(n - 1)}{2!}x^2 + \dots$$

$$+ \frac{n(n - 1)\dots(n - r + 1)}{r!}x^r + \dots.$$

The ratio test shows that this series is convergent in the range $|x| < 1$.

Example 6   Find the series expansion of $y = (1 - x^2)^{\frac{1}{2}}\sin^{-1}x$ in powers of x.

Differentiating once, we obtain

$$y' = 1 - x(1 - x^2)^{-\frac{1}{2}}\sin^{-1}x$$
$$= 1 - xy(1 - x^2)^{-1}.$$

Hence $(1 - x^2)y' + xy = 1 - x^2.$

We may apply Leibnitz's theorem to this result; differentiating $(n - 1)$ times, we obtain

$$(1 - x^2)y^{(n)} - 2x(n - 1)y^{(n-1)} - (n - 1)(n - 2)y^{(n-2)} \atop + xy^{(n-1)} + (n - 1)y^{(n-2)}} = \begin{cases} 0 & n \geqslant 4 \\ -2 & n = 3 \\ -2x & n = 2. \end{cases}$$

When $x = 0$, we have

$$y^{(n)}(0) - (n - 1)(n - 3)y^{(n-2)}(0) = \begin{cases} 0 & n \geqslant 4 \\ -2 & n = 3 \\ 0 & n = 2. \end{cases}$$

Evidently $y(0) = 0$, $y'(0) = 1$ from the original equations. Hence when $n = 2$, $y''(0) = 0$; similarly, $y^{(4)}(0) = y^{(6)}(0) = \dots = 0$. When $n = 3$, $y^{(3)}(0) = -2$, and generally, when n is odd and of the form $2m + 1$, we have

$$y^{(2m+1)}(0) = 2m(2m - 2)y^{(2m-1)}(0)   (m \geqslant 2)$$
$$= 2m(2m - 2)(2m - 2)(2m - 4)y^{(2m-3)}(0)$$
$$= 2m(2m - 2)(2m - 2)(2m - 4)\dots 6.4.4.2y^{(3)}(0)$$
$$= 2^{2m-2}m!\,(m - 1)!\,(-2).$$

Substituting these values into Maclaurin's power series, we obtain

$$y = x - \tfrac{1}{3}x^3 - \sum_{m=2}^{\infty} \frac{2^{2m-1}\, m!\, (m-1)!}{(2m+1)!}\, x^{2m+1}.$$

The ratio test shows that this series converges when $|x| < 1$.

The following method for simplifying the product of the odd integers should be noticed, since it sometimes arises in the calculation of $y^{(2n+1)}(0)$. If

$$I = (2n+1)(2n-1)(2n-3)\ldots 5.3.1,$$

we insert the missing even integers in both numerator and denominator:

$$I = \frac{(2n+1)(2n)(2n-1)(2n-2)(2n-3)\ldots 6.5.4.3.2.1}{(2n)(2n-2)\ldots 6.4.2}$$

$$= \frac{(2n+1)!}{2^n n!}.$$

Similarly, we have

$$(2n+1)^2(2n-1)^2(2n-3)^2 \ldots 5^2.3^2.1^2 = \frac{[(2n+1)!]^2}{2^{2n}(n!)^2}.$$

14.6 Stationary values of functions of one variable

The student should realise that the elementary approach to this subject does not exhaust the possibilities that may arise. If $dy/dx > 0$ in a particular range of values of x, y increases with x throughout this range. If d^2y/dx^2 is also positive, the gradient dy/dx is also increasing throughout the range, so the curve has its *concave* side upwards. If d^2y/dx^2 is negative, the concave side of the curve is downwards. Similarly, if dy/dx is negative throughout a given range, the values of y decrease with increasing x throughout the range.

If $dy/dx = 0$ at a point, and if d^2y/dx^2 is positive, elementary considerations show that y is a *minimum* at this point, while if d^2y/dx^2 is negative there, y is a *maximum*. If $d^2y/dx^2 = 0$ at a point where $dy/dx = 0$, we are unable, with this elementary reasoning, to distinguish the character of this *stationary value* or *turning point*.

If $dy/dx \neq 0$, but $d^2y/dx^2 = 0$, such a point is called a *point of inflexion*.

More generally, let us consider the shape of the curve $y = y(x)$ in the immediate neighbourhood of the general point $x = a$. Using Taylor's series, we have

$$y(a+h) = y(a) + hy'(a) + \tfrac{1}{2}h^2 y''(a) + \ldots + h^n y^{(n)}(a)/n! + \ldots,$$

where h is small. In particular, we consider stationary points, that is, points where $y'(a) = 0$. At such points, the tangent to the curve is parallel to the x-axis. Let the *first non-vanishing derivative* at $x = a$ be the nth ($n = 2$ in elementary cases). The shape of the curve in the immediate neighbourhood of $x = a$ is then given by

$$y(a + h) = y(a) + h^n y^{(n)}(a)/n!,$$

neglecting terms of the order h^{n+1}.

If n is even, and if $y^{(n)}(a) > 0$, we see that $h^n y^{(n)}(a) > 0$ for *both* $h > 0$ and $h < 0$. In other words, the value of y increases on *both* sides of $x = a$; the point is therefore a minimum. But if n is even, and if $y^{(n)}(a) < 0$, then $h^n y^{(n)}(a) < 0$ for *both* $h > 0$ and $h < 0$. The value of y therefore decreases on *both* sides of the point $x = a$, so the point is a maximum. But if n is odd, $h^n y^{(n)}(a)$ changes sign with h whatever the sign of $y^{(n)}(a)$; the point is therefore a point of inflexion.

We have therefore the test: Let s be the sign and n the order of the first non-vanishing derivative at the point $x = a$, where $y'(a) = 0$. Then

$$\begin{cases} n \text{ even, } s+, \text{ minimum;} \\ n \text{ even, } s-, \text{ maximum;} \\ n \text{ odd,} \qquad \text{point of inflexion.} \end{cases}$$

If the second or higher derivatives are awkward to calculate, graphical arguments may suffice to determine the character of the stationary point.

If the function y contains a factor which is a square root, it may be easier to consider instead the function y^2. Stationary points of y are also stationary points of y^2, but $dy^2/dx = 0$ possesses also a solution $y = 0$; *this does not necessarily yield* a stationary point for y, so care is evidently required.

Sometimes, we may have a particularly simple function, namely

$$y = ax^2 + 2hx + c.$$

Upon completing the square, we find

$$y = a(x + h/a)^2 + c - h^2/a,$$

possessing a stationary value $c - h^2/a$ when $x = -h/a$. More generally, if

$$y = a[f(x)]^2 + 2hf(x) + c,$$

y still has a stationary value $c - h^2/a$ *provided* the equation $f(x) = -h/a$ can be solved for x. Other stationary values for y may be found from the equation $f'(x) = 0$.

Example 7 Investigate the function $y = (1 + x^2 + px^4)e^{-x^2}$, for all values of the parameter p.

This is an even function of x; let $z = x^2$, giving

$$y = (1 + z + pz^2)e^{-z}.$$

Hence
$$\frac{dy}{dx} = \frac{dy}{dz}\cdot\frac{dz}{dx} = (1 + 2pz - 1 - z - pz^2)e^{-z}.2x.$$

This first derivative vanishes when

$$x = 0 \quad \text{and} \quad (2p - 1 - pz) = 0,$$

that is, when
$$x = 0 \quad \text{and} \quad z = x^2 = 2 - 1/p.$$

Evidently if

$p < 0$, then $z > 0$ and so 3 real values of x exist;

$\tfrac{1}{2} > p > 0$, then $z < 0$ and only 1 real value of x exists;

$p > \tfrac{1}{2}$, then $z > 0$ and 3 real values of x exist.

In order to investigate the nature of the stationary point at $x = 0$, rather than calculate the second derivative of y, we may expand y directly as a power series in x, yielding

$$y = (1 + x^2 + px^4)(1 - x^2 + \tfrac{1}{2}x^4 - \tfrac{1}{6}x^6 + \ldots)$$
$$= 1 + (p - \tfrac{1}{2})x^4 - (p - \tfrac{1}{3})x^6 + \ldots.$$

To test the nature of the stationary point at $x = 0$, we examine the first non-vanishing coefficient in this expansion: if

$p < 0$, then $p - \tfrac{1}{2} < 0$,

    so y is a maximum at $x = 0$;

$0 < p < \tfrac{1}{2}$, then $p - \tfrac{1}{2} < 0$,

    so y is a maximum at $x = 0$;

$p = \tfrac{1}{2}$, then $-(p - \tfrac{1}{3}) < 0$,

    so y is a maximum at $x = 0$;

$p > \tfrac{1}{2}$, then $p - \tfrac{1}{2} > 0$,

    so y is a minimum at $x = 0$.

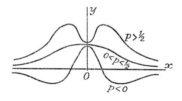

FIG. 71

Hence, on graphical evidence, the remaining two stationary values when $p < 0$ must be minima, and when $p > \tfrac{1}{2}$, they must be maxima.

Example 8 Investigate the function $y = (h + \cos x)(h + \sin x)$, $h > 0$.

Differentiating the given function y, we obtain

$$y' = (h + \cos x)\cos x - (h + \sin x)\sin x$$
$$= h(\cos x - \sin x) + \cos^2 x - \sin^2 x.$$

This first derivative vanishes when

$$\cos x - \sin x = 0 \quad \text{and} \quad h + \cos x + \sin x = 0.$$

The first equation has solutions $x = \frac{1}{4}\pi, \frac{5}{4}\pi$, in the range 0 to 2π, while the second equation is equivalent to

$$\sin(x + \tfrac{1}{4}\pi) = -h/\sqrt{2}. \tag{11}$$

If $h < \sqrt{2}$, this equation yields two further stationary points.

The second derivative of y is given by

$$y'' = h(-\sin x - \cos x) - 4\sin x \cos x.$$

The case $h > \sqrt{2}$. There are two stationary values given by $x = \frac{1}{4}\pi, \frac{5}{4}\pi$. When $x = \frac{1}{4}\pi$, we find that $y'' = -h\sqrt{2} - 2 < 0$; this point is therefore a maximum. When $x = \frac{5}{4}\pi$, $y'' = h\sqrt{2} - 2 > 0$, yielding a minimum.

The case $h < \sqrt{2}$. There are now two stationary points in addition to the values given by $x = \frac{1}{4}\pi, \frac{5}{4}\pi$. When $x = \frac{1}{4}\pi$ and $\frac{5}{4}\pi$, $y'' = -h\sqrt{2} - 2$ and $h\sqrt{2} - 2$; these are both negative, so y is a maximum at both these two values of x. The other two intermediate stationary points must therefore be minima without the necessity of calculating the value of y'' there.

The case $h = \sqrt{2}$. The solution of equation (11) is now $x + \frac{1}{4}\pi = \frac{3}{2}\pi$, so $x = \frac{5}{4}\pi$. In other words, there are only two stationary points given by $x = \frac{1}{4}\pi$ and $\frac{5}{4}\pi$. When $x = \frac{1}{4}\pi$, $y'' < 0$ as before, so y is a maximum there. But when $x = \frac{5}{4}\pi$, $y'' = h\sqrt{2} - 2 = 0$. We therefore calculate the higher derivatives of y:

$$y''' = h(-\cos x + \sin x) - 4(\cos^2 x - \sin^2 x),$$

vanishing when $x = \frac{5}{4}\pi$;

$$y^{(4)} = h(\sin x + \cos x) + 16\sin x \cos x$$

having the value 6 when $x = \frac{5}{4}\pi$. Hence y is a minimum there.

Example 9   An open bowl is formed by a segment of a hollow sphere. Express its volume and internal surface area in terms of the radius of the sphere. Find that form yielding the greatest volume for a given internal surface area.

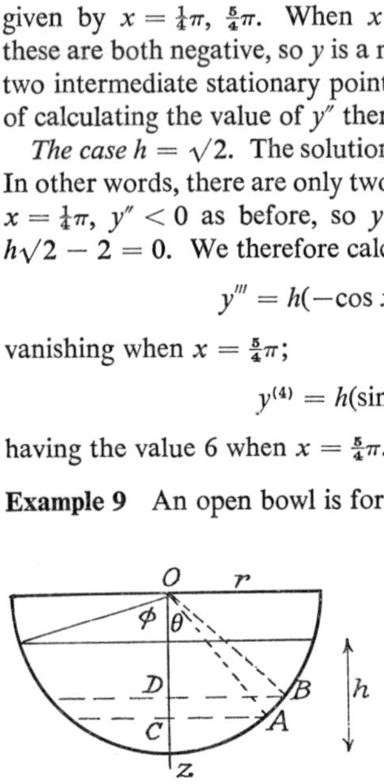

FIG. 72

The element of area traced out by the rotation of the line element AB about Oz is $2\pi r \sin \theta . r\, \delta\theta$ where $\theta = \angle zOA$. The total area is then

$$A = 2\pi r^2 \int_0^\phi \sin\theta\, d\theta = 2\pi r^2(1 - \cos\phi) = 2\pi rh,$$

where $h = r(1 - \cos\phi)$ is the depth of the bowl.

The element of volume is given by $\pi AC^2 . CD = \pi r^2 \sin^2\theta . r\, \delta\theta \sin\theta$, when the strip $ABCD$ is rotated about the axis Oz. The total volume is then

$$V = \pi r^3 \int_0^\phi \sin^3\theta\, d\theta = \pi r^3 \int_0^\phi (1 - \cos^2\theta)\sin\theta\, d\theta$$

$$= \pi r^3 \left[-\cos\theta + \tfrac{1}{3}\cos^3\theta \right]_0^\phi = \pi r^3(\tfrac{2}{3} - \cos\phi + \tfrac{1}{3}\cos^3\phi)$$

$$= \pi r^3 \left[\frac{2}{3} - \frac{r - h}{r} + \frac{1}{3}\left(\frac{r - h}{r}\right)^3 \right] = \tfrac{1}{3}\pi(3rh^2 - h^3)$$

upon simplification.

We require to examine the maximum of the function $V \propto 3rh^2 - h^3$, subject to the condition $A \propto rh = $ constant. We may regard V as a function of r alone, without explicitly eliminating h. Differentiating with respect to r, we obtain

$$\frac{dV}{dr} \propto 3h^2 + 6rh \frac{dh}{dr} - 3h^2 \frac{dh}{dr},$$

together with

$$h + r \frac{dh}{dr} = 0.$$

V is stationary when $dV/dr = 0$; eliminating dh/dr from the two equations, we obtain

$$\frac{dh}{dr} = -\frac{h}{r} = \frac{3h^2}{3h^2 - 6rh}.$$

The solution $h = 0$ yields an obvious minimum; the second solution is easily found to be $r = h$. The maximum volume is therefore attained when the form is a hemisphere.

14.7   Small increments and limits

Taylor's series enables us to write in the neighborhood of a point x

$$y(x + \delta x) = y(x) + \delta x y'(x) + \tfrac{1}{2} \delta x^2 y''(x) + \dots$$

Provided δx is small, the terms in this series decrease successively in magnitude. We often use a single symbol to denote all terms involving $\delta x^2, \delta x^3, \delta x^4, \dots$, namely $O(\delta x^2)$, where O stands for *"order of"*. We write therefore

$$y(x + \delta x) = y(x) + \delta x y'(x) + O(\delta x^2).$$

The increment in y may now be written as

$$y(x + \delta x) - y(x) = \delta y = \delta x y'(x) + O(\delta x^2). \tag{12}$$

In certain branches of mathematics, it proves convenient to write $\delta x = dx$, where dx stands for the *exact* finite small increment in x, being quite distinct from the dx in the derivative dy/dx, and from the dx attached to the integrand of an integral. The quantity $\delta x y'(x)$ is also denoted by dy, where this finite quantity *cannot claim to be the exact increment in y*. Hence

$$dy = y'(x)\, dx,$$

yielding upon division by the finite increment dx the rather ambiguous but helpful identity

$$\frac{dy}{dx} = \frac{dy}{dx}.$$

Such terms dy and dx are called *differentials*, and on no account should be regarded as vanishingly small, or *infinitesimals*; such a concept is not required in the development of the calculus. In the present text, however, we prefer neither to use the symbols dy and dx for differentials, nor indeed to adopt the definition just given.

Here, we shall generally use the unambiguous symbol δx to denote the differential of x, namely the finite small increment in x. Moreover, we shall use the unambiguous symbol δy to denote the differential of y, where δy is the *exact* small increment in y. However, the term $O(\delta x^2)$ occurring in equation (12) is seldom required, so we shall write

$$\delta y = y'(x)\,\delta x, \tag{13}$$

with a *mental note* that the second order terms are in fact present. The act of writing equation (13) down from the defining equation $y = y(x)$ will be termed the act of *"taking differentials"*.

This notation will prove to be of vital importance in the theory of partial differentiation. As an example of its use, let us prove the chain rule for differentiating a function of a function.

If $y = y(x)$ is given, the change of variable $x = x(t)$ yields y as a function of t; find dy/dt in terms of the derivatives of the given functions.

Taking differentials of both the given equations, we obtain

$$\delta y = \frac{dy}{dx}\,\delta x + O(\delta x^2), \qquad \delta x = \frac{dx}{dt}\,\delta t + O(\delta t^2).$$

Eliminating δx, we have

$$\delta y = \frac{dy}{dx}\cdot\frac{dx}{dt}\,\delta t + O(\delta t^2),$$

where all second order terms, including terms involving $\delta x\delta t$ are lumped together in the symbol $O(\delta t^2)$. Then

$$\frac{dy}{dt} = \lim_{\delta t \to 0}\frac{\delta y}{\delta t} = \lim_{\delta t \to 0}\left[\frac{dy}{dx}\cdot\frac{dx}{dt} + O(\delta t)\right] = \frac{dy}{dx}\cdot\frac{dx}{dt}.$$

Here, $O(\delta t^2)$ becomes $O(\delta t)$ upon division by δt, but in the limit, as $\delta t \to 0$, $O(\delta t)$ tends to zero.

This example shows that the original terms $O(\delta x^2)$ and $O(\delta t^2)$ need not be inserted, since they vanish when the limit is taken. The student should notice that a *limiting operation can only be performed on a ratio of small increments, and not on the small increments themselves.* The limit of equation (12) would be $0 = 0$, which is not very helpful!

Indeterminate forms and l'Hospital's rule. If y equals the ratio of the two given functions $f(x)$ and $g(x)$, namely $y = f(x)/g(x)$, the numerical value of y when $x = a$ is obtained by substituting $x = a$ in $f(x)$ and $g(x)$ *without any analytical simplification such as cancellation* beforehand. If exceptionally $f(a) = g(a) = 0$, y remains undefined at the point $x = a$; such a ratio is then termed an *indeterminate form*. On the other hand, a limiting value for y may exist as x approaches a.

We shall assume that both $f(x)$ and $g(x)$ possess Taylor-series expansions at $x = a$, namely

$$f(a + h) = f(a) + hf'(a) + \tfrac{1}{2}h^2f''(a) + \ldots = hf'(a) + \tfrac{1}{2}h^2f''(a) + \ldots$$
$$g(a + h) = hg'(a) + \tfrac{1}{2}h^2g''(a) + \ldots.$$

In the expansion of $f(a + h)$, let $f^{(m)}(a)$ be the first non-vanishing derivative at $x = a$, and let $g^{(n)}(a)$ be the first non-vanishing derivative of the function g at $x = a$. Then

$$y(a + h) = \frac{\dfrac{1}{m!} h^m f^{(m)}(a) + \dfrac{1}{(m + 1)!} h^{m+1} f^{(m+1)}(a) + \ldots}{\dfrac{1}{n!} h^n g^{(n)}(a) + \dfrac{1}{(n + 1)!} h^{n+1} g^{(n+1)}(a) + \ldots}.$$

If $m > n$,

$$y(a + h) = (n!/m!)h^{m-n}f^{(m)}(a)/g^{(n)}(a) + O(h^{m-n+1}).$$

As $h \to 0$, this expression also tends to zero, since the index of the term h^{m-n} is positive.

If $m < n$, y becomes infinite as $h \to 0$, since there is an excess of h's in the denominator.

If $m = n$,

$$y = \frac{f^{(n)}(a) + hf^{(n+1)}(a)/(n + 1) + \ldots}{g^{(n)}(a) + hg^{(n+1)}(a)/(n + 1) + \ldots}$$
$$\to f^{(n)}(a)/g^{(n)}(a)$$

as $h \to 0$. In other words, the limit of an indeterminate form equals the ratio of the first non-vanishing derivatives, *provided* these are of the same order.

If the Taylor series are known beforehand, or the Maclaurin power series if $x \to 0$, these series may be written down directly, and the limit noted by inspection. The above method, which merely calculates the coefficients of these series, is not needed in such cases.

An important limit. We shall now examine the limit of $y = (1 + n^{-1})^{nx}$ as n tends to infinity. The logarithm of this expression is

$$\log_e y = nx \log_e (1 + n^{-1}),$$

or

$$\log_e y = x \frac{\log (1 + h)}{h}$$

where $h = 1/n$. When $h = 0$, this expression is indeterminate; we therefore differentiate numerator and denominator with respect to h, and place $h = 0$ in the derivatives. This obviously yields

$$\log_e y \to x,$$

or $$y \to e^x.$$

We have therefore the standard result:

$$\lim_{n \to \infty} (1 + n^{-1})^{nx} = e^x.$$

Example 10   Find the limit of $y = (xe^x + 2 \cos x - \sin x - 2)/x^3$ as $x \to 0$.

Method i. The numerator must be expanded up to the term involving x^3, in order that the x^3 should be cancelled in the denominator. Direct expansion yields

$$y = \frac{x(1 + x + \tfrac{1}{2}x^2 + \tfrac{1}{6}x^3 + \ldots) + 2(1 - \tfrac{1}{2}x^2) - (x - \tfrac{1}{6}x^3) - 2}{x^3}$$

$$= \tfrac{2}{3} + \tfrac{1}{4}x + \ldots \to \tfrac{2}{3}.$$

Method ii. Successive differentiation of the numerator and denominator yields

$$\lim y = \lim \frac{xe^x + e^x - 2 \sin x - \cos x}{3x^2}$$

$$= \lim \frac{xe^x + 2e^x - 2 \cos x + \sin x}{6x}$$

$$= \lim \frac{xe^x + 3e^x + 2 \sin x + \cos x}{6}$$

$$= \tfrac{2}{3},$$

where the process is continued until a form different from $\tfrac{0}{0}$ is reached, at which stage a conclusion can be made.

Example 11   Find the limit of $y = (x^{-1} \cot x - x^{-2})$ as $x \to 0$.

This function, when written in the form $(x - \tan x)/x^2 \tan x$, takes the indeterminate form $\tfrac{0}{0}$ when $x = 0$. Hence, differentiating numerator and denominator successively as many times as required, we obtain

$$\lim y = \lim \frac{1 - \sec^2 x}{2x \tan x + x^2 \sec^2 x}$$

$$= \lim \frac{-2 \sec^2 x \tan x}{2 \tan x + 4x \sec^2 x + 2x^2 \sec^2 x \tan x}$$

$$= \lim \frac{-2 \sec^4 x - 4 \sec^2 x \tan^2 x}{2 \sec^2 x + 4 \sec^2 x + 8x \sec^2 x \tan x + \ldots}$$

$$= -\tfrac{1}{3}.$$

Example 12   Find the limit of

$$y = [(1 - 2n^{-1} - 3n^{-2})/(1 - 3n^{-1} - 28n^{-2})]^n \quad \text{as} \quad n \to \infty.$$

We first obtain linear factors in both numerator and denominator thus:

$$y = \left[\frac{(1 + n^{-1})(1 - 3n^{-1})}{(1 + 4n^{-1})(1 - 7n^{-1})}\right]^n.$$

Now replace $-3n^{-1}$, $4n^{-1}$, $-7n^{-1}$ by m^{-1}, p^{-1}, q^{-1} respectively, yielding

$$y = \frac{(1 + n^{-1})^n(1 + m^{-1})^{-3m}}{(1 + p^{-1})^{4p}(1 + q^{-1})^{-7q}}$$

$$\to \frac{e \cdot e^{-3}}{e^4 \cdot e^{-7}} = e,$$

as m, n, p, q tend to infinity.

14.8   Newton's method for the approximate solution of equations

Many equations in the unknown x cannot be solved explicitly for x; approximate numerical methods are necessary for their solution. Here, we shall consider *Newton's method*.

If the equation $f(x) = 0$ cannot be solved analytically, we first find a fairly good approximate solution $x = \alpha$, perhaps by using a carefully drawn large-scale graph. Then let $x = \alpha + \varepsilon$ be the exact solution, where ε is small. Using Taylor's expansion, we have

$$0 = f(\alpha + \varepsilon) = f(\alpha) + \varepsilon f'(\alpha) + \tfrac{1}{2}\varepsilon^2 f''(\alpha) + \dots.$$

This equation obviously cannot be solved for ε exactly, but since ε^2 is small, we may write

$$f(\alpha) + \varepsilon f'(\alpha) \doteqdot 0,$$

yielding

$$\varepsilon = -f(\alpha)/f'(\alpha),$$

neglecting terms of the order ε^2.   Hence a better solution is given by

$$\beta = \alpha - f(\alpha)/f'(\alpha).$$

We may repeat this process as many times as required; a better solution is given by

$$\gamma = \beta - f(\beta)/f'(\beta),$$

and so on, each stage giving greater numerical accuracy.

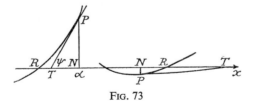

FIG. 73

Graphically, if N denotes the approximate solution and R the exact solution, a better solution is given by the point T where the tangent at P cuts the x-axis. For this method to be valid, the gradient at P must not be too small, otherwise the point T may be very far from the correct solution R.

Example 13 Solve the equation $\tan x = 1 + \frac{1}{2}x^2$, $(0 < x < \frac{1}{2}\pi)$.

We prepare the following table:

x	$\tan x$	$1 + \frac{1}{2}x^2$
0·92	1·3133	1·4232
0·94	1·3692	1·4418
0·96	1·4284	1·4608
0·98	1·4910	1·4802
1·00	1·5574	1·5000

An inspection of this table reveals that $\alpha = 0.98$ (radians) is the approximate solution. Then a better solution is

$$\beta = \alpha - \frac{f(\alpha)}{f'(\alpha)} = \alpha - \frac{\tan \alpha - 1 - \frac{1}{2}\alpha^2}{\sec^2 \alpha - \alpha}$$

$$= 0.98 - \frac{1 \cdot 4910 - 1 \cdot 4802}{3 \cdot 222 - 0 \cdot 98}$$

$$= 0.98 - \frac{0 \cdot 0108}{2 \cdot 242} = 0.98 - 0.0048 = 0.975$$

to three significant figures. A repetition of this process will not give any better result with four-figure tables. If greater accuracy is required, six-figure tables should be used, starting with this value 0·975.

If the first derivative $f'(\alpha)$ is small, the above process requires modification. From the equation to the second order in ε

$$0 = f(\alpha) + \varepsilon f'(\alpha) + \frac{1}{2}\varepsilon^2 f''(\alpha),$$

we obtain $\varepsilon \doteqdot \pm\sqrt{[-2f(\alpha)/f''(\alpha)]} \equiv \eta$

by neglecting $\varepsilon f'(\alpha)$, provided $f''(\alpha)$ is not small.

We now assume that ε can be expanded as a power series in η, namely

$$\varepsilon = \eta(1 + a\eta + b\eta^2 + \ldots),$$

where $a, b, \ldots$ are to be found. Substitution yields

$$0 = f(\alpha) + f'(\alpha)\eta(1 + a\eta + b\eta^2 + \ldots)$$
$$+ \tfrac{1}{2}f''(\alpha)\eta^2(1 + 2a\eta + a^2\eta^2 + 2b\eta^2 + \ldots)$$
$$+ \tfrac{1}{6}f'''(\alpha)\eta^3(1 + 3a\eta + \ldots).$$

Now $f'(\alpha)$, being small, will be expressible as a power of η; we therefore equate individual coefficients of powers of η to zero, obtaining simple equations for $a, b, \ldots$.

Example 14   Solve the equation $1 - e^{-x} = \cos x$, where x is large and positive.

It is obvious from a sketch that the graph of $1 - e^{-x}$ just cuts the tops off the maxima of the graph of $\cos x$ when x is large and positive. Hence $x = 2\pi n$ is an approximate solution where n is a large positive integer. Let $x = 2\pi n + \varepsilon$; then

$$1 - e^{-2\pi n - \varepsilon} = \cos \varepsilon.$$

Expanding this in powers of ε, we obtain

$$-s^2(1 - \varepsilon + \tfrac{1}{2}\varepsilon^2 + \ldots) = -\tfrac{1}{2}\varepsilon^2 + \tfrac{1}{24}\varepsilon^4 - \ldots,$$

where $s = e^{-\pi n}$ is small. We now equate the smallest term on the left-hand side, $-s^2$, and the smallest term on the right-hand side, $-\tfrac{1}{2}\varepsilon^2$, obtaining $\varepsilon \doteqdot \pm\sqrt{2}s$. Finally, a power series in the form

$$\varepsilon = \pm\sqrt{2}s(1 + as + bs^2 + \ldots)$$

is assumed, yielding upon substitution

$$-s^2 \pm \sqrt{2}s^3(1 + as) - s^4 + \ldots = -s^2(1 + 2as + 2bs^2 + a^2s^2) + \tfrac{1}{6}s^4 + \ldots$$

to the fourth order in s. Equating the coefficients of s^3 and s^4 respectively, we obtain

$$\pm\sqrt{2} = -2a, \quad \pm a\sqrt{2} - 1 = -2b - a^2 + \tfrac{1}{6},$$

yielding $a = \mp 1/\sqrt{2}, b = \tfrac{5}{6}$. Hence

$$x = 2\pi n \pm \sqrt{2}e^{-\pi n} - e^{-2\pi n} \pm \tfrac{5}{6}\sqrt{2}e^{-3\pi n}.$$

14.9   Curvature in Cartesian coordinates

If P is a point on the curve $y = f(x)$ given by $x = X$, then the *tangent line* at P is defined to be the limiting form of the chord PQ, as the point Q approaches P along the curve. The nearby point Q is given by

$$x = X + \delta X, \ y = f(X + \delta X) = f(X) + \delta X f'(X),$$

where only first order terms are required. The equation of the chord PQ is

$$\frac{y - f(X)}{\delta X f'(X)} = \frac{x - X}{\delta X},$$

or
$$y - f(X) = f'(X)(x - X)$$

in the limit; if the second order terms had been inserted, they would vanish in the limit. $f'(X)$ is the gradient of the tangent at P. Since this tangent line intersects the curve in two identical points at P, we say that the line has *two-point* contact with the curve at P.

The gradient of the *normal* at P is $-1/f'(X)$, so its equation is

$$y - f(X) = -(x - X)/f'(X).$$

Two distinct definitions of curvature are given here. Definition (i) may be omitted, although it appears to the author to be more fundamental. Definition (ii) is simple, but it leaves much to be desired as to its geometrical interpretation and significance.

Definition (i). If P is a given point on a curve, and if Q and R are two nearby points on the curve, the limiting form of the circumcircle of the triangle PQR as Q and R both approach P is the *circle of curvature* at P. The radius of this circle is the *radius of curvature* at P, and the reciprocal of the radius is the *curvature* at P. This circle is the unique circle having *three-point contact* with the curve at P.

Let P be the point $X, f(X) = f$,

Q be the point $X + h$, $\quad f(X) + hf'(X) + \tfrac{1}{2}h^2f''(X) = f + hf' + \tfrac{1}{2}h^2f''$,

R be the point $X + k$, $\quad f(X) + kf'(X) + \tfrac{1}{2}k^2f''(X) = f + kf' + \tfrac{1}{2}k^2f''$,

to the second order.

If the equation of their circumcircle is given by

$$(x - a)^2 + (y - b)^2 = r^2,$$

that is, by

$$x^2 + y^2 - 2ax - 2by + a^2 + b^2 - r^2 = 0,$$

upon substituting the coordinates of P, Q, R and retaining terms up to the second order only, we obtain the three equations:

$$X^2 \quad + \quad\quad f^2$$
$$- 2aX \quad - \quad 2bf \quad\quad + a^2 + b^2 - r^2 = 0, \quad (14)$$

$$(X^2 + 2hX + h^2) + (f^2 + 2hff' + h^2f'^2 + h^2ff'')$$
$$- 2a(X + h) - 2b(f + hf' + \tfrac{1}{2}h^2f'') + a^2 + b^2 - r^2 = 0, \quad (15)$$

$$(X^2 + 2kX + k^2) + (f^2 + 2kff' + k^2f'^2 + k^2ff'')$$
$$- 2a(X + k) - 2b(f + kf' + \tfrac{1}{2}k^2f'') + a^2 + b^2 - r^2 = 0, \quad (16)$$

correct to the second order. We now subtract equation (16) from (15), and divide by $(h - k)$, obtaining

$$2X + (h + k) + 2ff' + (f'^2 + ff'')(h + k) - 2a - 2bf' - bf''(h + k) = 0$$

now correct to the first order. In the limit, as h and k tend to 0, we conclude that

$$2X + 2ff' - 2a - 2bf' = 0. \quad (17)$$

Moreover, if we subtract equation (14) from (15), expression (17) is merely the coefficient of h, leaving

$$h^2(1 + f'^2 + ff'' - bf'') = 0$$

to the second order. In the limit, the third order correction terms (becoming first order terms upon division by h^2) vanish, leaving

$$1 + f'^2 + ff'' - bf'' = 0. \quad (18)$$

Solving equation (18) for b, we obtain

$$b = f + (1 + f'^2)/f''.$$

The solution of equation (17) for a then yields

$$a = X + ff' - bf' = X - (1 + f'^2)f'/f''.$$

Finally, equation (14) yields the value of r (denoted by ρ in the limit):

$$\begin{aligned} \rho^2 &= (X - a)^2 + (f - b)^2 \\ &= [(1 + f'^2)f'/f'']^2 + [(1 + f'^2)/f'']^2 \\ &= (1 + f'^2)^3/f''^2. \end{aligned}$$

Hence $\rho = (1 + f'^2)^{\frac{3}{2}}/f''.$

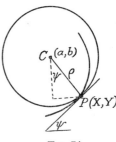

FIG. 74

The reciprocal of ρ, denoted by κ, is the curvature at P:

$$\kappa = f''/(1 + f'^2)^{\frac{3}{2}}.$$

Since $(f - b)/(X - a) = -1/f'$, we conclude that the centre of curvature (a, b) lies on the normal at P. The centre of curvature C in fact lies at a distance ρ from P along the normal on the concave side of the curve.

Definition (ii). For a circle of radius ρ, it is obvious that $\rho = ds/d\psi$, since the angle $\delta\psi$ between the tangents at two nearby points P and Q, where arc $PQ = \delta s$, is equal to the angles between the normals at P and Q. This arc length δs is related to the angle $\delta\psi$ subtended by PQ at the centre by the relation $\delta s = \rho\,\delta\psi$.

At a point P on a curve $y = f(x)$, the curve locally may be taken to approximate to a circle, in the sense that the arc length measured from P and the angle ψ are equal both for the curve and for the circle at P and in the neighbourhood of P. We therefore define the radius of curvature at P to be $ds/d\psi$, where s and ψ refer to the curve.

This result may easily be expressed in terms of x and $y = f(x)$. We have

$$\tan \psi = y';$$

differentiation with respect to x yields

$$\sec^2 \psi \frac{d\psi}{dx} = y''.$$

Hence

$$\rho = \frac{ds}{d\psi} = \frac{\sec^2 \psi}{y''} \cdot \frac{ds}{dx}.$$

But $dx/ds = \cos \psi$, so

$$\begin{aligned} \rho &= \sec^3 \psi/y'' \\ &= (1 + \tan^2 \psi)^{\frac{3}{2}}/y'' \\ &= (1 + y'^2)^{\frac{3}{2}}/y'' \end{aligned} \tag{19}$$

and $\kappa = y''/(1 + y'^2)^{\frac{3}{2}}.$

The curvature has the same sign as y'' if the positive root is taken; it is therefore positive when the concave side of the curve faces upwards.

The centre of curvature $C(a, b)$ is taken as that point on the normal at P distant ρ from P and on the concave side. Using Fig. 74, we see that

$$a = X - \rho \sin \psi = X - \frac{(1 + y'^2)^{\frac{3}{2}}}{y''} \cdot \frac{y'}{(1 + y'^2)^{\frac{1}{2}}}$$

$$= X - y'(1 + y'^2)/y'', \tag{20}$$

and

$$b = f(X) + \rho \cos \psi = f(X) + \frac{(1 + y'^2)^{\frac{3}{2}}}{y''} \cdot \frac{1}{(1 + y'^2)^{\frac{1}{2}}}$$

$$= f(X) + (1 + y'^2)/y'', \tag{21}$$

formulae identical with those found under definition (i).

Parametrically, if $x = x(t)$, $y = y(t)$, we have shown in section 14.1 that $dy/dx = y'/x'$ and $d^2y/dx^2 = (y''x' - x''y')/x'^3$, where the primes denote differentiation with respect to t. Hence

$$\kappa = \frac{1}{\rho} = \frac{y''x' - x''y'}{x'^3[1 + (y'/x')^2]^{\frac{3}{2}}} = \frac{y''x' - x''y'}{[x'^2 + y'^2]^{\frac{3}{2}}}. \tag{22}$$

If the curve is given implicitly in the form $f(x, y) = 0$, we require the theory of partial differentiation developed in chapter 15 to calculate ρ. Taking differentials, we have

$$\frac{\partial f}{\partial x}\, \delta x + \frac{\partial f}{\partial y}\, \delta y = 0,$$

so

$$\frac{dy}{dx} = \lim \frac{\delta y}{\delta x} = -\frac{\partial f/\partial x}{\partial f/\partial y}.$$

The second derivative is given by

$$\frac{d^2y}{dx^2} = \frac{\partial}{\partial x}\left(\frac{dy}{dx}\right) + \frac{\partial}{\partial y}\left(\frac{dy}{dx}\right)\frac{dy}{dx}$$

$$= -\frac{f_{xx}f_y - f_x f_{xy}}{f_y^2} + \frac{f_{yx}f_y - f_x f_{yy}}{f_y^2} \cdot \frac{f_x}{f_y}$$

$$= \frac{-f_{xx}f_y^2 + 2f_x f_y f_{xy} - f_{yy}f_x^2}{f_y^3}$$

where, for brevity, suffixes denote partial differentiation. Hence

$$\rho = \frac{(f_x^2 + f_y^2)^{\frac{3}{2}}}{-f_{xx}f_y^2 + 2f_x f_y f_{xy} - f_{yy}f_x^2}. \tag{23}$$

Example 15 Examine the curvature at a general point on the parabola $x = at^2$, $y = 2at$.

Since $y^2 = 4ax$, we have $dy/dx = 2a/y$ and $d^2y/dx^2 = -4a^2/y^3$. Hence

$$\rho = (y^2 + 4a^2)^{\frac{3}{2}}/(-4a^2).$$

At the vertex, $y = 0$, yielding $\rho = -2a$.

Parametrically, $x' = 2at$, $x'' = 2a$, $y' = 2a$, $y'' = 0$, so the formula for ρ becomes

$$\rho = \frac{(4a^2t^2 + 4a^2)^{\frac{3}{2}}}{-2a \cdot 2a} = -2a(1 + t^2)^{\frac{3}{2}}.$$

The coordinates of the centre of curvature are given by equations (20) and (21), where $dy/dx = y'/x' = 1/t$ and $d^2y/dx^2 = (y''x' - x''y')/x'^3 = -1/(2at^3)$. Hence, using α and β for the coordinates of the centre of curvature, we have

$$\alpha = at^2 - \frac{t^{-1}(1 + t^{-2})}{-(2at^3)^{-1}} = a(2 + 3t^2),$$

$$\beta = 2at + \frac{1 + t^{-2}}{-(2at^3)^{-1}} = -2at^3.$$

The equation of the circle of curvature at the general point becomes

$$(x - \alpha)^2 + (y - \beta)^2 = \rho^2,$$

or $\qquad [x - a(2 + 3t^2)]^2 + (y + 2at^3)^2 = 4a^2(1 + t^2)^3,$

which may be simplified to

$$x^2 + y^2 - 2ax(2 + 3t^2) + 4ayt^3 - 3a^2t^4 = 0.$$

For example, when $t = 1$, we have the point at the upper end of the latus rectum; $\rho = -2^{\frac{3}{2}}a$, $\alpha = 5a$, $\beta = -2a$, and the circle of curvature becomes

$$x^2 + y^2 - 10ax + 4ay - 3a^2 = 0.$$

Example 16 If $y = \operatorname{sech} \theta$ on the curve $x + \sqrt{(1 - y^2)} = \cosh^{-1}(1/y)$, find the circle of curvature at the point θ.

Parametrically, $x = \cosh^{-1}(\cosh \theta) - \sqrt{(1 - \operatorname{sech}^2 \theta)} = \theta - \tanh \theta$. Hence

$$y' = -\operatorname{sech} \theta \tanh \theta, \quad y'' = \operatorname{sech} \theta \tanh^2 \theta - \operatorname{sech}^3 \theta,$$

$$x' = 1 - \operatorname{sech}^2 \theta, \qquad x'' = 2 \operatorname{sech}^2 \theta \tanh \theta.$$

Substituting these values into equation (22), we obtain after reduction

$$\rho = \sinh \theta.$$

Moreover, $\qquad dy/dx = y'/x' = -\operatorname{cosech} \theta,$

and $\qquad \dfrac{d^2y}{dx^2} = \dfrac{d(-\operatorname{cosech} \theta)/d\theta}{dx/d\theta} = \dfrac{\cosh^3 \theta}{\sinh^4 \theta}.$

The coordinates of the centre of curvature are now given by equations (20) and (21):

$$a = \theta - \tanh \theta + \frac{\operatorname{cosech} \theta(1 + \operatorname{cosech}^2 \theta)}{\cosh^3 \theta/\sinh^4 \theta} = \theta,$$

$$b = \operatorname{sech} \theta + \frac{1 + \operatorname{cosech}^2 \theta}{\cosh^3 \theta/\sinh^4 \theta} = \cosh \theta.$$

Hence the circle of curvature has the equation

$$(x - \theta)^2 + (y - \cosh \theta)^2 = \sinh^2 \theta,$$

or $$x^2 + y^2 - 2x\theta - 2y \cosh \theta + \theta^2 + 1 = 0.$$

14.10   Further considerations of curvature

Newton's formula.   Let P be a point on the given curve, such that PT and PC are the tangent and normal at P respectively, where $PC = \rho$. If Q is a nearby point on the curve and on the circle of curvature at P, let us suppose that the perpendicular distances from Q to the two lines PC and PT may easily be written down;   in fact, let $PT = t$, $QT = n$

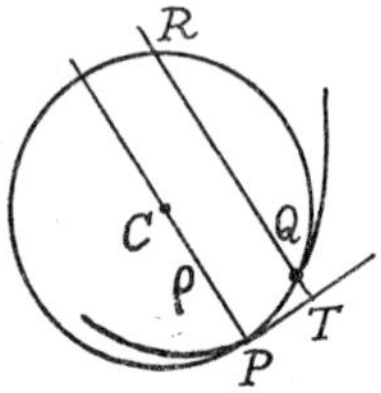

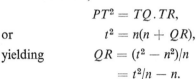

FIG. 75

For the circle, we have

$$PT^2 = TQ . TR,$$

or $$t^2 = n(n + QR),$$

yielding $$QR = (t^2 - n^2)/n$$
$$= t^2/n - n.$$

In the limit, as Q approaches P or as t and n tend to zero, QR becomes the diameter of the circle of curvature;   hence

$$\rho = \lim \tfrac{1}{2} t^2/n.$$

This formula is useful if the distances t and n can easily be written down, usually only at special points of symmetry of a given curve.

Example 17   Find the radius of curvature at the ends of the major axis of the ellipse $x^2/a^2 + y^2/b^2 = 1$.
From Fig. 76, at the point Q we have $t = y, n = a - x$; hence

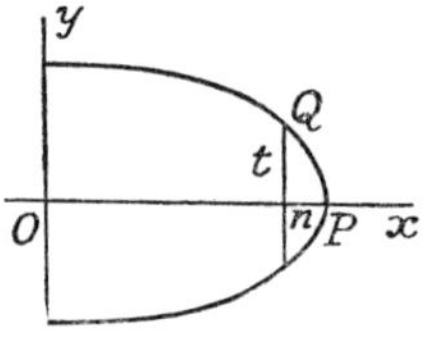

$$\rho = \lim_{x \to a} \frac{y^2}{2(a - x)} = \lim \frac{b^2(1 - x^2/a^2)}{2(a - x)}$$

$$= \lim \frac{b^2(a + x)}{2a^2} = b^2/a.$$

FIG. 76

At the end of the minor axis $\rho = a^2/b$. It is obvious that the use of this method would be complicated at a general point of the ellipse.

The evolute of a curve.   The locus of the centres of curvature of points on a given curve is called its *evolute*.

Referring to Fig. 74, if we let P be the point (x, y) and C the point (α, β), we have

$$\alpha = x - \rho \sin \psi, \quad \beta = y + \rho \cos \psi.$$

In order to find the gradient of the evolute, we form $d\beta/d\alpha$ thus:

$$\frac{d\beta}{d\alpha} = \frac{dy + \cos \psi \, d\rho - \rho \sin \psi \, d\psi}{dx - \sin \psi \, d\rho - \rho \cos \psi \, d\psi}.$$

But $\rho\,d\psi = ds$, and $\sin\psi\,ds = dy$, $\cos\psi\,ds = dx$; hence

$$\frac{d\beta}{d\alpha} = \frac{\cos\psi\,d\rho}{-\sin\psi\,d\rho} = -\cot\psi.$$

This is however the gradient of the normal CP. We conclude therefore that the normal at P to the given curve touches the evolute at C. In the light of section 15.7, we may say that the evolute is the *envelope* of the normals. Usually, the simplest method for finding the evolute of a given curve is to find the envelope of its normals; this avoids the calculation of the coordinates of C.

Example 18   Find the evolute of the parabola $y^2 = 4ax$.

In example 15, we have shown that $\alpha = 3at^2 + 2a$, $\beta = -2at^3$. This leads to

$$t^2 = (\alpha - 2a)/3a, \quad t^3 = -\beta/2a.$$

Cubing the first equation and squaring the second, we obtain

$$(\alpha - 2a)^3/27a^3 = \beta^2/4a^2.$$

The evolute therefore has the equation

$$27ay^2 = 4(x - 2a)^3.$$

This curve lies wholly to the right of the line $x = 2a$; it has in fact a cusp at the point $(2a, 0)$.

This evolute cuts the given parabola at the point $(at^2, 2at)$, where

$$27a(2at)^2 = 4(at^2 - 2a)^3,$$

or

$$27t^2 = (t^2 - 2)^3,$$

possessing the solution $t^2 = 8$, or $t = \pm 2\sqrt{2}$. The points of intersection are therefore $(8a, \pm 4a\sqrt{2})$.

14.11   Curvature in polar coordinates

Ox is the initial line and O is the *pole* or the origin; a point P is specified by the angle $\theta = \angle POx$ (positive when measured anticlockwise from Ox) and by the radius vector $r = OP$. If r is negative, the radius vector is cut off in the opposite direction along the line specified by the angle θ. The point with coordinates $-h$, θ is the same point as one with coordinates $+h$, $\theta + \pi$.

A curve is specified in such a coordinate system by equations of the form $r = f(\theta)$ or $f(r, \theta) = 0$. The angle measured anticlockwise from the outward radial direction PD to the tangent PT at P in the direction

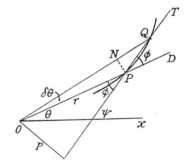

FIG. 77

of θ increasing is denoted by ϕ; this is the fundamental angle used in the theory of polar coordinates. Evidently for a small arc PQ, we have

$$\tan \phi \doteqdot PN/NQ \doteqdot r \, \delta\theta/\delta r,$$

yielding in the limit

$$\tan \phi = r \, d\theta/dr = r/(dr/d\theta).$$

It also follows that $\sin \phi = r \, d\theta/ds$ and $\cos \phi = dr/ds$.

Let p be the length of the perpendicular from O to the tangent at P, namely $p = r \sin \phi$. Differentiating this with respect to r, we obtain

$$\frac{dp}{dr} = \sin \phi + r \cos \phi \frac{d\phi}{dr}$$

$$= r \frac{d\theta}{ds} + r \frac{dr}{ds} \frac{d\phi}{dr}$$

$$= r \frac{d}{ds} (\theta + \phi)$$

$$= r \frac{d\psi}{ds} = r/\rho.$$

Hence

$$\rho = r \frac{dr}{dp} = r \left/ \frac{dp}{dr} \right. .$$

Before this equation can be used to calculate ρ, we must know p as a function of r. The p, r-equation, or *pedal equation*, of the curve $r = f(\theta)$ may easily be found. Since $p = r \sin \phi$, we have

$$p^{-2} = r^{-2} \operatorname{cosec}^2 \phi = r^{-2}(1 + \cot^2 \phi)$$

$$= \frac{1}{r^2}\left[1 + \frac{1}{r^2}\left(\frac{dr}{d\theta}\right)^2\right].$$

Finally, in $dr/d\theta$, θ is expressed in terms of r using the equation $r = f(\theta)$.

Example 19 Sketch the curve given by $r = \cos \frac{1}{2} \theta$.

We make the following observations:

As θ varies from 0 to $\frac{1}{2}\pi$, r decreases from 1 to $1/\sqrt{2}$, (AB)
As θ varies from $\frac{1}{2}\pi$ to π, r decreases from $1/\sqrt{2}$ to 0, (BO)
As θ varies from π to $\frac{3}{2}\pi$, r decreases from 0 to $-1/\sqrt{2}$, (OB)
As θ varies from $\frac{3}{2}\pi$ to 2π, r decreases from $-1/\sqrt{2}$ to -1, (BC)
As θ varies from 2π to $\frac{5}{2}\pi$, r increases from -1 to $-1/\sqrt{2}$, (CD)
As θ varies from $\frac{5}{2}\pi$ to 3π, r increases from $-1/\sqrt{2}$ to 0, (DO)
As θ varies from 3π to $\frac{7}{2}\pi$, r increases from 0 to $1/\sqrt{2}$, (OD)
As θ varies from $\frac{7}{2}\pi$ to 4π, r increases from $1/\sqrt{2}$ to 1, (DA)

The various segments of the curve produced are given in brackets.

Moreover, $\tan \phi = r/(dr/d\theta) = \cos \tfrac{1}{2}\theta/(-\tfrac{1}{2}\sin \tfrac{1}{2}\theta) = -2 \cot \tfrac{1}{2}\theta$. Hence at B, when $\theta = \tfrac{1}{2}\pi$, $\tan \phi = -2$, that is $\tan \angle yBT = -2$, or $\tan \angle OBT = 2$. At the

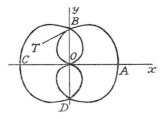

FIG. 78

origin, when $\theta = \pi$, $\tan \phi = 0$, showing that the tangent to the curve at O is directed along Ox. In other words, the tangent at O touches the initial line there.

Example 20 Find ϕ for the curve $r^2 = a^2 \cos 2\theta$, and find the radius of curvature by Newton's method at the point where $\theta = 0$.

Evidently the curve consists of two loops, with no real values of r when $\tfrac{1}{4}\pi < \theta < \tfrac{3}{4}\pi$, and $-\tfrac{3}{4}\pi < \theta < -\tfrac{1}{4}\pi$.

We note that $dr/d\theta = -a^2 \sin 2\theta/r$, so
$$\tan \phi = r/(dr/d\theta) = -\cot 2\theta = \tan (2\theta + \tfrac{1}{2}\pi).$$

It follows that $\phi = 2\theta + \tfrac{1}{2}\pi$.

By Newton's method, we have

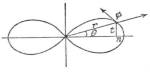

FIG. 79

$$\rho = \lim \frac{t^2}{2n} = \lim_{\theta \to 0} \frac{r^2 \sin^2 \theta}{2(a - r \cos \theta)}$$

$$= \tfrac{1}{2}a \lim \frac{\cos 2\theta \sin^2 \theta}{1 - \cos^{\frac{1}{2}} 2\theta \cos \theta}.$$

We expand numerator and denominator up to the term involving θ^2, obtaining

$$\rho = \tfrac{1}{2}a \lim \frac{(1 - 2\theta^2)\theta^2}{1 - (1 - 2\theta^2)^{\frac{1}{4}}(1 - \tfrac{1}{2}\theta^2)}$$

$$= \tfrac{1}{2}a \lim \frac{\theta^2}{1 - (1 - \theta^2)(1 - \tfrac{1}{2}\theta^2)}$$

$$= \tfrac{1}{2}a \lim \frac{\theta^2}{\tfrac{3}{2}\theta^2} = \tfrac{1}{3}a.$$

Example 21 Consider the curvature of the curve $r = 1 + 2 \cos \theta$ at the points where it intersects the initial line.

When $-1 < \cos \theta < -\tfrac{1}{2}$, r is negative; this produces two loops as shown in Fig. 80. We have $dr/d\theta = -2 \sin \theta$, so the pedal equation is given by

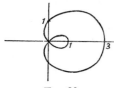

FIG. 80

$$\frac{1}{p^2} = \frac{1}{r^2}\left(1 + \frac{4 \sin^2 \theta}{r^4}\right) = \frac{1}{r^2} + \frac{4}{r^6}(1 - \cos^2 \theta)$$

$$= \frac{1}{r^2} + \frac{4}{r^6}[1 - \tfrac{1}{4}(r - 1)^2] = \frac{2r + 3}{r^4}.$$

Hence $\rho = r \left/ \frac{dp}{dr} = r \left/ \frac{d}{dr}\left(\frac{r^2}{\sqrt{(3 + 2r)}}\right) = \frac{(3 + 2r)^{\frac{3}{2}}}{6 + 3r}\right.\right.$.

The curve intersects the initial line where $\theta = 0$ and π, namely where $r = 3$ and -1; moreover $r = 0$ also gives a point of intersection. When $r = 0$, $\rho = 3^{\frac{3}{2}}/6 = \frac{1}{2}\sqrt{3}$; when $r = -1$, $\rho = \frac{1}{3}$ and when $r = 3$, $\rho = 9^{\frac{3}{2}}/15 = \frac{9}{5}$.

14.12   Some special curves

The cycloid. Let a circle of radius a roll without slipping along the line $y = 2a$, occupying the space $y \leqslant 2a$; a marked point P on the circumference of the circle is initially at the origin. The locus of P is called a *cycloid*. Parametrically, the point P is given by

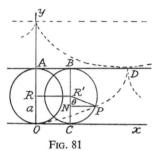

FIG. 81

$$x = OC + NP = AB + NP = a(\theta + \sin \theta),$$
$$y = a - R'N\quad = a(1 - \cos \theta),$$

where θ is the angle between the radius $R'P$ and its initial position RO.

Now $\quad dy/d\theta = a \sin \theta = 2a \sin \tfrac{1}{2}\theta \cos \tfrac{1}{2}\theta,$
$$dx/d\theta = a(1 + \cos \theta) = 2a \cos^2 \tfrac{1}{2}\theta.$$

Hence
$$\tan \psi = \frac{dy}{dx} = \frac{dy/d\theta}{dx/d\theta} = \tan \tfrac{1}{2}\theta,$$

yielding $\psi = \tfrac{1}{2}\theta$.

Moreover,
$$\left(\frac{ds}{d\theta}\right)^2 = \left(\frac{dx}{d\theta}\right)^2 + \left(\frac{dy}{d\theta}\right)^2 = 4a^2 \cos^2 \tfrac{1}{2}\theta,$$

whence
$$ds/d\theta = 2a \cos \tfrac{1}{2}\theta,$$

provided $\cos \tfrac{1}{2}\theta > 0$. If s is the arc length measured from O, we have

$$s = \int_0^{\theta} 2a \cos \tfrac{1}{2}\theta \, d\theta = 4a \sin \tfrac{1}{2}\theta.$$

From this we note immediately that $s^2 = 8ay$.

We also have
$$\rho = \frac{ds}{d\psi} = 2\frac{ds}{d\theta} = 4a \cos \tfrac{1}{2}\theta.$$

At the arch O of the cycloid, we have $\rho = 4a$ since $\theta = 0$. At the cusp D, $\theta = \pi$ and $\psi = \tfrac{1}{2}\pi$, so the tangent to the curve is vertical at D; moreover, $\rho = 0$ at that point.

If (X, Y) is the centre of curvature at P, we have

$$X = x - \rho \sin \psi = a\theta + a \sin \theta - 4a \sin \tfrac{1}{2}\theta \cos \tfrac{1}{2}\theta = a(\theta - \sin \theta),$$
$$Y = y + \rho \cos \psi = a - a \cos \theta + 4a \cos^2 \tfrac{1}{2}\theta = 3a + a \cos \theta.$$

The evolute must pass through the cusp D, since $\rho = 0$ there. Changing the origin to D, let $X = \xi + \pi a$, $Y = \eta + 2a$. Then

$$\xi = X - \pi a = a[(\theta - \pi) + \sin (\theta - \pi)],$$
$$\eta = Y - 2a = a[1 - \cos (\theta - \pi)].$$

This evolute is therefore a *congruent cycloid*, with parameter $(\theta - \pi)$; its arch is at the cusp of the original cycloid, and it occupies the space between the lines $y = 2a$ and $y = 4a$ as illustrated in Fig. 81.

The epicycloid. Let a circle of radius b roll without slipping round the circumference on the outside of a fixed circle of radius nb. The locus traced out by a fixed point P on the rolling curve is known as an *epicycloid*. In particular, if n is a rational fraction, the locus of P ultimately forms a closed curve.

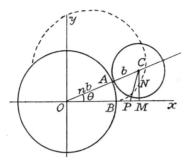

FIG. 82

Let the point P on the rolling circle be initially at B. If $\angle AOB = \theta$,
$$\text{arc } AP = \text{arc } AB = nb\theta,$$
so $\angle ACP = n\theta$. The coordinates of P are then given by
$$x = OM - PN = b(1 + n) \cos \theta - b \cos \angle CPN$$
$$= b(1 + n) \cos \theta - b \cos [\theta + \angle OCB]$$
$$= b(1 + n) \cos \theta - b \cos (n + 1)\theta,$$
$$y = CM - CN = b(1 + n) \sin \theta - b \sin (n + 1)\theta.$$

The gradient of the epicycloid at P is given by
$$\frac{dy}{dx} = \frac{dy/d\theta}{dx/d\theta} = \frac{\cos \theta - \cos (n + 1)\theta}{-\sin \theta + \sin (n + 1)\theta} = \tan (\tfrac{1}{2}n + 1)\theta,$$
from which it follows that $\psi = (\tfrac{1}{2}n + 1)\theta$.

Moreover,
$$ds^2 = dx^2 + dy^2$$
$$= b^2(n + 1)^2\{[\cos \theta - \cos (n + 1)\theta]^2 + [\sin \theta - \sin (n + 1)\theta]^2\} \, d\theta$$
$$= b^2(n + 1)^2(2 - 2 \cos n\theta) \, d\theta^2$$
$$= 4b^2(n + 1)^2 \sin^2 \tfrac{1}{2}n\theta \, d\theta^2;$$
hence
$$ds = 2b(n + 1) \sin \tfrac{1}{2}n\theta \, d\theta,$$
provided $\sin \tfrac{1}{2}n\theta$ is positive.

The radius of curvature is now given by
$$\rho = \frac{ds}{d\psi} = \frac{4b(n + 1)}{n + 2} \sin \tfrac{1}{2}n\theta.$$

Measured from B, the arc length s is given by
$$s = 2b(n + 1) \int_0^\theta \sin \tfrac{1}{2}n\theta \, d\theta = 4b(n + 1)(1 - \cos \tfrac{1}{2}n\theta)/n.$$

For one arch, θ varies from 0 to $2\pi/n$, so the length of the arch is $8b(n + 1)/n$. If n is an integer, there are n arches round the epicycloid, so its total length is $8b(n + 1)$.

The theory of the *hypocycloid*, in which the circle rolls round the inside of the fixed circle, may be treated *mutatis mutandis*.

The catenary. This is the curve specified by the equation $y = c \cosh (x/c)$; it is proved in texts on statics that a uniform flexible heavy chain assumes this form when hanging freely under gravity.

A useful parametric representation may be obtained by letting $y = c \sec \theta$. Then

$$x = c \cosh^{-1} (y/c) = c \cosh^{-1} \sec \theta$$
$$= c \log [\sec \theta + \sqrt{(\sec^2 \theta - 1)}]$$
$$= c \log (\sec \theta + \tan \theta).$$

The gradient at a point P on the catenary is

$$\tan \psi = \frac{dy}{dx} = \frac{dy/d\theta}{dx/d\theta} = \frac{c \sec \theta \tan \theta}{\dfrac{c}{\sec \theta + \tan \theta}.(\sec \theta \tan \theta + \sec^2 \theta)} = \tan \theta,$$

yielding $\psi = \theta$. Moreover,

$$ds^2 = dx^2 + dy^2 = (c^2 \sec^2 \theta + c^2 \sec^2 \theta \tan^2 \theta) \, d\theta^2 = c^2 \sec^4 \theta \, d\theta^2,$$

yielding

$$ds = c \sec^2 \theta \, d\theta.$$

Hence, upon integration,

$$s = c \tan \theta = c \tan \psi,$$

where $s = 0$ when $\theta = 0$, namely at the lowest point $(0, c)$.

The radius of curvature ρ is given by

$$\rho = \frac{ds}{d\psi} = c \sec^2 \theta = y^2/c.$$

Finally, we have

$$s = c \tan \psi = c\sqrt{(\sec^2 \psi - 1)} = \sqrt{(y^2 - c^2)}$$
$$= c\sqrt{[\cosh^2 (x/c) - 1]}$$
$$= c \sinh (x/c).$$

EXERCISES

Differentiation.

Differentiate the following functions:

(1)*. $(3x + 1)^5/(2 - x)^{10}$.

(2)*. $[x + \sqrt{(1 + x^2)}]^n$.

(3)*. $\cos x/(1 + \sin x)$.

(4)*. $\sec (x^{\frac{3}{2}})$.

(5)*. $a^x \tan x + \log (1 - \cos^3 x)$.

(6)*. $\sin^{-1} (\cos x), (0 < x < \pi)$.

(7)*. $\cos^{-1} [(1 - x^2)/(1 + x^2)]$.

(8)*. $\sin^{-1} [(1 + 2 \sin x)/(2 + \sin x)]$.

(9)*. $x\sqrt{(1 - x^2)} - \sin^{-1} \sqrt{(1 - x^2)}$.

(10)*. $\tan^{-1} \sqrt{[(1 - x)/(1 + x)]}$.

(11)*. $\tan^{-1} (\log x)$.

(12)*. $\tan^{-1} (x/e^{x^2}) + \tan^{-1} (e^{x^2}/x)$.

(13)*. $\tan^{-1} [(4\sqrt{x})/(1 - 4x)]$.

(14)*. $\tan^{-1} [2x/(1 - x^2)]$.

(15)*. $\cot^{-1}(x/\log x) + \cot^{-1}(\log x / x)$. (16)*. $x^n e^{\cos x}$.

(17)*. $\sin^{-1}[2x\sqrt{(1 - x^2)}] + \tan^{-1}\{\sqrt{[x/(1 - x)]}\}$.

(18)*. $\log[\sqrt{(x + a)} + \sqrt{(x + b)}]$. (19)*. $\log[\sqrt{(x^2 + 1)} + \sqrt{(x^2 - 1)}]$.

(20)*. $x\sqrt{(x^2 + 1)} + \log[x + \sqrt{(x^2 + 1)}]$.

(21)*. $\log[(1 - \cos x)/(1 + \cos x)]$.

(22)*. $\log(\sin x)$. (23)*. $(x + 1/x)^x$.

(24)*. $\log[x^2/\sqrt{(a^2 - x^2)}]$. (25)*. $\log(\tan e^{\sqrt{x}})$.

(26)*. $\log[(1 + x^2)/(1 - x^2)]^{\frac{1}{2}}$. (27)*. $\tan^{-1}(\tanh \frac{1}{2}x)$.

(28)*. $\log[x/\sqrt{(1 + x)}\sqrt[4]{(1 + x^2)}] - \frac{1}{2}\tan^{-1} x$.

(29)*. Obtain and simplify the first derivatives of the two functions

$$\cos^{-1}\left(\frac{a\cos x + b}{a + b\cos x}\right) \quad \text{and} \quad \tan^{-1}\left[\sqrt{\left(\frac{a - b}{a + b}\right)} \tan \frac{1}{2}x\right]$$

and explain the significance of your results.

(30)*. Find dy/dx, where $x = \cos 2\theta$ and $y = 2\theta + \sin 2\theta$.

(31)*. If $x = a\sin t - b\sin(at/b)$, $y = a\cos t - b\cos(at/b)$, where a and b are independent of t, obtain expressions for dy/dx and d^2y/dx^2 in terms of t.

(32)*. Find d^2y/dx^2 if $x = 3\cos\theta - \cos 3\theta$, $y = 3\sin\theta - \sin 3\theta$.

(33)*. If $y = t^m + t^{-m}$, $x = t + t^{-1}$, show that

(a) $(x^2 - 4)(dy/dx)^2 = m^2(y^2 - 4)$,

(b) $(x^2 - 4)d^2y/dx^2 + x\,dy/dx - m^2y = 0$.

(34)*. If $x = 2y - \tan^{-1} y$, find the value of d^2y/dx^2 when $y = 1$.

(35)*. If $y = 2x - \tan^{-1} x$, prove that $d^2x/dy^2 = -2x(1 + x^2)/(1 + 2x^2)^3$.

(36)*. Find dy/dx if $y = \sin[(x + y)^2]$.

(37)*. If $y = (1 + x)(25 - x^2)^{\frac{1}{2}}$, find the values of dy/dx and d^2y/dx^2 when $x = 3$.

(38)*. Find $d^3(e^{2x}\tan^{-1} x)/dx^3$ when $x = 0$.

(39)*. Find all the values of x that make $d^2y/dx^2 = 0$ when

$$y = \log\tan(2x + \tfrac{1}{4}\pi).$$

(40)*. If $y = \tan^{-1}[(\sinh\alpha\sin x)/(1 + \cosh\alpha\cos x)]$, where α is constant, show that $dy/dx = \sinh\alpha/(\cosh\alpha + \cos x)$, and also that

$$d^2(dx/dy)/dx^2 + dx/dy = \coth\alpha.$$

(41)*. Find the nth differential coefficient of $1/[(x - 1)^2(x - 2)]$.

(42)*. Find the nth differential coefficient of $1/[(x + 1)^2(x + 2)]$.

(43)*. If $y = \sec x$, prove that $y(d^2y/dx^2) = (dy/dx)^2 + y^4$.

(44)*. If $y = xe^y$, prove that $(1 - y)y' = e^y$, and $(1 - y)y'' = (2 - y)(y')^2$.

(45)*. If $y = e^x\sin x$, prove that $d^4y/dx^4 + 4y = 0$.

(46)*. If $y\sqrt{(a^2 + x^2)} = x$, find the value of

$$(a^2 + x^2)^2 d^2y/dx^2 + 2x(a^2 + x^2)\,dy/dx + a^2y.$$

(47)*. If $y = a\cos(\log bx) + b\sin(\log ax)$, show that

$$x^2 d^2y/dx^2 + x\,dy/dx + y = 0.$$

(48) *. If $y = A \sinh x + B \tanh x$, determine A and B so that
$$d^2y/dx^2 = (1 - \cosh^3 x) \tanh x \operatorname{sech}^2 x.$$

(49) *. Prove that the differential coefficient of the function $(x + 1)(x + 2) \ldots$ $(x + n)$ has the value $n! \, (1 + \frac{1}{2} + \frac{1}{3} + \ldots + n^{-1})$ when $x = 0$.

(50) *. A particle moves in a straight line describing a distance x in time t. If $t = ax^2 + bx + c$, where a, b, c are constants, prove that the acceleration is proportional to the cube of the velocity.

(51) *. If $y = e^{at}(b \cos bt - a \sin bt)$, show that both $dy/dx = 0$ and d^2y/dx^2 is negative at intervals of t measured by $2\pi/b$, and that then the successive values of y form a geometrical progression of ratio $e^{2\pi a/b}$.

(52) *. Show that for one value of the constant λ the differential coefficient of $y = \sin^{-1} [2x/(1 + x^2)] + \lambda \tan^{-1} [\sqrt{(x^2 + 1)} - x]$ is identically zero.

Leibnitz's theorem.

(53).   Find the $2n$th derivative of $x^2 \cosh x$.

(54).   Find the nth derivative of $e^{-ax} \cos ax$.

(55) *. By first proving that the nth derivative of $\cos \pi x$ with respect to x is $\pi^n \cos (\pi x + \frac{1}{2}n\pi)$, show that the $2m$th derivative of $x^2 \cos \pi x$ when $x = 1$ has the value $(-1)^{m+1}\pi^{2m-2}(\pi^2 + 2m - 4m^2)$.

(56) *. If $y = (2x - \pi)^5 \sin \frac{1}{2}x$, find the value of d^7y/dx^7 when $x = \frac{1}{2}\pi$.

(57) *. If $f(x) = \sin (k \sin^{-1} x)$, and if $f', f'', \ldots, f^{(n)}$ denote its successive derivatives with respect to x, show that
$$(1 - x^2)f'' - xf' + k^2f = 0,$$
and $(1 - x^2)f^{(n+2)} - (2n + 1)xf^{(n+1)} + (k^2 - n^2)f^{(n)} = 0.$

(58) *. Show that $(x^2 - 1)^n$ satisfies the equation
$$(x^2 - 1) \, dy/dx - 2nxy = 0.$$
Hence or otherwise prove that $d^n(x^2 - 1)^n/dx^n$ satisfies the equation
$$(x^2 - 1) \frac{d^2w}{dx^2} + 2x \frac{dw}{dx} - n(n + 1)w = 0.$$

(59) *. Prove that $D^{n+1}(xy) = (n + 1)D^ny + xD^{n+1}y$, where $D \equiv d/dx$. By taking $y = x^{n-1}e^{1/x}$, prove by induction that
$$D^n(x^{n-1}e^{1/x}) = (-1)^n e^{1/x}/x^{n+1}.$$

(60) *. Prove that the nth derivative of the function y/x is
$$(-1)^n n! \, x^{-n-1}\left(y - xy' + \frac{x^2y''}{2!} - \frac{x^3y'''}{3!} + \ldots + (-1)^n \frac{x^ny^{(n)}}{n!}\right),$$
where y is any function of x. Prove that
$$D^n(x^{-1}e^{-x}) = (-1)^n x^{-n-1}\left(n! - \int_0^x t^ne^{-t} \, dt\right).$$

Taylor's and Maclaurin's power series.

(61). Verify the first few terms of the following expansions:

(i) $e^{\sin x} = 1 + x + \frac{1}{2}x^2 - \frac{1}{8}x^4 + \ldots.$

(ii) $\log (1 + \sin x) = x - \frac{1}{2}x^2 + \frac{1}{6}x^3 - \ldots.$

(iii) $e^x \sin x = x + x^2 + 2x^3/3! - 2^2x^5/5! - 2^3x^6/6! - \dots$

(iv) $x \cot x = 1 - \frac{1}{3}x^2 - \frac{1}{45}x^4 - \frac{2}{945}x^6 - \dots$

(v) $x/(e^x + 1) = \frac{1}{2}x - \frac{1}{4}x^2 + \frac{1}{48}x^4 - \dots$

(vi) $\log(1 + x + x^2) = x + \frac{1}{2}x^2 - \frac{2}{3}x^3 + \frac{1}{4}x^4 + \dots$

(vii) $\tan(\frac{1}{4}\pi + x) = 1 + 2x + 2x^2 + \frac{8}{3}x^3 + \frac{10}{3}x^4 + \dots$

(viii) $\tan^{-1}(1 + x) = \frac{1}{4}\pi + \frac{1}{2}x - \frac{1}{4}x^2 + \frac{1}{12}x^3 - \dots$

(62) ⋆. Assuming the series for $\sin x$ and $\cos x$, find the series for $\log[(\sin x)/x]$ and $\log \cos x$ as far as the terms in x^4, and hence, or otherwise, show that if x is small, $\tan x$ is approximately equal to $xe^{x^2/3}$, the error being about $7x^5/90$.

(63) ⋆. Starting from an expansion of the function $1/(1 + x^2)$, find the expansion in powers of x of the function $\tan^{-1} x$. Prove that the tenth derivative of $\tan^{-1}(x^2)$ with respect to x has the value $2(9!)$ when $x = 0$.

(64) ⋆. Find the expansion for $e^x \sin^{-1} x$ up to and including the term in x^4.

(65) ⋆. If $y = e^{x \cos \alpha} \cos(x \sin \alpha)$, prove by induction that
$$y^{(n)}(x) = e^{x \cos \alpha} \cos(x \sin \alpha + n\alpha).$$
Hence obtain Maclaurin's series for y in ascending powers of x.

(66) ⋆. If $\log y = \sinh^{-1} x$, prove that
$$(1 + x^2)y'' + xy' - y = 0.$$
By differentiating this equation n times using Leibnitz's theorem, prove that $y^{(n+2)}(0) = -(n^2 - 1)y^{(n)}(0)$. Hence obtain the power series expansion of y in terms of x, assuming the expansion to be valid.

(67) ⋆. If $f(x) = \sinh^{-1} x$, prove that $(1 + x^2)f''(x) + xf'(x) = 0$. By using Leibnitz's theorem find the value of $f^{(n)}(x)$ when $x = 0$. Hence find the expansion of $\sinh^{-1} x$ in a series of ascending powers of x.

(68) ⋆. If the function $y(x)$ satisfies $y'' = xy$, by differentiating n times, show that, for $n \geq 1$, $y^{(n+2)}(0) = ny^{(n-1)}(0)$. Hence derive Maclaurin's expansion for y as an ascending power series in x such that $y = 1$, $y' = 0$ at $x = 0$.

(69) ⋆. If $y = (1 + x^2)^{\frac{1}{2}} \log[x + (1 + x^2)^{\frac{1}{2}}]$, prove that
$$(1 + x^2)(y' - 1) = xy.$$
Hence, assuming that the expression for y can be expanded as a series in ascending powers of x when $|x| < 1$, prove that this series is
$$y = x + \frac{x^3}{3} - \frac{2}{3}\frac{x^5}{5} + \frac{2}{3}\cdot\frac{4}{5}\frac{x^7}{7} - \frac{2}{3}\cdot\frac{4}{5}\cdot\frac{6}{7}\frac{x^9}{9} + \dots$$
and find the coefficient of x^{2n+1}.

(70) ⋆. If $x = \cos \theta$, $y = \cos n\theta$, and n is an integer > 1, prove that
$$(1 - x^2)y'' - xy' + n^2 y = 0.$$
Assuming that $y = a_0 + a_1 x + a_2 x^2 + \dots + a_n x^n$, where the a_k are constant, prove that $(k + 1)(k + 2)a_{k+2} + (n^2 - k^2)a_k = 0$ $(k = 0, 1, \dots, n - 2)$. Show that if n is even and greater than 2, then $a_4 = (-1)^{\frac{1}{2}n}n^2(n^2 - 4)/24$.

(71) ⋆. If $y = \sinh(m \sinh^{-1} x)$, prove that
$$(1 + x^2)y^{(n+2)}(x) + (2n + 1)xy^{(n+1)}(x) + (n^2 - m^2)y^{(n)}(x) = 0.$$
When $m = 5$, obtain y as a polynomial in x.

(72) ⋆. If $y = \cosh(\sin^{-1} x)$ prove

(i) $(1 - x^2)y'' - xy' - y = 0$,

(ii) $(1 - x^2)y^{(n+2)}(x) - (2n + 1)xy^{(n+1)}(x) = (n^2 + 1)y^{(n)}(x)$.

11

If $y = a_0 + a_1x + a_2x^2 + \ldots$, obtain an expression for a_{2n} and show that a_{2n+1} is zero.

(73)★. If $y = \cos \log (1 + x)$, prove that
$$(1 + x^2)y^{(n+2)}(x) + (2n + 1)(1 + x)y^{(n+1)}(x) + (n^2 + 1)y^{(n)}(x) = 0.$$
Show that, if y can be represented by the power series
$$a_0 + a_1x + a_2x^2 + \ldots + a_nx^n + \ldots,$$
then $(n + 1)(n + 2)a_{n+2} + (2n + 1)(n + 1)a_{n+1} + (n^2 + 1)a_n = 0$,
and determine the expansion up to and including the term in x^6.

(74)★. Assuming the existence of the Maclaurin power series, show that
$$2 \cos x \cosh x = \sum_{n=0}^{\infty} 2^{\frac{1}{2}n}[1 + (-1)^n]x^n \cos \tfrac{1}{4}n\pi/n!.$$

(75)★. If $f(x)$ is defined by the integral
$$f(x) = \int_0^x (1 - t^3)^{-\frac{1}{2}} \, dt,$$
prove that $2(1 - x^3)f''(x) = 3x^2f'(x)$. Deduce that
$$2f^{(n+2)}(0) = (2n - 1)n(n - 1)f^{(n-1)}(0).$$
Obtain Maclaurin's expansion for $f(x)$ as far as the term in x^{10}.

(76)★. If $y = [x + \sqrt{(1 + x^2)}]^m$, prove that
(i) $(1 + x^2)y'' + xy' - m^2y = 0$,
(ii) $(1 + x^2)y^{(n+2)}(x) + (2n + 1)xy^{(n+1)}(x) + (n^2 - m^2)y^{(n)}(x) = 0$.
If m is a positive integer (even or odd), prove that the value of $y^{(m+1)}(0)$ is $(2m)!/[2^m(m - 1)!]$.

(77)★. A function y satisfies, for all x, the differential equation
$$y''' - y'' + 2y' - y = 0$$
(and hence also the equation
$$y^{(4)} - y''' + 2y'' - y' = 0,$$
and so on). Given that $y = 0$, $y' = 1$, $y'' = 0$ when $x = 0$, calculate the values of y''', $y^{(4)}$, $y^{(5)}$, $y^{(6)}$ when $x = 0$, and use Maclaurin's expansion to estimate the value of y when $x = 1$. What degree of accuracy might reasonably be expected in the answer?

(78)★. If $y = \sin^{-1} x + (\sin^{-1} x)^2$, prove that $(1 - x^2)y'' - xy'$ is independent of x and deduce that, for $n \geqslant 1$,
$$(1 - x^2)y^{(n+2)}(x) - x(2n + 1)y^{(n+1)}(x) - n^2y^{(n)}(x) = 0.$$
Show that the value of $y^{(2r+1)}(0)$ is $[(2r)!]^2/[2^{2r}(r!)^2]$.

(79)★. By using Taylor's theorem, show that, if $-\tfrac{1}{2}\pi < \alpha < \tfrac{1}{2}\pi$, and if x^4 can be neglected
(i) $\tan^{-1}(x + \tan \alpha) = \alpha + x \cos^2 \alpha - x^2 \sin \alpha \cos^3 \alpha$
$$+ \tfrac{1}{3}x^3 \cos^4 \alpha(4 \sin^2 \alpha - 1),$$
(ii) $\sin^{-1}(x + \sin \alpha) = \alpha + x \sec \alpha + \tfrac{1}{2}x^2 \tan \alpha \sec^2 \alpha$
$$+ \tfrac{1}{6}x^3(3 \sec^5 \alpha - 2 \sec^3 \alpha).$$

(80)★. Show that, for small values of x,

$$\sec^2(\tfrac{1}{4}\pi + x) = 2 + 4x + ax^2 + bx^3 + cx^4 + \ldots,$$

and determine a, b and c. Expand $\sqrt{[2 + \sec^2(\tfrac{1}{4}\pi + x)]}$ in ascending powers of x as far as the term involving x^3.

Stationary values and points of inflexion.

(81)★. (i) Find the least value of each of the following expressions, x and θ being real: $\sqrt{(x^2 + 4x + 6)}$, $\cos^2\theta + 4\cos\theta + 6$.

(ii) Find the greatest value assumed by the function $x^2e^{-x^2}$. Sketch the graph of the function and indicate where it has inflexions.

(82)★. If $10y = (1 - x)^5x^{-3}$, show that y has two stationary values at one of which y is a maximum and at the other the graph of y has a point of inflexion. Show also that the graph has no other point of inflexion. Calculate the maximum value to two significant figures.

(83)★. If S is the total surface area of a right circular cone whose base is of radius r and if V is the volume of the cone, prove that $9V^2 = r^2(S^2 - 2\pi r^2S)$. Hence prove that the cone of maximum volume whose surface area is given has a vertical angle $2\sin^{-1}\tfrac{1}{3}$.

(84)★. A trapezium $ABCD$ is inscribed in a circle of radius r. The sides AB, CD are equal in length, and the side AD is a diameter of the circle. If each of the sides AB, CD subtends an angle θ at the centre of the circle, express the area S and the perimeter P of the trapezium in terms of θ. Find the maximum value of the area and of the perimeter.

(85)★. The points P and Q are on a circle of variable radius, and are such that the minor arc PQ is of given length. Prove that the area of the segment bounded by the arc and the chord PQ is greatest when the arc PQ is a semi-circle.

(86)★. Prove that $y = x^ne^{-x}$ has points of inflexion at two positive values of x when $n > 1$. Show that the product of the two values of y at these points of inflexion is $n^n(n - 1)^ne^{-2n}$.

(87)★. Sketch the graphs of the functions $1 + 2x$ and e^x with the same axes, and prove that the greatest value assumed by the function $1 + 2x - e^x$ is $\log(4/e)$.

Find the greatest value assumed by the function $\sinh(2x - e^x)$.

(88)★. Find the minimum value of y when $y^2 = ax^3 - x^4$. Sketch the curve represented by this equation, showing in particular that the whole curve must lie between $x = 0$ and $x = a$.

(89)★. The height and the circumference of a solid right circular cylinder together have a constant sum c. Express as a multiple of c the circumference of the cylinder whose total surface area is a maximum. Give evidence that your answer refers to a maximum area.

(90)★. Prove that there are just three normals to the curve $y = (1 + x^2)^{-1}$ which pass through the origin, and find where they meet the curve. Prove that the shortest distance from the origin to a point of the curve is $\sqrt{(2^{\frac{1}{3}} + 2^{-\frac{2}{3}} - 1)}$.

(91). Sketch the graph $y = (x^2 - 10x + 17)e^x$, showing the stationary points, points of inflexion and points where $y = 0$. What are the maximum and minimum values of y?

(92). The curve $y = e^x(x - 1)^2$ is given. Find the stationary values, indicating whether they are maxima or minima; find also the points of inflexion, and give a careful sketch of the curve.

(93)★. If $y = x^4 - 6c^2x^2 + bx + a$, determine the points of inflexion of this curve and show that the straight line through them has two further intersections with the curve such that the curve marks off three intervals on the line which are in the ratio $\sqrt{5} - 1 : 2 : \sqrt{5} - 1$.

(94)★. (i) Find all the maxima and minima of $(x^4 + 5x^2 + 8x + 8)e^{-x}$.

(ii) Find the minimum value of $a + b + c + x - 4(abcx)^{\frac{1}{4}}$, where a, b, c are positive constants, and sketch the graph. Hence show that

$$a + b + c + d - 4(abcd)^{\frac{1}{4}} \geqslant a + b + c - 3(abc)^{\frac{1}{3}},$$

for any positive numbers a, b, c, d.

(95)★. A right circular cone is circumscribed to a sphere of radius a, with the base of the cone touching the sphere. Find an expression for the volume of the cone in terms of a and the semi-vertical angle of the cone, and show that when the volume of the cone is a minimum it is double the volume of the sphere.

Find also the smallest volume of the cone if its semi-vertical angle is restricted to lie between $\sin^{-1}(\frac{1}{5})$ and $\sin^{-1}(\frac{1}{4})$ inclusive.

(96)★. Show that the distance between a point P on the curve $x = 2a \cos^3 t$, $y = 2a \sin^3 t$ and the point $(a, 0)$ is least when $8 \cos t = \sqrt{33} + 1$. Draw a rough graph of r against t as P completely describes the curve.

(97)★. (i) Find the stationary values of the function $x^4 - 8x^3 + 18x^2 - 14$ and state their nature.

(ii) Show that the points of inflexion of the curve $(1 + x^2)y + x - 1 = 0$ lie on the line $x + 4y = 3$.

(98). If $y = k(\sin \theta + \cos \theta - 1)^2 - \sin 2\theta$, show that $\theta = \frac{1}{4}\pi$ yields a maximum value of y if $k > 2 + \sqrt{2}$, and a minimum if $k < 2 + \sqrt{2}$. If $k = 2 + \sqrt{2}$, show $\theta = \frac{1}{4}\pi$ yields a minimum value of y.

(99). If $y = \theta \sin \theta + (1 + h) \cos \theta$, show that $\theta = 0$ yields a minimum value of y if $h < 1$, and a maximum if $h \geqslant 1$.

(100)★. An isosceles triangle OAB, $OA = OB$, has its vertices on the cardioid $r = a(1 + \cos \theta)$, O being the pole. Find the greatest area of the triangle.

(101)★. P is a variable point on a parabola of latus rectum $4a$ and vertex O. The ordinate at P meets the axis at M, and Q is the foot of the perpendicular from M to OP. Find the length OM when $QP - OQ$ is a maximum.

(102)★. If $y = \cos x/(\cos 2\alpha + \cos 2x)$, where α is a constant, show that, as x increases in the range $2n\pi < x < (2n + 1)\pi$, where n is any integer, y steadily increases, save when infinite. Show also that y has minimum values for $x = 2n\pi$. Sketch the graph of the function for $0 < \alpha < \frac{1}{2}\pi$.

(103)★. If t is a positive constant, determine the maximum and minimum values of $f(x) = 9(4 - 3x^2)(t - t^{-1} - x)$, and show that the difference between them is $4(t + t^{-1})^3$. Find the least value of this difference as the parameter t is varied.

(104)★. If $y^3 = x^2(6x - x^2 - 8)$, prove that the stationary values of y occur at $x = \frac{1}{4}(9 \pm \sqrt{17})$, and determine which of these values of x gives a maximum of y and which a minimum.

Limits.

(105)★. As $x \to 0$, find the limits of

(i) $x^2(e^x - e^{-x})/[(1 + x^3)^4 - (1 - x^3)^4]$.

(ii) $[2x - 2x^2 - \log(1 + 2x)]/(x^2 \tan^{-1} x)$.

(iii) $[\exp(\sin x) - 1 - x]/x^2$.

(iv) $(16 \sin \frac{1}{4}x - 2 \sin \frac{1}{2}x - 3x)/x^5$.

(v) $[\sqrt{(1 + 2x)} - \cos x - x]/x^3$.

(vi) $(\tan 3x - 3 \tan x)/x^3$.

(vii) $(e^{x^2} - 1)/(e^x - 1)^2$.

(viii) $(1 - \cos 2x - 2x^2 \cos x)/(2x^3 \tan x)$.

(ix) $[\sec(a + x) - \sec a]/[\tan(a + x) - \tan a]$.

(x) $(\sin^2 px - \sin^2 qx)/(1 - \cos rx)$.

(xi) $(\sin x - x \cos x)/x^3$.

(xii) $\dfrac{1}{x^4} \displaystyle\int_0^x (e^{t^2} - 1) \sin t \, dt$.

(106)★. Find the limits of

(i) $\sec x - \tan x$, as $x \to \frac{1}{2}\pi$.

(ii) $(\sqrt{x} - \sqrt{a})/(\sqrt[3]{x} - \sqrt[3]{a})$, as $x \to a$.

(iii) $[\tan(\log x) - \log(\tan \frac{1}{4}\pi x)]/\log x$, as $x \to 1$.

(iv) $e^{2x}(1 - \tanh x)$, as $x \to \infty$.

(107)★. Prove that $(x^n - a^n)/(x - a) \to na^{n-1}$ as $x \to a$, n being a positive integer. Find the limits as $n \to \infty$ of the following expressions

(i) $[1 + 3 + 5 + \ldots + (2n + 1)]/n^2$,

(ii) $n^2[\cos(\frac{1}{2}\theta/n) - \cos(\theta/n)]$.

(108)★. Find the limits as $n \to \infty$ of

$$(n + 2)^n/(n - 1)^n, \quad (1 + 2/n)^{-n}, \quad (1 - 1/n^2)^n.$$

(109)★. If $y > 0$, and $y^2(x - 2) = x(x + 1)^2$, prove that $\lim(y - x) = 2$ as $x \to \infty$. Sketch the curve given by $y^2(x - 2) = x(x + 1)^2$.

(110)★, If $y > 0$, and $y^2(x + 1) = x(2x + 1)(2x - 3)$, prove that

$$\lim_{x \to \infty} (2x - y) = 2 \quad \text{and} \quad \lim_{x \to -\infty} (2x + y) = 2.$$

Find the asymptotes of the curve $y^2(x + 1) = x(2x + 1)(2x - 3)$ and the point where the curve meets the axes and the asymptotes. Sketch the curve.

(111)★. If $y = \exp(\tan^{-1} x)$, where $\tan^{-1} x$ lies between $-\frac{1}{2}\pi$ and $+\frac{1}{2}\pi$, show that $(1 + x^2)y' = y$, and by successive differentiation of this equation, obtain, using Maclaurin's theorem, the expansion of y in ascending powers of x as far as the term in x^5.

Deduce that $[\exp(\tan^{-1} x) - e^x(1 - \frac{1}{3}x^3)]/x^5 \to \frac{1}{5}$ as $x \to 0$.

(112)★. Investigate the limits of $(1 + \cos x)/(x^2 - \pi^2)^2$ when (i) $x \to 0$, (ii) $x \to \pi$, (iii) $x \to \infty$.

The approximate solution of equations.

(113)★. Show that the equation $x^{1.5} - 24 \log_{10} x + 4 \sin 2x = 4 \cdot 12$ has a root lying between the values $x = 1$ and $x = 2$. Find its value correct to two decimal places by one application of Newton's approximation formula. (Take 1 radian = $57 \cdot 3°$.)

(114)★. Show that the area enclosed by the curve whose polar equation is $r = a \sec^2 \frac{1}{2}\theta$ and the lines $\theta = 0$ and $\theta = \alpha$ is $a^2(t + t^3/3)$, where $t = \tan \frac{1}{2}\alpha$. It is required to determine the value of α for which the area is equal to a^2. Taking as a first approximation the acute angle given by $t = \frac{3}{4}$, find a closer approximation, expressing the value of α in degrees correct to $0.1°$.

(115)★. Find, correct to three significant figures, the value of θ, lying between 0 and $\frac{1}{2}\pi$, which makes $\tan \theta/\theta^2$ a minimum.

(116)★. By considering the graphs of the equations $y = x^3$, $y = x + 0.1$, show that the cubic equation $x^3 - x - 0.1 = 0$ has three real roots, one positive and two negative. Find the value of the positive root correct to two decimal places.

(117)★. Show graphically that the equation $\sin x - \tanh x = 0$ has an infinity of real roots and find the smallest positive root correct to two decimal places.

(118)★. By drawing the graphs of $e^x - 1$ and $\log_e(x + 2)$, show that the equation $e^x - 1 = \log_e(x + 2)$ has two and only two real roots.

Find both the roots approximately, and find the larger root correct to two decimal places.

(119)★. Show that the function $y = x(x - 4)/(x^2 + 3)^{\frac{1}{2}}$ has one real turning point and find the corresponding value of x correct to two decimal places.

(120)★. Show graphically that the equation $\log_e (2x + 1) = 1 - x^2$ has only one real root, and find this root correct to three significant figures, given that $x = 0.5$ is a first approximation.

Curvature in Cartesian coordinates.

(121). Find the radius of curvature at the point $(2, 4)$ on the curve $y^2 = 2x^3$, and at the point where $x = \frac{1}{2}a$ on the curve $a^2y = x^3$.

(122)★. The normal at the point P on the curve $y = c \cosh(x/c)$ meets the x-axis at G. Prove that PG is equal to the radius of curvature at P.

(123)★. For the catenary $y = c \cosh(x/c)$ prove that $\rho = y^2/c$, and show that if K is the centre of curvature for the point P, and the normal at P meets Ox at G, then P is the mid-point of KG.

(124)★. The normal at a point P on the curve $y = a \cosh(x/a)$ meets the x-axis at N and C is the centre of curvature of the curve at P. Show that P bisects CN. The curve also cuts the y-axis at V and s is the length of the arc VP. Prove that $y^2 = a^2 + s^2$.

(125)★. Show that the radius of curvature at any point (x_1, y_1) of the rectangular hyperbola $x^2 - y^2 = a^2$ is $(x_1^2 + y_1^2)^{\frac{3}{2}}/a^2$ numerically, and that the corresponding centre of curvature is the point $(2x_1^3/a^2, -2y_1^3/a^2)$.

(126)★. Find the coordinates of the two points on the curve given by $x = at^2$, $y = 2at$ at which the radius of curvature is $125a/32$.

(127)★. Make a careful sketch of the curve $y(1 + x^2) = x - x^2$. Find the radius of curvature of this curve at the origin and the coordinates of the corresponding centre of curvature.

(128)★. P is the point on the parabola $y = ax^2 + bx$ at which $x = 1$. If the tangent at P makes $30°$ with the x-axis and the radius of curvature at P is 2 units of length, find the values of a and b and the coordinates of the centre of curvature at P.

(129)★. If $x = 2a \sin nt$ and $y = a \cos 2nt$, where a and n are constants, prove that the radius of curvature is $a(1 + 4 \sin^2 nt)^{\frac{3}{2}}$.

(130)★. The coordinates of a point P on a curve are given in terms of a parameter t by $x = a(\cos t + t \sin t)$, $y = a(\sin t - t \cos t)$. Find dy/dx and d^2y/dx^2 in terms of t and hence show that the radius of curvature at P is at. Find the coordinates of the centre of curvature at P.

(131)★. Find the radius of curvature at the point $(a \cos^3 \theta, a \sin^3 \theta)$ on the curve $x^{\frac{2}{3}} + y^{\frac{2}{3}} = a^{\frac{2}{3}}$, and show that the maximum value of the radius of curvature is $3a/2$.

(132)★. Show that the radius of curvature at the point t on the curve $x = 2a \sin t + a \sin 2t$, $y = 2a \cos t + a \cos 2t$ is $8a(\cos \frac{1}{2}t)/3$.

(133)★. Find the coordinates of the centre of curvature of the ellipse $x^2/a^2 + y^2/b^2 = 1$ at the point $(a \cos \theta, b \sin \theta)$, and show that at this point $a^2b^2\rho^2 = (a^2 \sin^2 \theta + b^2 \cos^2 \theta)^3$ where ρ is the radius of curvature.

Show that the locus of the centre of curvature has the equation

$$(ax)^{\frac{2}{3}} + (by)^{\frac{2}{3}} = (a^2 - b^2)^{\frac{2}{3}}.$$

(134)★. Find the value of the radius of curvature ρ at the point (at^2, at^3) on the curve $ay^2 = x^3$. Show that, if the normal at P meets the axes of x and y in the points X, Y respectively, $\rho = 3PX + 2PY$.

(135)★. Find d^2y/dx^2 and the radius of curvature at the point θ $(0 < \theta < \pi)$ on the *tractrix* $x = a(\log \cot \frac{1}{2}\theta - \cos \theta)$, $y = a \sin \theta$, and show that d^2y/dx^2 is positive. Also show that if (X, Y) are the coordinates of the centre of curvature at the point (x, y), then $X = x + a \cos \theta$, $Y = a^2/y$.

(136)★. If $x = e^t(\cos t + \sin t)$, $y = e^t(\cos t - \sin t)$ are the parametric equations of a curve, find the equation of the tangent at the point (x_0, y_0) where $t = t_0$. Find the radius of curvature at this point and prove that the coordinates of the centre of curvature are $(y_0, -x_0)$.

(137)★. Prove that the locus of the centres of curvature of the rectangular hyperbola $x = ct$, $y = c/t$ is $(x + y)^{\frac{2}{3}} - (x - y)^{\frac{2}{3}} = (4c)^{\frac{2}{3}}$.

(138)★. Prove that the centre of curvature at the point $P(at^2, 2at)$ on the parabola $y^2 = 4ax$ has coordinates $x = 2a + 3at^2$, $y = -2at^3$. A segment PQ of length a is measured along the tangent to the parabola at the point P in the direction of t increasing. Prove that the equation of the locus of Q is $x = a[t^2 + t/\sqrt{(1 + t^2)}]$, $y = a[2t + 1/\sqrt{(1 + t^2)}]$, and prove that the normal at Q to this locus passes through the centre of curvature at the point P on the parabola.

(139)★. A circle of radius a rolls externally on a fixed circle of radius $2a$. Show that, referred to axes through the centre of the fixed circle, the parametric equations to the curve described by a point P on the circumference of the rolling circle may be expressed in the form

$$x = 3a \cos \theta - a \cos 3\theta, \quad y = 3a \sin \theta - a \sin 3\theta.$$

Show that the radius of curvature at the point θ is $3a \sin \theta$. A is the point of contact of the two circles and K is the other point of intersection of PA with a circle of radius $\frac{1}{2}a$ touching the fixed circle internally at A. Show that PA is the normal at P to the locus of P and deduce that K is the centre of curvature at P of the locus of P.

(140)★. Prove that the line $lx + my + n = 0$ touches the curve $x^4 + y^4 = a^4$ if $l^{\frac{4}{3}} + m^{\frac{4}{3}} = (n/a)^{\frac{4}{3}}$.

Prove also that the radius of curvature of the curve at its points of intersection with the lines $y = \pm x$ is $2^{\frac{1}{4}} a/3$.

(141)★. A, A', B, B' are respectively the ends of the major and minor axes of an ellipse, centre O, and C is the fourth vertex of the rectangle A, O, B. Prove that the line through C perpendicular to AB cuts AA' in the centre of curvature at A and BB' in the centre of curvature at B.

Curvature in polar coordinates.

(142). By first finding the pedal equations, find the radius of curvature of the curves (i) $r = a\theta$, (ii) $r^6 = \cos 6\theta$, (iii) $r = a\sin^3 \tfrac{1}{3}\theta$.

(143)★. The *limaçon* $r = a - b\cos\theta$ $(a > b)$ is cut at A and B by a circle that touches the initial line $\theta = 0$ at the origin. Prove that the tangents to the limaçon at A and B intersect at a point on the circle.

(144)★. Prove that the (p, r) equation of the *cardioid* $r = 3a\cos^2 \tfrac{1}{2}\theta$ is $r^3 = 3ap^2$, and deduce that the radius of curvature at the point $P(r, \theta)$ on the cardioid is $2a\cos \tfrac{1}{2}\theta$.
If Q is a point on the curve such that PQ is a chord through the pole, prove that the normals at P and Q are perpendicular. Prove also that if C is the point of intersection of these normals, the radii of curvature at P and Q are proportional to PC and QC respectively.

(145)★. P and P' are points on the curve $r^2 = a^2 \cos 2\theta$ whose vectorial angles θ, θ', $(\theta' > \theta)$ are each positive and less than $\tfrac{1}{4}\pi$. If the tangents at P and P' intersect at right-angles at T, show that $\theta' = \theta + \tfrac{1}{6}\pi$ and that $OT^2 = \tfrac{3}{4}\sqrt{3}a^2 \cos (2\theta + \tfrac{1}{6}\pi)$, where O is the origin.

(146)★. If OQ, of length p, is the perpendicular from the origin O on to the tangent at P (r, θ) to the cardioid $r = a(1 + \cos\theta)$, show that $r^3 = 2ap^2$ and that the inclination ψ of OQ to the initial line is given by $2\psi = 3\theta$. If, with the same pole and initial line, the polar coordinates of Q are (r', θ') and p' is the length of the perpendicular from O to the tangent at Q to the locus of Q, show that

$$r' = 2a\cos^3 (\tfrac{1}{3}\theta') \quad \text{and} \quad r'^4 = 2ap'^3.$$

(147)★. Find the (p, r) equation of the curve $r^4 = a^4 \cos 4\theta$. If N is the foot of the perpendicular from the pole O onto the tangent at P, prove that the maximum value of the area of the triangle OPN occurs when P is a point for which $\cos 4\theta = \sqrt{(\tfrac{3}{5})}$.

ANSWERS TO EXERCISES

(1). $5(3x + 1)^4(8 + 3x)/(2 - x)^{11}$.　　(2). $n[x + \sqrt{(1 + x^2)}]^n/\sqrt{(1 + x^2)}$.
(3). $-\tfrac{1}{2}\sec^2 (\tfrac{1}{4}\pi - \tfrac{1}{2}x)$.　　(4). $\tfrac{3}{4}x^{-\frac{1}{4}} \sec x^{\frac{3}{4}} \tan x^{\frac{3}{4}}$.
(5). $a^x(\sec^2 x + \log_e a \tan x) + 3\cos^2 x \sin x/(1 - \cos^3 x)$.　　(6). -1.
(7). $2/(1 + x^2)$.　　(8). $\sqrt{3}/(2 + \sin x)$.　　(9). $2\sqrt{(1 - x^2)}$.
(10). $-1/2\sqrt{(1 - x^2)}$.　　(11). $1/\{x[1 + (\log x)^2]\}$.　　(12). 0.
(13). $2/(1 - 16x^2)\sqrt{x}$.　　(14). $2/(1 + x^2)$.　　(15). 0.
(16). $(n - x \sin x)x^{n-1}e^{\cos x}$.　　(17). $2/\sqrt{(1 - x^2)} + 1/[2\sqrt{x}\sqrt{(1 - x)}]$.
(18). $\tfrac{1}{2}/\sqrt{[(x + a)(x + b)]}$.　　(19). $x/\sqrt{(x^4 - 1)}$.　　(20). $2\sqrt{(x^2 + 1)}$.
(21). $2 \operatorname{cosec} x$.　　(22). $\cot x$.　　(23). $(x + 1/x)^x[\log (x + 1/x) + (x^2 - 1)/(x^2 + 1)]$.　　(24). $(2a^2 - x^2)/[x(a^2 - x^2)]$.
(25). $\tfrac{1}{2}x^{-\frac{1}{2}}e^{\sqrt{x}} \sec^2 (e^{\sqrt{x}}) \cot (e^{\sqrt{x}})$.　　(26). $2x/(1 - x^4)$.　　(27). $\tfrac{1}{2} \operatorname{sech} x$.
(28). $1/[x(1 + x)(1 + x^2)]$.　　(29). $(a^2 + b^2)^{\frac{1}{2}}/(a + b\cos x)$,
　　　$\tfrac{1}{2}(a^2 + b^2)^{\frac{1}{2}}/(a + b\cos x)$.　　(30). $-\cot\theta$.　　(31). $\cot [\tfrac{1}{2}t(a + b)/b]$,
　　　$-\tfrac{1}{4}[(a + b)/ab] \operatorname{cosec}^3 [\tfrac{1}{2}t(a + b)/b] \operatorname{cosec} [\tfrac{1}{2}t(a - b)/b]$.

(32). $\frac{1}{3}\sec^3 2\theta \operatorname{cosec} \theta$. (34). $-\frac{4}{27}$. (36). $2(x+y)\cos[(x+y)^2]/$
$\{1 - 2(x+y)\cos[(x+y)^2]\}$. (37). $1, -\frac{49}{16}$. (38). 10.

(39). $\frac{1}{4}n\pi, n$ integral. (41). $(-1)^{n+1}n!/(x-1)^{n+1} + (-1)^{n+1}(n+1)!/(x-1)^{n+2}$
$+ (-1)^n n!/(x-2)^{n+1}$. (42). $(-1)^{n+1}n!/(x+1)^{n+1} + (-1)^n(n+1)!/$
$(x+1)^{n+2} + (-1)^n n!/(x+2)^{n+1}$. (46). 0. (48). $A = -1, B = -\frac{1}{2}$.

(53). $[x^2 + 2n(2n-1)]\cosh x + 4nx\sinh x$. (54). $(a\sqrt2)^n e^{-ax}\cos(ax + \frac{3}{4}\pi n)$.

(56). $-_7C_5 5!\,2^5(\frac{1}{3})^2 \sin\frac{1}{6}\pi = -140 \times 2^5$. (62). $-x^2/6 - x^4/180, -\frac{1}{2}x^2 - x^4/12$.

(63). $x - \frac{1}{3}x^3 + \frac{1}{5}x^5 - \frac{1}{7}x^7 + \dots, |x| < 1$. (64). $x + x^2 + \frac{2}{3}x^4 + \frac{1}{3}x^4$.

(65). $\sum \cos(n\alpha)x^n/n!$. (66). $x + \sum_{r=0}^{\infty}(-1)^r(2r-2)!\,x^{2r}/[2^{2r-1}r!\,(r-1)!]$.

(67). $f^{(2n)}(0) = 0, f^{(2n+1)}(0) = (-1)^n[(2n)!]^2/2^{2n}(n!)^2; \sum f^{(2n+1)}(0)x^{2n+1}/(2n+1)!$.

(68). $1 + x^3/3! + 1.4x^6/6! + 1.4.7x^9/9! + 1.4.7.10x^{12}/12! + \dots$

(69). $(-1)^{n+1}2^{2n+1}(n-1)!\,n!/(2n+1)!$. (71). $5x + 20x^3 + 16x^5$.

(72). $[(2n-2)^2 + 1][(2n-4)^2 + 1]\dots(4^2+1)(2^2+1)/(2n)!$.

(73). $1 - \frac{1}{2}x^2 + \frac{1}{3}x^3 - \frac{5}{12}x^4 + \frac{1}{3}x^5 - \frac{19}{72}x^6$. (75). $x + \frac{1}{6}x^4 + \frac{3}{56}x^7 + \frac{17}{480}x^{10}$.

(77). $-2, -1, 3, 3; y(1) = 0.654$. (80). $a = 8, b = \frac{40}{3}, c = \frac{64}{3}$;
$2 + x + \frac{7}{4}x^2 + \frac{59}{24}x^3$. (81). (i) $\sqrt2, 3$; (ii) $1/e$.

(82). Max. $y = -\frac{625}{216} = -2.9$ when $x = -\frac{3}{2}$. (84). $S = r^2(\sin\theta + \frac{1}{2}\sin 2\theta)$,
$P = 2r(1 + \cos\theta + 2\sin\frac{1}{2}\theta)$; max. $S = \frac{3}{4}\sqrt3 r^2$, max. $P = 5r$.

(87). $(2e^{-2} - e^2/8)$. (88). $-3\sqrt{3}a^2/16$. (89). $\pi c/(2\pi - 1)$.

(90). $(0, 1), [\pm\sqrt{(\sqrt[3]{2} - 1)}, 1/\sqrt[3]{2}]$. (91). $8e, -4e^7$.

(92). Max: $(-1, 4/e)$, min: $(1, 0)$; $[\pm\sqrt2 - 1, (6 \mp 4\sqrt2)e^{-1\pm\sqrt2}]$.

(93). $x = \pm c, y = -5c^4 \pm bc + a$. (94). (i) Max: $x = 2, y = 60/e^2$,
infl: $x = 1, y = 22/e$, min: $x = 0, y = 8$. (97). (i) -14 at $x = 0$, min;
13 at $x = 3$, infl. (100). $\theta = \frac{1}{5}\pi, 1.56a^2$. (101). $(\sqrt{17} - 3)a$.

(103). $4(3t^2 - 1)^2/t^3, -4(t^2 - 3)^2/t$; 32. (104). $+$max; $-$min.

(105). (i) $\frac{1}{4}$. (ii) $-\frac{8}{3}$. (iii) $\frac{1}{2}$. (iv) $-\frac{1}{2500}$. (v) $\frac{1}{2}$. (vi) 8. (vii) 1. (viii) $\frac{1}{6}$.
(ix) $\sin a \cos a$. (x) $2(p^2 - q^2)/r^2$. (xi) $\frac{1}{3}$. (xii) $\frac{1}{4}$.

(106). (i) 0. (ii) $\frac{3}{2}a^{-6}$. (iii) $1 - \frac{1}{2}\pi$. (iv) 0. (107). (i) 1. (ii) $\frac{3}{4}\theta^2$.

(108). $e^3, e^{-2}, 1$. (110). $x = -1, 2x \pm y = 2; x = 0, -\frac{1}{2}, \frac{3}{2}, (4, \mp 6)$.

(111). $1 + x + \frac{1}{2}x^2 - \frac{1}{6}x^3 - \frac{7}{24}x^4 + \frac{1}{24}x^5$. (112). (i) $2/\pi^4$. (ii) $1/8\pi^2$. (iii) 0.

(113). 1.04. (114). $\tan\frac{1}{2}\alpha = 0.814, 78.3°$. (115). 0.948. (116). 1.05.

(117). 1.88. (118). $-1.5, 0.7; 0.67$. (119). Real root of $x^3 + 6x - 12 = 0$:
1.47. (120). 0.528. (121). $42.16, \frac{125}{192}a$. (126). $(\frac{9}{16}a, \pm\frac{3}{4}a)$.

(127). $-\sqrt2, (1, -1)$. (128). $a = 2/3\sqrt3, b = -1/\sqrt3, (0, 4/\sqrt3)$.

(130). $(a\cos t, a\sin t)$. (131). $3a\sin\theta\cos\theta$. (134). $\frac{1}{6}at(4 + 8t^2)^{\frac{3}{2}}$.

(135). $(\sec^4\theta\sin\theta)/a$. (136). $y + x\tan t_0 = e^{t_0}\sec t_0$; $\rho = -2e^{t_0}\cos t_0$.

(142). (i) $(a^2 + r^2)^{\frac{3}{2}}/(2a^2 + r^2)$. (ii) $1/7r^5$. (iii) $\frac{3}{4}\sqrt[3]{(ar^2)}$. (147). $p = r^5/a^4$.

CHAPTER 15

PARTIAL DIFFERENTIATION

15.1 Partial derivatives

We shall consider the subject first of all from an analytical point of view; its geometrical interpretation is considered later in section 15.8, but the student may refer to this immediately after the opening definitions given in this chapter.

We are given a function of several variables: $z = f(x, y, t, \ldots)$. To be specific, we shall consider the case of two *independent* variables x and y, but the general case may likewise be treated. We write

$$z = f(x, y) = z(x, y).$$

It is usual to replace the functional symbol f by z; confusion does not arise if care is taken. The z on the left, namely the *dependent* variable, denotes the numerical value of the function when particular values of x and y are inserted into the function. The z on the right denotes a functional symbol. Hence, for example, the expression

$$z = \exp(x + y^2) \sin \sqrt{(x^2 + y)}$$

is a function of the two variables x and y.

To examine the *continuity* of the function $z(x, y)$ at the point $P(x_0, y_0)$, we consider the value of the function at every neighbouring point $Q(x_0 + h, y_0 + k)$, namely $z(x_0 + h, y_0 + k)$, in the Oxy-plane. If the difference between the two values $z(x_0 + h, y_0 + k) - z(x_0, y_0)$ can be made as small as we please by making the distance $PQ = \sqrt{(h^2 + k^2)}$ as small as we please, we infer that the function is continuous at the point (x_0, y_0).

Thus the function $z(x, y) = (x - y)/(x + y)$, $z(0, 0) = 0$, is not continuous at the point $x = 0$, $y = 0$. For if we approach the point $(0, 0)$ in the Oxy plane along the line $y = mx$, then $z = (1 - m)/(1 + m)$ however small x and y may be. Near the origin, this certainly is not as near the value 0 as we please, for it may assume any value whatever depending on m.

The theory given in the following sections shows that it is necessary to introduce the derivatives of the function $z(x, y)$ in the following manner. The *partial differential coefficient of z with respect to x is* defined to be the function z or f differentiated with respect to x *with y held constant.* That is, at the definite point (X, Y), we have

$$\frac{\partial z}{\partial x} = \lim_{\delta x \to 0} \frac{f(X + \delta x, Y) - f(X, Y)}{\delta x}.$$

This partial derivative may variously be denoted by

$$\frac{\partial z}{\partial x}, \; D_x z, \; \left(\frac{\partial z}{\partial x}\right)_y, \; z_x, \; \frac{\partial f}{\partial x}, \; D_x f, \; \left(\frac{\partial f}{\partial x}\right)_y, \; f_x,$$

depending on circumstances; $\partial z/\partial x$ is the most usual, the pair of independent variables x and y being understood from the context. If it is required to indicate explicitly the other independent variable that is held constant, we write $(\partial z/\partial x)_y$, the suffix indicating the constant variable. If shorter notation is required, $D_x z$ or z_x may be used.

Similarly, $\partial z/\partial y$ is defined when x is held constant:

$$\frac{\partial z}{\partial y} = \lim_{\delta y \to 0} \frac{f(X, Y + \delta y) - f(X, Y)}{\delta y},$$

variously written as

$$\frac{\partial z}{\partial y}, \; D_y z, \; \left(\frac{\partial z}{\partial y}\right)_x, \; z_y, \; \frac{\partial f}{\partial y}, \; D_y f, \; \left(\frac{\partial f}{\partial y}\right)_x, \; f_y.$$

The student should note that whenever he writes down a partial differential coefficient such as $\partial z/\partial x$, he *must* make a mental note of the independent variables involved. If z is a function expressed in terms of x and y, *z may only be differentiated with respect to x and y but with respect to no other variables whatsoever.* Until the subject is thoroughly grasped, the student may well write $\partial z(x, y)/\partial x$ and $\partial z(x, y)/\partial y$.

Higher order derivatives may be defined. If $\partial z/\partial x$ is differentiated with respect to x with y constant ($\partial z/\partial x$ being a function of x and y), we write this second derivative as $\partial^2 z/\partial x^2$; while if it is differentiated with respect to y with x constant, we obtain the *mixed* derivative $\partial^2 z/\partial y \partial x$. Similarly, we may form the second derivatives $\partial^2 z/\partial y^2$ and $\partial^2 z/\partial x \partial y$. Third order derivatives as $\partial^3 z/\partial x^3$, $\partial^3 z/\partial x^2 \partial y$, etc., may likewise be formed. For brevity, we may write these as z_{xx}, z_{yx}, z_{yy}, z_{xy}, z_{xxx}, z_{xxy}, or $D_{xx} z$, $D_{yx} z$, $D_{yy} z$, $D_{xy} z$, $D_{xxx} z$, $D_{xxy} z$ respectively.

An important theorem, far from obvious for complicated functions, is that the two second order mixed derivatives are equal at most points, that is

$$\frac{\partial^2 z}{\partial y \partial x} = \frac{\partial^2 z}{\partial x \partial y}.$$

The condition usually stated for the validity of this theorem is that these two mixed derivatives should be continuous at the point in question, but less restricted conditions also exist.

Proof. Consider the function

$$F(x, y) = z(x + h, y + k) - z(x + h, y) - z(x, y + k) + z(x, y),$$

where h and k are finite increments. If we place

$$g(x, y) = z(x, y + k) - z(x, y),$$

we have
$$F(x, y) = g(x + h, y) - g(x, y)$$
$$= hg_x(x + \theta h, y)$$

where $0 < \theta < 1$ by the mean value theorem for one variable. It follows that

$$F(x, y) = h[z_x(x + \theta h, y + k) - z_x(x + \theta h, y)]$$
$$= hkz_{yx}(x + \theta h, y + \theta' k)$$

where $0 < \theta' < 1$ by the mean value theorem relating to the one variable y.

Similarly, by interchanging $z(x + h, y)$ and $z(x, y + k)$, we obtain

$$F(x, y) = khz_{xy}(x + \psi h, y + \psi' k),$$

where $0 < \psi < 1$ and $0 < \psi' < 1$. Hence

$$z_{xy}(x + \psi h, y + \psi' k) = z_{yx}(x + \theta h, y + \theta' k).$$

Provided z_{xy} and z_{yx} are continuous at the point (x, y), we may let h and k tend to zero, obtaining

$$z_{xy}(x, y) = z_{yx}(x, y),$$

thereby establishing the equality of these mixed derivatives under these conditions.

Example 1 Find the various partial derivatives of

$$z = x^3 y^5 \sin (x^2 + y^2).$$

We have directly

$$D_x z = 3x^2 y^5 \sin (x^2 + y^2) + 2x^4 y^5 \cos (x^2 + y^2),$$
$$D_{xx} z = 6xy^5 \sin (x^2 + y^2) + 14x^3 y^5 \cos (x^2 + y^2) - 4x^5 y^5 \sin (x^2 + y^2),$$
$$D_{yx} z = 15x^2 y^4 \sin (x^2 + y^2) + 6x^2 y^6 \cos (x^2 + y^2) + 10x^4 y^4 \cos (x^2 + y^2)$$
$$\qquad - 4x^4 y^6 \sin (x^2 + y^2),$$
$$D_y z = 5x^3 y^4 \sin (x^2 + y^2) + 2x^3 y^6 \cos (x^2 + y^2),$$
$$D_{yy} z = 20x^3 y^3 \sin (x^2 + y^2) + 22x^3 y^5 \cos (x^2 + y^2) - 4x^3 y^7 \sin (x^2 + y^2),$$
$$D_{xy} z = 15x^2 y^4 \sin (x^2 + y^2) + 10x^4 y^4 \cos (x^2 + y^2) + 6x^2 y^6 \cos (x^2 + y^2)$$
$$\qquad - 4x^4 y^6 \sin (x^2 + y^2).$$

15.2   The Taylor expansion of a function of two variables

If $z = z(x, y)$ is a given function of two independent variables x and y, we shall consider the increment δz as x varies from X to $X + \delta x$ and y from Y to $Y + \delta y$, namely

$$\delta z = z(X + \delta x, Y + \delta y) - z(X, Y).$$

The object of the expansion is to express this increment in terms of the derivatives of z at the point (X, Y); that is, we require to eliminate the δx and δy from within the functional brackets.

First of all, in the function $z(X + \delta x, Y + \delta y)$, we keep $Y + \delta y$ constant, expanding z as a Taylor series in the one variable x:

$$z(X + \delta x, Y + \delta y) = z(X, Y + \delta y) + \delta x D_x z(X, Y + \delta y)$$
$$+ \tfrac{1}{2}\delta x^2 D_{xx} z(X, Y + \delta y) + \dots$$
$$= (1 + \delta x D_x + \tfrac{1}{2}\delta x^2 D_{xx} + \dots) z(X, Y + \delta y),$$

where the left-hand bracket is an operator containing symbols indicating differentiation of the function standing on its right.

We now expand $z(X, Y + \delta y)$ as a Taylor series in y, with X constant:

$$z(X, Y + \delta y) = z(X, Y) + \delta y D_y z(X, Y) + \tfrac{1}{2}\delta y^2 D_{yy} z(X, Y) + \dots .$$

Hence
$$\delta z = -z(X, Y) + (1 + \delta x D_x + \tfrac{1}{2}\delta x^2 D_{xx} + \dots)$$
$$\times [z(X, Y) + \delta y D_y z(X, Y) + \tfrac{1}{2}\delta y^2 D_{yy} z(X, Y) + \dots] .$$

Carrying out the differentiations indicated, and retaining terms only up to the second order, we obtain

$$\delta z = \delta x D_x z + \delta y D_y z + \tfrac{1}{2}(\delta x^2 D_{xx} z + 2\delta x \delta y D_{xy} z + \delta y^2 D_{yy} z) + \dots .$$

This result may be written as (1)

$$\delta z = \frac{\partial z}{\partial x}\delta x + \frac{\partial z}{\partial y}\delta y + O(\delta x^2) \qquad (2)$$

if the second order terms are not explicitly required, or as

$$\delta z = \frac{\partial z}{\partial x}\delta x + \frac{\partial z}{\partial y}\delta y, \qquad (3)$$

understanding that the second order terms are implicitly included but not explicitly written down. We shall term the act of writing down equation (3) from the defining equation $z = z(x, y)$ the act of "*taking differentials*". We shall call the exact small increments $\delta x, \delta y, \delta z$ *differentials.* Expression (3) is called the *total differential* of the function $z(x, y)$.

Strictly, it is usual to denote the finite small increments δx and δy by dx and dy respectively, and to define the differential dz by the exact relation

$$dz = \frac{\partial z}{\partial x}dx + \frac{\partial z}{\partial y}dy;$$

under these circumstances dz is not the exact increment in the function z. We shall however avoid this notation, using expression (3) to denote the differential in z. Note that there is nothing in these definitions that requires δx, δy, δz or dx, dy, dz to be vanishingly small or infinitesimals. If such were the case, equations (1), (2) and (3) would merely read "$0 = 0$", which is not particularly revealing. We may in fact only take the limit of ratios, not of the differentials themselves.

15.3   Change of variable in first order differential coefficients

Standard case i.   If $z = f(x, y)$ is a given function of x and y, and if there exists a special relation between x and y in the form $y = g(x)$, we may formally regard the variable y as eliminated, yielding z as a function of one variable x alone, namely $z = j(x)$. Find dj/dx in terms of the derivatives of the two given functions.

As for all cases, we take differentials of the given functions:

$$\delta z = \frac{\partial f}{\partial x}\,\delta x + \frac{\partial f}{\partial y}\,\delta y, \qquad \delta y = \frac{dg}{dx}\,\delta x,$$

with second order terms implicitly implied. Eliminating δy, in order to obtain the relation between δx and δz, we obtain

$$\delta z = \frac{\partial f}{\partial x}\,\delta x + \frac{\partial f}{\partial y}\frac{dg}{dx}\,\delta x.$$

Finally,
$$\frac{dj}{dx} = \lim_{\delta x \to 0} \frac{\delta z}{\delta x} = \frac{\partial f}{\partial x} + \frac{\partial f}{\partial y}\frac{dg}{dx},$$

the second order terms (becoming first order upon division by δx) vanishing in the limit.

More usually, this problem and result would be expressed in the following notation. If the function $y = y(x)$ is substituted into the function $z = z(x, y)$, yielding $z = z(x)$, we have the result

$$\frac{dz}{dx} = \frac{\partial z}{\partial x} + \frac{\partial z}{\partial y}\frac{dy}{dx}. \tag{4}$$

The z on the left refers to $z(x)$, while the z on the right refers to $z(x, y)$; no confusion can ever arise if the student decides which are the independent variables in every derivative.

Example 2   If $z = x^2 y^3$, let $y = x^4$, and find dz/dx.
   Direct substitution yields
$$z = x^2(x^4)^3 = x^{14}, \tag{5}$$

yielding $dz/dx = 14x^{13}$. On the other hand, using formula (4), we have

$$\frac{dz}{dx} = \frac{\partial}{\partial x}(x^2 y^3) + \frac{\partial}{\partial y}(x^2 y^3)\frac{d}{dx}(x^4)$$
$$= 2xy^3 + 3x^2 y^2 . 4x^3$$
$$= 2x^{13} + 12x^{13}$$
$$= 14x^{13}$$

as before.

Note: The use of equation (5) implies *substitution before differentiation*, while the use of formula (4) implies *differentiation before substitution*.

Standard case ii. The substitution $x = x(t)$, $y = y(t)$ into the function $z = z(x, y)$ gives z as a function of t alone: $z = z(t)$. Find dz/dt in terms of the derivatives of the given three functions.

Taking differentials of the given functions, we obtain

$$\delta x = \frac{dx}{dt}\,\delta t, \qquad \delta y = \frac{dy}{dt}\,\delta t,$$

and

$$\delta z = \frac{\partial z}{\partial x}\,\delta x + \frac{\partial z}{\partial y}\,\delta y$$

$$= \left(\frac{\partial z}{\partial x}\frac{dx}{dt} + \frac{\partial z}{\partial y}\frac{dy}{dt}\right)\delta t,$$

second order terms being implied. Hence

$$\frac{dz}{dt} = \lim_{\delta t \to 0}\frac{\delta z}{\delta t} = \frac{\partial z}{\partial x}\frac{dx}{dt} + \frac{\partial z}{\partial y}\frac{dy}{dt}. \tag{6}$$

Distinguish carefully between the independent variables in z on the left and in z on the right.

Example 3 If $z = x^3 y^4$, let $x = t^2$, $y = t^3$; find dz/dt.
Directly, we have $z = t^{18}$, so $dz/dt = 18t^{17}$.
Using formula (6), which implies differentiation before substitution, we obtain

$$\frac{dz}{dt} = \frac{\partial}{\partial x}(x^3 y^4)\frac{d}{dt}(t^2) + \frac{\partial}{\partial y}(x^3 y^4)\frac{d}{dt}(t^3)$$

$$= 3x^2 y^4 . 2t + 4x^3 y^3 . 3t^2$$

$$= 6t^4 . t^{12} . t + 12t^6 . t^9 . t^2$$

$$= 18t^{17}.$$

Standard case iii. If $z(x, y) = 0$ is a given function of two variables, regard this equation solved for y in terms of x: $y = y(x)$. Find dy/dx in terms of the derivatives of z.

Such a function y is called an *implicit* function; if the function $z(x, y)$ is too complicated, usually neither y nor x can be solved explicitly in terms of the other, but in spite of this a curve is defined in the Oxy-plane, and its gradient dy/dx is required.

Taking differentials, we have

$$\frac{\partial z}{\partial x}\,\delta x + \frac{\partial z}{\partial y}\,\delta y = 0,$$

yielding

$$\frac{dy}{dx} = \lim_{\delta x \to 0}\frac{\delta y}{\delta x} = -\frac{\partial z/\partial x}{\partial z/\partial y}, \tag{7}$$

the implied higher order terms vanishing in the limit.

Example 4   The equation $x^5 + 2xy + y^5 = 0$ defines y in terms of x, even though an explicit formula cannot be found expressing y in terms of x. We have

$$\frac{dy}{dx} = -\frac{\partial(x^5 + 2xy + y^5)/\partial x}{\partial(x^5 + 2xy + y^5)/\partial y} = -\frac{5x^4 + 2y}{2x + 5y^4},$$

calculated at any particular point on the locus.

In particular, the point $(-1, -1)$ satisfies the equation; at this point the gradient is given by $dy/dx = -(5 - 2)/(5 - 2) = -1$.

Standard case iv.   If z is a function of the single variable u, namely $z = z(u)$, and if $u = u(x, y)$ is a function of the two variables x and y, elimination of u yields z as a function of x and y: $z = z(x, y)$. We require to find $\partial z/\partial x$ and $\partial z/\partial y$ in terms of the derivatives of the given functions.

Taking differentials, we have

$$\delta z = \frac{dz}{du}\,\delta u, \qquad \delta u = \frac{\partial u}{\partial x}\,\delta x + \frac{\partial u}{\partial y}\,\delta y,$$

yielding
$$\delta z = \frac{dz}{du}\frac{\partial u}{\partial x}\,\delta x + \frac{dz}{du}\frac{\partial u}{\partial y}\,\delta y.$$

Now $\partial z/\partial x$ is calculated with y constant, that is with $\delta y = 0$;   hence

$$\frac{\partial z}{\partial x} = \lim_{\substack{\delta x \to 0 \\ \delta y = 0}} \frac{\delta z}{\delta x} = \frac{dz}{du}\frac{\partial u}{\partial x}, \tag{8}$$

and
$$\frac{\partial z}{\partial y} = \lim_{\substack{\delta y \to 0 \\ \delta x = 0}} \frac{\delta z}{\delta y} = \frac{dz}{du}\frac{\partial u}{\partial y}. \tag{9}$$

In such a context, when z is a function of the composite variable u, we usually denote dz/du by z'.

Example 5   If $z = \sin(xy^2 + x^2y)$, we have
$$\partial z/\partial x = \cos(xy^2 + x^2y).(y^2 + 2xy),$$
$$\partial z/\partial y = \cos(xy^2 + x^2y).(2xy + x^2).$$
The act of changing sine to cosine corresponds to differentiating z with respect to u, that is, with respect to $(xy^2 + x^2y)$.

Example 6   If $z = xf(xy)$, where f is an arbitrary function, eliminate f.

Differentiating partially with respect to x and y, and using a prime to denote differentiation with respect to the composite variable xy, we obtain
$$\partial z/\partial x = f + xyf' = z/x + xyf',$$
$$\partial z/\partial y = x^2f'.$$

Eliminating f', we find
$$\frac{\partial z}{\partial x} = \frac{z}{x} + \frac{y}{x}\frac{\partial z}{\partial y},$$

or
$$x\frac{\partial z}{\partial x} - y\frac{\partial z}{\partial y} = z.$$

Standard case v. If the two functions $x = x(u, v)$ and $y = y(u, v)$ are given, we regard these as solved for u and v in terms of x and y. Find $\partial u/\partial x$, $\partial u/\partial y$, $\partial v/\partial x$, $\partial v/\partial y$ in terms of the derivatives of the given functions.

Taking differentials, we obtain

$$\delta x = \frac{\partial x}{\partial u}\,\delta u + \frac{\partial x}{\partial v}\,\delta v, \qquad \delta y = \frac{\partial y}{\partial u}\,\delta u + \frac{\partial y}{\partial v}\,\delta v,$$

yielding

$$\frac{\delta u}{\begin{vmatrix} D_v x & -\delta x \\ D_v y & -\delta y \end{vmatrix}} = \frac{-\delta v}{\begin{vmatrix} D_u x & -\delta x \\ D_u y & -\delta y \end{vmatrix}} = \frac{1}{\begin{vmatrix} D_u x & D_v x \\ D_u y & D_v y \end{vmatrix}}$$

in simpler notation. We define the determinant

$$J = \begin{vmatrix} D_u x & D_v x \\ D_u y & D_v y \end{vmatrix}$$

to be the *Jacobian* of the transformation. Then

$$\frac{\partial u}{\partial x} = \lim_{\substack{\delta x \to 0 \\ \delta y = 0}} \frac{\delta u}{\delta x} = \frac{\partial y/\partial v}{J},$$

$$\frac{\partial u}{\partial y} = \lim_{\substack{\delta y \to 0 \\ \delta x = 0}} \frac{\delta u}{\delta y} = -\frac{\partial x/\partial v}{J}.$$

Similarly, $\qquad \dfrac{\partial v}{\partial x} = -\dfrac{\partial y/\partial u}{J}, \qquad \dfrac{\partial v}{\partial y} = \dfrac{\partial x/\partial u}{J}.$

Note carefully the independent variables implied in each differentiation, u and v always go in pairs, as do x and y. These formulae need not be memorized; any individual case may be dealt with from first principles.

Example 7 If $x = r\cos\theta$, $y = r\sin\theta$, find $\partial r/\partial x$, $\partial r/\partial y$, $\partial\theta/\partial x$, $\partial\theta/\partial y$.

It is wrong to write $r = x/\cos\theta$, and $\partial r/\partial x = 1/\cos\theta$, since this is calculated with θ constant; but in the problem, it is understood that y should be constant in the derivative $\partial r/\partial x$.

We take differentials of the given equations:

$$\delta x = \delta r\cos\theta - r\sin\theta\,\delta\theta,$$
$$\delta y = \delta r\sin\theta + r\cos\theta\,\delta\theta.$$

Now $\partial r/\partial x$ implies that $\delta y = 0$, so $\delta\theta = -\delta r\tan\theta/r$ from the second equation.

The first equation then yields

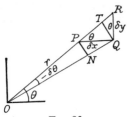

FIG. 83

$$\delta x = \delta r \cos \theta + \delta r \sin \theta \tan \theta = \delta r / \cos \theta.$$

Finally,
$$\frac{\partial r}{\partial x} = \lim_{\substack{\delta x \to 0 \\ \delta y = 0}} \frac{\delta r}{\delta x} = \cos \theta.$$

Similarly,

$$\frac{\partial r}{\partial y} = \sin \theta, \quad \frac{\partial \theta}{\partial x} = -\frac{\sin \theta}{r}, \quad \frac{\partial \theta}{\partial y} = \frac{\cos \theta}{r}. \quad (10)$$

The values of these derivatives may be deduced from the diagram in Fig. 83:

$$\left(\frac{\partial r}{\partial x}\right)_y = \frac{NQ}{PQ} = \cos \theta, \qquad (P \to Q \text{ with } y \text{ constant}),$$

$$\left(\frac{\partial r}{\partial y}\right)_x = \frac{TR}{QR} = \sin \theta, \qquad (Q \to R \text{ with } x \text{ constant}),$$

$$\left(\frac{\partial \theta}{\partial x}\right)_y = \frac{PN/r}{PQ} = -\frac{\sin \theta}{r}, \quad (P \to Q \text{ with } y \text{ constant}),$$

$$\left(\frac{\partial \theta}{\partial y}\right)_x = \frac{TQ/r}{RQ} = \frac{\cos \theta}{r}, \qquad (Q \to R \text{ with } x \text{ constant}),$$

where the signs of the elements must be carefully interpreted.

Standard case vi. If in the given function $z = z(x, y)$, we substitute $x = x(u, v)$ and $y = y(u, v)$, obtaining $z = z(u, v)$ as a function of u and v, it is required to find the partial derivatives of z with respect to u and v in terms of those with respect to x and y.

Taking differentials of the three given equations, we obtain

$$\delta z = \frac{\partial z}{\partial x} \delta x + \frac{\partial z}{\partial y} \delta y, \quad \delta x = \frac{\partial x}{\partial u} \delta u + \frac{\partial x}{\partial v} \delta v, \quad \delta y = \frac{\partial y}{\partial u} \delta u + \frac{\partial y}{\partial v} \delta v,$$

yielding upon elimination of δx and δy

$$\delta z = \frac{\partial z}{\partial x}\left(\frac{\partial x}{\partial u} \delta u + \frac{\partial x}{\partial v} \delta v\right) + \frac{\partial z}{\partial y}\left(\frac{\partial y}{\partial u} \delta u + \frac{\partial y}{\partial v} \delta v\right).$$

Hence
$$\frac{\partial z}{\partial u} = \lim_{\substack{\delta u \to 0 \\ \delta v = 0}} \frac{\delta z}{\delta u} = \frac{\partial z}{\partial x}\frac{\partial x}{\partial u} + \frac{\partial z}{\partial y}\frac{\partial y}{\partial u}, \quad (11)$$

and
$$\frac{\partial z}{\partial v} = \lim_{\substack{\delta v \to 0 \\ \delta u = 0}} \frac{\delta z}{\delta v} = \frac{\partial z}{\partial x}\frac{\partial x}{\partial v} + \frac{\partial z}{\partial y}\frac{\partial y}{\partial v}. \quad (12)$$

In all the cases *i, ii, iv, vi*, in which substitutions are made in the function *z*, the following general rule embracing all cases should be thoroughly grasped.

To differentiate with respect to p any function z which is expressed only in terms of the variables u, v, w, . . . each however functionally containing p, we differentiate z in turn with respect to ALL its variables u, v, w, . . . , completing each differentiation by the chain rule by a final differentiation with respect to p; that is

$$\frac{\partial z}{\partial p} = \frac{\partial z}{\partial u}\frac{\partial u}{\partial p} + \frac{\partial z}{\partial v}\frac{\partial v}{\partial p} + \frac{\partial z}{\partial w}\frac{\partial w}{\partial p} + \dots,$$

using d's instead of ∂'s if functions of a single variable arise.

Example 8 If $x = r \cos \theta$, $y = r \sin \theta$, prove that

$$\left(\frac{\partial z}{\partial x}\right)^2 + \left(\frac{\partial z}{\partial y}\right)^2 = \left(\frac{\partial z}{\partial r}\right)^2 + \frac{1}{r^2}\left(\frac{\partial z}{\partial \theta}\right)^2,$$

where *z* is any function of *x* and *y*, and hence of *r* and *θ*.

Right hand side to the left hand side. We have

$$\frac{\partial z}{\partial r} = \frac{\partial z}{\partial x}\frac{\partial x}{\partial r} + \frac{\partial z}{\partial y}\frac{\partial y}{\partial r} = \frac{\partial z}{\partial x}\cos \theta + \frac{\partial z}{\partial y}\sin \theta,$$

$$\frac{\partial z}{\partial \theta} = \frac{\partial z}{\partial x}\frac{\partial x}{\partial \theta} + \frac{\partial z}{\partial y}\frac{\partial y}{\partial \theta} = -\frac{\partial z}{\partial x}r \sin \theta + \frac{\partial z}{\partial y}r \cos \theta.$$

Dividing the second equation by *r*, and squaring and adding the two equations, we obtain the required result.

Left hand side to the right hand side. We have

$$\frac{\partial z}{\partial x} = \frac{\partial z}{\partial r}\frac{\partial r}{\partial x} + \frac{\partial z}{\partial \theta}\frac{\partial \theta}{\partial x} = \frac{\partial z}{\partial r}\cos \theta - \frac{\partial z}{\partial \theta}\frac{\sin \theta}{r}$$

using the previously calculated derivatives in example 7. Also

$$\frac{\partial z}{\partial y} = \frac{\partial z}{\partial r}\frac{\partial r}{\partial x} + \frac{\partial z}{\partial \theta}\frac{\partial \theta}{\partial y} = \frac{\partial z}{\partial r}\sin \theta + \frac{\partial z}{\partial \theta}\frac{\cos \theta}{r}.$$

Squaring and adding these two equations, we obtain the required result.

Example 9 If $z = z(v - w, w - u, u - v)$, show that

$$\frac{\partial z}{\partial u} + \frac{\partial z}{\partial v} + \frac{\partial z}{\partial w} = 0.$$

Whenever functions occur within functions, introduce temporary symbols representing them. Let $p = v - w, q = w - u, r = u - v$. Then

$$\frac{\partial z}{\partial u} = \frac{\partial z}{\partial p}\frac{\partial p}{\partial u} + \frac{\partial z}{\partial q}\frac{\partial q}{\partial u} + \frac{\partial z}{\partial r}\frac{\partial r}{\partial u}$$

$$= -\frac{\partial z}{\partial q} + \frac{\partial z}{\partial r};$$

similarly,
$$\frac{\partial z}{\partial v} = \frac{\partial z}{\partial p} \qquad -\frac{\partial z}{\partial r},$$

$$\frac{\partial z}{\partial w} = -\frac{\partial z}{\partial p} + \frac{\partial z}{\partial q}.$$

Addition yields the required result.

Euler's theorem on homogeneous functions. A function $z = z(x, y)$ of two or more variables x and y is said to be *homogeneous* of degree n if the act of replacing x by xt and y by yt merely multiplies the function by t^n. That is, if

$$z(xt, yt) = t^n z(x, y). \tag{13}$$

Examples of such functions are $x^3 + 4x^2y + 5y^3$ (of degree 3), $x^{-2} \sin(x/y)$ (of degree -2), $(x + y)(x^3 - 4y^3)^{-1}f(x/y)$ (of degree -2). We shall prove the result

$$x\frac{\partial z}{\partial x} + y\frac{\partial z}{\partial y} = nz. \tag{14}$$

Let $u = xt$, $v = yt$. We now differentiate equation (13) with respect to t, where the z on the left is a function of u and v, each being a function of t. We obtain

$$\frac{\partial z}{\partial u}\frac{\partial u}{\partial t} + \frac{\partial z}{\partial v}\frac{\partial v}{\partial t} = \frac{\partial}{\partial t}[t^n z(x, y)]$$

or

$$\frac{\partial z}{\partial u}x + \frac{\partial z}{\partial v}y = nt^{n-1}z(x, y).$$

Finally, placing $t = 1$, in which case $u = x$ and $v = y$, we obtain the required result (14).

In abbreviated notation, this result is

$$xD_x z + yD_y z = nz.$$

Differentiation in turn with respect to x and y yields

$$xD_{xx}z + D_x z + yD_{xy}z = nD_x z,$$
$$xD_{yx}z + yD_{yy}z + D_y z = nD_y z.$$

Multiplying the first of these equations by x and the second by y and adding, we obtain

$$x^2 D_{xx}z + 2xy D_{xy}z + y^2 D_{yy}z = (n - 1)(xD_x z + yD_y z)$$
$$= n(n - 1)z \tag{15}$$

from equation (14). This implies that homogeneous functions of degree s and of degree $1 - s$ both yield the same coefficient when substituted into equation (15).

Non-standard cases. Any substitution or transformation distinct from those given above should be regarded as non-standard; they should therefore be treated from first principles by taking differentials.

Example 10 If $u = f(u, v, w)$, $v = g(u, v, w)$, regard v as eliminated and w expressed as a function of u alone. Find dw/du.

Taking differentials of the two given functions, we obtain

$$\delta u = f_u\,\delta u + f_v\,\delta v + f_w\,\delta w,$$
$$\delta v = g_u\,\delta u + g_v\,\delta v + g_w\,\delta w.$$

Eliminating the unwanted differential δv, we have

$$\delta u = f_u\,\delta u + f_w\,\delta w + f_v\,(g_u\,\delta u + g_w\,\delta w)/(1 - g_v).$$

Hence
$$\frac{dw}{du} = \lim_{\delta u \to 0} \frac{\delta w}{\delta u} = \frac{1 - f_u - f_v g_u/(1 - g_v)}{f_w + f_v g_w/(1 - g_v)}.$$

Example 11 If $x^2 = y^2 + f(x^2 + z^2)$, where f is an arbitrary function, prove that

$$yz\,\frac{\partial y}{\partial x}\frac{\partial z}{\partial x} + xy\,\frac{\partial y}{\partial x} - xz\,\frac{\partial z}{\partial x} = 0.$$

Taking differentials, we obtain

$$2x\,\delta x = 2y\,\delta y + f'(x^2 + z^2).(2x\,\delta x + 2z\,\delta z).$$

Now the derivative $\partial y/\partial x$ implies that y is expressed as a function of x and z; hence

$$\frac{\partial y}{\partial x} = \lim_{\substack{\delta x \to 0 \\ \delta z = 0}} \frac{\delta y}{\delta x} = \frac{x - xf'}{y} = \frac{x}{y} - \frac{xf'}{y},$$

and
$$\frac{\partial z}{\partial x} = \lim_{\substack{\delta x \to 0 \\ \delta y = 0}} \frac{\delta z}{\delta x} = \frac{x - xf'}{zf'} = \frac{x}{zf'} - \frac{x}{z}.$$

Eliminating f', we obtain

$$\left(1 - \frac{y}{x}\frac{\partial y}{\partial x}\right)\left(1 + \frac{z}{x}\frac{\partial z}{\partial x}\right) = \frac{f'}{f'} = 1$$

yielding, upon multiplication, the required answer.

15.4 Change of variable in second order differential coefficients

We shall now calculate the second differential coefficients for the cases studied in the previous section. We merely use the rule stated in italics at the end of case vi.

Case i. If $z = z(x, y)$ and $y = y(x)$, then

$$\frac{dz}{dx} = \frac{\partial z}{\partial x} + \frac{\partial z}{\partial y}\frac{dy}{dx}, \tag{16}$$

and
$$\frac{d^2z}{dx^2} = \frac{d}{dx}\left(\frac{\partial z}{\partial x}\right) + \frac{d}{dx}\left(\frac{\partial z}{\partial y}\right)\frac{dy}{dx} + \frac{\partial z}{\partial y}\frac{d^2y}{dx^2}.$$

Note that dy/dx, being a function of x alone, can be differentiated directly to d^2y/dx^2. But $\partial z/\partial x$ and $\partial z/\partial y$ are both functions of x and y; they must therefore be differentiated with respect to both x and y:

$$\frac{d}{dx}\left(\frac{\partial z}{\partial x}\right) = \frac{\partial}{\partial x}\left(\frac{\partial z}{\partial x}\right)\frac{dx}{dx} + \frac{\partial}{\partial y}\left(\frac{\partial z}{\partial x}\right)\frac{dy}{dx}$$

$$= \frac{\partial^2 z}{\partial x^2} + \frac{\partial^2 z}{\partial y\,\partial x}\frac{dy}{dx},$$

a result obtained by replacing z in equation (16) by $\partial z/\partial x$. Similarly

$$\frac{d}{dx}\left(\frac{\partial z}{\partial y}\right) = \frac{\partial^2 z}{\partial x\,\partial y} + \frac{\partial^2 z}{\partial y^2}\frac{dy}{dx}.$$

Hence, finally

$$\frac{d^2 z}{dx^2} = \frac{\partial^2 z}{\partial x^2} + 2\frac{\partial^2 z}{\partial x\,\partial y}\frac{dy}{dx} + \frac{\partial^2 z}{\partial y^2}\left(\frac{dy}{dx}\right)^2 + \frac{\partial z}{\partial y}\frac{d^2 y}{dx^2}.$$

Case ii. If $z = z(x, y)$ and $x = x(t)$, $y = y(t)$, then

$$\frac{dz}{dt} = \frac{\partial z}{\partial x}\frac{dx}{dt} + \frac{\partial z}{\partial y}\frac{dy}{dt}, \qquad (17)$$

and $\qquad \dfrac{d^2 z}{dt^2} = \dfrac{d}{dt}\left(\dfrac{\partial z}{\partial x}\right)\dfrac{dx}{dt} + \dfrac{\partial z}{\partial x}\dfrac{d^2 x}{dt^2} + \dfrac{d}{dt}\left(\dfrac{\partial z}{\partial y}\right)\dfrac{dy}{dt} + \dfrac{\partial z}{\partial y}\dfrac{d^2 y}{dt^2}.$

Note that, dx/dt and dy/dt, being functions of t alone, can be differentiated directly with respect to t. But $\partial z/\partial x$ and $\partial z/\partial y$ are functions of x and y; they must therefore be differentiated with respect to *both* x and y, each differentiation being completed with respect to t by the chain rule:

$$\frac{d}{dt}\left(\frac{\partial z}{\partial x}\right) = \frac{\partial^2 z}{\partial x^2}\frac{dx}{dt} + \frac{\partial^2 z}{\partial y\,\partial x}\frac{dy}{dt},$$

a result obtained by replacing z in equation (17) by $\partial z/\partial x$. Also,

$$\frac{d}{dt}\left(\frac{\partial z}{\partial y}\right) = \frac{\partial^2 z}{\partial x\,\partial y}\frac{dx}{dt} + \frac{\partial^2 z}{\partial y^2}\frac{dy}{dt}.$$

Substitution finally yields

$$\frac{d^2 z}{dt^2} = \frac{\partial^2 z}{\partial x^2}\left(\frac{dx}{dt}\right)^2 + 2\frac{\partial^2 z}{\partial x\,\partial y}\frac{dx}{dt}\frac{dy}{dt} + \frac{\partial^2 z}{\partial y^2}\left(\frac{dy}{dt}\right)^2 + \frac{\partial z}{\partial x}\frac{d^2 x}{dt^2} + \frac{\partial z}{\partial y}\frac{d^2 y}{dt^2}.$$

Case iii. If $z(x, y) = 0$, we have seen that

$$\frac{dy}{dx} = -\frac{\partial z/\partial x}{\partial z/\partial y}.$$

This is a function of x and y; to differentiate it with respect to x, we use equation (16), obtaining

$$\frac{d^2y}{dx^2} = \frac{\partial}{\partial x}\left(-\frac{\partial f/\partial x}{\partial f/\partial y}\right) + \frac{\partial}{\partial y}\left(-\frac{\partial f/\partial x}{\partial f/\partial y}\right)\frac{dy}{dx}$$

$$= -\frac{f_{xx}f_y - f_x f_{xy}}{f_y^{\,2}} + \frac{f_{yx}f_y - f_x f_{yy}}{f_y^{\,2}} \cdot \frac{f_x}{f_y}$$

$$= -\frac{f_{xx}f_y^{\,2} - 2f_{xy}f_x f_y + f_{yy}f_x^{\,2}}{f_y^{\,3}}.$$

Case iv.   If $z = z(u)$ and $u = u(x, y)$, then

$$\frac{\partial z}{\partial x} = \frac{dz}{du}\frac{\partial u}{\partial x};\qquad\qquad(18)$$

hence

$$\frac{\partial^2 z}{\partial x^2} = \frac{\partial}{\partial x}\left(\frac{dz}{du}\right)\frac{\partial u}{\partial x} + \frac{dz}{du}\frac{\partial^2 u}{\partial x^2}$$

$$= \frac{d^2 z}{du^2}\left(\frac{\partial u}{\partial x}\right)^2 + \frac{dz}{du}\frac{\partial^2 u}{\partial x^2}$$

where $\partial(dz/du)/\partial x$ is found by substituting dz/du for z in equation (18). Similarly, $\partial^2 z/\partial y^2$ may be found.

Case v. If $x = x(u, v)$, $y = y(u, v)$, we have, for example,

$$\frac{\partial u}{\partial x} = \frac{\partial y/\partial v}{J},$$

where this is a function of u and v. Hence, differentiating this right hand side with respect to u and v, we obtain

$$\frac{\partial^2 u}{\partial x^2} = \frac{\partial}{\partial u}\left(\frac{\partial y/\partial v}{J}\right)\frac{\partial u}{\partial x} + \frac{\partial}{\partial v}\left(\frac{\partial y/\partial v}{J}\right)\frac{\partial v}{\partial x}$$

$$= \frac{\partial}{\partial u}\left(\frac{\partial y/\partial v}{J}\right)\frac{\partial y/\partial v}{J} - \frac{\partial}{\partial v}\left(\frac{\partial y/\partial v}{J}\right)\frac{\partial y/\partial u}{J}.$$

These derivatives may easily be evaluated for given functions. The remaining derivatives may be treated likewise.

Case vi. If $z = z(x, y)$ and $x = x(u, v)$, $y = y(u, v)$, then

$$\frac{\partial z}{\partial u} = \frac{\partial z}{\partial x}\frac{\partial x}{\partial u} + \frac{\partial z}{\partial y}\frac{\partial y}{\partial u}.$$

Sometimes it is convenient to use the identity of the operators

$$\frac{\partial}{\partial u} = \frac{\partial x}{\partial u}\frac{\partial}{\partial x} + \frac{\partial y}{\partial u}\frac{\partial}{\partial y},$$

where the operator on the left *must* act on a function of u and v, and the operator on the right *must* act on the same function expressed in terms of x and y. Hence

$$\frac{\partial^2 z}{\partial u^2} = \frac{\partial}{\partial u}\left(\frac{\partial z}{\partial u}\right) = \left(\frac{\partial x}{\partial u}\frac{\partial}{\partial x} + \frac{\partial y}{\partial u}\frac{\partial}{\partial y}\right)\left(\frac{\partial z}{\partial x}\frac{\partial x}{\partial u} + \frac{\partial z}{\partial y}\frac{\partial y}{\partial u}\right).$$

But this expression on the right is rather inconsistent, since the operators $\partial/\partial x$ and $\partial/\partial y$ demand that the bracket on which they operate be a function of x and y alone. But $\partial x/\partial u$ and $\partial y/\partial u$ occurring in this bracket are functions of u and v, so the required condition does not really hold. In practice however, the derivatives $\partial x/\partial u$ and $\partial y/\partial u$ may sometimes be expressed explicitly in terms of x and y for simplicity; the operational form for $\partial^2 z/\partial u^2$ may then be used (see example 13 below).

More directly, we have

$$\frac{\partial^2 z}{\partial u^2} = \frac{\partial}{\partial u}\left(\frac{\partial z}{\partial x}\frac{\partial x}{\partial u} + \frac{\partial z}{\partial y}\frac{\partial y}{\partial u}\right).$$

Now $\partial x/\partial u$ and $\partial y/\partial u$, being functions of u and v, may be differentiated directly. But $\partial z/\partial x$ and $\partial z/\partial y$ are functions of x and y; we must differentiate these with respect to x and y, completing the differentiation with respect to u by the chain rule, namely

$$\frac{\partial}{\partial u}\left(\frac{\partial z}{\partial x}\right) = \frac{\partial}{\partial x}\left(\frac{\partial z}{\partial x}\right)\frac{\partial x}{\partial u} + \frac{\partial}{\partial y}\left(\frac{\partial z}{\partial x}\right)\frac{\partial y}{\partial u}.$$

Hence

$$\frac{\partial^2 z}{\partial u^2} = \frac{\partial z}{\partial x}\frac{\partial^2 x}{\partial u^2} + \frac{\partial}{\partial u}\left(\frac{\partial z}{\partial x}\right)\frac{\partial x}{\partial u} + \frac{\partial z}{\partial y}\frac{\partial^2 y}{\partial u^2} + \frac{\partial}{\partial u}\left(\frac{\partial z}{\partial y}\right)\frac{\partial y}{\partial u}$$

$$= z_x x_{uu} + (z_{xx}x_u + z_{yx}y_u)x_u + z_y y_{uu} + (z_{xy}x_u + z_{yy}y_u)y_u$$

$$= z_x x_{uu} + z_y y_{uu} + z_{xx}x_u{}^2 + 2z_{xy}x_u y_u + z_{yy}y_u{}^2.$$

Similarly,

$$z_{vv} = z_x x_{vv} + z_y y_{vv} + z_{xx}x_v{}^2 + 2z_{xy}x_v y_v + z_{yy}y_v{}^2.$$

If, in particular, the given functions $x(u, v)$, $y(u, v)$ satisfy the Riemann-Cauchy conditions:

$$x_u = y_v, \quad x_v = -y_u,$$

implying, the student should note, that

$$x_{uu} + x_{vv} = 0, \quad y_{uu} + y_{vv} = 0, \quad x_u{}^2 + x_v{}^2 = y_u{}^2 + y_v{}^2,$$

we obtain upon addition

$$
\begin{aligned}
z_{uu} + z_{vv} &= z_x(x_{uu} + x_{vv}) + z_y(y_{uu} + y_{vv}) + z_{xx}(x_u{}^2 + x_v{}^2) \\
&\quad + 2z_{xy}(x_u y_u + x_v y_v) + z_{yy}(y_u{}^2 + y_v{}^2) \\
&= (x_u{}^2 + x_v{}^2)(z_{xx} + z_{yy}).
\end{aligned}
$$

Under these circumstances, if $z_{uu} + z_{vv} = 0$, so does $z_{xx} + z_{yy}$.
Finally, the mixed derivative is given by

$$
\begin{aligned}
\frac{\partial^2 z}{\partial v \partial u} &= \frac{\partial}{\partial v}\left(\frac{\partial z}{\partial x}\frac{\partial x}{\partial u} + \frac{\partial z}{\partial y}\frac{\partial y}{\partial u}\right) \\[4pt]
&= \frac{\partial z}{\partial x}\frac{\partial^2 x}{\partial v \partial u} + \frac{\partial}{\partial v}\left(\frac{\partial z}{\partial x}\right)\frac{\partial x}{\partial u} + \frac{\partial z}{\partial y}\frac{\partial^2 y}{\partial v \partial u} + \frac{\partial}{\partial v}\left(\frac{\partial z}{\partial y}\right)\frac{\partial y}{\partial u} \\[4pt]
&= z_x x_{vu} + (z_{xx}x_v + z_{yx}y_v)x_u + z_y y_{vu} + (z_{xy}x_v + z_{yy}y_v)y_u \\[4pt]
&= z_x x_{vu} + z_y y_{vu} + z_{xx}x_v x_u + z_{xy}(x_u y_v + x_v y_u) + z_{yy}y_v y_u.
\end{aligned}
$$

Example 12 If $z = xf(xy^2) + yg(x^2y)$, where f and g are arbitrary functions, eliminate f and g by showing that

$$2x^2 z_{xx} - 5xy z_{xy} + 2y^2 z_{yy} + 4xz_x + 4yz_y - 4z = 0.$$

Method. To eliminate two arbitrary functions, each a function of some composite variable of x and y, occurring in a function z, we form $z_x, z_y, z_{xx}, z_{xy}, z_{yy}$. Together with z, these provide six equations in f, g, f', g', f'', g'', where a prime denotes differentiation with respect to the relevant composite variable. Then either (a) a judicious examination of these six equations shows how to eliminate f, g, f', g', f'', g'' yielding a relation between z and its derivatives alone, or (b) direct substitution of the values of $z_x, z_y, z_{xx}, z_{xy}, z_{yy}$ into the given answer thereby verifies it. Method (b) is simpler, and is to be recommended particularly in complicated cases.
Differentiating, we obtain

$$z = xf(xy^2) + yg(x^2y), \tag{19}$$

$$z_x = f + xy^2 f' + 2xy^2 g', \tag{20}$$

$$z_y = 2x^2 yf' + g + x^2 yg', \tag{21}$$

$$z_{xx} = 2y^2 f' + xy^4 f'' + 2y^2 g' + 4x^2 y^3 g'', \tag{22}$$

$$z_{xy} = 4xyf' + 2x^2 y^3 f'' + 4xyg' + 2x^3 y^2 g'', \tag{23}$$

$$z_{yy} = 2x^3 f' + 4x^3 y^2 f'' + 2x^2 g' + x^4 yg''. \tag{24}$$

Substitution into the given answer immediately verifies it.

Or we may derive the answer without assuming it. Equation (20) multiplied by x plus equation (21) multiplied by y minus equation (19) (that is, to eliminate f and g), yields

$$xz_x + yz_y - z = 3x^2y^2(f' + g').$$ (25)

Equation (22) multiplied by $2x^2$ plus equation (24) multiplied by $2y^2$ minus equation (23) multiplied by $5xy$ (that is, to eliminate f'' and g'') yields

$$2x^2z_{xx} - 5xyz_{xy} + 2y^2z_{yy} = -12x^2y^2(f' + g')$$
$$= -4(xz_x + yz_y - z)$$

from equation (25).

Example 13 If $z = z(x, y)$ is transformed to $z = z(r, \theta)$ by the substitutions $x = r\cos\theta$, $y = r\sin\theta$, prove that

$$\frac{\partial^2 z}{\partial x^2} + \frac{\partial^2 z}{\partial y^2} = \frac{\partial^2 z}{\partial r^2} + \frac{1}{r}\frac{\partial z}{\partial r} + \frac{1}{r^2}\frac{\partial^2 z}{\partial \theta^2}.$$

From the right hand side to the left hand side. We have

$$z_r = z_x x_r + z_y y_r = z_x \cos\theta + z_y \sin\theta.$$

When we differentiate a second time with respect to r, we note that z_x and z_y, being functions of x and y, must first be differentiated with respect to both x and y:

$$z_{rr} = (z_{xx}x_r + z_{yx}y_r)\cos\theta + (z_{xy}x_r + z_{yy}y_r)\sin\theta$$
$$= (z_{xx}\cos\theta + z_{yx}\sin\theta)\cos\theta + (z_{xy}\cos\theta + z_{yy}\sin\theta)\sin\theta$$
$$= z_{xx}\cos^2\theta + 2z_{xy}\sin\theta\cos\theta + z_{yy}\sin^2\theta.$$

Similarly, $$z_\theta = z_x x_\theta + z_y y_\theta = -r\sin\theta z_x + r\cos\theta z_y.$$

When we differentiate again with respect to θ, we may differentiate the $\sin\theta$ and $\cos\theta$ directly, but z_x and z_y being functions of x and y must be differentiated with respect to x and y, each differentiation being completed with respect to θ by the chain rule:

$$z_{\theta\theta} = -r\cos\theta z_x - r\sin\theta z_y - r\sin\theta(z_{xx}x_\theta + z_{yx}y_\theta) + r\cos\theta(z_{xy}x_\theta + z_{yy}y_\theta)$$
$$= -r\cos\theta z_x - r\sin\theta z_y - r\sin\theta(-r\sin\theta z_{xx} + r\cos\theta z_{yx})$$
$$\quad + r\cos\theta(-r\sin\theta z_{xy} + r\cos\theta z_{yy})$$
$$= -r\cos\theta z_x - r\sin\theta z_y + r^2\sin^2\theta z_{xx} - 2r^2\sin\theta\cos\theta z_{xy} + r^2\cos^2\theta z_{yy}.$$

If, now, we form $z_{rr} + z_r/r + z_{\theta\theta}/r^2$, the result follows immediately.

From the left hand side to the right hand side. We will now require the derivatives $\partial r/\partial x$, $\partial r/\partial y$, $\partial\theta/\partial x$, $\partial\theta/\partial y$, with x or y respectively constant. A preliminary calculation is necessary to find these values. However, we may quote example 7:

$$\partial r/\partial x = \cos\theta, \quad \partial r/\partial y = \sin\theta, \quad \partial\theta/\partial x = -\sin\theta/r, \quad \partial\theta/\partial y = \cos\theta/r.$$

It should be noticed that these are in terms of r and θ, and not in terms of x and y. The operator method may therefore be used.

We have $$z_x = z_r r_x + z_\theta \theta_x = \cos\theta z_r - r^{-1}\sin\theta z_\theta,$$

yielding the operator $$D_x \equiv \cos\theta D_r - r^{-1}\sin\theta D_\theta.$$

Hence

$$z_{xx} = D_x(z_x) = (\cos\theta D_r - r^{-1}\sin\theta D_\theta)(\cos\theta z_x - r^{-1}\sin\theta z_\theta)$$
$$= \cos^2\theta z_{rr} - 2r^{-1}\sin\theta\cos\theta z_{r\theta} + r^{-2}\sin^2\theta z_{\theta\theta}$$
$$+ 2r^{-2}\sin\theta\cos\theta z_\theta + r^{-1}\sin^2\theta z_r$$

upon differentiating and collecting up terms.

Similarly,

$$z_{yy} = D_y(z_y) = (\sin\theta D_r + r^{-1}\cos\theta D_\theta)(\sin\theta z_r + r^{-1}\cos\theta z_\theta)$$
$$= \sin^2\theta z_{rr} + 2r^{-1}\sin\theta\cos\theta z_{r\theta} + r^{-2}\cos^2\theta z_{\theta\theta} - 2r^{-2}\sin\theta\cos\theta z_\theta$$
$$+ r^{-1}\cos^2\theta z_r$$

upon differentiating and collecting up terms.

Addition of these two equations yields the required result

Example 14 If the function $f(x, y, t)$ satisfies the equation $f_{xx} - f_{yt} = 0$, prove that the function $g(x, y, t) = t^{-\frac{1}{2}}f(u, v, w)$, where $u = x/t$, $v = y - x^2/4t$, $w = -1/t$, satisfies the same equation, namely $g_{xx} - g_{yt} = 0$.

Since $f(x, y, t)$ satisfies $f_{xx} - f_{yt} = 0$, we note that $f(u, v, w)$ satisfies $f_{uu} - f_{vw} = 0$. We now differentiate the function g thus:

$$g_x = t^{-\frac{1}{2}}(f_u u_x + f_v v_x + f_w w_x)$$
$$= t^{-\frac{1}{2}}(f_u/t - f_v x/2t),$$
$$g_{xx} = t^{-\frac{1}{2}}(f_{uu}u_x + f_{vu}v_x + f_{wu}w_x) - \tfrac{1}{2}t^{-\frac{3}{2}}f_v$$
$$- \tfrac{1}{2}xt^{-\frac{3}{2}}(f_{uv}u_x + f_{vv}v_x + f_{wv}v_x)$$
$$= t^{-\frac{3}{2}}(f_{uu}/t - f_{vu}x/2t) - \tfrac{1}{2}t^{-\frac{3}{2}}f_v - \tfrac{1}{2}xt^{-\frac{3}{2}}(f_{uv}/t - f_{vv}x/2t)$$
$$= t^{-\frac{5}{2}}f_{uu} - xt^{-\frac{5}{2}}f_{vu} - \tfrac{1}{2}t^{-\frac{3}{2}}f_v + \tfrac{1}{4}x^2t^{-\frac{5}{2}}f_{vv}.$$

Also

$$g_y = t^{-\frac{1}{2}}(f_u u_y + f_v v_y + f_w w_y)$$
$$= t^{-\frac{1}{2}}f_v,$$
$$g_{ty} = -\tfrac{1}{2}t^{-\frac{3}{2}}f_v + t^{-\frac{1}{2}}(f_{uv}u_t + f_{vv}v_t + f_{wv}w_t)$$
$$= -\tfrac{1}{2}t^{-\frac{3}{2}}f_v + t^{-\frac{1}{2}}(-f_{uv}x/t^2 + f_{vv}x^2/4t^2 + f_{wv}/t^2)$$
$$= -\tfrac{1}{2}t^{-\frac{3}{2}}f_v - xt^{-\frac{5}{2}}f_{uv} + \tfrac{1}{4}x^2t^{-\frac{5}{2}}f_{vv} + t^{-\frac{5}{2}}f_{wv}.$$

We now subtract these two derivatives, obtaining

$$g_{xx} - g_{ty} = t^{-\frac{5}{2}}(f_{uu} - f_{wv})$$
$$= 0$$

on account of the given equation satisfied by $f(u, v, w)$.

15.5 Small errors

If a function of several variables is given, namely $z = z(x, y, \ldots)$, the value of the function at $x = X$, $y = Y, \ldots$ is given by $z = z(X, Y, \ldots)$. If these values $X, Y, \ldots$ are obtained experimentally, small errors will usually occur; let the measured values be $X + \delta x$, $Y + \delta y, \ldots$. The exact error in z is then given by

$$z(X + \delta x, Y + \delta y, \ldots) - z(X, Y, \ldots).$$

However, we usually need only consider the first order terms in the Taylor expansion of this difference, namely

$$\text{error} = \delta z = \frac{\partial z}{\partial x}\,\delta x + \frac{\partial z}{\partial y}\,\delta y + \dots,$$

approximately, provided the second order terms are relatively negligible. On account of the linear relation existing between the independent errors δx, δy, ..., we speak of this result as the *principle of superposition of small errors*.

Sometimes the error in any variable may be expressed as a *percentage error*. If the error in x is $p\%$, then $\delta x = pX/100$. If the error is given as a *proportional* or *relative error* p, this implies that $\delta x = pX$. If the error in an angle y is given as k degrees, then $\delta y = k\pi/180$ measured in radians.

If z is a product of various functions, it may be convenient to differentiate logarithmically to obtain the first order error terms.

If δx lies in the restricted range $|\delta x| \leqslant \alpha$, and if δy lies in the range $|\delta y| \leqslant \beta$, etc., then the largest error in z is evidently

$$\max \delta z = \left|\frac{\partial z}{\partial x}\right|\alpha + \left|\frac{\partial z}{\partial y}\right|\beta + \dots,$$

this being either an increase or a decrease from the correct value. If the error δz is found by logarithmic differentiation, care is necessary, for various terms in, say, δx may arise:

$$\delta z = f(X,\ Y, \dots)\delta x + g(X,\ Y, \dots)\delta x + \dots.$$

The maximum error is *not* given by

$$\max \delta z = |f(X,\ Y, \dots)|\,\alpha + |g(X,\ Y, \dots)|\,\alpha + \dots,$$

rather we should write

$$\max \delta z = |f(X,\ Y, \dots) + g(X,\ Y, \dots)|\,\alpha + \dots.$$

In other words, the combined coefficients of δx, δy, ... must be formed before the modulus is taken. The method of taking the modulus should be carefully studied in the example below.

Example 15   The side b of a triangle ABC is calculated from a, B, C. If the maximum proportional error in a is p and the maximum magnitude of the error in either or both of B and C is α, find the magnitude of the maximum error in b.

In triangle ABC, we have from the sine formula

$$b = a \sin B/\sin A = a \sin B/\sin (B + C)$$

in terms of a, B, C. The use of logarithms simplifies the taking of differentials thus:

$$\log b = \log a + \log \sin B - \log \sin (B + C),$$

yielding

$$\frac{\delta b}{b} = \frac{\delta a}{a} + \frac{\cos B\, \delta B}{\sin B} - \frac{\cos (B + C)(\delta B + \delta C)}{\sin (B + C)},$$

so

$$\delta B = \frac{\sin B}{\sin (B + C)} \delta a + \left(\frac{a \cos B}{\sin (B + C)} - \frac{a \sin B \cos (B + C)}{\sin^2 (B + C)} \right) \delta B$$

$$- \frac{a \sin B \cos (B + C)}{\sin^2 (B + C)} \delta C$$

$$= \frac{\sin B}{\sin (B + C)} \delta a + \frac{a \sin C}{\sin^2 (B + C)} \delta B - \frac{a \sin B \cos (B + C)}{\sin^2 (B + C)} \delta C$$

upon simplification.

The maximum error in a is pa, since p is a proportional error.

Case i. If $B + C < \frac{1}{2}\pi$, $\cos (B + C) > 0$, so

$$\max \delta b = \frac{\sin B}{\sin (B + C)} ap + \frac{a \sin C}{\sin^2 (B + C)} \alpha + \frac{a \sin B \cos (B + C)}{\sin^2 (B + C)} \alpha$$

where we have taken the modulus of the last term by changing the minus sign to a plus sign. Simplification yields

$$\max \delta b = \frac{b}{a} ap + \left(\frac{a}{\sin A} \cdot \frac{c}{a} - a \cot A \frac{b}{a} \right) \alpha,$$

using $\cos (B + C) = -\cos A$. Hence

$$\max \delta b = pb + \frac{b}{\sin B} \cdot \frac{c - b \cos A}{a} \alpha = b(p + \alpha \cot B).$$

Case ii. If $B + C > \frac{1}{2}\pi$, $\cos (B + C) < 0$; hence

$$\max \delta b = \frac{\sin B}{\sin (B + C)} pa + \left(\frac{a \sin C}{\sin^2 (B + C)} - \frac{a \sin B \cos (B + C)}{\sin^2 (B + C)} \right) \alpha$$

where the last term together with its minus sign is now positive. Then

$$\max \delta b = pb + \frac{\alpha a}{\sin A} \cdot \frac{c + b \cos A}{a} = pb + \alpha(c \csc A + b \cot A).$$

15.6 Stationary values

In section 15.2, we have seen that the value of the function $z(x, y)$ in the neighbourhood of the point (X, Y) is given by

$$z(X + \delta x, Y + \delta y) = z(X, Y) + (\delta x z_x + \delta y z_y)$$
$$+ \tfrac{1}{2}(\delta x^2 z_{xx} + 2\delta x\, \delta y z_{xy} + \delta y^2 z_{yy})$$

to the second order, where all derivatives are calculated at (X, Y).

The point (X, Y) is said to be a *stationary point* if

$$\partial z/\partial x = \partial z/\partial y = 0$$

there; that is, if the first order increment vanishes for all small δx and δy. The expression $(\delta x^2 z_{xx} + 2\delta x\, \delta y z_{xy} + \delta y^2 z_{yy})$ then determines the main shape of the function in the neighbourhood of (X, Y).

If this bracket is positive for *all* small $\delta x, \delta y$, then z is a *minumum* at (X, Y).

If this bracket is negative for *all* small $\delta x, \delta y$, then z is a *maximum* at (X, Y), while if this bracket is neither positive nor negative definite, (X, Y) is called a *saddle-point*.

Using the results of section 4.3, sufficient conditions are

$$z_{xx} > 0, \quad z_{xx}z_{yy} - z_{xy}^2 > 0 \quad \text{for a minimum,}$$
$$z_{xx} < 0, \quad z_{xx}z_{yy} - z_{xy}^2 > 0 \quad \text{for a maximum,}$$
$$z_{xx}z_{yy} - z_{xy}^2 < 0 \quad \text{for a saddle-point.}$$

If the point (X, Y) yields a saddle-point, there are points near (X, Y) at which even the second order increments vanish. These are given by the lines through (X, Y) whose gradients dy/dx are specified by

$$\left(\frac{dy}{dx}\right)^2 z_{yy} + 2 \frac{dy}{dx} z_{xy} + z_{xx} = 0,$$

an equation possessing two real solutions if $z_{xx}z_{yy} - z_{xy}^2 < 0$, that is, only at a saddle-point. Such lines are called the *level lines* through (X, Y). In particular, if $z_{xx} + z_{yy} = 0$, these two lines are perpendicular, since the product of their gradients then equals -1. As the point (x, y) encircles the saddle-point, the difference $z(x, y) - z(X, Y)$ is first positive, then negative, positive, negative, as the level lines are crossed in turn.

The conditions just given for stationary values are not *necessary* conditions. If the tests are inconclusive, expansions of the function to higher powers of δx and δy are then necessary. This however is often a laborious calculation and should be avoided if the expansion, say, at the origin can be seen by inspection.

The theory for functions expressed in terms of three independent variables may similarly be examined, using the conditions for a positive definite quadratic form in three variables given in section 4.3.

Example 16   Find the stationary values of $z = x^3 + y^3 + 9(x^2 + y^2) + 12xy$.
Differentiating, we have

$$z_x = 3x^2 + 18x + 12y \propto x^2 + 6x + 4y,$$
$$z_y = 3y^2 + 18y + 12x \propto y^2 + 6y + 4x,$$
$$z_{xx} = 6x + 18 \propto x + 3,$$
$$z_{xy} = 12 \qquad \propto 2$$
$$z_{yy} = 6y + 18 \propto y + 3,$$

where any *common positive* factor may be dropped from the three second derivatives.

The stationary points are given by

$$x^2 + 6x + 4y = 0, \quad y^2 + 6y + 4x = 0.$$

Considerable ingenuity is sometimes needed to solve equations of this character. In this case, we may subtract, obtaining

$$(x - y)(x + y + 2) = 0,$$

so either $x = y$ or $y = -x - 2$.

When $x = y$, each equation becomes $x^2 + 10x = 0$; it follows that $(0, 0)$ and $(-10, -10)$ are stationary points.

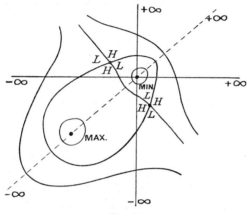

FIG. 84

When $y = -x - 2$, we have

$$x^2 + 6x + 4(-x - 2) = 0 \quad \text{or} \quad x^2 + 2x - 8 = 0,$$

with solutions $x = -4, 2$; two further stationary points are therefore $(-4, 2)$ $(2, -4)$.

We may now draw up the following table:

Point	z_{xx}	z_{yy}	z_{xy}	$z_{xx}z_{yy} - z_{xy}^2$	character
		proportional to			
$(0, 0)$	3	3	2	$5 > 0$	minimum
$(-10, -10)$	-7	-7	2	$45 > 0$	maximum
$(-4, 2)$	-1	5	2	$-9 < 0$	saddle-point
$(2, 4)$	5	-1	2	$-9 < 0$	saddle-point

Through the saddle-point $(-4, 2)$, the gradients y' of the level lines are given by

$$5y'^2 + 4y' - 1 = 0,$$

possessing the solutions $y' = -1, \frac{1}{5}$. Through the point $(2, -4)$, the level lines similarly are given by $y' = -1, 5$.

At these four stationary points, $z = 0, 1000, 28, 28$ respectively.

Fig. 84 provides a contour map of the function z, showing approximately how the four stationary points fit into the surface. Around the two saddle-points, L and H denote low and high respectively.

15.7   Envelopes

A *family* of curves in the Oxy-plane is specified by an equation of the form $f(x, y, \alpha) = 0$, where α is a parameter. Any permitted value of this parameter yields a member-curve of this family.

If a curve C exists that touches every member of this family, then C is known as the *envelope* of the family.

In section 14.10, we have seen that the evolute of a curve touches the normals of a curve at the centres of curvature. This implies that the envelope of the normals to a curve is the evolute of the curve.

Consider two nearby members of the family given by

$$f(x, y, \alpha) = 0, \quad f(x, y, \alpha + \delta\alpha) = 0.$$

To the first order, the equation of the second curve may be expressed in the form

$$f(x, y, \alpha) + \delta\alpha\, \partial f(x, y, \alpha)/\partial\alpha = 0,$$

or $\qquad\qquad\qquad \partial f(x, y, \alpha)/\partial\alpha = 0$

since $f(x, y, \alpha) = 0$. These two equations $f = \partial f/\partial\alpha = 0$ provide two simultaneous equations for the limiting point of intersection of these two nearby curves. If α is eliminated, we obtain the equation of the locus of the point of intersection of nearby curves. This locus is, in fact, the envelope.

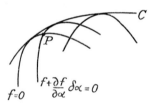

The fact that the curve $f(x, y, \alpha) = 0$ touches this locus at the limiting point P can be seen by evaluating the gradient at

Fig. 85

P to both curves. For the curve $f(x, y, \alpha) = 0$, we have

$$dy/dx = -f_x/f_y,$$

quoting case iii, section 15.3. For the locus of P, taking differentials of both $f = 0, f_\alpha = 0$, we have

$$f_x\, \delta x + f_y\, \delta y + f_\alpha\, \delta\alpha = 0,$$
$$f_{x\alpha}\, \delta x + f_{y\alpha}\, \delta y + f_{\alpha\alpha}\, \delta\alpha = 0,$$

yielding upon elimination of $\delta\alpha$,

$$\frac{dy}{dx} = \frac{f_{\alpha x}f_\alpha - f_{\alpha\alpha}f_x}{f_{\alpha\alpha}f_y - f_{y\alpha}f_\alpha}.$$

But at the point P, $f_\alpha = 0$, so

$$dy/dx = -f_x/f_y,$$

identical with the gradient of the curve $f(x, y, \alpha) = 0$. Hence the locus of the points P touches the curve at P, so it is, in fact, the envelope of the family.

Example 17 Find the envelope of the ellipse $x^2/a^2 + y^2/b^2 = 1$ if its area is the constant πA.

The area of the ellipse is subject to the condition $\pi ab = \pi A$, so the family of ellipses is given by

$$\frac{x^2}{a^2} + \frac{y^2 a^2}{A^2} = 1$$

where the members of the family are given by the parameter a. We differentiate partially with respect to this parameter, obtaining

$$-\frac{2x^2}{a^3} + \frac{2y^2 a}{A^2} = 0,$$

yielding $a^2 = \pm xA/y$. a is now eliminated:

$$x^2 \cdot \frac{y}{Ax} + \frac{y^2}{A^2} \cdot \frac{Ax}{y} = \pm 1,$$

simplifying to $xy = \pm\frac{1}{2}A$, representing two rectangular hyperbolae.

Example 18 Find the evolute of the parabola $y^2 = 4ax$.

The gradient of the tangent at the point $P(at^2, 2at)$ is $1/t$, so the gradient of the normal at P is $-t$. Its equation is

$$y - 2at = -t(x - at^2)$$

or $$y + t(x - 2a) - at^3 = 0.$$

To find the envelope of this line, we differentiate with respect to t obtaining

$$x - 2a - 3at^2 = 0,$$

or $$t^2 = (x - 2a)/3a.$$

To eliminate t, we replace t^3 by $t^2 . t$ in the equation of the normal, giving

$$y + t(x - 2a) - \frac{1}{3}t(x - 2a) = 0$$

or $$\frac{2}{3}t(x - 2a) = -y.$$

Finally, we square and eliminate t^2:

$$\frac{4}{9}(x - 2a)^3/3a = y^2,$$

or $$4(x - 2a)^3 = 27ay^2,$$

as already found in section 14.10.

15.8 Tangent planes and normals to surfaces

The function of two variables $z = z(x, y)$ may be represented on the Oxy-plane by contour lines drawn in the plane for constant z. More

12

usually, it may be represented in the three dimensional coordinate system $Oxyz$. For each point $P(x, y)$ in the Oxy-plane, the corresponding value of z (provided it is real) may be represented by the ordinate $z = PR$ standing vertically above P. The points R so defined generate a surface in space. This concept is a generalization of the method of representing planes, spheres and quadrics in three dimensions.

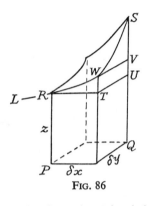

If a tangent line RL is drawn to the surface at R in the plane PRW parallel to the plane Oxz, evidently y is constant, so the gradient of the tangent line RL in this plane is given by $\partial z/\partial x$ calculated at R. Similarly, $\partial z/\partial y$ is the gradient of the tangent line at R drawn in the plane through R parallel to Oyz.

FIG. 86

As the point $P(x, y)$ is moved slightly to $Q(x + \delta x, y + \delta y)$, the ordinate erected from the plane Oxy changes from PR to QS. The increase is given by $\delta z = US$. This increase δz consists of two parts, WT and VS. Evidently,

$$WT = RT \tan \angle WRT \rightleftharpoons \delta x \frac{\partial z}{\partial x},$$

$$VS = WV \tan \angle SWV \rightleftharpoons \delta y \frac{\partial z}{\partial y}.$$

We have therefore the graphical interpretation of the equation

$$\delta z = \frac{\partial z}{\partial x} \delta x + \frac{\partial z}{\partial y} \delta y.$$

More generally, the equation $f(x, y, z) = 0$ defines z as an implicit function of x and y; this equation therefore represents a surface. The *normal* at the point R on the surface is the line perpendicular to RS, where RS denotes *every* small displacement on the surface; the direction ratios of RS may be taken to be $(\delta x, \delta y, \delta z)$. But these are related by the equation

$$\frac{\partial f}{\partial x} \delta x + \frac{\partial f}{\partial y} \delta y + \frac{\partial f}{\partial z} \delta z = 0.$$

Hence the line with direction ratios (f_x, f_y, f_z) calculated at R is perpendicular to every displacement $(\delta x, \delta y, \delta z)$ on the surface, so this line must be the normal at R.

The explicit equation $z(x, y) - z = 0$, when differentiated with respect to x, y, z, yields z_x, z_y, -1 for the direction ratios of the normal.

The equations of the tangent planes at the point (X, Y, Z) on the two surfaces $f(x, y, z) = 0$ and $z = z(x, y)$ are respectively given by

$$(x - X)f_x + (y - Y)f_y + (z - Z)f_z = 0$$

and $$(x - X)z_x + (y - Y)z_y - (z - Z) = 0.$$

Similarly, the equations of the normals to the two surfaces are given by

$$\frac{x - X}{f_x} = \frac{y - Y}{f_y} = \frac{z - Z}{f_z},$$

and $$\frac{x - X}{z_x} = \frac{y - Y}{z_y} = \frac{z - Z}{-1}.$$

Example 19 If the normal at the point $P(1, 1, 1)$ on the surface $3x + 2y^2 + z^3 = 6$ cuts the surface again in points Q and R, find the distance PM, where M is the mid-point of QR.

Generally, the direction ratios of the normal to the surface are given by $(3, 4y, 3z^2)$; at the point P these are $(3, 4, 3)$. The equation of the normal is given by

$$\tfrac{1}{3}(x - 1) = \tfrac{1}{4}(y - 1) = \tfrac{1}{3}(z - 1) = \lambda,$$

say, so this line cuts the surface in the points where

$$3(3\lambda + 1) + 2(4\lambda + 1)^2 + (3\lambda + 1)^3 = 6$$

or $$27\lambda^3 + 59\lambda^2 + 28\lambda = 0.$$

The parameters of Q and R are therefore given by

$$27\lambda^2 + 59\lambda + 28 = 0,$$

so the parameter of M, being the average of those of Q and R, is given by $-\tfrac{59}{54}$.

Finally, $$PM^2 = (3\lambda)^2 + (4\lambda)^2 + (3\lambda)^2$$
$$= 34\lambda^2,$$

yielding $PM = 59(\sqrt{34})/54$.

Example 20 Find the equation of the surface generated by the normals to the surface $x + 2yz + xyz^2 = 0$ at all points on the z-axis.

The direction ratios of the normal at a general point on the surface are given by $(1 + yz^2, 2z + xz^2, 2y + 2xyz)$. At the general point $(0, 0, t)$ on the z-axis, a point which lies on the surface, these ratios are $(1, 2t, 0)$, so the equation of the normal is

$$\frac{x}{1} = \frac{y}{2t} = \frac{z - t}{0}.$$

Eliminating t to find the surface generated by these normals, we obtain

$$y = 2xz.$$

The curvature of a surface.   This may be considered in an elementary way by choosing the origin at the point P on the surface $z = z(x, y)$ at which the curvature is required. Moreover, let the axis Pz be directed along the normal at P. To the second order, the equation of the surface in the neighbourhood of P is

$$\delta z = \tfrac{1}{2}(z_{xx}\delta x^2 + 2z_{xy}\delta x\,\delta y + z_{yy}\,\delta y^2),$$

since $z_x = z_y = 0$ at P because the plane Pxy is the tangent plane at P. More simply, we may write

$$Z = \tfrac{1}{2}(AX^2 + 2HXY + BY^2)$$

where X, Y, Z are small local coordinates near P.

The plane $Z = h$ (h small) cuts the surface just above or just below the tangent plane at P, in the plane curve given by

$$h = \tfrac{1}{2}(AX^2 + 2HXY + BY^2),$$

representing a conic known as the *indicatrix* at P. The point P is called

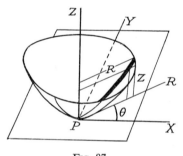

FIG. 87

an *elliptic, hyperbolic* or *parabolic point* according as this conic is an ellipse, hyperbola or parabola. If the conic is a circle, the point P is called an *umbilic*.

Consider the plane curve formed when the surface is cut by the plane $Y = \tan\theta X$ through the normal at P. Its X, Z equation is given by

$$Z = \tfrac{1}{2}(A + 2H\tan\theta + B\tan^2\theta)X^2.$$

If R is the distance measured along the line $Y = \tan\theta X$ in the plane PXY, we note that $R^2 = (1 + \tan^2\theta)X^2$, yielding

$$Z = \tfrac{1}{2}(A\cos^2\theta + 2H\sin\theta\cos\theta + B\sin^2\theta)R^2$$

as the equation of the curve with respect to the axes PR, PZ.

The radius of curvature of this curve is given by Newton's formula:

$$\rho_\theta = \lim (R^2/2Z) = (A\cos^2\theta + 2H\sin\theta\cos\theta + B\sin^2\theta)^{-1},$$

and the curvature by

$$\kappa_\theta = A\cos^2\theta + 2H\sin\theta\cos\theta + B\sin^2\theta.$$

By analogy with the equation of a central conic, we see that maximum and minimum values of κ_θ exist in perpendicular directions. The radii in these directions are called the *principal radii of curvature* at P.

Moreover, we note that

$$\kappa_{\theta+\frac{1}{2}\pi} = A \sin^2 \theta - 2H \cos \theta \sin \theta + B \cos^2 \theta,$$

yielding

$$\kappa_\theta + \kappa_{\theta+\frac{1}{2}\pi} = A + B,$$

a constant independent of θ. The sum of the curvatures in two perpendicular directions at P is therefore a constant, independent of θ.

Example 21 Examine the curvature at the points $(-10, -10, 1000)$ and $(-4, 2, 28)$ on the surface considered in example 16.

At the point $(-10, -10, 1000)$, the local coordinates (X, Y, Z) satisfy the equation

$$Z = \tfrac{1}{2}(-42X^2 + 24XY - 42Y^2),$$

quoting the values of the second derivatives from example 16. This yields

$$\kappa_\theta = -42 \cos^2 \theta + 24 \sin \theta \cos \theta - 42 \sin^2 \theta$$
$$= -42 + 12 \sin 2\theta.$$

This curvature has a maximum value -30 when $\theta = \tfrac{1}{4}\pi$ (or $\tfrac{5}{4}\pi$) and a minimum value -54 when $\theta = \tfrac{3}{4}\pi$ (or $\tfrac{7}{4}\pi$). These are the principal directions at the point, while the principal radii of curvature are $-\tfrac{1}{30}$ and $-\tfrac{1}{54}$.

At the point $(-4, 2, 28)$, we have similarly

$$Z = \tfrac{1}{2}(-6X^2 + 24XY + 30Y^2),$$

giving
$$\kappa_\theta = -6 \cos^2 \theta + 24 \sin \theta \cos \theta + 30 \sin^2 \theta$$
$$= -3(\cos 2\theta + 1) + 12 \sin 2\theta + 15(1 - \cos 2\theta)$$
$$= 12 \sin 2\theta - 18 \cos 2\theta + 12$$
$$= 6\sqrt{13} \sin (2\theta - \phi) + 12,$$

where $\tan \phi = \tfrac{3}{2}$. Hence max $\kappa_\theta = 6\sqrt{13} + 12$ when $\theta = \tfrac{1}{4}\pi + \tfrac{1}{2}\phi$, and min $\kappa_\theta = 12 - 6\sqrt{13}$ when $\theta = \tfrac{3}{4}\pi + \tfrac{1}{2}\phi$. At this point, we obviously have $\kappa_\theta = 0$ along the level lines through the point.

EXERCISES

(1). If $z = 5x^2y^3 - 7x^3y^5$, find $z_x, z_y, z_{xx}, z_{xy}, z_{yy}$.

(2). If $z = (x^2 - y^2)/(x^2 + y^2)$, find z_x, z_y, z_{xy}.

(3)$\star$. If $u = (x^2 + y^2)^{\frac{1}{2}} + x, v = (x^2 + y^2)^{\frac{1}{2}} - x$, write down u_x, v_x, u_y and v_y. Express x and y in terms of u and v and obtain x_u, x_v, y_u and y_v.

(4)$\star$. If $z^3 = (x^2 - xy + y^2) \tan^{-1}(y/x)$, show that $3(xz_x + yz_y) = 2z$.

(5)$\star$. If $z = (x + y)/\sqrt{(x^2 + y^2)}$, find $xz_x + yz_y$.

(6)$\star$. If $u(x, y) = x^2 - y^2$, find a function $v(x, y)$ such that $v_x = -u_y$ and $v_y = u_x$ for all x and y.

(7)$\star$. If $u = xv$, where v is a function of x and t, show that $D_{xx}u = x^{-1}D_x(x^2D_xv)$. Find $D_{xx}u$ when $v = t^n e^{-x^2/t}$.

(8)$\star$. Verify that $z = (k/2vt)\exp(-r^2/4vt)$, where k and v are constants, satisfies the partial differential equation $z_t = v(z_{rr} + r^{-1}z_r)$.

(9)$\star$. Verify that

$$V = \frac{2V_0}{\pi} \tan^{-1} \frac{\sin(\pi x/l)}{\sinh(\pi y/l)}$$

satisfies the differential equation $V_{xx} + V_{yy} = 0$ with the boundary conditions $V = 0$ if $x = 0$ or l, $V = V_0$ if $y = 0$, $V \to 0$ as $y \to \infty$.

(10)$\star$. If $u = 1/r$, where $r^2 = (x - a)^2 + (y - b)^2 + (z - c)^2$, prove that $u_{xx} + u_{yy} + u_{zz} = 0$.

(11)$\star$. If $V = x^n f(Y, Z)$, where $Y = y/x$ and $Z = z/x$, prove that $x V_x + y V_y + z V_z = nV$.

(12)$\star$. If $z^2 = xyF(x^2 - y^2)$, prove that $2xy(xz_y + yz_x) = z(x^2 + y^2)$.

(13)$\star$. If $V = f(xz, y/z)$, prove that $z V_z = x V_x - y V_y$.

(14)$\star$. If V is any function of r and θ, where $r = \sqrt{(x^2 + y^2 + z^2)}$ and $z \tan \theta = \sqrt{(x^2 + y^2)}$, prove that $x V_x + y V_y + z V_z = r V_r$.

(15)$\star$. If $x^2 = pu + qv$; $y^2 = qu - pv$, where p and q are constants, prove that $x_u . u_x = y_v . v_x = p^2/(p^2 + q^2)$, where x and y are functions of u and v, and u and v are functions of x and y.

(16)$\star$. If $z = x + y^2$, $t = x^2 - y$, show that $z_x = -t_y$ and that $x_z = -y_t = 1/(1 + 4xy)$, where z and t are functions of x and y, and x and y are functions of z and t.

(17)$\star$. If $u = x^2 + y^2$, $v = 2xy$, show that $x_u = y_v$.
If $z = f(u, v)$, prove also that $z_u - z_v = (z_x - z_y)/2(x - y)$.

(18)$\star$. If $z = F(x, y)$ is expressed in terms of u and v by the substitutions $u = x^2 - y^2$, $v = 2xy$, prove that $z_x^2 + z_y^2 = 4(x^2 + y^2)(z_u^2 + z_v^2)$.

(19)$\star$. If $z = (1 + x^3 + y^3)^{\frac{1}{3}}$, where the positive value is to be taken, and x, y are connected by the relation $x^2 + y^2 = 1$, show that $dz/dx = 3x(x - y)/2z$. Find the greatest value taken by z as x varies between -1 and $+1$.

(20)$\star$. If x, y, z are connected by the relations $f(x, y, z) = 0$, $x^2 + y^2 + z^2 = $ constant, prove that $dy/dx = -(zf_x - xf_z)/(zf_y - yf_z)$.

(21)$\star$. If $x^3 + y^3 + z^3 - 3xyz = a^3$, find the value of $\partial y/\partial x$.

(22)$\star$. If $u = \frac{1}{2} \log(x^2 + y^2)$ and $v = \tan^{-1}(y/x)$, prove that
   (i) $xu_v = 1$, where u is a function of x and v,
   (ii) $xz_x + yz_y = z_u$, where $z = f(u, v) = g(x, y)$.

(23)$\star$. Three variables x, y, z are related by the equation $f(x, y, z) = 0$, so that any one variable can be regarded as a function of the other two. Express x_y, y_z, z_x in terms of the partial derivatives f_x, f_y, f_z and prove that $x_y . y_z . z_x = -1$.

(24)$\star$. If u and v are two functions of x and y, and if u and v are not independent but connected by some relation $v = F(u)$, show that $u_x v_y - u_y v_x = 0$. Show that this equation is satisfied when $u = (x + y)/x$ and $v = (x + y)/y$, and find the expression for v in terms of u alone.

(25)$\star$. If z is a function of x and y and $y = ux$, prove that

$$\left(\frac{\partial z}{\partial x}\right)_y = \left(\frac{\partial z}{\partial x}\right)_u - \frac{u}{x}\left(\frac{\partial z}{\partial u}\right)_x .$$

(26)$\star$. The rate of increase of internal energy with volume, at constant temperature of a gas is

$$T\left(\frac{\partial p}{\partial T}\right)_v - p .$$

Evaluate this for a gas obeying Van der Waal's equation

$$(p + a/v^2)(v - b) = RT,$$

where a, b and R are constants, and deduce that as the volume increases from v_1 to v_2, the internal energy increases by $a(v_2 - v_1)/v_1 v_2$.

(27)*. Assuming that for a certain substance $dE = t\,d\phi - p\,dv$, where E is the internal energy, t the temperature, ϕ the entropy, p the pressure, and v the specific volume, and E is a function of v, ϕ only, prove that

$$\left(\frac{\partial t}{\partial v}\right)_\phi = -\left(\frac{\partial p}{\partial \phi}\right)_v.$$

(28)*. If p, v, t are such that each is a function of the other two, prove that

$$\left(\frac{\partial p}{\partial t}\right)_v = 1 \Big/ \left(\frac{\partial t}{\partial p}\right)_v.$$

(28)*. The state of a gas is specified by two independent variables and for an ideal gas the equation of state connecting the variables p, v and T is $pv = RT$, where R is a constant. Assuming the thermodynamic relation $T\,ds = dE + p\,dv$, where S and E are functions of these variables, prove that the internal energy E is a function of T only.

(29)*. Prove that $V = \log r$, where $r^2 = x^2 + y^2$, is a solution of the equation $V_{xx} + V_{yy} = 0$.

(30)*. If $V = r^{-1}f(ct - r) + r^{-1}g(ct + r)$, where f and g are arbitrary functions, show that $V_{tt} = c^2(V_{rr} + 2r^{-1}V_r)$.

(31)*. If $U = f(x^2 + y^2 + z^2)$, prove that

$$U_{xx} + U_{yy} + U_{zz} = 4(x^2 + y^2 + z^2)f'' + 6f'.$$

(32)*. If $z = x^n f(y/x)$, where $f(u)$ is an arbitrary function of u, prove that $xz_x + yz_y = nz$ and $x^2 z_{xx} + 2xyz_{xy} + y^2 z_{yy} = n(n-1)z$.
If $v = ze^{ax+by}$, with z as above, prove that $xv_x + yv_y = (ax + by + n)v$.

(33)*. Prove that the equation $x^2 z_{xx} + 2xyz_{xy} + y^2 z_{yy} + xz_x + yz_y = z$ is satisfied by $z = xf(y/x) + y^{-1}g(y/x)$, where f and g are arbitrary functions.

(34)*. If $z = f(x + y)g(x - y)$, where f and g are arbitrary functions, prove that $zz_{xx} - zz_{yy} = z_x^2 - z_y^2$.

(35)*. If V is a homogeneous function of x, y, z of degree n, show that $xV_x + yV_y + zV_z = nV$. If V also satisfies $V_{xx} + V_{yy} + V_{zz} = 0$, and $r^2 = x^2 + y^2 + z^2$, show that $U = r^{-2n-1}V$ satisfies the latter equation.

(36)*. If $V = x \log(x + r) - r$, where $r^2 = x^2 + y^2$, prove that

$$V_{xx} + V_{yy} = 1/(x + r).$$

(37)*. If $V(x, y)$ satisfies the equations $V_{xx} + V_{yy} = 0$, $xV_x + yV_y = mV$, show that $(D_{xx} + D_{yy})(V/r^n) = n(n - 2m)V/r^{n+2}$, where $r^2 = x^2 + y^2$.

(38)*. If $z = f(xy) + F(x/y)$, prove that $x^2 z_{xx} + xz_x = y^2 z_{yy} + yz_y$ and evaluate z_{xy}.

(39)*. If $z = xf(x + y) + yF(x + y)$, prove that $z_{xx} + z_{yy} = 2z_{xy}$.

(40)*. Find the possible values of n if the function $U = xr^n$ satisfies the equation $U_{xx} + U_{yy} = 0$, where $r^2 = x^2 + y^2$.
For each value of n obtain the function V which is such that $V_y = U_x$, $V_x = -U_y$, and V is zero on the x-axis.

(41)*. If $u = x^n[f(y + x) + g(y - x)]$, where f and g are arbitrary functions, prove that $u_{xx} - u_{yy} - 2nx^{-1}u_x + n(n + 1)x^{-2}u = 0$.

(42)*. If $f(z) = y/x$, prove that $z_x + f(z)z_y = 0$ and that
$$z_y{}^2 z_{xx} + z_x{}^2 z_{yy} = 2z_x.z_y.z_{xy}.$$

(43)*. If $z = f(x, y)$ and $x = \frac{1}{2}(u^2 - v^2)$, $y = uv$, show that

(i) $uz_v - vz_u = 2(xz_y - yz_x)$,   (ii) $z_{uu} + z_{vv} = (u^2 + v^2)(z_{xx} + z_{yy})$.

(44)*. If $z = f(u, v)$, where $u = xy$, $v = x + y$, show that
$$z_{xx} + z_{yy} = (v^2 - 2u)z_{uu} + 2vz_{uv} + 2z_{vv}.$$

(45)*. If $u = ax + by$, $v = bx - ay$, prove that

(i) $\left(\dfrac{\partial u}{\partial x}\right)_y \left(\dfrac{\partial x}{\partial u}\right)_v = \dfrac{a^2}{a^2 + b^2}$,   (ii) $\left(\dfrac{\partial y}{\partial v}\right)_x \left(\dfrac{\partial v}{\partial y}\right)_u = \dfrac{a^2 + b^2}{a^2}$,

(iii) $w_{xy} = ab(w_{uu} - w_{vv}) + (b^2 - a^2)w_{uv}$, where $w = f(x, y) = g(u, v)$.

(46)*. If z is a function of x and y, where $x = e^u \cos v$, $y = e^u \sin v$, express z_u and z_v in terms of z_x and z_y, and prove that
$$z_{uu} + z_{vv} = e^{2u}(z_{xx} + z_{yy}).$$

(47)*. The independent variables x, y are given in terms of the independent variables u, v by $x = \cosh u \cos v$, $y = \sinh u \sin v$. If z is a function of x and y, prove that

(i) $z_u{}^2 + z_v{}^2 = (\cosh^2 u - \cos^2 v)(z_x{}^2 + z_y{}^2)$,

(ii) $z_{uu} + z_{vv} = (\cosh^2 u - \cos^2 v)(z_{xx} + z_{yy})$.

(48)*. If $V = f(u, v) = g(x, y)$ where $u = x^2 + y^2$, $v = 2xy$, prove that

(i) $xV_x - yV_y = 2(u^2 - v^2)^{\frac{1}{2}}V_u$,

(ii) $V_{xx} - V_{yy} = 4(u^2 - v^2)^{\frac{1}{2}}(V_{uu} - V_{vv})$.

(49)*. Variables x, y are given in terms of new variables t, u by the equations $x = e^t$, $y = ue^{-t}$. If $y = f(x)$, prove that

(i) $x^2 \dfrac{dy}{dx} = \dfrac{du}{dt} - u$,   (ii) $x^3 \dfrac{d^2y}{dx^2} = \dfrac{d^2u}{dt^2} - 3\dfrac{du}{dt} + 2u$.

(50)*. Independent variables x, y are given in terms of independent variables r, θ by the equations $x = \cos \theta - r \sin \theta$, $y = \sin \theta + r \cos \theta$. Prove that
$$\theta_x = -\cos \theta/r, \; r_x = x/r, \; \theta_{xx} = \cos \theta(\cos \theta - 2r \sin \theta)/r^3.$$

(51)*. If z is a function of u and v where $u = \frac{1}{2}(x^2 - y^2)$, $v = xy$, prove that

(i) $z_{xx} - z_{yy} = 2u(z_{uu} - z_{vv}) + 4vz_{uv} + 2z_u$,

(ii) if $z = uf(u)$, then $z_{xy} = f + 2u(df/du) - v^2(d^2f/du^2)$.

(52)*. If $x = uv$ and $y = u/v$ and f is a function of x and y, prove that
$$f_x = \tfrac{1}{2}v^{-1}f_u + \tfrac{1}{2}u^{-1}f_v, \quad f_y = \tfrac{1}{2}vf_u - \tfrac{1}{2}v^2u^{-1}f_v,$$
and deduce that
$$f_{xy} = \tfrac{1}{4}(f_{uu} + u^{-1}f_u - vu^{-2}f_v - v^2u^{-2}f_{vv}).$$

(53)*. The independent variables x, y are transformed into new variables X, Y given by the equations $X = xy$, $Y = 1/y$. If a function $f(x, y)$ is thus transformed into $F(X, Y)$, prove that

(i) $yf_y(xf_x - yf_y) = YF_Y(XF_X - YF_Y)$,

(ii) $y(xf_{xy} - yf_{yy} - f_y) = Y(XF_{XY} - YF_{YY} - F_Y)$.

(54)⋆. The concentration c of a solute, at time t and distance x from a chosen origin, satisfies the equation $c_t = kc_{xx}$ where k is constant. Assuming that c can be of the form $f(u)$, where $u = x/t^{\frac{1}{2}}$, show that

$$2kf''(u) + uf'(u) = 0.$$

Deduce that $f(u) = A\int \exp(-u^2/4k)\, du + B$, where A and B are constants.

(55)⋆. For the transformation $x = \rho \cos w$, $y = \rho \sin w$, and $\rho = a \cosh u \cos v$, $z = a \sinh u \sin v$, applied to the function

$$F(x, y, z) = \phi(\rho, w, z) = \psi(u, v, w),$$

(i) express $F_{xx} + F_{yy}$ in terms of $\phi_{\rho\rho}$, ϕ_{ww} and ϕ_ρ,

(ii) show that the equation $F_{xx} + F_{yy} + F_{zz} = 0$ transforms into

$$\psi_{uu} + \psi_{vv} + \tanh u\, \psi_u - \tan v\, \psi_v + \frac{\sinh^2 u + \sin^2 v}{\cosh^2 u \cos^2 v}\, \psi_{ww} = 0.$$

Hence find a solution of this equation which is a function of u only.

Small errors.

(56)⋆. If $u = xe^y + ye^x$, prove that $u_{xx} + u_{yy} = u$.

If the value of x is slightly changed from 0 to δx, and that of y from 0 to δy, prove that the change δu in the value of u is approximately $\delta x + \delta y$. Find the corresponding value of δu if the value of x is changed from 1 to $1 + \delta x$ and that of y from 1 to $1 + \delta y$.

(57)⋆. If $f(x, y) = xe^{xy}$, and the values of x and y are slightly changed from 1 and 0 to $1 + \delta x$ and δy respectively so that δf, the change in f, is very nearly $3\delta x$, show that δy must be very nearly $2\delta x$.

(58)⋆. If $z = \sin \theta \sin \phi/\sin \psi$ and z is calculated for the values $\theta = 30°$, $\psi = 60°$, $\phi = 45°$, find approximately the change in the value of z if each of the angles θ and ψ is increased by the same small angle $\alpha°$ and ϕ is decreased by $\frac{1}{2}\alpha°$.

(59)⋆. The surface area of a cone, including the base, is calculated from measurements of r, the radius of the base, and V, the volume. If $r = 2$ feet and $V = 12$ cubic feet, what is the surface area? If an error of $\frac{1}{4}$ inch is made in the measurement of r, find the error in the calculated area.

(60)⋆. Show that the volume of a segment of a sphere is $\frac{1}{6}\pi h(h^2 + 3R^2)$, where h is the height of the segment and R is the radius of the base.

If the measurement of h is too large by a small amount α, and that of R is too small by an equal amount, show that the calculated volume is too large by an amount $\frac{1}{2}\pi\alpha(h - R)^2$ approximately. If the segment is a hemisphere, show that the error in the calculated volume is $\frac{2}{3}\pi\alpha^3$ exactly.

(61)⋆. The side BC of a triangle ABC is to be determined from measurements of the sides AB and AC and of the angle BAC. The measured values of the sides are liable to a small proportional error θ and the angle BAC to a small absolute error δA. Show that the calculated value of BC is liable to a proportional error

$$\theta + (bc/a^2) \sin A\, \delta A.$$

The measured values of b, c and A are 4, 5 and 120° respectively and are liable to errors of $\frac{1}{2}\%$, $\frac{1}{2}\%$ and 1° respectively. Show that the calculated value of a is liable to an error of approximately 1%.

(62)⋆. The points A and B, at a distance a apart on a horizontal plane, are in line with the base C of a vertical tower and on the same side of C. The elevations of the top of the tower from A and B are observed to be α and β ($\alpha < \beta$). Show that the distance BC is $a \sin \alpha \cos \beta \operatorname{cosec} (\beta - \alpha)$.

If the observations of the angles of elevation are uncertain by 4 minutes, show that the maximum possible percentage error in the calculated value of BC is approximately $\pi \sin (\alpha + \beta)/[27 \sin \alpha \cos \beta \tan (\beta - \alpha)]$.

(63)*. C is the mid-point of an arc ACB of a circle. The radius of the circle is estimated from the measurements of the lengths x and y of the chords AB, AC respectively. If there is the same actual small error $+\alpha$ in each of the measurements of x and y, find the corresponding error in the calculated value of the radius and verify that, when the arc subtends an angle 120° at the centre, this error in the radius is $-(2 - \sqrt{3})\alpha$.

Stationary values.

(64)*. Show that the function $z = 2x - y - \frac{1}{2}x^2 + x^3/y$ is stationary at $x = -1$, $y = -1$ and at another pair of values. Find the nature of the function at the point $(-1, -1)$.

(65)*. Find the stationary points of the function $x^4 + y^4 - 2x^2 + 2y^2$ and determine the nature of these points. Sketch the contour in which the surface $z = x^4 + y^4 - 2x^2 + 2y^2$ is cut by the plane $z = 0$.

(66)*. Write down an expression for the square of the distance from the point $A(0, 1, 0)$ to the point $P(u^2 + v^2, u^2 - v^2, 2uv)$ on the surface of the cone $x^2 = y^2 + z^2$. Hence find the values of u and v for which the distance AP is a minimum.

(67)*. If $z = 3x^2y^2 + 6xy^2 - 4y^3 + 18y$, find the stationary points of this function. Show that one of these points is a saddle-point and investigate the nature of the other.

(68)*. Show that the function $z = x^4 + y^4 - 4a^2xy$ has a saddle-point at the origin. Show also that z has two additional stationary points, and determine their nature.

(69)*. Show that the surface $z = 2x^3 - (x - y)^2 - 6y$ has two stationary ordinates z, of which one is a maximum and the other is neither a maximum nor a minimum. Sketch the sections of this surface made by planes containing the second of these ordinates and drawn parallel to the coordinate planes $x = 0$, $y = 0$.

(70)*. Show that the function $z = e^{-x}(x^2 - 5xy^2 + 4y^4)$ has a maximum value at the point $(2, 0)$ and investigate the behaviour of the function at the origin.

(71)*. If $z = (x^2 + y^2)^2 - 2(x^2 - y^2)$, find the points (x, y) at which z is a maximum or a minimum, and state which it is.

Discuss the behaviour of the function z near the point $(0, 0)$ by changing to polar coordinates (r, θ) and examining the sign of d^2z/dr^2 at that point for different values of θ, or in any other manner.

(72)*. Show that the function $z = (x + 2y + 2)/(x^2 + y^2 + 1)$ has stationary values at the points $(\frac{1}{5}, \frac{2}{5})$, $(-1, -2)$ and determine whether z is a maximum or a minimum at these points.

(73)*. Find the nature of the turning points of the function
$$z = 6x^2 + 8y^3 + 3(2x + y - 1)^2.$$

(74)*. Show that the expression $x^2 + y^2 + 2\lambda xy + x^2y^2$ where λ is a *positive* constant, has a minimum at $x = 0$, $y = 0$ if $\lambda < 1$, and that if $\lambda > 1$ it has a minimum at each of the points $x = -y = \pm\sqrt{(\lambda - 1)}$.

Envelopes.

(75). Find the envelope of the straight line $y = \alpha x + a\alpha^3$.

(76). Show that the envelope (the enveloping parabola) of the projectile paths $y = x \tan \theta - \frac{1}{2}gx^2V^{-2} \sec^2 \theta$ (paths of particles projected from the origin with constant velocity V but at varying angles θ) is the parabola $g^2x^2 = V^4 - 2gV^2y$.

(77). Show that the evolute (envelope of the normals) of the tractrix $x = a(u - \tanh u)$, $y = \operatorname{sech} u$ is a catenary.

(78). P and P' are the points $(at^2, 2at)$ and $(at^2, -2at)$ on the parabola $y^2 = 4ax$. Prove that the envelope of the circles on PP' as diameter is $y^2 = 4a(x + a)$.

(79). Repeat question 78 for the ellipse $x^2/a^2 + y^2/b^2 = 1$, showing that the envelope is $x^2/(a^2 + b^2) + y^2/b^2 = 1$.

(80). Prove that the envelope of the normals of the hyperbola $x = a \cosh \theta$, $y = b \sinh \theta$ is $(ax)^{\frac{2}{3}} - (by)^{\frac{2}{3}} = (a^2 + b^2)^{\frac{2}{3}}$.

Tangent planes and normals to surfaces.

(81)★. Find the equations of the tangent plane and of the normal to the surface $z^3 = axy$ at the point $(at, a/t, a)$.
Show that the line of intersection of the tangent plane with the plane $z = 0$ is a tangent to the hyperbola $4xy = a^2$, $z = 0$. Show also that the normal meets the plane $z = 0$ in a point which lies on the hyperbola
$$9(x - 3y)(3x - y) + 64a^2 = 0 = z.$$

(82)★. Find the equations of the tangent plane and normal to the surface $5z^2 + 4x^2y - 6xz^2 = 3$ at the point $P(1, 1, 1)$. If the normal at the point P meets the surface again at A and B, and if C is the mid-point of AB, show that the length of PC is $(31\sqrt{6})/4$.

(83)★. Find the equations of the two tangent planes to the surface $x^2 + y^3 + z^4 = 108$ which pass through the z-axis, and determine their points of contact. Find the y and z coordinates of all points P on the surface, not in any coordinate plane, such that the normal to the surface at P passes through the origin.

(84)★. Write down the equations of the tangent plane and normal at any point $P(x_1, y_1, z_1)$ of the surface $z(x^2 - y^2) - axy = 0$. Prove that (i) if the tangent plane at P meets the z-axis in Q, then PQ is perpendicular to the z-axis; (ii) the normals at points on the x-axis lie on the surface $xy + az = 0$.

(85)★. Show that the tangent plane at the point $P(\sin \theta, \cos \theta, c)$ to the surface $z^2(x^2 + y^2) = c^2$ meets the plane $z = 0$ in a line which touches the circle $x^2 + y^2 = 4$, $z = 0$.
Show that one of the points where the normal at P meets the surface again lies on the sphere $c^2(x^2 + y^2 + z^2) = 1 + c^6$.

(86)★. Prove that all points on the line given by $x = y$, $z = 0$ lie on the surface $(y - 1)(z - c)^2 - (x - 1)(z + c)^2 = 0$, and that the normals to the surface at these points lie on the surface $(x - y)(x + y - 2) - cz = 0$.

(87)★. Write down the equations of the normal to the surface $z = x^4 + 3x^2y^2 - 2xy^3$ at the point (α, β, γ). If the normal at P is parallel to the plane $x + y = 0$, but not in this plane, prove that P lies in the plane $2x - y = 0$.

(88)★. Write down the equations of the tangent plane and the normal at the point $P(x_0, y_0, z_0)$ of the surface $x^3 + y^3 = axyz + 1$, $(a \neq 0)$.

If the normal at P is parallel to the tangent plane at the point $(0, 1, 3/a)$, prove that P lies either in the plane $x - y = 0$ or in the plane $3(x + y) + az = 0$.

(89) ★. Obtain the equations of the tangent plane and normal at each of the points $(-a, -a, a)$ and $(-a, a, -a)$ on the surface $xyz + x^2(y + z) = a^3$. Prove that the normals intersect and find the equation of their common plane. Show that the tangent planes intersect in the line $x + 3a = 2y = 2z$.

(90) ★. Show that the tangent planes to the surface $x^4 - ay^3 - 2a^3z = 0$ at the points $P(a, -a, a)$ and $Q(a, a, 0)$ are parallel, and find the distance between them. The tangent plane at P intersects the coordinate axes at A, B, C respectively and the tangent plane at Q intersects them at D, E, F respectively. Show that the volume of the tetrahedron $OABC$ is 125 times that of $ODEF$, where O is the origin.

(91) ★. Prove that the tetrahedron formed by the coordinate planes and any tangent plane to the surface $xyz = a^3$ is of constant volume.

(92) ★. Find the equation of the tangent plane and normal to the surface $x^{-1} + y^{-1} + z^{-1} = a^{-1}$ at the point (x_1, y_1, z_1). If P is a point on the intersection of this surface and the plane $z = a$, show that the locus of intersection of the normal at P and the plane $z = 0$ is $(x + y)(x - y)^2 + 8a^3 = 0$.

(93) ★. Find the equation of the tangent plane at the point (p, q, r) on the surface $xyz = a(x^2 - y^2)$. Show that all planes drawn through either of the lines $y + x = 0$, $z = 0$; $y - x = 0$, $z = 0$, touch the surface at some point on these lines.

(94) ★. Write down the equations of the normal to the cubic surface $x^2 + y^2 + xyz\sqrt{2} = 1$ at any point $(\cos\theta, \sin\theta, 0)$ on its circle of intersection with the plane $z = 0$. Show that there are four points P on this circle such that the normals to the surface there are tangential to the surface elsewhere, and find the coordinates of these points P.

(95). Repeat example 21, (p. 347), for the stationary points on the surfaces given in examples 64, 65, 67, 69.

ANSWERS TO EXERCISES

(1). $10xy^3 - 21x^2y^5$, $15x^2y^2 - 35x^3y^4$, $10y^3 - 42xy^5$, $30xy^2 - 105x^2y^4$, $30x^2y - 140x^3y^3$.   (2). $4xy^2/(x^2 + y^2)^2$, $-4x^2y/(x^2 + y^2)^2$, $8xy(x^2 - y^2)/(x^2 + y^2)^3$.

(3). $x(x^2 + y^2)^{-\frac{1}{2}} \pm 1$, $y(x^2 + y^2)^{-\frac{1}{2}}$; $x = \frac{1}{2}(u - v)$, $y = (uv)^{\frac{1}{2}}$; $\frac{1}{2}$, $-\frac{1}{2}$, $\frac{1}{2}(v/u)^{\frac{1}{2}}$, $\frac{1}{2}(u/v)^{\frac{1}{2}}$.   (5). 0.   (6). $2xy$.

(7). $2x(2x^2 - 3t)t^{n-2}\exp(-x^2/t)$.   (19). $\sqrt{2}$.   (21). $(x^2 - yz)/(xz - y^2)$.

(24). $v = u/(u - 1)$.   (26). a/v^2.   (38). $f' + xyf'' - y^{-2}F' - xy^{-3}F''$.

(40). $n = 0, -2$; $V = y, -y/(x^2 + y^2)$.   (55). $A\tan^{-1}(e^x) + B$.

(56). $2e(\delta x + \delta y)$.   (58). $\pi\alpha(4\sqrt{2} - \sqrt{6})/2160$.

(59). Area $= \pi r^2 + r^{-1}\sqrt{(9V^2 + \pi^2r^2)} \rightleftharpoons 22 + 4\pi$ when $r = 2$;
 error $= (4\pi - \frac{1}{11})/48$ sq. ft.   (63). $r = y^2/\sqrt{(4y^2 - x^2)}$,
 $\delta r = \alpha y(4y^2 - 2x^2 + xy)/(4y^2 - x^2)^{\frac{3}{2}}$.   (64). $(-4, -8)$; min.

(65). $(0, 0)$, saddle-point; $(1, 0)$, min.; $(-1, 0)$, min.   (66). $u = \pm 1/\sqrt{2}, v = 0$.

(67). $(-1, 1)$, saddle-point; $(-1, -\frac{3}{2})$, min.   (68). $(a, a), (-a, -a)$, minima.

(69). $(1, -2)$, saddle-point; $(-1, -4)$, max.   (70). Min.

(71). $(1, 0)$, min.; $(-1, 0)$, min.; $(0, 0)$, saddle-point with $\theta = \pm\frac{1}{4}\pi$ as the level lines.

(72). Max., min.   (73). $(\frac{1}{4}, \frac{1}{4})$, min., $(\frac{4}{9}, -\frac{1}{3})$, saddle-point.

(75). $27ay^2 + 4x^3 = 0$.   (81). $x + yt^2 - 3tx + at = 0$;
 $(x - at) = (y - a/t)/t^2 = -(z - a)/3t$.   (82). $x + 2y - z = 2$,

$x - 1 = \frac{1}{2}(y - 1) = 1 - z.$ (83). $(\pm 18, -6, 0)$, $\pm x + 3y = 0$; $y = \frac{2}{3}$, $z = \pm 1/\sqrt{2}$.

(84). $(2z_1x_1 - ay_1)x - (2z_1y_1 + ax_1)y + (x_1^2 - y_1^2)z - ax_1y_1 = 0$;
$(x - x_1)/(2z_1x_1 - ay_1) = -(y - y_1)/(2z_1y_1 + ax_1) = (z - z_1)/(x_1^2 - y_1^2).$

(87). $(x - \alpha)/(4\alpha^3 + 6\alpha\beta^2 - 2\beta^3) = (y - \beta)/(6\alpha^2\beta - 6\alpha\beta^2) = -(z - \gamma).$

(88). $(3x_0^2 - ay_0z_0)x + (3y_0^2 - ax_0z_0) - ax_0y_0z = 3$;
$(x - x_0)/(3x_0^2 - ay_0z_0) = (y - y_0)/(3y_0^2 - ax_0z_0) = -(z - z_0)/ax_0y_0.$

(89). $x - 2z + 3a = 0$; $x + a = -\frac{1}{2}(z - a)$, $y = -a$; $x - 2y + 3a = 0$,
$x + a = -\frac{1}{2}(y - a)$, $z = -a$; $2x + y + z + 2a = 0$. (90). $4a/\sqrt{29}$.

(92). $x/x_1^2 + y/y_1^2 + z/z_1^2 = 1/a$, $x_1^2(x - x_1) = y_1^2(y - y_1) = z_1^2(z - z_1).$

(93). $x(qr - 2ap) + y(pr + 2aq) + zpq = pqr.$

(94). $(x - \cos\theta)/2\cos\theta = (y - \sin\theta)/2\sin\theta = z/\sqrt{2}\sin\theta\cos\theta$;
$\theta = \frac{1}{4}\pi, \frac{3}{4}\pi, \frac{5}{4}\pi, \frac{7}{4}\pi.$

CHAPTER 16

INTEGRATION AND SOME APPLICATIONS

16.1 Definition of an integral

If the differential coefficient of the function $y = F(x)$ is $f(x)$, we define the *definite integral* of $f(x)$ with respect to x from the *lower limit* of integration a to the *upper limit* b to be $F(b) - F(a)$. The function $F(x)$ is said to be the *indefinite integral* of $f(x)$. Integration is thereby regarded as the converse operation to differentiation, and we write

$$\int_a^b f(x)\, dx = F(b) - F(a)$$

and

$$\int f(x)\, dx = F(x).$$

A constant may always be added to an indefinite integral.

Clearly this definition, satisfactory in elementary theory, is very restricted, for it assumes that, given $f(x)$, a function $F(x)$ can be found possessing $f(x)$ as its derivative. Even for very elementary functions $f(x)$, such as $e^{1/x}$, $\sin(x^2)$, etc., no such function $F(x)$ exists. Yet the definite integral of such functions must be defined, but it is clearly not permissible to use the definition just given.

The following definition, by Riemann, may be adopted. To define the definite integral of the function $f(x)$ from $x = a$ to $x = b$, we divide the range $x = a$ to $x = b$ into a large number of strips of varying width; let δx be a typical width. If x' is any value of x within this width δx, we form the product $f(x')\, \delta x$, and then the sum $S = \Sigma f(x')\, \delta x$ for all widths. Finally, let the widths of all strips tend to zero, and we examine the value of S in this process. *If* the limit exists, and *if* the limit has the same value whatever may be the mode of subdivision of the range (a, b), then we define this limiting value to be the numerical value of the definite integral of $f(x)$ from a to b; moreover, this integral is defined to be the *area* under the curve $f(x)$ between the ordinates $x = a$, $x = b$ and the x-axis. A sufficient condition for the existence of this integral is that $f(x)$ should be continuous throughout the range $a \le x \le b$, but this is not a necessary condition.

This definition of the definite integral and the former one are identical in all cases where both definitions are applicable. A variable definite integral may be defined by forming the sum $S = \Sigma f(t')\, \delta t$ throughout the range (a, x); a definite integral that is a function of its upper limit x is thereby defined. To differentiate this with respect to x, the following (by no means rigorous) argument may be used. We consider the similar sum extended over the range a to $x + \delta x$, using the increment δx as the width of the final strip. The derivative of the integral is then given by

$$\lim_{\delta x \to 0} \frac{\lim S[a \text{ to } x + \delta x] - \lim S[a \text{ to } x]}{\delta x}$$

$$= \lim_{\delta x \to 0} \frac{\lim S[x \text{ to } x + \delta x]}{\delta x} \rightleftharpoons \lim_{\delta x \to 0} \frac{f(x')\, \delta x}{\delta x} = f(x)$$

exactly in the limit. We may therefore write

$$\frac{d}{dx} \int_a^x f(t)\, dt = f(x),$$

a result known as the fundamental theorem of the integral calculus.

16.2 Standard forms for integration

In these sections we shall only be concerned with integration as the converse of differentiation. Ultimately, all processes of indefinite integration rearrange the integrand $f(x)$ in order to render possible integration at sight, merely by quoting various elementary standard results. The student should be familiar with as many as possible of the following standard integrals, these being the converse of the various standard differential coefficients.

$\int x^n\, dx = x^{n+1}/(n + 1),\ n \neq -1;\ \int x^{-1}\, dx = \log_e x;\ \int e^x\, dx = e^x;$
$\int \sin x\, dx = -\cos x;\ \int \cos x\, dx = \sin x;\ \int \tan x\, dx = -\log(\cos x);$
$\int \cot x\, dx = \log(\sin x);\ \int \sec x\, dx = \log(\sec x + \tan x);$
$\int \operatorname{cosec} x\, dx = -\log(\operatorname{cosec} x + \cot x);\ \int dx/\sqrt{(1 - x^2)} = \sin^{-1} x;$
$\int dx/(1 + x^2) = \tan^{-1} x;\ \int dx/[x\sqrt{(x^2 - 1)}] = \sec^{-1} x;$
$\int \sec^2 x\, dx = \tan x;\ \int \operatorname{cosec}^2 x\, dx = -\cot x;$
$\int \sec x \tan x\, dx = \sec x;\ \int \operatorname{cosec} x \cot x\, dx = -\operatorname{cosec} x;$
$\int \sinh x\, dx = \cosh x;\ \int \cosh x\, dx = \sinh x;$
$\int \tanh x\, dx = \log(\cosh x);\ \int \coth x\, dx = \log(\sinh x);$
$\int \operatorname{sech} x\, dx = 2 \tan^{-1}(e^x);\ \int \operatorname{cosech} x\, dx = -2 \coth^{-1}(e^x);$
$\int dx/\sqrt{(x^2 + 1)} = \sinh^{-1} x = \log[x + \sqrt{(x^2 + 1)}];$
$\int dx/\sqrt{(x^2 - 1)} = \cosh^{-1} x = \log[x + \sqrt{(x^2 - 1)}];$
$\int dx/(1 - x^2) = \tanh^{-1} x = \tfrac{1}{2}\log[(1 + x)/(1 - x)];$
$\int dx/[x\sqrt{(1 - x^2)}] = \operatorname{sech}^{-1} x;\ \int dx/[x\sqrt{(1 + x^2)}] = \operatorname{cosech}^{-1} x.$

16.3   The use of algebraic and trigonometric identities

Some of the following examples involve standard techniques; others show that much ingenuity is required in special cases. We freely use the converse of "function of a function" occurring in differentiation; that is

$$\int \frac{df(g)}{dg} \cdot \frac{dg(x)}{dx} \, dx = f[g(x)].$$

Example 1   The integral

$$I = \int \frac{4x^5 \, dx}{x^4 - 1},$$

in which the integrand is of the form (polynomial)/(polynomial), should be evaluated by the use of partial fractions, after long division if necessary. We have

$$I = \int \left(4x + \frac{4x}{x^4 - 1} \right) dx$$

$$= \int \left(4x + \frac{1}{x - 1} + \frac{1}{x + 1} - \frac{2x}{x^2 + 1} \right) dx$$

$$= 2x^2 + \log (x - 1) + \log (x + 1) - \log (x^2 + 1)$$

$$= 2x^2 + \log [(x^2 - 1)/(x^2 + 1)].$$

Example 2   In the integral

$$I = \int \frac{4x + 7}{4 + (x + 1)^2} \, dx$$

part of the numerator proportional to the differential coefficient of the denominator is detached:

$$I = \int \frac{(4x + 4) \, dx}{4 + (x + 1)^2} + 3 \int \frac{dx}{4 + (x + 1)^2}$$

$$= 2 \log (x^2 + 2x + 5) + \tfrac{3}{2} \tan^{-1} [\tfrac{1}{2}(x + 1)].$$

Example 3   The following trigonometrical integrals should be noted:

$\int \sin^2 x \, dx = \tfrac{1}{2}\int (1 - \cos 2x) \, dx = \tfrac{1}{2}x - \tfrac{1}{4} \sin 2x.$

$\int \cos^2 x \, dx = \tfrac{1}{2}\int (1 + \cos 2x) \, dx = \tfrac{1}{2}x + \tfrac{1}{4} \sin 2x.$

$\int \sin^3 x \, dx = \int (1 - \cos^2 x) \sin x \, dx = -\cos x + \tfrac{1}{3} \cos^3 x.$

$\int \sin^4 x \, dx = \int (1 - \cos^2 x) \sin^2 x \, dx = \int (\sin^2 x - \tfrac{1}{4} \sin^2 2x) \, dx$

$\qquad = \tfrac{1}{2}x - \tfrac{1}{4} \sin 2x - \tfrac{1}{8}\int (1 - \cos 4x) \, dx$

$\qquad = \tfrac{3}{8}x - \tfrac{1}{4} \sin 2x + \tfrac{1}{32} \sin 4x.$

Example 4

$$\int \frac{d\theta}{1 + \sin \theta} = \int \frac{d\theta}{\sin^2 \tfrac{1}{2}\theta + \cos^2 \tfrac{1}{2}\theta + 2 \sin \tfrac{1}{2}\theta \cos \tfrac{1}{2}\theta}$$

$$= \int \frac{\sec^2 \tfrac{1}{2}\theta \, d\theta}{(1 + \tan \tfrac{1}{2}\theta)^2} = -\frac{2}{1 + \tan \tfrac{1}{2}\theta}.$$

Example 5

(i) $\int \dfrac{d\theta}{a \cos \theta + b \sin \theta} = (a^2 + b^2)^{-\frac{1}{2}} \int \dfrac{d\theta}{\sin \alpha \cos \theta + \cos \alpha \sin \theta} \left(\tan \alpha = \dfrac{a}{b} \right)$

$$= (a^2 + b^2)^{-\frac{1}{2}} \int \operatorname{cosec} (\alpha + \theta) \, d\theta$$

$$= -(a^2 + b^2)^{-\frac{1}{2}} \log \left[\operatorname{cosec} (\alpha + \theta) + \cot (\alpha + \theta) \right].$$

(ii) $\int \dfrac{d\theta}{(a \cos \theta + b \sin \theta)^2} = (a^2 + b^2)^{-1} \int \operatorname{cosec}^2 (\alpha + \theta) \, d\theta$

$$= -(a^2 + b^2)^{-1} \cot (\alpha + \theta).$$

Example 6 (This is one of the standard forms quoted in section 16.2).

$$\int \operatorname{sech} x \, dx = \int \dfrac{2 \, dx}{e^x + e^{-x}} = \int \dfrac{2e^x \, dx}{1 + (e^x)^2} = 2 \tan^{-1} (e^x).$$

Example 7

$$\int \dfrac{e^{2x} \, dx}{e^x - 1} = \int \dfrac{(e^{2x} - e^x + e^x) \, dx}{e^x - 1} = \int \left(e^x + \dfrac{e^x}{e^x - 1} \right) dx = e^x + \log (e^x - 1).$$

Example 8 Evaluate $I = \int (\sec^2 x + 2x \tan x) e^{x^2} \, dx$.

Integrals of this character often arise in the solution of first order linear differential equations; the integrand consists of an exponential function multiplied by an un-related (in the real sense) function, perhaps algebraic, perhaps trigonometric. Such integrals, which may be evaluated by using the method of integration by parts, can also be evaluated by inspection. In the final answer, the exponential function must still occur, since neither integration nor differentiation can remove it. The integral I must therefore be of the form $F(x)e^{x^2}$, where $F(x)$ is a function to be found. The derivative of this must be the integrand, so

$$[F'(x) + 2xF(x)]e^x \equiv (\sec^2 x + 2x \tan x)e^{x^2},$$

or $\qquad\qquad F'(x) + 2xF(x) \equiv \sec^2 x + 2x \tan x.$

Inspection yields $F(x) = \tan x$, yielding $I = \tan x \, e^{x^2}$.

16.4 Integration by change of variable

The equation $dF(x)/dx = f(x)$ implies the relation $F(x) = \int f(x) \, dx$, where, up to now, we have given no reason why the symbol dx should be attached to the integrand $f(x)$.

Let us now place $x = x(u)$, giving $F(x)$ as a function of u, namely $F[x(u)]$. Then

$$\dfrac{dF[x(u)]}{du} = \dfrac{dF(x)}{dx} \cdot \dfrac{dx}{du} = f(x) \dfrac{dx}{du} = f[x(u)] \dfrac{dx}{du},$$

by the chain rule. Integration yields

$$F[x(u)] = \int f[x(u)] \dfrac{dx}{du} \, du.$$

This formula shows that we have merely replaced, as it were, the symbol dx in the original integral by the symbol $(dx/du)\,du$. In the language of differentials, we have replaced the differential dx by its equivalent form $(dx/du)\,du$, but we must guard against thinking that the dx occurring in an integrand is a differential; it is merely a matter of convenient notation.

This method often changes the character of the integrand completely, reducing it to a standard integral.

Care is necessary when evaluating definite integrals by this method. If we require to calculate

$$\int_a^b f(x)dx = F(b) - F(a),$$

the limits of the new integral must be changed in order that they may refer to the new variable of integration u. If $u = c$ when $x = a$ and $u = d$ when $x = b$, we have

$$\int_c^d f[u(x)]\frac{dx}{du}\,du = \left[F[x(u)]\right]_c^d$$
$$= F[x(d)] - F[x(c)]$$
$$= F(b) - F(a).$$

In order to find c and d when a and b are given, the function inverse to $x = x(u)$ is required. If this is multi-valued, (as for example the inverse trigonometric functions), as x varies continuously from a and b, u must vary from c to the lowest value of d greater than c; u must not jump to a higher value of d for its upper limit. A rough graph is often helpful in ambiguous cases.

Example 9 In the integral $I = \int \sqrt{(a^2 - x^2)}\,dx$, we place $x = a \sin \theta$, this being a standard substitution for integrands containing the expression $\sqrt{(a^2 - x^2)}$. Then $dx = a \cos \theta\,d\theta$, yielding

$$I = a^2 \int \cos^2 \theta\,d\theta = \tfrac{1}{2}a^2(\theta + \tfrac{1}{2}\sin 2\theta)$$
$$= \tfrac{1}{2}a^2[\sin^{-1}(x/a) + (x/a)\sqrt{(1 - x^2/a^2)}]$$
$$= \tfrac{1}{2}a^2 \sin^{-1}(x/a) + \tfrac{1}{2}x\sqrt{(a^2 - x^2)}.$$

If
$$I = \int_{-a}^a \sqrt{(a^2 - x^2)}\,dx,$$

we must consider the inverse transformation $\theta = \sin^{-1}(x/a)$. When $x = -a$, we may take θ to be $-\tfrac{1}{2}\pi$, and when $x = a$, $\theta = \tfrac{1}{2}\pi$ (not $\tfrac{5}{2}\pi$, etc.). Hence

$$I = \left[\tfrac{1}{2}a^2(\theta + \tfrac{1}{2}\sin 2\theta)\right]_{-\frac{1}{2}\pi}^{\frac{1}{2}\pi} = \tfrac{1}{2}\pi a^2.$$

Example 10 Evaluate

$$I = \int_0^c x^2(x^2 + c^2)^{-\frac{3}{2}} \, dx.$$

In integrals containing roots of the expression $(x^2 + c^2)$, we may make the substitution $x = c \sinh \theta$ and $dx = c \cosh \theta \, d\theta$. When $x = 0$, $\theta = 0$ and when $x = c$, $\theta = \sinh^{-1} 1 = \log(1 + \sqrt{2})$. Hence

$$I = \int_0^{\log(1+\sqrt{2})} \frac{c^2 \sinh^2 \theta}{c^3 \cosh^3 \theta} c \cosh \theta \, d\theta$$

$$= \int_0^{\log(1+\sqrt{2})} \tanh^2 \theta \, d\theta$$

$$= \int_0^{\log(1+\sqrt{2})} (1 - \operatorname{sech}^2 \theta) \, d\theta$$

$$= \left[\theta - \tanh \theta \right]_0^{\log(1+\sqrt{2})}$$

$$= \log(1 + \sqrt{2}) - \tanh[\log(1 + \sqrt{2})]$$

$$= \log(1 + \sqrt{2}) - 1/\sqrt{2}.$$

Example 11 Evaluate the integral

$$I = \int_0^1 \frac{dx}{(x + 1)\sqrt{(x^2 + 1)}}.$$

Making the substitution $x = \tan \theta$ and $dx = \sec^2 \theta \, d\theta$, we have

$$I = \int_0^{\frac{1}{4}\pi} \frac{\sec^2 \theta \, d\theta}{(\tan \theta + 1)\sec \theta} = \int_0^{\frac{1}{4}\pi} \frac{d\theta}{\sin \theta + \cos \theta}$$

$$= \frac{1}{\sqrt{2}} \int_0^{\frac{1}{4}\pi} \frac{d\theta}{\cos(\theta - \frac{1}{4}\pi)}$$

$$= \frac{1}{\sqrt{2}} \left[\log[\tan(\theta - \frac{1}{4}\pi) + \sec(\theta - \frac{1}{4}\pi)] \right]_0^{\frac{1}{4}\pi}$$

$$= -2^{-\frac{1}{2}} \log(-1 + \sqrt{2})$$

$$= 2^{-\frac{1}{2}} \log(1 + \sqrt{2}).$$

Example 12 Evaluate the integral

$$I = \int_b^a \frac{x \, dx}{\sqrt{[(a - x)(x - b)]}}, \qquad (a > x > b).$$

A suitable change of variable for integrals involving $\sqrt{[(a - x)(x - b)]}$ is

$$a - x = (a - b)\cos^2 \theta,$$

with

$$dx = 2(a - b)\cos \theta \sin \theta \, d\theta$$

and

$$x - b = (a - b) - (a - x) = (a - b)\sin^2 \theta.$$

Hence

$$I = \int_0^{\frac{1}{2}\pi} \frac{[a - (a - b)\cos^2 \theta].2(a - b)\cos \theta \sin \theta \, d\theta}{(a - b)\cos \theta \sin \theta}$$

$$= 2\int_0^{\frac{1}{2}\pi} [a - (a - b)\cos^2 \theta] \, d\theta$$

$$= 2\left[a\theta - \tfrac{1}{2}(a - b)(\theta + \tfrac{1}{2}\sin 2\theta) \right]_0^{\frac{1}{2}\pi}$$

$$= \tfrac{1}{2}(a + b)\pi.$$

Example 13   Evaluate the integral

$$I = \int \frac{dx}{x\sqrt{(3x^2 + 2x - 1)}}.$$

In integrals of this character, we make the standard substitution $x = 1/u$, yielding

$$I = \int \frac{-u^{-2} \, du}{u^{-1}\sqrt{(3u^{-2} + 2u^{-1} - 1)}} = -\int \frac{du}{\sqrt{[4 - (u - 1)^2]}}$$

$$= \cos^{-1}[\tfrac{1}{2}(u - 1)]$$

$$= \cos^{-1}[(1 - x)/2x].$$

Example 14   Evaluate the integral $I = \int dx/(5 + 3\cos x)$.

An integral involving trigonometric functions may be reduced to algebraical form by the substitution $t = \tan \frac{1}{2}x$. Then

$$dt = \tfrac{1}{2}\sec^2 \tfrac{1}{2}x \, dx = \tfrac{1}{2}(1 + t^2) \, dx,$$

yielding

$$dx = 2 \, dt/(1 + t^2).$$

Moreover,

$$\sin x = 2t/(1 + t^2), \quad \cos x = (1 - t^2)/(1 + t^2), \quad \tan x = 2t/(1 - t^2).$$

Hence

$$I = \int \frac{2 \, dt/(1 + t^2)}{5 + 3(1 - t^2)/(1 + t^2)} = \int \frac{2 \, dt}{8 + 2t^2}$$

$$= \tfrac{1}{2}\tan^{-1}(\tfrac{1}{2}t)$$

$$= \tfrac{1}{2}\tan^{-1}(\tfrac{1}{2}\tan \tfrac{1}{2}x).$$

Note. If the integrand contains only $\sin^2 x$, $\cos^2 x$ or $\tan^2 x$, we may use the simpler substitution $t = \tan x$, in which case

$$dx = du/(1 + u^2), \quad \sin^2 x = u^2/(1 + u^2), \quad \cos^2 x = 1/(1 + u^2).$$

Example 15   Evaluate the integral

$$I = \int_1^2 \frac{dx}{x(1 + x^n)}.$$

In some examples, an obvious guess must be made for a suitable substitution; we choose $u = x^n$, so $du = nx^{n-1} dx$. Then

$$I = \int_1^{2^n} \frac{du}{nx^{n-1}.x(1+u)} = \int_1^{2^n} \frac{du}{nu(1+u)}$$

$$= \frac{1}{n} \int_1^{2^n} \left(\frac{1}{u} - \frac{1}{u+1}\right) du$$

$$= \frac{1}{n} \left[\log \frac{u}{u+1}\right]_1^{2^n}$$

$$= \frac{1}{n} \log \left(\frac{2^{n+1}}{2^n+1}\right).$$

Example 16   Evaluate the integral

$$I = \int_0^\infty \frac{dx}{(x^2+1) + x\sqrt{(x^2+1)}}.$$

We choose the substitution $x = \sinh u$, yielding

$$I = \int_0^\infty \frac{\cosh u \, du}{\cosh^2 u + \sinh u \cosh u} = \int_0^\infty \frac{du}{\cosh u + \sinh u}$$

$$= \int_0^\infty \frac{du}{e^u}$$

$$= -\left[e^{-u}\right]_0^\infty = 1.$$

Example 17   Evaluate the integral

$$I = \int \frac{(8 - x^2) \, dx}{\sqrt{(-3 + 4x - x^2)}}.$$

In examples where the integrand is of the form

$$(ax^2 + bx + c)/\sqrt{(Ax^2 + Bx + C)},$$

the numerator is rearranged to take the form

$ax^2 + bx + c \equiv \alpha$(the quadratic in the denominator)
    $+ \beta$(the derivative of the quadratic in the denominator) $+ \gamma$.

Each of the three parts thus formed may be dealt with separately. Integrals of the form $\int (ax^2 + bx + c)\sqrt{(Ax^2 + Bx + C)} \, dx$ may be treated similarly. In the present example, let

$$8 - x^2 \equiv \alpha(-3 + 4x - x^2) + \beta(4 - 2x) + \gamma$$

yielding $\alpha = 1$, $\beta = 2$, $\gamma = 3$.
    Hence

$$I = \int \sqrt{(-3 + 4x - x^2)} \, dx + \int \frac{2(4 - 2x) \, dx}{\sqrt{(-3 + 4x - x^2)}} + \int \frac{3 \, dx}{\sqrt{(-3 + 4x - x^2)}}$$

$$= \int \sqrt{[1 - (x - 2)^2]} \, dx + 4\sqrt{(-3 + 4x - x^2)} + 3 \int \frac{dx}{\sqrt{[1 - (x - 2)^2]}}.$$

The first integral has, in effect, been calculated in example 9; hence

$$I = \tfrac{1}{2} \sin^{-1}(x-2) + \tfrac{1}{2}(x-2)\sqrt{[1-(x-2)^2]} + 4\sqrt{(-3+4x-x^2)}$$
$$+ 3\sin^{-1}(x-2)$$
$$= \tfrac{7}{2} \sin^{-1}(x-2) + (\tfrac{1}{2}x+3)\sqrt{(-3+4x-x^2)}.$$

16.5   Integration by parts

This is the method generally employed if the integrand consists of the product of two unlike functions. Consider the product of the two functions u and $\int v \, dx$. Its derivative is given by

$$\frac{d}{dx}\left[u\left(\int v \, dx\right)\right] = uv + \frac{du}{dx}\left(\int v \, dx\right),$$

by the product rule. Integration then yields

$$u\left(\int v \, dx\right) = \int uv \, dx + \int \frac{du}{dx}\left(\int v \, dx\right) dx,$$

or $$\int uv \, dx = u\left(\int v \, dx\right) - \int \frac{du}{dx}\left(\int v \, dx\right) dx.$$

The success of this method (the formula being but an identity) depends on whether the final integral can be evaluated.

If both functions u and v are integrable, care is necessary as to which is integrated in the first step. If one of the functions is a power of x, this is usually left to be differentiated in the second integral, in order to diminish its index. Sometimes, the final integral must also be evaluated by another application of this method; in this case, the factor $(\int v \, dx)$ in the integrand *must* be integrated first, *not* the factor du/dx, otherwise we are merely undoing the work of the first application of the method, arriving back at the starting point. Sometimes neither u nor v should be integrated as they stand; rather the integrand should be prepared before integration (see example 23). On other occasions, it is necessary to insert a factor $v = 1$ into the integrand (see example 19).

Example 18

$$I = \int x \cos x \, dx = x \sin x - \int \sin x \, dx \quad \text{(taking } u = x, v = \cos x)$$
$$= x \sin x + \cos x.$$

If we had integrated the factor x first, the result

$$\int x \cos x \, dx = \tfrac{1}{2}x^2 \cos x + \tfrac{1}{2}\int x^2 \sin x \, dx$$

is correct, but not very helpful.

Example 19 Evaluate $I = \int \log x \, dx$.

Several integrals of this type may be evaluated by inserting a factor $v = 1$ in the integrand. We have

$$I = \int 1.\log x \, dx = x \log x - \int x(x^{-1}) \, dx = x \log x - x.$$

Similarly,

$$\int \sin^{-1} x \, dx = x \sin^{-1} x - \int x(1 - x^2)^{-\frac{1}{2}} \, dx = x \sin^{-1} x + \sqrt{(1 - x^2)},$$

$$\int \tan^{-1} x \, dx = x \tan^{-1} x - \int x(1 + x^2)^{-1} \, dx = x \tan^{-1} x - \tfrac{1}{2} \log (1 + x^2).$$

Example 20 Evaluate $I = \int e^{-ax} \cos bx \, dx$.

It is simpler to evaluate this integral with the aid of complex numbers (see example 9, chapter 7); integration by parts twice in succession is otherwise necessary. We have

$$I = b^{-1}e^{-ax} \sin bx + ab^{-1} \int e^{-ax} \sin bx \, dx$$

$$= b^{-1}e^{-ax} \sin bx + ab^{-1} \left[-b^{-1}e^{-ax} \cos bx - ab^{-1} \int e^{-ax} \cos bx \, dx \right],$$

yielding

$$(1 + a^2b^{-2})I = e^{-ax}(\sin bx - ab^{-1} \cos bx)/b,$$

and

$$I = e^{-ax}(b \sin bx - a \cos bx)/(a^2 + b^2).$$

Example 21

$$I = \int \sqrt{(a^2 - x^2)} \, dx = \int 1.\sqrt{(a^2 - x^2)} \, dx$$

$$= x\sqrt{(a^2 - x^2)} + \int x^2(a^2 - x^2)^{-\frac{1}{2}} \, dx$$

$$= x\sqrt{(a^2 - x^2)} - I + \int a^2(a^2 - x^2)^{-\frac{1}{2}} \, dx;$$

hence

$$I = \tfrac{1}{2}x\sqrt{(a^2 - x^2)} + \tfrac{1}{2}a^2 \sin^{-1} (x/a).$$

Example 22 If n is a positive integer,

$$I = \int_0^\infty x^n e^{-x} \, dx$$

$$= \left[-x^n e^{-x} \right]_0^\infty + n \int_0^\infty x^{n-1} e^{-x} \, dx.$$

But $x^n e^{-x} \to 0$ as $x \to \infty$, so

$$I = n \int_0^\infty x^{n-1} e^{-x} \, dx.$$

Similarly,

$$I = n(n-1) \int_0^\infty x^{n-2} e^{-x} \, dx$$

$$= n(n-1)(n-2)\ldots 2.1 \int_0^\infty e^{-x} \, dx$$

$$= n!$$

Example 23 Evaluate $I = \int e^{-1/x} x^{-4} \, dx$.

Since $e^{-1/x}$ cannot be integrated, the temptation is first to integrate x^{-4}; but it would then be found that the integrand of the final integral contained x^{-5}. This method of approach is therefore useless, so the integrand must be prepared in a different manner. We have

$$I = \int \frac{1}{x^2} \left(\frac{e^{-1/x}}{x^2} \right) dx = \frac{1}{x^2} e^{-1/x} + 2 \int \frac{e^{-1/x}}{x^3} \, dx$$

$$= \frac{1}{x^2} e^{-1/x} + 2 \int \frac{1}{x} \left(\frac{e^{-1/x}}{x^2} \right) dx$$

$$= \frac{1}{x^2} e^{-1/x} + 2 \left[\frac{1}{x} e^{-1/x} + \int \frac{e^{-1/x} \, dx}{x^2} \right]$$

$$= \left(\frac{1}{x^2} + \frac{2}{x} + 2 \right) e^{-1/x}.$$

Three times we have used the fact that the integral of $x^{-2} e^{-1/x}$ is $e^{-1/x}$.

Example 24 The following integral may similarly be evaluated:

$$\int \sin 2x \, e^{\sin x} \, dx = 2 \int \sin x (\cos x \, e^{\sin x}) \, dx$$

$$= 2 \sin x \, e^{\sin x} - \int \cos x \, e^{\sin x} \, dx$$

$$= 2 \sin x \, e^{\sin x} - e^{\sin x}.$$

16.6 Infinite integrals

If the definite integral $\int_a^X f(x) \, dx$ exists for all values of X (greater than a, say), then the integral is a function of its upper limit X; we write its value as $I(X)$. If $I(X)$ tends to a limit as $X \to \infty$, we say that I is an *infinite integral* in the limit, and we write

$$I = \lim_{X \to \infty} \int_a^X f(x) \, dx.$$

Strictly speaking, in worked examples, the finite upper limit X should first be substituted into the indefinite integral, and then the resulting expression should be examined for a limit. In elementary examples, however, "infinity" can often be "substituted" directly into the indefinite integral, although care is necessary in some cases. This statement means, of course, that the value of the limit is usually obvious by inspection.

Example 25   Evaluate the infinite integral $\displaystyle\int_{\sqrt{3}}^{\infty} \frac{x^2\,dx}{x^4 - 1}$

We have

$$I(X) = \int_{\sqrt{3}}^{X} \frac{x^2\,dx}{x^4 - 1} = \int_{\sqrt{3}}^{X} \left(\frac{\frac{1}{4}}{x - 1} - \frac{\frac{1}{4}}{x + 1} + \frac{\frac{1}{2}}{x^2 + 1} \right) dx$$

$$= \left[\frac{1}{4} \log \frac{x - 1}{x + 1} + \frac{1}{2} \tan^{-1} x \right]_{\sqrt{3}}^{X}$$

$$= \frac{1}{4} \log \frac{X - 1}{X + 1} + \frac{1}{2} \tan^{-1} X - \frac{1}{4} \log \frac{\sqrt{3} - 1}{\sqrt{3} + 1} - \frac{1}{2} \tan^{-1} \sqrt{3}.$$

Hence, in the limit,

$$I = \tfrac{1}{4}\pi - \tfrac{1}{4} \log (2 - \sqrt{3}) - \tfrac{1}{6}\pi$$

$$= \tfrac{1}{12}\pi - \tfrac{1}{4} \log (2 - \sqrt{3}).$$

Consider the positive continuous function $f(x)$, and the sequence $f(n)$, where n is a positive integer. If $f(x)$ has the additional property that it is a monotonically decreasing function, we have

$$\int_{n}^{n+1} f(x)\,dx = ABCD < AFCD = f(n).$$

Adding such contributions for all integral values of n from 0 to N, we obtain

$$\int_{0}^{N+1} f(x)\,dx < f(0) + f(1)$$

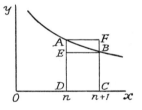

FIG. 88

$$+ f(2) + \ldots + f(N).$$

As many as necessary of the first terms of the sequence may be omitted if the monotonic property does not apply for small values of the integer n.

We now consider the limiting process $N \to \infty$. If the infinite sum on the right of the inequality converges, so does the integral; on the other hand, if the infinite integral does not converge, neither does the series.

Similarly,

$$\int_{n}^{n+1} f(x)\,dx > EBCD = f(n + 1),$$

yielding

$$\int_{0}^{N} f(x)\,dx > f(1) + f(2) + \ldots + f(N).$$

Hence, if the infinite series diverges, so does the integral, while if the integral converges, so does the series. In other words, *the integral and the series either converge or diverge together.*

Example 26   Show that $u_n = 1 + \frac{1}{2} + \frac{1}{3} + \ldots + n^{-1} - \log_e n$ tends to a limit.

The function $1/x$ is a positive monotonically decreasing function when $x > 0$. Hence, using Fig. 88, we have the inequalities

$$\frac{1}{r+1} < \int_r^{r+1} \frac{dx}{x} < \frac{1}{r},$$

where r is a positive integer. Adding all such inequalities from $r = 1$ to $r = n - 1$, we obtain

$$\frac{1}{2} + \frac{1}{3} + \ldots + n^{-1} < \log_e n < 1 + \frac{1}{2} + \frac{1}{3} + \ldots + (n-1)^{-1},$$

or
$$u_n - 1 < 0 < u_n - n^{-1}.$$
This may also be written as
$$n^{-1} < u_n < 1,$$

from which we conclude that u_n is bounded.

But
$$u_n - u_{n+1} = -\log_e n + \log_e (n+1) - (n+1)^{-1}$$
$$= ABCD - (n+1)^{-1} \quad \text{(see Fig. 88)}$$
$$= ABCD - EBCD = ABE > 0;$$

hence $u_n > u_{n+1}$. The sequence u_n is therefore monotonically decreasing and is bounded below; hence u_n has a limit, denoted by γ and called *Euler's constant.* Its value is $0\cdot5772156649\ldots$.

Infinite integrands.   If the integrand $f(x)$ is infinite when $x = a$, consider the integral

$$I(\varepsilon) = \int_{a+\varepsilon}^b f(x)\, dx$$

where $b > a + \varepsilon$, and ε is small. If $I(\varepsilon)$ tends to a limit as $\varepsilon \to 0$, we write the integral as $\int_a^b f(x)\, dx$, the value of this integral being the value of $I(\varepsilon)$ in the limit. Similar arguments apply if $b < a$, or if the integrand becomes infinite at the upper limit of integration.

Example 27   Evaluate the integral

$$I = \int_0^1 \log\left(\frac{1}{1-x^2}\right) dx.$$

The integrand becomes infinite at the upper limit of integration, which we therefore place equal to $X = 1 - \varepsilon$. The indefinite integral is found by parts:

$$\int 1.\log \frac{1}{1-x^2}\, dx = -x \log (1-x^2) - \int \frac{2x^2\, dx}{1-x^2}$$

$$= -x \log (1-x^2) - 2 \int \frac{(x^2 - 1 + 1)\, dx}{1-x^2}$$

$$= -x \log (1-x^2) + 2x - \log \frac{1+x}{1-x}.$$

The value of this expression at the lower limit $x = 0$ is zero, so

$$I(\varepsilon) = -X\log(1 - X) - X\log(1 + X) + 2X - \log(1 + X) + \log(1 - X)$$
$$= 2X - (1 + X)\log(1 + X) + (1 - X)\log(1 - X)$$
$$= 2 - 2\varepsilon - (2 - \varepsilon)\log(2 - \varepsilon) + \varepsilon\log\varepsilon.$$

But $\varepsilon\log\varepsilon \to 0$ as $\varepsilon \to 0$ (see example 29); hence $I = 2 - 2\log 2$.

More generally, if we wish to integrate from c to b where $c < a < b$ and $f(a) = \infty$, we may consider

$$I(\varepsilon, \eta) = \int_c^{a-\eta} f(x)\,dx + \int_{a+\varepsilon}^b f(x)\,dx$$

with $\varepsilon > 0$, $\eta > 0$. If both limits exist as ε and $\eta \to 0$, then a unique limit exists for the integral over the whole range $c < x < b$. But if neither limit exists separately, a limit may exist under special conditions. Let $\varepsilon = \eta$. Then *if* the limit of

$$I(\varepsilon) = \int_c^{a-\varepsilon} f(x)\,dx + \int_{a+\varepsilon}^b f(x)\,dx$$

exists as $\varepsilon \to 0$, then this limit is called the *principal value* of the integral, and we write the result as

$$P\int_c^b f(x)\,dx.$$

In effect, the two infinite areas on each side of $x = a$ cancel each other out.

For example, the reader may easily check that for $b > 0$, $c > 0$,

$$P\int_{-c}^b \frac{dx}{x} = \log\frac{b}{c}.$$

16.7   The logarithmic integral

The following two problems should be carefully noted.

Example 28   If $\log_e x$ is defined to equal the area under the graph $1/t$, from $t = 1$ to $t = x$, prove that $\log xy = \log x + \log y$.

From the definition,

$$\log xy = \int_1^{xy} t^{-1}\,dt.$$

If we substitute $t = xu$, this integral becomes

$$\log xy = \int_{1/x}^y u^{-1}\,du$$
$$= \int_{1/x}^1 u^{-1}\,du + \int_1^y u^{-1}\,du.$$

In the first integral, let $u = 1/v$ with $du = -dv/v^2$:

$$\log xy = -\int_x^1 v^{-1}\, dv + \int_1^y u^{-1}\, du$$

$$= \int_1^x v^{-1}\, dv + \int_1^y u^{-1}\, du$$

$$= \log x + \log y.$$

Example 29   Prove that $x^r \log x$ tends to zero as x tends to zero through positive values, however small r may be $(r > 0)$.

It is sufficient to prove that

$$rx^r \log x = x^r \log x^r = \varepsilon \log \varepsilon$$

tends to zero with ε.   Now $\log \varepsilon < 0$, so

$$0 < \varepsilon \int_\varepsilon^1 t^{-1}\, dt \qquad\qquad \text{(the integral is now positive)}$$

$$< \varepsilon \int_\varepsilon^1 t^{-\frac{3}{2}}\, dt \qquad\qquad \text{(increasing the integrand)}$$

$$= \varepsilon \left[-2t^{-\frac{1}{2}} \right]_\varepsilon^1$$

$$= \varepsilon[-2 + 2\varepsilon^{-\frac{1}{2}}]$$

$$= -2\varepsilon + 2\varepsilon^{\frac{1}{2}} \to 0 \text{ with } \varepsilon.$$

It follows that $\varepsilon \log \varepsilon$ lies between 0 and a value that tends to 0; in other words, $\varepsilon \log \varepsilon \to 0$ with ε.

A similar result applies to the exponential function.   If m and n are positive, $x^m e^{-nx}$ tends to zero as $x \to \infty$, however large m may be and however small n may be.

Since $y^{n/m} \log y \to 0$ as $y \to 0$, if we place $y = e^{-x}$, we have

$$-xe^{-xn/m} \to 0 \quad \text{as} \quad x \to \infty.$$

Taking the mth power, we obtain the required result.

16.8   Simpson's rule for approximate integration

Numerical methods must be used to evaluate definite integrals for which no indefinite integral can be found.   In other cases, a curve may be defined only by a set of experimentally derived points; the area under the curve may be required.

The *trapezoidal* rule consists of dividing the range of integration (a, b) into n equal subdivisions of width $h = (b - a)/n$.   Let the $(n + 1)$ ordinates for the function $y = f(x)$ then be given by

$$f(a) = y_0, y_1, y_2, \ldots, y_{n-1}, y_n = f(b).$$

Very approximately, we neglect the curvature of the n arcs so formed, replacing them by n chords; n trapezia are thereby formed. The area under the curve is approximately equal to the total area of these n trapezia, namely

$$\tfrac{1}{2}h(y_0 + y_1) + \tfrac{1}{2}h(y_1 + y_2) + \ldots + \tfrac{1}{2}h(y_{n-1} + y_n)$$
$$= \tfrac{1}{2}h(\text{twice the sum of the } n + 1 \text{ ordinates} -y_0 - y_n).$$

Simpson's rule improves upon this approximation, by replacing the chords by parabolic curves.

We divide the range of integration (a, b) into $2n$ equal subdivisions, of width $h = (b - a)/2n$. Let the ordinates at the values of x given by

$$x = a, a + h, a + 2h, \ldots, a + 2rh,$$
$$a + (2r + 1)h, a + (2r + 2)h, \ldots, a + 2nh$$

all be positive, with the values

$$y = y_0, y_1, y_2, \ldots, y_{2r}, y_{2r+1}, y_{2r+2}, \ldots, y_{2n}.$$

Consider the area under the curve from $x = a + 2rh$ to $x = a + (2r + 2)h$. We denote $a + (2r + 1)h$ by d, and let $x = d + t$; we also assume a parabolic curve of the general form $y = a + bt + ct^2$, defined by the three points $(-h, y_{2r})$, $(0, y_{2r+1})$, (h, y_{2r+2}). The area under this curve is

$$\int_{-h}^{h} (a + bt + ct^2)\, dt = 2(ah + \tfrac{1}{3}ch^3).$$

But substituting the three defining points into the equation of the parabola, we have

$$y_{2r} = a - bh + ch^2, \; y_{2r+1} = a, \; y_{2r+2} = a + bh + ch^2.$$

Then
$$y_{2r} + y_{2r+2} = 2a + 2ch^2.$$

The area is now given by

$$\tfrac{1}{3}h(4a + 2a + 2ch^2) = \tfrac{1}{3}h(4y_{2r+1} + y_{2r} + y_{2r+2}).$$

Similar contributions arise from each of the n pairs of strips. Totally, we have for the area

$$\tfrac{1}{3}h[(y_0 + 4y_1 + y_2) + (y_2 + 4y_3 + y_4) + \ldots + (y_{2n-2} + 4y_{2n-1} + y_{2n})]$$
$$= \tfrac{1}{3}h(2 \sum \text{even ordinates} + 4 \sum \text{odd ordinates} -y_0 - y_{2n}).$$

If M is the largest value of $|d^4y/dx^4|$ in the range (a, b), it can be shown that the error satisfies the inequality

$$\text{error} \leq (b - a)^5 M/[2880n^4].$$

Example 30   Using five ordinates, evaluate the integral

$$I = \int_1^2 \frac{\log_e r}{r-1}\, dr.$$

When $r = 1$, $1\cdot25$, $1\cdot5$, $1\cdot75$, 2 the integrand equals 1, $0\cdot8924$, $0\cdot8110$, $0\cdot7641$, $0\cdot6931$ respectively. With $h = 0\cdot25$, we have, using Simpson's formula,

$$I = \tfrac13 \times 0\cdot25[2(1 + 0\cdot8110 + 0\cdot6931) + 4(0\cdot8924 + 0\cdot7641) - 1\cdot6931]$$
$$= \tfrac13 \times 0\cdot25 \times 9\cdot9411 = 0\cdot828.$$

The trapezoidal rule also gives the value $0\cdot828$.

16.9   Derivatives of parametric integrals

If we are given a definite integral whose variable of integration is t, such that its integrand and its upper and lower limits are functions of a variable x, the integral defines a function of x:

$$I(x) = \int_{f(x)}^{g(x)} h(x, t)\, dt.$$

The differential coefficient $dI(x)/dx$ may be found formally as follows, but more careful analysis would show that restrictions are necessary on the functions involved. We have

$$I(x + \delta x) = \int_{f(x+\delta x)}^{g(x+\delta x)} h(x + \delta x, t)\, dt.$$

Expanding all functions to the first order, and subtracting $I(x)$ we obtain

$$I(x + \delta x) - I(x) = \int_{f+f'\,\delta x}^{g+g'\,\delta x} \left[h(x, t) + \frac{\partial}{\partial x} h(x, t)\, \delta x \right] dt - \int_f^g h(x, t)\, dt$$

$$= \int_{f+f'\,\delta x}^{f} h(x, t)\, dt + \int_f^g h(x, t)\, dt + \int_g^{g+g'\,\delta x} h(x, t)\, dt$$

$$+ \delta x \int_f^g \frac{\partial}{\partial x} h(x, t)\, dt - \int_f^g h(x, t)\, dt$$

$$= \delta x \int_f^g \frac{\partial}{\partial x} h(x, t)\, dt - h(x, f) f'\, \delta x + h(x, g) g'\, \delta x$$

to the first order. The last term arises, for example, by multiplying the integrand evaluated at the lower limit by the small width of integration. In the limit, the omitted second order terms disappear in the ratio $\delta I/\delta x$, yielding

$$\frac{dI(x)}{dx} = \int_f^g \frac{\partial h}{\partial x}\, dt + h(x, g)\frac{dg}{dx} - h(x, f)\frac{df}{dx}.$$

In particular, if the two limits are constants, we have

$$\frac{d}{dx} \int_a^b h(x, t)\, dt = \int_a^b \frac{\partial h}{\partial x}\, dt.$$

Sometimes the evaluation of parametric integrals is rendered more simple by differentiation first:

Example 31 Evaluate

$$I(x) = \int_0^{\frac{1}{2}\pi} \frac{\log\,(1 + x^2 \sin^2 \theta)}{\sin^2 \theta}\, d\theta.$$

Differentiating with respect to x, we obtain

$$\frac{dI}{dx} = \int_0^{\frac{1}{2}\pi} \frac{2x\, d\theta}{1 + x^2 \sin^2 \theta}\,.$$

Substituting $u = \tan \theta$, we find

$$\frac{dI}{dx} = 2x \int_0^\infty \frac{(1 + u^2)^{-1}\, du}{1 + x^2 u^2 (1 + u^2)^{-1}} = 2x \int_0^\infty \frac{du}{1 + (1 + x^2)u^2}$$

$$= 2x \left[\frac{\tan^{-1}\,[u\sqrt{(1 + x^2)}]}{\sqrt{(1 + x^2)}} \right]_0^\infty = \frac{\pi x}{\sqrt{(1 + x^2)}}\,.$$

We now integrate with respect to x, obtaining

$$I = \pi\sqrt{(1 + x^2)} + C.$$

In particular, the given integral vanishes when $x = 0$; the constant C must therefore have the value $-\pi$. Hence

$$I(x) = \pi[\sqrt{(1 + x^2)} - 1].$$

16.10 Reduction formulae

The definite integral $I_n = \int_a^b f(x, n)\, dx$ is given containing a parameter n, usually a positive integer, though *mutatis mutandis* negative integers may arise in certain problems.

By integration by parts and/or by algebraic rearrangement of the integrand, it is often possible to express I_n in terms of I_{n-1} (or I_{n-2}). In other words, an identity of the form

$$I_n \equiv g(n)I_{n-1} + h(n)$$

exists, where $g(n)$ and $h(n)$ depend only on n. Such an identity is known as a *reduction formula*. No general rule can be laid down for the derivation of reduction formulae from their defining integrals; each case must be treated on its own merits.

Repetition of this process finally enables I_n to be calculated, for since also

$$I_{n-1} \equiv g(n-1)I_{n-2} + h(n-1),$$

we conclude that

$$I_n \equiv g(n)[g(n-1)I_{n-2} + h(n-1)] + h(n),$$

and so on, until I_0 (or perhaps I_1) is attained, which we suppose easily to be integrable.

More generally, an integral may contain two parameters m and n. If, for example, $I(m, n)$ can be rearranged by diminishing m by unity and n by unity in turn, namely

$$I(m, n) = g(m, n)I(m - 1, n),$$
$$I(m, n) = h(m, n)I(m, n - 1),$$

then evidently

$$I(m, n) = g(m, n)h(m - 1, n)I(m - 1, n - 1)$$
$$= g(m, n)h(m - 1, n) \cdot g(m - 1, n - 1)h(m - 2, n - 1)$$
$$\times I(m - 2, n - 2),$$

and so on until $I(0, 0)$ is attained, supposed integrable.

Example 32   If

$$I_n = \int_0^{\frac{1}{2}\pi} \sin^n \theta \, d\theta,$$

we have

$$I_n = \int_0^{\frac{1}{2}\pi} \sin \theta \sin^{n-1} \theta \, d\theta$$

$$= \left[-\cos \theta \sin^{n-1} \theta \right]_0^{\frac{1}{2}\pi} + (n - 1) \int_0^{\frac{1}{2}\pi} \cos^2 \theta \sin^{n-2} \theta \, d\theta$$

$$= 0 + (n - 1) \int_0^{\frac{1}{2}\pi} (1 - \sin^2 \theta) \sin^{n-2} \theta \, d\theta \qquad (n \geqslant 2)$$

$$= (n - 1)(I_{n-2} - I_n).$$

Hence

$$nI_n = (n - 1)I_{n-2},$$

or

$$I_n = \frac{n - 1}{n} I_{n-2}.$$

Now $I_0 = \frac{1}{2}\pi$ and $I_1 = 1$, so applying this formula successively, we have when n is even:

$$I_n = \frac{(n - 1)(n - 3) \ldots 3.1}{n(n - 2) \ldots 4.2} I_0 = \frac{(n - 1)(n - 3) \ldots 3.1}{n(n - 2) \ldots 4.2} \cdot \frac{\pi}{2},$$

and when n is odd:

$$I_n = \frac{(n - 1)(n - 3) \ldots 4.2}{n(n - 2) \ldots 5.3} I_1 = \frac{(n - 1)(n - 3) \ldots 4.2}{n(n - 2) \ldots 5.3}.$$

These two useful formulae should be committed to memory.

Example 33 If

$$I_n = \int_0^a x^{2n}(a^2 - x^2)^{-\frac{1}{2}} dx,$$

we have

$$I_n = \int_0^a x^{2n-1} \cdot x(a^2 - x^2)^{-\frac{1}{2}} dx$$

$$= \left[-x^{2n-1}(a^2 - x^2)^{\frac{1}{2}} \right]_0^a + (2n - 1)\int_0^a x^{2n-2}(a^2 - x^2)^{\frac{1}{2}} dx \quad (n \geqslant 1)$$

$$= 0 + (2n - 1)\int_0^a x^{2n-2}(a^2 - x^2)(a^2 - x^2)^{-\frac{1}{2}} dx$$

$$= (2n - 1)[a^2 I_{2n-2} - I_n],$$

yielding

$$I_{2n} = \frac{2n - 1}{2n} a^2 I_{2n-2}.$$

Using this identity successively, we have

$$I_{2n} = \frac{2n - 1}{2n} a^2 \cdot \frac{2n - 3}{2n - 2} a^2 \cdot \frac{2n - 5}{2n - 4} a^2 \ldots \tfrac{1}{2}a^2 I_0.$$

But $I_0 = \tfrac{1}{2}\pi$, so

$$I_{2n} = \frac{(2n - 1)(2n - 3)\ldots 1}{2n(2n - 2)\ldots 2} a^{2n}(\tfrac{1}{2}\pi)$$

$$= \frac{2n(2n - 1)(2n - 2)(2n - 3)\ldots 2.1}{[2n(2n - 2)\ldots 2]^2} a^{2n}(\tfrac{1}{2}\pi)$$

$$= \frac{a^{2n}\pi(2n)!}{2^{2n+1}(n!)^2}.$$

Example 34★ If n is a positive integer, and $I_n = \int \text{cosec}^n x \, dx$, prove that

$$(n - 1)I_n - (n - 2)I_{n-2} + \cos x \, \text{cosec}^{n-1} x = 0.$$

Show that $8\int_{\frac{1}{4}\pi}^{\frac{1}{2}\pi} \text{cosec}^5 x \, dx = 7\sqrt{2} + 3 \log (\sqrt{2} + 1)$, and find

$$J = \int_{\frac{1}{4}\pi}^{\frac{1}{2}\pi} (3 - \cos 2x) \, \text{cosec}^5 x \, dx.$$

We have

$$I_n = \int \text{cosec}^2 x \, \text{cosec}^{n-2} x \, dx$$

$$= -\cot x \, \text{cosec}^{n-2} x - (n - 2)\int \cot x . \text{cosec}^{n-3} x \, \text{cosec} x \cot x \, dx$$

$$= -\cos x \, \text{cosec}^{n-1} x - (n - 2)\int \text{cosec}^{n-2} x(\text{cosec}^2 x - 1) \, dx$$

$$= -\cos x \, \text{cosec}^{n-1} x - (n - 2)(I_n - I_{n-2}),$$

yielding the required reduction formula.

13

Inserting the limits $\frac{1}{4}\pi$ and $\frac{1}{2}\pi$, we obtain

$$(n-1)I_n = (n-2)I_{n-2} + (\sqrt{2})^{n-2}.$$

When $n = 3$ and 5, we have

$$2I_3 = I_1 + \sqrt{2}, \quad 4I_5 = 3I_3 + 2\sqrt{2},$$

and

$$I_1 = \int_{\frac{1}{4}\pi}^{\frac{1}{2}\pi} \operatorname{cosec} x \, dx = \left[-\log\left(\operatorname{cosec} x + \cot x\right) \right]_{\frac{1}{4}\pi}^{\frac{1}{2}\pi} = \log\left(\sqrt{2}+1\right).$$

Then

$$I_3 = \tfrac{1}{2}[\sqrt{2} + \log(\sqrt{2}+1)],$$

and

$$8I_5 = 3[\sqrt{2} + \log(\sqrt{2}+1)] + 4\sqrt{2} = 7\sqrt{2} + 3\log(\sqrt{2}+1).$$

Finally,

$$J = \int_{\frac{1}{4}\pi}^{\frac{1}{2}\pi} (2 + 2\sin^2 x)\operatorname{cosec}^5 x \, dx$$

$$= 2I_5 + 2I_3$$

$$= \tfrac{11}{4}\sqrt{2} + \tfrac{7}{4}\log(\sqrt{2}+1).$$

Example 35 If

$$I_n = \int_0^\infty \frac{dx}{(x^2 + a^2)^n}$$

we have

$$I_n = \left[\frac{x}{(x^2+a^2)^n} \right]_0^\infty + \int_0^\infty \frac{x \cdot 2nx}{(x^2+a^2)^{n+1}} \, dx$$

$$= 0 + 2n \int_0^\infty \frac{x^2 + a^2 - a^2}{(x^2+a^2)^{n+1}} \, dx$$

$$= 2n(I_n - a^2 I_{n+1}),$$

or, upon changing n to $n-1$,

$$I_n = \frac{1}{a^2}\left(\frac{2n-3}{2n-2}\right)I_{n-1}.$$

Successive applications of this result yield

$$I_n = \frac{1}{a^2}\left(\frac{2n-3}{2n-2}\right) \cdot \frac{1}{a^2}\left(\frac{2n-5}{2n-4}\right) \cdots \frac{1}{a^2}\frac{1}{2}I_1.$$

But

$$I_1 = \left[\frac{1}{a}\tan^{-1} x \right]_0^\infty = \frac{\pi}{2a},$$

giving

$$I_n = \frac{\pi}{a^{2n-1}} \frac{(2n-3)(2n-5)\ldots3.1}{2^n(n-1)!}.$$

This result may be simplified by inserting the factor $(2n-2)(2n-4)\ldots2$ in both numerator and denominator, giving

$$I_n = \frac{\pi(2n-2)!}{(2a)^{2n-1}[(n-1)!]^2}.$$

Example 36   If

$$I(m, n) = \int_0^{\frac{1}{2}\pi} \cos^m x \sin^n x \, dx,$$

we have

$$I(m, n) = \int_0^{\frac{1}{2}\pi} \cos^m x \sin x . \sin^{n-1} x \, dx$$

$$= \left[-\frac{\cos^{m+1} x}{m + 1} \sin^{n-1} x \right]_0^{\frac{1}{2}\pi} + \frac{n - 1}{m + 1} \int_0^{\frac{1}{2}\pi} \cos^{m+2} x \sin^{n-2} x \, dx$$

$$= \frac{n - 1}{m + 1} [I(m, n - 2) - I(m, n)],$$

yielding

$$I(m, n) = \frac{n - 1}{m + n} I(m, n - 2).$$

Similarly,

$$I(m, n) = \frac{m - 1}{m + n} I(m - 2, n).$$

It is important to know whether m and n are odd or even. In particular, if both are odd, we have

$$I(2m + 1, 2n + 1) = \frac{2n}{2m + 2n + 2} I(2m + 1, 2n - 1)$$

$$= \frac{2n}{2m + 2n + 2} . \frac{2n - 2}{2m + 2n} I(2m + 1, 2n - 3)$$

$$= \frac{2n}{2m + 2n + 2} . \frac{2n - 2}{2m + 2n} \cdots \frac{2}{2m + 4} I(2m + 1, 1)$$

$$= \frac{n! \, (m + 1)!}{(m + n + 1)!} I(2m + 1, 1)$$

$$= \frac{n! \, (m + 1)!}{(m + n + 1)!} . \frac{2m}{2m + 2} I(2m - 1, 1)$$

$$= \frac{n! \, (m + 1)!}{(m + n + 1)!} . \frac{2m}{2m + 2} . \frac{2m - 2}{2m} \cdots \frac{2}{4} I(1, 1).$$

But $I(1, 1)$ may be evaluated directly, having the value $\frac{1}{2}$; hence

$$I(2m + 1, 2n + 1) = \frac{n! \, (m + 1)!}{(m + n + 1)!} . \frac{m!}{(m + 1)!} . \frac{1}{2} = \frac{m! \, n!}{2(m + n + 1)!}$$

16.11   Various elements and their integrals

In many mathematical and physical problems, the functional form of some variable, $V(x)$ say, is required to be determined. On the other hand, the specification of the problem enables us directly only to write down the increment of V, namely

$$\delta V(x) = f(x) \, \delta x + g(x) \, \delta x^2 + \dots .$$

Moreover, the only coefficient usually known from the specification of the problem is $f(x)$. Dividing by δx and proceeding to the limit, we have

$$\frac{dV(x)}{dx} = f(x),$$

from which we conclude that

$$V(x) = \int f(x)\,dx.$$

In other words, we need only concern ourselves with the first order increment, merely writing

$$\delta V(x) = f(x)\,\delta x,$$

and the notation adopted for integration enables us to change this directly to

$$V(x) = \int f(x)\,dx.$$

Strictly speaking, in many cases this method of approach is begging the question, for the variable sought, $V(x)$, is not even defined until its value is found. The first order increment $\delta V(x)$ cannot then be

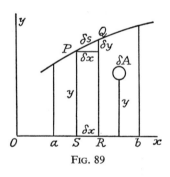

FIG. 89

written down, since if $V(x)$ has not been defined, we cannot write down anything about it. The above method of procedure is therefore not valid and, under these circumstances, a Riemann integral is necessary to define $V(x)$. We shall not, however, occupy ourselves with these more subtle points, and we shall write down the various first order increments, known as *elements*, by reference to a diagram.

Areas. If $y = y(x)$ is a given curve in Cartesian coordinates, the element of area $PQRS$ consisting of a strip of width δx parallel to Oy has the value $y\,\delta x$; hence

$$\text{area} = \int_a^b y\,dx.$$

The *mean value* of y is defined to be this area divided by $(b - a)$. If the curve is below Ox, the area is obviously negative.

If the chosen strip is of width δy and parallel to Ox, the area bounded by the curve $x = x(y)$ and the lines $y = c$ and d is

$$\text{area} = \int_c^d x\,dy.$$

In polar coordinates, the triangular element OPQ has the area

$$\tfrac{1}{2}OP.OQ \sin \angle POQ = \tfrac{1}{2}r^2 \, \delta\theta$$

to the first order; hence the area intercepted between the lines $\theta = \theta_1$ and θ_2 is

$$\text{area} = \int_{\theta_1}^{\theta_2} \tfrac{1}{2}r^2 \, d\theta,$$

when r is given as a function of θ. If θ increases by more than 2π, parts of the area will obviously be swept over more than once.

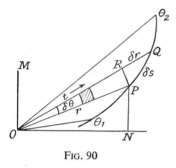

FIG. 90

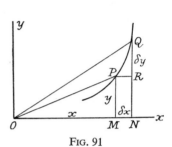

FIG. 91

For a curve given in Cartesian coordinates, usually expressed parametrically, we may find the area of a small triangular element with vertex O, measured positively if taken anticlockwise. If P is the point (x, y) and Q the point $(x + \delta x, y + \delta y)$, then

$$\begin{aligned}
\text{area } OPQ &= OQN - OPM - PRNM \quad \text{(to the first order)} \\
&= \tfrac{1}{2}(x + \delta x)(y + \delta y) - \tfrac{1}{2}xy - y \, \delta x \\
&= \tfrac{1}{2}(x \, \delta y - y \, \delta x).
\end{aligned}$$

Parametrically, if $x = x(t)$, $y = y(t)$,

$$\text{area } OPQ = \frac{1}{2}\left(x \frac{dy}{dt} - y \frac{dx}{dt} \right)\delta t,$$

so the total area OAB, where A has parameter a, and B has parameter b, is given by

$$\text{area} = \tfrac{1}{2}\int_a^b \left(x \frac{dy}{dt} - y \frac{dx}{dt} \right) dt.$$

For an ellipse, $x = a \cos \theta$, $y = b \sin \theta$; the whole area is traversed if θ varies from 0 to 2π. Hence

$$\begin{aligned}
\text{area} &= \tfrac{1}{2}\int_0^{2\pi} [a \cos \theta . b \cos \theta - b \sin \theta .(-a \sin \theta)] \, d\theta \\
&= \tfrac{1}{2}\int_0^{2\pi} ab \, d\theta = \pi ab.
\end{aligned}$$

Arc length. In Fig. 89, the chord δs has the value

$$\delta s = \sqrt{(\delta x^2 + \delta y^2)} = \sqrt{\left[1 + \left(\frac{dy}{dx}\right)^2\right]} \, \delta x$$

to the first order. The length of the arc from $x = a$ to $x = b$ is then

$$s = \int_a^b \sqrt{\left[1 + \left(\frac{dy}{dx}\right)^2\right]} \, dx.$$

Strictly speaking, this should be regarded as a *definition* of the arc length, rather than the value of something *already* defined.

If the curve is given parametrically, the arc length from A, with parameter a, to B, with parameter b, is given by

$$s = \int_a^b \sqrt{\left[\left(\frac{dx}{dt}\right)^2 + \left(\frac{dy}{dt}\right)^2\right]} \, dt.$$

In polar coordinates, referring to Fig. 90, we have

$$\delta s^2 = \delta r^2 + r^2 \, \delta\theta^2,$$

so the arc length between $\theta = \theta_1$ and θ_2 is given by

$$s = \int_{\theta_1}^{\theta_2} \sqrt{\left[r^2 + \left(\frac{dr}{d\theta}\right)^2\right]} \, d\theta.$$

Surfaces of revolution. If the curve $y = y(x)$ for $y > 0$ (see Fig. 89) is rotated through four right-angles around the axis Ox, a surface of revolution is produced. The element of arc δs traces out a thin frustum of a cone whose base radius is y. Since the element of area is $2\pi y \, \delta s$, the total area generated is

$$\text{area} = 2\pi \int_a^b y \sqrt{\left[1 + \left(\frac{dy}{dx}\right)^2\right]} \, dx.$$

In polar coordinates, the element of surface area when the curve is rotated about the initial line is (see Fig. 90)

$$2\pi PN \, \delta s = 2\pi r \sin\theta \sqrt{\left[r^2 + \left(\frac{dr}{d\theta}\right)^2\right]} \, \delta\theta,$$

so the total area generated is

$$\text{area} = 2\pi \int_{\theta_1}^{\theta_2} r \sin\theta \sqrt{\left[r^2 + \left(\frac{dr}{d\theta}\right)^2\right]} \, d\theta.$$

Volumes of revolution. In Cartesian coordinates, the element of volume of the thin frustum of a cone just considered in Fig. 89 has the value $\pi PS^2 \, \delta x = \pi y^2 \, \delta x$. The total volume is therefore

$$\text{volume} = \pi \int_a^b y^2 \, dx.$$

In polar coordinates, the element of volume usually considered is that traced out by the area element OPQ when rotated about the initial line ON. The small shaded area is $t \, \delta t \, \delta \theta$; this traces out a ring of radius $t \sin \theta$, so the volume of the ring is $2\pi t \sin \theta . t \, \delta t \, \delta \theta = 2\pi \sin \theta \, \delta \theta . t^2 \, \delta t$.

The total volume generated by all such elements along the triangle OPQ is found by integrating with respect to t, from 0 to r and keeping θ constant:

$$\text{volume} = 2\pi \sin \theta \, \delta \theta \int_0^r t^2 \, dt = \tfrac{2}{3}\pi r^3 \sin \theta \, \delta \theta.$$

This is usually memorized as the appropriate element of volume; the total volume generated by all such elementary triangles from $\theta = \theta_1$ to θ_2 is

$$\text{volume} = \tfrac{2}{3}\pi \int_{\theta_1}^{\theta_2} r^3 \sin \theta \, d\theta.$$

For a sphere, $r = a$, and we integrate from $\theta = 0$ to π, yielding

$$\text{volume} = \tfrac{2}{3}\pi \int_0^\pi a^3 \sin \theta = \tfrac{2}{3}\pi a^3 \left[-\cos \theta \right]_0^\pi = \tfrac{4}{3}\pi a^3.$$

Centroids and centres of area.   In Cartesian coordinates, the moment about Ox of the element of area $PQRS$ in Fig. 89 is $\tfrac{1}{2}y.y \, \delta x$. The total moment about Ox is therefore

$$\text{total moment} = \int_a^b \tfrac{1}{2}y^2 \, dx.$$

The y coordinate, $\bar{y}$, of the centre of area is defined to be this moment about Ox divided by the area, namely

$$\bar{y} = \tfrac{1}{2}\int_a^b y^2 \, dx \Big/ \int_a^b y \, dx.$$

The element of moment about Oy is $xy \, \delta x$, yielding similarly

$$\bar{x} = \int_a^b xy \, dx \Big/ \int_a^b y \, dx.$$

In polar coordinates, the centre of area of the elementary triangle OPQ in Fig. 90 is given by $x = \tfrac{2}{3}r \cos \theta$, $y = \tfrac{2}{3}r \sin \theta$ with respect to the axes OM, ON, this point being two thirds the way up the median through the vertex O. The elements of moment about the axes OM and ON respectively are $\tfrac{1}{3}r^3 \cos \theta \, \delta \theta$ and $\tfrac{1}{3}r^3 \sin \theta \, \delta \theta$. Hence

$$\bar{x} = \int_{\theta_1}^{\theta_2} \tfrac{1}{3}r^3 \cos \theta \, d\theta \Big/ \int_{\theta_1}^{\theta_2} \tfrac{1}{2}r^2 \, d\theta,$$

$$\bar{y} = \int_{\theta}^{\theta_2} \tfrac{1}{3}r^3 \sin \theta \, d\theta \Big/ \int_{\theta_1}^{\theta_2} \tfrac{1}{2}r^2 \, d\theta.$$

The moment about Ox of the element of arc PQ in Fig. 89 is $y\,\delta s$, so if $\bar{y}$ is the y coordinate of the centroid of the arc of total length s, it follows that

$$\bar{y}s = \int_{x=a}^{x=b} y\,ds.$$

Comparing this result with the formula for the area of the surface of revolution thus formed, we see that this area has the value $2\pi\bar{y}s$, namely the length of the arc multiplied by the distance travelled by the centroid of this arc. This result is known as one of the *theorems of Pappus*.

Similarly, if δA is any small element of area distant y from Ox as in Fig. 89, this traces out a ring of radius y as the volume of revolution is formed. Its volume is $2\pi y\,\delta A$, so the total volume is $2\pi \int y\,dA$. If $\bar{y}$ is the distance of the centroid of this area from Ox, the moment of the area about Ox must be $A\bar{y}$ and also $\int y\,dA$, where A is the total area of the plane curve. Hence the volume generated is $2\pi\bar{y}A$, namely the area multiplied by the distance travelled by the centroid of this area. This result is also known as one of the theorems of Pappus.

The main use of these theorems concerns rotation about a general axis $lx + my + n = 0$. If a closed curve, not intersected by this axis, has total area A and total perimeter s, and if $(\bar{x}_A, \bar{y}_A)$ and $(\bar{x}_s, \bar{y}_s)$ are the coordinates of the centroids of the area and of the bounding perimeter respectively, then the perpendicular distances of these points from the axis are

$$\frac{l\bar{x}_A + m\bar{y}_A + n}{\sqrt{(l^2 + m^2)}} \quad \text{and} \quad \frac{l\bar{x}_s + m\bar{y}_s + n}{\sqrt{(l^2 + m^2)}}.$$

Hence the volume and surface area generated by rotation of the closed curve about this axis are respectively

$$2\pi A\,\frac{|l\bar{x}_A + m\bar{y}_A + n|}{\sqrt{(l^2 + m^2)}} \quad \text{and} \quad 2\pi s\,\frac{|l\bar{x}_s + m\bar{y}_s + n|}{\sqrt{(l^2 + m^2)}}.$$

Moments of inertia and second moments of area. The concept of second moments of area is a geometrical concept, while that of moments of inertia is a physical concept relating to a lamina consisting of a mass distribution. We shall assume that the reader is familiar with the definitions of these terms from his knowledge of elementary dynamics. Here, we are only concerned with stating the relevant elements, not in proving various standard theorems.

For the plane lamina in Fig. 89, the area of the element $PQRS$ is $y\,\delta x$; since every part of it is at a distance x from Oy, its second moment of area about Oy is $x^2y\ \delta x$. The total second moment of area is given by

$$\int_a^b x^2y\ dx,$$

and the *radius of gyration* k_x about Oy is defined by

$$r_x{}^2 = \int_a^b x^2y\ dx \Big/ \int_a^b y\ dx.$$

About Ox, we may regard the element as a rod of length y. The square of its radius of gyration about one end is known to be $\frac{4}{3}(\frac{1}{2}y)^2 = \frac{1}{3}y^2$, so the element of second moment about Ox is $\frac{1}{3}y^2 . y\ \delta x$. It follows totally that

$$r_y{}^2 = \int_a^b \tfrac{1}{3}y^3\ dx \Big/ \int_a^b y\ dx.$$

On the other hand, an element parallel to Ox may be chosen if it is more suitable.

The *product of area* (or *product of inertia*) is defined with respect to two perpendicular axes. The definition of the element (see Fig. 89) is taken to be $xy\ \delta A$ for the small marked element δA. For the strip $PQRS$, the appropriate element is

$$x \sum y\ \delta A = x \textstyle\int y . \delta x\ dy = \tfrac{1}{2}xy^2\ \delta x.$$

Hence for the whole area, its product of area is

$$\tfrac{1}{2} \int_a^b xy^2\ dx.$$

For the solid of revolution generated by rotation of the curve about Ox, the volume element $\pi y^2\ \delta x$, being of circular shape, has the square of its radius of gyration equal to $\frac{1}{2}y^2$. Hence the total second moment about Ox is given by

$$\int_a^b \tfrac{1}{2}\pi y^4\ dx,$$

and the radius of gyration r by

$$r^2 = \int_a^b \tfrac{1}{2}\pi y^4\ dx \Big/ \int_a^b \pi y^2\ dx.$$

Other more appropriate elements may sometimes be chosen depending on the particular problem.

Example 37   Sketch the curve $xy^2 = a^2(a - x)$; find its area and the distance of its centroid from the origin.

Since $y = \pm a\sqrt{[(a - x)/x]}$, the curve consists of symmetrical upper and lower portions. Moreover y is real only when x lies in the range $0 < x \leqslant a$. The y-axis is an asymptote, and when $x = a$, $dy/dx = \infty$. This information enables us to sketch the curve shown in Fig. 92.

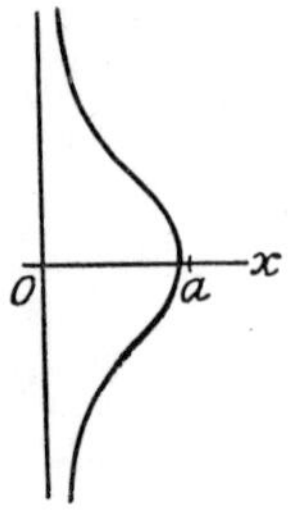

FIG. 92

The area is given by

$$A = 2 \int_0^a y \, dx = 2a \int_0^a \sqrt{[(a - x)/x]} \, dx.$$

The substitution $x = a \sin^2 \theta$ yields

$$A = 2a^2 \int_0^{\frac{1}{2}\pi} \cot \theta . 2 \sin \theta \cos \theta \, d\theta$$

$$= 4a^2 \int_0^{\frac{1}{2}\pi} \cos^2 \theta \, d\theta = \pi a^2.$$

Taking moments about Oy, we find for the total moment

$$2 \int_0^a xy \, dx = 4a^3 \int_0^{\frac{1}{2}\pi} \cos^2 \theta \sin^2 \theta \, d\theta = a^3 \int_0^{\frac{1}{2}\pi} \sin^2 2\theta \, d\theta = \tfrac{1}{4}\pi a^3.$$

By symmetry, the centroid lies on the axis Ox; its distance $\bar{x}$ from O is given by

$$\bar{x} = (\tfrac{1}{4}\pi a^3)/(\pi a^2) = \tfrac{1}{4}a.$$

Example 38 Find the length of the curve $3ay^2 = x^2(2x + a)$, from the origin to the point (a, a).

Taking the positive root, we have

$$y = x\sqrt{(2x + a)}/\sqrt{(3a)},$$

and

$$\frac{dy}{dx} = \frac{\sqrt{(2x + a)}}{\sqrt{(3a)}} + \frac{x}{\sqrt{(3a)}\sqrt{(2x + a)}} = \frac{3x + a}{\sqrt{(3a)}\sqrt{(2x + a)}}.$$

Hence

$$1 + \left(\frac{dy}{dx}\right)^2 = 1 + \frac{(3x + a)^2}{3a(2x + a)} = \frac{(3x + 2a)^2}{3a(2x + a)}.$$

The arc length is calculated from the positive square root of this quantity, namely

$$s = (3a)^{-\frac{1}{2}} \int_0^a \frac{(3x + 2a) \, dx}{\sqrt{(2x + a)}} = \tfrac{1}{2}(3a)^{-\frac{1}{2}} \int_0^a \frac{(6x + 3a + a) \, dx}{\sqrt{(2x + a)}}$$

$$= \tfrac{1}{2}(3a)^{-\frac{1}{2}} \int_0^a \left[3\sqrt{(2x + a)} + \frac{a}{\sqrt{(2x + a)}} \right] dx$$

$$= \tfrac{1}{2}(3a)^{-\frac{1}{2}} \left[(2x + a)^{\frac{3}{2}} + a\sqrt{(2x + a)} \right]_0^a$$

$$= (2 - \tfrac{1}{3}\sqrt{3})a.$$

Example 39 Sketch the curve $x = te^{-t}$, $y = t^2 e^{-t}$, and find the area of the loop.

We prepare a small table showing the general trend of values of x, y, t:

t	x	y
$-\infty$	$-\infty$	$+\infty$
$-$ve	$-$ve	$+$ve
0	0	0
$+$ve	$+$ve	$+$ve
$+\infty$	0	0

Moreover

$$\frac{dy}{dx} = \frac{dy/dt}{dx/dt} = \frac{2t - t^2}{1 - t},$$

which vanishes when $t = 0$ and becomes infinite when $t = \infty$. These facts enable us to sketch the graph as shown in Fig. 93.

Noting that $y = xt$, we find that the area of the loop is given by

$$\frac{1}{2}\int_0^\infty \left(x\frac{dy}{dt} - y\frac{dx}{dt}\right) dt$$

$$= \frac{1}{2}\int_0^\infty \left[x\left(x + t\frac{dx}{dt}\right) - xt\frac{dx}{dt}\right] dt$$

$$= \frac{1}{2}\int_0^\infty x^2 \, dt = \frac{1}{2}\int_0^\infty t^2 e^{-2t} \, dt = \tfrac{1}{8}$$

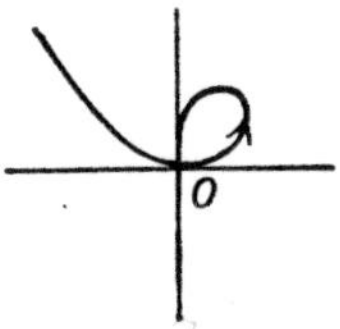

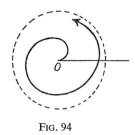

Fig. 93

after integrating by parts two times in succession.

Example 40 Sketch the curve $r = a \tanh \frac{1}{2}\theta$; find the area A swept out between $\theta = 0$ and 2α and the arc length s.

Since $\tanh \frac{1}{2}\theta$ starts at 0 and increases monotonically to unity as $r \to \infty$, a spiral is produced always lying inside the circle $r = a$.

As θ increases, the central part of the area is included again and again in the total area. We have

Fig. 94

$$A = \int_0^{2\alpha} \tfrac{1}{2}r^2 \, d\theta = \tfrac{1}{2}a^2 \int_0^{2\alpha} \tanh^2 \tfrac{1}{2}\theta \, d\theta$$

$$= \tfrac{1}{2}a^2 \int_0^{2\alpha} (1 - \operatorname{sech}^2 \tfrac{1}{2}\theta) \, d\theta$$

$$= \tfrac{1}{2}a^2 \left[\theta - 2\tanh \tfrac{1}{2}\theta\right]_0^{2\alpha}$$

$$= a^2(\alpha - \tanh \alpha).$$

The arc length s is given by

$$s = \int_0^{2\alpha} \sqrt{\left[r^2 + \left(\frac{dr}{d\theta}\right)^2\right]} \, d\theta = a\int_0^{2\alpha} \sqrt{(\tanh^2 \tfrac{1}{2}\theta + \tfrac{1}{4}\operatorname{sech}^4 \tfrac{1}{2}\theta)} \, d\theta$$

$$= \tfrac{1}{2}a\int_0^{2\alpha} \sqrt{(4 - 4\operatorname{sech}^2 \tfrac{1}{2}\theta + \operatorname{sech}^4 \tfrac{1}{2}\theta)} \, d\theta$$

$$= \tfrac{1}{2}a\int_0^{2\alpha} (2 - \operatorname{sech}^2 \tfrac{1}{2}\theta) \, d\theta$$

$$= \tfrac{1}{2}a\left[2\theta - 2\tanh \tfrac{1}{2}\theta\right]_0^{2\alpha}$$

$$= a(2\alpha - \tanh \alpha).$$

Example 41 The loop given by $r^2 = 4a^2 \cos^2 \theta - 2a^2$, $(0 < \theta < \tfrac{1}{4}\pi)$ rotates about the initial line to form a solid of revolution; find its volume V.

We use the element of area $\tfrac{1}{2}r^2 \, \delta\theta$ that produces the volume element $\tfrac{2}{3}\pi r^3 \sin \theta \, \delta\theta$. Hence

$$V = \tfrac{2}{3}\pi a^3 \int_0^{\frac{1}{4}\pi} (4\cos^2 \theta - 2)^{\frac{3}{2}} \sin \theta \, d\theta.$$

We substitute $\sqrt{2}\cos\theta = \sec t$, yielding

$$V = -\tfrac{2}{3}\pi a^3 \int_{\frac{1}{4}\pi}^0 (2\sec^2 t - 2)^{\frac{3}{2}}.(\sec t \tan t \, dt/\sqrt{2})$$

$$= \tfrac{4}{3}\pi a^3 \int_0^{\frac{1}{4}\pi} \tan^4 t \sec t \, dt.$$

But

$$I = \int \tan^4 t \sec t \, dt = \int (\sec t \tan t) \tan^3 t \, dt$$
$$= \sec t \tan^3 t - 3 \int \sec^3 t \tan^2 t \, dt$$
$$= \sec t \tan^3 t - 3 \int \sec t(1 + \tan^2 t) \tan^2 t \, dt,$$

so

$$4I = \sec t \tan^3 t - 3J,$$

where

$$J = \int \sec t \tan^2 t \, dt = \int (\sec t \tan t) \tan t \, dt$$
$$= \sec t \tan t - \int \sec^3 t \, dt$$
$$= \sec t \tan t - \int (1 + \tan^2 t) \sec t \, dt,$$

and

$$2J = \sec t \tan t - \int \sec t \, dt$$
$$= \sec t \tan t - \log (\sec t + \tan t).$$

Hence

$$4I = \sec t \tan^3 t - \tfrac{3}{2}\sec t \tan t + \tfrac{3}{2}\log (\sec t + \tan t).$$

The volume is therefore given by

$$V = \tfrac{1}{3}\pi a^3 \left[\sec t \tan^3 t - \tfrac{3}{2}\sec t \tan t + \tfrac{3}{2}\log (\sec t + \tan t) \right]_0^{\frac{1}{4}\pi}$$
$$= \tfrac{1}{3}\pi a^3 [\sqrt{2} - \tfrac{3}{2}\sqrt{2} + \tfrac{3}{2}\log (\sqrt{2} + 1)]$$
$$= \tfrac{1}{6}\pi a^3 [3 \log (1 + \sqrt{2}) - \sqrt{2}].$$

Example 42 Sketch the *cardioid* $r = a(1 + \cos \theta)$. Find (i) its area, (ii) its arc length, (iii) the position of its centroid, (iv) the volume generated when rotated about the tangent at $(2a, 0)$, (v) the volume generated when rotated about the initial line, (vi) the surface area generated when rotated about the initial line, (vii) the radius of gyration of the solid thus formed.

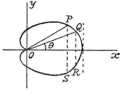

FIG. 95

As θ varies from 0 to $\tfrac{1}{2}\pi$, r decreases from $2a$ to a; as θ increases from $\tfrac{1}{2}\pi$ to π, r decreases from a to zero. Moreover, the curve is symmetrical about the initial line, yielding the curve given in Fig. 95.

(i) *Area.* This is given by

$$A = 2 \int_0^\pi \tfrac{1}{2}r^2 \, d\theta = a^2 \int_0^\pi (1 + \cos \theta)^2 \, d\theta = a^2 \int_0^\pi 4 \cos^4 \tfrac{1}{2}\theta \, d\theta.$$

Let $\theta = 2\phi$, yielding

$$A = 8a^2 \int_0^{\frac{1}{2}\pi} \cos^4 \phi \, d\phi = 8a^2 \frac{3.1}{4.2} \cdot \frac{\pi}{2} = \frac{3}{2}\pi a^2,$$

quoting the result of example 32 which applies to cosines as well as to sines.

(ii) *Arc length.* This is given by

$$s = 2 \int_0^\pi \sqrt{\left[r^2 + \left(\frac{dr}{d\theta} \right)^2 \right]} \, d\theta = 2a \int_0^\pi \sqrt{[(1 + \cos \theta)^2 + \sin^2 \theta]} \, d\theta$$

$$= 2a \int_0^\pi \sqrt{(2 + 2\cos \theta)} \, d\theta$$

$$= 4a \int_0^\pi \cos \tfrac{1}{2}\theta \, d\theta = 8a.$$

Note. In evaluating the arc length, the square root occurring in the integrand must be positive; it would therefore be wrong to use the above integral extended beyond the upper limit π.

(iii) *The centroid.* This will lie on the initial line. The element of moment of the elementary triangle OPQ about Oy is $\tfrac{2}{3}r \cos \theta . \tfrac{1}{2}r^2 \, \delta\theta$, so the total moment is

$$\tfrac{1}{3} \int_0^\pi r^3 \cos \theta \, d\theta = \tfrac{1}{3}a^3 \int_0^\pi (\cos \theta + 1)^3 \cos \theta \, d\theta$$

$$= \tfrac{1}{3}a^3 \int_0^\pi (\cos^4 \theta + 3\cos^3 \theta + 3\cos^2 \theta + \cos \theta) \, d\theta$$

$$= \tfrac{2}{3}a^3 \int_0^{\frac{1}{2}\pi} (\cos^4 \theta + 3\cos^2 \theta) \, d\theta \quad \begin{array}{l}\text{(the odd powers of } \cos \theta \\ \text{integrate to zero)}\end{array}$$

$$= \tfrac{2}{3}a^3 \left(\frac{3.1}{4.2} + \frac{3.1}{2} \right) \frac{\pi}{2} = \tfrac{5}{4}\pi a^3.$$

Hence $\bar{x} = (\tfrac{5}{4}\pi a^3)/(\tfrac{3}{2}\pi a^2) = \tfrac{5}{6}a$.

(iv) *Volume.* We use one of the theorems of Pappus. The distance of the centroid of the area from the tangent at the vertex $r = 2a$ is $\tfrac{7}{6}a$; hence

$$V = 2\pi(\tfrac{7}{6}a)A = 2\pi . \tfrac{7}{6}a . \tfrac{3}{2}\pi a^2 = \tfrac{7}{2}\pi^2 a^3.$$

(v) *Volume.* When the cardioid is rotated about the initial line, the volume generated is

$$V = \int_0^\pi \tfrac{2}{3}\pi r^3 \sin \theta \, d\theta = \tfrac{2}{3}\pi a^3 \int_0^\pi (1 + \cos \theta)^3 \sin \theta \, d\theta$$

$$= \tfrac{2}{12}\pi a^3 \left[-(1 + \cos \theta)^4 \right]_0^\pi = \tfrac{8}{3}\pi a^3.$$

(vi) *Surface area.* This is given by

$$\int 2\pi y \, ds = \int_0^\pi 2\pi r \sin\theta . a\sqrt{(2 + 2\cos\theta)} \, d\theta \qquad \text{(from ii)}$$

$$= 2\sqrt{2}\pi a^2 \int_0^\pi (1 + \cos\theta)^{\frac{3}{2}} \sin\theta \, d\theta$$

$$= \tfrac{4}{5}\sqrt{2}\pi a^2 \left[-(1 + \cos\theta)^{\frac{5}{2}} \right]_0^\pi = \tfrac{32}{5}\pi a^2.$$

(vii) *Radius of gyration.* The volume of the circular element $PQRS$ is $\pi y^2 \, \delta x$ and its radius of gyration squared is $\tfrac{1}{2} y^2$. The element of the second moment of volume about the initial line is therefore $\tfrac{1}{2}\pi y^4 \, \delta x$. Totally, the second moment is given by

$$I = \tfrac{1}{2}\pi \int y^4 \, dx = \tfrac{1}{2}\pi \int r^4 \sin^4\theta \, d(r\cos\theta)$$

$$= \tfrac{1}{2}\pi \int r^4 \sin^4\theta \, d[a(\cos\theta + \cos^2\theta)]$$

$$= -\tfrac{1}{2}\pi a^5 \int (1 + \cos\theta)^4 \sin^4\theta(\sin\theta + 2\sin\theta\cos\theta) \, d\theta$$

$$= -\tfrac{1}{2}\pi a^5 \int (1 + \cos\theta)^4 (1 + 2\cos\theta) \sin^5\theta \, d\theta.$$

To arrive at a positive answer, the limits of integration must agree with x increasing; θ varies therefore from π to 0. We substitute $u = 1 + \cos\theta$, obtaining

$$I = \tfrac{1}{2}\pi a^5 \int_0^2 u^6 (2 - u)^2 (2u - 1) \, du$$

$$= \tfrac{64}{35}\pi a^5$$

upon simplification. Hence $k^2 = I/(\text{volume}) = (\tfrac{64}{35}\pi a^5)/(\tfrac{2}{3}\pi a^3) = \tfrac{24}{35}a^2$.

See example 5, chapter 17, for another method of calculating this second moment of volume.

Example 43 If $\rho = m(a^2 - r^2)$ is the density at a distance r from the centre O of the plane face of a solid hemisphere of radius a, find (i) its total mass M, (ii) the position of its centre of mass, (iii) the radius of gyration k about the axis of symmetry.

(i) We take a hollow shell of radius r and thickness δr for an element; its mass is $2\pi r^2 \, \delta r . m(a^2 - r^2)$ yielding totally

$$M = 2\pi m \int_0^a r^2(a^2 - r^2) \, dr = 2\pi m \left[\tfrac{1}{3}a^2 r^3 - \tfrac{1}{5}r^5 \right]_0^a = \tfrac{4}{15}\pi m a^5.$$

(ii) The centre of mass of a hollow hemispherical shell is known to be at a distance $\tfrac{1}{2}r$ from O along its axis of symmetry. Hence the total moment about a line through O perpendicular to the axis is

$$\pi m \int_0^a r^3(a^2 - r^2) \, dr = \pi m \left[\tfrac{1}{4}a^2 r^4 - \tfrac{1}{6}r^6 \right]_0^a = \tfrac{1}{12}\pi m a^6.$$

Dividing by the mass, the distance of the centre of mass from O is $\tfrac{5}{16}a$.

(iii) The square of the radius of gyration of a hollow shell of radius r about its axis of symmetry should be known to be $\frac{2}{3}r^2$; this result applies equally well to a hemisphere as to a sphere. The value of the element of moment of inertia of the hollow hemisphere is therefore given by $\frac{2}{3}r^2 . 2\pi r^2 \rho \, \delta r$; the total is therefore given by

$$Mk^2 = \int_0^a \tfrac{4}{3}\pi r^4 \rho \, dr = \tfrac{4}{3}\pi m \int_0^a r^4(a^2 - r^2) \, dr = \tfrac{4}{3}\pi m \left[\tfrac{1}{5}a^2 r^5 - \tfrac{1}{7}r^7 \right]_0^a = \tfrac{8}{105}\pi m a^7.$$

Hence $k^2 = \frac{2}{7}a^2$.

EXERCISES

Use trigonometrical identities to integrate the following ⋆ integrals:

(1). $\displaystyle\int_0^{\frac{1}{2}\pi} \cos^3 x \, dx$

(2). $\displaystyle\int_0^{\frac{1}{6}\pi} \sin^2 \theta (\cos^3 \theta - 1) \, d\theta.$

(3). $\displaystyle\int_0^{\frac{1}{2}\pi} \frac{dx}{(1 + \cos x)^2}.$

(4). $\displaystyle\int_0^{\frac{3}{2}\pi} \frac{\sin^3 x \, dx}{\cos x}.$

(5). $\displaystyle\int_0^{\frac{1}{4}\pi} \sin^3 \theta \cos \theta \, d\theta.$

(6). $\displaystyle\int_0^{\frac{1}{4}\pi} \frac{\sin^3 \theta \, d\theta}{1 - \cos \theta}.$

(7). $\displaystyle\int_0^{\pi} \frac{\sin x \, dx}{2 + \cos x}.$

(8). $\displaystyle\int_0^{\frac{1}{2}\pi} \sin^4 x \cos 4x \, dx.$

(9). $\displaystyle\int \frac{d\theta}{\sin \theta (1 + \sin \theta)}.$

(10). $\displaystyle\int \frac{\sin^n x \, dx}{\cos^{n+2} x}.$

(11). $\displaystyle\int \frac{2 \sin^3 x - \sin 3x - 3 \sin^5 x}{\cos^2 x} \, dx.$

(12). $\displaystyle\int_0^1 \cosh^2 x \, dx.$

Integrate by parts the following ⋆ integrals:

(13). $\displaystyle\int_0^1 x e^x \, dx.$

(14). $\displaystyle\int_0^{\infty} x^2 e^{-\frac{1}{2}x} \, dx.$

(15). $\displaystyle\int x^3 e^{-x^2} \, dx.$

(16). $\displaystyle\int_0^{\frac{1}{2}\pi} e^x \sin 2x \, dx.$

(17). $\displaystyle\int x \sin^{-1} x \, dx.$

(18). $\displaystyle\int_0^{\frac{1}{4}\pi} x \cos^2 x \, dx.$

(19). $\displaystyle\int e^{4x} \cos 3x \, dx.$

(20). $\displaystyle\int \sin x \sinh x \, dx.$

(21). $\displaystyle\int x \tan^{-1}(x + 1) \, dx.$

(22). $\displaystyle\int \frac{x \sin^{-1} x \, dx}{\sqrt{(1 - x^2)}}.$

(23). $\displaystyle\int \log (1/t) \, dt.$

(24). $\displaystyle\int_0^{\frac{1}{2}\pi} \cos \theta \log (1 + \cos \theta) \, d\theta.$

(25). $\displaystyle\int \frac{\log_e (1 + x) \, dx}{x^2}.$

(26). $\displaystyle\int \tanh^{-1} u \, du.$

Integrate, using partial fractions, the following★ integrals:

(27). $\int \dfrac{dx}{(x+1)(x^2-1)}$.

(28). $\int_0^1 \dfrac{(x^2-2x)\,dx}{(2x+1)(x^2+1)}$.

(29). $\int \dfrac{(x^3+x+1)\,dx}{x^4+x^2}$.

(30). $\int \dfrac{x^3\,dx}{(x^2+1)(x-2)}$.

(31). $\int_0^1 \dfrac{dx}{(x+1)^3(x+2)}$.

(32). $\int_0^\infty \dfrac{x\,dx}{(x+1)^2(x^2+4)}$.

(33). $\int \dfrac{(3x-1)\,dx}{x^3+x^2+x+1}$.

(34). $\int \dfrac{(2x^3+7)\,dx}{(2x+1)(x^2+2)}$.

Integrate the following★, using the function of a function principle:

(35). $\int_1^2 \dfrac{1}{x}\log_e x\,dx$.

(36). $\int_1^{\sqrt3} \dfrac{dx}{(1+x^2)\tan^{-1}x}$.

(37). $\int_0^a x(a^2-x^2)^{\frac{5}{4}}\,dx$.

(38). $\int_1^2 \dfrac{e^{2x}\,dx}{e^x-1}$.

(39). $\int \dfrac{x^5\,dx}{(x^3+1)^3}$.

(40). $\int_0^{\frac{1}{2}\pi} \dfrac{\cos x\,dx}{\sqrt{(3+\cos 2x)}}$.

(41). $\int_0^{\frac{1}{2}\pi} \cos\theta\log(1+\sin\theta)\,d\theta$.

(42). $\int_0^\infty \dfrac{dx}{(1+e^x)(1-e^{-x})}$.

(43). $\int_0^1 \dfrac{x\,dx}{\sqrt{(1-x^2)}}$.

(44). $\int_0^{\frac{1}{2}\pi} \dfrac{\sin 2x\,dx}{1+\cos^2 x}$.

Integrate *without* a substitution the following★ integrals:

(45). $\int_0^1 x\sqrt{(x+1)}\,dx$.

(46). $\int_1^2 \dfrac{(x+1)\,dx}{\sqrt{(x+2)}}$.

(47). $\int \dfrac{dx}{\sqrt{(x+a)}-\sqrt{(x-a)}}$.

(48). $\int_0^1 \dfrac{x\,dx}{\sqrt{(2x^2-2x+1)}}$.

(49). $\int_0^{\frac{1}{6}} \dfrac{(1+2x)\,dx}{\sqrt{(1-9x^2)}}$.

(50). $\int_{\frac{1}{3}}^{\frac{1}{2}} \dfrac{dx}{\sqrt{[x(1+x)]}}$.

(51). $\int_1^3 \dfrac{dx}{\sqrt{[(3-x)(x-1)]}}$.

(52). $\int_1^\infty \dfrac{dx}{x\sqrt{(25x^2-1)}}$.

By a suitable change of variable, integrate the following★:

(53). $\int_3^4 \dfrac{dx}{x\sqrt{(4-x)}}$.

(54). $\int \dfrac{\sqrt{x}\,dx}{1+x}$.

(55). $\int_0^\infty \dfrac{dx}{(x^2+1)^2}$.

(56). $\int \dfrac{dx}{(x+1)\sqrt{(x+2)}}$.

(57). $\int_a^\infty \dfrac{dx}{x^2\sqrt{(a^2+x^2)}}$.

(58). $\int_{\frac{1}{2}a}^a \dfrac{dx}{x^2\sqrt{(a^2-x^2)}}$.

(59). $\displaystyle\int_0^\pi \frac{\sin x \, dx}{\sin x - 2\cos x + 2}$.

(60). $\displaystyle\int_0^\pi \frac{d\theta}{4 - 3\sin\theta}$.

(61). $\displaystyle\int_0^{\frac{1}{6}\pi} \frac{d\theta}{\cos\theta + \cos^3\theta}$.

(62). $\displaystyle\int_0^{\frac{1}{2}\pi} \frac{d\theta}{3 + 5\cos\theta}$.

(63). $\displaystyle\int_0^\pi \frac{d\theta}{a^2 - 2ab\cos\theta + b^2}$, $(a > b)$.

(64). $\displaystyle\int \frac{x^2(x+1)\,dx}{(x^2+1)^3}$.

(65). $\displaystyle\int_{\frac{1}{2}}^1 \frac{dx}{x\sqrt{(5x^2 - 4x + 1)}}$.

(66). $\displaystyle\int_{\frac{1}{4}}^{\frac{1}{2}} \frac{dx}{x\sqrt{(1 + 2x - 8x^2)}}$.

(67). $\displaystyle\int_0^a x\sqrt{\left(\frac{a-x}{a+x}\right)}\,dx$.

(68). $\displaystyle\int_{-\infty}^\infty \frac{dx}{\cosh x + \cos\alpha}$, $(0 < \alpha < \pi)$.

(69). $\displaystyle\int_1^a \frac{dx}{x\sqrt{(x^4 - 1)}}$, $(a > 1)$.

(70). $\displaystyle\int_a^b \sqrt{\left(\frac{b-x}{x-a}\right)}\,dx$.

(71). $\displaystyle\int_1^2 \frac{dx}{(x+1)\sqrt{(x^2 - 1)}}$.

(72). $\displaystyle\int_0^{\frac{1}{4}\pi} \cos\theta\sqrt{(\cos 2\theta)}\,d\theta$.

(73). $\displaystyle\int_0^{\frac{1}{2}\pi} \frac{dx}{a^2\cos^2 x + b^2\sin^2 x + c^2}$.

(74). $\displaystyle\int_0^1 \sqrt{(x^2 + 3)}\,dx$.

(75) ★. Show that

$$\int_0^\pi \frac{d\theta}{5 + 3\cos\theta} = \tfrac{1}{4}\pi .$$

Hence, or otherwise, evaluate

$$\int_0^\pi \frac{\cos\theta + 2\sin\theta}{5 + 3\cos\theta}\,d\theta.$$

(76) ★. Show that

$$\int_0^a f(x)\,dx = \int_0^a f(a - x)\,dx,$$

and prove that

$$\int_0^\pi \frac{x\,dx}{4 + \sin^2 x} = \pi^2(\sqrt 5)/20.$$

(77) ★. Prove that constants λ, μ, ν can be found, so

$$\lambda(\alpha x^2 + 1) + (\mu x + \nu)\,d(\alpha x^2 + 1)/dx \equiv x^2 + 1, \qquad (\alpha \neq 0).$$

Hence show that the integral $\int [(x^2 + 1)/(\alpha x^2 + 1)^2]\,dx$ can be expressed as a rational function of x only if $\alpha = -1$ or 0.

(78) ★. If $I = \displaystyle\int_0^\pi \frac{x\sin x\,dx}{1 + \cos^2 x}$, prove that $I = \displaystyle\int_0^\pi \frac{(\pi - x)\sin x\,dx}{1 + \cos^2 x}$, and hence, or otherwise, deduce that $I = \tfrac{1}{4}\pi^2$.

Simpson's rule for approximate integration.

(79) ★. Obtain an approximate value for $\log_e 2$ by applying Simpson's rule to $\displaystyle\int_1^2 dx/x$, dividing the interval into ten equal parts.

(80) ★. Find the approximate value of the integral $\displaystyle\int_1^3 \frac{dx}{1 + x}$ by using Simpson's formula and five ordinates.

(81)★. Find, correct to four decimal places, the value yielded for the integral $\int_0^1 \dfrac{4\,dx}{1+x^2}$ by Simpson's rule using five ordinates.

(82)★. Evaluate $\int_0^{\frac{1}{2}\pi} \sin^{\frac{3}{2}} x \, dx$ approximately by Simpson's rule, using five ordinates (i.e. at intervals of 15°).

(83)★. Evaluate $\int_0^{\frac{1}{2}\pi} \theta \sin^2 \theta \, d\theta$ to three decimal places both by an exact method and by Simpson's rule using five ordinates.

(84)★. Prove that the length of the whole perimeter of the ellipse given by the parametric equations $x = 3\cos\theta$, $y = 2\sin\theta$ is equal to

$$2\sqrt{2} \int_0^{\frac{1}{2}\pi} \sqrt{(13 - 5\cos 2\theta)}\, d\theta,$$

and evaluate this integral by Simpson's rule, dividing the range $(0, \frac{1}{2}\pi)$ into six equal intervals.

(85)★. Find by Simpson's rule an approximate value of the integral $\int_0^1 e^{-x^2}\, dx$ using the following table:

x	0·00	0·25	0·50	0·75	1·00
e^{-x^2}	1·0000	0·9394	0·7788	0·5698	0·3679

Compare the approximate value with that obtained by expanding e^{-x^2} as a series in ascending powers of x, and integrating term by term.

(86)★. The speed in ft./sec. of a train accelerating from rest is recorded at 5-second intervals as follows:

t sec.	0	5	10	15	20	25	30	35	40
v ft./sec.	0	3·9	10·4	18·1	26·4	35·4	44·7	54·5	64·5

Estimate the distance in feet covered in the 40 seconds.

Reduction formulae

(87)★. If $I_n = \int_0^\infty x^n e^{-x}\, dx$, prove that for n a positive integer, $I_n = nI_{n-1}$. Deduce that $I_n = n!$

(88)★. If $f_n(x) = \dfrac{1}{n!}\int_0^x t^n e^{-t}\, dt$, prove that $f_n(x) - f_{n-1}(x) = -\dfrac{x^n e^{-x}}{n!}$. Hence, or otherwise, evaluate the integral $\int_1^2 t^3 e^{-t}\, dt$.

(89)★. If $I_n = \int_0^1 \dfrac{x^n}{\sqrt{(1+x^2)}}\, dx$, prove that $nI_n = \sqrt{2} - (n-1)I_{n-2}$. Hence show that $I_5 = \frac{1}{15}(7\sqrt{2} - 8)$.

(90)★. If $I_n = \int \exp(-x^3)x^{3n+2}\, dx$, show that

$$3I_n - 3nI_{n-1} + \exp(-x^3)x^{3n} = 0,$$

and use this result to evaluate $\int_0^1 \exp(-x^3)x^8\, dx$.

(91)★. If $I_n = \int_0^{\frac{1}{4}\pi} \tan^n x \, dx$, show that, for $n \geqslant 2$, $I_n = (n-1)^{-1} - I_{n-2}$. Evaluate I_5 and I_6.

(92) $\star$. If $I_n = \displaystyle\int_0^1 x^p(1 - x)^n \, dx$, where p and n are positive, show that

$$(n + p + 1)I_n = nI_{n-1}.$$

If $p = \frac{1}{2}$, evaluate I_4.

(93) $\star$. If $I_n = \int x^n \sin x \, dx$, prove that

$$I_n = nx^{n-1} \sin x - x^n \cos x - n(n - 1)I_{n-2},$$

and evaluate I_5.

(94) $\star$. If $a \neq 0$, and $I_m = \int x^m e^{ax} \, dx$, find a reduction formula giving I_m in terms of I_{m-1}. Show that, if m is a positive integer,

$$\int_0^t x^m e^{ax} \, dx = \frac{(-1)^m m! \, e^{at}}{a^{m+1}} \left[1 - \frac{at}{1!} + \frac{(at)^2}{2!} - \ldots + \frac{(-1)^m (at)^m}{m!} \right] - \frac{(-1)^m m!}{a^{m+1}}.$$

(95) $\star$. If $I_n = \int \sec^n \theta \, d\theta$, show that, when $n \geqslant 1$,

$$(n - 1)I_n = \sec^{n-2} \theta \tan \theta + (n - 2)I_{n-2}.$$

Show that $8 \displaystyle\int_0^{\frac{1}{4}\pi} \sec^5 \theta \, d\theta = 7\sqrt{2} + 3 \log (1 + \sqrt{2})$. Evaluate $\displaystyle\int_0^a \frac{dx}{(2a^2 - x^2)^3}$.

(96) $\star$. Obtain a reduction formula expressing $\int (x^2 + a^2)^{\frac{1}{2}n} \, dx$ in terms of

$$\int (x^2 + a^2)^{\frac{1}{2}n-1} \, dx.$$

Prove that $\displaystyle\int_0^a (x^2 + a^2)^{\frac{3}{2}} \, dx = \frac{1}{8}a^4[7\sqrt{2} + 3 \log (1 + \sqrt{2})].$

(97) $\star$. If n is a positive integer, prove that

$$\frac{3n - 3}{(x^3 + 1)^n} = \frac{d}{dx}\left(\frac{x}{(x^3 + 1)^{n-1}} \right) + \frac{3n - 4}{(x^3 + 1)^{n-1}}.$$

Hence, if $I_n = \displaystyle\int_0^1 \frac{dx}{(x^3 + 1)^n}$, prove the reduction formula

$$3(n - 1)I_n = \frac{1}{2}^{n-1} + (3n - 4)I_{n-1}.$$

Deduce that $I_2 = \frac{1}{6} + \frac{2}{9} \log 2 + \frac{2}{27}\pi\sqrt{3}.$

(98) $\star$. If $I_n = \displaystyle\int_0^1 x^n \sqrt{(1 - x)} \, dx$, where n is a positive integer, prove that

$$(3 + 2n)I_n = 2nI_{n-1}.$$

Hence show $\qquad I_n = 2^{2n+2}n! \, (n + 1)!/(2n + 3)!.$

(99) $\star$. If $I_n = \displaystyle\int_0^\infty x^n \exp (-x^2) \, dx$, prove that, if $n > 0$, $I_n = 2I_{n+2}/(n + 1)$, and express I_n in terms of I_{n-2}. Deduce that $I_5 = 1$.

(100) $\star$. Prove that $d^2(\sin^n x)/dx^2 + n^2 \sin^n x = n(n - 1) \sin^{n-2} x$ where n is any constant.

If $I_n = \displaystyle\int_0^\pi e^{-x} \sin^n x \, dx$ show that $I_n = n(n - 1)I_{n-2}/(n^2 + 1)$ where n is an integer greater than 2. Show that $I_6 = \frac{144}{629}(1 - e^{-\pi})$.

(101)★. By differentiating $\sin\theta\cos\theta/(1 + \sin^2\theta)^n$ with respect to θ, and expressing the result in powers of y where $y = 1 + \sin^2\theta$, show that if $I_n = \int_0^{\frac{1}{2}\pi} \dfrac{d\theta}{(1 + \sin^2\theta)^n}$, then $4nI_{n+1} = (6n - 3)I_n - 2(n - 1)I_{n-1}$. Show that $I_1 = \frac{1}{4}\pi\sqrt{2}$, and hence that $I_2 = \frac{3}{16}\pi\sqrt{2}$.

(102)★. If $T_{m,n} = \int_{-1}^1 (1 - x)^m(1 + x)^n \, dx$, where $m \geqslant 0$, $n \geqslant 0$, show that

(i) $(n + 1)T_{m,n} = mT_{m-1,n+1}$, $(m \geqslant 1)$; (ii) $(m + n + 1)T_{m,n} = 2mT_{m-1,n}$ $(m \geqslant 1)$. Evaluate $T_{3,2}$.

(103)★. If $u(n, m) = \int_0^1 x^n(1 - x)^m \, dx$, and m, n are positive, prove that

$$(n + 1)u(n, m) = mu(n + 1, m - 1).$$

Using this result, evaluate the integral $\int_0^a x^{5/2}(a - x)^3 \, dx$.

(104)★. Show that, if $A(m, n) = \int_0^x t^m(t^2 + a^2)^n \, dt$, then

$$2(n + 1)A(m, n) = x^{m-1}(x^2 + a^2)^{n+1} - (m - 1)A(m - 2, n + 1); \quad (m > 1),$$

and $(2n + 1)A(0, n) = x(x^2 + a^2)^n + 2na^2A(0, n - 1)$.

Hence evaluate $\int_0^1 x^2\sqrt{(x^2 + 3)} \, dx$.

Applications of integration

(105)★. Sketch the curve $y^2(1 - x)(x - 2) = x^2$. Prove that the area between the curve and its asymptotes is 3π.

(106)★. Sketch the curve $y^2 = x^2(1 - x)/(3 + x)^2$ and show that the area of its loop is $4(10 - 9\log 3)/3$.

(107)★. Sketch the curve $16y^2 = x^2(2 - x^2)$ and find the area of one loop. Show that the total length of the curve is 2π.

(108)★. Sketch the general shape of the curve $y = (x - 1)^2/(x + 1)^4$. Prove that there is a maximum at which $y = \frac{1}{64}$. Prove that the area contained between the curve and the x-axis for $x > 1$ is $\frac{1}{6}$.

(109)★. Prove that the area included between the curves $y^2 = 4ax$ and $x^2 - 2ax + y^2 = 3a^2$ and the y-axis is $\frac{1}{3}(2\pi + 3\sqrt{3} - 8)a^2$.

(110)★. Sketch the curve $y = -\log(1 - x^2)$, and find its length from the origin to the point where $x = X$ $(0 < X < 1)$. Find also the area bounded by the curve, the x-axis, and the ordinate $x = X$. Show that, as $X \to 1$, this area tends to the limit $2 - 2\log 2$.

(111). If P and Q are the points at which t has the values 0 and π respectively on the cycloid $x = a(t + \sin t)$, $y = a(1 - \cos t)$, find the length of the arc PQ and the area bounded by this arc and the chord PQ.

(112)★. Show that, as θ increases from $-\pi$ to π, the point (x, y), where $x = a\cos^3\theta$, $y = a\sin^3\theta$ $(a > 0)$, describes a simple closed curve. Find the area which is enclosed by the curve.

(113)★. Show that the curve $x = ae^{-t}(t - 1)$, $y = xt$, has a loop given by $1 \leqslant t \leqslant \infty$, and find its area.

(114)★. Show that, as t varies from 0 to ∞, the point whose coordinates are given by $x = 3at/(1 + t^3)$, $y = 3at^2/(1 + t^3)$ describes a closed curve and show that the area enclosed by it is $3a^2/2$.

(115)★. Show that the finite area bounded by the parabola $l/r = 1 + \cos\theta$ and a chord through the focus which makes an angle $\pi/3$ with the axis is $16l^2/9\sqrt{3}$.

(116)★. Trace the curve whose polar equation is $r^2 = a^2 \cos 2\theta$. Show that, at the point P on the curve where $\theta = \pi/6$, the tangent to the curve is parallel to the initial line. Show also that the line OP divides the area of one loop of the curve in the ratio $2 - \sqrt{3} : 2 + \sqrt{3}$.

(117)★. Show that $\displaystyle\int_0^\pi \frac{d\theta}{1 + e\cos\theta} = \frac{\pi}{\sqrt{(1 - e^2)}}$ $\quad(0 < e < 1)$.

If each focal radius vector of an ellipse is produced a constant length c, show that the area between the curve so formed and the ellipse is $\pi c/(2b + c)$, b being the semi-minor axis of the ellipse.

(118)★. Starting from the point whose polar coordinates are $(a, 0)$, a point P moves in the plane in such a way that the direction of its motion always makes the same angle $\frac{1}{4}\pi$ with the radius vector OP. Prove that the equation of the locus of P is $r = ae^\theta$. Prove that the difference of the areas described by the radius vector OP as θ increases (i) from $2(n - 1)\pi$ to $2n\pi$, (ii) from $2n\pi$ to $2(n + 1)\pi$, is $a^2 e^{4n\pi} \sinh^2 2\pi$. Shade on a sketch the area so calculated when $n = 2$.

---

(119)★. Find the total length of the curve whose parametric equations are $x = a\sin^3 t$, $y = a\cos^3 t$, and prove that the shortest distance between the curve and the origin is $\frac{1}{2}a$.

(120)★. Sketch the curve given by $x = 4t$, $y = t^2 - 2\log_e t$ where t is a variable parameter, for values of t from 1 to 3. If A and B are the points corresponding to $t = 1$ and $t = 3$ respectively, calculate (i) the length of the arc AB, (ii) the area bounded by the arc AB, the x-axis and the ordinates through A and B.

(121)★. Sketch the curve $3ay^2 = x(x - a)^2$, where $a > 0$. Show that $dy/dx = \pm(3x - a)/[2\sqrt{(3ax)}]$ and hence show that the perimeter of the loop of the curve is $4a/\sqrt{3}$.

(122)★. Find the area of the region bounded by the two arcs of the parabolae $y^2 = ax$ $(a > 0)$, $x^2 = by$ $(b > 0)$. Show that, when $b = a$, the perimeter of this region is $[\frac{1}{2}\log(2 + \sqrt{5}) + \sqrt{5}]a$.

(123)★. Prove that the curve $x = \cos^3 t$, $y = 2\sin^3 t$ is of length $\frac{28}{3}$ and encloses an area $\frac{3}{4}\pi$.

(124)★. Trace the curve given by $x = a(2t - \sin 2t)$, $y = 2a\sin^2 t$ where t ranges from 0 to π. Prove that the length of the arc of the curve in this range is $8a$, and calculate the area between the arc and the x-axis.

---

(125)★. Prove that the area enclosed between the curve $x^2 - y^2 = a^2$ and the line $x = 2a$ is $2a^2\sqrt{3} - a^2\log_e(2 + \sqrt{3})$, and find the position of its mean centre. Find the volume generated when this area is revolved about the y-axis through four right-angles.

(126)★. A solid of revolution is formed by rotating the loop of the curve $ay^2 = x(x-a)^2$ about the x-axis. Prove that the volume of the solid is nine-sixteenths of the volume of the cylinder of the same length whose generators touch the solid along the circumference of its greatest circular cross-section.

(127)★. The area enclosed by the parabola $y^2 = 6ax + 16a^2$ and the ordinates $x = 0$, $x = 4a$ is rotated about the axis of x to form a solid of revolution. Show that the area of the curved surface of the solid is $436\pi a^2/9$. The volume generated by rotating about the x-axis the area enclosed by the parabola $y^2 = 5ax + 6a^2$ and the ordinates $x = a$, $x = 4a$ is removed from the above solid to leave a hollow vessel. Find the volume of the material of the vessel.

(128)★. A is the vertex and LL' ($= 4a$) the latus rectum of a parabola. Find the area generated when the arc AL is rotated through four right-angles (i) about the axis of the parabola, (ii) about LL'.

(129)★. Sketch in the same diagram the curves $xy^2 = a^2(a - x)$ and $(a - y)y^2 = a^2x$. Prove that they enclose an area $(\pi - 2)a^2$, and find the volume of the solid obtained by rotating this area through two right-angles about the line $y = 0$.

(130)★. The region bounded by a quadrant of a circle of radius a, and the tangents at its extremities, revolves through 360° about one of these tangents. Prove that the volume of the solid thus generated is $(10 - 3\pi)\pi a^3/6$, and the area of its curved surface $\pi(\pi - 2)a^2$.

(131)★. Prove that the volume generated when the area enclosed by the curve $x = a(1 - t^2)$, $y = 2a(1 + t)$ and the y-axis is rotated through 2π about the x-axis is five times the volume generated when the same area is rotated about the y-axis.

(132)★. Sketch the curve $y^2 = x^2(a - x)/(a + x)$, $(a > 0)$, and show that the tangents to the curve at the origin are perpendicular. Show also that the area enclosed by the loop of the curve is $(2 - \frac{1}{2}\pi)a^2$.
Show that the volume generated when the area enclosed by the loop is rotated through π about the x-axis is $\frac{1}{3}\pi a^3(6 \log 2 - 4)$.

(133)★. Show that the curve $r = 1 + 2 \cos \theta$ consists of an outer and an inner loop. If the area of the inner loop is rotated through two right-angles about the initial line, show that the volume so formed is $\pi/12$.

(134)★. The area enclosed by the lemniscate $r^2 = a^2 \cos 2\theta$ is rotated through two right-angles about the line $\theta = \frac{1}{2}\pi$. Prove that the volume of the solid formed is $\sqrt{2}\pi^2a^3/8$.

(135)★. Sketch the curve $r = a \cos^2 \theta$, showing that it consists of two loops. Show that the length of one loop is $a[2\sqrt{3} + \log (2 + \sqrt{3})]/\sqrt{3}$, and find the area enclosed by it. Find the distance between the initial line and a tangent to the curve parallel to the initial line, and show that the volume obtained by rotating one of the loops through 2π about this tangent is $\pi^2a^3/4\sqrt{3}$.

---

(136)★. Show that the centroid of the area bounded by the x-axis and the arc of the curve $y = a \sin x$ between the points $(0, 0)$, $(\pi, 0)$ is the point $(\frac{1}{2}\pi, \frac{1}{8}\pi a)$. Show also that the radius of gyration of this area about the x-axis is $(a\sqrt{2})/3$.

(137)★. The area bounded by the upper half of the parabola $y^2 = 4ax$, the x-axis and the ordinate $x = a$, is rotated through four right-angles about the tangent at the vertex. Prove that the volume of the solid so formed is $8\pi a^3/5$, and find the position of the centroid of this solid.

(138)*. ABC is a semicircle, with diameter AC of length $2a$. Show, by using the theorem of Pappus that the centroid of the area ABC is distant $4a/3\pi$ from AC. If OP and OQ are the bounding radii of a quadrant of a circle, and the semicircle with OP as diameter is cut away from the quadrant, find the position of the centroid of the area remaining.

(139)*. Sketch the curve $ay^2 = x^2(a - x)$ and find the area of its loop. Find also the position of the centroid of this area and deduce the volume of the solid formed when this area is rotated through 2π about a tangent to the curve at the origin.

(140)*. Sketch the curve $r^2 = a^2 \cos 2\theta$ and find the coordinates of the centroid of one of its loops.

(141)*. A circular lamina of radius a is constructed in such a way that its surface density varies as the 4th power of the distance from a fixed point, O, on the circumference. Using polar coordinates, with O as origin, show that the centroid lies at a distance $\frac{3}{4}a$ from O.

---

(142)*. A shell is formed by rotating the portion of the parabola $y^2 = 4ax$ for which $0 \leqslant x \leqslant 1$ through two right-angles about its axis. Prove that the area of its curved surface is $8\pi(2\sqrt{2} - 1)/3$, and that its radius of gyration k about the axis of rotation is given by $35k^2 = 8(5 + 3\sqrt{2})$.

(143)*. The area bounded by the curve $y^2 = 4a(b - x)$ and the y-axis is rotated through two right-angles about the x-axis. Show that the volume of the solid of revolution is $2\pi ab^2$, and find the radius of gyration of this solid about the y-axis.

(144)*. The area bounded by the curve $y = c \cosh(x/c)$, the coordinate axes and the line $x = a$ is occupied by a lamina of uniform thickness and mass M. Show that the moment of inertia of the lamina about the y-axis is $M[a^2 - 2ca \coth(a/c) + 2c^2]$.

(145)*. Find the moments of inertia of an elliptic lamina about its principal axes and also about the axis through the centre perpendicular to the plane of the lamina.

(146)*. The area bounded by the curve $y^2 = x^3$, the lines $y = 0$, $y = 1$, $x = -1$, rotates about the line $x = -1$. Find correct to one-tenth of a unit, the radius of gyration of the volume developed about the axis of rotation.

(147)*. The smaller of the two areas into which the latus rectum $x = ae$ divides the ellipse $x^2/a^2 + y^2/b^2 = 1$ is rotated through four right-angles about the line $x = 0$. Find the volume of the solid generated by the area and show that the radius of gyration of this solid about the line $x = 0$ is $\sqrt{(a^2 - \frac{3}{5}b^2)}$.

ANSWERS TO EXERCISES

(1). $\frac{2}{3}$. (2). $-\frac{1}{12}\pi + \frac{1}{8}\sqrt{3} + \frac{17}{480}$. (3). $\frac{2}{3}$. (4). $\log 2 - \frac{3}{8}$. (5). $\frac{1}{16}$.

(6). $\frac{5}{4} - \frac{1}{2}\sqrt{2}$. (7). $\log 3$. (8). $\frac{1}{32}\pi$.

(9). $-\log(\operatorname{cosec}\theta + \cot\theta) + \sec\theta - \tan\theta$. (10). $(\tan^{n+1} x)/(n + 1)$.

(11). $\cos^3 x$. (12). $\frac{1}{4}\sinh 2 + \frac{1}{2}$. (13). 1. (14). 16.

(15). $-\frac{1}{2}(x^2 + 1)e^{-x^2}$. (16). $\frac{2}{5}(1 + e^{\frac{1}{2}\pi})$.

(17). $(\frac{1}{2}x^2 - \frac{1}{4})\sin^{-1} x + \frac{1}{4}x\sqrt{(1 - x^2)}$. (18). $\frac{1}{16}\pi^2 - \frac{1}{4}$.

(19). $e^{4x}(4 \cos 3x + 3 \sin 3x)/25$. (20). $\frac{1}{2}(\sin x \cosh x - \sinh x \cos x)$.

(21). $\frac{1}{2}x^2 \tan^{-1}(x + 1) - \frac{1}{2}x + \frac{1}{2}\log(x^2 + 2x + 2)$.

(22). $x - \sqrt{(1 - x^2)}\sin^{-1} x$. (23). $t(1 - \log t)$. (24). $\frac{1}{2}\pi - 1$.

(25). $\log x - (1 + 1/x)\log(1 + x)$. (26). $u \tanh^{-1} u + \frac{1}{2}\log(1 - u^2)$.

(27). $\frac{1}{4}\log[(x - 1)/(x + 1)] + \frac{1}{2}/(x + 1)$. (28). $\frac{1}{2}\log 3 - \frac{1}{4}\pi$.

(29). $\log x - \tan^{-1} x - 1/x$.

(30). $x + \frac{3}{5}\log(x-2) + \frac{1}{5}\log(x^2+1) - \frac{1}{5}\tan^{-1} x$.　　(31). $\log\frac{4}{3} - \frac{1}{8}$.

(32). $(2\pi + 3\log 2 - 5)/25$.　　(33). $\log[(x^2+1)/(x+1)^2] + \tan^{-1} x$.

(34). $x + \frac{3}{2}\log(2x+1) - \log(x^2+2) - \frac{1}{2}\sqrt{2}\tan^{-1}(\frac{1}{2}\sqrt{2}x)$.

(35). $\frac{1}{2}(\log 2)^2$.　　(36). $\log\frac{4}{3}$.　　(37). $a^7/7$.　　(38). $e^2 - e + \log(e+1)$.

(39). $-(2x^3+1)/(x^3+1)^2$.　　(40). $\pi/4\sqrt{2}$.　　(41). $\log 4 - 1$.

(42). $\frac{1}{2}\log(\coth\frac{1}{2}x)$.　　(43). 1.　　(44). $\log\frac{5}{3}$.　　(45). $\frac{4}{15}(\sqrt{2}+1)$.

(46). $\frac{4}{3}$.　　(47). $[(x+a)^{\frac{3}{2}} + (x-a)^{\frac{3}{2}}]/3a$.　　(48). $2^{-\frac{1}{2}}\log(1+\sqrt{2})$.

(49). $\frac{1}{18}\pi - \frac{1}{9}\sqrt{3} + \frac{2}{9}$.　　(50). $\log\frac{3}{2}$.　　(51). π.　　(52). $\frac{1}{2}(\pi - 2\sec^{-1} 5)$.

(53). $\frac{1}{2}\log 3, 4 - x = u^2$.　　(54). $2\sqrt{x} - 2\tan^{-1}\sqrt{x}, x = u^2$.

(55). $\frac{1}{4}\pi, x = \tan\theta$.　　(56). $\log[\sqrt{(x+2)} - 1]/[\sqrt{(x+2)} + 1], x + 2 = u^2$.

(57). $(\sqrt{2}-1)/a^2, x = a\tan\theta$.　　(58). $a^{-2}\sqrt{3}, x = a\sin\theta$.

(59). $\frac{2}{5}(4\log 2 + \pi), t = \tan\frac{1}{2}x$.　　(60). $[\pi + 2\tan^{-1}(3/\sqrt{7})]/\sqrt{7}, t = \tan\frac{1}{2}\theta$.

(61). $\frac{1}{2}\log 3 + \frac{1}{4}\sqrt{2}\log[(2\sqrt{2}-1)^2/7], t = \tan\theta$.　　(62). $\frac{1}{4}\log 3, t = \tan\frac{1}{2}\theta$.

(63). $\pi/(a^2 - b^2), t = \tan\frac{1}{2}\theta$.

(64). $(2x^4 + x^3 - x)/8(1 + x^2)^2 + \frac{1}{8}\tan^{-1} x, x = \tan\theta$.

(65). $\log(\sqrt{2}+1), x = 1/y$.　　(66). $\log[(2+\sqrt{3})/3], x = 1/y$.

(67). $(1 - \frac{1}{4}\pi)a^2, x = a\sin\theta$.　　(68). $2\alpha/\sin\alpha, u = e^x$

(69). $\frac{1}{4}(\pi - 2\sin^{-1}(1/a^2)), x = 1/y$.　　(70). $\frac{1}{2}\pi(b-a), u^2 = (b-x)/(x-a)$.

(71). $1/\sqrt{3}, x + 1 = 1/y$.　　(72). $\pi/4\sqrt{2}, \sqrt{2}\sin\theta = \sin\phi$.

(73). $\frac{1}{2}\pi/\sqrt{[(a^2+c^2)(b^2+c^2)]}, t = \tan x$.　　(74). $1 + \frac{3}{4}\log 3, x = 3^{\frac{1}{3}}\sinh\theta$.

(75). $\frac{2}{3}\log 4 - \frac{1}{12}\pi$.　　(76). $\lambda = 1, \mu = (1-\alpha)/2\alpha, \nu = 0$.　　(79). 0·69315.

(80). 0·693.　　(81). 3·1416.　　(82). 0·370.　　(83). 0·867.　　(84). 15·9.

(85). 0·7468.　　(86). 1125 ft.　　(88). $16/e - 38/e^2$.　　(90). $(2 + e^{-1})/3$.

(91). $\frac{1}{2}\log 2 - \frac{1}{4}, \frac{13}{15} - \frac{1}{4}\pi$.　　(92). $2^5 4!/3.5.7.9.11$.

(93). $(5x^4 - 60x^2 + 120)\sin x - (x^5 - 20x^3 + 120x)\cos x$.

(94). $I_m = x^m e^{ax}/a - mI_{m-1}/a$.　　(95). $[14 + 3\sqrt{2}\log(1+\sqrt{2})]/64a^5$.

(96). $(1+n)I_n = x(x^2+a^2)^{\frac{1}{2}n} + a^2 nI_{n-2}$.　　(99). $I_n = \frac{1}{2}(n-1)I_{n-2}$.

(102). $\frac{16}{15}$.　　(103). $96a^{13/2}/13.11.9.7$.　　(104). $(10 - 9\log\sqrt{3})/8$.

(107). $\frac{1}{3}\sqrt{2}$.　　(110). $-X + \log[(1+X)/(1-X)]$; $2X - X\log(1-X^2)$, $-\log[(1+X)/(1-X)]$.　　(111). $4a, \frac{1}{2}\pi a^2$.　　(112). $3\pi a^2/8$.

(113). $a^2/8e^2$.　　(119). $6a$.　　(120). $4 + \log 3, \frac{152}{3} - 24\log 3$.　　(122). $ab/3$.

(124). $3\pi a^2$.　　(125). $2\sqrt{3}a[2\sqrt{3} - \log(2+\sqrt{3})], 4\pi\sqrt{3}a^3$.　　(127). $75\pi a^3/2$.

(128). $\frac{8}{3}\pi a^2(2\sqrt{2}-1), \frac{1}{2}\pi a^2[5\log(1+\sqrt{2}) + \sqrt{2}]$.　　(129). $\pi a^3(\log 2 - \frac{1}{3})$.

(135). $3\pi a^2/16, 2a/3\sqrt{3}$.　　(137). $x = \frac{3}{8}a$.

(138). $(\frac{3}{8}/\pi - \frac{1}{2})OP$ from OP, $(2/\pi)OP$ from OQ.

(139). $8a^2/15, 4a/7, 32\sqrt{2}\pi a^3/105$.　　(140). $a\pi/4\sqrt{2}$ from origin.

(143). $\sqrt{[b(b+4a)/6]}$.　　(145). $\frac{1}{4}\pi a^3 b, \frac{1}{4}\pi ab^3, \frac{1}{4}\pi ab(a^2+b^2)$.　　(146). 1·2.

(147). $\frac{4}{3}\pi b^4/a$.

CHAPTER 17

SIMPLE MULTIPLE INTEGRALS

17.1 Definitions

We are given the function of two variables $z = z(x, y)$, represented by a surface above the x,y-plane. Moreover, we are given a closed curve $y = f(x)$ in the x, y-plane; usually this consists of a number of distinct arcs, each defined by separate equations.

The equation $y = f(x)$ defines a cylinder standing on the closed curve in the x,y-plane. We seek the value of the volume within this cylinder intercepted between the x, y-plane and the surface $z = z(x, y)$. Let $P(x, y)$ be any point in an element of area δA within the closed curve in the x, y-plane. Then the value of the volume above δA is $z(x, y)\, \delta A$ approximately. We may sum such contributions for all elements of area within $y = f(x)$, obtaining $\Sigma\, z(x, y)\, \delta A$. Finally, if this

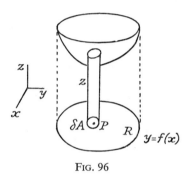

FIG. 96

sum tends to a unique limit V as the largest of the elements of area tends to zero (in such a way that its circumference also tends to zero), then this limit V is the required volume. We write

$$V = \iint_R z(x, y)\, dA,$$

where the region R is the area within $y = f(x)$ over which the integral is calculated. It should be noticed that the value of the limit must be independent of the mode of subdivision of the area within $y = f(x)$ into elements of area. The examination of sufficient conditions for this to be so is beyond the scope of this text; it suffices to say that the functions usually considered in elementary theory satisfy the conditions.

In particular, let the region R be the area within the rectangle bounded by the straight lines $x = a, b$ $(b > a)$ and $y = c, d$ $(d > c)$. Let $A(x)$ denote the area of the section standing above the ordinate at x between

$y = c$ and d; then the volume element is $A(x)\,\delta x$ for a thickness δx.

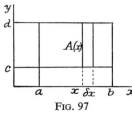

FIG. 97

Totally, we have

$$V = \int_a^b A(x)\,dx.$$

But the cross sectional area $A(x)$ is given by

$$A(x) = \int_c^d z(x, y)\,dy,$$

with x constant. Hence

$$V = \int_a^b \left[\int_c^d z(x, y)\,dy \right] dx.$$

Note that the last symbol dx on the right corresponds to the first set of limits a, b on the left. With this convention, we may write

$$V = \int_a^b \int_c^d z(x, y)\,dy\,dx.$$

If, instead, a strip is taken parallel to Ox, we find that

$$V = \int_c^d \int_a^b z(x, y)\,dx\,dy.$$

The interchange of the order of integration is only as simple as this when the four limits involved are constants.

In particular, if the integrand $z(x, y)$ is *separable*, that is, if it consists of a product of a function $u(x)$ of x alone and a function $v(y)$ of y alone, we have

$$V = \int_a^b \int_c^d u(x)v(y)\,dy\,dx = \int_a^b u(x) \int_c^d v(y)\,dy\,dx$$

$$= \left(\int_a^b u(x)\,dx \right)\left(\int_c^d v(y)\,dy \right).$$

Example 1   Find the volume between the planes $z = 0$, $x = -\tfrac{1}{2}\pi$, $x = \tfrac{1}{2}\pi$, $y = 0$, $y = \tfrac{1}{2}\pi$ and the surface $z = \sin(x + y)$.

We have directly

$$V = \int_0^{\frac{1}{2}\pi} \int_{-\frac{1}{2}\pi}^{\frac{1}{2}\pi} \sin(x + y)\,dx\,dy$$

$$= \int_0^{\frac{1}{2}\pi} \left[-\cos(x + y) \right]_{-\frac{1}{2}\pi}^{\frac{1}{2}\pi} dy = \int_0^{\frac{1}{2}\pi} [-\cos(y + \tfrac{1}{2}\pi) + \cos(y - \tfrac{1}{2}\pi)]\,dy$$

$$= \int_0^{\frac{1}{2}\pi} 2 \sin y\,dy = 2.$$

The region R is usually not as simple as a rectangle. In this case, because the limits are constant, it is immaterial whether we integrate first with respect to x or y.

Let us suppose, for any value of x, that the lower limit of integration

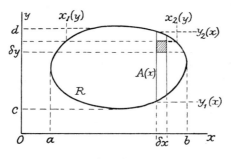

FIG. 98

with respect to y is $y_1(x)$ and the upper limit $y_2(x)$. Then the area $A(x)$ intercepted by the surface $z = z(x, y)$ for constant x is

$$A(x) = \int_{y_1(x)}^{y_2(x)} z(x, y)\, dy.$$

Then if x varies from a to b in order to traverse the whole region R, the total volume is given by

$$V = \int_a^b A(x)\, dx = \int_a^b \int_{y_1(x)}^{y_2(x)} z(x, y)\, dy\, dx.$$

It is clear that the integration with respect to y, involving limits which are functions of x, must be carried out first.

If the order of integration is reversed, integration with respect to x involves limits depending on y, namely $x_1(y)$ to $x_2(y)$:

$$V = \int_c^d \int_{x_1(y)}^{x_2(y)} z(x, y)\, dx\, dy.$$

Sometimes the region R, over which the integration extends, may be specified by inequalities; these must first be transformed into equations of curves.

Example 2 The region R consists of all points satisfying the inequalities $0 \leqslant x \leqslant 1, 0 \leqslant y \leqslant 1, 0 \leqslant x + y \leqslant 1$. Write down V in two ways.

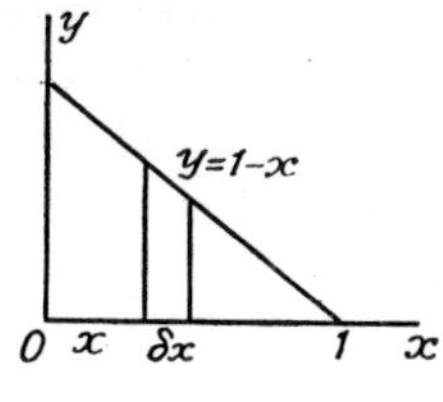

The region R lies above the line $y = 0$, to the right of the line $x = 0$ and below the line $x + y = 1$, as shown in Fig. 99.

FIG. 99

If integration with respect to y is carried out first, y varies from 0 to $1 - x$, for any given value of x. Finally, x varies from 0 to 1 in order that the vertical strips should traverse the whole region R, yielding

$$V = \int_0^1 \int_0^{1-x} z(x, y) \, dy \, dx.$$

But if we integrate first with respect to x, this must vary from 0 to $1 - y$, yielding

$$V = \int_0^1 \int_0^{1-y} z(x, y) \, dx \, dy.$$

Example 3   Interchange the order of integration in the integral

$$V = \int_2^4 \int_{4/x}^{\frac{1}{2}\sqrt{(20-x^2)}} z(x, y) \, dy \, dx.$$

The lower limit $y = 4/x$ and the upper limit $y = \frac{1}{2}\sqrt{(20 - x^2)}$ imply that we are dealing with two curves, namely $xy = 4$ and $x^2 + 4y^2 = 20$. The region of integration therefore lies between these two curves, from $x = 2$ to $x = 4$. But the points of intersection of these two curves in the first quadrant are $(2, 2)$ and $(4, 1)$, so the region of integration consists of that small area in the first quadrant common to both ellipse and hyperbola.

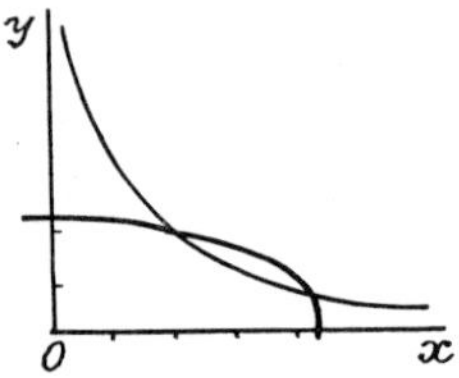

FIG. 100

Conversely, if we integrate with respect to x first along a strip parallel to Ox, x must vary from $4/y$ (on the hyperbola) to $\sqrt{(20 - 4y^2)}$ (on the ellipse). Finally y varies from 1 to 2 in order to embrace the required region:

$$V = \int_1^2 \int_{4/y}^{\sqrt{(20-4y^2)}} z(x, y) \, dx \, dy.$$

The volume between two surfaces.   Let two given surfaces $z = f(x, y)$ and $z = g(x, y)$ intersect in the curve C; let C' be the projection of this curve onto the x,y-plane. The x, y-equation of the curve C' is the same as the relation existing between the x and y coordinates of points on C; this is obtained merely by eliminating z from the defining equations, namely

$$f(x, y) = g(x, y).$$

The volume intercepted between the two surfaces consists of elementary cylinders of cross-sectional area δA and height $f(x, y) - g(x, y)$. Hence the total volume V is given by

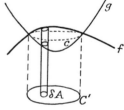

FIG. 101

$$V = \iint_R [f(x, y) - g(x, y)] \, dA$$

integrated over the region R within the curve $f(x, y) = g(x, y)$.

Example 4 Find the volume between the paraboloid $z = x^2 + y^2$ and the plane $2x + 2y + z = 2$.

The curve C' in the x, y-plane over which the integration is extended is

$$x^2 + y^2 = 2 - 2x - 2y,$$

namely the circle

$$(x + 1)^2 + (y + 1)^2 = 4.$$

Hence the volume V is given by

$$V = \int \int [(2 - 2x - 2y) - (x^2 + y^2)] \, dA,$$

the integrand being positive for values of x and y lying within C'; this fact may be checked by considering, for example, the centre $(-1, -1)$.

To simplify this, let $X = x + 1$, $Y = y + 1$, yielding

$$V = \int \int (4 - X^2 - Y^2) \, dA$$

integrated over the circle $X^2 + Y^2 = 4$. If we integrate with respect to Y first, the limits must be $\pm \sqrt{(4 - X^2)}$; X must then vary from -2 to $+2$:

$$V = \int_{-2}^{2} \int_{-\sqrt{(4-X^2)}}^{\sqrt{(4-X^2)}} (4 - X^2 - Y^2) \, dY \, dX$$

$$= \int_{-2}^{2} dX \left[4Y - X^2 Y - \tfrac{1}{3} Y^3 \right]_{-\sqrt{(4-X)^2}}^{\sqrt{(4-X^2)}}$$

$$= 2 \int_{-2}^{2} [(4 - X^2)\sqrt{(4 - X^2)} - \tfrac{1}{3}(4 - X^2)^{\frac{3}{2}}] \, dX$$

$$= 2 \int_{-2}^{2} \tfrac{2}{3}(4 - X^2)^{\frac{3}{2}} \, dX.$$

To integrate this, we let $X = 2 \sin \theta$, yielding

$$V = \tfrac{64}{3} \int_{-\frac{1}{2}\pi}^{\frac{1}{2}\pi} \cos^4 \theta \, d\theta = \tfrac{128}{3} \int_{0}^{\frac{1}{2}\pi} \cos^4 \theta \, d\theta = \tfrac{128}{3} \cdot \tfrac{3}{4} \cdot \tfrac{1}{2}(\tfrac{1}{2}\pi) = 8\pi.$$

17.2 Polar coordinates

The region R over which the double integral is evaluated may be defined in terms of polar coordinates r, θ. The element of area is $r \, \delta r \, \delta \theta$ and the function z must be expressed in terms of r and θ, namely $z = z(r, \theta)$. We write

$$V = \int \int z(r, \theta) \, r \, dr \, d\theta.$$

In particular, if the region R is bounded by the circles $r = a$ and $r = b$ $(a < b)$, and the lines $\theta = \theta_1$ and $\theta = \theta_2$ $(\theta_1 < \theta_2)$, then

$$V = \int_{\theta_1}^{\theta_1} \int_{a}^{b} z(r, \theta) r \, dr \, d\theta.$$

More generally, the region R may be bounded by the closed curve given by $r = r(\theta)$ in polar coordinates. First, we must integrate with θ constant along the elementary triangle with respect to r from 0 to $r(\theta)$, and then with respect to θ from 0 to 2π (or to any other desired limit). This yields

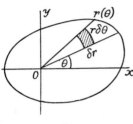

$$V = \int_0^{2\pi} \int_0^{r(\theta)} z(r, \theta)r \, dr \, d\theta.$$

Fig. 102

Second moments of area may also be found by this technique. The element of area being $r \, \delta r \, \delta\theta$, its second moment about Ox is $r \, \delta r \, \delta\theta \, . \, r^2 \sin^2 \theta$; hence

$$I_x = \int_0^{2\pi} \int_0^{r(\theta)} r^3 \sin^2 \theta \, dr \, d\theta$$

$$= \int_0^{2\pi} \left[\tfrac{1}{4} r^4 \sin^2 \theta \right]_0^{r(\theta)} d\theta = \tfrac{1}{4} \int_0^{2\pi} [r(\theta)]^4 \sin^2 \theta \, d\theta.$$

Similarly, about Oy, we have

$$I_y = \int_0^{2\pi} \int_0^{r(\theta)} r^3 \cos^2 \theta \, dr \, d\theta = \tfrac{1}{4} \int_0^{2\pi} [r(\theta)]^4 \cos^2 \theta \, d\theta.$$

Example 5   Find the moment of inertia about the initial line of the solid of revolution generated by rotating the cardioid $r = a(1 + \cos \theta)$ about the initial line.

The element of area $r \, \delta r \, \delta\theta$ generates a ring of radius $r \sin \theta$. Its volume is $2\pi r \sin \theta . r \, \delta r \, \delta\theta$, and its moment of inertia (assuming unit density) about the initial line is $2\pi r \sin \theta . r \, \delta r \, \delta\theta . (r \sin \theta)^2$. Upon integration along the elementary triangle, r varies from 0 to $a(1 + \cos \theta)$; then θ varies from 0 to π (obviously we need only integrate over the upper half of the cardioid). Totally, we have

$$I_x = 2\pi \int_0^{\pi} \int_0^{a(1+\cos\theta)} r^4 \sin^3 \theta \, dr \, d\theta = \tfrac{2}{5}\pi \int_0^{\pi} (1 + \cos \theta)^5 \sin^3 \theta \, d\theta.$$

Placing $\theta = 2\phi$, we have

$$I_x = \tfrac{2}{5}\pi \int_0^{\frac{1}{2}\pi} (2 \cos^2 \phi)^5 . 8 \sin^3 \phi \cos^3 \phi . 2 \, d\phi$$

$$= \frac{2^{10}\pi}{5} \int_0^{\frac{1}{2}\pi} \cos^{13} \phi (1 - \cos^2 \phi) \sin \phi \, d\phi = \frac{2^{10}\pi}{5} \left[\frac{\cos^{16} \phi}{16} - \frac{\cos^{14} \phi}{14} \right]_0^{\frac{1}{2}\pi} = \frac{64\pi}{35}.$$

Example 6   From the interior of the sphere $x^2 + y^2 + z^2 = 4a^2$, a cylindrical hole $x^2 + y^2 - 2ax = 0$ is removed. Find the volume that is removed.

We require the value of

$$V = 2 \int \int z \, dA = 2 \int \int \sqrt{(4a^2 - x^2 - y^2)} \, dA$$

integrated over the region within $(x - a)^2 + y^2 = a^2$. Polar coordinates may be introduced, with $x = r \cos \theta$, $y = r \sin \theta$, $\delta A = r \, \delta r \, \delta \theta$, while r varies from 0 to $2a \cos \theta$, and θ from 0 to $\frac{1}{2}\pi$ (and the result doubled). Hence

$$V = 4 \int_0^{\frac{1}{2}\pi} \int_0^{2a \cos \theta} \sqrt{(4a^2 - r^2)} r \, dr \, d\theta = 4 \int_0^{\frac{1}{2}\pi} \left[-\tfrac{1}{3}(4a^2 - r^2)^{\frac{3}{2}} \right]_0^{2a \cos \theta} d\theta$$

$$= \tfrac{4}{3} \int_0^{\frac{1}{2}\pi} [(2a)^3 - (2a \sin \theta)^3] \, d\theta \qquad (1)$$

$$= \tfrac{32}{3}a^3 \int_0^{\frac{1}{2}\pi} [1 - \sin \theta(1 - \cos^2 \theta)] \, d\theta$$

$$= \tfrac{32}{3}a^3 \left[\theta + \cos \theta - \tfrac{1}{3} \cos^3 \theta \right]_0^{\frac{1}{2}\pi} = \tfrac{32}{3}a^3(\tfrac{1}{2}\pi - \tfrac{2}{3}).$$

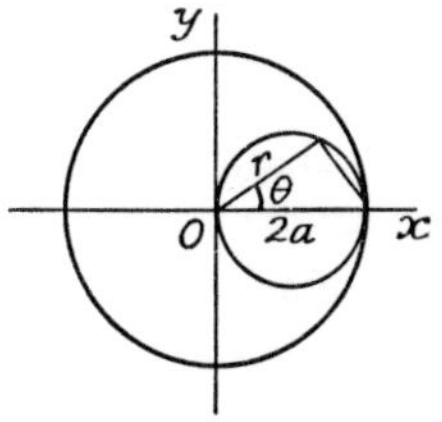

Fig. 103

A *word of warning* is necessary here. If the limits for θ were chosen to be $-\frac{1}{2}\pi$ and $\frac{1}{2}\pi$, it would be wrong merely to insert these limits and to change the factor $\frac{4}{3}$ to $\frac{2}{3}$ in equation (1), for evidently a different answer would be obtained. To rectify this error, we must note that, throughout, the term $\sqrt{(4a^2 - r^2)}$ is positive. Hence, when substituting the upper limit $2a \cos \theta$ after the first integration, we require $(4a^2 - 4a^2 \cos^2 \theta)^{\frac{3}{2}}$ to be positive; we may take this to be $(2a \sin \theta)^3$ if $0 < \theta \leqslant \frac{1}{2}\pi$ (as in the calculation), but we must use $-(2a \sin \theta)^3$ if $-\frac{1}{2}\pi \leqslant \theta < 0$ (that is, when the limit of integration is extended to $-\frac{1}{2}\pi$).

Example 7 Evaluate the integral $I = \int_0^\infty e^{-x^2} \, dx$.

We consider the volume between the x,y-plane in the first quadrant and the surface $z = e^{-x^2-y^2}$ for the three cases

(i) within the circle $r = a$,
(ii) within the square with sides $x = y = a$,
(iii) within the circle $r = a\sqrt{2}$.

If I_1, I_2, I_3 are the values of these three volumes, we have, since z is everywhere positive,

Fig. 104

$$I_1 < I_2 < I_3.$$

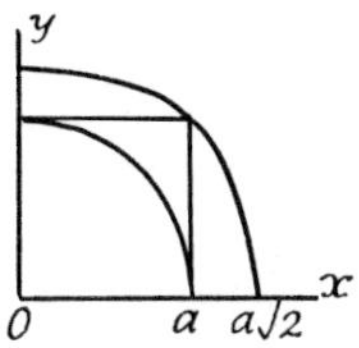

In polar coordinates, we have

$$I_1 = \int_0^a \int_0^{\frac{1}{2}\pi} e^{-r^2} r \, d\theta \, dr = \tfrac{1}{2}\pi \int_0^a e^{-r^2} r \, dr = \tfrac{1}{2}\pi \left[-\tfrac{1}{2}e^{-r^2} \right]_0^a = \tfrac{1}{4}\pi(1 - e^{-a^2}).$$

Similarly, $I_3 = \tfrac{1}{4}\pi(1 - e^{-2a^2})$. Finally, in Cartesian coordinates,

$$I_2 = \int_0^a \int_0^a e^{-x^2} e^{-y^2} \, dy \, dx = \int_0^a e^{-x^2} \, dx \cdot \int_0^a e^{-y^2} \, dy = \left(\int_0^a e^{-x^2} \, dx \right)^2.$$

The above inequalities now yield

$$\tfrac{1}{4}\pi(1 - e^{-a^2}) < \left(\int_0^a e^{-x^2} \, dx \right)^2 < \tfrac{1}{4}\pi(1 - e^{-2a^2}).$$

In the limit, as $a \to \infty$, we must have

$$\tfrac{1}{4}\pi \leqslant I^2 \leqslant \tfrac{1}{4}\pi;$$

in other words, $I = \tfrac{1}{2}\sqrt{\pi}$. It follows immediately that

$$\int_{-\infty}^{\infty} e^{-x^2}\, dx = \sqrt{\pi}.$$

17.3   Change of variable

A change of variable is made in the variables of integration in order to render more tractable both the integrand and the equations of the boundaries of the region of integration R.

For example, in the integral $V = \iint z(x, y)\, dA$, it is sometimes possible to change the variables from x and y to u and v where $x = x(u, v)$ and $y = y(u, v)$ in such a way that the boundaries of the region of integration reduce to the simple equations $u = $ constant, $v = $ constant. Variable limits of integration are thereby eliminated.

The integrand becomes $z[x(u, v), y(u, v)]$, but $du\, dv$ is *not* the appropriate element of area. The equations of transformation can formally be solved for u and v in terms of x and y: $u = u(x, y)$, $v = v(x, y)$. The curves $u = $ constant and $v = $ constant in the x, y-plane then subdivide the region R into a mesh of curves. An elementary parallelogram (the element of area) $ABCD$ is formed by the curves $u = u_0$,

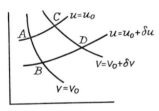

FIG. 105

$u = u_0 + \delta u$, $v = v_0$, $v = v_0 + \delta v$. If the coordinates of A, B, C are respectively (x_A, y_A), (x_B, y_B), (x_C, y_C), then

$$\delta A = \text{area } ABCD = 2\triangle ABC = \begin{vmatrix} 1 & 1 & 1 \\ x_A & x_B & x_C \\ y_A & y_B & y_C \end{vmatrix}$$

$$= \begin{vmatrix} x_B - x_A & x_C - x_A \\ y_B - y_A & y_C - y_A \end{vmatrix} \qquad \begin{aligned} &(\text{col}_2 - \text{col}_1; \\ &\ \text{col}_3 - \text{col}_1) \end{aligned}$$

$$= \begin{vmatrix} \dfrac{\partial x}{\partial u}\,\delta u & \dfrac{\partial x}{\partial v}\,\delta v \\[2mm] \dfrac{\partial y}{\partial u}\,\delta u & \dfrac{\partial y}{\partial v}\,\delta v \end{vmatrix}$$

$$= \begin{vmatrix} \partial x/\partial u & \partial x/\partial v \\ \partial y/\partial u & \partial y/\partial v \end{vmatrix} \delta u\, \delta v$$

to the first order. For example, $x_B - x_A$ is calculated along the curve $v =$ constant, while u increases by δu; the difference therefore equals $(\partial x/\partial u)\,\delta u$.

The determinant is the *Jacobian* of the transformation. A *positive* element of area is always required; if the Jacobian is negative, it must be changed in sign. The limits of integration for the new variables u and v should increase from the lower to the upper limit; they can be found from a diagram.

Example 8 The function $z = z(x, y)$ is integrated over the interior of the triangle $x = y = 0$, $x + y = 1$. Find a suitable change of variable so that all limits of integration should be constants.

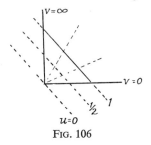

Let $v = y/x$ be chosen, so that the side $x = 0$ now becomes $v = \infty$ and the side $y = 0$ becomes $v = 0$.

Let $u = x + y$; the lines $u =$ constant are all parallel to the hypotenuse of the triangle. Clearly, u must vary from 0 to 1 in order that these lines should sweep over the complete triangle.

Fig. 106

But $x = u/(1 + v)$ and $y = uv/(1 + v)$, so the new element of area is

$$
\begin{vmatrix} \dfrac{\partial x}{\partial u} & \dfrac{\partial x}{\partial v} \\[2mm] \dfrac{\partial y}{\partial u} & \dfrac{\partial y}{\partial v} \end{vmatrix} \delta u\,\delta v = \begin{vmatrix} \dfrac{1}{1 + v} & \dfrac{-u}{(1 + v)^2} \\[2mm] \dfrac{v}{1 + v} & \dfrac{u}{(1 + v)^2} \end{vmatrix} \delta u\,\delta v = \frac{u\,\delta u\,\delta v}{(1 + v)^2}.
$$

The integral now becomes

$$
\int_0^\infty \int_0^1 z\left(\frac{u}{1 + v},\ \frac{uv}{1 + v}\right)\cdot\frac{u\,du\,dv}{(1 + v)^2}.
$$

Example 9 Find the volume between the plane $z = 0$ and the surface $z = e^{-x/y^2}$ bounded by the cylinder defined by $y = 1$, $y = 2$, $y^2 = x$, $y^2 = 2x$.

We choose $u = y$ and $v = y^2/x$; u then varies from 1 to 2 and v from 1 to 2. Moreover, $x = u^2/v$ and $y = u$, so the new element of area is given by

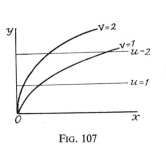

$$
\begin{vmatrix} \partial x/\partial u & \partial x/\partial v \\ \partial y/\partial u & \partial y/\partial v \end{vmatrix} \delta u\,\delta v
$$

$$
= \begin{vmatrix} 2u/v & -u^2/v^2 \\ 1 & 0 \end{vmatrix} \delta u\,\delta v = u^2\,\delta u\,\delta v/v^2.
$$

Hence

$$
V = \int_1^2 \int_1^2 e^{-1/v}\,\frac{u^2}{v^2}\,du\,dv
$$

$$
= \left[\tfrac{1}{3}u^3\right]_1^2\left[e^{-1/v}\right]_1^2 = \tfrac{7}{3}(e^{-\frac{1}{2}} - e^{-1}).
$$

Fig. 107

14

Example 10   Integrate the function

$$z = \frac{x^3 y}{\sqrt{\left(1 - \dfrac{x^2}{a^2} - \dfrac{y^2}{b^2}\right)}}$$

over the region inside the ellipse $x^2/a^2 + y^2/b^2 = 1$ in the first quadrant, using the substitution $x = a \sin \theta \cos \phi$, $y = b \sin \theta \sin \phi$.

Evidently the new element of area is given by

$$\begin{vmatrix} a \cos \theta \cos \phi & -a \sin \theta \sin \phi \\ b \cos \theta \sin \phi & b \sin \theta \cos \phi \end{vmatrix} \delta\theta \, \delta\phi = ab \sin \theta \cos \theta \, \delta\theta \, \delta\phi,$$

where this is positive at least in the ranges $0 < \theta \leqslant \frac{1}{2}\pi$, $0 < \phi < \frac{1}{2}\pi$.

When θ is eliminated, we have $\tan \phi = ay/bx$; ϕ therefore must vary from 0 to $\frac{1}{2}\pi$, in order that the lines $\phi = $ constant should rotate about the origin sweeping over the whole of the first quadrant.   When ϕ is eliminated, we obtain $x^2/a^2 + y^2/b^2 = \sin^2 \theta$, a series of ellipses; θ must vary from 0 to $\frac{1}{2}\pi$ in order that these ellipses should expand from zero to the required outer boundary.   Hence

$$V = \int_0^{\frac{1}{2}\pi} \int_0^{\frac{1}{2}\pi} \frac{a^3 \sin^3 \theta \cos^3 \phi . b \sin \theta \sin \phi}{\sqrt{(1 - \sin^2 \theta \cos^2 \phi - \sin^2 \theta \sin^2 \phi)}} . ab \sin \theta \cos \theta \, d\theta \, d\phi$$

$$= a^4 b^2 \int_0^{\frac{1}{2}\pi} \int_0^{\frac{1}{2}\pi} \sin^5 \theta \cos^3 \phi \sin \phi \, d\theta \, d\phi$$

$$= a^4 b^2 \int_0^{\frac{1}{2}\pi} \sin^5 \theta \, d\theta \int_0^{\frac{1}{2}\pi} \cos^3 \phi \sin \phi \, d\phi$$

$$= a^4 b^2 . \frac{4.2}{5.3} . \left[-\tfrac{1}{4} \cos^4 \phi \right]_0^{\frac{1}{2}\pi} = \tfrac{2}{15} a^4 b^2.$$

Example 11

Evaluate the integral $V = \displaystyle\int_0^a \int_0^a \frac{dx \, dy}{\sqrt{[a^2 + (x - y)^2]}}$ by using the substitution $u = x + y$, $v = y - x$.

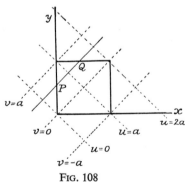

We have $x = \frac{1}{2}(u - v)$ and $y = \frac{1}{2}(u + v)$; the appropriate element of area is then given by

$$\begin{vmatrix} \tfrac{1}{2} & -\tfrac{1}{2} \\ \tfrac{1}{2} & \tfrac{1}{2} \end{vmatrix} \delta u \, \delta v = \tfrac{1}{2} \delta u \, \delta v.$$

The boundaries of the region of integration are not given by such simple forms as $u = $ constant, $v = $ constant. For any value of $v \geqslant 0$, u must be chosen in order that the represented point moves along the line $v = $ constant from P to Q.   At P $x = 0$, so $u = y = v$

FIG. 108

from the transformation equations. At Q, $y = a$, so $u = x + y = (y - v) + y = 2a - v$. To include the region $v < 0$, on the grounds of symmetry we double the value of the integral obtained when $v > 0$. Hence

$$V = 2 \int_0^a \int_v^{2a-v} \frac{\frac{1}{2} \, du \, dv}{\sqrt{(a^2 + v^2)}} = 2 \int_0^a \frac{(a - v) \, dv}{\sqrt{(a^2 + v^2)}}$$

$$= 2 \left[a \log \left[v + \sqrt{(a^2 + v^2)} \right] - \sqrt{(a^2 + v^2)} \right]_0^a$$

$$= 2a \log (1 + \sqrt{2}) - 2(\sqrt{2} - 1)a.$$

Example 12

Evaluate $I = \displaystyle\int_0^\infty e^{-x} \sqrt{x} \, dx$ by integrating $e^{-x-y} \sqrt{(xy)}$ over the first quadrant with the change of variable $x = \frac{1}{2}u(1 + v)$, $y = \frac{1}{2}u(1 - v)$.

Conversely, $u = x + y$ and $v = (x - y)/(x + y)$. The $u = $ constant curves are straight lines with gradient -1; u varies from 0 to ∞ to traverse the first quadrant. The $v = $ constant curves are straight lines through the origin, varying from -1 to $+1$ to cover the first quadrant.

The element of area is

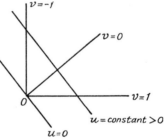

FIG. 109

$$\begin{vmatrix} \frac{1}{2}(1 + v) & \frac{1}{2}u \\ \frac{1}{2}(1 - v) & -\frac{1}{2}u \end{vmatrix} \delta u \, \delta v = -\frac{1}{2}u \, \delta u \, \delta v;$$

to be positive, we must take $\frac{1}{2}u \, \delta u \, \delta v$, since $u > 0$ throughout the region of integration. Then

$$V = \int_{-1}^1 \int_0^\infty e^{-u} \sqrt{[\frac{1}{4}u^2(1 - v^2)]} . \frac{1}{2}u \, du \, dv$$

$$= \frac{1}{4} \int_{-1}^1 \sqrt{(1 - v^2)} \, dv \int_0^\infty e^{-u} u^2 \, du$$

$$= \frac{1}{4} \int_{-\frac{1}{2}\pi}^{\frac{1}{2}\pi} \cos^2 \theta \, d\theta \left[-e^{-u} u^2 + 2 \int e^{-u} u \, du \right]_0^\infty \text{(when } v = \sin \theta\text{)}$$

$$= \frac{1}{4} . \frac{1}{2}\pi . \left[-2e^{-u} u + 2 \int e^{-u} \, du \right]_0^\infty = \frac{1}{4}\pi \left[-e^{-u} \right]_0^\infty = \frac{1}{4}\pi.$$

But it is obvious that $I^2 = V$, yielding $I = \frac{1}{2}\sqrt{\pi}$.

17.4   Triple integrals

A volume V is given in three dimensional space, together with a function of position $f(x, y, z)$. This function may be a varying mass density, a varying electric charge density, or any of the other scalar space distributions encountered in physical theory.

If δV is an element of volume, and (x, y, z) a point within δV, we form the product $f(x, y, z)\,\delta V$ and the sum $\Sigma f(x, y, z)\,\delta V$ taken over the whole interior of V. If this sum tends to a unique limit as all the elements of volume tend to zero, then we write this limit as the *triple integral*

$$\int \int \int f(x, y, z)\, dx\, dy\, dz$$

in Cartesian coordinates.

Spherical polar coordinates are required in the evaluation of many triple integrals. Let $OP = r$, $\angle zOP = \theta$ and ψ be the angle between the planes zOx and zOP. Then the spherical polar coordinates of the point P are (r, θ, ψ). Evidently,

$$x = ON \cos \psi = r \sin \theta \cos \psi,$$

$$y = r \sin \theta \sin \psi, \quad z = r \cos \theta.$$

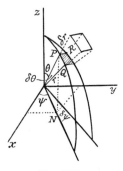

FIG. 110

The shaded element of area is situated on a sphere of radius r. We note that $PQ = r\,\delta\theta$ and $PR = r \sin \theta\,\delta\psi$, since PR lies on a circle of radius $r \sin \theta$ in the plane through P parallel to the plane Oxy. The element of area is therefore $r^2 \sin \theta\,\delta\theta\,\delta\psi$. If the radius of the sphere is now increased from r to $r + \delta r$, the volume element generated is $r^2 \sin \theta\,\delta r\,\delta\theta\,\delta\psi$.

More generally, the change of variable $x = x(u, v, w)$, $y = y(u, v, w)$ and $z = z(u, v, w)$ requires the introduction of the new element of volume:

$$\frac{\partial(x, y, z)}{\partial(u, v, w)}\,\delta u\,\delta v\,\delta w \equiv \begin{vmatrix} \dfrac{\partial x}{\partial u} & \dfrac{\partial x}{\partial v} & \dfrac{\partial x}{\partial w} \\[2mm] \dfrac{\partial y}{\partial u} & \dfrac{\partial y}{\partial v} & \dfrac{\partial y}{\partial w} \\[2mm] \dfrac{\partial z}{\partial u} & \dfrac{\partial z}{\partial v} & \dfrac{\partial z}{\partial w} \end{vmatrix}\,\delta u\,\delta v\,\delta w.$$

This formula is proved in more advanced texts on the calculus.

Example 13   Integrate the function $xyz\sqrt{(1 - x^2 - y^2 - z^2)}$ through the positive octant of the sphere of radius a and centre the origin.

In spherical polar coordinates, r must increase from 0 to a; θ must increase from 0 to $\tfrac{1}{2}\pi$; ψ must increase from 0 to $\tfrac{1}{2}\pi$. The integral equals

$$\int_0^{\frac{1}{2}\pi} \int_0^{\frac{1}{2}\pi} \int_0^a r^3 \sin^2 \theta \cos \theta \sin \psi \cos \psi . \sqrt{(1 - r^2)} . r^2 \sin \theta \, dr \, d\theta \, d\psi$$

$$= \int_0^{\frac{1}{2}\pi} \sin \psi \cos \psi \, d\psi \int_0^{\frac{1}{2}\pi} \sin^3 \theta \cos \theta \, d\theta \int_0^a r^5 \sqrt{(1 - r^2)} \, dr$$

$$= \left[\tfrac{1}{2} \sin^2 \psi \right]_0^{\frac{1}{2}\pi} \left[\tfrac{1}{4} \sin^4 \theta \right]_0^{\frac{1}{2}\pi} \int_0^{\frac{1}{2}\pi} a^7 \sin^5 \xi \cos^2 \xi \, d\xi \qquad (r = a \sin \xi)$$

$$= \tfrac{1}{8} a^7 \int_0^{\frac{1}{2}\pi} (\sin^5 \xi - \sin^7 \xi) \, d\xi = \tfrac{1}{8} a^7 (\tfrac{4}{5} . \tfrac{2}{3} - \tfrac{6}{7} . \tfrac{4}{5} . \tfrac{2}{3}) = \tfrac{1}{105} a^7.$$

Example 14 Integrate the function $(x + y + z)^n xyz$ over the interior of the tetrahedron bounded by the planes $x = y = z = 0$, $x + y + z = 1$, using the substitutions $u = x + y + z$, $uv = y + z$, $uvw = z$.

Evidently, $z = uvw$, $y = uv - uvw$, $x = u - uv$, so the new volume element is

$$\begin{vmatrix} 1 - v & -u & 0 \\ v - vw & u - uw & -uv \\ vw & uw & uv \end{vmatrix} \delta u \, \delta v \, \delta w = u^2 v \, \delta u \, \delta v \, \delta w.$$

As u varies from 0 to 1, the plane $x + y + z = $ constant sweeps over the interior from the origin to the boundary $x + y + z = 1$.

The surface $v = $ constant is $(y + z)/(x + y + z) = v$, a plane. Otherwise expressed, this is $(y + z)(1 - v) = vx$, a plane varying through the line $y + z = x = 0$. To sweep over the first quadrant, v must vary from 0 to 1.

The surface $w = $ constant is the plane $z = w(y + z)$ passing through the z axis; w must vary from 0 to 1 to sweep through the first quadrant. The integral becomes

$$\int_0^1 \int_0^1 \int_0^1 u^n . u(1 - v) . uv(1 - w) . uvw . u^2 v \, du \, dv \, dw$$

$$= \int_0^1 u^{n+5} \, du \int_0^1 (1 - v)v^3 \, dv \int_0^1 (1 - w)w \, dw$$

$$= 1/[120(n + 6)]$$

upon simplification.

EXERCISES

(1)★. Evaluate $\displaystyle\int_0^a dx \int_x^a \frac{x \, dy}{\sqrt{(x^2 + y^2)}}$ and state the region of the (x, y)-plane to which it refers. Change the order of integration, evaluate and verify that the two values are the same.

(2)★. Sketch the area over which the double integral $\displaystyle\int_0^c dx \int_x^c \frac{x \, dy}{\sqrt{(x^2 + y^2)}}$ is taken. By inverting the order of integration, show that the value of the integral is $\tfrac{1}{2}c^2(\sqrt{2} - 1)$.

(3) ★. Express the volume bounded by the cylinders $x^2 + y^2 = a^2$, $y^2 = 4a(z - a)$ and the plane $z = 0$ as a double integral with respect to x and y, and find the volume. Check your result by changing the variables of integration to polar coordinates r and θ.

(4) ★. Show that the volume contained between the cylinder $x^2 + y^2 = a^2$, the paraboloid $x^2 + y^2 = 2az$ and the plane $z = 0$ is given by

$$\frac{2}{a} \int_0^a \int_0^{\sqrt{(a^2 - y^2)}} (x^2 + y^2) \, dx \, dy.$$

Find the value of this integral.

(5) ★. (i) Draw a diagram of the x,y-plane indicating the area of integration for the double integral

$$\int_2^4 dx \int_{2\sqrt{(x-2)}}^{2\sqrt{x}} f(x, y) \, dy.$$

(ii) Show that $\displaystyle\int_0^1 dx \int_0^{1-x} f(x, y) \, dy = \int_0^1 dy \int_0^{1-y} f(x, y) \, dx.$

(iii) Determine the volume of the solid which is bounded by the surface $z = 1 - (x^2 + y^2)^3$, by the x,y-plane and the cylinder whose generators are parallel to the z-axis and whose cross-section in the x,y-plane is the loop of the curve $r^2 = \cos \theta$ which lies in $x \geqslant 0$.

(6) ★. (i) Show, by using polar coordinates, that the volume contained between the surface $z = (1 + x^2 + y^2)^{-n}$, $(n > 1)$, and $z = 0$ is $\pi/(n - 1)$.

(ii) Determine the volume which is bounded by the planes $z = 0$, $z = x + y$, $x = 0$, $y = a$, $y = 2a$ and the parabolic cylinder $y^2 = ax$.

(7) ★. Sketch the curve $r = a(1 + \cos \theta)$ and find the area which it encloses. Express as a double integral the second moment of this area about the line $\theta = \frac{1}{2}\pi$. Find the radius of gyration about this line.

(8) ★. If $x = pv$, $y = pv^\gamma$, where $\gamma > 1$, show that $(\gamma - 1)\iint dp \, dv = \iint y^{-1} \, dx \, dy$. Hence show that the area in the p,v-plane enclosed by the curves $pv = a_1$, $pv = a_2$, $pv^\gamma = b_1$, $pv^\gamma = b_2$, where a_1, a_2, b_1, b_2 are constants such that $a_1 > a_2 > 0$, $b_1 > b_2 > 0$, is $(a_1 - a_2)(\gamma - 1)^{-1} \log_e (b_1/b_2)$.

(9) ★. A uniform solid, of density ρ, occupies the space in the first octant bounded by the four planes $x = 0$, $y = 0$, $z = 0$, $z = x + y$ and the cylinder $x^2 + y^2 = a^2$. Express as repeated integrals (i) the mass of the solid and (ii) the first moment of the solid about the plane $z = 0$.

By evaluating these integrals show that the mass is $\frac{2}{3}\rho a^3$ and find the distance of the mass-centre of the solid from the plane $z = 0$.

(10) ★. (i) Sketch the area of integration in the x,y-plane for the integral

$$\int_0^a dx \int_{a-x}^{\sqrt{(a^2 - x^2)}} f(x, y) \, dy$$

and evaluate the integral if

$$f(x, y) = xy.$$

(ii) Determine the volume in the positive octant enclosed between the surfaces $z = 0$ and $z = y^2 \exp(-x^2 - y^2)$.

(11) ★. Sketch the area of integration in the x,y-plane for the integral

$$\int_0^a dx \int_0^{a-x} \frac{dy}{1 + (x + y)^2}.$$

Sketch the corresponding area of integration in the u,v-plane under the substitution $u = x + y, v = -x + y$, and use this substitution to evaluate the integral.

(12)*. Prove that the integral of $\exp(-x^2 - y^2)$ over a quadrant of the circle enclosed by $x^2 + y^2 = a^2$ is $\frac{1}{4}\pi[1 - \exp(-a^2)]$. Evaluate the integral

$$\int_0^\infty \exp(-x^2)\, dx,$$

and deduce the value of

$$\int_{-\infty}^\infty x^2 \exp(-x^2)\, dx.$$

(13)*. A variable point P has rectangular coordinates (x, y, z) given by $x = a \cos \theta \sin \theta \cos \phi$, $y = a \cos \theta \sin \theta \sin \phi$, $z = a \cos^2 \theta$, where a is a constant, and θ, ϕ are restricted so that $0 \leqslant \theta \leqslant \frac{1}{2}\pi$ and $0 \leqslant \phi < 2\pi$. What is the locus of P, and what is the geometrical significance of θ and ϕ?

The region enclosed by the sphere $x^2 + y^2 + z^2 = az$ is filled with matter whose density at (x, y, z) is $k\sqrt{(x^2 + y^2 + z^2)}$ where k is a constant. Show that the moment of inertia of the solid about Oz is $\frac{2}{189}\pi ka^6$.

(14)*. Transform the integral $\iint(x^2 - y^2)(x^2 + y^2)^{-1}\, dx\, dy$ into an integral in polar coordinates r, θ where $x = r \cos \theta, y = r \sin \theta$.

Evaluate the integral over the region in the first quadrant bounded by an arc of the parabola $y^2 = 4(1 - x)$ and the coordinate axes.

(15)*. Show that the volume between the spheres $x^2 + y^2 + z^2 = a^2$ and $x^2 + y^2 + z^2 = 4az$ is equal to $\int_0^{2\pi} \int_0^{\frac{1}{4}a\sqrt{15}} [\sqrt{(a^2 - r^2)} - 2a + \sqrt{(4a^2 - r^2)}]r\, dr\, d\theta$, where r, θ are polar coordinates, and evaluate this integral.

(16)*. Show in a diagram the region over which the double integral

$$\int_0^{a/\sqrt{2}} \int_x^{\sqrt{(a^2-x^2)}} xy(x + y)\, dy\, dx$$

is taken. By transforming into polar coordinates, show that the value of the integral is $\frac{1}{15}a^5$.

(17)*. (i) Exhibit by a diagram the region in the x,y-plane over which the repeated integral $\int_0^a dx \int_0^{\sqrt{(a^2-x^2)}} \sin[\pi(a^2 - x^2 - y^2)/a^2]\, dy$ extends. By conversion to polar coordinates, show that its value is $\frac{1}{2}a^2$.

(ii) Express as a repeated integral the volume contained between the cylinder $y^2 = 4ax$ and the planes $x + z = a, z = 0$. Show that this volume is $16a^3/15$.

(18)*. Sketch the area over which the double integral

$$\int_0^{a/\sqrt{2}} \int_y^{\sqrt{(a^2-y^2)}} \log_e(x^2 + y^2)\, dx\, dy$$

is taken, where $a > 0$. (i) By changing to polar coordinates, show that the value of the integral is $\frac{1}{4}\pi a^2(\log_e a - \frac{1}{2})$. (ii) Change the order of integration in the original integral, but do not carry through the integration.

(19)*. Interpret $\int_0^a dx \int_{\sqrt{(ax-x^2)}}^{\sqrt{(a^2-x^2)}} \dfrac{dy}{\sqrt{(a^2 - x^2 - y^2)}}$ as a double integral taken over an area, showing the area in a diagram. Evaluate the integral by transforming to polar coordinates.

(20) *. Sketch the area over which the double integral

$$\int_0^{2a} dx \int_0^{\sqrt{(2ax-x^2)}} \exp\left[-(x^2 + y^2)/a^2\right](x^2 + y^2)^{-1}xy \, dy$$

is taken, and by transforming to polar coordinates, show that it equals $a^2(3 + e^{-4})/16$.

(21) *. Sketch the parabola $x^2 = 4ay$ and the straight line $2y = 4a - x$ and find the coordinates of their points of intersection. Express as repeated integrals (i) the area enclosed by the parabola and the straight line and (ii) the moment of this area about the y-axis. Evaluate these integrals and show that the centroid of the area is at a distance a from the y-axis.

(22) *. By transforming into cylindrical coordinates u, ϕ, z, where $x = u \cos \phi$, $y = u \sin \phi$, show that $\iiint(x^2 + y^2 + z^2) \, dx \, dy \, dz$, taken throughout the interior of the cone $x^2 + y^2 - (1 - z)^2 = 0$ between the planes $z = 0$ and $z = 1$ has the value $2\pi/15$.

ANSWERS TO EXERCISES

(1). $a^2[\sqrt{2} + \frac{1}{2}\log(1 + \sqrt{2})]$.   (3). $17\pi a^3/16$.   (4). $\frac{1}{4}\pi a^3$.

(5). (i) Area between $x = 2$, $x = 4$, $y^2 = 4x$, $y^2 = 4(x - 2)$; (iii) $\frac{1}{2} - \frac{3}{128}\pi$.

(6). (ii) $\frac{137}{20}a^3$.   (7). $3\pi a^2/2$, $7a/4\sqrt{3}$.   (9). (ii) $\rho a^4(\pi + 2)/16$, $3a(\pi + 2)/32$.

(10). (i) $a^4/12$; (ii) $\pi/8$.   (11). $\frac{1}{2}\log(1 + a^2)$.   (12). $\frac{1}{2}\sqrt{\pi}$, $\frac{1}{2}\sqrt{\pi}$.

(14). $2\pi - \frac{20}{3}$.   (15). $\frac{13}{24}\pi a^3$.   (19). a.   (21). $(2a, a)$, $(-4a, 4a)$; $9a^2$, $-9a^3$.

CHAPTER 18

FOURIER SERIES

18.1 Some special integrals

The following integrals, though elementary, are used throughout the theory of Fourier series; their values should be known before the chapter is read, since they will be quoted without further explanation.

Let m and n be two non-negative integers.

Integral i. Consider

$$I = \int_0^{2\pi} \cos mx \cos nx \, dx.$$

If $m = n = 0$,

$$I = \int_0^{2\pi} dx = 2\pi.$$

If $m = n \neq 0$,

$$I = \int_0^{2\pi} \cos^2 mx \, dx = \tfrac{1}{2} \int_0^{2\pi} (1 + \cos 2mx) \, dx = \pi.$$

If $m \neq n$,

$$I = \tfrac{1}{2} \int_0^{2\pi} [\cos (m + n)x + \cos (m - n)x] \, dx$$

$$= \tfrac{1}{2} \left[\frac{\sin (m + n)x}{m + n} + \frac{\sin (m - n)x}{m - n} \right]_0^{2\pi} = 0.$$

If the upper limit is only π, we have obviously

$$I = \pi, \, (m = n = 0); \quad I = \tfrac{1}{2}\pi, \, (m = n \neq 0), \quad I = 0, \, (m \neq n).$$

Integral ii. Consider

$$J = \int_0^{2\pi} \sin mx \sin nx \, dx.$$

The trivial case $m = n = 0$ yields $J = 0$.

If $m = n \neq 0$,

$$J = \int_0^{2\pi} \sin^2 mx \, dx = \pi.$$

If $m \neq n$,

$$J = \tfrac{1}{2} \int_0^{2\pi} [\cos (m - n)x - \cos (m + n)x] \, dx = 0$$

as before. If the upper limit is only π, we have

$$J = \tfrac{1}{2}\pi, \, (m = n \neq 0); \quad J = 0, \, (m \neq n).$$

Integral iii. Consider

$$K = \int_0^{2\pi} \sin mx \cos nx \, dx.$$

For all *m* and *n* we have

$$K = \tfrac{1}{2} \int_0^{2\pi} [\sin (m + n)x + \sin (m - n)x] \, dx$$

$$= -\tfrac{1}{2} \left[\frac{\cos (m + n)x}{m + n} + \frac{\cos (m - n)x}{m - n} \right]_0^{2\pi} = 0,$$

omitting sin $(m - n)x$ and its integral if $m = n$. Integration over the range 0 to π does not arise in the theory of Fourier series.

The whole group of functions sin nx and cos nx are called *orthogonal* over the range $(0, 2\pi)$, for the integral of the product of any two of these functions over this range vanishes unless the integrand is merely the square of one of the functions. The group of functions sin nx forms an orthogonal set of functions over the range $(0, \pi)$ as well as over the range $(0, 2\pi)$; the functions cos nx form a similar group.

18.2   Fourier series of period 2π

A finite, single-valued function $y = f(x)$ is given in the range $0 < x < 2\pi$, (or in any other range of extent 2π, such as $-\pi < x < \pi$). The values and shape of the function outside the specified range do not enter into the theory.   Examples are

$y = 3x + 2 \ (0 < x < 2\pi)$;

$y = \cosh x \ (-\pi \leqslant x \leqslant \pi)$;

$y = x \ (0 \leqslant x \leqslant \pi), \quad y = 2\pi - x \ (\pi \leqslant x \leqslant 2\pi)$;

$y = 0 \ (0 < x < \tfrac{1}{2}\pi), \quad y = 1 \ (\tfrac{1}{2}\pi < x < \tfrac{3}{2}\pi), \quad y = 0 \ (\tfrac{3}{2}\pi < x < 2\pi)$.

The function $y = f(x)$ may be continuous throughout the range, or it may have a finite number of discontinuities; at a discontinuity, a strict inequality must be used in the two defining ranges of x terminating at the discontinuity, as in the fourth example above. The value of y at such a point need not be defined.

The graph of the function in the specified range of x is the fundamental graph which we are concerned in the theory of Fourier series. We now define a function $y = F(x)$ to be a periodic function with period 2π, such that $F(x) = f(x)$ over the range in which $f(x)$ is defined. In other words, the fundamental shape with which we started is merely repeated indefinitely along the whole x-axis. If a discontinuity occurs, either within the fundamental shape, or at its end, $F(x)$ is defined to be *the average of the two values of y at the discontinuity.*

If, for example, $f(x) = e^x$ $(0 < x < 2\pi)$, then $F(x)$ will be

$$
\begin{array}{cccc}
\cdot & \cdot & \cdot & \cdot & \cdot & \cdot & \cdot & \cdot & \cdot & \cdot & \cdot
\end{array}
$$

$$
\begin{aligned}
F(x) &= e^{4\pi+x} & (-4\pi < x < -2\pi), \\
F(x) &= e^{2\pi+x} & (-2\pi < x < 0), \\
f(x) = F(x) &= e^{x} & (0 < x < 2\pi), \\
F(x) &= e^{-2\pi+x} & (2\pi < x < 4\pi), \\
F(x) &= e^{-4\pi+x} & (4\pi < x < 6\pi),
\end{aligned}
$$

$$
\begin{array}{cccc}
\cdot & \cdot & \cdot & \cdot & \cdot & \cdot & \cdot & \cdot & \cdot & \cdot
\end{array}
$$

When $x = -4\pi, -2\pi, 0, 2\pi, 4\pi, \ldots$, a discontinuity occurs; $F(x)$ is defined to be the average value of the two values of $F(x)$ occurring there, namely $\frac{1}{2}(1 + e^{2\pi}) = e^{\pi} \cosh \pi$. These features are shown in Fig. 111.

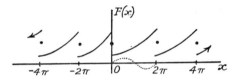

FIG. 111

It is absolutely necessary, for clarity of thought, for the student to sketch such a graph before proceeding further with any problem.

We seek to express $F(x)$ as an infinite linear sum of sines and cosines having the same period as $F(x)$, namely 2π. If n is a positive integer, the functions $\sin nx$ and $\cos nx$ possess this property. The lowest integer $n = 1$ yields $\sin x$ and $\cos x$; these are called the *fundamental* or *lowest harmonics* and their complete graphical shape fits *exactly* once into the range $(0, 2\pi)$ as indicated in Fig. 111. The second harmonics $\sin 2x$ and $\cos 2x$ evidently fit in twice. A constant term, written as $\frac{1}{2}a_0$ for reasons that will be evident later, is also obviously periodic.

We assume that

$$
F(x) = \tfrac{1}{2}a_0 + \sum_{1}^{\infty} a_n \cos nx + \sum_{1}^{\infty} b_n \sin nx, \tag{1}
$$

where the coefficients a_n and b_n are to be found. It is not obvious that such an assumption is even a possibility; it is only reasonable because the right hand side is periodic with period 2π as is the left hand side. It is also not obvious that no other functions periodic in 2π are required on the right hand side in order that the infinite series so formed should possess $F(x)$ as its sum; the functions $\tan nx$, $\cot nx$, $\sec nx$, $\operatorname{cosec} nx$ are however rejected on account of their infinities. The theoretical investigation of these questions is very complicated, and at this stage it is sufficient to accept the mathematician's word that sines and cosines are all that is needed, forming what is known as a *complete set*.

To find the values of the coefficients, we perform a series of integrations, interchanging the order of the summation sign and the integration sign. Again we adopt this as formally permissible, relying on more abstract analysis to give us the authority to do such a thing.

To find a_0, we merely integrate (1) from 0 to 2π, that is over the whole period for which $F(x)$ equals the given function $f(x)$. All the cosines and sines integrate to zero, yielding

$$\int_0^{2\pi} f(x)\,dx = \tfrac{1}{2}a_0 \int_0^{2\pi} dx = \pi a_0,$$

so

$$a_0 = \frac{1}{\pi} \int_0^{2\pi} f(x)\,dx.$$

To find a_m, we multiply by $\cos mx$ and integrate from 0 to 2π. All the integrals involved are of the type I and K considered in section 18.1; these all vanish except the cosine integral when $n = m$, so

$$\int_0^{2\pi} f(x) \cos mx\,dx = \int_0^{2\pi} a_m \cos^2 mx\,dx = a_m\pi,$$

or

$$a_m = \frac{1}{\pi} \int_0^{2\pi} f(x) \cos mx\,dx.$$

Note that a_0 has the same form as a_m; it was to ensure this that the factor $\tfrac{1}{2}$ was inserted in the constant term in (1).

To find b_m, we multiply (1) by $\sin mx$ and integrate from 0 to 2π. All the integrals involved are of the type J and K considered in section 18.1; these all vanish except the sine integral when $n = m$, so

$$\int_0^{2\pi} f(x) \sin mx\,dx = \int_0^{2\pi} b_m \sin^2 mx\,dx = b_m\pi,$$

or

$$b_m = \frac{1}{\pi} \int_0^{2\pi} f(x) \sin mx\,dx.$$

These integrals are calculated for general values of m (though, exceptionally, care is sometimes necessary for the cases $m = 0, 1, 2$) and inserted in (1), yielding the final result. The function $F(x)$ is thereby resolved into its harmonic components.

If any value of x is inserted in the series, the sum of this infinite series is $F(x)$. At a discontinuity in the graph of $F(x)$, the single-valued sum equals the average of the two values of $F(x)$ on each side of the discontinuity. This result can only be proved by abstract analysis, and the reader is asked to assume this fact.

The complex form for the Fourier series. A compact form for the series can be found by using complex exponentials. Inserting the values of the coefficients into (1), but changing x to t in the integrands in order to avoid confusion with the x in the series, we have

$$F(x) = \frac{1}{2\pi}\int_0^{2\pi} f(t)\,dt + \frac{1}{\pi}\sum_1^\infty \int_0^{2\pi} f(t)(\cos nt \cos nx + \sin nt \sin nx)\,dt$$

$$= \frac{1}{2\pi}\int_0^{2\pi} f(t)\,dt + \frac{1}{\pi}\sum_1^\infty \int_0^{2\pi} f(t) \cos [n(t - x)]\,dt$$

$$= \frac{1}{2\pi}\int_0^{2\pi} f(t)\,dt + \frac{1}{2\pi}\sum_1^\infty \int_0^{2\pi} f(t)[e^{in(t-x)} + e^{-in(t-x)}]\,dt$$

$$= \frac{1}{2\pi}\sum_{-\infty}^\infty \int_0^{2\pi} f(t)e^{in(t-x)}\,dt.$$

Example 1 Find the Fourier series of period 2π equal to x^2 when $0 < x < 2\pi$.

The graph of the periodic function $F(x)$ is shown in Fig. 112. At the discontinuities $x = -2\pi, 0, 2\pi, \ldots$, $F(x) = \frac{1}{2}(2\pi)^2$, this being the average value of $F(x)$ on

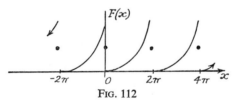

FIG. 112

each side of the discontinuity. We assume the form (1), which becomes for the range $0 < x < 2\pi$,

$$x^2 = \tfrac{1}{2}a_0 + \sum_1^\infty a_n \cos nx + \sum_1^\infty b_n \sin nx.$$

The coefficients are calculated by the method just developed:

$$a_0 = \frac{1}{\pi}\int_0^{2\pi} x^2\,dx = \tfrac{1}{3}(2\pi)^3/\pi = \tfrac{8}{3}\pi^2.$$

To find a_n, we multiply by $\cos nx$ and integrate from 0 to 2π:

$$a_n = \frac{1}{\pi}\int_0^{2\pi} x^2 \cos nx\,dx = \frac{1}{\pi}\left[\frac{x^2 \sin nx}{n} - \frac{2}{n}\int x \sin nx\,dx\right]_0^{2\pi}$$

$$= -\frac{2}{\pi n}\left[\frac{-x\cos nx}{n} + \frac{1}{n}\int \cos nx\,dx\right]_0^{2\pi}$$

$$= -\frac{2}{\pi n^2}\left[-x\cos nx + \frac{\sin nx}{n}\right]_0^{2\pi} = \frac{4}{n^2}.$$

To find b_n, we multiply by $\sin nx$ and integrate from 0 to 2π:

$$b_n = \frac{1}{\pi} \int_0^{2\pi} x^2 \sin nx \, dx = \frac{1}{\pi}\left[\frac{-x^2 \cos nx}{n} + \frac{2}{n}\int x \cos nx \, dx\right]_0^{2\pi}$$

$$= \frac{1}{\pi n}\left[-x^2 \cos nx + \frac{2x \sin nx}{n} - \frac{2}{n}\int \sin nx \, dx\right]_0^{2\pi}$$

$$= \frac{1}{\pi n}\left[-x^2 \cos nx + \frac{2 \cos nx}{n^2}\right]_0^{2\pi} = -\frac{4\pi}{n}.$$

Hence
$$F(x) = \tfrac{4}{3}\pi^2 + 4\sum_{n=1}^{\infty}\frac{1}{n^2}\cos nx - 4\pi\sum_{n=1}^{\infty}\frac{1}{n}\sin nx.$$

When $x = 0$, we see from the graph that $F(x) = \tfrac{1}{2}(2\pi)^2$, being the average value at a discontinuity. The series yields the result

$$2\pi^2 = \tfrac{4}{3}\pi^2 + 4\sum n^{-2},$$

or
$$\sum n^{-2} = \pi^2/6.$$

When $x = \pi$, $F(x) = \pi^2$; hence

$$\pi^2 = \tfrac{4}{3}\pi^2 + 4\sum(-1)^n n^{-2},$$

or
$$\sum(-1)^{n+1}n^{-2} = \pi^2/12.$$

The reader should note the useful result: $\cos n\pi = (-1)^n$; this is valid *only* when n is an integer.

Example 2   Find the Fourier series of period 2π such that $F(x) = x$ $(0 \leqslant x < \pi)$, $F(x) = 0$ $(\pi < x \leqslant 2\pi)$.

We assume that

$$F(x) = \tfrac{1}{2}a_0 + \sum_{n=1}^{\infty} a_n \cos nx + \sum_{n=1}^{\infty} b_n \sin nx, \qquad (2)$$

yielding, upon integration,

$$a_0 = \frac{1}{\pi}\int_0^{\pi} x \, dx = \tfrac{1}{2}\pi.$$

It should be carefully noticed that the integral of the right hand side of equation (2)

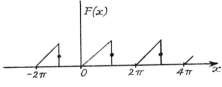

FIG. 113

is extended from 0 to 2π as usual; the functions concerned are not orthogonal over smaller ranges. But the integration of the left hand side from 0 to 2π is changed to 0 to π merely because the integrand is zero from π to 2π; the right hand side must not be similarly treated.

Again,

$$a_n = \frac{1}{\pi} \int_0^\pi x \cos nx \, dx = \frac{1}{\pi} \left[\frac{x \sin nx}{n} - \frac{1}{n} \int \sin nx \, dx \right]_0^\pi$$

$$= \frac{1}{\pi n^2} \left[\cos nx \right]_0^\pi = \frac{1}{\pi n^2} [(-1)^n - 1] = \begin{cases} 0 & (n \text{ even}) \\ -2/\pi n^2 & (n \text{ odd}). \end{cases}$$

Similarly,

$$b_n = \frac{1}{\pi} \int_0^\pi x \sin nx \, dx = \frac{1}{\pi} \left[-\frac{x \cos nx}{n} + \frac{1}{n} \int \cos nx \, dx \right]_0^\pi$$

$$= \frac{1}{\pi n} \left[-x \cos nx + \frac{\sin nx}{n} \right]_0^\pi = -(-1)^n/n.$$

Hence

$$F(x) = \tfrac{1}{4}\pi - \sum_{\substack{n=1 \\ \text{odd}}}^\infty \frac{2}{\pi n^2} \cos nx - \sum_{n=1}^\infty \frac{(-1)^n}{n} \sin nx$$

$$= \tfrac{1}{4}\pi - \frac{2}{\pi} \sum_{n=0}^\infty \frac{\cos (2n + 1)x}{(2n + 1)^2} - \sum_{n=1}^\infty \frac{(-1)^n}{n} \sin nx,$$

where n is replaced by $2n + 1$ in order to ensure that only odd integers occur. In particular, when $x = 0$, $F(x) = 0$, yielding

$$\frac{\pi^2}{8} = \frac{1}{1^2} + \frac{1}{3^2} + \frac{1}{5^2} + \frac{1}{7^2} + \dots.$$

18.3 Half-range Fourier series

Whenever the Fourier series of a given function is required, the graph of the periodic function should first of all be drawn and the period ascertained. As presented above, the given function $f(x)$ is defined over the whole period $0 < x < 2\pi$, so no ambiguity can arise. But other cases may occur.

A function $F(x)$ is called an *even* function if $F(x) = F(-x)$, while it is an *odd* function if $F(-x) = -F(x)$. Examples of even functions are $1 + x^2$, $\cosh x$, $\cos 3x$, while examples of odd functions are $x - x^3$, $\sinh x$, $x^2 \sin^3 x$. The Maclaurin power series of an even function consists only of even powers of x, while for an odd function it consists only of odd powers.

Half-range Fourier series are specified in the following manner. A function $f(x)$ is defined only in the range $0 < x < \pi$, and the additional information is given that it is either an odd or an even function. This implies that the graph of the function is also determined in the range $-\pi < x < 0$, so in fact the period must be taken to be 2π, the fundamental periodically-repeated shape being in fact defined from $-\pi$ to $+\pi$.

Moreover, the Fourier series of an even function must consist only of cosine terms, since any sine terms, being odd, would prevent the complete series from enjoying the even property. Similarly, odd functions require only sine terms in their Fourier series.

These observations provide another method for specifying the problem: Expand the function $f(x)$, $0 < x < \pi$, as a Fourier cosine series. This statement implies that the function is even, so in effect the definition of $f(x)$ is extended to include the range $-\pi < x < 0$; the period is 2π.

Exceptionally, the shape of the graph in the range $-\pi < x < 0$ may be the same as that in the range $0 < x < \pi$. The period is therefore only π, but the correct answer is still obtained if a period of 2π is used.

If an odd function is to equal $f(x)$ in the range $0 < x < \pi$, we assume that

$$F(x) = \sum_{n=1}^{\infty} b_n \sin nx;$$

this equals $f(x)$ only in the range $0 < x < \pi$. If instead the function is given to be even, we assume the series

$$F(x) = \tfrac{1}{2}a_0 + \sum_{n=1}^{\infty} a_n \cos nx;$$

this equals $f(x)$ in the range $0 < x < \pi$.

In finding the coefficients, it is not wrong to integrate over the whole range, namely $-\pi$ to π, but it is not necessary. If this complete range is used, the value of the function in the range $-\pi < x < 0$ must be taken to be $-f(-x)$ or $f(-x)$ respectively, *not* $f(x)$. It is better merely to integrate over half the range, namely from 0 to π, since integrals of the form I and J only enter the calculations; these vanish for this restricted range of integration if $m \neq n$ (see section 18.1).

Example 3   Find the Fourier series of $\cos x$ $(0 < x < \pi)$ as an odd function.

We take 2π to be the period, and we assume a series of the form

$$F(x) = \sum_{n=1}^{\infty} b_n \sin nx.$$

To find b_m, we multiply by $\sin mx$ and integrate from 0 to π:

$$\int_0^{\pi} \cos x \sin mx \, dx = b_m \int_0^{\pi} \sin^2 mx \, dx = \tfrac{1}{2}\pi b_n.$$

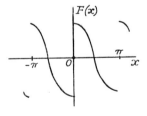

FIG. 114

Hence

$$b_m = \frac{1}{\pi} \int_0^\pi [\sin (m + 1)x + \sin (m - 1)x]\, dx$$

$$= -\frac{1}{\pi} \left[\frac{\cos (m + 1)x}{m + 1} + \frac{\cos (m - 1)x}{m - 1} \right]_0^\pi \quad (\text{if } m \neq 1)$$

$$= -\frac{1}{\pi} \left[\frac{(-1)^{m+1}}{m + 1} + \frac{(-1)^{m-1}}{m - 1} - \frac{1}{m + 1} - \frac{1}{m - 1} \right]$$

$$= \begin{cases} 0 & (m \text{ odd}) \\ 4m/\pi(m^2 - 1) & (m \text{ even}). \end{cases}$$

Exceptionally, if $m = 1$,

$$b_1 = \frac{2}{\pi} \int_0^\pi \cos x \sin x \, dx = 0.$$

Hence

$$F(x) = \frac{4}{\pi} \sum_{\substack{n=2 \\ \text{even}}}^\infty \frac{n \sin nx}{n^2 - 1} = \frac{8}{\pi} \sum_{n=1}^\infty \frac{n \sin 2nx}{4n^2 - 1}\,.$$

Example 4 Expand the function $\frac{1}{2}\pi - x$, $(0 < x < \pi)$ as a Fourier cosine series.

The question implies that the function is even, so in effect the fundamental shape is defined from $-\pi$ to $+\pi$, giving a period of 2π. Let

$$F(x) = \tfrac{1}{2}a_0 + \sum_{n=1}^\infty a_n \cos nx.$$

To find a_0 we integrate from 0 to π, obtaining

$$\int_0^\pi (\tfrac{1}{2}\pi - x)\, dx = \tfrac{1}{2}\pi a_0$$

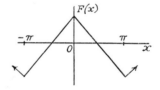

FIG. 115

yielding $a_0 = 0$. Similarly, we have

$$\int_0^\pi (\tfrac{1}{2}\pi - x) \cos mx \, dx = \tfrac{1}{2}\pi a_m,$$

yielding $\quad a_m = \dfrac{2}{\pi} \left[\dfrac{(\tfrac{1}{2}\pi - x) \sin mx}{m} + \dfrac{1}{m} \int \sin mx \, dx \right]_0^\pi$

$$= \frac{2}{\pi} \left[-\frac{\cos mx}{m^2} \right]_0^\pi = \frac{2}{\pi m^2} [-(-1)^m + 1] = \begin{cases} 0 & (m \text{ even}) \\ 4/\pi m^2 & (m \text{ odd}). \end{cases}$$

Hence

$$F(x) = \frac{4}{\pi} \sum_{n=0}^\infty \frac{\cos (2n + 1)x}{(2n + 1)^2}\,.$$

In this last example, the even coefficients vanish, leaving only odd coefficients; the condition for this may be seen from the beginning.

If $f(x)$ is defined for $0 < x < \pi$, and if $F(x)$ is to be an odd function whose Fourier series consists only of the terms sin x, sin $3x$, sin $5x$, . . . , then each of these terms possesses the property

$$\sin n(\pi - x) = \sin nx$$

when n is odd. Hence $f(x)$ must satisfy the condition

$$f(x) = f(\pi - x)$$

for $0 < x < \pi$; that is, $f(x)$ must be an even function about the value $x = \tfrac{1}{2}\pi$.

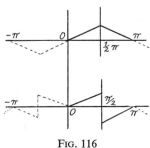

If on the other hand $F(x)$ is to be an even function whose Fourier series consists only of the terms cos x, cos $3x$, cos $5x$, . . . , then each of these terms possesses the property

$$\cos n(\pi - x) = -\cos nx$$

when n is odd. Hence

$$f(x) = -f(\pi - x)$$

Fɪɢ. 116

for $0 < x < \pi$; that is, $F(x)$ must be an odd function about the value $x = \tfrac{1}{2}\pi$.

18.4   Fourier series of general period

If $f(x)$ is defined for $0 < x < l$, and if $F(x)$ is defined to be of period l, then $F(x)$ cannot be arranged as a sum of functions of the type cos nx and sin nx whose periods are 2π. We therefore seek those functions whose period is l. These are given by

$$\cos 2\pi x/l, \cos 4\pi x/l, \cos 6\pi x/l, \ldots, \sin 2\pi x/l, \ldots,$$

the fundamental harmonics being cos $2\pi x/l$ and sin $2\pi x/l$ whose fundamental shapes fit in exactly once into the range $0 < x < l$.

We therefore assume

$$F(x) = \tfrac{1}{2}a_0 + \sum_{n=1}^{\infty} a_n \cos \frac{2\pi nx}{l} + \sum_{n=1}^{\infty} b_n \sin \frac{2\pi nx}{l}.$$

To find a_m and b_m, we multiply respectively by cos $2\pi mx/l$ and sin $2\pi mx/l$ and integrate over the complete period, namely from 0 to l. All the trigonometrical functions involved are orthogonal over such a range.

On the other hand, if $f(x)$ is defined in the range $0 < x < l$ together with the information that either an even or an odd function is to be formed, this implies that the period is $2l$. The cosines and sines assumed must now be $\cos \pi nx/l$ and $\sin \pi nx/l$; that is,

$$F(x) = \tfrac{1}{2}a_0 + \sum_{n=1}^{\infty} a_n \cos \pi nx/l \qquad \text{if } F(x) \text{ is even,}$$

$$F(x) = \sum_{n=1}^{\infty} b_n \sin \pi nx/l \qquad \text{if } F(x) \text{ is odd.}$$

The integration need be extended only over the range $0 < x < l$.

Example 5 Find the Fourier series for $\cosh x$ $(0 < x < 1)$ as a cosine series.

The question implies that the function is of period 2; we therefore consider functions of the form $\cos \pi nx$, since the lowest harmonic $\cos \pi x$ fits in exactly once into the range $-1 < x < 1$. Let

$$F(x) = \tfrac{1}{2}a_0 + \sum_{n=1}^{\infty} a_n \cos \pi nx.$$

Between 0 and 1, we have

$$\cosh x = \tfrac{1}{2}a_0 + \sum_{n=1}^{\infty} a_n \cos \pi nx.$$

To find a_0 we integrate this from 0 to 1, obtaining $\tfrac{1}{2}a_0 = \sinh 1$.
To find a_m we integrate from 0 to 1 after multiplication by $\cos \pi mx$:

$$\int_0^1 \cosh x \cos \pi mx \, dx = \tfrac{1}{2}a_m.$$

Integration by parts yields

$$a_m = 2\left[\sinh x \cos \pi mx + \pi m \int \sinh x \sin \pi mx \, dx \right]_0^1$$

$$= 2(-1)^m \sinh 1 + 2\pi m \left[\cosh x \sin \pi mx - \pi m \int \cosh x \cos \pi mx \, dx \right]_0^1$$

$$= 2(-1)^m \sinh 1 + 2\pi^2 m^2(\tfrac{1}{2}a_m);$$

hence
$$a_m = \frac{2(-1)^m \sinh 1}{1 + \pi^2 m^2}.$$

The Fourier series is

$$F(x) = \sinh 1 + \sum_{m=1}^{\infty} \frac{2(-1)^m \sinh 1 \cos \pi mx}{1 + \pi^2 m^2}.$$

In particular, when $x = 1$, we obtain

$$1 + \coth 1 = \sum_{m=0}^{\infty} \frac{2}{1 + \pi^2 m^2}.$$

18.5   Harmonic analysis

If the function $f(x)$ $(0 < x < 2\pi)$ is not specified by means of a mathematical function but by a discrete set of points on a graph, approximate methods must be used to resolve the function into its harmonic components.

Let the range $0 \leqslant x \leqslant 2\pi$ be divided into p equal subdivisions, each of width $h = 2\pi/p$; we shall designate the $p + 1$ values of x by

$$0 = x_0, x_1, x_2, \ldots, x_r, \ldots, x_{p-1}, x_p = 2\pi.$$

Using the trapezoidal rule for approximate integration (see section 16.8), we have

$$a_n = \frac{1}{\pi} \int_0^{2\pi} f(x) \cos nx \, dx \doteqdot \tfrac{1}{2}h(2\textstyle\sum \text{ordinates} - \text{the two end ordinates})/\pi$$

$$= \frac{1}{p}\left[2 \sum_{r=0}^{p} f(x_r) \cos nx_r - f(0) - f(2\pi) \cos 2\pi n \right]$$

$$= \frac{2}{p} \sum_{r=0}^{p-1} f(x_r) \cos nx_r,$$

provided the two end values $f(0)$ and $f(2\pi)$ are equal in value; this will be so if no discontinuity occurs there. Similarly,

$$b_n \doteqdot \frac{2}{p} \sum_{r=0}^{p-1} f(x_r) \sin nx_r,$$

where the end values of $f(x) \sin nx$ vanish for all values of n.

If we use a 12 ordinate scheme, for which $h = \tfrac{1}{6}\pi$ radians $= 30°$, we have

$$a_n = \frac{1}{12}\left[2 \sum_{r=0}^{12} f(30r) \cos 30nr - f(0) - f(360) \right]$$

$$= \frac{1}{6} \sum_{r=0}^{11} f(30r) \cos 30nr$$

if $f(0) = f(360)$, and

$$b_n = \frac{1}{6} \sum_{r=0}^{11} f(30r) \sin 30nr.$$

Any simplifying features should be noticed before calculations begin. For example, if the given data satisfies $f(\pi + x) = -f(x)$, only odd harmonics can be present both for the sines and for the cosines.

Numerical work should be tabulated in vertical columns, using the following scheme for $p = 12$.

x	$f(x)$	$\cos x$	$f(x) \cos x$	$\sin x$	$f(x) \sin x$	$\cos 2x$	$f(x) \cos 2x$	$\sin 2x$	$f(x) \sin 2x$
0		1		0		1		0	
30		0·866		0·5		0·5		0·866	
60		0·5		0·866		−0·5		0·866	
90		0		1		−1		0	
120		−0·5		0·866		−0·5		−0·866	
150		−0·866		0·5		0·5		−0·866	
180		−1		0		1		0	
210		−0·866		−0·5		0·5		0·866	
240		−0·5		−0·866		−0·5		0·866	
270		0		−1		−1		0	
300		0·5		−0·866		−0·5		−0·866	
330		0·866		−0·5		0·5		−0·866	
sum									
$\frac{1}{6}$ sum	$a_0 =$		$a_1 =$		$b_1 =$		$a_2 =$		$b_2 =$

If the function is even and given only in the range $0 < x < \pi$, we need only integrate over this half range. For p subdivisions of width $h = \pi/p$,

$$a_n = \frac{2}{\pi} \int_0^{\pi} f(x) \cos nx \, dx$$

$$\doteq \frac{2}{p} \left[2 \sum_{r=0}^{p} f(x_r) \cos nx_r - f(0) - f(\pi) \cos n\pi \right]$$

$$= \frac{4}{p} \sum_{r=0}^{p-1} f(x_r) \cos nx_r + \frac{2}{p} [f(0) + (-1)^n f(\pi)],$$

and

$$b_n = \frac{4}{p} \sum_{r=0}^{p-1} f(x_r) \sin nx_r$$

if an odd function is required.

Example 6 Find the first and second harmonics for the function with period 360° specified by

$x°$	0	30	60	90	120	150	180	210	240	270	300	330
$f(x)$	180	276	364	436	488	522	556	558	550	516	440	318

We draw up the following table as previously described:

x	$f(x)$	$\cos x$	$f(x) \cos x$	$\sin x$	$f(x) \sin x$	$\cos 2x$	$f(x) \cos 2x$	$\sin 2x$	$f(x) \sin 2x$
0	180	1	180	0	0	1	180	0	0
30	276	0·866	239·0	0·5	138	0·5	138	0·866	239·0
60	364	0·5	182	0·866	315·2	−0·5	−182	0·866	315·2
90	436	0	0	1	436	−1	−436	0	0
120	488	−0·5	−244	0·866	422·6	−0·5	−244	−0·866	−422·6
150	522	−0·866	−452·1	0·5	261	0·5	261	−0·866	−452·1
180	556	−1	−556	0	0	1	556	0	0
210	558	−0·866	−483·2	−0·5	−279	0·5	279	0·866	483·2
240	550	−0·5	−275	−0·866	−476·3	−0·5	−275	0·866	476·3
270	516	0	0	−1	−516	−1	−516	0	0
300	440	0·5	220	−0·866	−381·0	−0·5	−220	−0·866	−381·0
330	318	0·866	275·4	−0·5	−159	0·5	159	−0·866	−275·4
sum	5204		−913·9		−238·5		−300		−17·4
$\frac{1}{6}$ sum	$a_0 = 867$		$a_1 = -152$		$b_1 = -40$		$a_2 = -50$		$b_2 = -3$

We have therefore the result

$$f(x) = 433 - 152 \cos x - 50 \cos 2x + \ldots - 40 \sin x - 3 \sin 2x + \ldots.$$

EXERCISES

(1). Prove that the Fourier series, with period 2π, equal to -1 when $-\pi < x < 0$ and to $+1$ when $0 < x < \pi$, is

$$(4/\pi)(\sin x + \tfrac{1}{3} \sin 3x + \tfrac{1}{5} \sin 5x + \tfrac{1}{7} \sin 7x + \ldots).$$

(2)*. A periodic function of x, of period 2π, has the values

$$-\tfrac{1}{2}\pi \text{ for } -\pi < x \leqslant -\tfrac{1}{2}\pi, \quad x \text{ for } -\tfrac{1}{2}\pi \leqslant x \leqslant \tfrac{1}{2}\pi, \quad \tfrac{1}{2}\pi \text{ for } \tfrac{1}{2}\pi \leqslant x < \pi.$$

Show that the function can be represented by the Fourier series

$$\left(1 + \frac{2}{\pi}\right) \sin x - \tfrac{1}{2} \sin 2x + \left(\frac{1}{3} - \frac{2}{9\pi}\right) \sin 3x$$

$$- \tfrac{1}{4} \sin 4x + \left(\frac{1}{5} + \frac{2}{25\pi}\right) \sin 5x + \ldots.$$

(3). Find the odd Fourier series for the periodic function whose period is 2π, and which is equal to $\cosh x$ in the range $0 < x < \pi$. Hence show that

$$\tfrac{1}{4}\pi \operatorname{sech} \tfrac{1}{2}\pi = \sum_{0}^{\infty} (-1)^n / [(2n + 1) + (2n + 1)^{-1}].$$

(4)*. A periodic function $F(x)$ of period 2π in x can be expressed as a Fourier series containing only sine terms. In the range of x from 0 to π it is defined by $F(x) = x$, $(0 \leqslant x \leqslant \tfrac{1}{2}\pi)$; $F(x) = \pi - x$, $(\tfrac{1}{2}\pi \leqslant x \leqslant \pi)$. Draw a graph of the function to cover two whole periods and find its Fourier series.

(5)*. A thin flexible string is stretched tightly between fixed points whose Cartesian coordinates are $(0, 0)$ and $(l, 0)$. If the mid-point of the string is now displaced to the point $(\tfrac{1}{2}l, h)$, the two portions of the string being straight, show with the aid of suitable graphs how the displaced form of the string can be represented (a) by an infinite series of sines or (b) by an infinite series of cosines. Show that the series of

$$\text{sines is } \frac{8h}{\pi^2} \left[\frac{\sin (\pi x/l)}{1^2} - \frac{\sin (3\pi x/l)}{3^2} + \frac{\sin (5\pi x/l)}{5^2} - \ldots \right].$$

(6)*. A function of x, $F(x)$, has period 2π and

$$F(x) = 2x \text{ for } 0 < x < \tfrac{1}{2}\pi, \quad F(x) = 2(\pi - x) \text{ for } \tfrac{1}{2}\pi < x < \pi.$$

If its Fourier series contains sine terms only sketch the graph of the function in the range $0 \leqslant x \leqslant 2\pi$ and find the general term of the series.

(7)*. Find the Fourier sine series representing the function

$$y = \sin 2x \text{ when } 0 \leqslant x \leqslant \tfrac{1}{2}\pi, \quad y = 0 \text{ when } \tfrac{1}{2}\pi \leqslant x \leqslant \pi,$$

in the range $0 \leqslant x \leqslant \pi$. Sketch the graph of the function represented by the series in the range $-2\pi \leqslant x \leqslant 2\pi$.

(8)*. An odd function $F(x)$ of period 2π is defined as follows:

$$F(x) = 0, \ (0 \leqslant x \leqslant \tfrac{1}{4}\pi); \quad F(x) = x - \tfrac{1}{4}\pi, \ (\tfrac{1}{4}\pi \leqslant x \leqslant \tfrac{1}{2}\pi);$$
$$F(x) = \tfrac{3}{4}\pi - x, \ (\tfrac{1}{2}\pi \leqslant x \leqslant \tfrac{3}{4}\pi); \quad F(x) = 0, \ (\tfrac{3}{4}\pi \leqslant x \leqslant \pi).$$

Sketch the graph of the function for $-2\pi \leqslant x \leqslant 2\pi$, and show that

$$F(x) = \frac{4}{\pi}\left[\left(1 - \frac{1}{\sqrt{2}}\right)\frac{\sin x}{1^2} - \left(1 + \frac{1}{\sqrt{2}}\right)\frac{\sin 3x}{3^2}\right.$$
$$\left. + \left(1 + \frac{1}{\sqrt{2}}\right)\frac{\sin 5x}{5^2} - \left(1 - \frac{1}{\sqrt{2}}\right)\frac{\sin 7x}{7^2} + \dots\right].$$

(9)*. A function $F(x)$, of period 2π in x, is such that

$$F(x) = 3x \text{ for } 0 \leqslant x \leqslant \tfrac{1}{3}\pi, \quad F(x) = \pi \text{ for } \tfrac{1}{3}\pi \leqslant x \leqslant \tfrac{1}{2}\pi$$

and the corresponding Fourier series contains sines of odd multiples of x only. Sketch the graph of $F(x)$ from $x = 0$ to 2π and obtain the first five non-vanishing terms of the Fourier series. By considering the value $F(\tfrac{1}{4}\pi)$ obtain a series expression for π^2.

(10)*. The even function $F(x)$ of period 2π is such that $F(x) = \sin x$ when $0 \leqslant x \leqslant \pi$. Show that the Fourier series is

$$\frac{2}{\pi} - \frac{4}{\pi}\left[\frac{\cos 2x}{1.3} + \frac{\cos 4x}{3.5} + \frac{\cos 6x}{5.7} + \dots\right].$$

(11).* Prove that, for $0 < x < \pi$,

$$\pi - 2x = (8/\pi)(\cos x + 3^{-2}\cos 3x + 5^{-2}\cos 5x + \dots).$$

To what function is the series equal in the range $-\pi < x < 0$? From the given result deduce that, in the range $-\tfrac{1}{2}\pi < x < \tfrac{1}{2}\pi$,

$$\sin x - 3^{-2}\sin 3x + 5^{-2}\sin 5x - \dots = \tfrac{1}{4}\pi x.$$

(12)*. Show that, if $a \neq 0$, and $-\pi \leqslant x \leqslant \pi$,

$$a\pi \cosh ax = \sinh a\pi + 2a^2 \sinh a\pi \sum_{n=1}^{\infty}(-1)^n\frac{\cos nx}{a^2 + n^2}.$$

Deduce the value of $\displaystyle\sum_{n=1}^{\infty}\frac{1}{a^2 + n^2}$.

(13)*. A function $F(x)$ is such that $F(x) = x$ for $0 \leqslant x \leqslant \tfrac{1}{2}\pi$, and $F(x) = \tfrac{1}{2}\pi$ for $\tfrac{1}{2}\pi \leqslant x \leqslant \pi$. Express $F(x)$ as a Fourier series involving cosines only, and sketch the graph of the series outside the range $0 \leqslant x \leqslant \pi$.
Sketch also the graph of the Fourier sine series which equals $F(x)$ in the range $0 \leqslant x \leqslant \pi$.

(14)*. Obtain the Fourier series of the function $F(x) = |x|$ in the range $-\pi \leqslant x \leqslant \pi$. Assuming that the series converges to the function, state the sum of the series when $\pi < x < 2\pi$. Show that

$$\sum_{n=1}^{\infty}1/n^2 = \pi^2/6.$$

(15)*. A periodic function $F(x)$, whose period is $\tfrac{1}{2}\pi$, is zero in the ranges $-\tfrac{1}{4}\pi < x < -\alpha$ and $\alpha < x < \tfrac{1}{4}\pi$, while in the range $-\alpha < x < \alpha$, $F(x)$ has the constant value $1/\alpha$. Show that $F(x)$ can be expanded in the Fourier series

$$F(x) = \frac{8}{\pi}\left[\tfrac{1}{2} + \sum_{n=1}^{\infty}\frac{\sin 4n\alpha}{4n\alpha}\cos 4nx\right].$$

(16)★. Obtain the Fourier series of the function defined by

$$F(x) = x, \; (0 \leqslant x \leqslant \pi); \quad F(x) = 2\pi - x, \; (\pi \leqslant x \leqslant 2\pi); \quad F(x + 2\pi) = F(x).$$

By considering the value of the function for a particular value of x, prove that

$$\pi^2/8 = 1/1^2 + 1/3^2 + 1/5^2 + \dots.$$

(17)★. Obtain the Fourier expansion of an even function $F(x)$ defined by

$$F(x) = x, \; (0 \leqslant x < \tfrac{1}{3}\pi); \quad F(x) = 0, \; (\tfrac{1}{3}\pi < x < \tfrac{2}{3}\pi);$$
$$F(x) = x - \tfrac{2}{3}\pi, \; (\tfrac{2}{3}\pi \leqslant x < \pi),$$

and simplify the coefficients of the first four terms.

(18)★. The Fourier series of a function $F(x)$ of period 2π does not contain sines of multiples of x. Also $F(x) = \cos x$ when $0 \leqslant x \leqslant \tfrac{1}{2}\pi$ and $F(x) = 0$ when $\tfrac{1}{2}\pi \leqslant x \leqslant \pi$. Sketch the graph of $F(x)$ for one complete period and show that its Fourier series is

$$\frac{1}{\pi} + \frac{1}{2}\cos x + \frac{2}{\pi}\sum_{n=1}^{\infty}\frac{(-1)^{n+1}}{4n^2 - 1}\cos 2nx.$$

Sum the series $1/1.3 - 1/3.5 + 1/5.7 - \dots$.

(19)★. Express $F(x)$ as a cosine series, given that

$$F(x) = \tfrac{1}{4}\pi^2 - x^2, \; (0 \leqslant x \leqslant \tfrac{1}{2}\pi); \quad F(x) = 0, \; (\tfrac{1}{2}\pi \leqslant x \leqslant \pi).$$

(20)★. A function $F(x)$ is such that $F(x) = F(x + 2\pi)$ and $F(x) = \tfrac{1}{4}x^2$ for $-\pi \leqslant x \leqslant \pi$. Sketch the graph of $F(x)$ from $x = -2\pi$ to 2π and state what terms are absent from the Fourier expansion of $F(x)$ in the range $-\pi$ to π of x. Obtain the general term in this series and deduce the value of

$$\sum_{n=1}^{\infty} n^{-2}.$$

(21)★. Find the Fourier series of period 2π which will represent

$$\tfrac{1}{8}\pi^2 - \tfrac{1}{4}\pi x, \; (0 \leqslant x \leqslant \pi); \quad \tfrac{1}{4}\pi x - \tfrac{3}{8}\pi^2, \; (\pi \leqslant x \leqslant 2\pi).$$

What does the series represent at the endpoints and outside these intervals?

(22). If $F(x) = k - |x|$ for $-2k \leqslant x \leqslant 2k$, and if $F(x)$ has period $4k$, show that its Fourier series is

$$\frac{8k}{\pi^2}\sum_{n=0}^{\infty}\frac{1}{(2n + 1)^2}\cos\left(\frac{(2n + 1)\pi x}{2k}\right).$$

(23)★. Prove that the Fourier series for the periodic function, with period 2π, defined by $F(x) = e^{-x}$ in the range $0 < x < 2\pi$, is

$$\frac{1 - e^{-2\pi}}{\pi}\left(\tfrac{1}{2} + \sum_{n=1}^{\infty}\frac{n\sin nx + \cos nx}{n^2 + 1}\right).$$

(24). Prove that the Fourier series with period 2π representing the function $F(x) = \sin x \; (0 \leqslant x \leqslant \pi)$ and $F(x) = 0 \; (\pi \leqslant x \leqslant 2\pi)$ is given by

$$F(x) = \frac{1}{\pi}\left(1 + \frac{\pi}{2}\sin x - \frac{2}{1.3}\cos 2x - \frac{2}{3.5}\cos 4x - \frac{2}{5.7}\cos 6x - \dots\right).$$

(25). Prove that the Fourier series with period 2π representing the function $F(x) = \cos kx$ in the range $0 < x < 2\pi$ is given by

$$\pi F(x) = \frac{\sin 2\pi k}{2k} + k\sin 2\pi k\sum_{n=1}^{\infty}\frac{\cos nx}{k^2 - n^2} + (\cos 2\pi k - 1)\sum_{n=1}^{\infty}\frac{n\sin nx}{k^2 - n^2}.$$

(26). Find the first and second harmonics of the following function whose period is 360°:

x	0	30	60	90	120	150	180	210	240	270	300	330
$f(x)$	27·20	36·93	41·34	40·36	35·64	28·69	20·26	11·22	3·75	0·97	5·00	15·01

(27). By first showing that only odd harmonics are present, find the first and third harmonics of the following function whose period is 360°:

x	0	30	60	90	120	150	180	210	240	270	300	330
$f(x)$	28	346	517	560	523	326	−28	−346	−517	−560	−523	−326

(28). By first showing that odd harmonics only are present, find the first, third and fifth harmonics of the following odd function:

x	0	30	60	90	120	150
$f(x)$	0	1·50	6·53	14·25	6·53	1·50

ANSWERS TO EXERCISES

(3). $\dfrac{2}{\pi} \displaystyle\sum_{n=1}^{\infty} \dfrac{1-(-1)^n \cosh \pi}{n + 1/n} \sin nx.$ 　　(4). $\dfrac{4}{\pi} \displaystyle\sum_{n=1}^{\infty} \dfrac{(-1)^{n+1}}{(2n-1)^2} \sin (2n-1)x.$

(6). $\dfrac{8}{\pi} \displaystyle\sum_{n=0}^{\infty} \dfrac{(-1)^n}{(2n+1)^2} \sin (2n+1)x.$ 　　(7). $b_1 = \tfrac{4}{3}\pi,\ b_2 = \tfrac{1}{2},\ b_n = \dfrac{4 \sin \frac{1}{2}n\pi}{\pi(4 - n^2)}.$

(9). $\dfrac{12}{\pi} \displaystyle\sum_{n=1}^{\infty} \dfrac{\sin \frac{1}{3}(2n-1)\pi \sin (2n-1)x}{(2n-1)^2},$

$\pi^2 = 8\sqrt{3} \left(\dfrac{1}{1^2} + \dfrac{1}{5^2} - \dfrac{1}{7^2} - \dfrac{1}{11^2} - \dfrac{1}{13^2} - \dfrac{1}{17^2} + \dfrac{1}{19^2} + \dfrac{1}{25^2} + \dots \right).$

(11). $\pi + 2x.$ 　　(12). $\dfrac{\pi \coth a\pi}{2a} - \dfrac{1}{2a^2}.$ 　　(13). $\dfrac{3\pi}{8} - \dfrac{2}{\pi} \displaystyle\sum_{n=1}^{\infty} \dfrac{1-\cos \frac{1}{2}n\pi}{n^2} \cos nx.$

(14). $\dfrac{\pi}{2} - \dfrac{4}{\pi} \displaystyle\sum_{n=1}^{\infty} \dfrac{\cos (2n-1)x}{(2n-1)^2},\ y = 2\pi - x.$ 　　(16). $\dfrac{\pi}{2} - \dfrac{4}{\pi} \displaystyle\sum_{n=1}^{\infty} \dfrac{\cos (2n-1)x}{(2n-1)^2}.$

(17). $\tfrac{1}{2}a_0 = \tfrac{1}{9}\pi,\ a_n = 2 [\frac{1}{3}\pi n \sin \frac{1}{3}n\pi + \cos \frac{1}{3}n\pi - \cos \frac{2}{3}n\pi + (-1)^n - 1]/\pi n^2,$
$a_1 = 1/\sqrt{3} - 2/\pi,\ a_2 = 1/\sqrt{3},\ a_3 = -8/3\pi,\ a_4 = -1/\sqrt{3}.$

(18). $\tfrac{1}{4}\pi - \tfrac{1}{2}.$ 　　(19). $\tfrac{1}{2}a_0 = \tfrac{1}{12}\pi^2,\ a_n = 2(2 \sin \frac{1}{2}n\pi - \pi n \cos \frac{1}{2}n\pi)/\pi n^3.$

(20). $\dfrac{\pi^2}{12} + \displaystyle\sum_{n=1}^{\infty} \dfrac{(-1)^n \cos nx}{n^2},\ \tfrac{1}{6}\pi^2.$ 　　(21). $\displaystyle\sum_{n=0}^{\infty} \dfrac{\cos (2n-1)x}{(2n-1)^2}.$

(26). $f(x) = 22\!\cdot\!20 + 3\!\cdot\!47 \cos x + 1\!\cdot\!53 \cos 2x + 19\!\cdot\!70 \sin x + 1\!\cdot\!29 \sin 2x.$
(27). $f(x) = 14 \cos x + 11 \cos 3x + 599 \sin x + 37 \sin 3x.$
(28). $f(x) = 9\!\cdot\!0 \sin x - 3\!\cdot\!75 \sin 3x + 1\!\cdot\!5 \sin 5x.$

CHAPTER 19

FIRST ORDER DIFFERENTIAL EQUATIONS

19.1 Definitions

A *differential equation*, involving the *dependent* variable y and the *independent* variable x, is a relationship existing between x, y and the various derivatives of y, namely dy/dx, d^2y/dx^2, ... For convenience, these derivatives may be written as $y', y'', \ldots$, or as $Dy, D^2y, \ldots$, using the notation introduced in section 14.3. The *solution* of such an equation is attained when either y is expressed explicitly in terms of x, or when a relation between x and y is found such that all the derivatives are eliminated. The process of solution consists of remoulding the equation in order to render possible an integration and the simultaneous introduction of an *arbitrary constant*.

If the highest order derivative occurring in the equation is d^ny/dx^n, we call the equation an nth *order differential equation*. If dy/dx is the only derivative that occurs, the equation is a *first order* equation. In the process of solving an nth order equation, n successive integrations must be carried out, either explicitly or implicitly; each integration introduces an arbitrary constant. The final solution will then contain n arbitrary constants; this result is called the *general solution* of the equation. The value of these n constants can be determined to satisfy n postulated conditions, such as specified values of $y, Dy, D^2y, \ldots,$ $D^{n-1}y$ when $x = 0$. Sometimes, other solutions of the equation may exist, that are not obtained from the general solution merely by giving the n constants special values; these are called *singular solutions*.

Sometimes, $y, Dy, D^2y, \ldots$ may be raised to various powers, such as $(Dy)^4$; the highest index occurring is the *degree* of the equation. Powers of the independent variable x are disregarded in deciding the degree of an equation.

An equation is *linear* if it is of the first degree and if no products exist between the terms $y, Dy, D^2y, \ldots.$

19.2 Formation of differential equations

Differential equations usually arise in theoretical physics and engineering through the application of fundamental laws to particular problems.

432

On the other hand, we may be given a function

$$y = y(x, A, B, C, \ldots)$$

containing n arbitrary constants, and we may form the differential equation giving rise to this function as a solution. The technique is elementary, but it arises occasionally. We differentiate repeatedly n times, obtaining

$$y' = y'(x, A, B, C, \ldots),$$
$$\cdots \cdots \cdots \cdots \cdots$$
$$y^{(n)} = y^{(n)}(x, A, B, C, \ldots).$$

We now eliminate the constants $A, B, C, \ldots$ from these $n + 1$ equations, obtaining a relationship between $x, y, y', \ldots, y^{(n)}$.

Example 1   Find the differential equation of the tangents to a parabola.

In parametric form, the general point on the parabola $y^2 = 4ax$ is $(at^2, 2at)$. The gradient being $1/t$, the equation of the tangent is

$$y - 2at = (x - at^2)/t,$$

or
$$ty = x + at^2.$$

Here, t is the arbitrary parameter. Differentiating with respect to x, we obtain $ty' = 1$; so the elimination of t yields

$$x(y')^2 + a - yy' = 0.$$

This equation is of the first order but of the second degree. The equation provides a relationship between x, y, y' at every point on every tangent to the parabola.

Example 2   Find the differential equation for every circle in a plane.

The general circle is given by

$$(x - a)^2 + (y - b)^2 = r^2,$$

containing three arbitrary constants a, b, r. Differentiating three times, we obtain

$$(x - a) + (y - b)y' = 0,$$
$$1 + (y - b)y'' + (y')^2 = 0,$$
$$(y - b)y''' + 3y'y'' = 0.$$

Eliminating $(x - a)$ and $(y - b)$ from these three equations, we obtain

$$\begin{vmatrix} 1 & y' & 0 \\ 0 & y'' & 1 + (y')^2 \\ 0 & y''' & 3y'y'' \end{vmatrix} = 0,$$

or
$$3y'(y'')^2 = y'''[1 + (y')^2].$$

19.3   Separable equations

If the given first order equation can be solved for dy/dx such that its value is expressed as the product of a function $f(x)$ of x alone and a function $g(y)$ of y alone, then *separation is* possible.   If

$$\frac{dy}{dx} = f(x)g(y),$$

in preparation for integration we may write this conventionally as

$$\frac{dy}{g(y)} = f(x)\,dx,$$

which yields, upon integration,

$$\int \frac{dy}{g(y)} = \int f(x)\,dx + A.$$

Example 3   Solve the equation

$$y \tan x \frac{dy}{dx} = (25 - y^2) \sec^2 x,$$

such that $y = 3$ when $x = \tfrac{1}{4}\pi$.

Separating the variables, we have

$$\frac{y\,dy}{25 - y^2} = \frac{\sec^2 x\,dx}{\tan x},$$

yielding upon integration

$$-\tfrac{1}{2} \log (25 - y^2) = \log \tan x + A,$$

or
$$(25 - y^2)^{-\frac{1}{2}} = B \tan x$$

when the logarithms are removed.   (*Note that the added arbitrary constant A becomes the multiplied arbitrary constant B*).

Inserting the given values for x and y, we find $B = \tfrac{1}{4}$.

Various standard types of first order equations may be reduced to separable form.   If

$$\frac{dy}{dx} = f(ax + by + c)$$

where the right hand side is a function of the linear expression $ax + by + c$, we eliminate y in favour of the new dependent variable $z = ax + by + c$.   Then

$$\frac{dz}{dx} = a + b\frac{dy}{dx} = a + bf(z).$$

This equation is obviously separable, yielding

$$\int \frac{dz}{a + bf(z)} = x + A.$$

Example 4 Solve the equation $dy/dx = \sin(x + y)$.

Making the substitution $z = x + y$, we have

$$\frac{dz}{dx} = 1 + \frac{dy}{dx} = 1 + \sin z$$
$$= \cos^2 \tfrac{1}{2}z + \sin^2 \tfrac{1}{2}z + 2 \sin \tfrac{1}{2}z \cos \tfrac{1}{2}z$$
$$= (\cos \tfrac{1}{2}z + \sin \tfrac{1}{2}z)^2$$
$$= 2 \cos^2 (\tfrac{1}{2}z - \tfrac{1}{4}\pi).$$

Hence $\qquad dx = \tfrac{1}{2} \sec^2 (\tfrac{1}{2}z - \tfrac{1}{4}\pi) \, dz,$

yielding $\qquad x = \tan (\tfrac{1}{2}z - \tfrac{1}{4}\pi) + A,$

or $\qquad x = \tan (\tfrac{1}{2}x + \tfrac{1}{2}y - \tfrac{1}{4}\pi) + A.$

Example 5 Solve the equation $dy/dx = (2x + y + 3)/(4x + 2y + 1)$.

The variable terms of the numerator are proportional to the variable terms of the denominator. We therefore substitute $z = 2x + y + 3$, yielding

$$\frac{dz}{dx} = 2 + \frac{dy}{dx} = 2 + \frac{z}{2z - 5} = \frac{5z - 10}{2z - 5}.$$

Integration yields

$$5x + A = \int \left(\frac{2z - 5}{z - 2}\right) dz = \int \left(2 - \frac{1}{z - 2}\right) dz$$
$$= 2z - \log (z - 2)$$
$$= 4x + 2y + 6 - \log (2x + y + 1),$$

or, finally, $\qquad 2y - x - \log (2x + y + 1) = B,$

where the constant 6 may be absorbed into the arbitrary constant.

Another common type of equation is given by

$$\frac{dy}{dx} = f\left(\frac{y}{x}\right),$$

the function on the right commonly being called a *homogeneous* function. We make the substitution $t = vx$, yielding upon differentiation

$$\frac{dy}{dx} = v + x \frac{dv}{dx} \, ;$$

that is $\qquad f(v) = v + x \frac{dv}{dx} \, .$

This equation is now separable; integration yields

$$\int \frac{dv}{f(v) - v} = \log x + A.$$

Example 6   Solve the equation $x(dy/dx) = y + \sqrt{(x^2 - y^2)}$.
 Let $y = vx$, giving

$$\frac{dy}{dx} = v + x\frac{dv}{dx} = v + \sqrt{(1 - v^2)}.$$

Hence

$$\frac{dv}{\sqrt{(1 - v^2)}} = \frac{dx}{x},$$

yielding upon integration

$$\sin^{-1} v = \log x + A,$$

or $\sin^{-1}(y/x) = \log x + A.$

This may finally be solved for y:

$$y = x \sin (\log x + A).$$

 Equations of the type

$$\frac{dy}{dx} = \frac{ax + by + c}{Ax + By + C},$$

where $aB \neq Ab$, may also be reduced to homogeneous type. Let the
two lines

$$ax + by + c = 0, \quad Ax + By + C = 0$$

intersect in the unique point (x_0, y_0). The simple change of variables
$x = X + x_0$, $y = Y + y_0$ (that is, taking parallel axes through the
point of intersection) now yields

$$\frac{dY}{dX} = \frac{dy}{dx} = \frac{a(X + x_0) + b(Y + y_0) + c}{A(X + x_0) + B(Y + y_0) + C}$$

$$= \frac{aX + bY + (ax_0 + by_0 + c)}{AX + BY + (Ax_0 + By_0 + C)} = \frac{aX + bY}{AX + BY}$$

which is now an equation homogeneous in X and Y.
 This type of equation may also be solved by the change of variable

$$X = Ax + By + C, \quad Y = ax + by + c.$$

For $\delta X = A\,\delta x + B\,\delta y, \quad \delta Y = a\,\delta x + b\,\delta y;$

hence, upon division,

$$\frac{dY}{dX} = \frac{a + b\dfrac{dy}{dx}}{A + B\dfrac{dy}{dx}} = \frac{a + b\dfrac{Y}{X}}{A + B\dfrac{Y}{X}} = \frac{aX + bY}{AX + BY},$$

the same equation as before.
 In other examples, suitable substitutions must be found by intelligent
inspection, as in example 8 below.

Example 7 Solve the equation $dy/dx = 2(x + y - 1)/(3x + y + 1)$.

The two lines $x + y - 1 = 0$, $3x + y + 1 = 0$ intersect in the point $(-1, 2)$; we therefore let $x = X - 1$, $y = Y + 2$, yielding

$$\frac{dY}{dX} = \frac{2X + 2Y}{3X + Y}.$$

We now place $Y = vX$, giving

$$\frac{dY}{dX} = v + X\frac{dv}{dX} = \frac{2 + 2v}{3 + v},$$

or

$$X\frac{dv}{dX} = \frac{2 + 2v}{3 + v} - v = \frac{(1 - v)(2 + v)}{3 + v}.$$

Separating this, and integrating, we obtain

$$\log X + A = \int \frac{(3 + v)\, dv}{(1 - v)(2 + v)}$$

$$= \tfrac{1}{3}\int \left(\frac{4}{1 - v} + \frac{1}{2 + v}\right) dv$$

$$= -\tfrac{4}{3}\log (1 - v) + \tfrac{1}{3}\log (2 + v),$$

simplifying to

$$\frac{2 + v}{(1 - v)^4} = Bx^3.$$

Now $v = Y/X$, so the solution becomes

$$\frac{2X + Y}{(X - Y)^4} = B,$$

or finally

$$2x + y = B(x - y + 3)^4.$$

Example 8 Solve the following equation, subject to the condition that $y = 0$ when $x = 1$:

$$\frac{dy}{dx} = \frac{(x + y)^2 - (x - y)}{(x - y) + (x + y)^2}.$$

We make the substitutions: $u = x + y$, $v = x - y$. Now $\delta u = \delta x + \delta y$ and $\delta v = \delta x - \delta y$, yielding

$$\frac{du}{dv} = \frac{1 + \dfrac{dy}{dx}}{1 - \dfrac{dy}{dx}} = \frac{1 + \dfrac{u^2 - v}{v + u^2}}{1 - \dfrac{u^2 - v}{v + u^2}} = \frac{u^2}{v}.$$

The equation is now separable; integration yields

$$-u^{-1} = \log v + A,$$

or

$$v = Be^{-1/u},$$

or, finally,

$$x - y = Be^{-1/(x+y)}.$$

The point $(1, 0)$ must lie on this locus. This yields $B = e$, so

$$x - y = e^{1-1/(x+y)}.$$

19.4   Exact equations

In section 15.2, we have seen that the first order increment for the equation $z(x, y) = A$ is given by

$$\frac{\partial z}{\partial x} \, \delta x + \frac{\partial z}{\partial y} \, \delta y = 0. \tag{1}$$

Conversely, if this first order equation is given, we may deduce that its solution is $z(x, y) = A$.

In this section we shall conventionally write dx and dy for δx and δy.

If an equation

$$f(x, y) \, dx + g(x, y) \, dy = 0 \tag{2}$$

is given, it may or it may not be expressible in the form (1). If it is thus expressible, a function $z(x, y)$ exists, such that

$$\frac{\partial z}{\partial x} = f, \qquad \frac{\partial z}{\partial y} = g.$$

Differentiating with respect to y and x respectively, we obtain

$$\frac{\partial^2 z}{\partial y \, \partial x} = \frac{\partial f}{\partial y}, \qquad \frac{\partial^2 z}{\partial x \, \partial y} = \frac{\partial g}{\partial x}.$$

Since these mixed derivatives must be equal, we have derived a necessary condition to be satisfied by $f(x, y)$ and $g(x, y)$ in order that equation (2) should be identical with (1). This condition is

$$\frac{\partial f}{\partial y} = \frac{\partial g}{\partial x}.$$

If this condition is satisfied, equation (2) is called *exact*, and *only* under these circumstances can a function z be found.

The function z may be found either by inspection or by integration. Integrating $\partial z/\partial x = f$, we obtain

$$z = \int f(x, y) \, dx + Y(y),$$

where $Y(y)$ is an arbitrary function of y introduced upon partial integration with respect to x. Differentiating this with respect to y, we obtain

$$\frac{\partial z}{\partial y} = \frac{\partial}{\partial y} \int f(x, y) \, dx + \frac{dY(y)}{dy} = g(x, y).$$

It will be found that the variable x disappears from this latter equation, enabling $Y(y)$ to be found. The final solution is then $z = A$.

If equation (2) is not exact as it stands, it may be rendered exact by multiplying it by what is termed an *integrating factor* $J(x, y)$; that is, we assume that the new equation

$$(Jf)\,dx + (Jg)\,dy = 0$$

is exact. The condition for this is

$$\frac{\partial}{\partial y}\,(Jf) = \frac{\partial}{\partial x}\,(Jg),$$

which yields the function J. In elementary work, however, a hint must be provided in the problem, in order to calculate J from this equation.

Example 9 Solve the equation

$$\frac{dy}{dx} = \frac{3x^2y^2 + 1 - y}{x - 2y - 2x^3y}.$$

Arranged in the form

$$(3x^2y^2 + 1 - y)\,dx + (2x^3y + 2y - x)\,dy = 0,$$

we note that

$$\frac{\partial}{\partial y}\,(3x^2y^2 + 1 - y) = \frac{\partial}{\partial x}\,(2x^3y + 2y - x) = 6x^2y - 1,$$

so the equation is exact. Hence a function z exists such that

$$\partial z/\partial x = 3x^2y^2 + 1 - y, \quad \partial z/\partial y = 2x^3y + 2y - x.$$

The integral of the first equation is

$$z = x^3y^2 + x - xy + Y(y),$$

where $Y(y)$ is an unknown function of y. Differentiation yields

$$\partial z/\partial y = 2x^3y - x + dY/dy = 2x^3y + 2y - x$$

or $dY/dy = 2y$. We conclude that $Y = y^2$, yielding the final solution

$$z = x^3y^2 + x - xy + y^2 = A.$$

Example 10 By assuming an integrating factor of the form $xf(y)$, solve the equation

$$(3x \sin y + 2 \sin^3 y)\,dx + (2x^2 \cos y + 4x \sin^2 y \cos y)\,dy = 0.$$

The equation is not exact as it stands, since the test is negative. But multiplying by $xf(y)$, we assume that the equation

$$(3x^2 \sin y + 2x \sin^3 y)f(y)\,dx + (2x^3 \cos y + 4x^2 \sin^2 y \cos y)f(y)\,dy = 0$$

is exact. The test yields the equation

$$\frac{\partial}{\partial y}\,[(3x^2 \sin y + 2x \sin^3 y)f(y)] = \frac{\partial}{\partial x}\,[(2x^3 \cos y + 4x^2 \sin^2 y \cos y)f(y)]$$

or $(3x^2 \sin y + 2x \sin^3 y)f' + (3x^2 \cos y + 6x \sin^2 y \cos y)f$

$$= (6x^2 \cos y + 8x \sin^2 y \cos y)f$$

or $\qquad 3x^2(\sin y\,f' - \cos y\,f) = -2x \sin^2 y(\sin y\,f' - \cos y\,f).$

15

Clearly $\sin y f' = \cos y f$, yielding $f(y) = \sin y$. No constant of integration need be introduced when integrating to find an integrating factor.

Hence a function z exists such that

$$\partial z/\partial x = 3x^2 \sin^2 y + 2x \sin^4 y, \quad \partial z/\partial y = (2x^3 \sin y + 4x^2 \sin^3 y) \cos y.$$

It follows by inspection that $z = x^3 \sin^2 y + x^2 \sin^4 y$. The final solution is therefore

$$x^3 \sin^2 y + x^2 \sin^4 y = A.$$

19.5   Equations not of the first degree

Equations soluble for dy/dx.   In this context, we often write $p \equiv dy/dx$. If a given equation contains $p, p^2, p^3, \ldots$, we may sometimes solve the equation for p, after which we may use one of the methods developed above.

Example 11   Solve the equation $xp^2 - 2py + x = 0$.
Solving this as a quadratic in p, we find that

$$p = \frac{dy}{dx} = \frac{y \pm \sqrt{(y^2 - x^2)}}{x} .$$

We have now two first order equations to solve. We place $y = vx$, giving

$$v + x\frac{dv}{dx} = \frac{dy}{dx} = v \pm \sqrt{(v^2 - 1)},$$

or $dv/\sqrt{(v^2 - 1)} = \pm dx/x.$

Integration yields
$$\log [v + \sqrt{(v^2 - 1)}] = \pm\log x + A.$$
Finally, $v + \sqrt{(v^2 - 1)} = Bx$ or B/x,
that is, $y + \sqrt{(y^2 - x^2)} = Bx^2$ or B.

Clairaut's equation.   Theorem.   If the family of curves specified by the general solution of a first order differential equation has an envelope, then the equation of this envelope is also a solution of the differential equation. It is called a *singular solution*, since it cannot be obtained from the general solution merely by giving the arbitrary constant a particular value.

That this must be so is obvious. For the differential equation merely provides a relationship between x, y and dy/dx at *every* point on *every* member of a family of curves. But at the point of contact of one of these curves and the envelope, x, y, and dy/dx have the same values for the envelope as for the curve of the family. Hence, x, y and dy/dx at every point on the envelope satisfy the differential equation.

All equations considered thus far have had solutions of the form $f(x, y) = A$. Clearly such a family cannot have an envelope, for partial differentiation with respect to the parameter A (see section 15.7) yields nothing of consequence. Evidently a differential equation is needed such that the arbitrary constant in its general solution occurs in a more complicated way than merely by addition. *Clairaut's equation* possesses this property.

Consider the equation

$$y = px + f(p),$$

where $p \equiv dy/dx$ and where f is an arbitrary function. For example, we may consider

$$y = x \frac{dy}{dx} + \left(\frac{dy}{dx}\right)^3.$$

Differentiation with respect to x yields

$$p = p + xp' + \frac{df}{dp} p',$$

or

$$p'\left(x + \frac{df}{dp}\right) = 0,$$

where the prime denotes differentiation with respect to x. Hence, firstly, $p' = 0$ yielding $p = A$, in which case

$$y = Ax + f(A), \tag{3}$$

representing a family of straight lines determined by the parameter A. Secondly, we may have $x = -df/dp$. Substituting into the original equation,

$$y = -p \frac{df}{dp} + f(p).$$

This second solution $x = -df/dp$, $y = -p\, df/dp + f(p)$, expressed parametrically, is the singular solution, since it is quite distinct from the general solution (3) containing the arbitrary constant A. That this singular solution is the envelope of the general solution may easily be seen by finding the envelope of (3). Differentiating with respect to A, we obtain $x = -df/dA$, from which it follows that $y = -A\, df/dA + f(A)$. This parametric form of the envelope is identical with the singular solution.

Example 12 Solve the equation $y = px + p^n$.

Quoting the above results, the general solution is obtained by placing $p = A$, namely

$$y = Ax + A^n.$$

The parametric form of the singular solution is

$$x = -np^{n-1}, \quad y = -p(np^{n-1}) + p^n = (1 - n)p^n.$$

The elimination of p yields

$$(1 - n)^{n-1}x^n = (-1)^n n^n y^{n-1}.$$

19.6   Linear first order equations

If f and g are functions of x, we consider the general *linear equation* of the first order:

$$\frac{dy}{dx} + f(x)y = g(x).$$

Note that the coefficient of dy/dx must be unity, rendered thus by division if necessary.

We multiply the given equation by an integrating factor $J(x)$ to be found:

$$J\frac{dy}{dx} + fJy = gJ.$$

We may choose J so that the left hand side of this equation equals

$$\frac{d}{dx}(Jy) = J\frac{dy}{dx} + y\frac{dJ}{dx}.$$

We therefore make the choice

$$fJ = \frac{dJ}{dx},$$

yielding $$J = \exp\left(\int f\,dx\right).$$

With this particular value for J, the equation becomes

$$\frac{d}{dx}(Jy) = gJ,$$

or $$Jy = \int gJ\,dx + A.$$

Finally, the solution for y is given by

$$y = \frac{1}{J}\int gJ\,dx + \frac{A}{J}.$$

The integration of $\int gJ\,dx$ may be straightforward; sometimes its value can be seen by inspection and at other times the method of example 23, chapter 16 must be used.

Example 13 below illustrates the general method, while examples 14, 15 and 16 show how certain equations can be reduced to linear form by appropriate changes of variable. The above bookwork, showing how J is calculated, need not be reproduced every time a linear equation is solved; no more working need be written down than that shown in example 13.

Example 13 Solve the following equation such that $y = 2$ when $x = 0$:

$$\cos x \frac{dy}{dx} + (\cos x + \sin x)y = 2 + \sin 2x.$$

We first divide by $\cos x$, obtaining

$$\frac{dy}{dx} + (1 + \tan x)y = 2 \sec x + 2 \sin x.$$

The integrating factor is

$$\exp \left[\int (1 + \tan x)\,dx \right] = \exp (x - \log \cos x) = e^x/\cos x = e^x \sec x.$$

Multiplying the equation by this integrating factor, we have

$$\frac{d}{dx}(ye^x \sec x) = 2(\sec x + \sin x)e^x \sec x.$$

Hence
$$ye^x \sec x = 2 \int (\sec^2 x + \tan x)e^x\,dx + A$$

$$= 2 \tan x e^x + A$$

by inspection. Finally, the general solution is

$$y = 2 \sin x + Ae^{-x} \cos x.$$

Substituting $x = 0$ and $y = 2$, we find that $A = 2$; the required solution is therefore

$$y = 2(\sin x + e^{-x} \cos x).$$

Example 14 Find the general solution of the equation

$$(y^5 - xy)\frac{dy}{dx} = 1.$$

This equation is not linear in y as it stands, but if we write the equation as

$$\frac{dx}{dy} + xy = y^5,$$

it is now linear with x as the dependent variable.

The integrating factor is $\exp \left(\int y\,dy \right) = \exp (\tfrac{1}{2}y^2)$, so the equation becomes

$$d\,[x \exp (\tfrac{1}{2}y^2)]/dy = y^5 \exp (\tfrac{1}{2}y^2).$$

Integration now yields

$$x \exp\left(\tfrac{1}{2}y^2\right) = \int y^4 \cdot y \exp\left(\tfrac{1}{2}y^2\right) dy + A$$

$$= y^4 \exp\left(\tfrac{1}{2}y^2\right) - 4\int y^3 \exp\left(\tfrac{1}{2}y^2\right) dy + A$$

$$= y^4 \exp\left(\tfrac{1}{2}y^2\right) - 4y^2 \exp\left(\tfrac{1}{2}y^2\right) + 8\int y \exp\left(\tfrac{1}{2}y^2\right) dy + A$$

$$= (y^4 - 4y^2 + 8) \exp\left(\tfrac{1}{2}y^2\right) + A,$$

by integration by parts, preparing the integrand suitably at each integration. Hence the general solution is

$$x = y^4 - 4y^2 + 8 + A \exp\left(-\tfrac{1}{2}y^2\right).$$

Example 15 Solve the equation

$$x^2 y \frac{dy}{dx} - xy^2 = 1.$$

This is not an equation linear in y, but if we write $y^2 = u$, we have

$$\tfrac{1}{2}x^2 \frac{du}{dx} - xu = 1,$$

or

$$\frac{du}{dx} - \frac{2u}{x} = \frac{2}{x^2}.$$

This equation is now linear in u. Its integrating factor is

$$\exp\left(-2\int dx/x\right) = \exp\left(-2 \log x\right) = 1/x^2,$$

so the equation becomes

$$\frac{d}{dx}\left(\frac{u}{x^2}\right) = \frac{2}{x^4}.$$

Integration yields

$$u/x^2 = -\tfrac{2}{3}/x^3 + A,$$

$$u = y^2 = -\tfrac{2}{3}x^{-1} + Ax^2.$$

Example 16 The previous example is a particular case of the more general equation known as *Bernoulli's equation*:

$$\frac{dy}{dx} + f(x)y = g(x)y^n.$$

Let $u = y^{1-n}$, yielding

$$\frac{du}{dx} = (1-n)y^{-n}\frac{dy}{dx}.$$

Eliminating dy/dx, we obtain

$$\frac{y^n}{1-n}\frac{du}{dx} + f(x)y = g(x)y^n,$$

or

$$\frac{du}{dx} + (1-n)f(x)u = (1-n)g(x)$$

upon division by y^n. The equation is now linear with u as the dependent variable.

19.7 Families of curves

Orthogonal trajectories. A one-parameter family of curves is given, namely a family defined by the equation $f(x, y, t) = 0$; each value of t yields a curve of the family. The problem is to find a second family of curves, such that each curve of the first family intersects each curve of the second family orthogonally (i.e. at right-angles).

We first form the differential equation of the first family, by differentiating with respect to x and eliminating t. This provides a relation between x, y and dy/dx at every point P on every curve C of the first family. The curve C' through P, orthogonal to C, must be such that

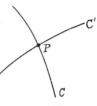

Fig. 117

its gradient dy/dx at P is minus the reciprocal of the gradient dy/dx of the curve C at P. Hence to find the differential equation of the orthogonal family, we merely replace dy/dx by $-1/(dy/dx)$ in the differential equation of the first family. Integration of the resulting equation yields the required family of curves.

Example 17 As a trivial example, consider the family of straight lines through the origin: $y = mx$. Since $dy/dx = m$, the differential equation of the family is

$$y = x \frac{dy}{dx}$$

upon elimination of m. Hence the differential equation of the orthogonal family is given by

$$y = -x \left/ \frac{dy}{dx} \right.,$$

or $\qquad\qquad x\, dx + y\, dy = 0.$

Integration yields $\qquad x^2 + y^2 = A,$

a family of concentric circles whose common centre is the origin.

Example 18 Find the family of curves orthogonal to the family
$$y^2 = (x^3 - a^3)/3x.$$

To eliminate the parameter a, we write $x^3 - 3xy^2 = a^3$, yielding upon differentiation

$$3x^2 - 3y^2 - 6xy \frac{dy}{dx} = 0.$$

The differential equation of the orthogonal family is given by

$$x^2 - y^2 + 2xy \left/ \frac{dy}{dx} \right. = 0,$$

or $\qquad\qquad \dfrac{dy}{dx} = \dfrac{2xy}{y^2 - x^2}.$

The function on the right hand side is homogeneous, so we may use the substitution $y = vx$; the equation is, however, also exact:

$$2xy\,dx + (x^2 - y^2)\,dy = 0.$$

Inspection shows that

$$x^2y - \tfrac{1}{3}y^3 = \text{constant},$$

or

$$y(3x^2 - y^2) = A.$$

Equations of curves deduced from given geometrical properties. A

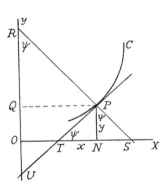

FIG. 118

curve C is given in the x,y-plane, and the tangent and normal are drawn at any point P on the curve. A relationship is given between some of the various lengths $PN = y$, $ON = x$, $OT = x - y \cot \psi$, PT, PS, NS, RP, OR, TN, OP, etc., all of which can be expressed in terms of x, y, ψ. If we place $\tan \psi$ equal to dy/dx, we obtain the differential equation of the family of curves with the given property.

Note: When a diagram is drawn, *always* draw it such that $x > 0$, $y > 0$, $dy/dx > 0$, $d^2y/dx^2 > 0$, as indicated in Fig. 118; otherwise false signs may be used. It may be an advantage to use polar coordinates in examples where the length OP is required.

Example 19   If $NS = QR$, find the family of curves with this property, and the particular curve passing through the point (4, 4) but not through the origin.

From Fig. 118, we see that $NS = y \tan \psi$ and $QR = x \cot \psi$. Hence

$$y \tan \psi = x \cot \psi,$$

or

$$(dy/dx)^2 = x/y.$$

Clearly the curves must lie in either the first or third quadrants in order that x/y should be positive.

The equation is separable, taking the form

$$y^{\frac{1}{2}}\,dy = \pm x^{\frac{1}{2}}\,dx,$$

yielding upon integration

$$y^{\frac{3}{2}} = \pm x^{\frac{3}{2}} + A.$$

We have, in fact, two families of curves: (i) $y^{\frac{3}{2}} = x^{\frac{3}{2}} + A$ and (ii) $y^{\frac{3}{2}} + x^{\frac{3}{2}} = A$. To pass through (4, 4), we have either (i) $A = 0$ or (ii) $A = 16$. The former curve would pass through the origin, so the required curve is

$$y^{\frac{3}{2}} + x^{\frac{3}{2}} = 16.$$

The graphical method of isoclines. Every first order differential equation may formally be arranged in the form $dy/dx = f(x, y)$. At any point (x, y), the value of dy/dx can be calculated. Such points are called *ordinary* points, unless exceptionally $f(x, y)$ is indeterminate, in which case such points are called *singular* points.

On a graph with axes Ox, Oy, at each point $P(x, y)$ a small line segment may be drawn whose gradient equals the calculated value of dy/dx at P. When enough of these segments have been inserted, the general trend of the curves satisfying the equation can be traced in.

The best way to draw the line segments is first to sketch the loci in the plane on which dy/dx has simple constant values, such as ± 2, ± 1, 0, etc.

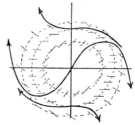

Example 20 Sketch the curves satisfying the equation $dy/dx = 2 - x^2 - y^2$.

The gradient dy/dx has the constant value m on the curves $x^2 + y^2 = 2 - m, (m \leqslant 2)$. The gradient is 1 on the circle $x^2 + y^2 = 1$; it is 2 at the origin, 0 on the circle of radius $\sqrt{2}$, and -1 on the circle of radius $\sqrt{3}$. These circles are shown on the diagram together with the line segments with the appropriate gradient. The heavy lines show typical solutions sketched in, joining the ends of neighbouring line segments.

FIG. 119

EXERCISES

Solve the following differential equations, finding in particular those solutions passing through the specified points, when given. ($D \equiv d/dx$).

(1)★. $Dy = e^y \sin x$, $(0, 0)$.

(2)★. $\sqrt{(1 + x^2)} \, Dy = xe^y$, $(0, 0)$.

(3)★. $(1 - x^2) \, Dy = 1 + \cos 2y$, $(0, \tfrac{1}{4}\pi)$.

(4)★. $(x + 1) \, Dy = x\sqrt{(y + 1)}$, $(0, 0)$.

(5)★. $Dy = (1 + y^2)/(1 + x^2)$.

(6)★. $Dy = y/\sqrt{(1 + x^2)}$.

(7)★. $y \, Dy = \sin x \, e^{x+2y}$.

(8)★. If $x \, Dy = y^2 - y$ and $y = 2$ when $x = 1$, prove $Dy = \tfrac{1}{2}y^2$.

(9)★. $Dy = (3x - y + 3)/(3x - y - 1)$.

(10)★. $Dy = \cos (x + y)$, $(0, \tfrac{1}{2}\pi)$.

(11)★. $Dy = (x + 2y + 1)/(x + 2y + 3)$.

(12)★. $(x + 2y + 1) \, Dy = x + 2y$.

(13)★. If $Dy = (x + y)^2$ and $y = \tfrac{1}{3}$ when $x = \tfrac{1}{3}$, calculate, correct to three significant figures, the value of y when $x = 0.7$.

(14)★. $x \, Dy = y + \sqrt{(x^2 + y^2)}$.

(15)★. $(2x + y) \, Dy = x + 2y$, $(1, 0)$.

(16)*. $y(x + y\,Dy) = x(x\,Dy - y)$.

(17)*. $x\,Dy = y(\log y - \log x)$.

(18)*. $Dy = (3x^2 - 3xy + y^2)/(2x^2 + 3xy)$,　　(1, −2).

(19)*. $2y(x + y)\,Dy - 3x^2 + y^2 = 0$.

(20)*. $(x^2 - y^2)\,Dy = xy$,　　(0, 1).

(21)*. $xy\,Dy = 2x^2 + 3xy + 2y^2$,　　(1, 0).

---

(22)*. $Dy = (x - y)/(x - 8y + 7)$.

(23)*. $Dy = (4x - 2y + 4)/(2x + y - 2)$.

(24)*. $Dy = (4x + 3y - 3)/(3x + y - 2)$.

(25)*. $(x + y + 2)\,Dy + (x - y + 2) = 0$.

(26)*. $Dy = (x + 3y - 1)/(4 - 3x - y)$,　　(1, 0).

---

(27)*. $(x^2 - 4xy - 2y^2 + 2x)\,dx + (y^2 - 4xy - 2x^2 + 3y)\,dy = 0$.

Solve the following four equations by first finding n so the appended factor is an integrating factor:

(28)*. $(4x^2 + 2xy + 6y)\,dx + (2x^2 + 9y + 3x)\,dy = 0$,　　$(x + y)^n$.

(29)*. $(5x^2 + 12xy - 3y^2)\,dx + (3x^2 - 2xy)\,dy = 0$,　　x^n.

(30)*. $xy^2\,dx - x^2y\,dy = 0$,　　$(x^2 + y^2)^n$.

(31)*. $(4x^3y + 12x^5y^2)\,dx + (6x^4 + 14x^6y + 33y^5)\,dy = 0$,　　y^n.

---

(32)*. $Dy + y/x = x^3$,　　(1, 2).

(33)*. $Dy = xy/a^2 + bx$.

(34)*. $Dy + y\cot x = \cos x$,　　$(\tfrac{1}{2}\pi, 1)$.

(35)*. $\cos x\,Dy + y\sin x = x\sin 2x + x^2$.

(36)*. $(1 + 3x)\,Dy + (3 - 9x)y = 3$.

(37)*. $Dy + y\cos x = \sin x\cos x$.

(38)*. $(x - 1)\,Dy + xy = (x - 1)e^x$,　　(0, 0).

(39)*. $dx/dy = \cos 2y - x\cot y$,　　$(\tfrac{1}{2}, \tfrac{1}{2}\pi)$.

(40)*. $(1 + x^2)^{\frac{3}{2}}\,Dy + x\sqrt{(1 + x^2)}y = 1$.

(41)*. $x\,Dy + (x - 1)y = x^3$,　　(1, 1).

(42)*. $x(x^2 - 1)\,Dy + y = x^3$.

(43)*. $Dy - y\tan x + (\sec^2 x + 1)\tan x = 0$, (0, 2). Find the maximum value of y for values of x lying between $-\tfrac{1}{2}\pi$ and $\tfrac{1}{2}\pi$.

(44)*. $x(1 - x^2)\,Dy - (x^2 - 2x - 1)y = 2x + 1$,　　$(2, \tfrac{1}{2})$.

(45)*. $x\cos x\,Dy + (x\sin x - \cos x)y - x^2 = 0$,　　$(\pi, -\pi)$.

(46)*. $(1 + x^2)\,Dy - xy = (1 + x^2)x^2$.

(47)*. $(1 + x)^2\,Dy + (1 - x^2)y = x$.

(48)*. $x\,Dy + (x + 1)y = x^2e^x$.

(49)*. $y + x(x + 1)\,Dy = x(x + 1)^2\exp(-x^2)$.

(50)*. $(1 - x^2)\,Dy = x(\sin^{-1} x - y)$.

---

(51)*. $xy^2\,Dy - 2y^3 = 2x^3$,　　(1, 1).

(52)*. $Dy = -2y \tan x + y^2 \tan^2 x,$ (0, 1).

(53)*. $Dy + y \tan x = y^3 \sec^3 x,$ (0, 1).

(54)*. $2x\,Dy + y = 2x^2(x + 1)y^3,$ (1, 1).

(55)*. $(y^2 - 2x)\,Dy = y.$

(56)*. $(1 - xy)\,Dy = y^2,$ (0, 1).

(57)*. $x\,Dy + x + \sin(x + y) = 0.$

Find the general and singular solutions of the following three equations, where $p \equiv Dy$:

(58)*. $y = px + p^3.$

(59)*. $y = px - \log p.$

(60)*. $y = px - e^p.$

(61)*. A tank contains 100 gallons of water. Brine, containing 2 lb. of salt to the gallon, flows in at the rate of 3 gallons per minute and the mixture (kept uniform by agitation) flows out at the same rate. If, at the end of t minutes after the brine begins to flow, there are x lb. of salt in the tank, prove that $(6 - 0{\cdot}03x)\,dt = dx$. Prove that at the end of an hour the tank contains about 167 lb. of salt.

(62)*. A thick-walled pipe having internal and external radii R_1 and R respectively, is subjected to internal and external pressures P_1 and zero respectively. The pressure p at distance r from the axis is such that $d\,(pr)/dr = ap - b$, a and b being constants. Show that

$$(R/R_1)^{1-a} = 1 + (1 - a)P_1/b.$$

(63)*. In a reversible chemical reaction the yield x at time t satisfies the differential equation $dx/dt = k_1(1 - x)(2 - x) - k_2x^2$ and $x = 0$ when $t = 0$. It is known that the value of x tends to $\tfrac{1}{2}$ in equilibrium. Prove that

$$\log[(1 + \tfrac{1}{2}x)/(1 - 2x)] = 5k_1t.$$

If $x = 0{\cdot}4$ when $t = 10$, find t when $x = 0{\cdot}49$.

(64)*. The tangent at any point P on a curve meets the x-axis in T and O is the origin. Find the differential equation of the family of curves for which OT is equal to the ordinate at P. Solve it, and hence show that the equation of the family of curves is $y = ce^{-x/y}$, where c is an arbitrary constant.

(65)*. Find the differential equation representing the families of curves which are such that the rectangular axes of x and y cut off equal intercepts from the tangent and the normal respectively at any point. Integrate this differential equation.

(66)*. N is the foot of the ordinate at a point P on a plane curve, and T, U are the respective points at which the tangent and normal at P meet the x-axis. If $TN - NU = 2ON$, where O is the origin, find the differential equation of the curve, and hence show that the curve belongs to a family of parabolae. Find the two members which pass through the point $(-\tfrac{3}{4}, 1)$.

(67)*. The normal to a plane curve at a variable point P meets the axes of x and y at Q and R respectively. The orthogonal projection of PQ on the x-axis is equal to that of PR on the y-axis. Find the equation of the curve, given that it passes through (1, 1) but not through (0, 0).

(68)*. The tangent to a plane curve at a point $P(x, y)$ meets the axes of x and y in A and B respectively. If $PA:PB = kx:y$, where k is a constant, find the differential equation of the family to which the curve belongs.

Integrate the equation, and show that the curves of the family are rectangular hyperbolae with their centres on a fixed straight line.

(69)★. Prove that the differential equation $p^2 + p\phi(x, y) - 1 = 0$, $(p = dy/dx)$, represents a system of plane curves such that two pass through every point and intersect at right-angles. Find the system of curves for which $\phi(x, y) = -2y/x$.

(70)★. The normal at $P(x, y)$, a point on a plane curve, meets the x- and y-axes at Q and R respectively on opposite sides of P, such that $RP/RQ = x^2/y^2$. Find the equation of the curve, given that it passes through the point $(1, 1)$.

(71)★. The perpendicular from the origin to the normal at $P(x, y)$ on a plane curve is of length y. Find the differential equation of the curve and integrate it. Find the orthogonal trajectories of the family of curves having the above property.

(72)★. The parabolae of a family have their vertices on the line $2x + 3y = 0$. For every $a > 0$ the parabola with its vertex at $(-9a, 6a)$ has its focus at $(-8a, 6a)$. Find the differential equation of the family. Show that the orthogonal trajectories form the family $(y + 2x)^2 = c(y + x)$.

(73)★. Find the curves for which the tangent, the normal and the perpendicular to the radius vector at the origin, form a triangle of constant area.

(74)★. Find the differential equation of the family of curves given by $x^2 - y^2 + 2\lambda xy = 1$, where λ is a parameter. Show that the differential equation of the orthogonal trajectories of this family is $(x^2 + y^2)(x + y\,Dy) = x - y\,Dy$, and solve this equation.

(75)★. Show that the two plane curves, whose polar equations are $r = f(\theta)$ and $r = F(\theta)$ respectively, cut at right-angles at points of intersection for which $f'(\theta)F'(\theta) + r^2 = 0$. Find in the form $r = F(\theta)$ the equation of the family of curves each of which intersects every member of the family $r = a(2\cos\theta + 1)$ orthogonally, a being a parameter.

(76)★. Find the equation of the system of orthogonal trajectories of the family of curves whose equation in polar coordinates is $r = a(1 - \cos\theta)$, where a is a parameter. Sketch a typical curve of the system.

ANSWERS TO EXERCISES

(1). $y = \log\sec x$.   (2). $e^{-y} = 2 - \sqrt{(1 + x^2)}$.
(3). $\tan y - 1 = \log[(1 + x)/(1 - x)]$.
(4). $2\sqrt{(y + 1)} - 2 = x - \log(1 + x)$.   (5). $y - x = A(1 + xy)$.
(6). $Ay = x + \sqrt{(1 + x^2)}$.   (7). $-\frac{1}{4}(1 + 2y)e^{-2y} = \frac{1}{2}(\sin x - \cos x)e^x + A$.
(9). $x - y = 2\log(3x - y - 3) + A$.   (10). $\tan\frac{1}{2}(x + y) = x + 1$.
(11). $3(y - x) + 2\log(3x + 6y + 5) = A$.
(12). $\log(3x + 6y + 1) + 3y - 3x = A$.   (13). 0.808.
(14). $A^2x^2 - 2Ay - 1 = 0$.   (15). $x + y = (x - y)^3$.   (16). $x^2 + y^2 = Ay$.
(17). $y = xe^{Ax+1}$.   (18). $(3x + y)^2(x - 2y) = Ax$.
(19). $3xy^2 + 2y^3 - 3x^3 = A$.   (20). $x^2 + 2y^2\log y = 0$.
(21). $(y + 2x)^2 = 4x^2(y + x)$.   (22). $x^2 - 2xy + 8y^2 - 14y = A$.
(23). $4xy + y^2 - 4y - 4x^2 - 8x = A$.
(24). $(2x - y - 1)^5 = A(10x + 5y - 7)$.
(25). $2\tan^{-1}[y/(x + 2)] + \log[y^2 + (x + 2)^2] = A$.
(26). $x^2 + y^2 + 6xy - 2x - 8y = A$.
(27). $2x^3 - 12x^2y - 12y^2x + 6x^2 + 2y^3 + 9y^2 = A$.

(28). $n = 1$; $x^4 + 2x^3y + 6y^2x + 3x^2y + x^2y^2 + 3y^3 = A$.

(29). $n = 2$, $x^5 + 3x^4y - x^3y^2 = A$.

(30). $n = -2$; $(x^2 - y^2)/(x^2 + y^2) = A$.

(31). $n = 5$; $x^4y^6 + 2x^6y^7 + 3y^{11} = A$. (32). $y = (x^5 + 9)/5x$.

(33). $y = -a^2b + A\exp(x^2/2a^2)$. (34). $y = \frac{1}{2}\sin x + \frac{1}{2}\operatorname{cosec} x$.

(35). $y = x^2 \sin x + A \cos x$.

(36). $y = -(3x + 2)/(1 + 3x)^2 + Ae^{3x}/(1 + 3x)^2$.

(37). $y = \sin x - 1 + Ae^{-\sin x}$.

(38). $y = \frac{1}{4}(2x - 3)e^x/(x - 1) + \frac{3}{4}e^{-x}/(x - 1)$.

(39). $x = \frac{1}{3}\cot y(3 - 2\cos^2 y) + \frac{1}{2}\operatorname{cosec} y$.

(40). $y = (\tan^{-1} x + A)/\sqrt{(1 + x^2)}$. (41). $y = x^2 - x + xe^{-x}$.

(42). $y = x + Ax/\sqrt{(x^2 - 1)}$.

(43). $y = 2 \sec x - \tan^2 x$; $y = 2$ when $x = 0$.

(44). $y = [2(1 - x)\log(x - 1) + 3]/x(1 + x)$. (45). $y = x(\sin x + \cos x)$.

(46). $y = \frac{1}{2}x(x^2 + 1) - \frac{1}{2}\sqrt{(x^2 + 1)}\log[x + \sqrt{(x^2 + 1)}] + A\sqrt{(x^2 + 1)}$.

(47). $y = -1/(1 + x) + Ae^x/(1 + x)^2$.

(48). $y = \frac{1}{4}e^x(2x^2 - 2x + 1)/x + Ae^{-x}/x$. (49). $y = x(A - \frac{1}{2}e^{-x^2})/(x + 1)$.

(50). $y = \sin^{-1} x - \frac{1}{2}\sqrt{(1 - x^2)}\log[(1 + x)/(1 - x)] + A\sqrt{(1 - x^2)}$.

(51). $y^3 = 3x^6 - 2x^3$. (52). $1/y = \frac{1}{2}\tan x + \frac{1}{2}(2 - x)\sec^2 x$.

(53). $y^{-2} = \sec^2 x - 2\sec^2 x\log(\sec x + \tan x)$. (54). $y^{-2} = 4x - 2x^2 - x^3$.

(55). $x = \frac{1}{4}y^2 + A/y^2$. (56). $xy = \log y$.

(57). $\operatorname{cosec}(x + y) + \cot(x + y) = Ax$.

(58). $y = cx + c^3$, $4x^3 + 27y^2 = 0$. (59). $y = cx - \log c$, $y = 1 + \log x$.

(60). $y = cx - e^c$, $y = x\log x - x$. (63). $23\cdot1$. (64). $Dy = y/(x - y)$.

(65). $Dy = (x + y)/(x - y)$, $\tan^{-1}(y/x) = c + \frac{1}{2}\log(x^2 + y^2)$.

(66). $y\,Dy = -x \pm \sqrt{(x^2 + y^2)}$, $y^2 = c^2 + 2cx$, $c = 2, -\frac{1}{2}$.

(67). $x^{\frac{2}{3}} + y^{\frac{2}{3}} = 2$. (68). $y^2 = kx^2\,Dy$, $x - y = 0$.

(69). $y + \sqrt{(x^2 + y^2)} = c$ or cx^2. (70). $y^2/x^2 = 1 - 2\log x$.

(71). $Dy = (y^2 - x^2)/2xy$, $x^2 + y^2 = cx$, $x^2 + y^2 = cy$.

(72). $Dy = y/(2x + 3y)$. (73). $2A\sin^{-1}\sqrt{(r/2A)} - \sqrt{(2Ar - r^2)} = c \pm \theta$.

(74). $Dy = y(x^2 + y^2 + 1)/x(x^2 + y^2 - 1)$, $(x^2 + y^2)(x^2 + y^2 + 2) = 4x^2 + c$.

(75). $r^2 = c\sin\theta(1 - \cos\theta)$. (76). $r = c(1 + \cos\theta)$.

CHAPTER 20

SECOND ORDER DIFFERENTIAL EQUATIONS

20.1 Equations in which the independent variable is absent

If a relationship is given between y, dy/dx and d^2y/dx^2 such that the independent variable x is absent explicitly, we write $dy/dx = p$ and observe that

$$\frac{d^2y}{dx^2} = \frac{d}{dx}\,p = \frac{d}{dy}\,p.\frac{dy}{dx} = p\,\frac{dp}{dy}\,.$$

The equation is now a relationship between y, p and dp/dy; that is, it is a first order equation with p as the dependent variable and y as the independent variable. This equation is solved for p in terms of y; a second integration, if possible, then gives y in terms of x.

Similarly, if y is absent explicitly in a relationship between x, dy/dx and d^2y/dx^2, the equation is really a relationship between x, p and dp/dx. This first order equation in p may be solved for p in terms of x, and integration then yields y in terms of x.

In dynamics, if a force $F(x)$ per unit mass acts on a particle moving along the x-axis, the equation of motion is

$$\frac{d^2x}{dt^2} = F(x),$$

an equation in which the independent variable t is absent. Writing $v = dx/dt$, the equation reduces to

$$v\,\frac{dv}{dx} = F(x);$$

this integrates to

$$\tfrac{1}{2}v^2 = \int F(x)\,dx + A.$$

This equation relates the kinetic energy per unit mass to the work done by the forces acting on the particle.

Example 1 Solve the following equation, such that $y = dy/dx = 0$ when $x = 0$:

$$\frac{d^2y}{dx^2} = 1 + \left(\frac{dy}{dx}\right)^2.$$

We write $dy/dx = p$, giving

$$p\frac{dp}{dx} = 1 + p^2,$$

or

$$p\,dp/(1 + p^2) = dy.$$

Integrating, we obtain

$$\tfrac{1}{2}\log(1 + p^2) = y + A.$$

In order that y and p should vanish together, we choose $A = 0$; it follows that

$$p = \sqrt{(e^{2y} - 1)},$$

or

$$\frac{e^y\,dy}{e^y\sqrt{(e^{2y} - 1)}} = dx.$$

Integrating a second time, we obtain

$$\sec^{-1}(e^y) = x + B.$$

Finally, $B = 0$ in order that x and y should vanish together, yielding the solution

$$e^y = \sec x.$$

20.2 The homogeneous linear equation with constant coefficients

We are given the linear equation with constant coefficients:

$$a\,D^2y + b\,Dy + cy = 0,$$

where $D \equiv d/dx$. The equation is called *homogeneous* since no term appears on the right hand side independent of y. The solution of this equation may be found formally by the following method, but in any problem, the final simple answer should always be quoted, *never proved*.

Let λ, μ be the two roots of the associated *auxiliary quadratic*

$$aq^2 + bq + c = 0.$$

The equation may now be re-expressed in the form

$$D^2y - (\lambda + \mu)\,Dy + \lambda\mu y = 0,$$

or

$$D(Dy - \lambda y) = \mu(Dy - \lambda y).$$

Solving for $Dy - \lambda y$, we obtain

$$Dy - \lambda y = Ce^{\mu x},$$

where C is an arbitrary constant.

This is now a first order linear equation. Its integrating factor is $e^{-\lambda x}$, so the equation becomes

$$D(ye^{-\lambda x}) = Ce^{(\mu - \lambda)x},$$

$$ye^{-\lambda x} = \begin{cases} \dfrac{Ce^{(\mu - \lambda)x}}{\mu - \lambda} + A & \text{if } \lambda \neq \mu, \\ Cx + A & \text{if } \lambda = \mu. \end{cases}$$

Finally, the general solution is given by

$$y = Ae^{\lambda x} + Be^{\mu x} \qquad (\lambda \neq \mu),$$
$$y = (A + Bx)e^{\lambda x} \qquad (\lambda = \mu).$$

These solutions should be thoroughly memorized. Similarly, if the third order equation

$$(aD^3 + bD^2 + cD + d)y = 0$$

is given, and if λ, μ, ν are the roots of the auxiliary cubic

$$aq^3 + bq^2 + cq + d = 0,$$

then

$$y = Ae^{\lambda x} + Be^{\mu x} + Ce^{\nu x} \qquad (\mu \neq \nu, \nu \neq \lambda, \lambda \neq \mu),$$
$$y = (A + Bx)e^{\lambda x} + Ce^{\nu x} \qquad (\lambda = \mu \neq \nu),$$
$$y = (A + Bx + Cx^2)e^{\lambda x} \qquad (\lambda = \mu = \nu).$$

The extension to higher order equations is obvious.

If one root should vanish, one term occurring in y is merely a constant.

In particular, if λ and μ are conjugate complex numbers with the values $m \pm in$, we may rearrange the solution to exhibit real functions only:

$$y = Ae^{(m+in)x} + Be^{(m-in)x}$$
$$= e^{mx}(A \cos nx + Ai \sin nx + B \cos nx - Bi \sin nx)$$
$$= e^{mx}(C \cos nx + D \sin nx),$$

where C and D are arbitrary constants, usually real. Using the ordinary method for expressing the sum of a cosine and a sine as a sine only (or a cosine), we may write this solution in the form

$$y = Ae^{mx} \sin (nx + \varepsilon),$$

where A is an arbitrary *amplitude* constant and ε an arbitrary *phase* constant.

For example, the equation governing *simple harmonic motion*

$$\frac{d^2y}{dt^2} + n^2y = 0$$

possesses an auxiliary quadratic with roots $\pm in$, so

$$y = C \cos nt + D \sin nt = A \sin (nt + \varepsilon).$$

For an nth order equation, n *initial conditions* may be specified, enabling the values of the n arbitrary constants to be calculated.

Example 2   Solve the equation $(D^2 + 4D + c)y = 0$, when $c = 3$, 4 or 5.

When $c = 3$, the roots of the auxiliary quadratic $q^2 + 4q + c = 0$ are -1, -3; when $c = 4$, they are -2, -2; when $c = 5$, they are $-2 \pm i$.

For three cases, the solutions respectively are

$$y = Ae^{-x} + Be^{-3x}; \quad y = (A + Bx)e^{-2x}; \quad y = e^{-2x}(C \cos x + D \sin x).$$

Example 3   If j is the current flowing in a circuit consisting of a resistance R, an inductance L and a capacitance C in series, the equation satisfied by j is

$$\frac{d^2j}{dt^2} + \frac{R}{L}\frac{dj}{dt} + \frac{1}{LC}j = 0.$$

The solution of the auxiliary quadratic is

$$-\frac{R}{2L} \pm \sqrt{\left(\frac{R^2}{4L^2} - \frac{1}{LC}\right)}.$$

If $R^2/4L^2 > 1/LC$, both roots are real and negative; the current is therefore damped and non-oscillatory; if $R^2/4L^2 = 1/LC$, the current is critically damped, but if $R^2/4L^2 < 1/LC$, the solution is

$$j = Ae^{-Rt/2L} \sin\left[\left(\frac{1}{LC} - \frac{R^2}{4L^2}\right)^{\frac{1}{2}}t + \varepsilon\right],$$

representing an oscillatory current with diminishing amplitude.

20.3   The inhomogeneous equation

If the linear *inhomogeneous* equation

$$aD^2y + bDy + cy = h(x)$$

is given, where $h(x)$ is a function of x, let $y_1(x)$ denote any one solution of the equation. This cannot be the general solution, since this must contain two arbitrary constants. Let the general solution, if possible, be $y = y_1 + u$, where u, to be found, must contain the two arbitrary constants.

Substituting, we obtain

$$aD^2(y_1 + u) + bD(y_1 + u) + c(y_1 + u) = h(x),$$

or $aD^2u + bDu + cu + aD^2y_1 + bDy_1 + cy_1 = h(x).$

Since y_1 satisfies the original differential equation, we conclude that

$$a\,D^2u + b\,Du + cu = 0.$$

In other words, the function u is the solution of the corresponding homogeneous equation, with $h(x)$ eliminated. Evidently u can easily be found; moreover it will contain the two required arbitrary constants. When u is added to y_1, we obtain the general solution of the equation. The solution y_1 is called the *particular integral*, while the function u is called the *complementary function*.

Methods for finding the particular integral are considered in the next section; here, it may be observed that if $h(x)$ is a constant d, then $y_1 = d/c$ provided $c \neq 0$. If $c = 0$ but $b \neq 0$, $y_1 = dx/c$ is a suitable particular integral.

Example 4   Solve the equation $(D^2 - 5D + 6)y = 12$, such that $y = 5$ and $Dy = 8$ when $x = 0$.

The roots of the auxiliary quadratic $q^2 - 5q + 6 = 0$ are 2 and 3; the complementary function is therefore $Ae^{2x} + Be^{3x}$.

The particular integral is obviously $y = \frac{12}{6} = 2$. Hence the general solution is

$$y = Ae^{2x} + Be^{3x} + 2.$$

When $x = 0$, we have

$$y = 5 = A + B + 2, \; Dy = 8 = 2A + 3B,$$

yielding $A = 1$, $B = 2$. The required solution is

$$y = e^{2x} + 2e^{3x} + 2.$$

20.4   Methods for finding the particular integral

Theorem.   If y_1 is a particular integral for the equation

$$a \, D^2y + b \, Dy + cy = h_1(x),$$

and if y_2 is a particular integral for the equation

$$a \, D^2y + b \, Dy + cy = h_2(x),$$

then $y_1 + y_2$ is a particular integral for the equation

$$a \, D^2y + b \, Dy + cy = h_1(x) + h_2(x).$$

This result follows merely by adding the two equations satisfied by y_1 and y_2. It follows that if the general function $h(x)$ consists of the sum of various types of functions, then each part may be dealt with separately, and the results added.

We shall consider the following cases: (i) $h(x)$ is a polynomial in x; (ii) $h(x) = e^{\alpha x}$; (iii) $h(x)$ consists of hyperbolic or trigonometric sines and cosines; (iv) $h(x)$ consists of products of functions of types (i), (ii) and (iii). The methods, given for second order equations, are applicable to equations of all orders.

(i) $h(x)$ *a polynomial in x of degree n.*   We formally write the equation

$$(a \, D^2 + b \, D + c)y = h(x)$$

in the form

$$y = \frac{1}{aD^2 + bD + c} \, h(x),$$

regarding $1/(a \, D^2 + b \, D + c)$ as an operator, that operates on the function placed *on its right*. The validity of the following method can be demonstrated by more complete analysis; here we merely state it as a mechanical device that the student must learn.

The expression $1/(a\,D^2 + b\,D + c)$ is expanded by the binomial theorem (using partial fractions if necessary), yielding a power series in D. These D's in the numerator now imply differentiation; when they operate on the polynomial $h(x)$, the resulting polynomial is the required particular integral. The student should check each particular integral to make sure that it does in fact satisfy the original equation. If, exceptionally, $c = 0$, one term D must remain in the denominator upon expansion; the term $1/D$ is interpreted as implying integration. In such a case, an arbitrary constant of integration need never be added, since all the necessary constants appear in the complementary function.

In practice, we assert that the operational equivalent of $1/(aD^2 + bD + c)$ is its binomial expansion in powers of D up to D^n.

The validity of this process may be demonstrated by extending the following simple result to include every possible case. If $(1 - \alpha D)^{-1}$ operates on a polynomial $h(x)$ of degree n, we assert that it is equivalent operationally to $1 + \alpha D + \alpha^2 D^2 + \ldots + \alpha^n D^n$. For it is required that $(1 - \alpha D).[(1 - \alpha D)^{-1} h(x)]$ should yield $h(x)$ when this operational equivalent is employed. This equivalent form yields

$$(1 - \alpha D)(1 + \alpha D + \ldots + \alpha^n D^n)h(x) = (1 - \alpha^{n+1} D^{n+1})h(x) = h(x),$$

since $D^{n+1}h(x) \equiv 0$ for a polynomial of degree n.

Example 5 Solve the equation $(D^2 + 3D + 2)y = 4x^2 + 2x + 1$, such that $y = Dy = 0$ when $x = 0$.

The roots of the auxiliary quadratic $q^2 + 3q + 2 = 0$ are -1 and -2, so the complementary function is $Ae^{-x} + Be^{-2x}$.

The particular integral is given by

$$y = \frac{1}{D^2 + 3D + 2}(4x^2 + 2x + 1).$$

When this operator is expanded in powers of D, we need only calculate the expansion up to D^2. Using partial fractions, we obtain

$$y = \left(\frac{1}{D+1} - \frac{1}{D+2}\right)(4x^2 + 2x + 1)$$

$$= [(1 - D + D^2) - \tfrac{1}{2}(1 - \tfrac{1}{2}D + \tfrac{1}{4}D^2)](4x^2 + 2x + 1)$$

$$= (\tfrac{1}{2} - \tfrac{3}{4}D + \tfrac{7}{8}D^2)(4x^2 + 2x + 1)$$

$$= (2x^2 + x + \tfrac{1}{2}) - \tfrac{3}{4}(8x + 2) + \tfrac{7}{8}(8)$$

$$= 2x^2 - 5x + 6.$$

The general solution is therefore

$$y = Ae^{-x} + Be^{-2x} + 2x^2 - 5x + 6.$$

When $x = 0$, we have

$$y = 0 = A + B + 6, \quad Dy = 0 = -A - 2B - 5,$$

yielding $A = -7$, $B = 1$. Hence

$$y = -7e^{-x} + e^{-2x} + 2x^2 - 5x + 6.$$

Example 6 Find the general solution of the equation $(D^2 - D)y = 4x + 3$.

The roots of the auxiliary quadratic $q^2 - q = 0$ are 0 and 1, so the complementary function is $A + Be^x$.

The particular integral is

$$y = \frac{1}{D^2 - D}(4x + 3)$$

$$= -\frac{1}{D} \cdot \frac{1}{1 - D}(4x + 3)$$

$$= -\frac{1}{D}(1 + D + D^2)(4x + 3)$$

$$= -\left(\frac{1}{D} + 1 + D\right)(4x + 3)$$

$$= -[(2x^2 + 3x) + (4x + 3) + 4]$$

$$= -(2x^2 + 7x + 7).$$

Hence the general solution is

$$y = A + Be^x - (2x^2 + 7x + 7).$$

The constant 7 is irrelevant, since it can be combined with the arbitrary constant A, yielding finally

$$y = A + Be^x - 2x^2 - 7x.$$

(ii*a*) *h(x) an exponential function.* Consider the equation

$$(aD^2 + bD + c)y = ke^{\alpha x},$$

where k and α are constants. This equation may usually be satisfied by a particular integral of the form $y = Ce^{\alpha x}$, where C is to be found. Substitution yields

$$C(a\alpha^2 + b\alpha + c)e^{\alpha x} = ke^{\alpha x},$$

so $$C = k/(a\alpha^2 + b\alpha + c).$$

Hence if we write formally

$$y = \frac{1}{aD^2 + bD + c} ke^{\alpha x}, \tag{1}$$

the operator is interpreted merely by replacing D by α, namely by the constant (complete with sign) occurring in the index of the exponential. This simple method breaks down if $a\alpha^2 + b\alpha + c = 0$, that is, if α is a root of the auxiliary quadratic.

Example 7 Find the general solution of $(D^2 - 4D + 13)y = 20e^{3x}$.

The roots of the auxiliary quadratic are $2 \pm 3i$, so the complementary function is given by $e^{2x}(A \cos 3x + B \sin 3x)$.

The particular integral is

$$y = \frac{1}{D^2 - 4D + 13}(20e^{3x})$$

$$= \frac{1}{9 - 12 + 13}(20e^{3x}) = 2e^{3x}.$$

Hence, generally, $y = e^{2x}(A\cos 3x + B\sin 3x) + 2e^{3x}.$

(ii*b*) *h(x) an exponential function.* We now concern ourselves with the special case when $a\alpha^2 + b\alpha + c = 0$; first, we require the following result.

If $f(x)$ is any function of x, consider the nth derivative of $e^{\alpha x}f(x)$ using Leibnitz' theorem:

$$D^n[e^{\alpha x}f(x)] \equiv \alpha^n e^{\alpha x}f(x) + {}_nC_1\alpha^{n-1}e^{\alpha x}Df(x) + {}_nC_2\alpha^{n-2}e^{\alpha x}D^2f(x)$$
$$+ \ldots + e^{\alpha x}D^nf(x)$$
$$\equiv e^{\alpha x}[\alpha^n + {}_nC_1\alpha^{n-1}D + {}_nC_2\alpha^{n-2}D^2 + \ldots + D^n]f(x)$$
$$\equiv e^{\alpha x}(D + \alpha)^nf(x).$$

In other words, $e^{\alpha x}$ may be removed to the left outside the scope of the operator merely by changing D to $D + \alpha$. Even if $f(x)$ is a constant, this rule still applies.

More generally, if $P(D)$ is any polynomial in D, we have similarly

$$P(D)[e^{\alpha x}f(x)] \equiv e^{\alpha x}P(D + \alpha)f(x),$$

since the rule just deduced is applicable to every term in the polynomial.

When finding particular integrals of differential equations, the polynomial in D stands in the denominator; we therefore require to interpret expressions of the form

$$\frac{1}{P(D)}[e^{\alpha x}f(x)].$$

However $e^{\alpha x}f(x)$ is treated, the exponential part can never be removed; hence this expression must equal $e^{\alpha x}$ multiplied by some unknown function $g(x)$, say. That is, we assume

$$\frac{1}{P(D)}[e^{\alpha x}f(x)] \equiv e^{\alpha x}g(x).$$

This statement is equivalent to

$$e^{\alpha x}f(x) \equiv P(D)[e^{\alpha x}g(x)]$$
$$\equiv e^{\alpha x}P(D + \alpha)g(x).$$

Hence $f(x) \equiv P(D + \alpha)g(x),$

or $\dfrac{f(x)}{P(D + \alpha)} \equiv g(x).$

We conclude, then, that

$$\frac{1}{P(D)}\left[e^{\alpha x}f(x)\right] \equiv e^{\alpha x}\frac{1}{P(D+\alpha)}f(x).$$

Hence we may take $e^{\alpha x}$ outside the scope of an operator regardless of whether this operator consists of a polynomial in D either in its numerator or in its denominator.

Hence if $a\alpha^2 + b\alpha + c = 0$ in equation (1) above, $e^{\alpha x}$ is taken to the left outside the influence of the operator by replacing D by $D + \alpha$. The resulting operator then operates on the polynomial k, which in this case is merely a constant. Under these circumstances, formal expansion by the binomial is not necessary; we may merely take the lowest power of D in the new denominator and integrate accordingly.

Example 8 Solve the equation $(D^2 - 3D + 2)y = 3e^x$, satisfying the initial conditions $y = 0$, $Dy = 4$ when $x = 0$.

The roots of the auxiliary quadratic are 1 and -2, so the complementary function is $Ae^x + Be^{-2x}$.

The particular integral cannot be found by the method (ii$a$); using method (ii$b$) and replacing D by $D + 1$, we obtain

$$y = \frac{1}{(D-1)(D+2)}\,3e^x = e^x\frac{1}{D(D+3)}\,3 = e^x x,$$

where we have used only the lowest power of D, that is $3D$, in the denominator. The binomial expansion would produce the same result. Hence

$$y = Ae^x + Be^{-2x} + xe^x.$$

When $x = 0$, we have

$$y = 0 = A + B, \quad Dy = 4 = A - 2B + 1.$$

Hence $A = 1$, $B = -1$, yielding

$$y = (1 + x)e^x - e^{-2x}.$$

Example 9 Solve the equation $(D^3 - 2D^2 - 4D + 8)y = 8e^{2x}$.

The roots of the auxiliary cubic are 2, 2, -2, so the complementary function is

$$y = (A + Bx)e^{2x} + Ce^{-2x}.$$

The particular integral, using method (ii$b$), is given by

$$y = \frac{1}{(D-2)^2(D+2)}\,8e^{2x} = e^{2x}\frac{1}{D^2(D+4)}\,8 = e^{2x}\frac{1}{4D^2}\,8 = x^2e^{2x},$$

where, in the new denominator, we have retained only the lowest power of D. Hence the general solution is

$$y = (A + Bx + x^2)e^{2x} + Ce^{-2x}.$$

Note: The particular integral *must* contain functions quite distinct from those occurring in the complementary function. In this example, e^{2x} and xe^{2x} already occur in the complementary function; the particular integral must therefore contain x^2e^{2x}.

(iii) *Hyperbolic and trigonometric functions.* Hyperbolic sine and cosine functions are replaced by their exponential forms, while cos αx and sin αx are replaced by Rl $e^{i\alpha x}$ and Im $e^{i\alpha x}$ respectively, keeping the symbols Rl and Im to the left of all the i's that may occur. Methods (ii$a$) and (ii$b$) are then used to find the particular integrals. Other texts may provide quite different rules for trigonometric functions, but in our text we prefer to keep the number of rules to a minimum.

Example 10 Solve the equation $(D^2 + 2D + 1)y = 8 \cosh x$.

The complementary function is evidently $(A + Bx)e^{-x}$, while the particular integral is

$$y = \frac{1}{D^2 + 2D + 1}\, 4(e^x + e^{-x})$$

$$= \frac{1}{D^2 + 2D + 1}\, 4e^x + \frac{1}{D^2 + 2D + 1}\, 4e^{-x}$$

$$= \tfrac{1}{4} 4e^x + e^{-x}\frac{1}{D^2}\, 4 = e^x + 2x^2 e^{-x},$$

upon replacing D by 1 for the first exponential and D by $D - 1$ for the second exponential. Hence

$$y = (A + Bx + 2x^2)e^{-x} + e^x.$$

Example 11 Solve the equation $(D^2 - 4)y = 4 \sinh^2 x$.

The complementary function is $Ae^{2x} + Be^{-2x}$, and the particular integral is

$$y = \frac{1}{D^2 - 4}\, 2(\cosh 2x - 1)$$

$$= \frac{-1}{D^2 - 4}\, 2 + \frac{1}{D^2 - 4}\, e^{2x} + \frac{1}{D^2 - 4}\, e^{-2x}$$

$$= \tfrac{1}{2} + e^{2x}\frac{1}{(D+2)^2 - 4}\, 1 + e^{-2x}\frac{1}{(D-2)^2 - 4}\, 1$$

$$= \tfrac{1}{2} + e^{2x}\frac{1}{4D}\, 1 - e^{-2x}\frac{1}{4D}\, 1$$

$$= \tfrac{1}{2} + \tfrac{1}{4}xe^{2x} - \tfrac{1}{4}xe^{-2x}$$

retaining only the lowest powers of D in each denominator. The general solution is

$$y = (A + \tfrac{1}{4}x)e^{2x} + (B - \tfrac{1}{4}x)e^{-2x} + \tfrac{1}{2}.$$

Example 12 Solve the equation $(D^2 + 2D + 5)y = 34 \cos 2x$.

The roots of the auxiliary quadratic are $-1 \pm 2i$, so the complementary function is $e^{-x}(A \cos 2x + B \sin 2x)$. The particular integral is

$$y = \text{Rl}\,\frac{1}{D^2 + 2D + 5}\, 34e^{2ix} = \text{Rl}\,\frac{1}{-4 + 4i + 5}\, 34e^{2ix}$$

$$= \text{Rl}\,\tfrac{34}{17}(1 - 4i)(\cos 2x + i \sin 2x)$$

$$= 2(\cos 2x + 4 \sin 2x),$$

where we have replaced D by $2i$. Hence, generally,

$$y = e^{-x}(A \cos 2x + B \sin 2x) + 2 \cos 2x + 8 \sin 2x,$$

The particular integral may also be evaluated as follows: After substituting $D = 2i$, we use polar coordinates.

$$y = \text{Rl} \, \frac{1}{1 + 4i} \, 34e^{2ix} = \text{Rl} \, \frac{34e^{2ix}}{\sqrt{17}e^{i\alpha}} \qquad (\tan \alpha = 4)$$

$$= \text{Rl} \, 2\sqrt{17}e^{i(2x-\alpha)} = 2\sqrt{17} \cos (2x - \alpha).$$

Example 13   Solve the equation $(D^2 + 9)y = 6 \cos 3x + 6 \sin 3x$.

The roots of the auxiliary quadratic are $\pm 3i$, so the complementary function is $A \cos 3x + B \sin 3x$. The particular integral is given by

$$y = (\text{Rl} + \text{Im}) \, \frac{1}{D^2 + 9} \, 6e^{3ix} = (\text{Rl} + \text{Im})e^{3ix} \, \frac{1}{(D + 3i)^2 + 9} \, 6$$

$$= (\text{Rl} + \text{Im})e^{3ix} \, \frac{1}{D^2 + 6i \, D} \, 6$$

$$= -(\text{Rl} + \text{Im})e^{3ix}ix$$

$$= -x(\cos 3x - \sin 3x).$$

Hence the general solution is

$$y = (A - x) \cos 3x + (B + x) \sin 3x.$$

(iv) *Products of the above functions.* Functions of the form $e^{\alpha x} \cosh \beta x$, $e^{\alpha x} \cos \beta x$, etc., may be expressed solely in terms of exponential functions, either with real or complex indices.

Functions of the type $e^{\alpha x}$ multiplied by a polynomial in x should be treated according to method (ii*b*), by taking the exponential function to the left, and allowing the resulting operator to operate on the polynomial according to rule (i). Examples 14 and 15 below illustrate these methods, but example 16 is of a special character.

Example 14   Find the particular integral for $(D^2 + 2D + 5)y = e^{-x} \sin^2 x$.

We have

$$y = \frac{1}{D^2 + 2D + 5} \, \tfrac{1}{2}e^{-x}(1 - \cos 2x)$$

$$= \frac{1}{D^2 + 2D + 5} \tfrac{1}{2}e^{-x} - \tfrac{1}{2} \text{Rl} \, \frac{1}{D^2 + 2D + 5} \, e^{(-1+2i)x}$$

$$= \tfrac{1}{8}e^{-x} - \tfrac{1}{2} \text{Rl} \, e^{(-1+2i)x} \, \frac{1}{(D - 1 + 2i)^2 + 2(D - 1 + 2i) + 5} \, 1$$

$$= \tfrac{1}{8}e^{-x} - \tfrac{1}{2} \text{Rl} \, e^{(-1+2i)x} \, \frac{1}{D^2 + 4iD} \, 1$$

$$= \tfrac{1}{8}e^{-x} - \tfrac{1}{2} \text{Rl} \, e^{-x}e^{2ix}(-\tfrac{1}{4}ix) \qquad \text{(using the lowest power of } D\text{)}$$

$$= \tfrac{1}{8}e^{-x} - \tfrac{1}{8}xe^{-x} \sin x.$$

Example 15 Solve the equation $(D^2 - 3D + 2)y = x^2 e^x$.

The complementary function is $Ae^x + Be^{2x}$, and the particular integral is

$$y = \frac{1}{D^2 - 3D + 2} x^2 e^x = e^x \frac{1}{(D+1)^2 - 3(D+1) + 2} x^2$$

$$= e^x \frac{1}{D^2 - D} x^2$$

$$= -e^x \frac{1}{D}(1 + D + D^2 + D^3)x^2$$

$$= -e^x \left(\frac{1}{D} + 1 + D + D^2\right)x^2$$

$$= -e^x(\tfrac{1}{3}x^3 + x^2 + 2x + 2).$$

This last constant 2 is immaterial, since it reproduces part of the complementary function; hence, generally,

$$y = (A - 2x - x^2 - \tfrac{1}{3}x^3)e^x + Be^{2x}.$$

Example 16 Solve the equation $(D^2 - 4D + 4)y = e^{2x}/x$.

The function $1/x$ on the right hand side is unlike the other functions already considered. Normally, the above methods do not apply to any other types of functions, but there is something special in the present equation. Using the above methods, we obtain for the complementary function $(A + Bx)e^{2x}$, and for the particular integral

$$y = \frac{1}{(D-2)^2} \frac{e^{2x}}{x} = e^{2x} \frac{1}{D^2} \frac{1}{x} = e^{2x} \frac{1}{D} \log x = e^{2x}(x \log x - x).$$

The general solution is therefore

$$y = (A + Bx + x \log x)e^{2x}.$$

This method is applicable to any equation of the form

$$(D - \alpha)^2 y = e^{\alpha x} f(x),$$

whatever the form of the function $f(x)$, for the particular integral is

$$y = \frac{1}{(D-\alpha)^2} e^{\alpha x} f(x) = e^{\alpha x} \frac{1}{D^2} f(x) = e^{\alpha x} \iint f(x) \, dx^2.$$

20.5   Change of the dependent variable

The more general linear equation of the second order with variable coefficients may be written in the form

$$D^2 y + f(x) \, Dy + g(x)y = h(x), \tag{2}$$

where f, g and h are functions of x. Unlike the first order linear equation, this equation possesses no general solution expressible in terms of

f, g and h. However, in special circumstances, a change of the dependent variable y may reduce the equation to one with constant coefficients. It is not usually possible to guess the appropriate change of variable, so a hint is usually supplied.

Let $y = \phi(x)u$, where ϕ is a *given* function of x. Then

$$Dy = \phi\, Du + (D\phi)u,$$
$$D^2y = \phi\, D^2u + 2(D\phi)\, Du + (D^2\phi)u.$$

Equation (2) becomes upon substitution,

$$[\phi\, D^2u + 2(D\phi)\, Du + (D^2\phi)u] + f(x)[\phi\, Du + (D\phi)u]$$
$$+ g(x)\phi u = h(x),$$

or $\quad \phi\, D^2u + (2D\phi + f\phi)\, Du + (D^2\phi + f\, D\phi + g\phi)u = h.$

If this method is applicable, division by ϕ should yield constant coefficients. In particular, ϕ may always be chosen so that the coefficient of Du vanishes, namely $2\, D\phi + f\phi = 0$. This implies that

$$\phi = \exp\left[-\tfrac{1}{2}\int f(x)\, dx\right].$$

On other occasions, the dependent variable y may be given as a function of the new dependent variable u by a relationship of the form $y = \psi(u)$. Denoting differentiation with respect to u by a prime, we have

$$Dy = \psi'(u)\, Du, \quad D^2y = \psi''(u)\, (Du)^2 + \psi'(u)\, D^2u.$$

These are substituted into equation (2), yielding after division an equation with constant coefficients.

Example 17   The substitution $y = zx^n$ reduces the equation

$$x^2\, D^2y + (4x + 3x^2)\, Dy + (2 + 6x + 2x^2)y = x$$

to one possessing constant coefficients for a suitable value of n. Find n, and the general solution of the equation.

Since $y = zx^n$, we have

$$Dy = x^n\, Dz + nx^{n-1}z,$$
$$D^2y = x^n\, D^2z + 2nx^{n-1}\, Dz + n(n-1)x^{n-2}z,$$

yielding, upon substitution,

$$x^2[x^n\, D^2z + 2nx^{n-1}\, Dz + n(n-1)x^{n-2}z] + (4x + 3x^2)(x^n\, Dz + nx^{n-1}z)$$
$$+ (2 + 6x + 2x^2)x^n z = x,$$

or $\quad x^{n+2}\, D^2z + (2nx^{n+1} + 4x^{n+1} + 3x^{n+2})\, Dz$
$$+ [n(n-1)x^n + 4nx^n + 3nx^{n+1} + 2x^n + 6x^{n+1} + 2x^{n+2}]z = x.$$

The choice $n = -2$ yields
$$D^2 z + 3\,Dz + 2z = x,$$
possessing the complementary function $Ae^{-x} + Be^{-2x}$, and the particular integral

$$z = \frac{1}{D^2 + 3D + 2}\,x = \tfrac{1}{2}(1 - \tfrac{3}{2}D)x = \tfrac{1}{2}x - \tfrac{3}{4}.$$

Hence
$$z = Ae^{-x} + Be^{-2x} + \tfrac{1}{2}x - \tfrac{3}{4},$$
and
$$y = x^{-2}(Ae^{-x} + Be^{-2x} + \tfrac{1}{2}x - \tfrac{3}{4}).$$

20.6 Change of the independent variable

If, in equation (2), we make the *given* substitution $x = x(t)$, or conversely, $t = t(x)$, we obtain

$$\frac{dy}{dx} = \frac{dy}{dt}\cdot\frac{dt}{dx}, \qquad \frac{d^2y}{dx^2} = \frac{d^2y}{dt^2}\left(\frac{dt}{dx}\right)^2 + \frac{dy}{dt}\cdot\frac{d^2t}{dx^2}.$$

The equation should reduce to one with constant coefficients, provided the function $x(t)$ is correctly chosen.

Example 18 Using the substitution $t = \sqrt{x}$, find the general solution of the equation

$$4x\frac{d^2y}{dx^2} + 2(1 - \sqrt{x})\frac{dy}{dx} - 6y = e^{3\sqrt{x}}.$$

We have
$$\frac{dy}{dx} = \frac{dy}{dt}\cdot\frac{1}{2\sqrt{x}}, \qquad \frac{d^2y}{dx^2} = \frac{d^2y}{dt^2}\cdot\frac{1}{4x} - \frac{dy}{dt}\cdot\frac{1}{4x^{\frac{3}{2}}},$$

transforming the given equation into

$$4x\left(\frac{d^2y}{dt^2}\cdot\frac{1}{4x} - \frac{dy}{dt}\cdot\frac{1}{4x^{\frac{3}{2}}}\right) + 2(1 - \sqrt{x})\frac{dy}{dt}\cdot\frac{1}{2\sqrt{x}} - 6y = e^{3\sqrt{x}},$$

simplifying to
$$\frac{d^2y}{dt^2} - \frac{dy}{dt} - 6y = e^{3t}.$$

The complementary function is $Ae^{3t} + Be^{-2t}$, while, if $D \equiv d/dt$, the particular integral is

$$y = \frac{1}{(D - 3)(D + 2)}e^{3t} = e^{3t}\frac{1}{D(D + 5)}1 = \tfrac{1}{5}te^{3t},$$

using the lowest power of D. Hence

$$y = Ae^{3t} + Be^{-2t} + \tfrac{1}{5}te^{3t} = (A + \tfrac{1}{5}\sqrt{x})e^{3\sqrt{x}} + Be^{-2\sqrt{x}}.$$

Example 19 Solve the *homogeneous* equation

$$x^2\frac{d^2y}{dx^2} - 7x\frac{dy}{dx} + 16y = x^4 \log x.$$

This equation is of a standard type, and its form should be noted; x^2 multiplies D^2y and x multiplies Dy. The standard substitution should be learnt, since it is not always given.

Let $x = e^t$, implying that $dx/dt = x$; then

$$\frac{dy}{dx} = \frac{dy}{dt} \bigg/ \frac{dx}{dt} = \frac{1}{x}\frac{dy}{dx}, \quad \frac{d^2y}{dx^2} = \frac{1}{x^2}\frac{d^2y}{dt^2} - \frac{1}{x^2}\frac{dy}{dt}.$$

The equation becomes

$$\left(\frac{d^2y}{dt^2} - \frac{dy}{dt}\right) - 7\frac{dy}{dt} + 16y = te^{4t},$$

or

$$\frac{d^2y}{dt^2} - 8\frac{dy}{dt} + 16y = te^{4t}.$$

The complementary function is $(A + Bt)e^{4t}$, while, if $D \equiv d/dt$, the particular integral is

$$y = \frac{1}{(D - 4)^2} te^{4t} = e^{4t}\frac{1}{D^2}t = \tfrac{1}{6}e^{4t}t^3.$$

Hence, generally,

$$y = (A + Bt + \tfrac{1}{6}t^3)e^{4t} = [A + B\log x + \tfrac{1}{6}(\log x)^3]x^4.$$

20.7   Simultaneous differential equations

If two relationships are given between the two dependent variables x and y together with their derivatives and the independent variable t, these constitute two *simultaneous differential equations* for x and y. The formal steps by which such sets of equations may be solved are as follows:

Step (i).   Gather the terms in x and y respectively together, using $D \equiv d/dt$.

Step (ii).   Decide which of the two variables x and y is to be eliminated. If y, say, combine suitably the two equations in order to eliminate *all* the derivatives of y but *not* y itself. This new equation expresses y explicitly in terms of t, x and the derivatives of x. If y does not occur explicitly in the given equations, express the lowest order derivative of y in terms of t, x and the derivatives of x.

Step (iii).   Eliminate y completely; care must be taken to obtain the equation of lowest order satisfied by x. Solve this equation for x, introducing as many arbitrary constants as necessary. If initial conditions are given, *solve for all the arbitrary constants at this stage.*

Step (iv).   Find y, using the equation obtained in step (ii).

While this is the general method, illustrated in examples 20 and 21 below, sometimes a certain symmetry in the given equations enables special methods to be used. Examples 22 and 23 demonstrate these methods. In particular, equations that arise in oscillation problems are often similar to those considered in example 22.

Example 20   If $D \equiv d/dt$, find the general solution of the equations

$$Dy + y - 3x = t, \quad Dx + 2x - 2y = -t.$$

Step (i). We rearrange these equations thus

$$(D + 1)y - 3x = t, \tag{3}$$
$$-2y + (D + 2)x = -t. \tag{4}$$

Step (ii) After deciding to eliminate x (this choice is arbitrary), we observe that equation (3) gives x directly in terms of y, Dy and t; no new equation need therefore be formed.

Step (iii). To eliminate x completely, we consider

$$(D + 2)(\text{equation 3}) + 3(\text{equation 4}),$$

obtaining
$$(D + 2)(D + 1)y - 6y = (D + 2)t - 3t$$
or
$$(D^2 + 3D - 4)y = 1 - t.$$

The complementary function is $Ae^{-4t} + Be^t$, while the particular integral is

$$y = \frac{1}{D^2 + 3D - 4}(1 - t) = \frac{1}{3D - 4}(1 - t) = -\tfrac{1}{4}(1 + \tfrac{3}{4}D)(1 - t) = \tfrac{1}{4}t - \tfrac{1}{16}.$$

Hence
$$y = Ae^{-4t} + Be^t + \tfrac{1}{4}t - \tfrac{1}{16}.$$

Step (iv). Using equation (3), we have

$$3x = (D + 1)y - t = -3Ae^{-4t} + 2Be^t + \tfrac{1}{4}t + \tfrac{3}{16} - t,$$

yielding
$$x = -Ae^{-4t} + \tfrac{2}{3}Be^t - \tfrac{1}{4}t + \tfrac{1}{16}.$$

Note that the same arbitrary constants must appear in both x and y.

Example 21   Solve the two equations

$$Dx + Dy + y = t, \quad D^2x + 3x + D^2y + 7y = e^{2t},$$

such that $Dx = -\tfrac{19}{3}$ and $Dy = 3$ when $t = 0$.

Step (i). The equations are

$$Dx + (D + 1)y = t, \tag{5}$$
$$(D^2 + 3)x + (D^2 + 7)y = e^{2t}. \tag{6}$$

Step (ii). After deciding to eliminate x, we first consider

$$(\text{equation 6}) - D(\text{equation 5}),$$

yielding
$$3x + (7 - D)y = e^{2t} - 1. \tag{7}$$

Step (iii). In order to eliminate x completely, we may consider

$$3(\text{equation 5}) - D(\text{equation 7}),$$

yielding
$$[3(D + 1) - D(7 - D)]y = 3t - 2e^t,$$
or
$$(D^2 - 4D + 3)y = 3t - 2e^t.$$

Solving for y, we obtain directly

$$y = Ae^t + Be^{3t} + (t + \tfrac{4}{3}) + 2e^{2t}.$$

Using equation (5), we note that $y = t - Dx - Dy$, so when $t = 0$, we have $y = -Dx - Dy = \frac{19}{3} - 3 = \frac{10}{3}$. Hence, when $t = 0$,

$$y = \tfrac{10}{3} = A + B + \tfrac{4}{3} + 2,$$
$$Dy = 3 = A + 3B + 1 + 4,$$

yielding $A = 1$, $B = -1$, and

$$y = e^t - e^{3t} + t + \tfrac{4}{3} + 2e^{2t}.$$

Step (iv). Using equation (7), we obtain the value of x:

$$x = \tfrac{1}{3}[e^{2t} - 1 + (D - 7)y]$$
$$= \tfrac{1}{3}[e^{2t} - 1 - 6e^t + 4e^{3t} + 1 - 7t - \tfrac{28}{3} - 10e^{2t}]$$
$$= -2e^t + \tfrac{4}{3}e^{3t} - \tfrac{7}{3}t - \tfrac{28}{9} - 3e^{2t}.$$

Example 22 These equations are of a special type and should be recognized immediately. Solve the equations

$$D^2x + 2\,Dy - 2x = 0, \tag{8}$$
$$D^2y - 2\,Dx - 2y = e^t. \tag{9}$$

generally, and subject to the conditions $x = y = Dx = Dy = 0$ and when $t = 0$.

The following method applies in cases where x in the first equation is replaced by y in the second, and where y in the first is replaced by $-x$ in the second.

All the coefficients being real, consider the combination

$$\text{(equation 8)} + i\text{(equation 9)},$$

where $x + iy = z$. We obtain

$$D^2z - 2i\,Dz - 2z = ie^t.$$

The roots of the auxiliary quadratic are $i \pm 1$, so the complementary function is

$$Ae^{(1+i)t} + Be^{(-1+i)t}.$$

The particular integral is

$$z = \frac{1}{D^2 - 2i\,D - 2}\,ie^t = \frac{ie^t}{1 - 2i - 2} = \tfrac{1}{5}i(2i - 1)e^t = -\tfrac{1}{5}(2 + i)e^t.$$

yielding
$$z = Ae^{(1+i)t} + Be^{(-1+i)t} - \tfrac{1}{5}(2 + i)e^t. \tag{10}$$

When we evaluate the real and imaginary parts of z, we must notice that the constants A and B may be complex. Let us therefore write

$$z = x + iy = (C + i\,D)e^t e^{it} + (E + iF)e^{-t}e^{-t} - \tfrac{1}{5}(2 + i)e^t.$$

Hence $\quad x = \text{Rl}\,z = e^t(C \cos t - D \sin t) + e^{-t}(E \cos t - F \sin t) - \tfrac{2}{5}e^t,$

$\qquad\quad y = \text{Im}\,z = e^t(D \cos t + C \sin t) + e^{-t}(F \cos t + E \sin t) - \tfrac{1}{5}e^t.$

When $t = 0$, we have $z = x + iy = 0$ and $Dz = Dx + i\,Dy = 0$, from the given initial conditions. Equation (10) yields

$$z = 0 = A + B - \tfrac{1}{5}(2 + i),$$
$$Dz = 0 = (1 + i)A + (-1 + i)B - \tfrac{1}{5}(2 + i),$$

from which it follows that $A = \tfrac{1}{2}$, $B = \tfrac{1}{10}(2i - 1)$. Hence

$$x = \tfrac{1}{2}e^t \cos t + e^{-t}(-\tfrac{1}{10} \cos t - \tfrac{1}{5} \sin t) - \tfrac{2}{5}e^t,$$
$$y = \tfrac{1}{2}e^t \sin t + e^{-t}(\tfrac{1}{5} \cos t - \tfrac{1}{10} \sin t) - \tfrac{1}{5}e^t.$$

Example 23 This set of equations is also of a special type, and should be recognized immediately. Solve the equations

$$D^2x + 2\,Dy + x = \cosh t,$$
$$D^2y + 2\,Dx + y = \sinh t,$$

such that $x = y = Dx = Dy = 0$ when $t = 0$.

In these equations, x and y in the first equation are replaced respectively by y and x in the second. If we let $x + y = u$ and $x - y = v$, then successive addition and subtraction of the given equations yield

$$(D^2 + 2\,D + 1)u = e^t,$$
$$(D^2 - 2\,D + 1)v = e^{-t}.$$

The solution for u is

$$u = (A + Bt)e^{-t} + \tfrac{1}{4}e^t.$$

When $t = 0$, $u = 0 = A + \tfrac{1}{4}$ and $Du = 0 = B - A + \tfrac{1}{4}$, yielding $A = -\tfrac{1}{4}$, $B = -\tfrac{1}{2}$. Hence

$$u = (-\tfrac{1}{4} - \tfrac{1}{2}t)e^{-t} + \tfrac{1}{4}e^t.$$

The solution for v is

$$v = (C + Dt)e^t + \tfrac{1}{4}e^{-t}.$$

When $t = 0$, $v = 0 = C + \tfrac{1}{4}$ and $Dv = 0 = C + D - \tfrac{1}{4}$, yielding $C = -\tfrac{1}{4}$, $D = \tfrac{1}{2}$. Hence

$$v = (-\tfrac{1}{4} + \tfrac{1}{2}t)e^t + \tfrac{1}{4}e^{-t}.$$

Finally,
$$x = \tfrac{1}{2}(u + v) = \tfrac{1}{2}t \sinh t,$$
$$y = \tfrac{1}{2}(u - v) = \tfrac{1}{2}\sinh t - \tfrac{1}{2}t \cosh t.$$

20.8 An oscillatory system of one particle

Suppose a particle of unit mass moves along the axis Ox under the action of the following forces: (i) a *restoring force* proportional to its distance from O, n^2x say; (ii) a *resistive force* proportional to the velocity, $-2k\dot{x}$ say, (iii) an applied force $a \cos \omega t$, where a and ω are constants.

If dots denote differentiation with respect to time, the equation of motion of the particle is

$$\ddot{x} = -n^2x - 2k\dot{x} + a \cos \omega t,$$

or, if $D \equiv d/dt$,

$$(D^2 + 2k\,D + n^2)x = a \cos \omega t.$$

The roots of the auxiliary quadratic are $-k \pm \sqrt{(k^2 - n^2)}$, and the particular integral is

$$x = \mathrm{Rl}\, \frac{1}{D^2 + 2k\,D + n^2}\, ae^{i\omega t} = \mathrm{Rl}\, \frac{ae^{i\omega t}}{(n^2 - \omega^2) + 2ki}$$

$$= \frac{a(n^2 - \omega^2) \cos \omega t + 2ak\omega \sin \omega t}{(n^2 - \omega^2)^2 + 4k^2\omega^2}.$$

Various cases must now be considered:

$k^2 > n^2$.   The general solution is

$$x = A \exp\{[-k + \sqrt{(k^2 - n^2)}]t\} + B \exp\{[-k - \sqrt{(k^2 - n^2)}]t\}$$
$$+ \text{ particular integral.}$$

Both the exponential functions decay to zero as t increases, leaving the particular integral as the only remaining *steady state* solution.

$k^2 < n^2$.   The general solution is

$$x = e^{-kt}\{A \cos[t\sqrt{(n^2 - k^2)}] + B \sin[t\sqrt{(n^2 - k^2)}]\}$$
$$+ \text{ particular integral.}\quad (11)$$

Again the complementary function vanishes as t becomes large, leaving the particular integral as the steady state solution ($k > 0$).

$k = 0$.   The general solution is

$$x = A \cos nt + B \sin nt + a\,(\cos \omega t)/(n^2 - \omega^2).$$

Forced oscillations of period $2\pi/\omega$ are impressed upon the natural oscillations of the system of period $2\pi/n$.

$k = 0$, $\omega = n$.   If the period of the impressed force equals the *natural period* of the system, the particular integral is

$$x = \text{Rl}\;\frac{1}{D^2 + n^2}\,ae^{int} = \text{Rl}\;ae^{int}\;\frac{1}{D^2 + 2inD}\,1 = \frac{at \sin nt}{2n}.$$

Hence $x = A \cos nt + B \sin nt + (at/2n) \sin nt.$

The amplitude of the oscillations therefore builds up to infinity with time; this is the phenomenon of *resonance*.   In practice, under such circumstances, k is small but not zero.   Solution (11) then becomes

$$x = e^{-kt}(A \cos nt + B \sin nt) + (a/2kn) \sin nt.$$

The complementary function, being the *transient solution*, disappears ultimately with increasing t through the factor e^{-kt}, although k is small.

The particular integral yields a steady state solution of finite but large amplitude $a/2kn$.

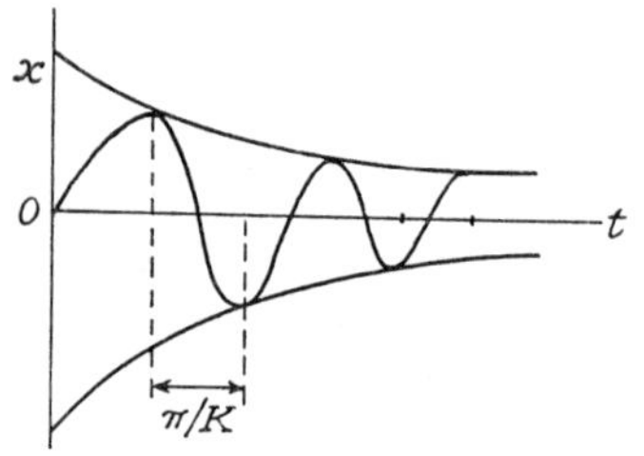

If $k^2 < n^2$, and if there is no applied force $a \cos \omega t$, the equation

$$(D^2 + 2kD + n^2)x = 0$$

possesses the complementary function only as its solution; this may be expressed in the form

$$x = Ae^{-kt} \sin(pt + \varepsilon),$$

FIG. 120

where $p = \sqrt{(n^2 - k^2)}$.   This represents decaying oscillatory motion.

The value of x is stationary when $Dx = 0$, namely when

$$-kAe^{-kt} \sin (pt + \varepsilon) + pAe^{-kt} \cos (pt + \varepsilon) = 0,$$

or $$\tan (pt + \varepsilon) = p/k.$$

Hence successive values of pt differ by π; that is, successive values of t yielding stationary values of x differ by π/p.

If T and $T + \pi/p$ are two such values of the time, the ratio of the successive maximum amplitudes of x is given by

$$\frac{Ae^{-k(T+\pi/p)} \sin [p(T + \pi/p) + \varepsilon]}{Ae^{-kT} \sin (pT + \varepsilon)} = -e^{-k\pi/p}.$$

The minus sign arises since the particle is successively at rest on opposite sides of the origin.

20.9 An oscillatory system of two particles

Two particles may be connected together in various ways, as the following examples show; at any time t their positions may be specified by the two variables x and y respectively. The equations of motion of the two particles provide two equations for the dependent variables x and y in terms of the time t. Here, we shall be concerned with the *free* oscillations of such a system, with no impressed forces additional to those arising within the system itself. The variables x and y are measured from their respective equilibrium positions. The resulting equations will form a set of two simultaneous differential equations, such that each term in each equation involves only x, y or their derivatives. Moreover, we assume that there are no resistive forces acting on the particles; the first derivatives of x and y will not therefore appear in the equations.

The two equations of motion will reduce to the following form (or to an equivalent form):

$$(aD^2 + b)x + cy = 0,$$
$$(fD^2 + g)y + hx = 0,$$

where $D \equiv d/dt$, and where a, b, c, f, g, h are constants.

Owing to the special form of these equations, we may seek a solution in the form

$$x = X \cos pt, \quad y = Y \cos pt,$$

(or $x = X \sin pt$, $y = Y \sin pt$, or any combination of these two forms). Here, X and Y are constant amplitudes to be determined, and $2\pi/p$ is the period, again to be found, of both x and y. Substitution yields

$$(-ap^2 + b)X + cY = 0, \qquad (12)$$
$$hX + (-fp^2 + g)Y = 0.$$

X and Y may be eliminated:

$$\begin{vmatrix} -ap^2 + b & c \\ h & -fp^2 + g \end{vmatrix} = 0,$$

yielding two values p^2, p_1^2 and p_2^2 say. Finally the ratio $X:Y$ is found from equation (12):

$$X:Y = c:ap_1^2 - b \quad \text{and} \quad c:ap_2^2 - b$$

for the two cases.

We obtain therefore the four distinct solutions

$$x = c \cos p_1 t, \quad y = (ap_1^2 - b) \cos p_1 t,$$
$$x = c \sin p_1 t, \quad y = (ap_1^2 - b) \sin p_1 t,$$
$$x = c \cos p_2 t, \quad y = (ap_2^2 - b) \cos p_2 t,$$
$$x = c \sin p_2 t, \quad y = (ap_2^2 - b) \sin p_2 t.$$

Such simple solutions as these are called *normal modes of oscillation*; for each of them, x and y oscillate *in phase* with the same frequency but with different amplitudes. The general solution consists of an arbitrary linear combination of these four solutions; the four constants may be determined from the initial conditions, namely from the given values of x, y, Dx, Dy when $t = 0$.

Example 24 OAB is a light inextensible string of length $17a$, such that $OA = 13a$. O is a fixed point, and a particle of mass $4m$ is attached to the string at A and a

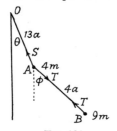

particle of mass $9m$ at B. The system performs small oscillations about the vertical through O, such that OA and AB make small angles θ and ϕ respectively to the downward vertical.

Find the normal modes of the system, and find that solution satisfying the initial conditions $\theta = \alpha$, $\phi = D\theta = D\phi = 0$ when $t = 0$.

To the first order, there is no vertical motion, so the tensions in the strings are given by $T = 9mg$, $S = 13mg$.

To the first order, the horizontal distances of A and B from the vertical through O are $13a\theta$ and $13a\theta + 4a\phi$

FIG. 121

respectively. Hence the horizontal equations of motion are

$$4m.13a\ddot{\theta} = T \sin \phi - S \sin \theta, \quad 9m(13a\ddot{\theta} + 4a\ddot{\phi}) = -T \sin \phi,$$

or
$$52a\ddot{\theta} = 9g\phi - 13g\theta, \quad 13a\ddot{\theta} + 4a\ddot{\phi} = -g\phi,$$

or
$$(52a D^2 + 13g)\theta - 9g\phi = 0, \quad 13a D^2\theta + (4a D^2 + g)\phi = 0.$$

Assuming a solution in the form $\theta = T \cos pt$, $\phi = F \cos pt$, we obtain, upon substitution,

$$(-52ap^2 + 13g)T - 9gF = 0, \quad -13ap^2 T + (-4ap^2 + g)F = 0. \tag{13}$$

Eliminating T and F, we have

$$\begin{vmatrix} -52ap^2 + 13g & -9g \\ -13ap^2 & -4ap^2 + g \end{vmatrix} = 0,$$

simplifying to $\qquad 16a^2p^4 - 17agp^2 + g^2 = 0,$

with the solutions $p = \frac{1}{4}n$ and $p = n$, where $n^2 = g/a$.

When $p^2 = g/16a$, from the first of equations (13) we may take

$$T:F = 9g:(-52ap^2 + 13g) = 9g:39g/4 = 12:13,$$

so $\qquad\qquad \theta = 12 \cos \frac{1}{4}nt, \quad \phi = 13 \cos \frac{1}{4}nt,$

and $\qquad\qquad \theta = 12 \sin \frac{1}{4}nt, \quad \phi = 13 \sin \frac{1}{4}nt.$

When $p^2 = g/a$, we find that $T:F = 3:-13$, yielding

$$\theta = 3 \cos nt, \quad \phi = -13 \cos nt,$$

$$\theta = 3 \sin nt, \quad \phi = -13 \sin nt.$$

These four solutions constitute the normal modes of oscillation of the system. The general solution is

$$\theta = 12A \cos \tfrac{1}{4}nt + 12B \sin \tfrac{1}{4}nt + 3C \cos nt + 3D \sin nt,$$

$$\phi = 13A \cos \tfrac{1}{4}nt + 13B \sin \tfrac{1}{4}nt - 13C \cos nt - 13D \sin nt.$$

When $t = 0$, we have $\theta = \alpha, \phi = D\theta = D\phi = 0$; hence

$$\alpha = 12A + 3C, \quad 0 = 13A - 13C, \quad 0 = 12B.\tfrac{1}{4}n + 3Dn, \quad 0 = 13B.\tfrac{1}{4}n - 13Dn,$$

yielding $A = C = \tfrac{1}{15}\alpha, B = D = 0$.

Example 25 An unstretched elastic string OAB of modulus $72amk^2$ is such that $OA = 8a, AB = 3a$. Masses m and $6m$ are attached at A and B respectively. The system hangs in equilibrium from O freely under gravity, and then, in small vertical displacements, x and y denote the increases in the equilibrium lengths of OA and AB respectively. Find the normal modes of oscillation for the system.

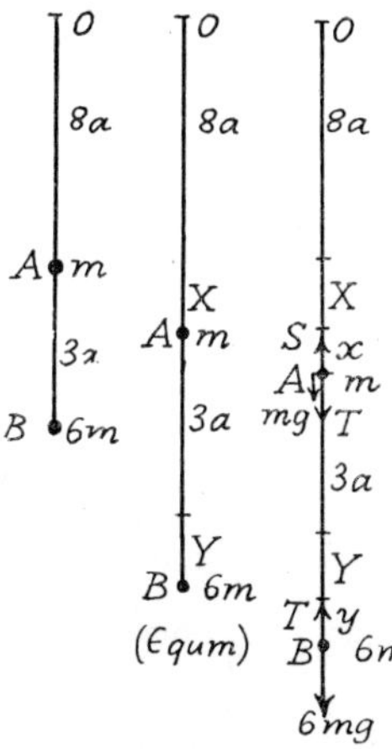

Let X and Y be the equilibrium extensions of OA and AB; then generally, A is at a depth $8a + X + x$ below O and B is at a depth $11a + X + Y + x + y$ below O. The tensions are given by

$$T = 72amk^2(X + x)/8a = 9mk^2(X + x),$$

$$S = 72amk^2(Y + y)/3a = 24mk^2(Y + y).$$

The two equations of motion are

$$m\ddot{x} = S + mg - T$$

$$= 24mk^2(Y + y) + mg - 9mk^2(X + x),$$

$$6m(\ddot{x} + \ddot{y}) = 6mg - S$$

$$= 6mg - 24mk^2(Y + y).$$

FIG. 122

In equilibrium, $x = y = \ddot{x} = \ddot{y} = 0$; hence in each equation all terms involving g, X, Y cancel, leaving

$$\ddot{x} = 24k^2y - 9k^2x, \quad \ddot{x} + \ddot{y} = -4k^2y,$$

or $\qquad (D^2 + 9k^2)x - 24k^2y = 0, \quad D^2x + (D^2 + 4k^2)y = 0.$

We now assume solutions of the form $x = \xi \cos pt$, $y = \eta \cos pt$, yielding

$$(-p^2 + 9k^2)\xi - 24k^2\eta = 0, \quad -p^2\xi + (-p^2 + 4k^2)\eta = 0. \tag{14}$$

Eliminating ξ and η, we obtain

$$\begin{vmatrix} -p^2 + 9k^2 & -24k^2 \\ -p^2 & -p^2 + 4k^2 \end{vmatrix} = 0,$$

simplifying to $\quad\quad\quad\quad p^4 - 37p^2k^2 + 36k^4 = 0$

possessing the roots $p = 6k$ and k.

When $p = 6k$, using the first equation (14), we may take $\xi:\eta = 8:-9$, and when $p = k$, we have $\xi:\eta = 3:1$. Hence the normal modes may be taken to be

$$x = 8 \cos 6kt, \quad y = -9 \cos 6kt,$$
$$x = 8 \sin 6kt, \quad y = -9 \sin 6kt,$$
$$x = 3 \cos kt, \quad y = \cos pt,$$
$$y = 3 \sin kt, \quad y = \sin pt.$$

The general solution consists of an arbitrary linear combination of these four independent solutions.

Example 26 $ABCD$ is an inextensible string whose tension $T = 6amk^2$, such that $AB = BC = CD = a$. Masses $3m$ and $8m$ are attached at B and C respectively, while A and D are two fixed points. Motion is constrained to take place in a horizontal plane through $ABCD$. If, at time $t = 0$, $x = y = 5d$, $\dot{x} = \dot{y} = 0$, where x and y are the small horizontal displacements of B and C respectively, find x and y at the general time t.

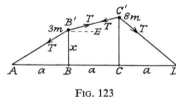

FIG. 123

The forces acting on the particles are resolved perpendicular to $ABCD$, using the tangents of the small angles $B'AB$, $C'B'E$, $C'DC$. The two equations of motion are

$$3m\ddot{x} = -Tx/a + T(y - x)/a, \quad 8m\ddot{y} = -T(y - x)/a - Ty/a,$$

or $\quad\quad\quad \ddot{x} = -4k^2x + 2k^2y, \quad 4\ddot{y} = 3k^2x - 6k^2y,$

or $\quad\quad (D^2 + 4k^2)x - 2k^2y = 0, \quad -3k^2x + (4D^2 + 6k^2)y = 0.$

Assuming solutions of the form $x = X \cos pt$, $y = Y \cos pt$, and eliminating X and Y, we obtain $\quad\quad \begin{vmatrix} -p^2 + 4k^2 & -2k^2 \\ -3k^2 & -4p^2 + 6k^2 \end{vmatrix} = 0,$

possessing the roots $p^2 = k^2$ and $6k^2$. When $p^2 = k^2$, we have $X:Y = 2:3$, and when $p^2 = 6k^2$, we have $X:Y = 1:-1$. The normal modes are therefore

$$x = 2 \cos kt, \quad y = 3 \cos kt,$$
$$x = 2 \sin kt, \quad y = 3 \sin kt,$$
$$x = \cos \sqrt{6}kt, \quad y = -\cos \sqrt{6}kt,$$
$$x = \sin \sqrt{6}kt, \quad y = -\sin \sqrt{6}kt.$$

The general solution is an arbitrary linear combination of these four solutions, using the constants A, B, C, D, say. When $t = 0$, we have $x = y = 5d$, $\dot{x} = \dot{y} = 0$, yielding

$$5d = 2A + C, \quad 5d = 3A - C, \quad 0 = 2kB + \sqrt{6k}D, \quad 0 = 3kB - \sqrt{6k}D.$$

Hence $A = 2d$, $C = d$, $B = D = 0$ and

$$x = 4d \cos kt + d \cos \sqrt{6}kt, \quad y = 6d \cos kt - d \cos \sqrt{6}kt.$$

20.10   Power-series solutions

Usually, equations of the form

$$f(x)\, D^2y + g(x)\, Dy + h(x)y = 0$$

$(D \equiv d/dx)$, where $f(x)$, $g(x)$, $h(x)$ are simple polynomials in x, cannot be solved in terms of the elementary functions with which the student is familiar. However, solutions often exist that are infinite power series in x; if exceptionally these series can be summed in terms of the elementary functions, we say that the solutions are expressed in *closed form*. There is no reason why the first term in the power series should be a constant; some unknown power of x may be necessary for the first term.

We therefore assume

$$y = x^c(a_0 + a_1x + a_2x^2 + a_3x^3 + \ldots + a_rx^r + \ldots) \qquad (15)$$

where the constants c, a_0, a_1, a_2, $\ldots$ are to be found. We stipulate that $a_0 \neq 0$, in order to be quite definite as to where the series is to start; we may in fact choose $a_0 = 1$. Formal differentiation yields

$$Dy = ca_0x^{c-1} + (c + 1)a_1x^c + (c + 2)a_2x^{c+1} + \ldots$$
$$+ (c + r)a_rx^{c+r-1} + \ldots, \qquad (16)$$
$$D^2y = c(c - 1)a_0x^{c-2} + (c + 1)ca_1x^{c-1} + (c + 2)(c + 1)a_3x^c + \ldots$$
$$+ (c + r)(c + r - 1)a_rx^{c+r-2} + \ldots. \qquad (17)$$

These series are inserted into the given differential equation. In order that the left hand side should vanish for all values of x in the range of convergence of series (15), we equate to zero the total coefficient of every power of x. The equation associated with the lowest index of x is called the *indicial equation*; it yields two values of c. The other equations then provide systematically the values of a_1, a_2, a_3, $\ldots$ in terms of a_0 for each value of c.

The final series should be tested for convergence.

If the two values of c differ by an integer, this method for finding the a's for one of these values of c may break down. Also, if the two values of c are identical, only one series is produced. A second series involving logarithms may be produced in these cases, but in this text, we shall not consider these more advanced techniques.

Sometimes, for one value of c, all the a's beyond a certain stage may vanish, yielding a finite series. On other occasions, the resulting infinite series (either one or both) can be summed, yielding a solution in closed form.

Example 27   Solve the equation $4x\,D^2y + 2Dy + y = 0$.

Inserting the series (15), (16) and (17), we obtain

$$4c(c-1)a_0x^{c-1} + 4(c+1)ca_1x^c + 4(c+2)(c+1)a_2x^{c+1} + 4(c+3)(c+2)a_3x^{c+2} + \ldots$$
$$+ 2ca_0x^{c-1} \qquad + 2(c+1)a_1x^c \quad + 2(c+2)a_2x^{c+1} \qquad\qquad + 2(c+3)a_3x^{c+2} + \ldots$$
$$+ a_0x^c \qquad\qquad + a_1x^{c+1} \qquad\qquad\qquad + a_2x^{c+2} + \ldots = 0.$$

Equating the coefficients of x^c, x^{c+1}, $\ldots$ to zero, we obtain

$$4c(c-1)a_0 + 2ca_0 = 0, \qquad\qquad \text{or} \quad 2c(2c-1)a_0 = 0,$$
$$4(c+1)ca_1 + 2(c+1)a_1 + a_0 = 0, \qquad \text{or} \quad 2(c+1)(2c+1)a_1 = -a_0,$$
$$4(c+2)(c+1)a_2 + 2(c+2)a_2 + a_1 = 0, \quad \text{or} \quad 2(c+2)(2c+3)a_2 = -a_1,$$
$$4(c+3)(c+2)a_3 + 2(c+3)a_3 + a_2 = 0, \quad \text{or} \quad 2(c+3)(2c+5)a_3 = -a_2, \text{ etc.}$$

The roots of the indicial equation are $c = 0$ and $c = \frac{1}{2}$, and

$$a_1 = -a_0/2(c+1)(2c+1),$$
$$a_2 = -a_1/2(c+2)(2c+3)$$
$$ = a_0/4(c+1)(c+2)(2c+1)(2c+3),$$
$$a_3 = -a_2/2(c+3)(2c+5)$$
$$ = -a_0/8(c+1)(c+2)(c+3)(2c+1)(2c+3)(2c+5).$$

With $a_0 = 1$ and $c = 0$, we obtain

$$a_1 = -1/2 = -1/2!,$$
$$a_2 = 1/4.2.3 = 1/4!,$$
$$a_3 = -1/8.2.3.3.5 = -1/6!,$$

so the first power-series solution is given by

$$y_1 = 1 - \frac{x}{2!} + \frac{x^2}{4!} - \frac{x^3}{6!} + \ldots = \cos\sqrt{x}.$$

With $a_0 = 1$ and $c = \frac{1}{2}$, we obtain

$$a_1 = -1/2.\tfrac{3}{2}.2 = -1/3!,$$
$$a_2 = 1/4.\tfrac{3}{2}.\tfrac{5}{2}.2.4 = 1/5!,$$
$$a_3 = -1/8.\tfrac{3}{2}.\tfrac{5}{2}.\tfrac{7}{2}.2.4.6 = -1/7!,$$

so the second power-series solution is given by

$$y_2 = x^{\frac{1}{2}}\left(1 - \frac{x}{3!} + \frac{x^2}{5!} - \frac{x^3}{7!} + \ldots\right) = \sin\sqrt{x}.$$

Both series are convergent for all values of x; the ratio test may be used to demonstrate this.

The general solution is therefore $y = A \cos \sqrt{x} + B \sin \sqrt{x}$; this shows that the unsuspected change of the independent variable $t = \sqrt{x}$ enables the equation to be solved by elementary methods.

Example 28   Solve the equation $2x(1 - x) D^2y + (1 - x) Dy + 3y = 0$.

Inserting the series assumed above, we obtain

$$2c(c - 1)a_0x^{c-1} + 2(c + 1)ca_1x^c + 2(c + 2)(c + 1)a_2x^{c+1} + 2(c + 3)(c + 2)a_3x^{c+2} + \ldots$$
$$- 2c(c - 1)a_0x^c - 2(c + 1)ca_1x^{c+1} \qquad - 2(c + 2)(c + 1)a_2x^{c+2} + \ldots$$
$$+ ca_0x^{c-1} \qquad + (c + 1)a_1x^c \quad + (c + 2)a_2x^{c+1} \qquad + (c + 3)a_3x^{c+2} + \ldots$$
$$- ca_0x^c \qquad - (c + 1)a_1x^{c+1} \qquad - (c + 2)a_2x^{c+2} - \ldots$$
$$+ 3a_0x^c \qquad + 3a_1x^{c+1} \qquad + 3a_2x^{c+2} + \ldots = 0.$$

Equating to zero the various coefficients of x^{c-1}, x^c, $\ldots$, we obtain

$$2c(c - 1)a_0 + ca_0 = 0,$$
$$[2(c + 1)c + (c + 1)]a_1 = [2c(c - 1) + c - 3]a_0,$$
$$[2(c + 2)(c + 1) + (c + 2)]a_2 = [2(c + 1)c + (c + 1) - 3]a_1, \text{ etc.}$$

Hence $c = 0$ or $\frac{1}{2}$, and

$$(2c + 1)a_1 = (2c - 3)a_0,$$
$$(2c + 3)a_2 = (2c - 1)a_1,$$
$$(2c + 5)a_3 = (2c + 1)a_2, \text{ etc.}$$

When $c = 0$, we find that $a_1 = -3$, $a_2 = -a_1/3 = 1$, $a_3 = a_2/5 = \frac{1}{5}$, when $a_0 = 1$. These values yield the series

$$y_1 = 1 - 3x + \frac{3x^2}{1.3} + \frac{3x^3}{3.5} + \ldots,$$

convergent if $|x| < 1$.

When $c = \frac{1}{2}$, with $a_0 = 1$, we find that $a_1 = -1$, $a_2 = a_3 = \ldots = 0$, giving $y_2 = x^{\frac{1}{2}}(1 - x)$.

The general solution is a linear combination of y_1 and y_2.

Example 29   Solve the *Airy equation* $D^2y = xy$.

Inserting the power series given above, we obtain

$$c(c - 1)a_0x^{c-2} + (c + 1)ca_1x^c + (c + 2)(c + 1)a_2x^c$$
$$+ (c + 3)(c + 2)a_3x^{c+1} + \ldots - a_0x^{c+1} - a_1x^{c+2} - a_2x^{c+3} - \ldots = 0.$$

Equating coefficients of the various powers of x, we obtain the equations

$$c(c - 1)a_0 = 0,$$
$$(c + 1)ca_1 = 0,$$
$$(c + 2)(c + 1)a_2 = 0,$$
$$(c + 3)(c + 2)a_3 = a_0,$$
$$(c + 4)(c + 3)a_4 = a_1, \text{ etc.}$$

The first equation gives $c = 0$ or 1. When $c = 0$, a_1 is arbitrary in the second equation, but $a_2 = 0$ in the third equation. Any arbitrary coefficient may be placed equal to zero (this is convenient, but not necessary). Then $a_1 = a_4 = a_7 = \ldots = 0$, and $a_2 = a_5 = a_8 = \ldots = 0$, and

$$3.2a_3 = a_0, \quad 6.5a_6 = a_3, \quad 9.8a_9 = a_6, \ldots,$$

yielding, when $a_0 = 1$,

$$a_3 = 1/2.3, \quad a_6 = 1/2.3.5.6, \quad a_9 = 1/2.3.5.6.8.9.$$

Hence $\qquad y_1 = 1 + \dfrac{x^3}{2.3} + \dfrac{x^6}{2.3.5.6} + \dfrac{x^9}{2.3.5.6.8.9} + \ldots,$

a series convergent for all values of x.

When $c = 1$, we must choose $a_1 = a_2 = 0$, implying that a_4, a_7, a_5, a_8, etc., all vanish. When $a_0 = 1$, we have

$$a_3 = 1/3.4, \quad a_6 = 1/3.4.6.7, \quad a_9 = 1/3.4.6.7.9.10,$$

yielding the convergent series

$$y = x + \frac{x^4}{3.4} + \frac{x^7}{3.4.6.7} + \frac{x^{10}}{3.4.6.7.9.10} + \ldots.$$

The general solution is $Ay_1 + By_2$.

20.11   The Laplace transform

By means of the *Laplace transform*, the solution of differential equations with given initial conditions may be found directly, *without* the necessity of finding the general solution containing arbitrary constants.

If y is a function of x, the integral $\displaystyle\int_0^\infty e^{-sx}y(x)\,dx$ (provided it exists) is defined to be the Laplace transform of the function y; we write

$$\mathscr{L}(y) = \int_0^\infty e^{-sx}y(x)\,dx,$$

and notice that it is a function of s alone. Conversely, if $\mathscr{L}(y)$ is given as a function of s, the function $y(x)$ giving rise to it may be found. More advanced methods are necessary to show how $y(x)$ can be calculated, but in elementary work a table of Laplace transforms is all that is required.

It follows from the definition that $\mathscr{L}(y + z) = \mathscr{L}(y) + \mathscr{L}(z)$ and $\mathscr{L}(Ay) = A\mathscr{L}(y)$, where y and z are functions of x and A is a constant.

We shall now calculate the transforms of the more important elementary functions.

(i) If $y = 1$, then $\mathscr{L}(1) = \displaystyle\int_0^\infty e^{-sx}\,dx = \frac{1}{s}.$

(ii) If $y = x^n$, we differentiate the parametric integral (i) n times with respect to s, obtaining

$$\int_0^\infty (-x)^n e^{-sx}\,dx = \frac{(-1)^n n!}{s^{n+1}}.$$

Cancelling the factor $(-1)^n$, we obtain $\mathscr{L}(x^n) = n!/s^{n+1}$.

(iii) If $y = e^{-ax}$, then $\mathscr{L}(e^{-ax}) = \displaystyle\int_0^\infty e^{-ax}e^{-sx}\,dx = \dfrac{1}{s+a}$ provided $s > -a$ for convergence.

(iv) If $F(s)$ denotes the transform of $y(x)$, then

$$F(s) = \int_0^\infty e^{-sx}\,y(x)\,dx,$$

and hence $F(s+a) = \displaystyle\int_0^\infty e^{-(s+a)x}\,y(x)\,dx = \int_0^\infty e^{-sx}[e^{-ax}y(x)]\,dx.$

It follows that $F(s+a)$ is the transform of $e^{-ax}y(x)$.

(v) If $y = x^n e^{-ax}$, we use result (iv) and replace s by $s+a$ in result (ii), obtaining $\mathscr{L}(x^n e^{-ax}) = n!/(s+a)^{n+1}$.

(vi) If $y = \cos kx$, we place $a = -ik$ and ik in turn in result (iii), obtaining

$$\mathscr{L}(\cos kx) = \tfrac{1}{2}\left(\dfrac{1}{s-ik} + \dfrac{1}{s+ik}\right) = \dfrac{s}{s^2+k^2}.$$

(vii) Integrating by parts, we have

$$\mathscr{L}\left(\dfrac{dy}{dx}\right) = \int_0^\infty e^{-sx}\dfrac{dy}{dx}\,dx = \left[y(x)e^{-sx}\right]_0^\infty - \int_0^\infty y(-se^{-sx})\,dx = -y(0) + s\mathscr{L}(y)$$

(viii) Replacing y by dy/dx in (vii), we obtain

$$\mathscr{L}\left(\dfrac{d^2y}{dx^2}\right) = -y'(0) + s\mathscr{L}\left(\dfrac{dy}{dx}\right) = s^2\mathscr{L}(y) - y'(0) - sy(0).$$

All the remaining Laplace transforms given in the table below may be derived directly from these cases; the student should verify every one.

$y(x)$	$\mathscr{L}(y)$
1	$1/s$
x^n	$n!/s^{n+1}$
e^{-ax}	$1/(s+a)$
$x^n e^{-ax}$	$n!/(s+a)^{n+1}$
$\cos kx$	$s/(s^2+k^2)$
$\sin kx$	$k/(s^2+k^2)$
$\cosh kx$	$s/(s^2-k^2)$
$\sinh kx$	$k/(s^2-k^2)$
$1 - \cos kx$	$k^2/s(s^2+k^2)$
$kx - \sin kx$	$k^3/s^2(s^2+k^2)$
$x\cos kx$	$(s^2-k^2)/(s^2+k^2)$
$x\sin kx$	$2ks/(s^2+k^2)$
$\sin kx - kx\cos kx$	$2k^3/(s^2+k^2)^2$
$e^{-ax}\cos kx$	$(s+a)/[(s+a)^2+k^2]$
$e^{-ax}\sin kx$	$k/[(s+a)^2+k^2]$
$x\,e^{-ax}\cos kx$	$[(s+a)^2-k^2]/[(s+a)^2+k^2]^2$
$x\,e^{-ax}\sin kx$	$2k(s+a)/[(s+a)^2+k^2]^2$

This table enables us to write down the Laplace transform of all elementary functions expressible in terms of the functions given in the left hand column.

Conversely, if $\mathscr{L}(y)$ is a given function of s, being in elementary work equal to (polynomial in s)/(polynomial in s), then the function $y(x)$ giving rise to $\mathscr{L}(y)$ may be deduced by resolving $\mathscr{L}(y)$ into the various elementary functions given on the right hand side of the table. Partial fractions may be employed to effect the rearrangement. To this end, the following table may be more convenient.

$\mathscr{L}(y)$	$y(x)$
$1/s$	1
$1/s^n$	$x^{n-1}/(n-1)!$, n a positive integer
$1/(s-a)$	e^{ax}
$1/(s^2+a^2)$	$(\sin ax)/a$
$s/(s^2+a^2)$	$\cos ax$
$1/(s^2-a^2)$	$(\sinh ax)/a$
$s/(s^2-a^2)$	$\cosh ax$
$1/(s^2+a^2)^2$	$(\sin ax - ax \cos ax)/2a^3$
$s/(s^2+a^2)^2$	$(x \sin ax)/2a$

Example 30   Find the Laplace transform of $y(x) = -\frac{1}{6} + \frac{1}{2}e^x - \frac{1}{2}e^{2x} + \frac{1}{6}e^{3x}$.

Using the table, and quoting the transforms for 1, e^x, e^{2x}, e^{3x}, we have

$$\mathscr{L}(y) = -\frac{1}{6s} + \frac{1}{2(s-1)} - \frac{1}{2(s-2)} - \frac{1}{6(s-3)} = \frac{1}{s(s-1)(s-2)(s-3)}.$$

Example 31   Find the Laplace transform of

$$y(x) = \frac{1}{4}(x^2 - 3x + \frac{3}{2})e^x - \frac{1}{24}e^{-x} - \frac{1}{3}[\cos \frac{1}{2}\sqrt{3}x - \sqrt{3}\sin \frac{1}{2}\sqrt{3}x]e^{\frac{1}{2}x}.$$

Using the table, and quoting the transforms for x^2e^x, xe^x, e^x, e^{-x}, $e^{\frac{1}{2}x}\cos \frac{1}{2}\sqrt{3}x$, $e^{\frac{1}{2}x}\sin \frac{1}{2}\sqrt{3}x$, we have

$$\mathscr{L}(y) = \frac{1}{2(s-1)^3} - \frac{3}{4(s-1)^2} + \frac{3}{8(s-1)} - \frac{1}{24(s+1)}$$

$$- \frac{(s - \frac{1}{2}) - \sqrt{3}.(\frac{1}{2}\sqrt{3})}{3[(s-\frac{1}{2})^2 + \frac{3}{4}]} = \frac{1}{(s-1)^3(s^3+1)}$$

upon simplification.

Example 32   Find the inverse transform of $\mathscr{L}(y) = 2/[s(s+1)(s^2+1)]$.

In partial fractions, we find that

$$\mathscr{L}(y) = \frac{2}{s} - \frac{1}{s+1} - \frac{1+s}{s^2+1}.$$

Quoting the second table for $1/s$, $1/(s-a)$, $1/(s^2+a^2)$ and $s/(s^2+a^2)$, we obtain

$$y(x) = 2 - e^{-x} - \sin x - \cos x.$$

Example 33 Find the inverse transform of $\mathscr{L}(y) = 4/(s^4 + 4)$.
In real partial fractions, we find that

$$\mathscr{L}(y) = \frac{1 + \frac{1}{2}s}{s^2 + 2s + 2} + \frac{1 - \frac{1}{2}s}{s^2 - 2s + 2} \,;$$

completing the square for the denominators yields

$$\mathscr{L}(y) = \frac{\frac{1}{2}(s + 1) + \frac{1}{2}}{(s + 1)^2 + 1} + \frac{\frac{1}{2} - \frac{1}{2}(s - 1)}{(s - 1)^2 + 1} \,.$$

Quoting the second table for $1/(s^2 + a^2)$ and $s/(s^2 + a^2)$, and using the result (iv), we obtain

$$y(x) = \tfrac{1}{2}e^{-x} \cos x + \tfrac{1}{2}e^{-x} \sin x + \tfrac{1}{2}e^{x} \sin x - \tfrac{1}{2}e^{x} \cos x$$
$$= \sin x \cosh x - \cos x \sinh x.$$

20.12 The solution of differential equations

Using the method of the Laplace transformation, we require to solve the second order linear differential equation

$$a\,D^2y + b\,Dy + cy = f(x),$$

subject to the initial conditions that $y(0)$ and $Dy(0)$ are given.

We take the Laplace transform of the given equation, using the results (vii) and (viii) derived in the previous section; the resulting equation may be called the *subsidiary equation*. We obtain

$$a[s^2\mathscr{L}(y) - Dy(0) - sy(0)] + b[s\mathscr{L}(y) - y(0)] + c\mathscr{L}(y) = \mathscr{L}(f),$$

yielding

$$\mathscr{L}(y) = \frac{a\,Dy(0) + asy(0) + by(0) + \mathscr{L}(f)}{as^2 + bs + c} \,.$$

Finally, the inverse transform y is found by rearranging the right hand side (using partial fractions if necessary) and then by using the tables.

Simultaneous equations in which x and y are the dependent variables may be solved similarly, by taking the Laplace transform of the given equation, by introducing the initial conditions and by solving for $\mathscr{L}(x)$ and $\mathscr{L}(y)$. Finally, x and y may be written down from the tables (using t as the independent variable instead of x occurring in the tables).

Example 34 Solve the equation $D^2y + 5Dy + 6y = 0$ when $y(0) = 2$, $Dy(0) = -3$.
We take the Laplace transform of the given equation, obtaining

$$[s^2\mathscr{L}(y) + 3 - 2s] + 5[s\mathscr{L}(y) - 2] + 6\mathscr{L}(y) = 0;$$

this yields

$$\mathscr{L}(y) = \frac{7 + 2s}{s^2 + 5s + 6} = \frac{3}{s + 2} - \frac{1}{s + 3} \,.$$

Finally, using the tables we obtain

$$y = 3e^{-2x} - e^{-3x}.$$

Example 35 Solve the equation $D^2y + 5Dy + 6y = e^{-2x}$ when $y(0) = 1$ and $Dy(0) = -2$.

The subsidiary equation is

$$[s^2\mathscr{L}(y) + 2 - s] + 5[s\mathscr{L}(y) - 1] + 6\mathscr{L}(y) = 1/(s + 2)$$

yielding $\qquad \mathscr{L}(y) = \dfrac{s + 3 + 1/(s + 2)}{s^2 + 5s + 6} = \dfrac{1}{(s + 2)^2} - \dfrac{1}{s + 3}.$

Finally, using the tables, we obtain

$$y = xe^{-2x} - e^{-3x}.$$

Example 36 Solve the simultaneous equations $D^2x = p\,Dy$, $D^2y = a - p\,Dx$, such that $x = y = Dx = Dy = 0$ when $t = 0$.

Taking the Laplace transforms of x and y (using, of course, integration with respect to t in the process), we obtain

$$s^2\mathscr{L}(x) = ps\mathscr{L}(y), \quad s^2\mathscr{L}(y) = a/s - ps\mathscr{L}(x).$$

Solving these for $\mathscr{L}(x)$ and $\mathscr{L}(y)$, we have

$$\mathscr{L}(x) = \frac{a}{p}\left(\frac{1}{s^2} - \frac{1}{s^2 + p^2}\right), \quad \mathscr{L}(y) = \frac{a}{p^2}\left(\frac{1}{s} - \frac{s}{s^2 + p^2}\right).$$

Finally, using the tables, we obtain

$$x(t) = (a/p^2)(pt - \sin pt), \quad y(t) = (a/p^2)(1 - \cos pt).$$

20.13 Laplace transforms of some special functions

Periodic functions. If $y(x)$ is a periodic function with period 2π, its Laplace transform is given as usual by

$$\mathscr{L}(y) = \int_0^\infty e^{-sx}y(x)\,dx.$$

This may be simplified as follows: Let $x = t - 2\pi$; then since $y(x) = y(t - 2\pi) = y(t)$, we have

$$\mathscr{L}(y) = \int_{2\pi}^\infty e^{-s(t-2\pi)}y(t)\,dt,$$

or

$$\mathscr{L}(y)e^{-2\pi s} = \int_{2\pi}^\infty e^{-st}y(t)\,dt.$$

Subtraction yields

$$\mathscr{L}(y)(1 - e^{-2\pi s}) = \left(\int_0^\infty - \int_{2\pi}^\infty\right)e^{-sx}y(x)\,dx$$

$$= \int_0^{2\pi} e^{-sx}y(x)\,dx.$$

Hence

$$\mathscr{L}(y) = \frac{1}{1 - e^{-2\pi s}} \int_0^{2\pi} e^{-sx} y(x)\, dx.$$

The range of integration is now extended only over one complete period.

Example 37   Find the Laplace transform of the function with period 2π defined by $y = 1$ when $0 < x < \pi$, $y = -1$ when $\pi < x < 2\pi$.

Using the above formula, we have

$$\mathscr{L}(y) = \frac{1}{1 - e^{-2\pi s}} \left(\int_0^{\pi} e^{-sx}\, dx - \int_{\pi}^{2\pi} e^{-sx}\, dx \right)$$

$$= \frac{1}{1 - e^{-2\pi s}} \left(\frac{e^{-s\pi} - 1}{-s} - \frac{e^{-2\pi s} - e^{-\pi s}}{-s} \right)$$

$$= \frac{(1 - e^{-\pi s})^2}{s(1 - e^{-2\pi s})} = \frac{1 - e^{-\pi s}}{s(1 + e^{-\pi s})} = \frac{\tanh \tfrac{1}{2} s\pi}{s}.$$

The step function.   In certain problems, it is necessary to introduce a new function into $y(x)$ at and beyond the point $x = a$. This may be accomplished by using Heaviside's *step function* $H(x - a)$, defined to be unity when $x > a$ and zero when $x < a$. Its Laplace transform is

$$\mathscr{L}[H(x - a)] = \int_0^{\infty} e^{-sx} H(x - a)\, dx = \int_a^{\infty} e^{-sx}\, dx = \frac{e^{-sa}}{s}.$$

At a later point $x = b$, the value $y = 1$ may be removed again by subtracting $H(x - b)$. The function $y = H(x - a) - H(x - b)$, where $b > a$, is such that $y = 0$ when $x < a$, $y = 1$ when $a < x < b$, $y = 0$ when $x > b$. Its Laplace transform is

$$\mathscr{L}(y) = (e^{-sa} - e^{-sb})/s.$$

If $\mathscr{L}(y)$ is the Laplace transform of $y(x)$, then we shall prove that $e^{-sa}\mathscr{L}(y)$ is the transform of $y(x - a)H(x - a)$. The graph of this function is identical with that of $y(x)$ shifted a distance a to the right; its value is zero to the left of $x = a$. Its Laplace transform is given by

$$\int_0^{\infty} e^{-sx} y(x - a)H(x - a)\, dx = \int_a^{\infty} e^{-sx} y(x - a)\, dx$$

$$= \int_0^{\infty} e^{-s(t+a)} y(t)\, dt = e^{-sa}\mathscr{L}(y)$$

where we have used the substitution $t = x - a$. Hence the inverse transform of $e^{-sa}\mathscr{L}(y)$ is found by replacing x by $x - a$ in $y(x)$ and multiplying by $H(x - a)$.

Example 38 A constant E.M.F. E is introduced into a series $L - R$ circuit from the time $t = a$ to $t = b$. Find the current for $t > b$, assuming that $j = 0$ initially.

The differential equation for the current j is

$$L\, dj/dt + Rj = \text{E.M.F.}$$

The Laplace transform is given by

$$Ls\mathscr{L}(j) + R\mathscr{L}(j) = E(e^{-sa} - e^{-sb})/s,$$

yielding

$$\mathscr{L}(j) = \frac{E(e^{-sa} - e^{-sb})}{s(Ls + R)} = \frac{E}{R}(e^{-sa} - e^{-sb})\left(\frac{1}{s} - \frac{L}{Ls + R}\right).$$

The inverse transform of $\dfrac{E}{R}\left(\dfrac{1}{s} - \dfrac{L}{Ls + R}\right)$ is $E(1 - e^{-Rt/L})/R$; hence the inverse

transforms of $\dfrac{E}{R}\,e^{-sa}\left(\dfrac{1}{s} - \dfrac{L}{Ls + R}\right)$ and $\dfrac{E}{R}\,e^{-sb}\left(\dfrac{1}{s} - \dfrac{L}{Ls + R}\right)$ are given respec-

tively by $E(1 - e^{-R(t-a)/L})H(t - a)/R$ and $E(1 - e^{-R(t-b)/L})H(t - b)/R$. Hence

$$j(t) = \frac{E}{R}(-e^{-R(t-a)/L} + e^{-R(t-b)/L}) \qquad (t > b > a)$$

$$= \frac{E}{R}\,e^{-Rt/L}[e^{Rb/L} - e^{Ra/L}].$$

Example 39 A uniform beam $OABC$ of length $6a$, whose weight per unit length is w and whose flexural rigidity is B, is clamped horizontally at O. Weights $3wa$, $2wa$, wa hang from A, B, C respectively, where $OA = AB = BC = 2a$. Find the deflexion at a general point P of the beam.

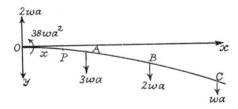

FIG. 124

The reaction at O is $12wa$, while the clamping couple must be $38wa^2$. The bending moment Bd^2y/dx^2 at P equals the sum of the anticlockwise moments about P of all forces acting on the left of P. As P moves to the right through A and B, the additional moments introduced may be taken care of by the step function. We have

$$Bd^2y/dx^2 = \tfrac{1}{2}wx^2 + 38wa^2 - 12wax + 3wa(x - 2a)H(x - 2a)$$
$$+ 2wa(x - 4a)H(x - 4a).$$

The Laplace transform of this equation is given by

$$Bs^2\mathscr{L}(y) = \frac{w}{s^3} + \frac{38wa^2}{s} - \frac{12wa}{s^2} + 3wae^{-2sa}\frac{1}{s^2} + 2wae^{-4sa}\frac{1}{s^2}$$

yielding

$$B\mathscr{L}(y) = \frac{w}{s^5} + \frac{38wa^2}{s^3} - \frac{12wa}{s^4} + 3wae^{-2sa}\frac{1}{s^4} + 2wae^{-4sa}\frac{1}{s^4}.$$

The inverse transform finally gives the deflexion:

$$By = \frac{wx^4}{24} + 19wa^2x^2 - 2wax^3 + \tfrac{1}{2}wa(x - 2a)^3H(x - 2a)$$
$$+ \tfrac{1}{3}wa(x - 4a)^3H(x - 4a).$$

The impulse function. In certain problems, the concept of an *impulse* is an idealization of great importance. Consider the function $y = 1/\varepsilon$ for $a < x < a + \varepsilon$ and zero elsewhere. Its Laplace transform is

$$\mathscr{L}(y) = \int_a^{a+\varepsilon} \frac{e^{-sx}}{\varepsilon} \, dx = \frac{e^{-s(a+\varepsilon)} - e^{-sa}}{-\varepsilon s}.$$

As $\varepsilon \to 0$, the function merely becomes an infinite spike at $x = a$, but such that the area under the function remains unity. This idealized function is known as *Dirac's delta function* $\delta(x - a)$, and we have

$$\mathscr{L}[\delta(x - a)] = \lim e^{-sa}\left(\frac{e^{-s\varepsilon} - 1}{-\varepsilon s}\right) = e^{-sa}.$$

If $a = 0$, the impulse occurs at the origin; we have $\mathscr{L}[\delta(x)] = 1$.

Example 40 At the time $t = 0$, a large voltage V is applied for a short time ε to a series $R - L - C$ circuit. Idealizing this as an impulsive voltage $E = V\varepsilon$ at $t = 0$, find the resulting current in the circuit, assuming that no charge or current is present initially, and that $CR^2 < 4L$.

The differential equations for the circuit are

$$L\frac{dj}{dt} + Rj + \frac{q}{C} = \text{E.M.F.}, \quad j = \frac{dq}{dt},$$

where q is the charge on the condenser. The Laplace transforms are

$$(Ls + R)\mathscr{L}(j) + \mathscr{L}(q)/C = E, \quad \mathscr{L}(j) = s\mathscr{L}(q),$$

where E is the transform of the impulse at $t = 0$. Eliminating $\mathscr{L}(q)$, we obtain

$$\mathscr{L}(j) = \frac{Es}{Ls^2 + Rs + C^{-1}} = \frac{(E/L)s}{\left(s + \dfrac{R}{2L}\right)^2 + \dfrac{1}{CL} - \dfrac{R^2}{4L^2}} = \frac{(E/L)s}{\left(s + \dfrac{R}{2L}\right)^2 + \alpha^2}$$

say, where α is real. Hence

$$\mathscr{L}(j) = \frac{\dfrac{E}{L}\left(s + \dfrac{R}{2L}\right) - \dfrac{ER}{2L^2}}{\left(s + \dfrac{R}{2L}\right)^2 + \alpha^2},$$

yielding

$$j(t) = \frac{E}{L}e^{-Rt/2L}\cos\alpha t - \frac{ER}{2L^2}e^{-Rt/2L}\frac{\sin\alpha t}{\alpha}$$

$$= \frac{E}{L\alpha}e^{-Rt/2L}(\alpha\cos\alpha t - \frac{R}{2L}\sin\alpha t).$$

EXERCISES

(1)*. If a and b are arbitrary constants, find the second order differential equation whose solution is $y = a \sec x + b \tan x$.

Solve the following differential equations, either generally, or satisfying the specified conditions.

(2). $D^2y + 2Dy - 15y = 0$.

(3). $D^2y - 6Dy + 9y = 0$.

(4). $D^2y - 4Dy + 13y = 0$.

(5)*. $a^2D^2y - 2abDy + 4b^2y = 4b^3x^2$.

(6)*. $5D^2y + 2Dy + y = 2x + 3$, $y = -1$, $Dy = 0$ when $x = 0$.

(7)*. $D^2y - 10Dy + 24y = 24x$, $y = Dy = 0$ when $x = 0$.

(8)*. $D^2y + Dy - 2y = 3e^{-x} - 1$, $y = 0$ when $x = 0$ and y is finite when $x = +\infty$. Find the values of x for which (i) $y = 0$, (ii) $Dy = 0$, (iii) $D^2y = 0$, and sketch the graph of y against x for $x \geqslant 0$.

(9)*. $D^2y + 2Dy + 5y = 4e^{-x}$, $y = Dy = 0$ when $x = 0$.

(10)*. $D^2y - Dy - 2y = e^{2x}$.

(11)*. $D^2y + 3Dy + 2y = e^{-x}$.

(12)*. $4D^2y - 4Dy + y = 8e^{\frac{1}{2}x}$, $y = 0$, $Dy = 1$ when $x = 0$.

(13)*. $D^2y + 4Dy + 4y = x^2 + e^{-2x}$, $y = \frac{1}{2}$, $Dy = 0$ when $x = 0$.

(14)*. $D^2y - 9y = \cosh 3x + x^2$.

(15)*. $D^2y - 6Dy + 9y = e^{3x} + e^{-3x}$.

(16)*. $D^2y + 4Dy + 4y = \cosh 2x$.

(17)*. $D^2y - 6Dy + 9y = \cosh 3x$, $y = Dy = 0$ when $x = 0$.

(18)*. $D^2y + 6Dy + 9y = e^{-3x} \cosh 3x$.

(19)*. $D^2y + 3Dy + 2y = xe^{-x}$.

(20)*. $D^2y - 2Dy + y = (x + 1)^2e^{2x}$.

(21)*. $D^2y - Dy - 6y = xe^{3x}$.

(22)*. $D^2y - 3Dy + 2y = xe^x$.

(23)*. $D^2y - 4Dy + 4y = 6xe^{2x}$.

(24)*. $D^2y - 2Dy + y = e^x/(1 - x)^2$.

(25)*. $D^2y - 4Dy - 5y = \cos x$.

(26)*. $D^2y + 4Dy + 5y = 8 \cos x$, $y = Dy = 0$ when $x = 0$.

(27)*. $D^2y + 4Dy + 5y = 40 \sin 3x$, $y = Dy = 0$ when $x = 0$.

(28)*. $D^2y + 4y = 12 \cos 4x$, $y = 1$ when $x = \frac{1}{4}\pi$, $y = -3$ when $x = \frac{1}{2}\pi$. Hence show that y is a maximum when $x = n\pi \pm \pi/6$, where n is an integer.

(29)*. $D^2y + 4y = x + \cos 2x$, $y = 0$ when $x = 0$.

(30)*. $2D^2y + 3Dy - 2y = x^2 + \sin 2x$.

(31)*. $D^2y - 2Dy + y = \cos x + \sin x$.

(32)*. $D^2y - 2Dy + 2y = e^x \sin x$, $y = 0$ when $x = 0$ and $\frac{1}{2}\pi$.

(33) *. $D^2y + 2Dy + 5y = 34 \sin x \cos x$.

(34) *. $D^2y + 2Dy + 3y = e^{-x} \cos x$.

(35) *. $2D^2y + Dy - y = e^x \sin 2x$.

(36) *. $D^2y + 2Dy + 5y = x + e^{-x} \cos 3x$.

(37) *. $D^2y - 2Dy + 2y = e^x(1 + \sin x)$, $y = 0$ when $x = 0$ and $\frac{1}{2}\pi$.

(38) *. $D^3y - Dy = 1$, $y = 0$ when $x = 0, +a, -a$.

(39) *. $D^3y - 2D^2y - Dy + 2y = x^2 + 3x$.

(40) *. $D^3y + Dy - 2y = e^{-x}$.

(41) *. $D^3y - 8y = 16 \sin 2x$.

(42) *. $D^3y + D^2y + Dy + y = \cos x$, $y = Dy = D^2y = 0$ when $x = 0$.

(43) *. $D^3y - 3D^2y + 4y = e^{2x} \sin x$.

(44) *. $D^3y + 2D^2y + Dy + 2y = e^x + \cos 2x$.

(45) *. $1 + (Dy)^2 = 2xDyD^2y$, $y = Dy = 0$ when $x = 1$.

(46) *. $2D^2y + (Dy)^2 + y = 0$, $y = 1$, $Dy = 0$ when $x = 0$.

(47) *. $(1 + y^2)D^2y = y[1 + (Dy)^2]$, $y = 1$, $Dy = 0$ when $x = 0$.

(48) *. If an e.m.f. $E \sin \omega t$ is applied to a circuit containing a resistance R, an inductance L and a condenser of capacity C, the charge q on the condenser at time t satisfies $LD^2q + RDq + q/C = E \sin \omega t$, where $D \equiv d/dt$ and the current $j = Dq$. If $R = 2\sqrt{(L/C)}$, solve the equation for q, and show that in the steady state the maximum value of the current is $\omega EC/(1 + LC\omega^2)$.

By changing either the dependent or independent variable as indicated, solve the following differential equations subject to any specified conditions.

(49) *. $x^2D^2y + (3x^2 + 4x)Dy + (2x^2 + 6x + 2)y = 0$, $\quad y = z/x^2$; $\ y = e^{-2}$ when $x = 1$ and $y = e^2$ when $x = -1$.

(50) *. $x^2D^2y + (4x^2 + 6x)Dy + (3x^2 + 12x + 6)y = 0$, $\quad y = z/x^3$; $\ y = 1/e$, $Dy = -4/e$ when $x = 1$.

(51) *. $x^2D^2y + 2x(x + 2)Dy + 2(x + 1)^2y = e^{-x} \cos x$, $y = zx^n$ (find n).

(52) *. $x^2D^2y + xDy + 4x^2y = \frac{1}{4}(y - x^{\frac{5}{2}})$, $y = zx^{-\frac{1}{2}}$.

(53) *. $x^2D^2y + 4x(x + 1)Dy + (8x + 2)y = \cos x$, $y = zx^n$ (find n).

(54) *. $yD^2y + (Dy)^2 = 2y^2$, $y^2 = z$; $\ y = Dy = 1$ when $x = 0$.

(55) *. $4x^2D^2y + 4xDy + (4x^2 - 1)y = 0$, $y = zx^{-\frac{1}{2}}$; $\ y = 0$ when $x = \frac{1}{2}\pi$ and $y = 1$ when $x = \pi$.

(56) *. $4xD^2y + 2(1 - \sqrt{x})Dy - 6y = e^{-2\sqrt{x}}$, $z = \sqrt{x}$.

(57) *. $(x + 1)^2D^2y - 3(x + 1)Dy + 4y = x^2$, $x = e^t - 1$; $\ y = Dy = 0$ when $x = 0$.

(58) *. $(1 + x^2)D^2y + xDy + y = 1 + x^2$, $x = \sinh t$; $\ y = Dy = 0$ when $x = 0$.

(59) *. $4xD^2y + 2Dy + y = 2x$, $z = \sqrt{x}$.

(60) *. $x^2D^2y - 10xDy + 24y = 6x^2$, $x = e^t$; $\ y = 1$, $Dy = 1$ when $x = 1$.

(61) *. $4x^2D^2y - 3y = 4x^2$.

(62) *. $x^2D^2y + 3xDy + y = 1/x$.

(63) *. $x^2D^2y - 3xDy + 4y = 6x^2 \log x + 6/x$, $y = 0$, $Dy = 1$ when $x = 1$.

(64) *. A circular disc of radius R rotating about its axis has transverse stress y/r at distance r from the axis. When $r = 0$ this stress is given by $(y/r)_0 = \frac{1}{8}CR^2(3 + 1/m)$, where C and m are constants, and at all points of the disc the stress remains finite. It is known that

$$r^2\frac{d^2y}{dr^2} + r\frac{dy}{dr} - y = -Cr^3(1 + 3/m).$$

Using the substitution $r = e^u$, show that at distance r from the axis the transverse stress is given by $\frac{1}{8}C[(3 + 1/m)R^2 - (1 + 3/m)r^2]$.

(65). $x^5D^2y - xy = 1$; $y = ux$, $x = 1/z$.

Solve the following simultaneous differential equations, either generally, or satisfying the specified conditions, ($D \equiv d/dt$).

(66) *. $Dy + ay = x$, $Dx + ax = y$; $x = 0$ and $y = 1$ when $t = 0$.

(67) *. $Dy + y = 3x$, $Dx + 2x = 2y$; $x = 0$ and $Dy = \frac{1}{2}$ when $t = 0$.

(68) *. $Dx + Dy + x = 0$, $2Dx + Dy - y = 1$; $x = y = 0$ when $t = 0$.

(69) *. $(D - 2)^2x = Dy$, $(D + 2)y = e^t$; $x = y = Dx = 0$ when $t = 0$.

(70) *. $Dy + y = z + e^t$, $Dz + z = y + e^t$; $y = 6$ and $z = 0$ when $t = 0$.

(71) *. $Dx + 5x + y = e^{-t}$, $-x + Dy + 3y = e^{-2t}$; $x = \frac{1}{2}$ and $y = \frac{2}{3}$ when $t = 0$. As t increases indefinitely, show that the ratio $x:y$ tends to $2:1$.

(72) *. $D^2x + 2x + 3y = 0$, $D^2y + 2x + y = 0$; $x = y = Dy = 0$ and $Dx = 10$ when $t = 0$.

(73) *. $D^2x + 2Dy + x = a \sin t$, $D^2y + 2Dx + y = a \cos t$; $x = y = Dx = Dy = 0$ when $t = 0$.

(74) *. $4Dx + 5x - 3y = 4e^t$, $4Dy - 5y + 3x = 4e^t$; $x = y = 0$ when $t = 0$.

(75) *. $3Dx + 2x - y = t$, $2Dy + y - x = 5e^{-t}$; $x = y = 0$ when $t = 0$.

(76) *. $D^2x - D^2y + x - y = 5e^{2t}$, $2Dx = Dy - y$; $x = 1$, $y = 2$ and $Dx = 0$ when $t = 0$.

(77) *. $D^2x + 5Dy - 4x = 3 \sin 2t$, $D^2y - 5Dx - 4y = 0$; $x = y = Dy = 0$ and $Dx = 1$ when $t = 0$.

(78) *. $2D^2x + x - y = 3 \cos 2t$, $3D^2y - x + 2y = 0$.

(79) *. Show that the general solution of the equations

$$D^2x = n^2(4y - 5x), \quad D^2y = n^2(4x - 5y)$$

is
$$x = P \sin nt + Q \cos nt + R \sin 3nt + S \cos 3nt,$$
$$y = P \sin nt + Q \cos nt - R \sin 3nt - S \cos 3nt,$$

where P, Q, R, S are arbitrary constants. If when $t = 0$, $x = a$, $y = Dx = Dy = 0$ show that $y/x = \tan nt \tan 2nt$.

(80) *. If x, y, z are functions of t such that

$$x + y + z = t^2, \quad 2Dx + Dz = y - 3x, \quad 3Dy + Dz = x + y,$$

show that $D^2x + 3Dx - 4x = -6$. Find x, y, z if $x = 0$, $y = 2$ when $t = 0$.

In questions (81)–(92), $D \equiv d/dt$.

(81) *. The equation $D^2x + 2\lambda Dx + (\lambda^2 + n^2)x = 0$, $(n \neq 0)$ represents the damped oscillation of a particle moving in a straight line, x being the displacement at time t. Find x in terms of t, given that $x = a$ and $Dx = 0$ when $t = 0$.

If the equation of motion is $D^2x + 4Dx + 5x = 2a \sin t$, prove that, with the same initial conditions as before,

$$x = \tfrac{1}{4}ae^{-2t}(9 \sin t + 5 \cos t) + \tfrac{1}{4}a(\sin t - \cos t),$$

and show that the particle ultimately describes simple harmonic oscillations of amplitude $\tfrac{1}{4}a\sqrt 2$.

(82). A particle P, of mass m, moves in a straight line through a point O under the action of (i) a force $m(k^2 + n^2)x$ towards O, where $x = OP$ and k, n are positive constants; (ii) a resistance whose magnitude is $2km$ times the speed of the particle; (iii) a force $mae^{-kt} \cos pt$ in the direction of increasing x. Write down the equation of motion of the particle and find x in terms of t given that $x = Dx = 0$ when $t = 0$. From this solution find the solution with the same initial conditions when $p = n$.

(83)*. An elastic string AB, of unstretched length a, may be stretched to a total length $2a$ by the application of a force mg. The string has a mass m at its lower end B and its upper end A is oscillating in a vertical line about a fixed point O. At time t the distances of A and B below O are $\alpha \sin \omega t$ and $(2a + x)$ respectively where α is small. If the air resistance to the motion is given by $2kmn$ times the velocity of B derive the equation of motion of the mass m in a simple form using the notation $n^2 = g/a$. If $0 < k < 1$, show that, whatever the initial conditions, x tends to

$$\alpha n^2 \sin (\omega t - \varepsilon)/[\sqrt\{(n^2 - \omega^2)^2 + 4k^2n^2\omega^2\}]$$

as t increases. Draw a diagram illustrating the variation of $\tan \varepsilon$ against ω/n in the case $k = \tfrac{1}{2}$ for the range $0 \leqslant \omega/n \leqslant \infty$.

(84). A particle of mass m is suspended from the lower end of a light elastic string of natural length a and modulus $(k^2 + p^2)am$. When the particle is hanging in equilibrium, the upper end of the string is moved vertically, so that its displacement at time t is $\alpha \sin [t\sqrt(k^2 + p^2)]$; while the particle is acted on by a resistance $2mkv$ when the speed of the particle is v. It is understood that α is small enough for the string always to be in tension. If the amplitude of the ultimate oscillations of the particle is to lie in the range $(\tfrac{3}{8}d, \tfrac{5}{8}d)$, show that k must satisfy the inequalities $\tfrac{3}{4}k < p < \tfrac{4}{3}k$.

(85)*. A particle of mass m, suspended from the lower end of a light spiral spring, has a natural period of $2\pi/n$. When the particle hangs in equilibrium the upper end of the spring is moved vertically so that its displacement measured vertically downwards is $a \sin nt$ at time t, The amplitude of the resulting oscillation is prevented from becoming excessive by the application of a frictional resistance which is of magnitude mkv, $(k < 2n)$, when the speed of the particle is v. Prove that the depth of the particle at time t below its equilibrium position satisfies the differential equation $D^2x + kDx + n^2x = n^2a \sin nt$.

Find the displacement of the particle at time t after the disturbing motion began and show that the ultimate motion of the particle will be a simple harmonic oscillation of amplitude less than $\tfrac{3}{2}a$ provided that $k > \tfrac{4}{3}n$.

(86)*. A particle of mass m is attached to the lower extremity of a light elastic string of unstretched length a, and modulus of elasticity λ. The upper end of the string is caused to move in a vertical line, with simple harmonic motion of period $2\pi/p$ and amplitude b. Show that if $a + x$ is the length of the string at time t, then x satisfies the equation $D^2x + \lambda x/ma = g + bp^2 \sin (pt + \alpha)$, where α is a constant.

Solve this equation, and show that if $\lambda = map^2$, the amplitude of the oscillations of the particle increases without limit.

(87)*. A light elastic string AB, of natural length a and modulus of elasticity $2mg$, lies on a smooth horizontal table. The end A of the string is fixed to the table and a particle of mass m is attached to the string at B. An inelastic string BC passes over the smooth edge of the table and then under a small movable pulley of mass m. The end C is fixed so that the two parts of the string supporting the pulley are vertical and the strings lie in a vertical plane perpendicular to the edge of the table. The system is released when $AB = a$ and the string BC is taut. If x is the length of AB after time t, show that $5aD^2x + 2g(4x - 5a) = 0$.

Solve this equation to show that the particle oscillates, and find the period and the amplitude of the oscillation. What is the amplitude of the oscillation of the pulley?

(88)*. A light string of length $4a$ has its ends A and B attached to fixed points on a smooth horizontal table and is under constant tension T. Masses $2m$ and m are attached to points P and Q of the string respectively, where $AP = PQ = a$. If the system performs small oscillations in which the displacements x and y of P and Q, respectively, are horizontal and perpendicular to the string, show that x and y satisfy the simultaneous differential equations

$$D^2x + \omega^2(2x - y) = 0, \; D^2y + \omega^2(3y - 2x) = 0 \text{ where } \omega = \sqrt{(T/2ma)}.$$

Find the general solution for x and show that it is the sum of two simple harmonic oscillations with periods $2\pi/\omega$ and π/ω. If, at time $t = 0$, $x = y = 0$ and $Dx = Dy = V$, show that, at time t, $x = y = (V/\omega) \sin \omega t$.

(89)*. A taut string connects the points A and D on a smooth horizontal table. To the string are attached two equal masses m at points B and C such that $AB = a$, $BC = sa$, $CD = a$, and the tension of the string in the equilibrium position is mn^2a. If the particles are disturbed from this position and perform small horizontal transverse oscillations so that x, y are their displacements at time t write down the equations of motion of the particles.

Hence show that the solutions for x, y are of the form

$$x = A_1 \cos (p_1t + \varepsilon_1) + A_2 \cos (p_2t + \varepsilon_2),$$

$$y = A_1 \cos (p_1t + \varepsilon_1) + A_2 \cos (p_2t + \varepsilon_2)$$

where $p_1 = n\sqrt{(1 + 2/s)}$, $p_2 = n$. Sketch the two normal modes of oscillation.

(90)*. A light string of length $7a$ has two particles of equal mass m attached to one end and to a point distance $4a$ from that end. It hangs freely from the other end under gravity. If the system performs small oscillations in which the particles move approximately horizontally in the same vertical plane, show that the equations for the displacements x, y of the upper and lower particles are

$$(12D^2 + 11n^2)x = 3n^2y, \; (4D^2 + n^2)y = n^2x$$

where $n^2 = g/a$. Prove that x and y are each the sum of two oscillations of periods $2\pi/n$, $2\pi(\sqrt{6})/n$. Find x and y in terms of t, given that, at $t = 0$, $Dx = Dy = 0$, $x = b$, $y = 0$.

(91)*. Two particles, A and B, of equal mass m are attached to the ends of a light spring which exerts a tension of amount s per unit extension. Initially the particles are at rest on a smooth horizontal table with the spring just taut, and a constant force of magnitude sa is then applied to particle B in the direction AB. Obtain the differential equations for the displacements, x and y, of the particles A and B respectively at time t, and show that $y + x = \frac{1}{4}a\omega^2t^2$, $y - x = \frac{1}{2}a(1 - \cos \omega t)$, where $m\omega^2 = 2s$.

(92)*. Three particles, each of mass m, are attached at equal intervals a to a light string of length $4a$ which is stretched to a tension T and fixed at the ends on a smooth horizontal table. Write down the equations of motion for small horizontal transverse vibrations of the system.

Show that solutions exist in the form $x = \alpha \cos(pt + \varepsilon)$, $y = \beta \cos(pt + \varepsilon)$, $z = \gamma \cos(pt + \varepsilon)$, where x, y, z are the transverse displacements of the particles at time t, and $\alpha, \beta, \gamma, p, \varepsilon$ are constants, provided that p^2 has one of the values $2n^2$, $(2 + \sqrt{2})n^2$, $(2 - \sqrt{2})n^2$, where $n^2 = T/ma$. Determine $\alpha:\beta:\gamma$ in each case and illustrate the results with rough sketches.

Find two independent power-series solutions of the following differential equations, expressing the series in closed form when possible.

(93)*. $x^2D^2y + xDy + (x^2 - \tfrac{1}{4})y = 0$.

(94)*. $D^2y + x^2y = 0$.

(95)*. $2xD^2y + (3 - 2x)Dy - 2y = 0$.

(96)*. $2x^2D^2y + (x^3 - x)Dy + y = 0$.

(97)*. $x^2D^2y + x^2Dy + (x - 2)y = 0$.

(98)*. $2x(1 + x)D^2y + (1 + 6x)Dy + 2y = 0$.

(99)*. $xD^2y + (2 - x^2)Dy + xy = 0$.

(100)*. $(x^2 + 2x)D^2y + Dy - 2y = 0$.

(101)*. $2xD^2y + (1 - x)Dy + 2y = 0$.

(102)*. $(1 - x^2)D^2y - 7xDy - 9y = 0$.

(103)*. $2x^2D^2y + (2x^2 - x)Dy + y = 0$.

(104)*. $(1 - x^2)D^2y - 4xDy - 2y = 0$.

(105)*. $4xD^2y + (4x + 3)Dy + y = 0$.

(106)*. $(1 - x^2)D^2y + xDy - y = 0$.

(107)*. $(1 - x^2)D^2y - xDy + 4y = 0$.

---

(108). Find the Laplace transforms of the following functions: (i) $1 + 2x + 3x^2$; (ii) $1 - e^{-x} - xe^{-x}$; (iii) $\sinh 2x - \sin 2x$; (iv) $3e^x - \tfrac{1}{3}x^3 - x^2 - 2x - 3$.

(109). Find the inverse transforms of the following:
(i) $1/s(s - 2)$; (ii) $(s^3 - 5s + 4)/s^2(s - 1)^2$; (iii) $(s + 3)/(s^2 - 1)(s - 2)$;
(iv) $(s + 7)/(s^2 + 6x + 10)$; (v) $1/s^2(s^2 + 4)$.

(110). Using the Laplace transform solve the equations with the given conditions: (6), (7), (9), (12), (13), (17), (26), (27), (42), (66), (67), (68), (69), (70), (72), (73).

(111). Verify the Laplace transforms of the following functions with period 2π:

If $y = 1(0 < x < X)$, $y = 0(X < x < 2\pi)$, $\mathscr{L}(y) = \dfrac{1 - e^{-sX}}{s(1 - e^{-2\pi s})}$.

If $y = x \ (0 < x < 2\pi)$, $\mathscr{L}(y) = \dfrac{1}{s^2} - \dfrac{2\pi e^{-2\pi s}}{s(1 - e^{-2\pi s})}$.

If $y = \sin \tfrac{1}{2}x \ (0 < x < 2\pi)$, $\mathscr{L}(y) = \dfrac{\coth s\pi}{2(s^2 + \tfrac{1}{4})}$.

If $y = \sin x \ (0 < x < \pi)$, $y = 0 \ (\pi < x < 2\pi)$, $\mathscr{L}(y) = \dfrac{1}{(s^2 + 1)(1 - e^{-\pi s})}$.

(112). If $y = n$ for $(n - 1)l < x < nl$ where $n = 1, 2, 3, \ldots$, prove that
$$\mathscr{L}(y) = 1/[s(1 - e^{-sl})].$$

ANSWERS TO EXERCISES

(1). $D^2y - \tan x \, Dy - y \sec^2 x = 0.$ (2). $y = Ae^{3x} + Be^{-5x}.$

(3). $y = (Ax + B)e^{3x}.$ (4) $y = e^{2x}(A \cos 3x + B \sin 3x).$

(5). $y = ax + bx^2 + e^{bx/a}[A \cos (\sqrt{3} \, bx/a) + B \sin (\sqrt{3} \, bx/a)].$

(6). $y = 2x - e^{-x} \sin 2x - 1.$ (7). $y = \frac{5}{12} + x - \frac{3}{4}e^{4x} + \frac{1}{3}e^{6x}.$

(8). $y = e^{-2x} - \frac{3}{2}e^{-x} + \frac{1}{2},$ (i) 0, log 2, (ii) log $\frac{4}{3}$, (iii) log $\frac{8}{3}$.

(9). $y = e^{-x}(1 - \cos 2x).$ (10). $y = Ae^{-x} + Be^{2x} + \frac{1}{3}xe^{2x}.$

(11). $y = Ae^{-2x} + (B + x)e^{-x}.$ (12). $y = (x + x^2)e^{\frac{1}{2}x}.$

(13). $y = (\frac{1}{8} + \frac{3}{4}x)e^{-2x} + \frac{1}{2}x^2 e^{-2x} + \frac{3}{8} - \frac{1}{2}x + \frac{1}{4}x^2.$

(14). $y = Ae^{3x} + Be^{-3x} + \frac{1}{6}x \sinh 3x - \frac{1}{9}(x^2 - \frac{2}{9}).$

(15). $y = (Ax + B)e^{3x} + \frac{1}{2}x^2e^{3x} + \frac{1}{36}e^{-3x}.$

(16). $y = (Ax + B)e^{-2x} + \frac{1}{32}e^{2x} + \frac{1}{4}x^2e^{-2x}.$

(17). $y = (Ax + B)e^{3x} + \frac{1}{72}e^{-3x} + \frac{1}{4}x^2e^{3x}.$

(18). $y = (Ax + B)e^{-3x} + \frac{1}{18} + \frac{1}{18}e^{-6x}.$

(19). $y = Ae^{-x} + Be^{-2x} + \frac{1}{2}(x^2 - 2x)e^{-x}.$

(20). $y = (Ax + B)e^x + e^{2x}(x^2 - 2x + 3).$

(21). $y = Ae^{3x} + Be^{-2x} + e^{3x}(5x^2 - 2x)/50.$

(22). $y = Ae^x + Be^{2x} - \frac{1}{2}(x^2 + 2x)e^x.$ (23). $y = (Ax + B)e^{2x} + x^3e^{2x}.$

(24). $y = (Ax + B)e^x - e^x \log (1 - x).$

(25). $y = Ae^{5x} + Be^{-x} - (3 \cos x + 2 \sin x)/26.$

(26). $y = \cos x + \sin x - e^{-2x}(\cos x + 3 \sin x).$

(27). $y = 3e^{-2x}(\cos x + 3 \sin x) - \sin 3x - 3 \cos 3x.$

(28). $y = 2 \cos 2x - \cos 4x.$ (29). $y = \frac{1}{4}x(1 + \sin 2x) + A \sin 2x.$

(30). $y = Ae^{-2x} + Be^{\frac{1}{2}x} - \frac{1}{4}(2x^2 + 6x + 13) - (5 \sin 2x + 3 \cos 2x)/68.$

(31). $y = (Ax + B)e^x + \frac{1}{2}(\cos x - \sin x).$ (32). $y = -\frac{1}{2} xe^x \cos x.$

(33). $y = e^{-x}(A \cos 2x + B \sin 2x) + \sin 2x - 4 \cos 2x.$

(34). $y = e^{-x}(A \cos \sqrt{2}x + B \sin \sqrt{2}x) + e^{-x} \cos x.$

(35). $y = Ae^{\frac{1}{2}x} + Be^{-x} - e^x(3 \sin 2x + 5 \cos 2x)/68.$

(36). $y = e^{-x}(A \cos 2x + B \sin 2x) + \frac{1}{5}x - \frac{2}{25} - \frac{1}{5}e^{-x} \cos 3x.$

(37). $y = e^x(1 - \cos x - \sin x) - \frac{1}{2}x \cos x \, e^x.$ (38). $y = a \sinh x/\sinh a - x.$

(39). $y = Ae^x + Be^{-x} + Ce^{2x} + \frac{1}{2}x^2 + 2x + 2.$

(40). $y = Ae^x + e^{-\frac{3}{2}x}(B \cos \frac{1}{2}\sqrt{7}x + C \sin \frac{1}{2}\sqrt{7}x) - \frac{1}{4}e^{-x}.$

(41). $y = Ae^{2x} + e^{-x}(B \cos \sqrt{3}x + C \sin \sqrt{3}x) + \cos 2x - \sin 2x.$

(42). $y = -\frac{1}{4}e^{-x} + \frac{1}{4}\cos x + \frac{1}{4}x(\sin x - \cos x).$

(43). $y = Ae^{-x} + (Bx + C)e^{2x} + \frac{1}{10}e^{2x}(\cos x - 3 \sin x).$

(44). $y = Ae^{-2x} + B \cos x + C \sin x + \frac{1}{6}e^x - \frac{1}{12}(\cos 2x + \sin 2x).$

(45). $y = \frac{2}{3}(x - 1)^{\frac{3}{2}}.$ (46). $y = \frac{1}{4}(4 - x^2).$

(47). $x = \sqrt{2} \log [y + \sqrt{(y^2 - 1)}].$

(48). $q = (A + Bt)e^{-t/\sqrt{(LC)}} + E[(C^{-1} - L\omega^2) \sin \omega t - 2\sqrt{(L/C)}\omega \cos \omega t]/$
     $(C^{-1} + L\omega^2)^2.$ (49). $y = e^{-2x}/x^2.$ (50). $y = e^{-x}/x^3.$ (51). $n = -2;$
     $y = e^{-x}(A \cos x + B \sin x)/x^2 + \frac{1}{2}x^{-1}e^{-x} \sin x.$

(52). $y = x^{-\frac{1}{2}}(A \cos 2x + B \sin 2x) - x^{\frac{3}{2}}/16.$

(53). $n = -2;$ $y = [A + Be^{-4x} + \frac{1}{17}(4 \sin x - \cos x)]/x^2.$ (54). $y = e^x.$

(55). $y = -\sqrt{(\pi/x)} \cos x.$ (56). $y = Ae^{3\sqrt{x}} + Be^{-2\sqrt{x}} - \frac{1}{5}\sqrt{x}e^{-2\sqrt{x}}.$

(57). $y = (A + Bt + \frac{1}{2}t^2)e^{2t} - 2e^t + \frac{1}{4}, A = \frac{7}{4}, B = -\frac{3}{2}.$

(58). $y = \frac{3}{5} + \frac{1}{5}x^2 - \frac{3}{5} \cos (\sinh^{-1} x).$

(59). $y = A \cos \sqrt{x} + B \sin \sqrt{x} + 2x - 4$.   (60). $y = x^2 + \frac{1}{5}x^3 - \frac{1}{5}x^8$.

(61). $y = Ax^{-\frac{1}{2}} + Bx^{\frac{3}{2}} + \frac{4}{5}x^2$.   (62). $y = (A \log x + B)/x + \frac{1}{2}(\log x)^2/x$.

(63). $y = (A \log x + B)x^2 + x^2(\log x)^3 + 2/3x$, $A = 3$, $B = -\frac{2}{3}$.

(65). $y = x(Ae^{1/x} + Be^{-1/x} - 2 - x^{-2})$.

(66). $x = e^{-at} \sinh t$, $y = e^{-at} \cosh t$.

(67). $x = \frac{1}{5}e^{-4t} - \frac{1}{5}e^t$, $y = -\frac{1}{5}e^{-4t} - \frac{3}{10}e^t$.

(68). $x = \sin t$, $y = \cos t - \sin t - 1$.

(69). $x = (\frac{1}{2}t - \frac{3}{8})e^{2t} + \frac{1}{8}e^t + \frac{1}{24}e^{-2t}$, $y = \frac{1}{3}(e^t - e^{-2t})$.

(70). $y = e^t + 3e^{-2t} + 2$, $z = e^t - 3e^{-2t} + 2$.

(71). $x = (-\frac{1}{4}t + \frac{19}{36})e^{-4t} - \frac{1}{4}e^{-2t} + \frac{2}{9}e^{-t}$, $y = (\frac{1}{4}t - \frac{7}{36})e^{-4t} + \frac{3}{4}e^{-2t} + \frac{1}{9}e^{-t}$.

(72). $x = 3 \sin 2t + 4 \sinh t$, $y = 2 \sin 2t - 4 \sinh t$.

(73). $x = \frac{1}{2}a(\sin t - \sinh t)$, $y = \frac{1}{2}a(\cosh t - \cos t)$.

(74). $x = \frac{1}{4}(te^t + 3 \sinh t)$, $y = \frac{1}{4}(3te^t + \sinh t)$.

(75). $x = -e^{-t} + 6e^{-t/6} + t - 5 - te^{-t}$, $y = -2e^{-t} + 9e^{-t/6} + t - 7 + te^{-t}$.

(76). $x = -\frac{8}{3}e^{-t} - \frac{1}{3}e^{2t} + 4 \cos t - 2 \sin t$,
$y = -\frac{8}{3}e^{-t} - \frac{4}{3}e^{2t} + 6 \cos t + 2 \sin t$.

(77). $x = \frac{1}{6} \sin 4t - \sin t + \frac{2}{3} \sin 2t$, $y = -\frac{1}{6} \cos 4t + \cos t - \frac{5}{6} \cos 2t$.

(78). $x = A \cos t + B \sin t + C \cos t/\sqrt{6} + D \sin t/\sqrt{6} - \frac{10}{23} \cos 2t$,
$y = -A \cos t - B \sin t + \frac{2}{3}C \cos t/\sqrt{6} + \frac{2}{3}D \sin t/\sqrt{6} + \frac{1}{23} \sin 2t$.

(80). $x = \frac{3}{2}(1 - e^{-4t})$, $y = \frac{1}{2}(4t - 5 - e^{-4t})$, $z = t^2 - 2t - 4 + 2e^{-4t}$.

(81). $x = ae^{-\lambda t}(n \cos nt + \lambda \sin nt)/n$.

(82). $D^2x + 2kDx + (k^2 + n^2)x = ae^{-kt} \cos pt$, $x = ae^{-kt}[\cos pt - \cos nt - (k/n) \sin nt]/(n^2 - p^2)$, $x = (at/2p)e^{-kt} \sin pt$.

(83). $D^2x + 2knDx + n^2x = \alpha n^2 \sin \omega t$.

(85). $x = e^{-\frac{1}{2}kt} \left[\dfrac{na}{k} \cos [\frac{1}{2}t\sqrt{(4n^2 - k^2)}] + \dfrac{na}{\sqrt{(4n^2 - k^2)}} \sin [\frac{1}{2}t\sqrt{(4n^2 - k^2)}] \right]$
$- \dfrac{na}{k} \cos nt$.

(86). $x = A \cos [t\sqrt{(\lambda/ma)}] + B \sin [t\sqrt{(\lambda/ma)}] + gma/\lambda + mabp^2 \sin(pt + \alpha)/(\lambda - map^2)$.

(87). $x = \frac{1}{4}a\{5 - \cos [t\sqrt{(8g/5a)}]\}$, $\pi\sqrt{(5a/2g)}$, $\frac{1}{4}a$, $\frac{1}{4}a$.

(88). $x, y = (A, A) \cos \omega t + (B, B) \sin \omega t + (C, -2C) \cos 2\omega t + (D, -2D) \sin 2\omega t$.

(89). $D^2x + n^2(1 + s)x/s + n^2y/s = 0$, $D^2y + n^2(1 + s)y/s - n^2x/s = 0$.

(90). $x = b(9 \cos nt + \cos nt/\sqrt{6})/10$, $y = b(-3 \cos nt + 3 \cos nt/\sqrt{6})/10$.

(91). $mD^2x + sx - sy = 0$, $mD^2y + sy - sx = sa$.

(92). $amD^2x = T(-2x + y)$, $amD^2y = T(x - 2y + z)$, $amD^2z = T(y - 2z)$;
$1:0:1$, $1: \pm\sqrt{2}:1$.   (93). $(\sin x)/\sqrt{x}$, $(\cos x)/\sqrt{x}$.

(94). $y_1 = 1 - \dfrac{1.2}{4!}x^4 + \dfrac{1.2.5.6}{8!}x^8 - \dfrac{1.2.5.6.9.10}{12!}x^{12} + \dots$,

$y_2 = x - \dfrac{2.3}{5!}x^5 + \dfrac{2.3.6.7}{9!}x^9 - \dfrac{2.3.6.7.10.11}{13!}x^{13} + \dots$.

(95). $y_1 = e^x/\sqrt{x}$, $y_2 = 1 + \dfrac{2x}{3} + \dfrac{(2x)^2}{3.5} + \dfrac{(2x)^3}{3.5.7} + \dfrac{(2x)^4}{3.5.7.9} + \dots$.

(96). $y_1 = x - \dfrac{1}{2.5}x^3 + \dfrac{1.3}{2.4.5.9}x^5 - \dots$,

$y_2 = x^{\frac{1}{2}}\left(1 - \dfrac{1}{3.4}x^2 + \dfrac{1.5}{3.4.7.8}x^4 - \dots\right)$.

(97). $y_1 = 1/x$, $y_2 = x^2\left(\frac{1}{3} - \frac{1}{4}x + \frac{1}{5.2!}x^2 - \frac{1}{6.3!}x^3 + \frac{1}{7.4!}x^4 - \ldots\right)$.

(98). $y_1 = 1 - \frac{2}{1}x + \frac{2.4}{1.3}x^2 - \frac{2.4.6}{1.3.5}x^3 + \frac{2.4.6.8}{1.3.5.7}x^4 - \ldots$,

$\qquad y_2 = x^{\frac{1}{2}}\left(1 - \frac{3}{2}x + \frac{3.5}{2.4}x^2 - \frac{3.5.7}{2.4.6}x^3 + \frac{3.5.7.9}{2.4.6.8}x^4 - \ldots\right)$.

(99). $y_1 = x - 1/x$, $y_2 = 1 - \frac{1}{3!}x^2 - \frac{1}{5!}x^4 - \frac{1.3}{7!}x^6 - \frac{1.3.5}{9!}x^8 - \ldots$.

(100). $y_1 = 1 + 2x + \frac{2}{3}x^2$, $y_2 = x^{\frac{1}{2}}(1 + \frac{1}{2}x)^{\frac{3}{2}}$.

(101). $y_1 = 3 - 6x + x^2$, $y_2 = x^{\frac{1}{2}}\left(1 + \frac{-3}{3!}x + \frac{-3.-1}{5!}x^2 + \frac{-3.-1.1}{7!}x^3 + \ldots\right)$

(102). $y_1 = 1 + \frac{3^2}{2!}x^2 + \frac{3^2.5^2}{4!}x^4 + \ldots$, $y^2 = x + \frac{4^2}{3!}x^3 + \frac{4^2.6^2}{5!}x^5 + \ldots$.

(103). $y_1 = x^{\frac{1}{2}}e^{-x}$, $y_2 = x\left(1 - \frac{2}{3}x + \frac{1}{1.3.5}(2x)^2 - \frac{1}{1.3.5.7}(2x)^3 + \ldots\right)$.

(104). $1/(1 - x^2)$, $x/(1 - x^2)$.

(105). $y_1 = 1 - \frac{1}{3}x + \frac{1.5}{3.7}\frac{x^2}{2!} - \frac{1.5.9}{3.7.11}\frac{x^3}{3!} + \ldots$,

$\qquad y_2 = x^{\frac{1}{4}}\left(1 - \frac{2}{5}x + \frac{2.6}{5.9}\frac{x^2}{2!} - \frac{2.6.10}{5.9.13}\frac{x^3}{3!} + \ldots\right)$.

(106). $y_1 = x$, $y_2 = 1 + \frac{x^2}{2!} + \frac{1^2.x^4}{4!} + \frac{1^2.3^2.x^6}{6!} + \ldots$.

(107). $y_1 = 1 - 2x^2$, $x\sqrt{(1 - x^2)}$.   (108). (i) $(s^2 + 2s + 6)/s^3$; (ii) $1/s(s + 1)^2$;
(iii) $16/(s^4 - 16)$; (iv) $(s^3 + 2)/s^4(s - 1)$.   (109). (i) $\frac{1}{2}(e^{2x} - 1)$;
(ii) $3 + 4x - 2e^x$; (iii) $-2e^x + \frac{1}{3}e^{-x} + \frac{5}{3}e^{2x}$; (iv) $e^{-3x}(\cos x + 4\sin x)$;
(v) $\frac{1}{4}x - \frac{1}{8}\sin 2x$.

CHAPTER 21

THE SOLUTION OF PARTIAL DIFFERENTIAL EQUATIONS BY THE METHOD OF SEPARATION OF VARIABLES

21.1 The general solution of the wave equation

In one dimension, the *wave equation* is given by

$$\frac{\partial^2 y}{\partial x^2} = \frac{1}{c^2}\frac{\partial^2 y}{\partial t^2}. \tag{1}$$

This equation arises when we consider the *transverse* vibrations of a stretched string.

If the string is displaced slightly from its equilibrium position along Ox, the element AB is of length δx to the first order. Its mass is $\rho\delta x$ where ρ is the mass per unit length of the string. If y is the small transverse displacement of the element at position x and at time t, the rate of change of momentum perpendicular to Ox is $\rho\delta x\,\partial^2 y/\partial t^2$.

If T is the constant tension in the string, its component perpendicular to Ox at A

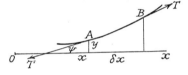

FIG. 125

is $-T\sin\psi$, while at B it is $+T\sin\psi + \delta x\partial(T\sin\psi)/\partial x$. If the string is constrained to vibrate horizontally, these are the only two forces acting on the element; the total force is

$$\frac{\partial}{\partial x}(T\sin\psi)\,\delta x \doteqdot T\frac{\partial}{\partial x}\tan\psi\,\delta x = T\frac{\partial^2 y}{\partial x^2}\,\delta x$$

to the first order, since ψ is small. The equation of motion of the element now yields

$$T\frac{\partial^2 y}{\partial x^2} = \rho\frac{\partial^2 y}{\partial t^2},$$

identical with equation (1) if $c^2 = T/\rho$.

To find the general solution of equation (1), we make the standard change of variable: $u = x + ct$, $v = x - ct$. Using suffixes to denote partial differentiation, we have

$$y_x = y_u + y_v, \quad y_{xx} = y_{uu} + 2y_{uv} + y_{vv},$$
$$y_{tt} = cy_u - cy_v, \quad y_{tt} = c^2 y_{uu} - 2c^2 y_{uv} + c^2 y_{vv}.$$

Equation (1) simplifies to

$$y_{uv} \equiv \frac{\partial^2 y}{\partial u\,\partial v} = 0.$$

495

Partial integration with respect to u yields $\partial y/\partial v = h(v)$, where $h(v)$ is an arbitrary function of v. Integration with respect to v now yields

$$y = f(v) + g(u),$$

where the arbitrary function $h(v)$ integrates to the arbitrary function $f(v)$, and where we add the arbitrary function $g(u)$, which would disappear when differentiated partially with respect to v. Hence

$$y = f(x - ct) + g(x + ct).$$

Consider the solution $y = f(x - ct)$. At $x + \delta x$ and $t + \delta t$, y has the same value as at x and t if $\delta x - c\,\delta t = 0$. Hence the shape represented by the function $f(x - ct)$ moves bodily to the right with speed $dx/dt = c$ and without change of form. Similarly, $y = g(x + ct)$ represents a shape propagated without change of form with speed c to the left.

In particular, let the shape of the string be given by $y = p(x)$ initially when $t = 0$, and let the initial velocity distribution of all points on the string be specified by $\partial y/\partial t = q(x)$ when $t = 0$. Then at $t = 0$, we have

$$p(x) = f(x) + g(x),$$
and
$$q(x) = -cf'(x) + cg'(x)$$

where t is placed equal to 0 after differentiation with respect to t. Integrating, we obtain

$$c^{-1}\int q(x)\,dx = -f(x) + g(x) = r(x),$$

say. It follows that

$$f(x) = \tfrac{1}{2}[p(x) - r(x)], \quad g(x) = \tfrac{1}{2}[p(x) + r(x)].$$

Finally, the argument of f is replaced by $x - ct$ and that of g by $x + ct$, yielding the solution satisfying the initial conditions:

$$y = \tfrac{1}{2}[p(x - ct) - r(x - ct) + p(x + ct) + r(x + ct)].$$

Example 1 When $t = 0$, the initial form of the infinite straight string is given by $y = a(1 - \cos x + 3 \sin x)$, where a is small. The initial velocity distribution for all points is given by $\partial y/\partial t = ca \sin x$. Find y generally as a function of x and t.

Let $y = f(x - ct) + g(x + ct)$, so at $t = 0$ we have

$$y = f(x) + g(x) = a(1 - \cos x + 3 \sin x),$$
$$\partial y/\partial t = -cf'(x) + cg'(x) = ca \sin x,$$
or
$$-f(x) + g(x) = -a \cos x$$

upon integration. Hence

$$f(x) = \tfrac{1}{2}a(1 + 3 \sin x), \quad g(x) = \tfrac{1}{2}a(1 - 2 \cos x + 3 \sin x).$$

Changing the arguments from x to $x - ct$ and $x + ct$ respectively, we obtain the required solution

$$y = \tfrac{1}{2}a[1 + 3\sin(x - ct) + 1 - 2\cos(x + ct) + 3\sin(x + ct)]$$
$$= a[1 - \cos(x + ct) + 3\sin x \cos ct].$$

The object of this present chapter is not to consider general solutions of partial differential equations which require arbitrary functions, but rather to consider a special type of solution known as a *separated* solution. Problems with specified boundary conditions in space as well as initial conditions in time may easily be dealt with using these separated solutions.

21.2   The general theory of separated solutions

The most general linear equation that we shall consider takes the form,

$$f(x)\frac{\partial^2 u}{\partial x^2} + g(x)\frac{\partial u}{\partial x} + h(x)u + j(y)\frac{\partial^2 u}{\partial y^2} + k(y)\frac{\partial u}{\partial y} + m(y)u = 0,$$

where f, g, h, j, k, m are functions of the one variable indicated. In practice, equations are much more simple than this general equation.

Equations of this type possess *separated solutions*, namely solutions of the form

$$u = X(x)\,Y(y),$$

a product of a function X of x alone with a function Y of y alone. Such a particular solution must be distinguished from the general solution. Evidently

$$\partial u/\partial x = X'Y, \quad \partial^2 u/\partial x^2 = X''Y, \quad \partial u/\partial y = XY', \quad \partial^2 u/\partial y^2 = XY'',$$

where a prime attached to X or Y denotes differentiation with respect to x or y respectively. Substitution yields

$$f(x)X''Y + g(x)X'Y + h(x)XY + j(y)XY'' + k(y)XY' + m(y)XY = 0.$$

Finally, division by XY gives

$$\frac{f(x)X'' + g(x)X' + h(x)X}{X} = -\frac{j(y)Y'' + k(y)Y' + m(y)Y}{Y}.$$

The left hand side is a function of x alone, while the right hand side is a function of y alone; since x and y are independent we must conclude that each side of the equation equals a constant, C say, The particular form of this constant (positive, negative, a perfect square, etc.) is chosen to suit the problem. We obtain two equations

$$f(x)X'' + g(x)X' + h(x)X - CX = 0,$$
$$j(y)Y'' + k(y)Y' + m(y)Y + CY = 0.$$

For progress to be made, the solution of these two ordinary differential equations must be easily obtained. If $X_1(x)$ and $X_2(x)$ are two independent solutions of the first equation, and $Y_1(y)$ and $Y_2(y)$ of the second, we have

$$X = AX_1(x) + BX_2(x), \quad Y = DY_1(y) + EY_2(y).$$

The final separated solution for u is

$$u = (AX_1 + BX_2)(DY_1 + EY_2).$$

Clearly, out of the constants A, B, D, E, there are only three that are arbitrary; the parameter C contained implicitly in X_1, X_2, Y_1, Y_2 makes a fourth constant. Different values of C yield different solutions. In particular, a linear combination of such separated solutions for various values of C also satisfies the original linear equation.

Example 2 Find the separated solutions of the equation

$$\frac{\partial^2 y}{\partial x^2} - 4y = \frac{\partial y}{\partial t}$$

such that $y \to 0$ as $x \to \infty$ and as $t \to \infty$.

Assuming a separated solution of the form $y = X(x)T(t)$, we have

$$X''T - 4XT = XT',$$

or
$$(X'' - 4X)/X = T'/T,$$

each side being a constant. Choosing this constant to be $m^2 + 4m$ (designed to simplify the coefficients in the equation for X), we have

$$X'' = (m + 2)^2 X, \quad T' = (m^2 + 4m)T.$$

Hence
$$X = Ae^{(m+2)x} + Be^{-(m+2)x}, \quad T = Ce^{(m^2+4m)t},$$

and
$$y = e^{(m^2+4m)t}[Ae^{(m+2)x} + Be^{-(m+2)x}],$$

the constant C not being required in the product.

To satisfy the condition that $y \to 0$ as $t \to \infty$, we require $m^2 + 4m < 0$, that is, $-4 < m < 0$. If $-4 < m < -2$, we must choose $B = 0$, otherwise $Be^{-(m+2)x}$ would not tend to zero as $x \to \infty$. Hence

$$y = Ae^{(m^2+4m)t}e^{(m+2)x}, \qquad (-4 < m < -2), \tag{2}$$

while if $-2 < m < 0$, we require $A = 0$, yielding

$$y = Be^{(m^2+4m)t}e^{-(m+2)x} \qquad (-2 < m < 0).$$

It is obvious that this second solution merely repeats the first, being symmetrical about $m = -2$. Hence (2) represents all separated solutions with the required property; $m = -3$ is the only possible integer, giving $y = Ae^{-3t}e^{-x}$.

Note: The *separation constant* $m^2 + 4m$ is greater than -4 for real values of m. If we choose the constant to be less than -4, the solution for X consists of sines and cosines; these must be rejected since they do not tend to zero as $x \to \infty$.

Example 3 Find the separated solutions for the equation

$$\frac{\partial^2 u}{\partial r^2} + \frac{1}{r}\frac{\partial u}{\partial r} + \frac{1}{r^2}\frac{\partial^2 u}{\partial \theta^2} = 0.$$

Find the single-valued function u that is finite within the circle $r = 1$, and such that $u = 2 \sin 5\theta - 3 \cos 7\theta$ on the circle $r = 1$.

We assume that $u = R(r)T(\theta)$, where R and T are functions of r and θ respectively. Then

$$R''T + R'T/r + RT''/r^2 = 0,$$

or

$$\frac{R'' + R'/r}{R/r^2} = -\frac{T''}{T}.$$

Each side of this equation is a constant, which we choose to be n^2. Hence

$$R'' + R'/r - n^2 R/r^2 = 0, \qquad T'' + n^2 T = 0.$$

The solution for T is obviously $T = A_n \cos n\theta + B_n \sin n\theta$, while the solution for R is easily found to be $C_n r^n + D_n r^{-n}$. Hence

$$u = (C_n r^n + D_n r^{-n})(A_n \cos n\theta + B_n \sin n\theta), \qquad (3)$$

where n is any number except zero. If $n = 0$, $T'' = 0$ yielding $T = A_0\theta + B_0$, while the equation $R'' + R'/r = 0$ has the solution $R = C_0 + D_0 \log r$. Hence

$$u = (C_0 + D_0 \log r)(A_0\theta + B_0). \qquad (4)$$

An arbitrary linear combination of (3) and (4) for various values of n is also a solution.

We now choose the constants so that as many as possible of the given conditions are satisfied by each separated solution. For u to be single-valued, $\cos n\theta$ and $\sin n\theta$ require n to be an integer; A_0 must be zero since θ is not single-valued. In order that u should be finite when $r = 0$ we require $D_0 = D_n = 0$ and $n \geqslant 0$. The separated solutions must now be of the form

$$u = r^n(A_n \cos n\theta + B_n \sin n\theta) \qquad n \geqslant 0.$$

Hence the most general solution satisfying all these conditions is

$$u = A_0 + \sum_{n=1}^{\infty} r^n(A_n \cos n\theta + B_n \sin n\theta). \qquad (5)$$

Finally, when $r = 1$, we are given that

$$2 \sin 5\theta - 3 \cos 7\theta \equiv A_0 + \sum_{n=1}^{\infty} (A_n \cos n\theta + B_n \sin n\theta).$$

Clearly, we only require $n = 5$ and 7. We choose $A_7 = -3$, $B_5 = 2$; all the other coefficients must vanish. Hence

$$u = -3r^7 \cos 7\theta + 2r^5 \sin 5\theta.$$

Example 4 Repeat example 3, with the boundary condition that $u = U$ for $0 < \theta < \pi$ and zero for $\pi < \theta < 2\pi$ on the circle $r = a$.

In electrostatics, this problem would correspond to finding the potential within a long straight cylindrical tube of radius a, with the top half maintained at the potential U and the lower portion earthed.

Using equation (5), we have, when $r = a$,

$$\left.\begin{array}{l} U(0 < \theta < \pi) \\ 0(\pi < \theta < 2\pi) \end{array}\right\} = A_0 + \sum_{n=1}^{\infty} a^n(A_n \cos n\theta + B_n \sin n\theta).$$

To find the coefficients, we treat the problem as a Fourier series.

A_0 is found by integrating from 0 to 2π:

$$\int_0^\pi U \, d\theta = \int_0^{2\pi} A_0 \, d\theta;$$

yielding $A_0 = \frac{1}{2}U$.

A_n is found by integrating from 0 to 2π after multiplication by $\cos n\theta$:

$$a^n A_n \pi = \int_0^\pi U \cos n\theta \, d\theta = 0.$$

B_n is found by integration from 0 to 2π after multiplication by $\sin n\theta$:

$$a^n B_n \pi = \int_0^\pi U \sin n\theta \, d\theta = U \left[\frac{-\cos n\theta}{n}\right]_0^\pi = \frac{U}{n}[1 - (-1)^n] = \begin{cases} 0 & \text{if } n \text{ is even} \\ 2U/n & \text{if } n \text{ is odd.} \end{cases}$$

Hence

$$u = \tfrac{1}{2}U + \frac{2U}{\pi} \sum \frac{r^n}{na^n} \sin n\theta \qquad\qquad (n \text{ odd})$$

$$= \tfrac{1}{2}U + \frac{2U}{\pi} \sum_{m=1}^{\infty} \frac{r^{2m-1}}{(2m-1)a^{2m-1}} \sin (2m - 1)\theta.$$

21.3   The separated solutions for the wave equation

Let the separated function $y = X(x)T(t)$ satisfy equation (1); we obtain the equation $c^2 X''T = XT''$, or

$$X''/X = T''/c^2T = -n^2,$$

where $-n^2$ is the separation constant. Hence

$$X = A_n \cos nx + B_n \sin nx, \quad T = C_n \cos nct + D_n \sin nct.$$

We usually write this solution in the form

$$y = \genfrac{}{}{0pt}{}{\sin}{\cos} nx \genfrac{}{}{0pt}{}{\sin}{\cos} nct,$$

implying that all the four combinations are possible solutions. We may also write the separated solution in the form

$$y = F_n \cos (nx + \alpha_n) \cos (nct + \beta_n);$$

four constants are involved in each solution.

For a stretched string, the problem is usually stated as follows:

The two ends of the finite string of length l are permanently fixed in space; that is, $y = 0$ for all t when $x = 0$ and $x = l$. When $t = 0$, the shape of the displaced string is given to be $y = f(x)$, while when $t = 0$ the distribution of velocity along the string is given to be $\partial y/\partial t = g(x)$.

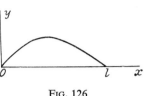

Fig. 126

We find those separated solutions satisfying the end conditions at $x = 0$ and $x = l$; then by using the methods of Fourier analysis we find the constants from the conditions at $t = 0$.

At $x = 0$, $\cos nx \neq 0$; hence $\cos nx$ is rejected, that is, we choose $A_n = 0$. This leaves $X = B_n \sin nx$. At $x = l$, we require $\sin nl = 0$ in order that y should vanish for all t. This implies $nl = m\pi$ (m an integer). Hence the separated solution must be of the form

$$y = \sin (m\pi x/l)[C_m \cos (m\pi ct/l) + D_m \sin (m\pi ct/l)]. \tag{6}$$

These solutions are the normal modes of oscillation of the system. The period is $2l/mc$.

Generally, y must be a linear combination of solutions (6) for all integers m. Obviously only positive integers need be considered; terms with negative integers can be absorbed directly into terms given by the positive integers.

When $t = 0$, we have

$$f(x) = y = \sum_{m=1}^{\infty} C_m \sin \frac{m\pi x}{l}, \quad g(x) = \frac{\partial y}{\partial t} = \sum_{m=1}^{\infty} \frac{m\pi c}{l} D_m \sin \frac{m\pi x}{l}.$$

To find the constants, we multiply by $\sin (m\pi x/l)$ and integrate from 0 to l, obtaining

$$\int_0^l f(x) \sin \frac{m\pi x}{l} \, dx = \tfrac{1}{2} C_m l, \quad \int_0^l g(x) \sin \frac{m\pi x}{l} \, dx = \frac{m\pi c}{l} D_m \cdot \tfrac{1}{2} l.$$

This completes the solution of the problem.

Example 5 When $t = 0$, let the string of length π be at rest, and let its shape be given by $a(\pi x - x^2)$ where a is small.

Proceeding from first principles, we find that the separated solutions are

$$y = \frac{\sin}{\cos} nx \frac{\sin}{\cos} nct.$$

To satisfy the condition $y = 0$ at $x = 0$ we reject $\cos nx$, and to satisfy the condition $y = 0$ at $x = \pi$ we choose n to be a positive integer in order that $\sin n\pi$ should vanish. When $t = 0$, the condition $\partial y/\partial t = 0$ is introduced by rejecting the term $\sin nct$, since its derivative does not vanish. Hence the separated solution reduces to

$$y = C_n \sin nx \cos nct.$$

The general solution is

$$y = \sum_{n=1}^{\infty} C_n \sin nx \cos nct.$$

When $t = 0$, we have

$$a(\pi x - x^2) = \sum_{n=1}^{\infty} C_n \sin nx.$$

Multiplying by $\sin nx$ and integrating from 0 to π, we obtain

$$\tfrac{1}{2}C_n\pi = a\int_0^{\pi} (\pi x - x^2)\sin nx\, dx = a\left[(\pi x - x^2)\frac{\cos nx}{-n} + \int (\pi - 2x)\frac{\cos nx}{n}\, dx\right]_0^{\pi}$$

$$= a\left[(\pi - 2x)\frac{\sin nx}{n^2} + 2\int \frac{\sin nx}{n^2}\, dx\right]_0^{\pi} = \frac{2a}{n^3}\left[-\cos nx\right]_0^{\pi}$$

$$= \frac{2a}{n^3}[1 - (-1)^n] = \begin{cases} 4a/n^3 & \text{if } n \text{ is odd} \\ 0 & \text{if } n \text{ is even.} \end{cases}$$

Hence

$$y = \frac{8a}{\pi}\sum_{m=1}^{\infty} \frac{\sin(2m-1)x \cos(2m-1)ct}{(2m-1)^3}.$$

21.4 The partial differential equation of heat conduction

In deriving this differential equation, we use the following fundamental physical law. *The rate of flow of heat normally across an element of area in a conducting body is proportional to the space-rate of decrease of temperature normally across the area.* If n denotes the normal to the element of area δS (usually n is drawn in the direction of x, y or z), the heat flowing across the area in time δt in the direction of n is $-k(\partial\theta/\partial n)\,\delta S\,\delta t$, where θ is the temperature and k the *conductivity* of the material, regarded as constant. Since the derivative $\partial\theta/\partial n$ is regarded as positive, the minus sign ensures that the heat flows from the hotter to the cooler side of the area element.

Consider the heat flowing in time δt into the volume element with sides δx, δy, δz. If θ is the temperature at the middle of the box, then the temperature at the mid-point of the side $ABCD$ is $\theta - \tfrac{1}{2}(\partial\theta/\partial x)\,\delta x$, while at the mid-point of the opposite face $EFGH$ it is $\theta + \tfrac{1}{2}(\partial\theta/\partial x)\,\delta x$.

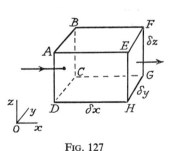

FIG. 127

The quantity of heat passing across $ABCD$ to the right (inwards) is

$$-k \frac{\partial}{\partial x}\left[\theta - \tfrac{1}{2}\frac{\partial \theta}{\partial x}\, \delta x\right]\delta y\, \delta z\, \delta t,$$

while across $EFGH$ to the right (outwards) the quantity is

$$-k \frac{\partial}{\partial x}\left[\theta + \tfrac{1}{2}\frac{\partial \theta}{\partial x}\, \delta x\right]\delta y\, \delta z\, \delta t.$$

The total quantity flowing inwards over these two faces is

$$k \frac{\partial^2 \theta}{\partial x^2}\, \delta x\, \delta y\, \delta z\, \delta t.$$

Similar contributions from the other four faces yield for the total quantity of heat entering the box

$$k\left(\frac{\partial^2 \theta}{\partial x^2} + \frac{\partial^2 \theta}{\partial y^2} + \frac{\partial^2 \theta}{\partial z^2}\right)\delta x\, \delta y\, \delta z\, \delta t.$$

If there are no sources of heat and no absorption of heat inside the element of volume, this inflow of heat raises the temperature of the material from θ to $\theta + (\partial\theta/\partial t)\, \delta t$ in time δt. If ρ is the density and C the specific heat, the heat required is $C\rho\, \delta x\, \delta y\, \delta z(\partial\theta/\partial t)\, \delta t$.

Equating these two expressions, the first being the cause and the second the effect, we obtain

$$K\left(\frac{\partial^2 \theta}{\partial x^2} + \frac{\partial^2 \theta}{\partial y^2} + \frac{\partial^2 \theta}{\partial z^2}\right) = \frac{\partial \theta}{\partial t}.$$

where $K = k/C\rho$, a constant.

For steady heat flow, there is no variation of temperature with respect to t, so $\partial\theta/\partial t = 0$. If heat is constrained to flow only in the x-direction (as for example in an idealized refrigerator door neglecting edge effects), the equation for θ is

$$d^2\theta/dx^2 = 0$$

with the solution

$$\theta = Ax + B.$$

A and B are found from the given temperatures on each side of the door.

For steady flow in a plate in the x, y-plane, insulated above and below so that heat is constrained to flow only in the plane, the equation for θ is

$$\frac{\partial^2 \theta}{\partial x^2} + \frac{\partial^2 \theta}{\partial y^2} = 0, \tag{7}$$

identical with the two-dimensional equation for the electric potential in electrostatics.

17

Finally, for time-varying flow in which heat is constrained to flow along an insulated rod placed along the x-axis, the heat flow is governed by the equation

$$K \frac{\partial^2 \theta}{\partial x^2} = \frac{\partial \theta}{\partial t}. \tag{8}$$

21.5 Steady heat flow in rectangular plates

A rectangular plate bounded by the sides $x = y = 0$, $x = a$, $y = b$ is given. One of the values a or b may be infinite, in which case the plate is called a *semi-infinite* plate.

In the simpler problems, we postulate the following conditions:

(a) For a semi-infinite plate, $\theta = 0$ at infinity. The two infinite sides may either be at the constant temperature $\theta = 0$ for all time, or they may both be insulated or one may be insulated and the other kept at $\theta = 0$. The temperature of the one finite side is to be an arbitrary distribution fixed for all time.

(b) If the plate is finite in extent, the temperature of one side must be specified arbitrarily; the other three sides may indifferently be kept either at the temperature $\theta = 0$ or insulated.

In case (b), two, three or four sides may be sources of heat by the addition of the simpler solutions for cases in which one side at a time is a source of heat, the other sides being kept at $\theta = 0$.

An insulated side is one over which there is no heat flow; the derivative of θ along its normal must vanish.

The method of solution is to find the separated solutions that satisfy the conditions along all the sides except that side containing the source of heat. The conditions along this last side are introduced by Fourier analysis.

Let $\theta = X(x)Y(y)$ be a separated solution, giving $X''Y + XY'' = 0$ when substituted into equation (7). Then

$$X''/X = -Y''/Y = \text{constant}.$$

If the constant is positive, m^2 say, we have either

$$X = A_m e^{mx} + B_m e^{-mx} \quad \text{or} \quad X = A_m \sinh mx + B_m \cosh mx$$

and $$Y = C_m \cos my + D_m \sin my.$$

Briefly, we write

$$\theta = e^{\pm mx} \frac{\sin}{\cos} my, \quad (9), \qquad \theta = \frac{\sinh}{\cosh} mx \frac{\sin}{\cos} my. \tag{10}$$

If the separation constant is negative, $-n^2$ say, we have

$$\theta = e^{\pm ny} \frac{\sin}{\cos} nx, \quad (11), \qquad \theta = \frac{\sinh}{\cosh} ny \frac{\sin}{\cos} nx. \tag{12}$$

Other combinations may sometimes be used, such as

$$\theta = \sin (nx + \alpha) \sinh (ny + \beta),$$

but in the applications considered here, it is suggested that the forms (9)–(12) are the most suitable.

If the separation constant vanishes, we obviously have

$$\theta = (A_0 x + B_0)(C_0 y + D_0).$$

There is never any doubt as to which form is to be used. With m and n both positive: if the plate extends to infinity in the $+x$-direction, use e^{-mx}; in the $-x$-direction, use e^{mx}; in the $+y$-direction, use e^{-ny}; in the $-y$-direction, use e^{ny}. For a rectangular plate with the source of heat parallel to the y-axis, use (10), while if the source of heat is parallel to the x-axis, use (12).

The argument (x or y) of the trigonometrical functions must be the same as the argument of the function specifying the given temperature distribution.

We may now consider various cases that arise:

(i) For the semi-infinite plate extending to $x = +\infty$, the sides $y = 0$ and $y = b$ are kept at $\theta = 0$, while the side $x = 0$ has the given temperature distribution $\theta = f(y)$, $0 < y < b$. Using solution (9), we have

$$\theta = e^{-mx} \, {\sin \atop \cos} \, my$$

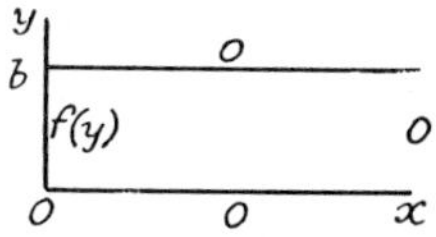

FIG. 128

as the separated solution. When $y = 0$, we require $\theta = 0$, so $\cos my$ is rejected. When $y = b$, we require $\theta = 0$, implying that $\sin mb = 0$; we therefore choose $m = p\pi/b$, where p is an integer. The sum of all such separated solutions yields the general solution:

$$\theta = \sum_{p=1}^{\infty} B_p e^{-p\pi x/b} \sin (p\pi \, y/b).$$

When $x = 0$, we have

$$f(y) = \sum_{p=1}^{\infty} B_p \sin (p\pi \, y/b),$$

from which it follows by Fourier analysis that

$$\tfrac{1}{2} b B_p = \int_0^b f(y) \sin (p\pi y/b) \, dy.$$

(ii) If, in case (i), the edges $y = 0$ and $y = b$ are insulated, we use the solution $\theta = e^{-mx} \cos my$, since its derivative with respect to y vanishes when $y = 0$. We choose $m = p\pi/b$ in order that this derivative should also vanish when $y = b$. Generally,

$$\theta = \sum_{p=0}^{\infty} A_p e^{-p\pi x/b} \cos (p\pi y/b).$$

The integer $p = 0$ is permitted here, yielding θ = constant as one separated solution. In the following Fourier analysis, note that A_0 need not vanish, showing that the temperature at infinity need not be zero.

(iii) If, in case (i), the edge $y = 0$ is maintained at $\theta = 0$ but the edge $y = b$ is insulated, we insert an additional plate in the space

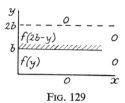

FIG. 129

$b < y < 2b$, such that its temperature distribution is an exact mirror image of that in the original plate with respect to the insulated side. The side $y = 2b$ is thus kept at $\theta = 0$, while along the side $x = 0$ ($b < y < 2b$) we use $f(2b - y)$ as the source of heat. Owing to the perfect symmetry thus achieved, heat can flow neither up nor down across the edge $y = b$, so in effect the edge is insulated.

Using the solution $\theta = e^{-mx} \sin my$, we require $\theta = e^{-mx} \sin 2mb$ to vanish when $y = 2b$, yielding $m = p\pi/2b$. Hence, generally

$$\theta = \sum_{p=1}^{\infty} B_p e^{-p\pi x/2b} \sin (p\pi y/2b).$$

When $x = 0$,

$$bB_p = \int_0^b f(y) \sin (p\pi y/2b) \, dy + \int_b^{2b} f(2b - y) \sin (p\pi y/2b) \, dy;$$

this obviously vanishes when p is even.

(iv) For the rectangular plate $x = y = 0$, $x = a$, $y = b$, three sides of which are maintained at $\theta = 0$ while the side $x = a$ is maintained at the temperature $f(y)$, we use solution (10). When $y = 0$ we require $\theta = 0$ so cos my is rejected. When $y = b$ we require sin mb to vanish, so $m = p\pi/b$. When $x = 0$, we require θ to vanish, so cosh mx is rejected, yielding for the separated solution

$$\theta = \sinh (p\pi x/b) \sin (p\pi y/b).$$

Generally, the solution

$$\theta = \sum_{p=1}^{\infty} B_p \sinh (p\pi x/b) \sin (p\pi y/b)$$

FIG. 130

satisfies the conditions along these three sides. Finally, when $x = a$, we have

$$f(y) = \sum_{p=1}^{\infty} B_p \sinh (p\pi a/b) \sin (p\pi y/b),$$

yielding

$$\tfrac{1}{2}bB_p \sinh (p\pi a/b) = \int_0^b f(y) \sin (p\pi y/b) \, dy.$$

(v) If the side $x = 0$ is insulated in case (iv), we reject sinh $(p\pi x/b)$ and retain cosh $(p\pi x/b)$, since the derivative of this latter function vanishes when $x = 0$.

(vi) If the sides $y = 0$, $y = b$ and $x = a$ are maintained at $\theta = 0$ while the distribution of temperature along $x = 0$ is $\theta = f(y)$, we must reject cos my and choose $m = p\pi y/b$, leaving

$$\theta = [A_p \cosh (p\pi x/b) + B_p \sinh (p\pi x/b)] \sin (p\pi y/b).$$

When $x = a$, we require θ to vanish; hence
$$A_p \cosh (p\pi a/b) + B_p \sinh (p\pi a/b) = 0,$$
or
$$B_p = -A_p \coth (p\pi a/b).$$
When $x = 0$, we have
$$f(y) = \sum_{p=1}^{\infty} A_p \sin (p\pi y/b),$$
from which the A_p may be determined by Fourier analysis. Hence, generally,
$$\theta = \sum_{p=1}^{\infty} A_p \left[\cosh (p\pi x/b) - \frac{\cosh (p\pi a/b)}{\sinh (p\pi a/b)} \sinh (p\pi x/b) \right] \sin (p\pi y/b)$$
$$= \sum_{p=1}^{\infty} A_p \frac{\sinh [p\pi(a-x)/b]}{\sinh (p\pi a/b)} \sin (p\pi y/b).$$

This is identical with the solution obtained in case (iv), with x replaced by $a - x$. That this should be so is obvious, for the origin has merely been changed from O to Q in Fig. 130, and the plate turned over.

(vii) Consider case (vi) but with the edges $y = 0$ and $y = b$ insulated. We use $\cos (p\pi y/b)$ instead of $\sin (p\pi y/b)$ throughout. The special separated solution when $p = 0$ must also be included.

(viii) Consider case (vi) but with the edge $y = 0$ at zero temperature and the edge $y = b$ insulated. We insert a similar plate in the region $b < y < 2b$, such that its temperature distribution is the mirror image of the original plate with respect to the insulated edge $y = b$. That is, the edge $y = 2b$ is kept at $\theta = 0$, and the temperature distribution along the edge $x = 0$ $(b < y < 2b)$ is $\theta = f(2b - y)$.

(ix) Consider case (xiii) but with the edge $x = 0$ insulated. We use cosh instead of sinh throughout, since its derivative vanishes when $x = 0$.

Many combinations can be assumed involving two, three or four sides as sources of heat. If, for example, sides (a) and (b) are given as heat sources, with sides (c) and (d) maintained at $\theta = 0$ or insulated, solve the two problems: (α) Side (a) as the source, side (b) at $\theta = 0$, sides (c) and (d) as given; and (β) side (a) at $\theta = 0$, side (b) as the source, sides (c) and (d) as given. The required result is obtained by adding these two solutions together.

The following example illustrates many of these principles:

Example 6 For the square plate whose sides are of length π, the edge $x = 0$ is maintained at $\theta = 0$, $y = \pi$ is insulated, $x = \pi$ is kept the temperature $\theta = 200$ while $y = 0$ is kept at $\theta = 100$. Find θ in the steady state as a function of x and y.

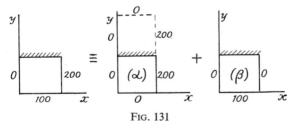

FIG. 131

Figure. 131 demonstrates that two distinct problems are involved.

(α) The side $y = 0$ is kept at $\theta = 0$. Using solution (10), we insert the additional plate in the range $\pi < y < 2\pi$, its temperature distribution being the mirror image of that in the original plate with respect to the insulated edge $y = \pi$. We reject cosh mx and cos my in order to ensure that $\theta = 0$ when $x = 0$ and $y = 0$. When $y = 2\pi$, we require sin my to vanish, so $m = \frac{1}{2}p$, where p is a positive integer. Generally, then,

$$\theta = \sum_{p=1}^{\infty} B_p \sinh \tfrac{1}{2}px \sin \tfrac{1}{2}py,$$

becoming when $x = \pi$,

$$200 = \sum_{p=1}^{\infty} B_p \sinh \tfrac{1}{2}p\pi \sin \tfrac{1}{2}py.$$

To find B_p, we multiply by sin $\frac{1}{2}py$ and integrate from 0 to 2π, obtaining

$$\pi B_p \sinh \tfrac{1}{2}p = \int_0^{2\pi} 200 \sin \tfrac{1}{2}py \, dy = \frac{200}{\tfrac{1}{2}p} \left[-\cos \tfrac{1}{2}py \right]_0^{2\pi}$$

$$= \frac{400}{P} [1 - (-1)^p] = \begin{cases} 800/p & \text{if } p \text{ is odd} \\ 0 & \text{if } p \text{ is even.} \end{cases}$$

Hence

$$\theta = \frac{800}{\pi} \sum_{n=1}^{\infty} \frac{\sinh \left[\frac{1}{2}(2n-1)x\right] \sin \left[\frac{1}{2}(2n-1)y\right]}{(2n-1) \sinh \left[\frac{1}{2}(2n-1)\pi\right]}. \tag{13}$$

(β) The side $x = \pi$ is now maintained at $\theta = 0$ and the side $y = 0$ at $\theta = 100$. Using solution (12), cos nx is rejected since it does not vanish when $x = 0$. When $x = \pi$, we require sin $nx = 0$, so n must be a positive integer, leaving

$$\theta = (A_n \cosh ny + B_n \sinh ny) \sin nx.$$

When $y = \pi$, we have $\partial\theta/\partial y = 0$, so

$$A_n \sinh n\pi + B_n \cosh n\pi = 0.$$

Finally, when $y = 0$,

$$100 = \sum_{n=1}^{\infty} A_n \sin nx,$$

yielding

$$\tfrac{1}{2}\pi A_n = \int_0^{\pi} 100 \sin nx \, dx = \frac{100}{n} \left[-\cos nx \right]_0^{\pi} = \frac{100}{n} [1 - (-1)^n]$$

$$= \frac{200}{n} \text{ only if } n \text{ is odd.}$$

Hence

$$A_n = \frac{400}{n\pi} \quad \text{and} \quad B_n = -A_n \tanh n\pi = -\frac{400}{n\pi} \tanh n\pi.$$

The solution therefore becomes

$$\theta = \frac{400}{\pi} \sum_{n \text{ odd}} n^{-1} (\cosh ny - \tanh n\pi \sin ny) \sin nx$$

$$= \frac{400}{\pi} \sum_{n=1}^{\infty} \frac{\cosh \left[(2n-1)(\pi - y)\right]}{(2n-1) \cosh \left[(2n-1)\pi\right]} \sin \left[(2n-1)x\right]. \tag{14}$$

The complete solution is given by the sum of the solutions (13) and (14).

At the mid-point of the square, $x = \frac{1}{2}\pi$, $y = \frac{1}{2}\pi$, the first two terms of solution (13) yield $\theta = 73$, while the first term of solution (14) yields $\theta = 53$. The total temperature of the mid-point is therefore 126.

21.6   Time-varying heat flow in an insulated rod

Let $\theta = X(x)T(t)$ be a separated solution of equation (8). Substitution yields $KX''T = XT'$, or $X''/X = T'/KT = $ constant. If this constant is negative, $-n^2$ say, we obtain the solutions

$$T = \exp\left(-Kn^2 t\right), \quad X = A_n \cos nx + B_n \sin nx,$$

or

$$\theta = \frac{\sin}{\cos} nx \exp\left(-Kn^2\, t\right). \tag{15}$$

If the constant is positive, $+m^2$ say, we have

$$\theta = \frac{\sinh}{\cosh} mx \exp\left(Km^2 t\right). \tag{16}$$

We now impose the condition that θ remains finite as $t \to \infty$; solution (16) is therefore rejected, while (15) is retained. All the solutions tend to zero as t becomes large except when $n = 0$; θ is then a constant.

A rod of length l is given. Its two ends indifferently are maintained at $\theta = 0$ or are insulated after the initial time $t = 0$. At $t = 0$, a known temperature distribution $\theta = f(x)$ exists along the rod. We choose those separated solutions that satisfy the conditions at the two ends of the rod, and finally the initial condition $\theta = f(x)$ is introduced by Fourier analysis.

(i) If both ends are maintained at $\theta = 0$, we reject the solution $\cos nx$, since this does not vanish when $x = 0$. In order that $\sin nx$ should vanish when $x = l$, we require $\sin nl = 0$; that is, $n = p\pi/l$ where p is a positive integer. Generally, then, the solution

$$\theta = \sum_{p=1}^{\infty} B_p \sin\left(p\pi x/l\right) \exp\left(-Kp^2\pi^2 t/l^2\right)$$

satisfies the two end conditions. Finally, when $t = 0$,

$$f(x) = \sum_{p=1}^{\infty} B_p \sin\left(p\pi x/l\right),$$

yielding

$$\tfrac{1}{2} l B_p = \int_0^l f(x) \sin\left(p\pi x/l\right) dx.$$

(ii) If both ends are insulated, we use $\cos nx$ instead of $\sin nx$ throughout, since its derivative vanishes when $x = 0$ and l if $n = p\pi/l$. The integer $p = 0$ is now retained, and the initial constant A_0 in the solution

$$\theta = \sum_{p=0}^{\infty} A_p \cos\left(p\pi x/l\right) \exp\left(-Kp^2\, \pi^2 t/l^2\right)$$

is the final temperature of the rod after the trapped heat has averaged itself out through the rod.

(iii) If the end $x = 0$ is kept at $\theta = 0$, while the end $x = l$ is insulated, we insert in the space $l \leqslant x \leqslant 2l$ a similar rod, the temperature distribution along which is a mirror image in the insulated end $x = l$ of the distribution along the original rod; no heat can flow across $x = l$. In this extra rod, the temperature distribution at $t = 0$ is $\theta = f(2l - x)$. The problem is thus reduced to case (i) with l replaced by $2l$; generally

$$\theta = \sum_{p=1}^{\infty} B_p \sin (p\pi x/2l) \exp (-Kp^2\pi^2 t/4l^2).$$

At time $t = 0$,

$$\left.\begin{array}{ll} f(x) & (0 \leqslant x < l) \\ f(2l - x) & (l < x < 2l) \end{array}\right\} = \sum_{p=1}^{\infty} B_p \sin (p\pi x/2l).$$

Hence

$$lB_p = \int_0^l f(x) \sin (p\pi x/2l)\, dx + \int_l^{2l} f(2l - x) \sin (p\pi x/2l)\, dx;$$

this vanishes if p is an even integer.

Example 7   The end $x = 0$ of a rod of length π is kept at $\theta = 0$, while the other end is insulated. At time $t = 0$, the temperature distribution along the rod is $100(\pi - x)/\pi$. Find θ generally.

We use the separated solution

$$\theta = \sin nx \exp (-Kn^2 t)$$

satisfying the condition $\theta = 0$ when $x = 0$. We insert a similar rod in the section $\pi \leqslant x \leqslant 2\pi$, maintaining the end $x = 2\pi$ at $\theta = 0$, such that its initial temperature distribution is

$$100[\pi - (2\pi - x)]/\pi = 100(x - \pi)/\pi.$$

We require $\sin nx$ to vanish when $x = 2\pi$; hence $n = \frac{1}{2}p$, where p is a positive integer. Generally,

$$\theta = \sum_{p=1}^{\infty} B_p \sin \tfrac{1}{2}px \exp (-Kp^2 t/4).$$

When $t = 0$, we have

$$\left.\begin{array}{ll} 100(\pi - x)/\pi & (0 \leqslant x \leqslant \pi) \\ 100(x - \pi)/\pi & (\pi \leqslant x \leqslant 2\pi) \end{array}\right\} = \sum_{p=1}^{\infty} B_p \sin \tfrac{1}{2}px,$$

yielding

$$\pi B_p = \frac{100}{\pi} \int_0^\pi (\pi - x) \sin \tfrac{1}{2}px\, dx + \frac{100}{\pi} \int_\pi^{2\pi} (x - \pi) \sin \tfrac{1}{2}px\, dx = \frac{400}{p}$$

if p is odd only, after integration by parts. Hence

$$\theta = \frac{400}{\pi} \sum_{m=1}^{\infty} (2m - 1)^{-1} \sin [\tfrac{1}{2}(2m - 1)x] \exp [-K(2m - 1)^2 t/4].$$

21.7   The diffusion equation

The *concentration* C of a solution at a given point P equals the mass of solute dissolved in a volume element δV enclosing P divided by δV. It is an experimental fact that *diffusion* takes place in a liquid in the absence of convection currents, solute passing from regions of higher to lower concentrations. This process is governed by *Fick's law*, which states that the rate of transfer of solute across an element δS is proportional to the concentration gradient, namely

$$\text{rate of diffusion} = -K \frac{\partial C}{\partial n} \delta S,$$

where n is the normal to the area. This is identical with the fundamental law of heat transfer, and so, if K is constant, the partial differential equation satisfied by C must be

$$K \left(\frac{\partial^2 C}{\partial x^2} + \frac{\partial^2 C}{\partial y^2} + \frac{\partial^2 C}{\partial z^2} \right) = \frac{\partial C}{\partial t},$$

simplifying to

$$K \frac{\partial^2 C}{\partial x^2} = \frac{\partial C}{\partial t} \tag{17}$$

for diffusion along Ox only.

If one end of the tube along which diffusion takes place is closed, $\partial C/\partial x = 0$ at that end; if the end is open to pure solvent, $C = 0$ there. Hence the mathematical equation and boundary conditions are identical with those of heat conduction, and so the problems given in section 21.6 may be interpreted in the light of diffusion processes rather than for the conduction of heat.

The separated solutions (15) may be used to solve the following problems:

A hollow straight tube of length l filled with solution is given. Its two ends are indifferently kept open to pure solvent for which $C = 0$ or kept permanently closed. At $t = 0$, a known concentration distribution $C = f(x)$ exists along the tube. Find C as a function of x and t. Cases (i), (ii) and (iii) of section 21.6 are immediately applicable, *mutatis mutandis*.

Example 8   The end $x = 0$ of a tube of length π is filled with solution; its end $x = 0$ is open to pure solvent $C = 0$, while the other end is closed. At time $t = 0$, the concentration distribution is given to be $C_0(\pi - x)/\pi$. Find C as a function of x and t.

The problem mathematically is identical with problem 7; we merely replace θ by C and 100 by C_0.

Example 9   An infinitely long straight tube is filled with liquid for which $C = 0$. At time $t = 0$, the free end $x = 0$ is suddenly brought into contact with solution at concentration C_0, and this concentration is maintained for all t. Find C in the tube as a function of x and t.

The following solution should be treated as bookwork. We change the independent variables x and t in equation (17) to u and v, where $u = xt^{-\frac{1}{2}}$, $v = t$. Then

$$C_x = C_u u_x + C_v v_x = C_u t^{-\frac{1}{2}},$$

and

$$C_{xx} = C_{uu} t^{-1} = C_{uu} v^{-1}.$$

Moreover, $C_t = C_u u_t + C_v v_t = C_u(-\tfrac{1}{2}xt^{-\frac{3}{2}}) + C_v = C_u(-\tfrac{1}{2}u/v) + C_v.$

The equation then becomes

$$KC_{uu} v^{-1} = -\tfrac{1}{2}uC_u/v + C_v,$$

or, upon separation,

$$KC_{uu} + \tfrac{1}{2}uC_u = vC_v.$$

If we now assume the separated solution $C = U(u)V(v)$, we obtain

$$KU''V + \tfrac{1}{2}uU'V = vUV',$$

or

$$(KU'' + \tfrac{1}{2}uU')/U = vV'/V.$$

Each side of this equation must be a constant; in particular, we choose the constant to be zero, yielding $V =$ constant, and

$$\frac{d}{du}\left(\frac{dU}{du}\right) = -\frac{u}{2K}\frac{dU}{du}.$$

This equation is an ordinary equation separable in U' and U:

$$\frac{dU'}{U'} = -\frac{u\,du}{2K},$$

integrating to $\log U' = -\tfrac{1}{4}u^2/K + \text{constant},$

or $U' = A \exp(-\tfrac{1}{4}u^2/K).$

Finally, $U = A \displaystyle\int_0^u \exp(-\tfrac{1}{4}u^2/K)\,du + B.$

It follows that a solution of equation (17) is

$$C = UV = A\int_0^{x/\sqrt{t}} \exp(-\tfrac{1}{4}u^2/K)\,du + B.$$

This solution may be made to fit all the imposed conditions. When $t = 0$, we have

$$C = A\int_0^{\infty} \exp(-\tfrac{1}{4}u^2/K)\,du + B$$
$$= A\sqrt{(\pi K)} + B$$

(see section 17.2). To vanish for all x, we choose $A = -B/\sqrt{(\pi K)}$, yielding

$$C = B\left[1 - \frac{1}{\sqrt{(\pi K)}}\int_0^{x/\sqrt{t}} \exp(-\tfrac{1}{4}u^2/K)\,du\right].$$

Finally, when $x = 0$, this gives $C = B$, which must have the given value C_0; hence

$$C = C_0\left[1 - \frac{1}{\sqrt{(\pi K)}}\int_0^{x/\sqrt{t}} \exp(-\tfrac{1}{4}u^2/K)\,du\right].$$

This may be arranged in standard form by writing $z = \frac{1}{2}u/\sqrt{K}$, giving

$$C = C_0\left[1 - \frac{2}{\sqrt{\pi}}\int_0^{x/2\sqrt{(Kt)}} \exp(-z^2)\,dz\right]$$

$$= C_0\{1 - \mathrm{erf}\,[x/2\sqrt{(Kt)}]\},$$

where the function erf w is defined by

$$\mathrm{erf}\,w = \frac{2}{\sqrt{\pi}}\int_0^w \exp(-z^2)\,dz,$$

and for which extensive tables exist (see section 24.10).

EXERCISES

Where possible partial differentiation
is denoted by a suffix.

(1)*. If $f(u)$ is an arbitrary function of u and if $z^2 = x^2 + f(y - z)$, prove that $zz_x + xz_y = x$.

(2)*. Obtain the second order partial differential equation of which $u = f(x + 2y) + F(x + 3y)$ is the solution.

(3)*. If $f(x, t)$ satisfies $c^2 f_{xx} = f_{tt}$, and c is a non-zero constant, prove that $f(x, t) = F(x + ct) + G(x - ct)$ for suitable functions F and G.
  If $c = 2$ and $f(x, t) = 2\exp(-x^2)$, $\partial f/\partial t = 4x\exp(-x^2)$ when $t = 0$, find $\partial f/\partial t$ when $t > 0$ and $x = 0$.

(4)*. Show that a solution of the partial differential equation $y_{tt} = 4y_{xx}$ is $y = f(x - 2t) + g(x + 2t)$.
  Find a solution for which $y = 1 + 3\sin x - \cos x$ and $y_{tt} = 6\cos x + 2\sin x$, when $t = 0$.

(5)*. Find the most general solution of the equation $z_{xx} = z_{yy}$ in terms of two arbitrary functions. Find a solution of the equation which satisfies the conditions $z = 0$ when $x = a$, $z = \sin py$ when $x = 0$.

(6)*. A function $Z(r, t)$ satisfies $\dfrac{1}{r^2}\dfrac{\partial}{\partial r}\left(r^2\dfrac{\partial Z}{\partial r}\right) = \dfrac{1}{c^2}\dfrac{\partial^2 Z}{\partial t^2}$ where c is a constant.
By introducing the new dependent variable $W = rZ$ and the independent variables $u = r + ct$ and $v = r - ct$, reduce the differential equation to $\partial^2 W/\partial u\,\partial v = 0$. Hence show that the general solution Z is of the form $Z = (U + V)/r$, where U is an arbitrary function of $r + ct$ only and V is an arbitrary function of $r - ct$ only.

(7)*. Find all the functions $F(x)$ such that $V = e^{2y}F(x)$ satisfies the equation
$$V_{xx} + 5V_x + V_{yy} = 0.$$

(8)*. Find a solution of the equation $z_{xx} + 2kz_x - z_{tt} = 0$, where k is positive, in the form $z = f(z)\sin kt$, given that $z = 0$ when $x = 0$, for all values of t, and $z = 1/(ke)$ when $x = 1/k$ and $t = \pi/(2k)$. Show that as $x \to \infty$, $z \to 0$ for all values of t.

(9)*. The current j in a cable satisfies the equation $j_{xx} = 2k^{-1}j_t + j$. By assuming a solution of the type $j = XT$, where X is a function of x alone and T is a function of t alone, show that if $j = 0$ when $x = l$, and $\partial j/\partial t = -ae^{-kt}$ when $x = 0$, the current is given by
$$j = ae^{-kt}\sin(l - x)/[k\sin l].$$

(10)★. Assuming that $u = r^{-1}F(r) \cos(\omega t + \alpha)$ is a solution of the partial differential equation $u_{rr} + 2r^{-1}u_r = c^{-2}u_{tt}$, where ω, α and c are constants, and $F(r)$ is a function of r only, obtain the ordinary differential equation satisfied by $F(r)$ and give the general solution for $F(r)$.

Given that, for all values of t, (i) u is finite at $r = 0$, (ii) $u_r = 0$ at $r = a$, and that u is not identically zero, prove that $\omega a/c = \beta$ must satisfy the equation $\beta = \tan \beta$.

(11)★. If u satisfies the equation $\dfrac{1}{r}\dfrac{\partial}{\partial r}\left(r\dfrac{\partial u}{\partial r}\right) + \dfrac{1}{r^2}\dfrac{\partial^2 u}{\partial \theta^2} + k^2 u = 0$, where k is a constant, show that $u = r^{-\frac12}f(r) \cos \frac12\theta$ is a solution, where $f(r)$ is a function of r, provided that $f(r)$ satisfies a certain differential equation. Write down the general solution for $f(r)$.

Obtain the solution for u which is of the above form and satisfies the conditions $u = 0$ when $r = a$, $u = \cos \frac12\theta$ when $r = b$ for all values of θ.

(12)★. If the equation $\dfrac{\partial^2 \phi}{\partial r^2} + \dfrac{1}{r}\dfrac{\partial \phi}{\partial r} + \dfrac{1}{r^2}\dfrac{\partial^2 \phi}{\partial \theta^2} = 0$ is satisfied by $\phi = V \cos n\theta$, where V is a function of r only and n is a positive integer, determine a differential equation for V. Solve this equation and hence find ϕ, given that ϕ is finite when $r = 0$, and $\partial\phi/\partial\theta = -n$ when $r = a$ and $\theta = \pi/2n$.

(13)★. Assuming that the equation $\dfrac{\partial}{\partial r}\left(r^2\dfrac{\partial \phi}{\partial r}\right) + \dfrac{1}{\sin \theta}\dfrac{\partial}{\partial \theta}\left(\sin \theta\,\dfrac{\partial \phi}{\partial \theta}\right) = 0$ can be satisfied by $\phi = f(r) \cos \theta$, find the differential equation satisfied by $f(r)$ and show that $f(r) = Ar + B/r^2$ where A and B are arbitrary constants.

Find the values of A and B if $\phi_r = \cos \theta$ when $r = a$ and $\phi_r = 0$ when $r = \infty$.

(14)★. If $y = F(x) \cos \omega t$, where ω is a constant greater than 1, is a solution of the equation $y_{xx} + 2y_x = y_{tt}$, find the ordinary differential equation satisfied by $F(x)$. Obtain the general solution of this equation and hence a solution of the equation for y in the above form. Given that this solution satisfies the conditions $y = 0$ at $x = 0$ and at $x = l$, for all values of t, and does not vanish identically, prove that ω must have one of the values given by $\omega^2 = 1 + n^2\pi^2/l^2$, where $n = 1, 2, \ldots$.

(15)★. A string of length l is stretched between two points, one fixed and the other vibrating transversely. The motion of the string is determined by the equation $z_{xx} = c^{-2}z_{tt}$, where $z(x, t)$ is the transverse displacement at time t at a point at distance x from the fixed end, and c is constant. The motion of the end points is given by $z(0, t) = 0$, $z(l, t) = a \sin pt$ for all t. Show that, in general, there is a solution in the form $z = f(x) \sin pt$, and determine $f(x)$. In what circumstances does this solution fail?

(16)★. Show that the equation $\dfrac{\partial^2 V}{\partial x^2} + \dfrac{\partial^2 V}{\partial y^2} = 0$ becomes $\dfrac{\partial^2 V}{\partial \lambda^2} + \dfrac{\partial^2 V}{\partial \theta^2} = 0$ when x and y are replaced by the new variables λ and θ, where r and θ are polar coordinates and $\lambda = \log r$. Given that

$V = 0$ on $\theta = 0$ and $\theta = \frac13\pi$, $\quad V = 0$ on $r = 1$, $\quad V = 63 \sin 3\theta$ on $r = 2$,

find V in all parts of the plane as a function of r and θ.

(17)★. Show that $u = Ae^{mx} \cos(\omega t + mx) + Be^{-mx} \cos(\omega t - mx)$ is a solution of $u_{xx} = 2u_t$, where A, B, m and ω are constants, provided that $m^2 = \omega$.

Find the values of the constants, given the conditions (i) $m > 0$, (ii) u remains finite as $x \to \infty$, (iii) $u = \cos t$ when $x = 0$.

(18)*. Prove that the equation $V_{xx} + V_{yy} = 0$ transforms, by the substitution $x = r \cos \theta$, $y = r \sin \theta$, to $V_{rr} + r^{-1}V_r + r^{-2}V_{\theta\theta} = 0$. Obtain the general solution of this equation in the form $V = f(r)F(\theta)$.

Hence determine V so that $V_r = 0$ when $r = a$, $V \to r \cos \theta$ when $r \to \infty$.

(19)*. Obtain the solution of the equation $V_{xx} + V_{tt} + 6V_x + 9V = 0$ in the form $V = f(x)g(t)$, satisfying the following conditions: (i) V is periodic in t, (ii) $V = 0$ when $x = 0$ for all values of t, (iii) $V_{xt} = 6 \cos 3t$ when $x = 0$ for all values of t.

(20)*. If $\partial\rho/\partial t + \partial(\rho u)/\partial x = 0$, where $\rho = f(x + ct)$, show that $\partial[(u + c)\rho]/\partial x = 0$. Given also that $u = u_0$ when $x = 0$, for all values of t, show that

$$u = -c + (u_0 + c)f(ct)/f(x + ct).$$

(21). Show that the equation $z_{xx} = (z_{tt} + kz_t)/c^2$, where k and c are constants, has solutions of the form

$$z = \begin{smallmatrix} \cos \\ \sin \end{smallmatrix} mx \begin{smallmatrix} \cos \\ \sin \end{smallmatrix} pt \; e^{-kt/2},$$

where the constants m and p satisfy $p^2 = m^2c^2 - \tfrac{1}{4}k^2$.

(22)*. A uniform string whose length is $2l$ and mass $2lm$ is stretched at tension T between two fixed points, the mid-point of the string being displaced a small distance b perpendicular to the string and then released, show that the subsequent motion of the string, referred to axes through its mid-point, is given by the equation in which $mc^2 = T$:

$$y = \frac{8b}{\pi^2} \sum_{r=0}^{\infty} \frac{1}{(2r+1)^2} \cos \frac{(2r+1)\pi x}{2l} \cos \frac{(2r+1)\pi ct}{2l}.$$

(23). A string is stretched between two fixed points and motion is started by drawing aside through a distance a a point on the string distant one-fifth of the length l of the string from one end. Show that the displacement at any instant will be given by the equation

$$y = \frac{25a}{2\pi^2} \sum_{n=1}^{\infty} \frac{1}{n^2} \sin \frac{n\pi}{5} \sin \frac{n\pi x}{l} \cos \frac{n\pi ct}{l}.$$

Find the distribution of temperature in the steady state for plates specified by the following boundary conditions:

(24)*. $y = 0$ at $\theta = 0$, $y = 6$ at $\theta = 0$, $x = \infty$ at $\theta = 0$, $x = 0$ at $\theta = 50 \sin (\pi y/6)$.

(25). $x = 0$ insulated, $x = \pi$ insulated, $y = \infty$ at a finite value of θ, $y = 0$ at $\theta = (\pi x - x^2)$.

(26). $y = 0$ at $\theta = 0$, $y = \pi$ insulated, $x = \infty$ at $\theta = 0$, $x = 0$ at $\theta = 100y/\pi$.

(27)*. $x = 0$ at $\theta = 0$ $x = \pi$ at $\theta = 0$, $y = 0$ insulated, $y = \pi$ at $\theta = 100$.

(28). $x = 0$ at $\theta = 0$, $x = 2\pi$ at $\theta = 0$, $y = 0$ insulated, $y = \pi$ at $\theta = T$.

Find the distribution of temperature for rods specified by the following end and initial conditions:

(29)*. $x = 0$ at $\theta = 0$, $x = \pi$ at $\theta = 0$, $\theta = x(\pi - x)$ at $t = 0$.

(30)*. $x = 0$ at $\theta = 0$, $x = a$ at $\theta = 0$, $\theta = V_0 \sin (\pi x/a) + V_1 \sin (2\pi x/a)$ at $t = 0$.

(31)*. $x = 0$ insulated, $x = \pi$ insulated, $\theta = \pi x - x^2$ at $t = 0$.

(32)*. $x = 0$ insulated, $x = \pi$ insulated, $\theta = V_0 x$ at $t = 0$.

(33)*. $x = 0$ at $\theta = 0$, $x = 1$ at $\theta = 0$, at $t = 0$: $\theta = \theta_0$ $(0 < x < \tfrac{1}{2})$, $\theta = 0$ $(\tfrac{1}{2} < x < 1)$. Find θ when $x = \tfrac{1}{2}$.

(34). $x = 0$ at $\theta = 0$, $x = \pi$ insulated, $\theta = 100(\pi - x)/\pi$ at $t = 0$.

(35). To what problems in diffusion theory do examples (29)–(34) correspond?

ANSWERS TO EXERCISES

(2). $6u_{xx} - 5u_{xy} + u_{yy} = 0.$ (3) $-16t \exp(-4t^2).$

(4). $y = 1 + 3 \sin(x + 2t) - \cos(x + 2t).$ (5). $z = f(x + y) + g(x - y);$
$z = \sin py \sin[p(a - x)] \operatorname{cosec} pa.$ (7). $F(x) = Ae^{-4x} + Be^{-x}.$

(8). $z = xe^{-kx} \sin kt.$ (10). $F(r) = A \cos(\omega r/c) + B \sin(\omega r/c).$

(11). $f(r) = A \cos kr + B \sin kr$; $u = (b/r)^{\frac{1}{2}} \sin[k(r - a)] \operatorname{cosec}[k(b - a)] \cos \frac{1}{2}\theta.$

(12). $V = Ar^n + Br^{-n}$; $\phi = (r/a)^n \cos n\theta.$

(13). $r^2 f'' + 2rf' - 2f = 0$; $\phi = -(a^3/2r^2) \cos \theta.$

(14). $F = e^{-x}\{A \cos[t\sqrt{(\omega^2 - 1)}] + B \sin[t\sqrt{(\omega^2 - 1)}]\}$, $A = 0.$

(15). $f(x) = a \sin(px/c)/\sin(pl/c)$; fails when $pl = n\pi c.$

(16). $V = 8(r^3 - r^{-3}) \sin 3\theta.$ (17). $A = 0$, $B = 1.$

(18). $V = (Ar^n + Br^{-n})(C \cos n\theta + D \sin \theta)$, $V = (r + a^2/r) \cos \theta.$

(19). $V = \frac{1}{3}(1 - e^{-6x}) \sin 3t.$ (24) $50e^{-\pi x/6} \sin(\pi y/6).$

(25). $\frac{1}{6}\pi^2 - \sum\limits_{m=1}^{\infty} \cos 2mx \, e^{-2my}/m^2.$

(26). $\dfrac{800}{\pi^2} \sum\limits_{n=0}^{\infty} \dfrac{(-1)^n}{(2n + 1)^2} \sin[\frac{1}{2}(2n + 1)y]e^{-\frac{1}{2}(2n+1)x}.$

(27). $\dfrac{400}{\pi} \sum\limits_{n=0}^{\infty} \dfrac{\sin(2n + 1)x \cosh(2n + 1)y}{(2n + 1) \cosh(2n + 1)\pi}.$

(28). $\dfrac{4T}{\pi} \sum\limits_{n=1}^{\infty} \operatorname{sech}[(\frac{1}{2} + n)\pi](2n + 1)^{-1} \sin[(\frac{1}{2} + n)x] \cosh[(\frac{1}{2} + n)y].$

(29). $\dfrac{8}{\pi} \sum\limits_{n=0}^{\infty} (2n + 1)^{-3} \exp[-K(2n + 1)^2 t] \sin[(2n + 1)x].$

(30). $V_0 \exp(-K\pi^2 t/a^2) \sin(\pi x/a) + V_1 \exp(-4K\pi^2 t/a^2) \sin(2\pi x/a).$

(31). $\frac{1}{6}\pi^2 - \sum\limits_{n=1}^{\infty} n^{-2} \exp(-4Kn^2 t) \cos 2nx.$

(32). $\frac{1}{2}V_0 l - \dfrac{4V_0 l}{\pi^2} \sum\limits_{n=1}^{\infty} (2n - 1)^{-2} \exp[-K(2n - 1)^2 \pi^2 t/l^2] \cos[(2n - 1)\pi x/l].$

(33). $\dfrac{4\theta_0}{\pi} \sum\limits_{n=1}^{\infty} n^{-1} \sin^2 \frac{1}{4}\pi n \sin \pi n x \exp(-Kn^2\pi^2 t).$

(34). $\dfrac{400}{\pi^2} \sum\limits_{n=0}^{\infty} \left(\dfrac{\pi}{2n + 1} - \dfrac{2(-1)^n}{(2n + 1)^2}\right) \sin(n + \frac{1}{2})x \exp[-K(n + \frac{1}{2})^2 t].$

CHAPTER 22

TOPICS IN ELEMENTARY STATICS

22.1 The equilibrium of a rigid body under a system of forces

Forces of *magnitude* F_i act at various points P_i of a lamina; we shall restrict ourselves to forces whose directions lie in the plane of the lamina. Arbitrary perpendicular axes Ox, Oy are chosen in the lamina; let the direction of the force F_i make an angle θ_i with Ox. We are concerned with the *reduction* of this set of forces to a simpler but equivalent system.

The *components* of the force F_i are $X_i = F_i \cos \theta_i$ and $Y_i = F_i \sin \theta_i$ acting in the x and y-directions respectively; the force F_i is equivalent in all respects to the combination or *sum* of the two forces X_i and Y_i. It is evident that $F_i = \sqrt{(X_i^2 + Y_i^2)}$.

At O, we introduce two forces of magnitude $F_i \cos \theta_i$ along the $+x$ and $-x$ directions respectively, and likewise two forces $F_i \sin \theta_i$ in the $+y$ and $-y$ directions. Such an insertion does not affect the given system, since each pair introduced cancels to zero.

Now the X_i to the right at P_i and the X_i to the left at O constitute a *couple* of *moment* $-X_i y_i$, while the Y_i upwards at P_i and the

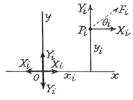

FIG. 132

Y_i downwards at O constitute a couple of moment $Y_i x_i$, where the anticlockwise sense is positive. The individual force F_i at P_i is thus equivalent to a couple $Y_i x_i - X_i y_i$ and an identical force F_i with components X_i, Y_i acting at O.

Every force is treated similarly, and using the property of arithmetical addition of the respective force components and of the couples, we obtain the result that the whole system is equivalent to

A couple $G = \sum(Y_i x_i - X_i y_i)$, together with

a force with components $X = \sum X_i = \sum F_i \cos \theta_i$ and
$Y = \sum Y_i = \sum F_i \sin \theta_i$ acting at O.

If this couple G and the two components X and Y all vanish, the given force system is in *equilibrium*. If $X = Y = 0$, the system reduces to a couple G. If at least one of X and Y does not vanish, the system reduces to a definite single *resultant*. This is a force with components X and Y, acting along that line about any point $P(x, y)$ of which the

517

given system possesses no moment. Recalling that a couple G has the same moment about all points in the plane, we have, taking moments about $P(x, y)$,

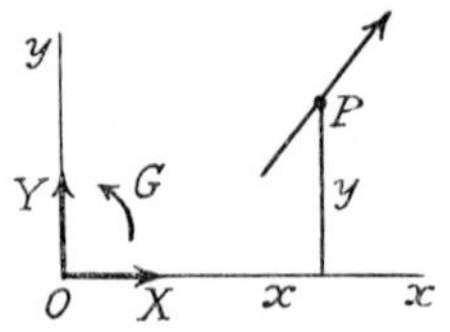

$$Xy - Yx + G = 0.$$

This is the *line of action* of the resultant of the given system.

If, in any given problem, the system is specified by a large number of forces, the best method of treatment is to find the total components X and Y at the origin, and the couple G.

FIG. 133

The equilibrium of a rigid body (lamina) is specified by three equations:

(i) the total component of all forces in an arbitrary x direction $= 0$,
(ii) the total component of all forces in an arbitrary y direction $= 0$,
(iii) the total moment of all forces about an arbitrary point $= 0$.

In general, it can be seen that *three* unknown forces must be introduced into a given system in order that these with the given system should be in equilibrium. If two rigid bodies are freely jointed at a hinge, six unknown forces may totally be introduced; each body provides three equations to yield their values. The two components of the reaction at the hinge are included in this total.

The reader should recall the following theorems which are useful in solving problems.

The triangle of forces. If three forces in equilibrium meet at a point, then they may be represented by the three sides of a triangle taken in order. *Lami's theorem* is equivalent to this: If the three forces P, Q, R are in equilibrium meeting at the point O, then

$$P/\sin \angle QOR = Q/\sin \angle ROP = R/\sin \angle POQ.$$

The polygon of forces. If n forces in equilibrium meet at a point, then they may be represented (in magnitude and direction) by the n sides of a closed n-sided polygon.

The following types of forces may be encountered.

(*a*) If two smooth bodies are in contact, the only force between them is a *normal reaction R* acting at the point of contact, and directed into each body away from the point of contact. If, in particular, one end of a rod r rests on a smooth body b, the normal reaction R is directed along the normal to b. This also defines what would otherwise be an indeterminate normal to r at its tip. When drawing a diagram for bodies in contact, it is suggested that a small gap should always be left between them, as in Fig. 134.

(*b*) A string AB attached to two bodies at A and B respectively transmits a *tension T*. T acts on each body, being directed from A to B on body b_1 and from B to

A on b_2. It is essential that $T > 0$. If the string is *elastic*, with *modulus* λ and *unstretched length a*, the tension T equals $\lambda x/a$ when it is extended to a length $(a + x)$. This same rule applies to a *spring*, except that x can now be negative for a *compression*, yielding a *thrust*.

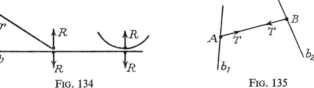

FIG. 134   FIG. 135

(c) If AB is a *light rod* or *strut* in Fig. 135, it can sustain either a tension (as shown) or a thrust. For a thrust, T would be negative as drawn, but if the arrows are reversed in the diagram, a positive value of T would now indicate a thrust.

(d) If two bodies are freely jointed together at A, the joint may be removed if a general force is introduced at the hinge, specified by the forces X and Y shown in the diagram. If the hinge is stiff, equal and opposite couples G should be introduced as shown.

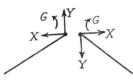

FIG. 136

(e) The *weight W* of a body acts vertically downwards at its centre of gravity. For a uniform rod, its weight acts at its mid-point.

In this connection, *internal* and *external* forces should be carefully distinguished. Newton's third law states that *to any force corresponds an equal and opposite force*; that is, there exists no such thing as an isolated force. This law is usually enunciated in the form that to every *action* corresponds an equal and opposite *reaction*, suggesting that there is a difference between action and reaction, that one is the cause and the other the effect. In Figs. 134, 135 and 136, R, T, X, Y, G demonstrate the use of this law. If *both* the forces that constitute a force pair are regarded as forming part of a system of forces, then these two forces are *internal* forces within the system. But if *only one* force of a force pair is regarded as acting within the system, then this force is an *external* force. The weight of a body is usually an external force; for the other member of the force pair is external to the system, acting at the centre of the earth.

(f) If two bodies in contact at a point A are both rough, a tangential *frictional*

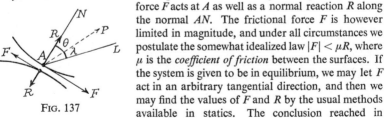

FIG. 137

force F acts at A as well as a normal reaction R along the normal AN. The frictional force F is however limited in magnitude, and under all circumstances we postulate the somewhat idealized law $|F| < \mu R$, where μ is the *coefficient of friction* between the surfaces. If the system is given to be in equilibrium, we may let F act in an arbitrary tangential direction, and then we may find the values of F and R by the usual methods available in statics. The conclusion reached in such a problem is an *inequality*, namely

$$|F|/R < \mu,$$

where F and R are the calculated values. But if the body is given to be on the point of slipping, under which circumstances the maximum friction possible is said to be *limiting friction, F* may be replaced even in the diagram by μR provided its direction is chosen *to oppose the tendency to relative movement.* The answer to such a problem is always an *equality.*

Graphical methods may often be used in friction problems. If $\mu = \tan \lambda$, where λ is the *angle of friction,* the resultant reaction P of R and F must lie within the acute angle formed by AN and the line AL where $\angle NAL = \lambda$. In particular, if three forces act on a body: P_1, P_2 and P (the last force being the resultant reaction at the point A), then if P_1 and P_2 intersect in a point B, it follows that P must pass through B for equilibrium. If $\angle NAP = \theta$, we must have

$$\tan \theta \leqslant \tan \lambda = \mu.$$

The value of $\tan \theta$ can be found by geometrical considerations; its value substituted into the inequality $\tan \theta \leqslant \mu$ provides the solution to the problem.

Example 1★ The moments of a system of forces about the points $(2, 1)$, $(-3, 4)$, $(1, -3)$ are $11, -15, 15$ respectively. Find the magnitude and equation of the line of action of that force acting at the point $(3, 2)$ which when added to the system, reduces it to a couple. Prove that the resultant couple is 13.

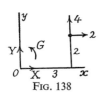

FIG. 138

Let the given system be equivalent to a force (X, Y) at O together with a couple G. Taking anticlockwise moments about the three given points, we have

$$X - 2Y + G = 11,$$
$$4X + 3Y + G = -15,$$
$$-3X - Y + G = 15,$$

yielding $X = -2, Y = -4, G = 5$. We therefore introduce a force with components $(+2, +4)$ at the point $(3, 2)$. Its magnitude is $2\sqrt{5}$, making an angle $\tan^{-1}\frac{1}{2}$ with Ox, so its line of action is specified by

$$(y - 2) = \tfrac{1}{2}(x - 3) \qquad \text{or} \qquad 2y - x - 1 = 0.$$

Using X, Y, G and this force $(2, 4)$ acting at the point $(3, 2)$, we take anticlockwise moments about O, obtaining for the resultant couple

$$\text{couple} = G + 4 \times 3 - 2 \times 2 = 13.$$

Example 2★ Forces with components $(1, 2)$, $(3, -1)$, $(-1, -1)$, (P, Q) act at the points $(1, 1)$, $(2, -1)$, $(-2, -1)$, (x_1, y_1) respectively. (i) Show that this is a couple if $P = -3, Q = 0$. (ii) If on the other hand the system is equivalent to a force $(2, 1)$ acting at $(1, 2)$ show that $x_1 + y_1 + 6 = 0$.

Let the system reduce to a force (X, Y) at O together with a couple G. Then resolving and taking moments about O, we obtain

$$X = 1 + 3 - 1 + P = 3 + P,$$
$$Y = 2 - 1 - 1 + Q = Q,$$
$$G = (2.1 - 1.1) + (-1.2 + 3.1) + (1.2 - 1.1) + (Qx_1 - Py_1)$$
$$ = 3 + Qx_1 - Py_1.$$

(i) To reduce to a couple, $X = Y = 0$, yielding $P = -3, Q = 0$.

(ii) If the system is equivalent to a force $(2, 1)$ acting at $(1, 2)$, we require $X = 2$, $Y = 1$, yielding $P = -1$, $Q = 1$. Moreover the given system must have no total moment about $(1, 2)$. Taking moments, we have

$$0 = G + X.2 - Y.1 = 3 + Qx_1 - Py_1 + 2X - Y = x_1 + y_1 + 6.$$

Example 3★ A rod AB of mass m and length $2l$ is smoothly hinged to a vertical wall at A. It is kept inclined at an acute angle 2θ to the upward vertical by an elastic string, of modulus λ and natural length l, attached to B and to a point C on the wall vertically above A, where $AC = 2l$. If $\sin \theta = 3/5$, prove that $\lambda = 3\,mg/7$. Find the magnitude and direction of the reaction at A.

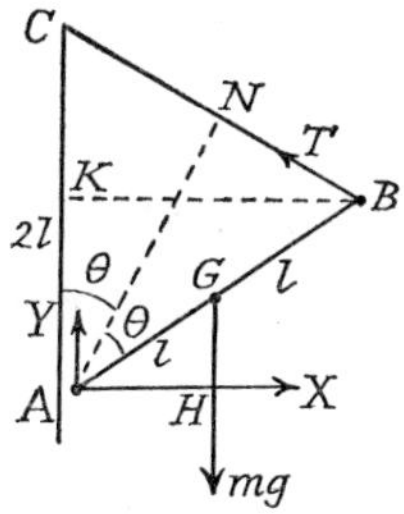

The stretched length of the string is given by

$$CB = 2NB = 4l \sin \theta = 12l/5,$$

so the extension is $7l/5$. The tension is therefore $7\lambda/5$.

Taking moments about A (chosen so as to avoid the unknown reaction at A), we have

$$T.AN = mg.AH$$

or

$$\tfrac{7}{5}\lambda.2l \cos \theta = mg.l \sin 2\theta$$

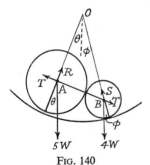

FIG. 139

yielding $\lambda = 3mg/7$.

Noting that $\angle CBK = 90° - \angle BCK = \angle CAN = \theta$, we have upon resolving horizontally,

$$X = T \cos \theta = \tfrac{7}{5}\lambda.\tfrac{4}{5} = \tfrac{12}{25}\, mg,$$

and vertically,

$$Y = mg - T \sin \theta = mg - \tfrac{7}{5}\lambda.\tfrac{3}{5} = \tfrac{16}{25}\, mg.$$

The magnitude of the resultant reaction at A is $\sqrt{(X^2 + Y^2)} = \tfrac{4}{5}\, mg$, while its angle of elevation above the horizontal is $\tan^{-1}(Y/X) = \tfrac{4}{3}$.

Example 4 Two smooth spheres of weights $5W$, $4W$ and of radii $2a$, a respectively, rest in equilibrium in a hollow sphere of radius $6a$. Find the three reactions between the spheres.

Since $OA = 4a$, $AB = 3a$, $OB = 5a$, we deduce that $\angle OAB = 90°$, and that $\cos (\theta + \phi) = \tfrac{4}{5}$. Three forces $5W$, R, T act through the centre of A of the first sphere, and three forces $4W$, S, T act through B. Lami's theorem is applicable in each case, yielding

$$\frac{5W}{\sin 90} = \frac{R}{\sin (90 + \theta)} = \frac{T}{\sin (180 - \theta)},$$

$$\frac{4W}{\sin (90 + \theta + \phi)} = \frac{S}{\sin (90 - \theta)} = \frac{T}{\sin (180 - \phi)},$$

or

$$5W = \frac{R}{\cos \theta} = \frac{T}{\sin \theta}$$

and

$$\frac{4W}{\cos (\theta + \phi)} = \frac{S}{\cos \theta} = \frac{T}{\sin \phi}.$$

FIG. 140

Equating T/W in both sets of ratios, and inserting the value of $\cos (\theta + \phi)$, we find that $\sin \theta = \sin \phi$, or $\theta = \phi$. Hence $\cos 2\theta = \tfrac{4}{5}$, yielding $\cos \theta = 3/\sqrt{10}$ and $\sin \theta = 1/\sqrt{10}$. It follows that

$$R = 5W \cos \theta = 15W/\sqrt{10}, \quad S = 5W \cos \theta = 15W/\sqrt{10},$$
$$T = 5W \sin \theta = 5W/\sqrt{10}.$$

Example 5 A ladder rests against a vertical wall of coefficient of friction μ' and on

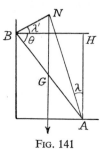

FIG. 141

horizontal ground of coefficient of friction μ. If the ladder is on the point of slipping, prove that $\tan \theta = (1 - \mu\mu')/2\mu$, where θ is the angle between the ladder and the horizontal.

Friction must be limiting at both ends of the ladder at the same time. The top end B tends to slip downwards, so friction must act vertically upwards; the lower end A tends to slip to the right, so friction must act to the left. The weight of the ladder acts through the mid-point G; the resultant force at B acts along BN making an angle λ' to the normal BH; at A the resultant force acts along AN making an angle λ to the normal AH. Here, $\tan \lambda = \mu$, $\tan \lambda' = \mu'$. All three forces must meet in N.

The problem is now entirely geometrical. In triangle BNG,

$$BG/NG = \sin \angle BNG/\sin \angle NGB,$$

and in triangle NGA,

$$GA/NG = BG/NG = \sin \angle GNA/\sin \angle NAG;$$

hence

$$\frac{\sin (90 - \lambda')}{\sin (\theta + \lambda')} = \frac{\sin \lambda}{\sin (90 - \theta - \lambda)}$$

or

$$\cos \lambda' \cos (\theta + \lambda) = \sin \lambda \sin (\theta + \lambda'),$$

or

$$\cos \lambda' (\cos \theta \cos \lambda - \sin \theta \sin \lambda) = \sin \lambda (\sin \theta \cos \lambda' + \cos \theta \sin \lambda').$$

Division by $\cos \theta \cos \lambda \cos \lambda'$ gives

$$1 - \tan \theta \tan \lambda = \tan \lambda (\tan \theta + \tan \lambda')$$

or

$$1 - \mu \tan \theta = \mu(\tan \theta + \mu').$$

The solution for $\tan \theta$ is

$$\tan \theta = (1 - \mu\mu')/2\mu.$$

Example 6★ A non-uniform rod of length $2a$ rests horizontally in equilibrium with its ends on two planes, each inclined at $45°$ to the horizontal. The angle of friction at both ends is $30°$. Show that there is a length of the rod $a\sqrt{3}$ within which its centre of gravity must lie.

If the centre of gravity G lies to the left of the mid-point M, the resultant reaction at A must make an angle less than or equal to $30°$ to the left of the normal at A; at B it makes an angle less than or equal to $30°$ to the left of the normal at B. If these two reactions intersect in P, then PG must be vertical for equilibrium. As G varies on the rod, the directions AP, BP adjust themselves to produce equilibrium.

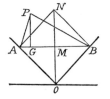

FIG. 142

In particular, GM is greatest when $\angle PAN = \angle PBN = 30°$. Examining the figure, we see that this implies that P, N, A, B are cyclic points, with AB as the diameter of the circle $ABPN$, since $\angle ANB = 90°$. Then $PM = a$, and

$$\angle PMG = 90 - \angle PMN = 90 - 2\angle PBM = 90 - 2 \times 30 = 30°.$$

Hence $GM = a \cos 30 = \tfrac{1}{2}a\sqrt{3}$. A similar contribution exists to the right of M; the maximum range in which G lies is therefore $a\sqrt{3}$.

Example 7* Two rough rods AB, AC are rigidly fastened together at A and held in a vertical plane with A uppermost and $\angle BAC = 90°$, so that they are equally inclined to the vertical. Two small rings, each of mass m, slide on the rods, one on AB and the other on AC. The rings are joined by an inextensible string to the mid-point of which is attached a mass $2m$. If the rings are on the point of sliding downwards when the string makes an angle θ with the upward vertical, prove that $\tan \theta = 2(1 - \mu)/(1 + \mu)$ where μ is the coefficient of friction between each ring and rod.

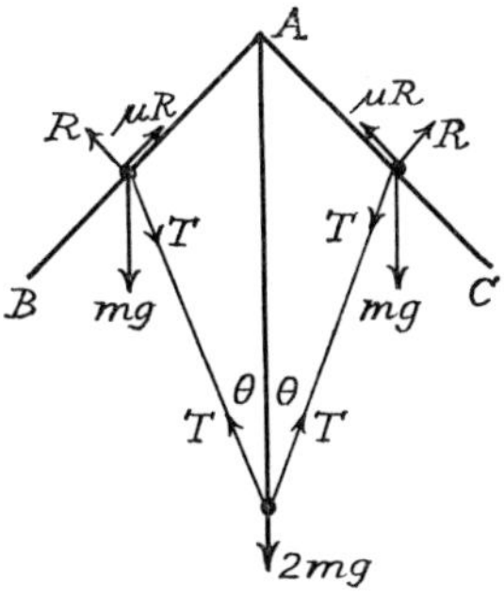

Limiting friction μR acts upwards on each ring along each rod. Resolving vertically for the mass $2m$, we have

$$2T \cos \theta = 2mg.$$

Fig. 143

Resolving along the rod for one ring, we obtain

$$\mu R = mg \cos 45 + T \cos (45 + \theta).$$

Resolving normally to the rod for one ring, we obtain

$$R = mg \sin 45 + T \sin (45 + \theta).$$

We now divide to eliminate R, and at the same time substitute the value of T:

$$\mu = \frac{\cos 45 + \cos (45 + \theta)/\cos \theta}{\sin 45 + \sin (45 + \theta)/\cos \theta}$$

$$= \frac{2 \cos 45 \cos \theta - \sin 45 \sin \theta}{2 \sin 45 \cos \theta + \cos 45 \sin \theta} = \frac{2 - \tan \theta}{2 + \tan \theta}.$$

Hence $\tan \theta = 2(1 - \mu)/(1 + \mu)$.

Revision of graphical statics. The stresses in a freely joined light *framework* may be found graphically by various methods, one of which is known as *Bow's notation*. The equilibrium of the pins at each joint is considered by drawing a polygon of forces, one for each pin. Economy in the number of lines drawn is achieved by using only *one* line in the stress diagram to represent the *two* equal and opposite stresses at each end of any member of the framework. The spaces between the forces are represented by letters. Then if the member AB in the framework has the marked spaces X and Y on each side of it, in the stress diagram a line XY parallel to AB represents the stress in AB. All the external forces may be calculated, and the external letters established in the stress diagram first. The internal letters may be found last. The stress in AB is equal to the length of the line XY (to a suitable scale); whether the stress is a thrust or a tension may be discovered by tracing the directions of the forces round the various polygons.

Example 8 In the framework shown in Fig. 144, all the triangles are equilateral. Find the thrusts in each member if loads 1, 2, 1, 6, 6 act at A, B, C, E, F respectively, and if the framework is supported at D, G.

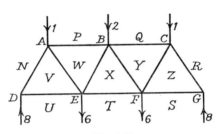

FIG. 144

The spaces between the forces are denoted by N, P, Q, R, S, T, U, V, W, X, Y, Z as shown. The upward external forces at D and G are obviously 8 units each.

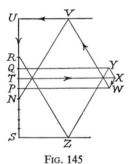

FIG. 145

The points N, P, Q, R, S, T, U are found first, being the spaces between the known external forces. UT is 6 units downwards, TS is 6 down, SR is 8 up, RQ is 1 down, QP is 2 down, PN is 1 down, NU is 8 up.

The internal points V, W, X, Y, Z are now found. For example, V is found by drawing UV horizontally parallel to the member DE and by drawing NV parallel to DA. The stresses in the 11 members are found by measurement or calculation of the lengths in the stress diagram. At the pin E, the polygon of forces is $UTXWV$; UT acts downwards (given); hence TX is to the right, XW downwards, WV upwards and VU to the left. This implies that the force in EF is a tension, in EB a thrust, in EA a tension and in ED a tension. We obtain:

$$\begin{aligned}
\text{Thrust in } DA, \quad CG &= \text{length } NV, \quad ZR = 16a/\sqrt{3}, \\
\text{thrust in } AB, \quad BC &= \text{length } PW, \quad QY = 15a/\sqrt{3}, \\
\text{tension in } DE, \quad FG &= \text{length } VU, \quad ZS = 8a/\sqrt{3}, \\
\text{tension in } AE, \quad CF &= \text{length } VW, \quad YZ = 14a/\sqrt{3}, \\
\text{thrust in } BE, \quad BF &= \text{length } WX, \quad XY = 2a/\sqrt{3}, \\
\text{tension in } EF \quad &= \text{length } TX \quad = 16a/\sqrt{3}.
\end{aligned}$$

22.2   Shearing forces and bending moments

AB is a light beam held horizontally in equilibrium under the action of a number of external forces perpendicular to its length. The force X_i acts at the point P_i at a distance x_i from the end A. For equilibrium we have upon resolving vertically and taking moments about A:

$$\sum_{i=1}^{n} X_i = 0; \qquad \sum_{i=1}^{n} x_i X_i = 0.$$

Let P be any point on the beam such that $x_r < x < x_{r+1}$. Then the portion AP is in equilibrium because the portion PB exerts a *shearing*

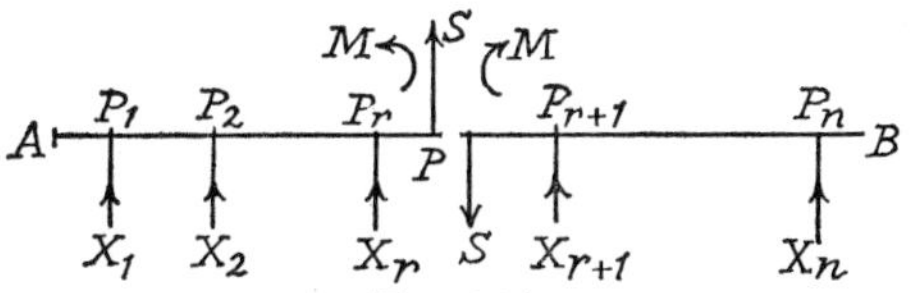

FIG. 146

force S on AP at P; similarly AP exerts a shearing force S in the opposite sense on PB at P. Similarly, PB exerts a couple on AP known as the *bending moment M* at P, and PA exerts an equal and opposite couple on PB. The shearing force S is taken as *positive* if it acts *upwards on the left of a cross-section at P;* the bending moment M is taken as *positive* if it acts *anticlockwise on the left of a cross-section at P.*

Resolving for AP, we have

$$S = -\sum_{i=1}^{r} X_i, \tag{1}$$

and taking moments about P, we obtain

$$M = \sum_{i=1}^{r} X_i(x - x_i). \tag{2}$$

A shearing force diagram and a bending moment diagram may be sketched, on which S and M are plotted against x. As P varies and passes through one of the points P_i at which a discrete force X_i acts, the force X_i is suddenly included in the sum (1). This means that at all points of discrete loading, a discontinuity of value X_i occurs in the shearing force diagram. The bending moment diagram however exhibits a continuous curve, for the term $X_i(x - x_i)$ is suddenly introduced as P passes through P_i; this is zero at P_i and varies continuously thereafter. The gradient of the bending moment diagram suffers a discontinuity at such points of discrete loading.

If the beam is continuously loaded, either uniformly or non-uniformly, let $f(t)$ be the downward force per unit length at a point

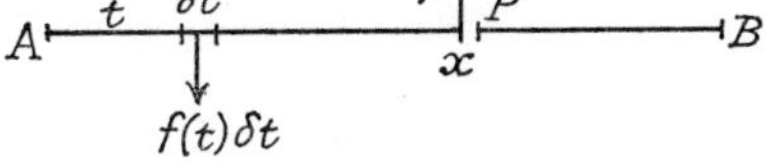

FIG. 147

distant t from A. Then $f(t)\,\delta t$ is the downward force on the element δt, so totally at P,

$$S = \int_0^x f(t)\,dt.$$

Taking moments about P, we have

$$M = -\int_0^x (x - t)f(t)\, dt = \int_0^x tf(t)\, dt - xS.$$

If these equations are differentiated with respect to x, we obtain the differential relationships between S, M and the loading function f:

$$\frac{dS}{dx} = f(x),$$

$$\frac{dM}{dx} = xf(x) - S(x) - x\frac{dS}{dx} = -S,$$

or

$$\frac{d^2M}{dx^2} = -\frac{dS}{dx} = -f(x).$$

In particular, if the beam is of uniform weight w per unit length, then $S = wx$ and $M = \frac{1}{2}wx^2$.

Example 9   A uniform beam ABC, where $AB = 30a$, $BC = 10a$, rests horizontally on supports at A and B. Its weight is $6w$ per unit length and a load $24aw$ is suspended at C. Plot the shearing force and bending moment diagrams and find where the numerical value of the bending moment is greatest.

The weight of the beam $240aw$ acts at the mid-point; hence, taking moments about A, we find that the upward reaction R at B is given by

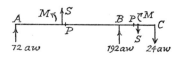

FIG. 148

$$R.30a = 240aw.20a + 24aw.40a,$$

yielding $R = 192aw$. The reaction at A is then found to be $72aw$.

Let $AP = x$. Then for $0 < x < 30a$, resolving and taking moments about P for the portion AP, we obtain

$$S = 6wx - 72aw, \quad M = 72awx - 3wx^2.$$

When $30a < x < 40a$, by considering the portion PC, we have

$$S = -24aw - 6w(40a - x),$$

$$M = -24aw(40a - x) - 3w(40a - x)^2.$$

The shearing force diagram consists of two straight lines, discontinuous when $x = 30a$ at B; the bending moment diagram consists of the arcs of two parabolae, continuous when $x = 30a$ but such that the gradient suffers a discontinuity there.

The maximum value of $|M|$ occurs either at a true stationary point of the graph or at the end point of one of the arcs of the parabolae. We note that $dM/dx = 0$ when $S = 0$, namely when $x = 12a$ within the range $0 < x < 30a$. Hence

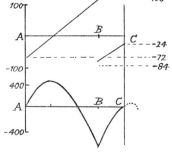

FIG. 149

$$\text{max } M = 72aw.12a - 3w(12a)^2 = 432a^2w.$$

We note that the bending moment vanishes when $x = 24a$, and that a greatest value of $|M|$ exists at the cusp $x = 30a$. At this point, we have

$$M = 72aw.30a - 3w(30a)^2 = -540a^2w.$$

It follows that throughout the whole range $0 < x < 40a$, the maximum value of $|M|$ is $540a^2w$.

Example 10 An isosceles triangular lamina, whose base is h and whose height is $36h$, rests horizontally, supported at its vertex A and by a horizontal rod perpendicular to its symmetrical median, three quarters of the way down this median from the vertex. If its weight is w per unit area, find the value of the bending moment everywhere and its greatest value.

The total weight of the lamina is $18wh^2$ acting at its centre of gravity two thirds of the way down the median from A. If R is the reaction due to the rod at $x = 27h$, we obtain by taking moments about A:

$$18wh^2.24h = R.27h,$$

yielding $R = 16wh^2$. The reaction at A is then found to be $2wh^2$.

The weight of the triangle whose median is AP is

$$\tfrac{1}{2}wxy = \tfrac{1}{2}wx.\tfrac{1}{36}x = \tfrac{1}{72}wx^2$$

acting at a point distant $\tfrac{1}{3}x$ from P. Hence, at P,

$$M = 2wh^2x - \tfrac{1}{3}.\tfrac{1}{72}wx^3.$$

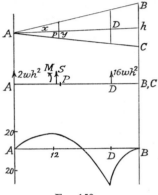

FIG. 150

To find the largest value of M, we calculate dM/dx. This value, $2wh^2 - \tfrac{1}{72}wx^2$, vanishes when $x = 12h$ lying between A and D. At this point, $M = 16wh^3$. Moreover, at the cusp at D where $x = 27h$, we find that $M = -37\tfrac{1}{8}wh^3$. It follows that $|M|$ is greatest at the rod D.

When $27h < x < 36h$, we have

$$M = 2wh^2x - \tfrac{1}{216}wx^3 + 16wh^2(x - 27h)$$
$$= 18wh^2x - \tfrac{1}{216}wx^3 - 16.27wh^3.$$

It may be checked that $dM/dx = 0$ when $x = 36h$, since the shearing force vanishes there. This stationary point for M is irrelevant in our search for max $|M|$, since $M = 0$ at a free end.

22.3   The deflexion of a beam

The bending moment at any section of a stressed beam is established by means of the elastic forces within the material of the beam. We shall measure x horizontally and y vertically downwards, in order that displacements downwards should be positive. It is assumed that plane cross-sections remain plane upon bending; changes in cross-section are ignored. Portions of the beam on its convex side are elongated relative to those of the concave side. A certain strip along the beam, originally a plane horizontal strip, suffers neither contraction

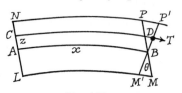

FIG. 151

nor elongation; this is the *neutral plane AB* along which we take the *x* axis.

$LM = AB = NP = x$ are unstretched positions; NP extends to NP', LM contracts to LM'. Consider the *filament CD*, at the signed distance z from AB. The extension is $z\theta$, where $\angle PBP' = \theta$; the relative elongation (*strain*) is $z\theta/x$. If T is the force (tension) acting on the end of the filament at D, and if the cross-sectional area of the filament is δS, the *stress* equals $T/\delta S$. Finally, if E is *Young's modulus* for the material, we have

$$T/\delta S = Ez\theta/x,$$

or
$$T = Ez\,\delta S\,\theta/x.$$

The total tension over the section $P'BM'$ is $\Sigma Ez\,\delta S\,\theta/x$, which must vanish under *simple bending* for which no total tension exists. Hence $\Sigma z\,\delta S = 0$, so the line cut by the neutral plane on the section at $P'BM'$ must contain the centroid of the section.

If θ is small, and if ρ is the radius of curvature at B, we have $x = \rho\theta$.

The clockwise bending moment M over the section at B is produced by these internal elastic forces, acting *on* the portion $NP'M'L$ by the rest of the beam. Taking moments about the horizontal line through B, we have

$$M = \sum Tz = \sum Ez^2\,\delta S\,\theta/x = E(\sum z^2\,\delta S)/\rho = EI/\rho,$$

where $I = \Sigma z^2\,\delta S$ is the second moment of area of the cross-section at B about the horizontal line through B perpendicular to the plane depicted in Fig. 151. The product EI, commonly denoted by B, is termed the *flexural rigidity* of the beam; for simple beams it is a constant.

Finally, if the curvature is small, we have $\rho = 1/(d^2y/dx^2)$, yielding

$$M = EI\,d^2y/dx^2. \tag{3}$$

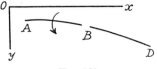

FIG. 152

At any point B, note that M equals the anticlockwise moment about B of all forces acting on AB, or the clockwise moment about B of all forces acting on BD.

If the beam rests on supports at various points, normal reactions act there and contribute to M; similarly the weight of the beam or a variable distribution of load contribute to M. If one end is clamped, a *clamping couple* exists in addition to a reaction at the clamp. For one beam, only two direct equations (found by resolving and taking moments) are available for these unknowns; those in excess of two must be treated as unknowns throughout the analysis. Moreover, if the beam rests on a support at a point D, then the functional form of M on one side of D differs from that on the other side of D. Equation (3) therefore possesses different integrals and arbitrary constants on each side of D. These two solutions are joined together by using the physical facts that both y and dy/dx are continuous at D.

Example 11 ABC is a uniform beam whose weight is w per unit length, such that $AB = a$, $BC = 3a$. It is supported freely at B and is maintained in a horizontal

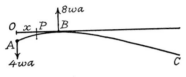

FIG. 153

position by a weight $4wa$ suspended from A. Prove that the ratio of the deflexion at A to that at C is $35:243$.

If $AP = x$ and if $0 < x < a$, the bending moment M at P equals the sum of the anticlockwise moments about P of forces acting on AP:

$$EIy'' = M = \tfrac{1}{2}wx^2 + 4wax$$

yielding

$$EIy' = \tfrac{1}{6}wx^3 + 2wax^2 + D,$$

$$EIy = \tfrac{1}{24}wx^4 + \tfrac{2}{3}wax^3 + Dx + F.$$

Similarly for points between B and C we have

$$EIy'' = \tfrac{1}{2}w(4a - x)^2,$$

yielding

$$EIy' = -\tfrac{1}{6}w(4a - x)^3 + G$$

$$EIy = \tfrac{1}{24}w(4a - x)^4 + Gx + H.$$

At B, where $x = a$, both y' and y are continuous and $y = 0$. Moreover, $y' = 0$ at B since the vertical reaction $8wa$ must be normal to the beam. Hence

$$EIy' = \tfrac{1}{6}wa^3 + 2wa^3 + D = -\tfrac{1}{6}w(3a)^3 + G = 0,$$

$$EIy = \tfrac{1}{24}wa^4 + \tfrac{2}{3}wa^4 + Da + F = \tfrac{1}{24}w(3a)^4 + Ga + H = 0,$$

yielding $D = -\tfrac{13}{6}wa^3$, $G = \tfrac{9}{2}wa^3$, $F = \tfrac{35}{24}wa^4$, $H = -\tfrac{63}{8}wa^4$.

At A, $x = 0$, so the deflexion there is given by $EIy = F$; at C, $x = 4a$, so the deflexion is given by $EIy = 4aG + H$. The ratio of these deflexions is

$$\frac{F}{4aG + H} = \frac{\tfrac{35}{24}}{4 \times \tfrac{9}{2} - \tfrac{63}{8}} = \frac{35}{243}.$$

Example 12 A uniform beam AB of length a is clamped horizontally at one end A, and the other end B is supported freely on the same horizontal level as the clamp. Find the position of maximum deflexion, taking $24w$ as the weight per unit length of the beam.

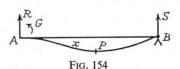

FIG. 154

The unknown reactions R and S together with a clamping couple G are introduced. Since the weight of the beam is $24wa$, we have by resolving

$$R + S = 24wa,$$

and by taking moments about A,

$$G + Sa = 12wa^2.$$

The anticlockwise moment of forces on AP about P is $G - Rx + 12wx^2$, so the equation for the deflexion is

$$EIy'' = G - Rx + 12wx^2$$

subject to the conditions that $y = y' = 0$ when $x = 0$ and that $y = 0$ when $x = a$. Integrating, we obtain

$$EIy' = Gx - \tfrac{1}{2}Rx^2 + 4wx^3$$

where the constant of integration is zero. The second integration yields

$$EIy = \tfrac{1}{2}Gx^2 - \tfrac{1}{6}Rx^3 + wx^4$$

again with a zero constant of integration.

Finally, when $x = a$, we have

$$0 = \tfrac{1}{2}Ga^2 - \tfrac{1}{6}Ra^3 + wa^4,$$

or

$$0 = 3G - Ra + 6wa^2.$$

Taken with equations (4) and (5), we find that $G = 3wa^2$, $R = 15wa$, $S = 9wa$.

The maximum deflexion occurs where $y' = 0$, namely where

$$G - \tfrac{1}{2}Rx + 4wx^2 = 0,$$

reducing to

$$8x^2 - 15ax + 6a^2 = 0.$$

The solutions of this equation are $x = (15 \pm \sqrt{33})a/16$. We choose the negative sign only since this is the only value of x lying in the range $0 < x < a$.

Example 13* A horizontal beam, of length a and weight w per unit length, is clamped horizontally at one end, and supported freely at a point distant $\tfrac{1}{4}a$ from the other end. If the height of the support is adjusted so that both ends are at the same level, show that the beam is horizontal at the free end, and find where the deflexion is greatest.

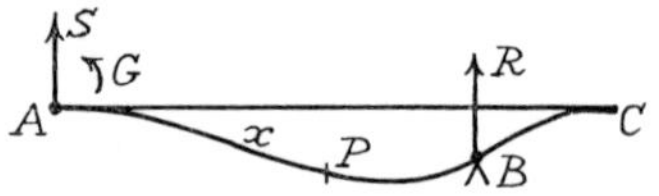

FIG. 155

The reactions R, S and the clamping couple G are introduced as shown. The weight of the beam wa acts at its mid-point, so resolving vertically and taking moments about A, we obtain

$$R + S = wa \quad \text{and} \quad G + \tfrac{3}{4}Ra = \tfrac{1}{2}wa^2,$$

or, upon elimination of R,

$$\tfrac{3}{4}aS = G + \tfrac{1}{4}wa^2. \tag{6}$$

If $AP = x$, when $0 < x < \frac{3}{4}a$ we have

$$EIy'' = G - Sx + \tfrac{1}{2}wx^2,$$

yielding

$$EIy' = Gx - \tfrac{1}{2}Sx^2 + \tfrac{1}{6}wx^3, \qquad (y' = 0 \text{ when } x = 0)$$

$$EIy = \tfrac{1}{2}Gx^2 - \tfrac{1}{6}Sx^3 + \tfrac{1}{24}wx^4. \qquad (y = 0 \text{ when } x = 0).$$

When P lies between B and C the bending moment may be found by taking clockwise moments about P of forces acting on PC:

$$By'' = \tfrac{1}{2}w(a - x)^2,$$

yielding

$$By' = -\tfrac{1}{6}w(a - x)^3 + L,$$

$$By = \tfrac{1}{24}w(a - x)^4 + L(x - a), \qquad (y = 0 \text{ when } x = a).$$

When $x = \frac{3}{4}a$, both y' and y must be continuous; hence

$$EIy' = \tfrac{3}{4}Ga - \tfrac{9}{32}Sa^2 + \tfrac{27}{384}wa^3 = -\tfrac{1}{384}wa^3 + L,$$

$$EIy = \tfrac{9}{32}Ga^2 - \tfrac{9}{128}Sa^3 + \tfrac{81}{6144}wa^4 = \tfrac{1}{6144}wa^4 - \tfrac{1}{4}La.$$

Solving these two equations with equation (6), we obtain $L = 0$, $G = \tfrac{1}{18}wa^2$ and $S = \tfrac{11}{27}wa$. The fact that $L = 0$ implies that $y' = 0$ when $x = a$.

The maximum deflexion occurs when $y' = 0$. Between $x = 0$ and $x = \frac{3}{4}a$ we have

$$\tfrac{1}{18}wa^2x - \tfrac{11}{54}wax^2 + \tfrac{1}{6}wx^3 = 0,$$

or

$$9x^2 - 11ax + 3a^2 = 0.$$

The only valid solution is $x = (11 - \sqrt{13})a/18$.

22.4 Theory of struts

If forces act at the ends of a beam both normally and tangentially along the beam, both these forces contribute to the bending moment at a point P. The integration of equation (3) is then quite different from that considered in examples 11–13.

Example 14★ A light vertical rod AB of length h is clamped at its lower end A, and a load W is placed on the end B. B is constrained to remain vertically above A, but other points are displaced sideways. If y is the displacement sideways from AB of a point P distant x from A, and M is the moment of the couple exerted by the clamp, show if y is small that

$$EIy'' = M(h - x)/h - Wy.$$

Solve this equation, and establish that $\alpha h = \tan \alpha h$ where $\alpha^2 = W/EI$. Show that the maximum displacement occurs where $x = (2/\alpha) \tan^{-1} \alpha h$.

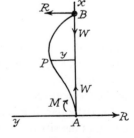

FIG. 156

At B, a horizontal reaction R is exerted by the guide on the rod; at A, the reaction has components W and R as shown. At P, the bending moment equals the clockwise moment about P of all forces acting on AP:

$$EIy'' = M - Wy - Rx.$$

Since there must be no bending moment at B, we have $M - Rh = 0$, yielding

$$EIy'' = M - Wy - Mx/h$$

or
$$EIy'' + Wy = M(h - x)/h$$

when R is eliminated.

The complementary function of this second order equation is

$$y = C \cos \alpha x + D \sin \alpha x,$$

and the particular integral is

$$y = M(h - x)/hW,$$

yielding
$$y = C \cos \alpha x + D \sin \alpha x + M(h - x)/hW$$

for the general solution. When $x = 0$, both y and y' vanish, giving

$$C + M/W = 0, \qquad \alpha D - M/hW = 0.$$

Hence
$$y = -(M/W) \cos \alpha x + (M/Wh\alpha) \sin \alpha x + M(h - x)/hW.$$

Finally, when $x = h$ we require $y = 0$, giving

$$\tan \alpha h = \alpha h,$$

possessing a series of solutions for αh. Let $p = \alpha h$ ($\pi < p < \frac{3}{2}\pi$) be the smallest positive solution. This result implies that there must be a relationship between EI, W, h for buckling to be possible, namely $Wh^2 = EIp^2$. If W is gradually increased from zero, buckling will suddenly take place when it attains this critical value.

The maximum displacement occurs when $y' = 0$, namely when

$$0 = (M/W)\alpha \sin \alpha x + (M/Wh) \cos \alpha x - M/Wh,$$

or
$$\alpha h \sin \alpha x + \cos \alpha x = 1.$$

Expressed in terms of half angles, this equation is

$$2\alpha h \sin \tfrac{1}{2}\alpha x \cos \tfrac{1}{2}\alpha x = 2 \sin^2 \tfrac{1}{2}\alpha x,$$

giving
$$\alpha h = \tan \tfrac{1}{2}\alpha x,$$

or
$$x = (2/\alpha) \tan^{-1} \alpha h.$$

22.5 Revision notes on hydrostatics

If δS is a small element of area within a liquid at rest, the liquid on one side of δS exerts a normal force across δS on the liquid on the other side of δS. The *pressure p* at a point within δS is defined to be the limiting value of this normal force divided by δS. Moreover the pressure p at the point P is independent of direction; whatever the orientation of the element δS at P, the normal force across it is $p \, \delta S$.

In particular, if P is at a depth h below the free surface of a liquid of constant density σ, then $p = \sigma g h$ in absolute units. If an atmospheric pressure Π exists above the free surface, the pressure at P is $\sigma g h + \Pi$. If a liquid of density σ_1 and depth h_1 rests on the top of a liquid of density σ_2, then the pressure at a depth h_2 in the second liquid is

$$p = \sigma_1 g h_1 + \sigma_2 g h_2.$$

The total force on a submerged plane area. Let the plane area A be submerged in liquid of density σ, such that its normal makes an angle θ with the vertical. Let δS be an element of area of this submerged lamina, at depth h. The force exerted by the liquid *above* on the element

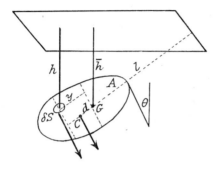

FIG. 157

is given by $p\ \delta S = \sigma g h\ \delta S$ normal to the lamina. All such forces being parallel, the *total thrust* is obtained by addition, namely $\sigma g \Sigma h\ \delta S$. But if $\bar{h}$ is the depth of the centroid of the area A, we have $\Sigma h\ \delta S = \bar{h} A$. Hence the total thrust equals $\sigma g \bar{h} A$. Its horizontal and vertical components are $\sigma g \bar{h} A \sin\theta$ and $\sigma g \bar{h} A \cos\theta$ respectively. The vertical component is merely the weight of liquid vertically above A (or that would be above A were it not for some submerged obstacle between A and the free surface). If an atmospheric pressure exists at the free surface, the total thrust is increased by ΠA.

The centre of pressure. This is the point of the lamina at which the resultant thrust acts. To find this point, it is necessary in general to take moments about two axes, but in elementary examples, any vertical axis of symmetry naturally contains the centre of pressure, so its depth is all that we need calculate.

Let y be the distance between horizontal lines drawn in the lamina through δS and G. Then the moment about this line through G of the element of thrust on δS is

$$\sigma g h y\ \delta S = \sigma g (\bar{h} + y \sin\theta) y\ \delta S.$$

The total moment is then given by

$$\sigma g (\Sigma\ \bar{h} y\ \delta S + \sin\theta \Sigma\ y^2\ \delta S) = \sin\theta \sigma g I,$$

since $\Sigma y\ \delta S = 0$. Here, I is the second moment of area about the line through G. If d is the distance between the line through G and a parallel line through the centre of pressure C, this total moment also equals the moment of the total thrust acting at C, namely

$$d . \sigma g \bar{h} A = \sin \theta \, \sigma g I,$$

yielding $d = \sin \theta \, I / \bar{h} A.$

Finally, if k is the radius of gyration of the area about this line through G, then $I = Ak^2$, yielding

$$d = \sin \theta \, k^2 / \bar{h} = k^2 / l$$

where l is the distance between G and the water-line.

If the lamina is vertical, $l = \bar{h}$, so the centre of pressure is at a depth $k^2 / \bar{h}$ below G.

If k^2 is not known, it must be found by integration; under these circumstances it may be more direct to integrate the element of moment itself. However, for elementary shapes, k^2 should be known.

For a *rectangle* of horizontal width $2a$ and length $2b$, G is at the centre and $k^2 = \frac{1}{3}b^2$. For a *circle* of radius a, G is at the centre and $k^2 = \frac{1}{4}a^2$.

For a *vertical triangle*, with one edge in the liquid surface, and of height H, we proceed as follows: The square of the radius of gyration about $A'A''$, distant $\frac{1}{3}H$ from the water line, must be the same as that for the rectangle on the same base and with the same height, namely $\frac{1}{3}(\frac{1}{2}H)^2$. Hence, by the principle of parallel axes, the square of the radius of gyration about $G'G''$ containing the centroid G one-third of the way down the median is given by $\frac{1}{3}(\frac{1}{2}H)^2 - (\frac{1}{6}H)^2 = \frac{1}{18}H^2$. Hence the depth of

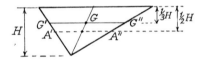

FIG. 158

the centre of pressure below the centroid is $\frac{1}{18}H^2 / \frac{1}{3}H = \frac{1}{6}H$. Finally the depth of the centre of pressure below the liquid surface is $\frac{1}{6}H + \frac{1}{3}H = \frac{1}{2}H$.

Similarly, if one vertex of a vertical triangle is in the liquid surface, and if the opposite side is horizontal at depth H, then the centre of pressure lies on the median at a depth $\frac{3}{4}H$.

More complicated figures can be subdivided into triangles and rectangles; sometimes parts must be added or subtracted from the main figure in order to yield the two standard triangles just considered. If liquids of various densities form horizontal layers, the resultant centre of pressure is found by dividing the total thrust up into several distinct parts, as example 15 shows.

Example 15 Liquid of depth $2a$ and density $\frac{1}{2}\sigma$ rests on top of liquid of depth $2a$ and density σ. A vertical rectangular plate of height $4a$ is submerged with one edge in the surface. Find the depth of the centre of pressure.

To reduce this problem to the standard cases, we regard the whole liquid as being of density $\frac{1}{2}\sigma$, plus extra liquid for the lower portion of height $2a$ of density $\frac{1}{2}\sigma$. The total thrust on the left-hand portion of the figure is $\frac{1}{2}\sigma g.2a.4ab$, while the depth of its centre of pressure is given by

$$2a + \tfrac{1}{3}(2a)^2/2a = \tfrac{8}{3}a.$$

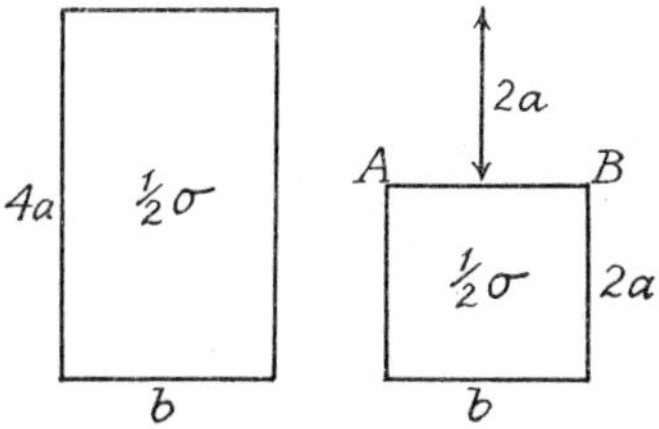

The total thrust on the right-hand portion is $\frac{1}{2}\sigma g.a.2ab$ while its centre of pressure is at the depth $a + (\frac{1}{3}a^2)/a = \frac{4}{3}a$ below AB. Its total depth is therefore $\frac{10}{3}a$.

If d is the depth of the resultant centre of pressure, we have

$d \times$ total thrust

= total moment about the surface,

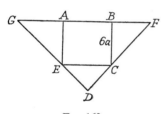

FIG. 159

namely $\qquad d(4\sigma g a^2 b + \sigma g a^2 b) = 4\sigma g a^2 b.\tfrac{8}{3}a + \sigma g a^2 b.\tfrac{10}{3}a,$

giving $\qquad\qquad d = (\tfrac{32}{3} + \tfrac{10}{3})a/5 = \tfrac{14}{5}a.$

Example 16 A plane lamina $ABCDE$, consisting of a square $ABCE$ of side $6a$ and an isosceles triangle CDE with $\angle CDE = 90°$, is immersed vertically in a uniform liquid with the edge AB in the surface. Find the depth of the centre of pressure.

The sides DC and DE are continued to the liquid surface, thereby forming a series of triangles each with one edge in the surface. The depth of D is clearly $9a$. We note that

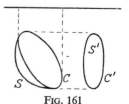

FIG. 160

thrust on $ABCDE$

= thrust on GFD − thrust on GAE

− thrust on BFC

= thrust on GFD − 2 × thrust on GAE,

moment of thrust on $ABCDE$ about GF

= moment of thrust on GFD

− 2 × moment of thrust on GAE.

But the area of GFD is $81a^2$, the depth of its centroid is $3a$ and of its centre of pressure $\frac{9}{2}a$. For GAE, the values are $18a^2$, $2a$, $3a$ respectively. Hence, if d is the depth of the centre of pressure of $ABCDE$, we have

$$d(\sigma g.81a^2.3a - 2\sigma g.18a^2.2a) = \sigma g.81a^2.3a.\tfrac{9}{2}a - 2\sigma g^2.18a^2.2a.3a,$$

giving

$$d = \frac{81.3.\frac{9}{2} - 2.18.2.3}{81.3 - 2.18.2}a = \frac{195}{38}a.$$

Thrust on a curved surface. A curved surface S is given bounded by the closed rim C. The vertical component of the total fluid thrust over C must equal the weight of liquid vertically above C, as indicated by the vertical dotted lines in Fig. 161. This vertical component acts at the centre of gravity of this volume of liquid. Moreover, this result is quite

FIG. 161

18

independent of whether there is or is not any liquid actually above S; a solid obstacle may be placed between S and the liquid surface. The result depends only on the pressure at points of S, and this in turn depends only on the total head of liquid. If S is a closed surface, the vertical upthrust must equal the weight of liquid that would be contained within S, and it acts at the centre of gravity of this liquid.

Let the rim C be projected horizontally onto a vertical plane yielding a plane area S' bounded by a rim C'. The liquid between S and S' is in horizontal equilibrium, so the horizontal thrust across S must equal the horizontal thrust across S'. Since S' is a plane area, the total thrust across it and also its centre of pressure can easily be found.

There can be no resultant horizontal thrust on a closed surface S.

The combination of the horizontal and vertical thrusts thus found yields the resultant thrust.

Floating bodies.   If a body of volume V and specific gravity s floats in liquid of specific gravity s', let us suppose that only a portion V' is submerged. The upthrust produced by the liquid on the body, being the weight of liquid with volume V', is equal to $V'\sigma g s'$, acting at the *centre of buoyancy*, namely the centre of gravity of such a volume V' of liquid. The weight of the body $V\sigma g s$ acts at its centre of gravity.

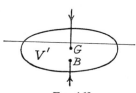

FIG. 162

If this body floats freely in equilibrium (with the stability of this equilibrium, however, we are not concerned), the line GB must be vertical, and $V'\sigma g s' = V\sigma g s$, or $V's' = Vs$.

If it is required to maintain the body in equilibrium in any other position for which GB is not vertical, an additional external force must be applied at some suitable point. If only one force is applied, it must be vertical. Let U be the upthrust acting at the centre of buoyancy B; let W equal the weight of the body acting at G, and let T be the applied vertical force acting at P. Resolving for equilibrium, we have

$$T + U = W,$$

and taking moments about P say,

$$Ua = Wb.$$

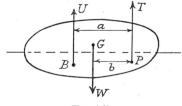

FIG. 163

These two equations enable us to find two unknowns that may be introduced into the problem.

Thrust on part of a closed surface containing liquid. S is part of a closed surface containing liquid, while P is a plane surface across its rim. At the highest point of S we assume that the pressure is zero. U, V, X, Y are the fluid thrusts *on the sides* shown in the diagram. These forces act in the opposite sense *on the liquid* of weight W. For the equilibrium of the liquid, we have $U = X$, $V = Y - W$.

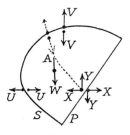

FIG. 164

Now X and Y may easily be calculated, since P is a plane surface; hence U and V may be found. From these values, the magnitude and direction of the resultant thrust on S may be found. Moreover, the resultant of X and Y acts normally to the plane P at its centre of pressure. If this line of action cuts the vertical through G in A, then the resultant of U and V must pass through this point A.

Example 17 A square lamina of side $2a$ and of uniform thickness floats vertically in water with one vertex immersed; the water-line making an angle $\theta < 45°$ with one immersed side. Find the length of the water-line if the lamina can be supported by a vertical force applied to its centre.

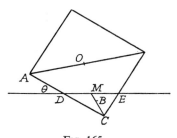

FIG. 165

Since the external force and the weight of the lamina act at its midpoint O, the only other force, namely the liquid upthrust, must also act in this same vertical line. Hence the centre of buoyancy B is vertically below O.

The horizontal distance of O from the vertical through A is $AO \cos (45 - \theta)$; the horizontal distance of B from the vertical through A is

$$AD \cos \theta + DM + MB \cos \angle EMC.$$

These two distances must be equal. Now $AO = a\sqrt{2}$, $AD = 2a - DC = 2a - DE \cos \theta$, $DM = \frac{1}{2}DE$, $MB = \frac{1}{3}MC = \frac{1}{3}MD = \frac{1}{6}DE$, and $\angle EMC = 2\angle MDC = 2\theta$, since M is the centre of the circle CDE. Hence

$$a\sqrt{2} \cos (45 - \theta) = (2a - DE \cos \theta) \cos \theta + \frac{1}{2}DE + \frac{1}{6}DE \cos 2\theta,$$

or $\quad a(\cos \theta + \sin \theta) = 2a \cos \theta + DE(\frac{1}{2} - \cos^2 \theta + \frac{1}{3}\cos^2 \theta - \frac{1}{6})$,

or $\quad a(\sin \theta - \cos \theta) = DE(\frac{1}{3} - \frac{2}{3}\cos^2 \theta) = \frac{1}{3}DE (\sin^2 \theta - \cos^2 \theta)$.

Hence $\qquad\qquad\qquad DE = 3a/(\cos \theta + \sin \theta)$.

Example 18★ $ABCD$ is the central cross-section of a uniform rectangular block, for which $AB = 4a$, $BC = 3a$. The block floats in water with the edges through B and D in the surface and is supported by a string attached to A, which is out of the water. Show that the string is vertical, and prove that the tension in the string is one quarter of the weight of the block. Find also the specific gravity of the block.

If s is the specific gravity of the block of unit thickness, its weight W is $12a^2s$ practical units, assuming unit density for water. Since this and the upthrust $U = 6a^2$, acting at G' the centroid of BCD, are both vertical, it follows that T must be vertical. Resolving vertically, we obtain

$$12a^2s = T + 6a^2, \tag{7}$$

and taking moments about G, we have

$$T(4a \cos \angle ABD - BG)$$
$$= 6a^2 . \tfrac{1}{3}(BG - BC \cos \angle CBD),$$

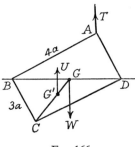

Fig. 166

or $\quad T(\tfrac{16}{5}a - \tfrac{5}{2}a) = 2a^2(\tfrac{5}{2}a - \tfrac{9}{2}a).$

Hence $\quad T = 2a^2 \dfrac{25 - 18}{32 - 25} = 2a^2.$

From equation (7), we now obtain $s = \tfrac{2}{3}$. Finally, the weight of the block is $W = 12a^2s = 8a^2$, showing that $T = \tfrac{1}{4}W$.

Example 19★ A uniform solid wooden hemisphere, of radius a, is smoothly pivoted to a point on the circumference of its base to the bottom of a tank of water. The hemisphere is in equilibrium and is just covered by the water. Find (i) the angle which the base makes with the horizontal; (ii) the angle which the resultant thrust on the curved surface of the hemisphere makes with the vertical.

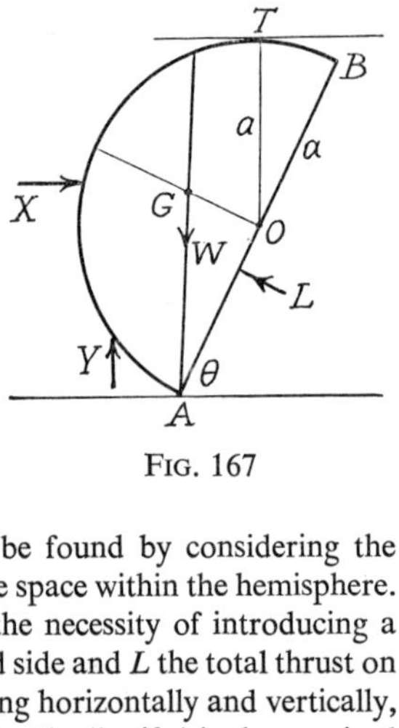

The total liquid force on the hemisphere consists of the vertical upthrust $\tfrac{2}{3}\pi a^3$ acting at G, the centre of gravity of the displaced liquid ($OG = \tfrac{3}{8}a$). The weight of the hemisphere also acts at G, and the only other force acting must be a vertical reaction at A. For equilibrium, these three forces must lie in the same straight line, so G is vertically above A. Hence

$$\tan \theta = \tan \angle OGA = OA/OG = \tfrac{8}{3},$$

Fig. 167

The thrusts on the sides of the hemisphere may be found by considering the equilibrium of a similar volume of water occupying the space within the hemisphere. Such a volume is of course in equilibrium without the necessity of introducing a reaction at A. If X and Y are the thrusts on the curved side and L the total thrust on the plane base, we have $L = \pi a^2 . a$; hence, by resolving horizontally and vertically, we obtain $X = \pi a^3 \sin \theta$ and $Y = \tfrac{2}{3}\pi a^3 - \pi a^3 \cos \theta$. Finally, if ϕ is the required angle, we have

$$\tan \phi = \frac{X}{Y} = \frac{\sin \theta}{\tfrac{2}{3} - \cos \theta} = \frac{24}{2\sqrt{73} - 9}.$$

EXERCISES

(1)★. The triangle ABC is isosceles and right-angled at A; BCD is an equilateral triangle on the other side of BC. Forces of 3, 2, 3, 10, 14 lb. wt. act along AB, BC, CA, BD, CD in the direction indicated by the order of the letters. Prove that the line of action of the resultant force is at a distance $(\sqrt{3}/15)AB$ from A. (Use the internal and external bisectors at A as axes.)

(2)*. $ABCD$ is a square; forces of magnitudes 3, 2, 4, 3, P units act along AB, CB, CD, AD, DB respectively in directions indicated by the order of the letters. If the system is equivalent to a couple, find the value of P.

(3)*. A system of coplanar forces has anticlockwise moments M, $\frac{2}{3}M$, $\frac{3}{2}M$, respectively about the points $(0, 0)$; $(a, 0)$; $(0, 2a)$ in its plane. Calculate the magnitude of the resultant of the forces and prove that the equation of its line of action is $3y - 4x + 12a = 0$.

(4)*. Two equal uniform rods AB, BC each of weight W are smoothly jointed at B, and the ends A and C are joined by a light string. The system hangs in a vertical plane suspended from A, and C is lower than B. If AB, BC make acute angles θ, ϕ respectively with the vertical, show that

$$3 \sin \theta = \sin \phi, \quad 2T = W \sin \phi \operatorname{cosec} \tfrac{1}{2}(\theta + \phi),$$

where T is the tension in the string.

(5)*. Two planes inclined at 30° to the horizontal meet in a horizontal line. Two smooth cylinders, each of weight W and radius a, rest one in contact with each plane and in contact with each other. A third cylinder of weight W' and radius b rests on top of the two cylinders, touching each along a generator. Find the pressure between the cylinders of radius a. Show that, if $b > a$, equilibrium is possible whatever be the ratio W'/W, but that if $b < a$, equilibrium is possible only if

$$W'/W < [2\sqrt{(b^2 + 2ab)}]/[\sqrt{3}a - \sqrt{(b^2 + 2ab)}].$$

(6)*. A uniform rod AB of weight W and length $2a$ is suspended horizontally by two light strings AC, BD, each of length l. The supports C, D are at the same level; the distance between them is $2a$. The rod is twisted through an angle 2θ by applying a couple in a horizontal plane. Show that, if the strings make angles ϕ with the vertical and L is the moment of the couple,

$$l \sin \phi = 2a \sin \theta, \quad L\sqrt{(l^2 - 4a^2 \sin^2 \theta)} = Wa^2 \sin 2\theta.$$

(7). Two equal square plates of side a are fixed rigidly together along a horizontal edge, such that each plate, being higher than this edge, is inclined at 45° to the horizontal. A rod rests in a vertical plane against the interior surface of one plate and over the remaining horizontal edge of the other plate. Find the length of the rod if it makes an angle θ to the horizontal.

(8)*. Two ladders AB, BC of the same weight W and the same length are smoothly hinged together at their upper ends B. The ladders stand with their lower ends A, C on level ground, each ladder being inclined at an angle θ to the vertical. A man, also of weight W, stands on the ladder AB two-thirds of the way up. If the centre of gravity of each ladder is at its mid-point, calculate the horizontal and vertical components of the reaction at B.

If the coefficient of friction at A and C is 0·4, find the greatest value of θ for which equilibrium is possible.

(9)*. AB, BC are two uniform rods each of weight W and length $10a$. They are freely hinged at B and held in a vertical plane. A is attached to a fixed horizontal axis at a distance $14a$ above the horizontal plane and at right-angles to AB. C rests on a rough horizontal plane and B is $6a$ above the plane. AB can turn freely about A and C is on the same side of A as B. Show that, if the coefficient of friction at C is $\frac{1}{5}$, the least couple that must be applied to the rod AB in the plane ABC to make C move away from A is $61Wa/9$.

(10)*. A thin uniform plate has the shape of the parabola $y^2 = 4x$ lying between the vertex and the latus rectum. It is held in equilibrium by a horizontal force at the vertex so that the latus rectum is horizontal and in contact with a plane which is inclined at 15° to the horizontal. Find the inclination of the plate to the horizontal when it is about to slide up the plane, the coefficient of friction being 0·87.

(11)*. Three equal hemispheres having their bases downwards are placed in contact with each other on a rough horizontal table; if a smooth sphere of the same radius and made of the same substance be placed upon them, show that there will be equilibrium or not according as the coefficient of friction between the hemispheres and the table be greater or less then $\sqrt{2}/5$.

(12)*. A uniform rod rests in contact with two equally rough pegs, passing above one and below the other. The pegs are fixed at a distance a apart, and the line joining them makes an angle θ with the horizontal. Show that if equilibrium is possible the length of the rod must be greater than $a(1 + \mu^{-1} \tan \theta)$. It may be assumed that $\tan \theta > \mu$.

(13)*. A light string connects a point B of a light thin rod AC to a point D of a rough vertical wall. The rod is moved so as to be normal to the wall, the end A touching the wall vertically below D. The coefficient of friction at A is μ, and the string is inclined at an angle θ to the rod. A weight W is attached to the rod at E. Show that if E is between A and B, the rod will remain in equilibrium provided $BE < \mu BA/(\mu + \tan \theta)$. Show also that if $\tan \theta < \mu$, the rod will remain in equilibrium for any position of E between B and C.

(14)*. A framework is made of light rods, smoothly jointed together, forming two equilateral triangles ABC and BCD, with AC horizontal and B above AC. The framework is free to turn in a vertical plane about a pivot through C. A weight of 10 tons is suspended from D and balanced by a weight suspended from A. Find the reaction at C and the stresses in the rods.

(15)*. A framework of five equal light rods AB, BC, CD, DE, EA, freely jointed at their ends, is suspended in a vertical plane with AB horizontal by vertical strings attached to A and B. A load of 10 lb. wt. is hung from the lowest point D and the framework is kept in the form of a regular pentagon $ABCDE$ by a sixth light rod joining E and C. Find the stresses in the rods, indicating which are in tension and which are in thrust.

---

(16)*. A horizontal girder of length 16 ft. rests on two supports 5 ft. from each end. The part of the girder between the supports carries a uniformly distributed load of 160 lb. per ft.; the projecting parts carry uniformly distributed loads of 80 lb. per ft. Calculate the shearing force and the bending moment at any point of the girder at distance x ft. from the mid-point, and show your results on a diagram. (The specified loads include the weight of the girder.)

(17)*. A uniform heavy rod $ABCDE$ of weight W and length a is suspended in a horizontal position by vertical strings attached to the rod at B and D, and a weight W is hung from C; $AB = a/6$, $AC = a/3$, $AD = 2a/3$. Find the tensions in the strings at B and D. Prove that there are two points of the rod (other than the ends) at which the bending moment vanishes, and find the distances of these points from the end A.

(18)*. The end B of a rod AB of length a is attached rigidly to the midpoint of a second rod CD of length b so that the two rods are at right-angles. Both rods may be assumed rigid and their weight neglected. The rod CD is pivoted freely about a fixed point at C, and the end D rests against a stop vertically below C. A load W is attached at A. Find the bending moment and shearing force at any point of CD, and exhibit your results in a diagram.

(19)⋆. A uniform straight rod of length $2a$ and weight $2wa$ is smoothly hinged at one end, and is supported at a point on the same horizontal level distant $3a/2$ from the hinge. A load wa is suspended from the midpoint of the rod. Find the shearing force and bending moment at all points of the rod, and give diagrams to illustrate your results.

(20)⋆. A uniform straight beam of length $2a$ and weight $2aw$ rests horizontally on supports at its ends, and a load of weight $2aw$ is suspended from the beam at distance $a/3$ from one end. Calculate the shearing force and bending moment at distance x from this end; illustrate your results by means of a diagram. Determine where the value of the bending moment is numerically greatest.

(21)⋆. A uniform beam of length $2l$ and weight $2wl$ rests symmetrically on two supports at the same level and a distance $2a$ apart. Show by a series of sketched graphs (not more than four) how the bending moment M varies along the bar for different values of a/l, from a small value up to $a/l = 1$. Find the value of a/l for which the greatest value of $|M|$ is as small as possible.

(22)⋆. A uniform bar, of negligible weight, rests across two smooth pegs, which are at the same level and are situated at the points of trisection of the bar. A weight hangs from the mid-point of the bar. Find the ratio of the sag at the mid-point to the elevation of either end above the level of the pegs.

(23)⋆. A light beam of length l rests on two supports at the same level, one at each end. The beam is subjected to a continuous loading, proportional to distance from one end. Determine the point of the beam at which the deflexion is a maximum.

(24)⋆. A uniform beam, of length $4l$ and weight w per unit length, is supported at two points on the same level, distant l and $3l$ from an end of the beam. Show that the deflexion at the ends is $7wl^4/24EI$ and find the height of the mid-point above the supports.

(25)⋆. A uniform beam AB, of length l and weight wl, rests on smooth rigid supports at its ends A, B and at its mid-point M. A and B are on the same level but M is at a small depth d below AB. Determine d in order that the reactions at the three supports shall be equal.

(26)⋆. A heavy uniform beam of length l is supported at the end A and at the point B where $AB = 2l/3$, both A and B being at the same horizontal level. Prove that the beam is horizontal at B, and find at what distance from A the sag below the level of the supports is greatest.

(27)⋆. A uniform beam AB, of length l and weight W, is clamped horizontally at B and rests on a support, on the same level as B, at the point C where $AC = AB/3$. Determine the reaction at the support and show that the deflexion at A is $5Wl^3/1944EI$.

(28)⋆. A uniform beam of length $2l$ and weight W is clamped horizontally at one end and supported at its mid-point so that the free end is at the same level as the clamp. Find the reactions at the supports and the deflexion and slope at the mid-point.

(29)⋆. A beam of constant flexural rigidity EI and length $2a$, clamped horizontally at both ends, has a concentrated load $4wa$ at its mid-point C. The load intensity is w per unit length over AC and $2w$ over CB. Show that the bending moment at A is $23wa^2/16$ and find the deflexion at C.

(30) *. A loaded beam AB of length l is clamped horizontally at one end A. The weight of the beam and its load are uniformly distributed along AB but the moment of inertia I of the cross-section of the beam is $k(2l - x)$, where k is constant and x is the distance of the section from the end A. Find the deflexion of the free end B.

(31) *. A uniform beam of length $2l$ and constant flexural rigidity EI is clamped horizontally at one end and pinned to the same level at the other. The load intensity at any point is proportional to the product of the distances of the point from the ends. Show that the reaction at the clamp is $13/20$ of the total load and find the deflexion at the mid-point.

(32) *. A light uniform pole of length l and constant flexural rigidity EI is fixed vertically in the ground at its lower end A, and its upper end B is acted upon by a force T which makes an angle α with the downward vertical. The consequent small horizontal deflexion of B is a. Taking the origin at A, measuring x vertically up and y horizontally, state the bending moment at any point $P(x, y)$ of the pole and show that

$$(D^2 + n^2)y = n^2a + n^2(l - x) \tan \alpha$$

where $D = d/dx$ and $EIn^2 = T \cos \alpha$. Solve this differential equation and show that $na = \tan \alpha \, (\tan nl - nl)$.

(33) *. A light thin strut of length l and constant flexural rigidity EI is clamped vertically at its lower end A. At its upper end O (which is vertically above A) the strut is acted upon by a vertical downward force T and a horizontal force R. Taking axes Ox vertically downwards and Oy horizontally (in the sense opposite to R) show that the deflexion y of the strut at any point satisfies the equation

$$EID^2y + Ty = -Rx,$$

where $D = d/dx$. Solve this equation and hence show that if T is gradually increased from zero the strut will remain straight and R will be zero until T reaches a critical value given by the smallest positive root of the equation $\tan nl = nl$ where $EIn^2 = T$.

(34) *. A uniform beam, of length l and weight w per unit length, is clamped horizontally at its ends at the same horizontal level and is acted upon by equal inward horizontal forces P at its ends. If M is the moment of the clamping couple and y is the vertical deflexion at a distance x from one end, prove that

$$EID^2y + Py = M - \tfrac{1}{2}wx(l - x),$$

where $D = d/dx$. Obtain the solution of this equation, subject to the given conditions, and show that $Mn^2 = w - \tfrac{1}{2}wnl \cot \tfrac{1}{2}nl$, where $P = EIn^2$.

(35) *. A light uniform tie rod of length $2l$ has its ends kept horizontal and at the same level. It is subject to constant horizontal tensions T acting through the ends and carries a concentrated load W at its mid-point. Show that the differential equation for the deflexion y at a distance x ($<l$) from one end is

$$EID^2y = Ty + M - \tfrac{1}{2}Wx$$

where $D = d/dx$ and M is the bending moment at an end. Solve this, using hyperbolic functions, and show that M is equal to $(\tfrac{1}{2}W/n) \tanh \tfrac{1}{2}nl$ and the deflexion at the load is $Wl[1 - (2/nl) \tanh \tfrac{1}{2}nl]/2T$, where $EIn^2 = T$.

(36) *. A trapezium $ABCD$ has $AB = a$, $CD = b$, and $AD = BC$. AB and DC are parallel and distant h apart. The trapezium is immersed in a fluid of density ρ with its plane vertical and the edge AB in the surface, which is free from atmospheric pressure. Determine the fluid thrusts on the triangular parts ABD, BDC, and hence prove that the depth of the centre of pressure of the whole trapezium is

$$h(a + 3b)/2(a + 2b).$$

(37)★. A triangle ABC is immersed vertically in water with AB in the surface. Prove that the depth of the centre of pressure of the triangle is one-half the depth of C.

A square of side a is immersed vertically in a liquid, of density ρ, with one vertex in the surface and a diagonal horizontal. Prove that the thrust on the square is $\rho a^3/\sqrt{3}$ and find the depth of the centre of pressure.

(38)★. A uniform rectangular lamina $ABCD$ is immersed in water with AB in the surface and BC, AD vertical. If $AB = 2a$ and $BC = 2b$, prove that the depth of the centre of pressure of the lamina is $4b/3$.

If E is the mid-point of BC and F is the mid-point of DC, find the position of the centre of pressure of the quadrilateral $AECF$.

(39)★. A hollow metal cube of side $2a$ has a square opening of side a in its upper face. One end of a vertical pipe of length $4a$ and of square cross-section of side a is soldered to the edges of the opening. The vessel formed is filled with liquid of total weight W. Find the thrust on the base of the vessel and explain why it is larger than W. Find also the magnitude and the line of action of the thrust on one of the vertical faces of the cube.

(40)★. Two equal light hemispherical shells can be fitted together to form a sphere which is water-tight on closing two small catches which are at points A and B at opposite ends of a diameter of the common rim of the two hemispheres. If the sphere is placed with the point A resting on a horizontal table and is filled with a weight W of water poured through a small hole near B, find the least pair of equal and opposite forces that must be applied at B to prevent the hemispheres from separating when the catch B is released.

(41)★. If the area enclosed by the parabola $x^2 = 4ay$, with the line $y = 4a$ as surface line and vertex downwards, is immersed in liquid with its plane vertical, find the depth of the centre of pressure.

(42)★. A cubical box, filled with water, is closed by a water-tight lid of negligible weight, which can turn freely about one edge of the cube, and a string is tied symmetrically round the box in a plane which bisects the edge about which the lid turns. The box is placed on a horizontal table with the plane of the lid vertical and the edge about which the lid turns uppermost. Prove that the tension of the string equals one-third of the weight of water.

(43)★. A uniform square lamina of side $2a$ is held vertically with two edges immersed in water, one edge being inclined at θ to the horizontal, where $\theta < \pi/4$, and the length of the water-line section being c. By finding the centre of buoyancy, show that the lamina can be held in this position by a vertical force applied at its centre provided that $c(\cos \theta + \sin \theta) = 3a$.

(44)★. A uniform rod of specific gravity s is suspended at its ends by two vertical strings, and it hangs inclined to the vertical with a fraction $1/n$ of its length immersed in water. Prove that both strings will be taut if $n^2s > 2n - 1$. The rod is to be supported in the same position by a single string, the other two strings being removed. Find where it must be fastened to the rod, given that $s = 2/n$.

(45)★. A solid cone of radius a cm. and height h cm. is joined to a solid cylinder of the same radius and height, the base of the cone being in contact with one end of the cylinder. The specific gravity of the cone is s_1, and that of the cylinder is s_2. The solid formed floats when completely immersed in a liquid of specific gravity s. Prove that $s_1 + 3s_2 = 4s$.

Show that in order to keep the axis of symmetry of the immersed solid horizontal, a couple must be applied. Find the magnitude and sense of this couple when $s_1 = \frac{3}{2}, s_2 = \frac{5}{6}, s = 1$ and $a = h = 4$.

(46)★. The cross-section of a uniform rod of weight W is a right-angled isosceles triangle. The triangle ABC, right-angled at A, is the mid-section. Show that the rod may float in water with the face in which AB lies horizontal, the edge in which C lies under water, and the face in which AC lies half immersed, if a certain force is applied at B. Find the magnitude and direction of this force.

(47)★. A uniform rod of length $2a$ is hinged freely at its upper end to a fixed point at a height less than $2a/3$ above the surface of water. If the specific gravity of the rod is $\frac{8}{9}$, prove that, in equilibrium, two-thirds of its length is immersed in the water. Calculate the action at the hinge as a fraction of the weight of the displaced water.

ANSWERS TO EXERCISES

(2). $\sqrt{2}$.　　(3). $5M/12a$.　　(5). $(W + \frac{1}{2}W')\sqrt{3} - \frac{1}{2}aW'/\sqrt{(b^2 + 2ab)}$.

(7). $4a/[\sqrt{2}\cos\theta\,(\cos\theta + \sin\theta)^2]$.　　(8). $\frac{5}{6}W\tan\theta, \frac{1}{3}W, \tan\theta = \frac{16}{25}$.

(10). $15\cdot1°$.　　(14). 15 tons; AB, BD: $10/\sqrt{3}$ tension; AC: $5/\sqrt{3}$ thrust; BC: $10/\sqrt{3}$ thrust; CD: $20/\sqrt{3}$ thrust.　　(15). AB: 5 tan 18° tension; AE, BC: 5 sec 18° tension; ED, DC: 5 sec 54° tension; EC: $5(\sec 18° + \tan 54°)$ thrust.　　(16). $0 < x < 3$, $S = 160x$, $M = -280 - 80x^2$; $3 < x < 8$, $S = -80(8 - x)$, $M = -40(8 - x)^2$.　　(17). $(1 - \frac{1}{3}\sqrt{6})a, a/\sqrt{3}$.

(18). $S = Wa/b$; $M = -Wax/b, 0 < x < \frac{1}{2}b$; $M = -Wax/b + Wa, \frac{1}{2}b < x < b$.

(19). x measured from the hinged end: $S = -wa + wx$, $M = wax - \frac{1}{2}wx^2$, $0 < x < a$; $S = wx$, $M = -\frac{1}{2}wx^2 + wa^2$, $a < x < \frac{3}{2}a$; $S = -2wa + wx$, $M = -\frac{1}{2}wx^2 + 2wax - 2wa^2$, $\frac{3}{2}a < x < 2a$.　　(20). $S = -\frac{2}{3}aw + wx$, $M = \frac{2}{3}awx - \frac{1}{2}wx^2, 0 < x < \frac{1}{3}a$; $S = -\frac{2}{3}aw + wx$, $M = -\frac{1}{2}wx^2 + \frac{2}{3}wax + \frac{2}{9}wa^2, \frac{1}{3}a < x < 2a$; M is greatest when $x = \frac{2}{3}a$.　　(21). $2 - \sqrt{2}$.　　(22). $\frac{1}{3}$.

(23). $l\sqrt{(1 - 2\sqrt{\frac{2}{15}})}$ from the given end.　　(24). $wl^4/24EI$.　　(25). $7wl^4/1152EI$.

(26). $(1 + \sqrt{33})l/36$.　　(27). $17W/24$.　　(28). $-\frac{1}{8}W, \frac{5}{8}W, 11Wl^3/240EI$, $Wl^2/60EI$.　　(29). $11wa^4/48EI$.　　(30). $y = wl^3(5 - 6\log 2)/12Ek$.

(31). $169l^3W/480EI$.　　(32). $y = (a + l\tan\alpha)(1 - \cos nx) + \tan\alpha(\sin nx - nx)/n$.

(33). $y = R(l\sin nx - x\sin nl)/T\sin nl$.

(34). $y = (Mn^2 - w)(1 - \cos nx)/Pn^2 - \frac{1}{2}wl(nx - \sin nx)/nP + \frac{1}{2}wx^2/P$.

(35). $y = M(\cosh nx - 1)/T + \frac{1}{2}W(nx - \sinh nx)/nT$.　　(36). $\frac{1}{6}ah^2\rho g, \frac{1}{3}bh^2\rho g$.

(37). $7\sqrt{2}a/12$.　　(38). $19b/14$ from AB, $15a/14$ from AD.　　(39). $2W, 5W/3$, $14a/15$ from base.　　(40). $3W/8$.　　(41). $16a/7$.　　(44). a/n from top end.

(45). 32π gm. wt. cm.　　(46). $W/5$ vertically upwards.　　(47). $\frac{3}{4}$.

CHAPTER 23

TOPICS IN ELEMENTARY AND ADVANCED DYNAMICS

23.1 Résumé of dynamical principles applied to a particle

The *force* acting on a particle should *always* be thought of as the *cause* and the associated *rate of change of momentum* as the *effect*; with suitable units, the laws of dynamics identify the values of the cause and the effect. Any other approach to the subject usually leads to confusion of thought and to wrong equations being written down.

Let the particle of mass m (lbs. or grams) be situated at time t (secs.) at the point with coordinates (x, y) (ft. or cms.) with respect to a fixed two-dimensional coordinate system. If the total force components (F_x, F_y) act on the particle at this moment, and if they are measured in poundals or dynes, then the two *equations of motion* of the particle are

$$F_x = m\ddot{x}, \quad F_y = m\ddot{y},$$

where dots denote differentiation with respect to time. These equations, together with the initial conditions $x = a$, $y = b$, $\dot{x} = u$, $\dot{y} = v$ at $t = 0$ define the succeeding motion for all time if the conditions remain unchanged. In particular, the weight of the particle contributes to the force an amount mg *absolute* units vertically downwards, where g is the acceleration due to gravity. It should be noted that in theoretical dynamics, in which absolute units are used throughout, g enters the equations through weights but by *no other means whatsoever*. To convert absolute units of force (poundals or dynes) to *practical* units (lbs. wt. or grams wt.) we divide by g.

The method by which these equations may be integrated depends upon circumstances. If F_x and F_y are given in terms of t, a double integration with respect to t may be carried out. If, as is more often the case, F_x and F_y are functions of position, namely of x, y, we write $\ddot{x} = \dot{x}\, d\dot{x}/dx$ and $\ddot{y} = \dot{y}\, d\dot{y}/dy$ and seek to integrate with respect to x and y. This gives the velocity components as functions of position. A further integration then yields x and y in terms of t, though this can seldom be carried out even for simple systems. If F_x and F_y are given in terms of $\dot{x}$ and $\dot{y}$, we write again $\ddot{x} = \dot{x}\, d\dot{x}/dx$, $\ddot{y} = \dot{y}\, d\dot{y}/dy$, and integrate to find the velocity components in terms of position. These principles of integration may most easily be applied to motion constrained to take place along a straight line, say Ox. The given force may then be a resistance, usually given as a function of the velocity $\dot{x}$ (see sections 20.8, 23.2).

Work. If the point of application of a particular force (F_x, F_y) moves from (x, y) to $(x + \delta x, y + \delta y)$, the *work* done by the force is defined to be $F_x\,\delta x + F_y\,\delta y$ (ft. lbs. wt., ft. pdls., cm. gms. wt., ergs). In vector language, work is the *scalar product* of the force vector and the displacement vector. If the point of application moves along a given curve between the points (a, b) and (c, d), the total work is

$$\int_{x=a}^{x=c} F_x\,dx + \int_{y=b}^{y=d} F_y\,dy$$

integrated along the curve.

The *energy* of a particle in a particular state, with respect to a particular force acting on it, is the work done by an *equal and opposite force* when the state of the particle is changed from a standard state to its particular state. Not all forces produce mechanical energy. Forces that produce energy must be such that no total work is done when the state of the particle is brought back to its original state. Friction is therefore excluded. The author would stress this all-embracing definition of energy, since he finds that students usually have very hazy ideas as to the exact nature of energy. Strictly speaking, it is a definition rather than a physical entity, merely being the first integral of the equations of motion.

The potential energy of a particle. If the axis Oy is measured vertically upwards, let $y = 0$ be the standard height (state) of the particle. The force acting on it is the weight mg absolute units downwards, so its gravitational potential energy at a height $y = h$ above the standard level equals the work done by the force mg *upwards* when moved through this distance h. The result is $V = mgh$.

The potential energy of a stretched elastic string. If zero extension of an elastic string of modulus λ and natural length a is taken as the standard state, and if the general extension x is taken as the general state of the system, then its potential energy equals the work done by a force equal and opposite to the tension in the string in extending the string from zero extension to extension x. When the extension is s, this force is $T = \lambda s/a$ in the direction of s. For an additional small extension δs, the element of work is $T\,\delta s$. Hence, totally,

$$V = \int_0^x T\,ds = \int_0^x \frac{\lambda s\,ds}{a} = \frac{\lambda x^2}{2a}\,.$$

Kinetic energy. This is the work T done by a force F in overcoming the inertia of a particle, when its speed is increased from zero (the standard state) to v (the general state). Now $F = m\ddot{x}$, and the element of work is $F\,\delta x$. Hence, totally,

$$T = \int m\ddot{x}\,dx = \int m\dot{x}\frac{d\dot{x}}{dx}\,dx = \int_0^v m\dot{x}\,d\dot{x} = \tfrac{1}{2}mv^2 \text{ absolute units.}$$

The conservation of energy. A *conservative force* is one for which potential energy exists. If a conservative force (F_x, F_y) acts on a particle of mass m, the equations of motion are

$$m\ddot{x} = F_x, \qquad m\ddot{y} = F_y$$

or
$$m\dot{x}\frac{d\dot{x}}{dx} = F_x, \qquad m\dot{y}\frac{d\dot{y}}{dy} = F_y.$$

Integrating and adding, we obtain

$$\tfrac{1}{2}m(\dot{x}^2 + \dot{y}^2) = \int(F_x\,dx + F_y\,dy) + \text{constant,}$$

or
$$\tfrac{1}{2}mv^2 - \int(F_x\,dx + F_y\,dy) = \text{constant.}$$

Now the potential energy of the particle is $-\int(F_x\,dx + F_y\,dy)$, where the minus sign occurs because in the definition of energy the force used is that *opposite* to the force acting on the particle. Hence

$$T + V = \text{constant.}$$

The separation of energy into kinetic and potential forms thus appears to be a mathematical artifice designed to simplify calculations; the sum of these two forms is the important quantity. The conservation equation is merely a first integral of the equations of motion.

Example 1 A horizontal plank of mass M and of length $24a$ hangs in equilibrium by two elastic strings attached at each end of the plank to a point O. Each string is of natural length $6a$ and of modulus λ. The distance of the plank below O is $5a$. A mass m is slowly placed on the middle point of the plank; find m if the plank falls a distance $11a$ before coming instantaneously to rest.

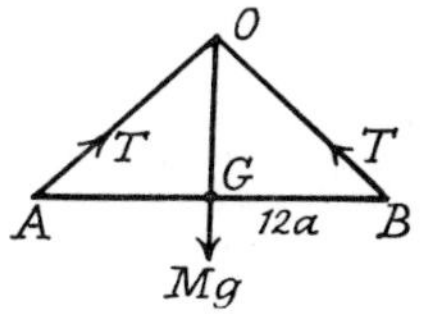

FIG. 168

In equilibrium, $OG = 5a$, $GB = 12a$, yielding $OB = OA = 13a$. The extension in each string is therefore $7a$, giving $T = 7a\lambda/6a = 7\lambda/6$. But resolving vertically, we have

$$Mg = 2T\sin\angle OBG = 2T.\tfrac{5}{13};$$

hence $\lambda = \tfrac{6}{7}T = \tfrac{6}{7}.\tfrac{13}{10}Mg = \tfrac{39}{35}Mg.$

When the plank has fallen an additional distance x, we have

$$OB = \sqrt{[(5a + x)^2 + 144a^2]},$$

so the potential energy of the two strings is $(\lambda/6a)(OB - 6a)^2$. The potential energy of the combined mass with respect to its initial position is $-(M + m)gx$. The equation of conservation of energy is then

$$\tfrac{1}{2}(M + m)v^2 - (M + m)gx + (\lambda/6a)(OB - 6a)^2 = (\lambda/6a)(7a)^2,$$

where the constant on the right-hand side equals the initial elastic energy. Now we are given that $v = 0$ when $x = 11a$; hence $OB = 20a$, giving

$$(\lambda/6a)[(14a)^2 - (7a)^2] = 11(M + m)ga,$$

or
$$\tfrac{13}{70}Mg(196 - 49)a = 11(M + m)ga,$$

or
$$\tfrac{13}{10}.\tfrac{21}{11}M = M + m.$$

This yields $m = \tfrac{163}{110}M$.

Power. Power is the rate at which a force does work, namely the work done per second. If a force F moves its point of application by a distance δx in time δt, the work done is $F\,\delta x$ in time δt. Hence the power, or rate of doing work, is Fv, where $v = dx/dt$. In particular, if F is measured in lbs. wt. and v in ft. per sec., then the quantity $Fv/550$ is termed the *horse-power*.

Two equations may usually be written down in horse-power problems. If T lbs. wt. is the tractive force acting on a body that suffers a resistance R lbs. wt., then we have

$$Tv = 550H, \quad (T - R)g = m\,dv/dt. \qquad (1)$$

Both R and H may be functions of the speed v. If the speed is given to be steady, we conclude that $T = R$ since $dv/dt = 0$. In horse-power problems, special attention should be paid to the units used.

Example 2 If a body is subject to a constant resistance R lbs. wt., and if the horse-power H is also constant, find the velocity-time relationship if $v = 0$ when $t = 0$.

Eliminating T from the two equations just given, we obtain

$$\frac{550Hg}{v} - Rg = m\frac{dv}{dt},$$

or
$$\frac{g\,dt}{m} = \frac{v\,dv}{550H - Rv},$$

or
$$\frac{Rg\,dt}{m} = \left(-1 + \frac{550H}{550H - Rv}\right)dv.$$

Integrating, we obtain

$$\frac{Rgt}{m} + C = -v - \frac{550H}{R}\log(550H - Rv).$$

Choosing C so v and t vanish together, we have

$$\frac{Rgt}{m} = -v - \frac{550H}{R} \log \left(\frac{550H - Rv}{550H} \right).$$

As $t \to \infty$, $v \to 550H/R$, being that value of v for which there is no acceleration.

Example 3* A train, whose weight is 270 tons, is pulled on the level by an engine which develops $20v(1 - v/100)$ horse-power when the speed is v miles per hour. The frictional resistance is proportional to the square of the speed, and the maximum speed is 50 miles per hour. If a speed of v miles per hour is attained, starting from rest, in t hours, prove that

$$dv/dt = (15/77)(50 - v)(100 + v),$$

and show that the time taken to attain 20 miles per hour is about 1·4 min.
  We eliminate T in equations (1), obtaining

$$m \frac{dv}{dt} = \frac{550Hg}{v} - Rg.$$

We replace R by kv^2 lbs. wt., H by $20v(1 - v/100)$ with v in miles per hour, g by 32, v ft. per sec. in the equation by $\frac{88}{60}v$ where v is in miles per hour, t secs. in the equation by $3600t$ where t is in hours, and m by 270×2240 lbs. Then

$$\frac{270 \times 2240 \times 88}{3600 \times 60} \frac{dv}{dt} = \frac{550 \times 32 \times 20v(1 - v/100)}{88v/60} - 32kv^2.$$

It is given that $dv/dt = 0$ when $v = 50$; hence

$$\frac{550 \times 32 \times 20 \times 60(1 - \frac{1}{2})}{88} = 32 \times 50 \times 50k,$$

yielding $k = \frac{3}{2}$. Substituting this value, and simplifying, we obtain

$$dv/dt = 15(50 - v)(100 + v)/77.$$

Arranged for integration, this equation becomes

$$\frac{77}{150} \left(\frac{dv}{50 - v} + \frac{dv}{100 + v} \right) = 15 \, dt,$$

yielding

$$\frac{77}{150} \log \left(\frac{100 + v}{50 - v} \right) - \frac{77}{150} \log 2 = 15t,$$

choosing the constant of integration so that $v = 0$ when $t = 0$. Finally, when $v = 20$ miles per hour, we have

$$t = \frac{77}{150 \times 15} \log_e \frac{120}{2 \times 30} \text{ hours} = \frac{154}{75} \log_e 2 \text{ minutes}.$$

The numerical value of t is 1·4 minutes.

Impulse. Sudden changes in the velocity of a particle are idealized by the introduction of the concept of an *impulse*. Since $F = m\, dv/dt$, we have generally

$$\int_{t_1}^{t_2} F\, dt = \int_{v_1}^{v_2} m\, \frac{dv}{dt}\, dt = mv_2 - mv_1;$$

that is, the increase in momentum is represented by the area under the force-time graph. To deal quantitatively with a sudden increase in velocity, we let $F \to \infty$ and the time during which it acts tend to zero in such a way that the area under the force-time curve remains finite. Its value is the impulse J, being the increase in momentum produced by the impulsive force. We write

$$J = mv_2 - mv_1, \tag{2}$$

where J, v_2 and v_1 all have the *same sense and direction*. In any problem, impulsive tensions and reactions must be inserted; equation (2) refers then to the *total* impulse acting on the particle in the direction in which the velocity components v_1 and v_2 are calculated.

In a collision between two smooth bodies, an additional equation is required. We use *Newton's law*, which states that the positive relative velocity after collision along the common normal equals a constant e multiplied by the positive relative velocity before the collision. The constant e is known as the *coefficient of restitution;* if $e = 1$, the bodies are known as perfectly elastic.

The student should realise that sudden energy changes take place when an impulse acts; the total energy content of a system before an impulse acts is different from the total energy after the application of the impulse.

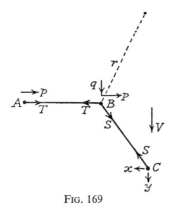

FIG. 169

Example 4 Three particles A, B, C, each of mass m, are joined by equal light strings AB, BC on a smooth horizontal table, such that $\angle ABC = 135°$; C is given a velocity V perpendicular to AB such that the string BC first of all is slack. (i) If the string BC cannot sustain an impulsive tension greater than I, show that $V < 7\sqrt{2}\, I/4m$. (ii) Find the magnitude of the velocity of C relative to A immediately after BC becomes tight.

S and T are the impulsive tensions in the two strings BC and AB. The velocity components immediately after the action of the impulses are x, y for C, p and q for B and p for A. Here, we have used the principle that for a taut string each end must have the same velocity component along the string. The five dynamical equations now become

for A to the right: $T = mp$,   (3)

for B to the right: $S/\sqrt{2} - T = mp$,   (4)

for B downwards: $S/\sqrt{2} = mq$,   (5)

for C downwards: $-S/\sqrt{2} = my - mV$,   (6)

for C to the left: $S/\sqrt{2} = mx$.   (7)

The kinematical condition on the velocity components at B and C is

$$q/\sqrt{2} + p/\sqrt{2} = y/\sqrt{2} - x/\sqrt{2},$$

or
$$q + p = y - x. \tag{8}$$

Equations (3), (4), (7) yield

$$2p = x, \tag{9}$$

which represents the conservation of momentum in the direction AB.

Using equations (5), (3), (6), (7), we eliminate p, q, x, y from (8), obtaining

$$S/\sqrt{2} + T = mV - S/\sqrt{2} - S/\sqrt{2},$$

or
$$3S/\sqrt{2} + T = mV.$$

Also, using equations (3) and (7), we eliminate p and x from equation (9), obtaining

$$2T = S/\sqrt{2}.$$

Hence, $T = mV/7$, $S = 2\sqrt{2}\, mV/7$. Now it is given that $S \leqslant I$, so we conclude that $V \leqslant 7I/2\sqrt{2}m$.

Using these values of S and T, we find that $p = V/7$, $x = 2V/7$, $y = 5V/7$. The components of the velocity of C relative to A are therefore $3V/7$ and $5V/7$; the magnitude of this velocity is $\sqrt{34}\, V/7$.

Motion in a fixed circle. If a particle of mass m is constrained to move in a fixed circle of radius a, its position at a point P at time t is specified by the angle θ made by the radius vector to the particle and a fixed radius. In Cartesian coordinates, we may write

$$x = a \cos \theta, \quad y = a \sin \theta.$$

Differentiating, we obtain

$$\dot{x} = -a\dot{\theta} \sin \theta, \quad \dot{y} = a\dot{\theta} \cos \theta,$$
$$\ddot{x} = -a\ddot{\theta} \sin \theta - a\dot{\theta}^2 \cos \theta, \quad \ddot{y} = a\ddot{\theta} \cos \theta - a\dot{\theta}^2 \sin \theta.$$

The *outward* radial acceleration f_r is given by

$$f_r = \ddot{x} \cos \theta + \ddot{y} \sin \theta = -a\dot{\theta}^2,$$

and the tangential acceleration f_θ is given by

$$f_\theta = \ddot{y} \cos \theta - \ddot{x} \sin \theta = a\ddot{\theta}.$$

In particular, if $\dot\theta = \omega$, a constant, the *inward* radial acceleration is $\omega^2 a = v^2/a$, where the speed v equals $a\dot\theta$.

The external forces, such as weight, together with the forces of constraint (tension in a radial string, or the normal reaction due to a circular wire, etc.) and perhaps a tangential resistive force, are resolved tangentially and radially *inwards*, and equated to the corresponding rates of change of momentum, namely to $ma\ddot\theta$ and $m\dot\theta^2/a$ respectively. In the absence of friction, energy is conserved; the kinetic energy of the particle is taken to be $\frac{1}{2}mv^2 = \frac{1}{2}ma^2\dot\theta^2$.

The fact that the particle tends to fly outwards, and indeed often does so, does *not* indicate that there is a force $ma\dot\theta^2$ acting on it radially *outwards* producing this tendency. If the particle flies outwards, it means that there is not sufficient force directed radially *inwards* to produce the requisite amount of rate of change of momentum $ma\dot\theta^2$ *inwards*. It is the author's grave experience, amongst students and lecturers alike, that usually only mathematicians appreciate this point, and that in engineering text-books much false thinking exists regarding the forces that are operative in circular-motion problems.

Example 5★ Two particles, P and Q, each of mass m, are joined by a light inextensible string. P is held at the top of a horizontal cylinder of radius a. Q hangs freely in space over the cylinder, and then P is released from rest. Show that P leaves the cylinder when the radius to P makes an angle α with the vertical, given by $2\cos\alpha = 1 + \alpha$. Show that the tension at this moment is $\frac{1}{2}mg(1 - \sin\alpha)$.

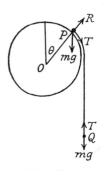

A tension T exists in the string as shown in the diagram. The acceleration of P consists of the component $a\dot\theta^2$ radially inwards and $a\ddot\theta$ tangentially in the direction θ increasing. The acceleration of Q is $a\ddot\theta$ vertically downwards. The three equations of motion are therefore

$$ma\dot\theta^2 = mg\cos\theta - R,$$
$$ma\ddot\theta = T + mg\sin\theta,$$
$$mg - T = ma\ddot\theta.$$

FIG. 170

The integration of these equations is avoided if we write down the equation of energy conservation. The kinetic energy of both particles is $\frac{1}{2}ma^2\dot\theta^2$; the potential energy of Q with respect to its initial position is $-mga\theta$, and that of P is $-mga(1 - \cos\theta)$. The total energy being zero, we have

$$0 = ma^2\dot\theta^2 - mga\theta - mga(1 - \cos\theta),$$

or

$$a^2\dot\theta^2 = ga\theta + ga(1 - \cos\theta).$$

We may now find the values of R and T in terms of position. The first equation of motion yields

$$R = mg\cos\theta - ma\dot\theta^2 = mg\cos\theta - m[g\theta + g(1 - \cos\theta)].$$

The particle leaves the cylinder when $R = 0$, yielding $\theta = \alpha$, where $2\cos\alpha = 1 + \alpha$.

At this moment, we have

$$T = mg - ma\ddot{\theta}$$

$$= mg - ma\dot{\theta}\,\frac{d\dot{\theta}}{d\theta}$$

$$= mg - \tfrac{1}{2}ma\,\frac{d\dot{\theta}^2}{d\theta}$$

$$= mg - \tfrac{1}{2}m\,\frac{d}{d\theta}[g\theta + g(1 - \cos\theta)]$$

$$= \tfrac{1}{2}mg(1 - \sin\alpha).$$

Simple harmonic motion. If the position of a particle is specified by means of the coordinate x and if its equation of motion is of the form

$$\ddot{x} = -n^2 x,$$

the motion is said to be *simple harmonic*. Sometimes, x may be re-stricted in magnitude, for the method of establishing the equation of motion may break down if x becomes too large. For example, an elastic string must remain taut throughout the motion; in intervals of time for which it is slack another equation must be used.

One solution of the equation is $x = a \sin nt$, where a is the amplitude, and such that $x = 0$ when $t = 0$ and such that the particle is moving in the $+x$-direction at $t = 0$. Alternatively, we may use $x = a \cos nt$, where the particle is at rest at the extreme right of its path at $t = 0$. The velocity of the particle is connected with its position by the formula

$$v = \pm n\sqrt{(a^2 - x^2)},$$

the sign being chosen according to circumstances. The period of the oscillations is $2\pi/n$, and the frequency is $n/2\pi$.

Small oscillations. Many oscillatory systems are not simple har-monic in character, but if the amplitude of the oscillation is small enough, the motion of most systems approximates very closely to simple harmonic motion. Let the position of a particle be specified by a general coordinate q (a length, or an angle, for example). We shall denote its potential energy by $V(q)$; its kinetic energy will contain the term $\dot{q}^2$ perhaps multiplied by a function of q, say $f(q)$. For a con-servative system,

$$V(q) + f(q)\dot{q}^2 = \text{constant}.$$

Let us consider motion in the neighbourhood of a particular position q_0; denote $q - q_0$ by x. Then if x and $\dot{x}$ are small, we have by Taylor's series

$$V(q_0) + xV'(q_0) + \tfrac{1}{2}x^2 V''(q_0) + \ldots + f(q_0)\dot{x}^2 + \ldots = \text{constant}$$

to the second order. In particular, we choose q_0 to be such that $V'(q_0)$ vanishes there. Then

$$x^2 V''(q_0) + 2f(q_0)\dot{x}^2 = \text{constant}$$

provided $|x|$ is small. Differentiating with respect to t, we obtain

$$2x\dot{x}V''(q_0) + 4f(q_0)\dot{x}\ddot{x} = 0,$$

or
$$\ddot{x} + [V''(q_0)/2f(q_0)]x = 0.$$

Now $f(q_0) > 0$, since kinetic energy is always positive. Hence if $V''(q_0)$ is positive, motion is simple harmonic; $|x|$ remains very small so the equations derived are always valid. The period is

$$2\pi/\sqrt{[V''(q_0)/2f(q_0)]}.$$

If $V''(q_0)$ is negative, no oscillations can take place; $|x|$ becomes large and the approximations used are no longer valid.

We conclude that small oscillations are possible about a point q_0, where this value yields a minimum value of $V(q)$.

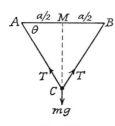

FIG. 171

Example 6★ An endless light elastic string of natural length $2a$ passes round two smooth pegs at a horizontal distance a apart. A heavy particle is attached to the string, which in equilibrium forms an equilateral triangle. Show that the period of small oscillations is $2\pi\sqrt{(2\sqrt{3}\, a/7g)}$.

Generally, let $\angle BAC = \theta$. In equilibrium, we have $2T\cos 30° = mg$, or $T = mg/\sqrt{3}$. In this position, the extension is a, so the modulus λ is given by the equation $mg/\sqrt{3} = T = \lambda a/2a$, yielding $\lambda = 2mg/\sqrt{3}$.

In the general position, the kinetic and potential energies are given by

$$T = \tfrac{1}{2}m\left(\frac{d}{dt}MC\right)^2 = \tfrac{1}{2}m\left(\frac{d}{dt}(\tfrac{1}{2}a\tan\theta)\right)^2 = \tfrac{1}{8}ma^2\sec^4\theta\,\dot{\theta}^2,$$

$$V = -mg\,MC + \frac{\lambda}{4a}(AB + 2AC - 2a)^2$$

$$= -\tfrac{1}{2}mga\tan\theta + \frac{mg}{2\sqrt{3}a}(a\sec\theta - a)^2.$$

Now $T + V = \text{constant}$. Since $\theta = 60°$ is the equilibrium position, we place $\theta = \tfrac{1}{3}\pi + \varepsilon$ and expand to the second order in ε and $\dot{\varepsilon}$. After considerable simplification, the energy equation reduces to

$$\dot{\varepsilon}^2 + 7g\varepsilon^2/2\sqrt{3}a = \text{constant},$$

from which we conclude that the period is $2\pi\sqrt{(2\sqrt{3}\, a/7g)}$.

23.2   Motion in a resisting medium

We shall consider the vertical motion under gravity of a particle of unit mass. In the first problem, we consider resistance proportional to the velocity, and in the second problem, resistance proportional to the square of the velocity.

Example 7   Let the resistance be kv per unit mass, where v is the velocity.

Let the axis Ox be the upward vertical, and let the particle be projected upwards from O with velocity u. The upward force acting on the particle is $-g - kv$, so the equation of motion

$$\frac{dv}{dt} = -g - kv$$

will yield v as a function of time t. Arranging this equation in the form suitable for integration, we obtain

$$\int_u^v \frac{dv}{g + kv} = -t,$$

where this choice of limits ensures that $v = u$ when $t = 0$. The integral is

$$\log(g + kv) - \log(g + ku) = -kt,$$

or

$$\frac{g + kv}{g + ku} = e^{-kt}.$$

In particular, the time to reach the maximum height is given by the condition $v = 0$; hence

$$t = k^{-1} \log[(g + ku)/g].$$

Throughout the motion, if kt is small, we have

$$g + kv = (g + ku)e^{-kt}$$
$$= (g + ku)(1 - kt + \tfrac{1}{2}k^2t^2 - \ldots)$$
$$= g - gkt - \tfrac{1}{2}gk^2t^2 + ku - k^2ut \text{ correct to the order } k^2,$$

yielding

$$v = u - gt - kt(u - \tfrac{1}{2}gt).$$

The last term $-kt(u - \tfrac{1}{2}gt)$ is the correction term that must be added to v in the case when there is no resistance.

The equation of motion may also be written in the form

$$v\frac{dv}{dx} = -g - kv.$$

Arranged as an integral such that $x = 0$ when $v = u$, we have

$$\int_u^v \left(1 - \frac{g}{g + kv}\right) dv = -kx,$$

integrating to

$$v - u - \frac{g}{k} \log \frac{g + kv}{g + ku} = -kx.$$

If h is the greatest height attained, $x = h$ when $v = 0$; hence

$$h = \frac{1}{k}\left[u + \frac{g}{k}\log\frac{g}{g + ku}\right] \tag{10}$$

$$= \frac{1}{k}\left[u - \frac{g}{k}\log\left(1 + \frac{ku}{g}\right)\right]$$

$$= \frac{1}{k}\left[u - \frac{g}{k}\left(\frac{ku}{g} - \frac{k^2u^2}{2g^2} + \frac{k^3u^3}{3g^3} - \cdots\right)\right]$$

$$= \frac{u^2}{2g} - \frac{ku^3}{3g^2},$$

exhibiting the first order correction term that must be subtracted from the value of h under conditions of no resistance.

Let us now measure x vertically downwards from the highest point. The equation of motion is

$$v\frac{dv}{dx} = g - kv,$$

where the force g per unit mass is now positive downwards, but the resistance kv, being upwards, must have a negative sign.

Arranged for integration, the equation becomes

$$\int_0^v \left(1 - \frac{g}{g - kv}\right) dv = -kx,$$

yielding
$$v + \frac{g}{k}\log\frac{g - kv}{g} = -kx.$$

If the particle falls through a distance h to its original starting point, the velocity of return is given by

$$-kh = v + \frac{g}{k}\log\left(1 - \frac{kv}{g}\right) \tag{11}$$

$$= v - \frac{g}{k}\left(\frac{kv}{g} + \frac{k^2v^2}{2g^2} + \frac{k^3v^3}{3g^3} + \cdots\right)$$

or
$$h = \frac{v^2}{2g} + \frac{kv^3}{3g^2}.$$

Combining the upward and downward motion, that is equations (10) and (11), we obtain

$$v + \frac{g}{k}\log\frac{g - kv}{g} = -kh = -u - \frac{g}{k}\log\frac{g}{g + ku},$$

or
$$u + v = \frac{g}{k}\log\frac{g + ku}{g - kv}$$

yielding the relationship between the upward and downward velocities at any given point. If k is small, the approximate solution of this equation may easily be checked to be $v = u - 2u^2k/3g$.

Example 8 Let the resistance be kv^2 per unit mass.

Let the particle be projected vertically up Ox with velocity u from O. The equation of motion is

$$v \frac{dv}{dx} = -g - kv^2.$$

Arranged for integration, this becomes

$$\int_u^v \frac{v\, dv}{g + kv^2} = -x,$$

or
$$\log(g + kv^2) - \log(g + ku^2) = -2kx.$$

If the greatest height reached is h when $v = 0$, we obtain

$$h = \tfrac{1}{2}k^{-1} \log[(g + ku^2)/g]. \tag{12}$$

If the particle falls from rest from this highest point, the equation of motion is now

$$v \frac{dv}{dx} = g - kv^2,$$

where Ox is taken vertically downwards. Arranged for integration, this is,

$$\int_0^v \frac{v\, dv}{g - kv^2} = x,$$

or
$$\log[(g - kv^2)/g] = -2kx.$$

The velocity attained after a fall of depth h is given by

$$\log[g/(g - kv^2)] = 2kh. \tag{13}$$

Eliminating h between equations (12) and (13), we obtain the relation between u and v at a particular level:

$$g/(g - kv^2) = (g + ku^2)/g,$$

simplifying to
$$\frac{1}{v^2} = \frac{1}{u^2} + \frac{k}{g}.$$

To the first order in k, this may be solved giving $v = u - u^3 k/2g$.

When falling, the particle attains its *terminal velocity* v_T when its acceleration tends to zero. Its acceleration being $g - kv^2$, we see that $v_T = \sqrt{(g/k)}$. Hence

$$\frac{1}{v^2} = \frac{1}{u^2} + \frac{1}{v_T{}^2}.$$

23.3 Rotation of a rigid body about a fixed axis

General theory. Consider a lamina rotating about a fixed point O in its own plane. Let δm be the mass of a small particle P of the lamina, rigidly attached to the system; we denote the distance OP by r. Let F be the external force perpendicular to OP and F' the internal force perpendicular to OP acting on P. The acceleration of P perpendicular to OP is $r\dot\omega$ where ω is the angular velocity of the lamina, so the equation of motion of the particle in the direction perpendicular to OP is

$$F + F' = r\dot\omega\, \delta m.$$

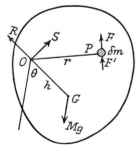

Fig. 172

A similar equation exists for all particles, but we may not take the sum of all these equations since the forces act in various directions. However, if we multiply by r, a couple is obtained. The equations may now be added, yielding

$$\sum Fr + \sum F'r = \sum \dot{\omega} r^2 \, \delta m.$$

But $\sum Fr = G$, the sum of the moments of all external forces about O; $\sum F'r = 0$, since the internal forces occur in equal and opposite pairs; $\sum r^2 \, \delta m = I$, the *moment of inertia* of the lamina about O. Hence the equation of motion of the lamina is

$$G = I\dot{\omega}, \tag{14}$$

where this formula has been proved *only for a fixed axis of rotation.*

The kinetic energy of the system is derived from the sum of the energies of the individual particles, namely

$$T = \tfrac{1}{2}\sum (r\omega)^2 \, \delta m = \tfrac{1}{2}\omega^2 \sum r^2 \, \delta m = \tfrac{1}{2}I\omega^2.$$

Moments of inertia. The reader should recall the following standard results for bodies of mass M:

(i) Rod of length $2a$ about its mid-point, $I = \tfrac{1}{3}Ma^2$.

(ii) Rectangle of sides $2a$, $2b$, about a diameter bisecting the sides of length $2a$, $I = \tfrac{1}{3}Ma^2$.

(iii) Hoop of radius a about an axis through its centre perpendicular to the hoop, $I = Ma^2$.

(iv) Circle of radius a about an axis through its centre perpendicular to the circle, $I = \tfrac{1}{2}Ma^2$.

(v) Circle of radius a about a diameter, $I = \tfrac{1}{4}Ma^2$.

(vi) Sphere of radius a about a diameter, $I = \tfrac{2}{5}Ma^2$.

For every case, if we write $I = Mk^2$, where M is the total mass of the body, we call k the *radius of gyration* of the body about the axis.

Moments of inertia about other axes may be found by using the following standard theorems:

(i) *Theorem of parallel axes.* If I_G equals the moment of inertia of a body about an axis l through the centre of gravity, then $I_G + Mh^2$ is the moment of inertia about an axis parallel to l and distant h from l. Thus the moment of inertia about a tangent line to a circle is given by $I = \tfrac{1}{4}Ma^2 + Ma^2 = \tfrac{5}{4}Ma^2$.

(ii) *Theorem of perpendicular axes.* If I_x and I_y are the moments of inertia about two perpendicular lines Ox and Oy in a lamina, then $I_x + I_y$ is the moment of inertia of the lamina about an axis through O perpendicular to the lamina.

Rotation about a fixed horizontal axis. The weight of the lamina acts at the centre of gravity G (see Fig. 172). The reaction at the axis O is designated by a component R along GO and a component S perpendicular to GO. The equations of motion of the point G may be written down by quoting a result proved in the next section: all the mass may be regarded as concentrated at G and all the external forces may be regarded as acting at G. The acceleration of G is $h\dot\theta^2$ along GO radially inwards and $h\ddot\theta$ perpendicular to GO. Resolving the forces in these directions, we obtain

$$R - Mg\cos\theta = Mh\dot\theta^2, \quad S - Mg\sin\theta = Mh\ddot\theta.$$

The rotational equation of motion may be found by taking anti-clockwise moments about the fixed axis O:

$$-Mgh\sin\theta = I\ddot\theta, \tag{15}$$

where I is the moment of inertia of the lamina about O. By replacing $\ddot\theta$ by $\dot\theta\, d\dot\theta/d\theta$, we may integrate equation (15), obtaining

$$Mgh\cos\theta = \tfrac{1}{2}I\dot\theta^2 + \text{constant},$$

or $$Mgh(\cos\theta - \cos\alpha) = \tfrac{1}{2}I\dot\theta^2,$$

assuming the initial conditions $\dot\theta = 0$ when $\theta = \alpha$.

The value of R is now given by

$$R = Mg\cos\theta + 2M^2h^2g(\cos\theta - \cos\alpha)/I,$$

and by using equation (15), we find that S has the value

$$S = Mg\sin\theta - M^2h^2g\sin\theta/I.$$

Finally, if k equals the radius of gyration about an axis through G, we have $I = M(k^2 + h^2)$ from the theorem of parallel axes. Hence

$$S = Mg\sin\theta \cdot k^2/(h^2 + k^2).$$

If θ is small, equation (15) may be written approximately

$$I\ddot\theta + Mgh\theta = 0.$$

Motion is simple harmonic, with the period

$$2\pi\sqrt{(I/Mgh)} = 2\pi\sqrt{[(h^2 + k^2)/gh]}.$$

The length of the *simple equivalent pendulum* is $(h^2 + k^2)/h$.

Example 9★ A point O of the surface of a uniform solid sphere of radius a and mass M is freely attached to a fixed support, and the sphere is released from rest in a position where OG makes an angle α with the downward vertical, where G is the centre of the sphere. Show that the motion of OG is similar to that of a simple pendulum of length $7a/5$.

If $\alpha = \tfrac{1}{2}\pi$, prove that the greatest value of the horizontal pull on the support during the motion is $15Mg/14$.

The moment of inertia about a parallel axis through G is $\tfrac{2}{5}Ma^2$; the theorem of parallel axes then yields the moment of inertia about the axis through O, namely $\tfrac{2}{5}Ma^2 + Ma^2 = \tfrac{7}{5}Ma^2$.

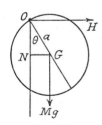

Fig. 173

The kinetic energy of the sphere is $\frac{1}{2}.\frac{7}{5}Ma^2\dot{\theta}^2$, while the potential energy with respect to its initial position is $-Mga(\cos\theta-\cos\alpha)$. Since there is no total initial energy, we have

$$7Ma^2\dot{\theta}^2 - 10Mga(\cos\theta - \cos\alpha) = 0.$$

The corresponding equation for a simple pendulum of length l is

$$\dot{\theta}^2 - 2g(\cos\theta - \cos\alpha)/l = 0.$$

Hence $l = 7a/5$.

If $\alpha = \frac{1}{2}\pi$, we have $7a\dot{\theta}^2 = 10g\cos\theta$.

If H is the horizontal reaction at O, the horizontal equation of motion of G is

$$\begin{aligned}
H = M\, d^2NG/dt^2 &= Ma\, d^2(\sin\theta)/dt^2 = Ma\, d(\cos\theta\,\dot{\theta})/dt \\
&= Ma(\cos\theta\,\ddot{\theta} - \sin\theta\,\dot{\theta}^2) \\
&= Ma(\tfrac{1}{2}\cos\theta\, d\dot{\theta}^2/d\theta - \sin\theta\,\dot{\theta}^2) \\
&= M[\tfrac{1}{2}\cos\theta\, d(\tfrac{10}{7}g\cos\theta)/d\theta - \sin\theta\,.\tfrac{10}{7}g\cos\theta] \\
&= Mg(-\tfrac{5}{7}\cos\theta\sin\theta - \tfrac{10}{7}\sin\theta\cos\theta) \\
&= -\tfrac{15}{14}Mg\sin 2\theta.
\end{aligned}$$

The maximum numerical value of H occurs when $\theta = \frac{1}{4}\pi$, namely $H = \frac{15}{14}Mg$.

Example 10★ A particle of mass m is attached to one end of a uniform rod of mass $2m$. The other end rests on a rough horizontal table. The rod is released from rest with the rod inclined to the vertical at the angle $\frac{1}{3}\pi$. If the rod does not slip *initially*, prove that $\mu \geqslant \frac{1}{2}\sqrt{3}$.

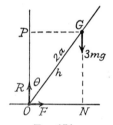

FIG. 174

Initially, $\dot{\theta} = 0$ and $\theta = \frac{1}{3}\pi$. The vertical and horizontal equations of motion of the centre of gravity G are

$$\begin{aligned}
R - 3mg &= 3m\, d^2(h\cos\theta)/dt^2 \\
&= 3mh(-\sin\theta\,\ddot{\theta} - \cos\theta\,\dot{\theta}^2) \\
F &= 3m\, d^2(h\sin\theta)/dt^2 \\
&= 3mh(\cos\theta\,\ddot{\theta} - \sin\theta\,\dot{\theta}^2),
\end{aligned}$$

where h is the distance OG. This is obviously given by

$$3mh = 2ma + m.2a,$$

yielding $h = \frac{4}{3}a$. Moreover, the moment of inertia of the system about O is given by $(\frac{4}{3}.2m.a^2 + m.4a^2) = \frac{20}{3}ma^2$, so clockwise rotational motion about the fixed point O is given by the equation

$$3mgh\sin\theta = \tfrac{20}{3}ma^2\ddot{\theta}.$$

We are only concerned with the initial values of R and F, so no integration is necessary; we insert the initial conditions $\dot{\theta} = 0$ and $\theta = \frac{1}{3}\pi$, obtaining

$$R = 3mg - 3mh\sin\tfrac{1}{3}\pi\,\ddot{\theta},$$
$$F = 3mh\cos\tfrac{1}{3}\pi\,\ddot{\theta},$$
$$3gh\sin\tfrac{1}{3}\pi = \tfrac{20}{3}a^2\ddot{\theta}.$$

Eliminating $\ddot{\theta}$, we obtain $R = \frac{6}{5}mg$ and $F = \frac{3}{5}\sqrt{3}mg$.

If no slipping takes place (and only then are the above equations valid) we require $\mu \geqslant F/R$. This yields $\mu \geqslant \frac{1}{2}\sqrt{3}$.

23.4 The general motion of a lamina in a plane

We now remove the restriction that rotation takes place about a fixed point of the lamina.

Let the coordinates of the centre of gravity G be (x_g, y_g) with respect to a fixed system of axes, and let (x, y) and (r, θ) be the Cartesian and polar coordinates respectively of an element P of mass δm with respect to parallel axes through G. The two equations of motion of P are given by

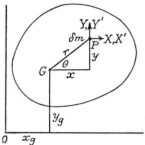

Fig. 175

$$X + X' = \delta m(\ddot{x}_g + \ddot{x}),$$
$$Y + Y' = \delta m(\ddot{y}_g + \ddot{y}),$$

where the accelerations must be measured with respect to fixed axes. Here, X, Y are the components of external force acting on P, and X', Y' are the components of internal force.

Adding similar equations for all particles, we obtain

$$\Sigma X + \Sigma X' = \Sigma \ddot{x}_g \, \delta m + \Sigma \ddot{x} \, \delta m, \quad \Sigma Y + \Sigma Y' = \Sigma \ddot{y}_g \, \delta m + \Sigma \ddot{y} \, \delta m.$$

But $\Sigma X = F_x$, $\Sigma Y = F_y$, the total components of external force regardless of the points at which they act; $\Sigma X' = \Sigma Y' = 0$ since internal forces occur in equal and opposite pairs; $\Sigma \ddot{x}_g \, \delta m = M \ddot{x}_g$, $\Sigma \ddot{y}_g \, \delta m = M\ddot{y}_g$ where M is the total mass of the lamina; $\Sigma \ddot{x} \, \delta m = \Sigma \ddot{y} \, \delta m = 0$ since $\Sigma x \, \delta m = \Sigma y \, \delta m = 0$, G being the centre of gravity. Hence

$$F_x = M\ddot{x}_g, \quad F_y = M\ddot{y}_g;$$

namely *the centre of gravity of the lamina moves as if all the external forces were concentrated there and as if all the mass were concentrated there.* In some problems, it may be necessary to specify the acceleration of G in terms of polar coordinates. We have already used this principle in examples 9 and 10.

Taking anticlockwise moments about G of all forces acting on P, we obtain

$$(Y + Y')x - (X + X')y = \delta m(\ddot{y}_g + \ddot{y})x - \delta m(\ddot{x}_g + \ddot{x})y. \quad (16)$$

The sum of similar equations for all particles of the lamina is

$$\Sigma(Yx - Xy) + \Sigma Y'x - \Sigma X'y$$
$$= \ddot{y}_g \Sigma x \, \delta m - \ddot{x}_g \Sigma y \, \delta m + \Sigma \delta m(\ddot{y}x - \ddot{x}y).$$

But $\Sigma(Yx - Xy) = G$, the sum of the moments of all external forces about the centre of gravity; $\Sigma Y'x = \Sigma X'y = 0$ since internal forces occur in equal and opposite pairs; $\Sigma x \, \delta m = \Sigma y \, \delta m = 0$ since G is the centre of gravity, and

$$\Sigma \, \delta m(\ddot{y}x - \ddot{x}y) = \Sigma \, \delta m \, \frac{d}{dt} (\dot{y}x - \dot{x}y)$$

$$= \Sigma \, \delta m \, \frac{d}{dt} [(r \cos \theta \, \dot{\theta})(r \cos \theta) - (-r \sin \theta \, \dot{\theta})(r \sin \theta)]$$

$$= \Sigma \, \delta m \, \frac{d}{dt} (r^2 \dot{\theta}) = \Sigma r^2 \, \delta m \ddot{\theta} = I \ddot{\theta},$$

where I is the moment of inertia of the lamina about the perpendicular axis through O. Hence the rotational equation of motion about G reduces to

$$G = I \ddot{\theta}. \tag{17}$$

This equation should be compared with equation (14). *This equation may only be used*

 (i) *if rotation takes place about a fixed axis, or*
 (ii) *if the quantities G and I refer to the centre of gravity of a moving lamina.*

The kinetic energy. For the single particle P, we have

$$\text{K.E.} = \tfrac{1}{2} \, \delta m[(\dot{x}_g + \dot{x})^2 + (\dot{y}_g + \dot{y})^2]$$

where the velocity components with respect to fixed axes must be used. Totally,

$$T = \tfrac{1}{2}\Sigma \, \delta m(\dot{x}_g{}^2 + 2\dot{x}_g\dot{x} + \dot{x}^2 + \dot{y}_g{}^2 + 2\dot{y}_g\dot{y} + \dot{y}^2).$$

But $\tfrac{1}{2}\Sigma \, \delta m(\dot{x}_g{}^2 + \dot{y}_g{}^2) = \tfrac{1}{2}M(\dot{x}_g{}^2 + \dot{y}_g{}^2) = \tfrac{1}{2}MV^2$, where V is the velocity of the centre of gravity; $\Sigma \dot{x}_g\dot{x} \, \delta m = \Sigma \dot{y}_g\dot{y} \, \delta m = 0$ since $\Sigma x \, \delta m = \Sigma y \, \delta m = 0$,

and $\quad \tfrac{1}{2}\Sigma \, \delta m(\dot{x}^2 + \dot{y}^2) = \tfrac{1}{2}\Sigma \, \delta m[(-r \sin \theta \, \dot{\theta})^2 + (r \cos \theta \, \dot{\theta})^2]$

$$= \tfrac{1}{2}\Sigma \, \delta m r^2 \dot{\theta}^2 = \tfrac{1}{2}I\dot{\theta}^2.$$

Hence $\quad T = \tfrac{1}{2}MV^2 + \tfrac{1}{2}I\dot{\theta}^2,$

consisting of two parts, namely the translational part $\tfrac{1}{2}MV^2$ as if all the mass were concentrated at and moving with the centre of gravity, and the rotational part $\tfrac{1}{2}I\dot{\theta}^2$ relative to the centre of gravity.

Moment of momentum about a fixed point. We shall now find the moment of the external forces about a fixed point O in space, where O is not necessarily a fixed point in the body. Equation (16) becomes

$$(Y + Y')(x_g + x) - (X + X')(y_g + y)$$
$$= \delta m(\ddot{y}_g + \ddot{y})(x_g + x) - \delta m(\ddot{x}_g + \ddot{x})(y_g + y).$$

The sum of the left-hand side is of course merely G_O, the total moment of external forces about O. Hence

$$G_O = \sum \delta m \frac{d}{dt} [(\dot{y}_g + \dot{y})(x_g + x) - (\dot{x}_g + \dot{x})(y_g + y)]$$

$$= \frac{d}{dt} \sum \delta m (\dot{y}_g x_g + \dot{y}x - \dot{x}_g y_g - \dot{x}y)$$

$$= \frac{d}{dt} [M(\dot{y}_g x_g - \dot{x}_g y_g) + I_g \dot{\theta}]$$

where I_g is the moment of inertia about G as before. Moreover, $(\dot{y}_g x_g - \dot{x}_g y_g)$ is merely the moment of the velocity of G about O; more simply we may denote this by hV, where V is the velocity of G acting at a distance h from O. Hence

$$G_O = \frac{d}{dt}(MhV + I_g \dot{\theta}), \tag{18}$$

namely the rate of change of the *moment of momentum* $MhV + I_g \dot{\theta}$ about O, where O is any point fixed in space but not necessarily in the lamina.

In particular, if one point O of a lamina is suddenly fixed so that rotation about O only is now possible, the only forces that produce this sudden change act at O. This implies that $G_O = 0$, so the moment of momentum $MhV + I_g \dot{\theta}$ remains unchanged, having the same value before and after the point is fixed. This enables us to calculate the new angular velocity. If pure rotation now takes place about O with angular velocity ω, we have $V = h\omega$, so the moment of momentum has the value

$$(Mh^2\omega + I_g\omega) \equiv I_0\omega$$

in keeping with the theorem of parallel axes, where I_0 is the moment of inertia about O. This special simplification in form is only possible if O is a point fixed in the lamina as well as in space.

The method for solving problems that require the use of equation (17) is as follows: First, draw the diagram, indicating all the external forces acting on the body. Locate the centre of gravity, choose a suitable angle for measuring the angular velocity and for finding the acceleration components of the centre of gravity with respect to fixed axes. Finally, write down the equations of motion for translation and rotation. If energy is conserved, the conservation equation may be written down. In initial value problems, the velocities but not the accelerations may be equated to zero.

Example 11* A smooth rod, of mass M and length $2a$, is held vertically with its lower end in contact with a smooth plane inclined at an angle α to the horizontal. If the rod is released from rest, find its initial angular acceleration and the initial reaction of the plane.

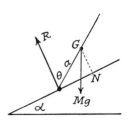

Let the general position of the rod be designated by the angle θ between the rod and the normal to the plane. The translational equation of motion of G along the outward normal is

$$R - Mg\cos\alpha = M\frac{d^2}{dt^2}NG$$

FIG. 176

$$= Ma\frac{d^2}{dt^2}\cos\theta = -Ma(\sin\theta\,\ddot\theta + \cos\theta\,\dot\theta^2),$$

while taking moments about G for the clockwise rotational equation of motion, we obtain

$$Ra\sin\theta = \tfrac{1}{3}Ma^2\,\ddot\theta.$$

Initially, $\theta = \alpha$ and $\dot\theta = 0$, yielding the particular equations

$$R - Mg\cos\alpha = -Ma\sin\alpha\ddot\theta, \quad Ra\sin\alpha = \tfrac{1}{3}Ma^2\ddot\theta.$$

Solving these two equations for the initial values of $\ddot\theta$ and R, we find

$$\ddot\theta = \frac{3g\cos\alpha\sin\alpha}{a(1 + 3\sin^2\alpha)}, \qquad R = \frac{Mg\cos\alpha}{1 + 3\sin^2\alpha}.$$

Example 12 A rough sphere of radius a and mass m rolls on the outside of a fixed rough sphere of radius b. It starts from rest in the uppermost position. By finding (i) where it leaves the surface if no slipping takes place, (ii) where slipping first takes place, show that (ii) occurs before (i).

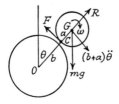

The position of the rolling sphere is specified by the angle θ made by the common radius OCG to the vertical. The velocity of the centre G is then $(a + b)\dot\theta$. If ω is the angular velocity of the sphere, the velocity of the point of contact C on the rolling sphere must be zero for no slipping. Hence

FIG. 177

the velocity of G + the velocity of C relative to $G = 0$,

or $$(a + b)\dot\theta - \omega a = 0.$$

The acceleration components of G are $(b + a)\dot\theta^2$ radially inwards and $(a + b)\ddot\theta$ tangentially. Hence the translational equations of motion of G are

$$mg\cos\theta - R = m(a + b)\dot\theta^2,$$
$$mg\sin\theta - F = m(a + b)\ddot\theta.$$

By taking moments about G, we obtain the clockwise rotational equation of motion of the sphere:

$$Fa = \tfrac{2}{5}ma^2\dot\omega.$$

If we now eliminate F in order to integrate the equations, we obtain

$$mg\sin\theta - \tfrac{2}{5}ma\dot\omega = m(a + b)\ddot\theta,$$

or $$g\sin\theta = \tfrac{7}{5}(a + b)\ddot\theta.$$

Integration with respect to θ yields

$$-g \cos \theta + \text{constant} = \tfrac{7}{10}(a + b)\dot\theta^2,$$

or
$$g(1 - \cos \theta) = \tfrac{7}{10}(a + b)\dot\theta^2.$$

This equation expresses of course the conservation of energy, with zero initial total energy.

We now calculate the value of R:

$$R = mg \cos \theta - m(a + b)\dot\theta^2 = mg \cos \theta - \tfrac{7}{10}mg(1 - \cos \theta)$$
$$= \tfrac{1}{7}mg(17 \cos \theta - 10),$$

while
$$F = \tfrac{2}{5}ma\dot\omega = \tfrac{2}{5}m(a + b)\ddot\theta = \tfrac{2}{7}mg \sin \theta.$$

If no slipping takes place, the sphere leaves the surface when $R = 0$, namely when $\cos \theta = \tfrac{10}{17}$. However, in order that no slipping should take place, we require $F/R < \mu$, namely

$$2 \sin \theta/(17 \cos \theta - 10) < \mu.$$

Hence slipping takes place as soon as $2 \sin \theta = \mu(17 \cos \theta - 10)$, which obviously occurs before the particle leaves the surface.

Example 13★ A uniform circular disc is projected with its plane vertical, along a line of greatest slope of a plane of inclination α to the horizontal. Initially the disc has no angular velocity and its centre is moving up the plane with velocity V. If the coefficient of friction between the disc and the plane is $\tfrac{1}{2} \tan \alpha$, show that slipping ceases after a time $2V/(5g \sin \alpha)$. Show, also, that the disc comes to instantaneous rest after moving a total distance $2V^2/(5g \sin \alpha)$.

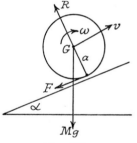

Initially, $v = V$ and $\omega = 0$. As long as slipping takes place, $F = \tfrac{1}{2} \tan \alpha\, R$. The equations of motion of G are

$$-\tfrac{1}{2} \tan \alpha\, R - mg \sin \alpha = mv, \qquad R = mg \cos \alpha$$

FIG. 178

parallel to and normal to the plane respectively. The clockwise rotational equation of motion about G is

$$\tfrac{1}{2} \tan \alpha\, Ra = \tfrac{1}{2}ma^2\dot\omega.$$

Eliminating R, we obtain

$$-\tfrac{3}{2}g \sin \alpha = \dot v, \qquad g \sin \alpha = a\dot\omega.$$

Integration with respect to t yields

$$-\tfrac{3}{2}g \sin \alpha\, t = v - V, \qquad g \sin \alpha\, t = a\omega.$$

Slipping ceases as soon as $v = a\omega$, namely when

$$V - \tfrac{3}{2}g \sin \alpha\, t = g \sin \alpha\, t,$$

yielding $t = \tfrac{2}{5}V/g \sin \alpha$.

Moreover, if x measures distance up the plane, we have

$$v = dx/dt = V - \tfrac{3}{2}g \sin \alpha\, t;$$

therefore
$$x = Vt - \tfrac{3}{4}g \sin \alpha\, t^2.$$

The distance travelled while slipping takes place is then given by $x = \frac{7}{25} V^2/g \sin \alpha$, using the value of t just found.

Slipping ceases as soon as $v = a\omega = g \sin \alpha\, t = \frac{2}{7}V$. After this, energy is conserved up to the position of instantaneous rest. If X denotes the additional distance travelled, the potential energy gained is $mgX \sin \alpha$, while the kinetic energy lost is given by

$$\tfrac{1}{2}mv^2 + \tfrac{1}{2}I\omega^2 = \tfrac{1}{2}mv^2 + \tfrac{1}{4}mv^2 = \tfrac{3}{4}mv^2 = \tfrac{3}{25}mV^2.$$

Equating these two values, we deduce that $X = \frac{3}{25} V^2/g \sin \alpha$. The total distance travelled is finally given by

$$x + X = (\tfrac{7}{25} + \tfrac{3}{25})V^2/g \sin \alpha = \tfrac{2}{5}V^2/g \sin \alpha.$$

Example 14★ The door of a stationary railway carriage stands open and perpendicular to the length of the train. The train starts off with acceleration f and at the same time the door is given an angular velocity Ω in the direction towards the front of the train, so as to shut the door. Show that, if the door can be regarded as a smoothly-hinged uniform rectangular plate of width $2a$, then Ω must be at least of magnitude $\sqrt{(3f/2a)}$ in order to close the door.

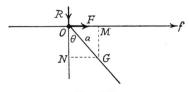

FIG. 179

Let the door make an angle θ to the normal ON. Initially, $\theta = 0$, $\dot{\theta} = \Omega$. If R and F denote the components of the reaction at the hinge as shown, the two equations of motion of G are

$$R = m\frac{d^2}{dt^2}MG = ma\frac{d^2}{dt^2}\cos \theta = -ma(\sin \theta\,\ddot{\theta} + \cos \theta\,\dot{\theta}^2),$$

$$F = mf + m\frac{d^2}{dt^2}NG = mf + ma\frac{d^2}{dt^2}\sin \theta = mf + ma(\cos \theta\,\ddot{\theta} - \sin \theta\,\dot{\theta}^2).$$

The anticlockwise equation of motion about G is given by

$$Ra \sin \theta - Fa \cos \theta = \tfrac{1}{3}ma^2\ddot{\theta}.$$

Eliminating R and F in order to integrate with respect to θ, we obtain upon simplification

$$-f\cos \theta = \tfrac{4}{3}a\ddot{\theta} = \tfrac{4}{3}a\dot{\theta}\,d\dot{\theta}/d\theta,$$

with the integral

$$-f\sin \theta = \tfrac{2}{3}a(\dot{\theta}^2 - \Omega^2).$$

When $\theta = \tfrac{1}{2}\pi$, we have $\dot{\theta}^2 = \Omega^2 - \tfrac{3}{2}f/a > 0$ in order that this position should be attained. Hence $\Omega > \sqrt{(3f/2a)}$.

Note. The student should repeat this calculation using radial and transverse reactions at O and radial and transverse accelerations of G relative to O combined with f.

Example 15★ A uniform circular disc of radius a rolls without slipping with its plane vertical, on a rough horizontal table, the speed of the centre being v. If the disc strikes a rough inelastic step of height $h\,(<a)$ show that it will begin to turn about the top of the step with angular speed $(3a - 2h)v/3a^2$, assuming that it maintains contact with the step. Show, also, that the disc will surmount the step if

$$v^2 > 12a^2gh/(3a - 2h)^2.$$

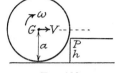

During the initial period of rolling, $v = a\omega$. Motion is suddenly changed as the disc strikes the top of the step, so we use equation (18) expressing the fact that the

FIG. 180

moment of momentum about P is instantaneously conserved. Before the impact, this consists of the two clockwise contributions

moment of linear momentum of G about P + moment of momentum of the

$$\text{disc relative to } G = mv(a - h) + \tfrac{1}{2}ma^2\omega = mv(\tfrac{3}{2}a - h).$$

Just after impact, motion is one of pure rotation about P with angular velocity Ω say. The moment of momentum is given by

$$I_P\Omega = (I_G + ma^2)\Omega = \tfrac{3}{2}ma^2\Omega.$$

These two values are identical, yielding $\Omega = (3a - 2h)v/3a^2$.

After the impact, energy is conserved. The kinetic energy just after impact is one of pure rotation about P, namely $\tfrac{1}{2}.\tfrac{3}{2}ma^2.\Omega^2$. In order that the disc should surmount the step, this available kinetic energy must be greater than the potential energy required, namely mgh. The inequality $\tfrac{3}{4}ma^2\Omega^2 > mgh$ immediately yields the required answer.

23.5 The impulsive motion of a lamina in a plane

If, in Fig. 175, X and Y now denote the external components of impulse and X', Y' the internal components of impulse acting on the element P, we have the two impulsive equations

$$X + X' = \delta m(\dot{x}_g + \dot{x}), \quad Y + Y' = \delta m(\dot{y}_g + \dot{y}),$$

where these velocity components represent the *increases* due to the impulse. Adding, and using the same argument as before, we obtain

$$I_x = M\dot{x}_g, \quad I_y = M\dot{y}_g,$$

where I_x and I_y denote the total external components of impulse. In other words, *the centre of gravity behaves as if all the mass were concentrated there and as if all the external impulses were concentrated there.*

Rotationally, we take moments of impulse about G, obtaining

$$\Sigma(Yx - Xy) + \Sigma Y'x - \Sigma X'y = \Sigma\,\delta m[(\dot{y}_g + \dot{y})x - (\dot{x}_g + \dot{x})y],$$

leading, as before, to $$H = I\dot{\theta},$$

where H denotes the total external anticlockwise moment of impulse about G, I the moment of inertia about G, $\dot{\theta}$ the increase in the anticlockwise angular velocity due to the impulse.

19

This formula may also be applied to impulsive rotational motion about a fixed axis of rotation not situated at G, but in general about no other point *except G or a fixed axis.*

If various bodies are freely hinged together, these three equations may be written down for each body, provided equal and opposite impulsive reactions are introduced at each hinge. Impulsive couples may also be introduced at hinges which are not free. Kinematical equations must also be written down for the hinges. The resulting equations may usually be solved most quickly by substituting the dynamical impulsive equations into the kinematical ones.

The kinetic energy generated by impulses. For one particle P, this is

$$T = \tfrac{1}{2}\,\delta m(u^2 + v^2) = \tfrac{1}{2}(X + X')u + \tfrac{1}{2}(Y + Y')v,$$

where the velocity components u and v are generated from rest. Totally,

$$T = \tfrac{1}{2}\Sigma[(X + X')u + (Y + Y')v] = \tfrac{1}{2}\Sigma Xu + \tfrac{1}{2}\Sigma Yv,$$

since $\Sigma X'u = \Sigma Y'v = 0$. Verbally, this result may be stated as

$T = \tfrac{1}{2}\Sigma$ impulse $\times$ velocity created at the point of application
in the direction of the impulse.

More generally, if the motion is not started from rest, we have:

increase in $T = \Sigma$ impulse $\times$ mean velocity at the point
of application in the direction of the impulse.

Example 16 Two equal uniform rods AB, BC, of mass m and length $2a$, are freely hinged at B; they move on a smooth horizontal table with velocity $7V$ perpendicular to the straight line ABC. The midpoint of AB strikes a small peg fixed to the table. Find the loss of kinetic energy if e is the coefficient of restitution.

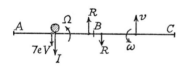

Fig. 181

Introduce the impulsive reactions I, R, the velocities of the mid-points $7eV$, v and the angular velocities ω, Ω as shown.

The two translational impulsive equations for the centres of gravity are

$$I - R = 7meV + 7mV, \qquad -R = mv - 7mV.$$

The two rotational impulsive equations about the centres of gravity are

$$Ra = \tfrac{1}{3}ma^2\Omega, \qquad Ra = \tfrac{1}{3}ma^2\omega.$$

The kinematical equation is given by the common velocity of B:

$$a\Omega - 7eV = v - a\omega.$$

Multiplying the kinematical equation by m, we substitute the dynamical equations into it, obtaining

$$3R - 7emV = -R + 7mV - 3R,$$

giving $R = mV(1 + e)$. The values of the other unknowns I, v, $\omega = \Omega$ follow immediately. We have in particular

$$I = R + 7mV(1 + e) = 8mV(1 + e).$$

Now I is the only external impulse. We conclude that the gain in kinetic energy equals I multiplied by the mean of the velocities in the direction of I, namely

$$\text{gain} = \tfrac{1}{2}I(eV - V) = -4mV^2(1 - e^2).$$

The loss in energy of the system is therefore $4mV^2(1 - e^2)$.

Example 17★ A chain of three equal uniform rods AB, BC, CD, each of mass M, freely jointed together at B and C, is at rest on a smooth table, with the rods lying along three sides of a square $ABCD$. It is set in motion by an impulse J in the direction AD, applied at A to the rod AB. Prove that the velocity with which D starts to move is $J/6M$.

We introduce the reactions R, S as indicated, the velocities u, v, w of the centres of gravity of the three rods, and the angular velocities ω, Ω.

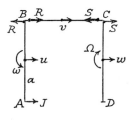

FIG. 182

The translational impulsive equations of the centres are

$$J - R = Mu, \quad R - S = Mv, \quad S = Mw,$$

while the rotational equations are

$$(J + R)a = \tfrac{1}{3}Ma^2\omega, \qquad Sa = \tfrac{1}{3}Ma^2\Omega.$$

The kinematical equations expressing common horizontal velocities at B and C respectively are

$$v = U - a\omega, \qquad v = w + a\Omega.$$

Substituting the dynamical equations into the kinematical ones, we obtain

$$R - S = J - R - 3(J + R), \qquad R - S = S + 3S,$$

yielding $R = -5J/12$, $S = -J/12$. Hence $w = S/M = -J/12M$, and $a\Omega = 3S/M = -J/4M$. Finally, the velocity of D is given by $w - \Omega a$ to the right, namely $J/6M$.

Example 18★ A uniform circular disc of mass M is rotating in its own plane about a vertical axis through its centre with angular velocity ω when a particle of mass $\tfrac{1}{2}M$, moving with negligible velocity, suddenly adheres to the rim. Find the subsequent angular velocity of the disc and the impulse on the particle (a) when the axis is fixed, (b) when the axis is free.

For the case (a), the moment of momentum about O, being a fixed axis, is conserved. Initially it is $I_0\omega = \tfrac{1}{2}Ma^2\omega$. Finally, it is $(I_0 + \tfrac{1}{2}Ma^2)\Omega$ about O, namely $Ma^2\Omega$. It follows that $\Omega = \tfrac{1}{2}\omega$.

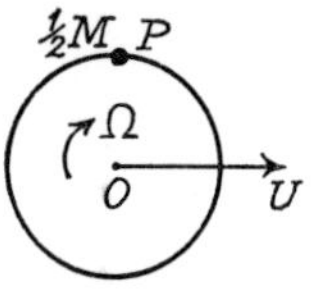

The velocity gained by the particle equals $a\Omega$ or $\tfrac{1}{2}a\omega$, so the impulse on the particle must equal $\tfrac{1}{2}Ma\Omega = \tfrac{1}{4}Ma\omega$.

For case (b), the new velocity of O is u, and that of the particle is $u + a\Omega$. Since there is no external impulse on the system, linear momentum is conserved, namely

$$0 = Mu + \tfrac{1}{2}M(u + a\Omega),$$

FIG. 183

or $u = -\tfrac{1}{3}a\Omega$. Moreover, the moment of momentum is conserved about any point.

In particular, the original value about P is $I_0\omega = \frac{1}{2}Ma^2\omega$. The final value is $\frac{1}{2}Ma^2\Omega$ — Mua clockwise, where the last part refers to the moment of momentum of the centre of gravity of the disc about P. The particle does not contribute to the total. Hence

$$\tfrac{1}{2}Ma^2\omega = \tfrac{1}{2}Ma^2\Omega - Mua = \tfrac{1}{2}Ma^2\Omega + \tfrac{1}{3}Ma^2\Omega = \tfrac{5}{6}Ma^2\Omega,$$

yielding $\Omega = \frac{3}{5}\omega$.

The velocity gained by the particle is

$$u + a\Omega = -\tfrac{1}{3}a\Omega + a\Omega = \tfrac{2}{3}a\Omega = \tfrac{2}{5}a\omega.$$

Hence the impulse on the particle is $\frac{1}{3}M.\frac{2}{5}a\omega = \frac{2}{15}Ma\omega$.

23.6   The equations of motion in polar coordinates

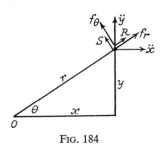

FIG. 184

In certain problems, it is more convenient to use polar coordinates; we therefore require the *radial* and *transverse* accelerations directed outwards and perpendicular to the radius vector.

We differentiate the equations $x = r \cos\theta$, $y = r\sin\theta$ with respect to time, obtaining

$$\dot{x} = \dot{r}\cos\theta - r\sin\theta\,\dot\theta, \quad \ddot{x} = \ddot{r}\cos\theta - 2\dot{r}\sin\theta\,\dot\theta - r\sin\theta\,\ddot\theta - r\cos\theta\,\dot\theta^2,$$
$$\dot{y} = \dot{r}\sin\theta + r\cos\theta\,\dot\theta, \quad \ddot{y} = \ddot{r}\sin\theta + 2\dot{r}\cos\theta\,\dot\theta + r\cos\theta\,\ddot\theta - r\sin\theta\,\dot\theta^2.$$

The radial and transverse velocity and acceleration components are then found to be

$$v_r = \dot{x}\cos\theta + \dot{y}\sin\theta = \dot{r},$$
$$v_\theta = \dot{y}\cos\theta - \dot{x}\sin\theta = r\dot\theta,$$
$$f_r = \ddot{x}\cos\theta + \ddot{y}\sin\theta = \ddot{r} - r\dot\theta^2,$$
$$f_\theta = \ddot{y}\cos\theta - \ddot{y}\sin\theta = r\ddot\theta + 2\dot{r}\dot\theta.$$

If R and S are the radial and transverse components of force acting on a particle of mass m, the equations of motion are

$$R = m(\ddot{r} - r\dot\theta^2), \quad S = m(r\ddot\theta + 2\dot{r}\dot\theta).$$

In particular, the second equation may be written in the form

$$Sr = m(r^2\ddot\theta + 2r\dot{r}\dot\theta) = \frac{d}{dt}(mr^2\dot\theta) = \frac{d}{dt}(mrv_\theta) = \frac{dh}{dt},$$

where $h = mrv_\theta$ is the moment of momentum of the particle about the fixed origin O. If the transverse force S vanishes, we have $h = $ constant. It follows that $r^2\dot\theta$ is a constant, its value being determined by the initial conditions of projection of the particle.

The method of integration if S vanishes.   Let $R(r)$ be the radial force per unit mass, and h the constant moment of momentum per unit mass. Then

$$R = \ddot{r} - r\dot{\theta}^2 \quad \text{and} \quad r^2\dot{\theta} = h.$$

Eliminating $\dot{\theta}$, we obtain

$$\ddot{r} = R + h^2/r^3,$$

integrating to

$$\tfrac{1}{2}\dot{r}^2 = \int (R + h^2/r^3)\, dr + \text{constant.} \tag{19}$$

A second integration then gives r in terms of time.

Equation (19) gives $\dot{r}$ in terms of r; moreover we have $\dot{\theta} = h/r^2$. Division yields $dr/d\theta$ in terms of r, and the integral of this relationship yields the polar equation of the path of the particle.

The energy equation.   If $R(r)$ is a conservative force, we may find the potential energy associated with it. Its value equals the work done by the external force $-R(r)$ as its point of application is moved from the standard position $r = a$ to the general position, namely

$$V = -\int_a^r R(r)\, dr,$$

where a is usually 0 or ∞. Equation (19) now gives

$$\tfrac{1}{2}\dot{r}^2 = \int_a^r R(r)\, dr - \frac{h^2}{2r^2} + \text{constant,}$$

or

$$\tfrac{1}{2}(\dot{r}^2 + r^2\dot{\theta}^2) - \int_a^r R(r)\, dr = \text{constant.} \tag{20}$$

The first term on the left is the total kinetic energy per unit mass of the particle. This conservation equation, being a first integral of the equations of motion, may be written down straight away; the value of the constant depends on the initial conditions.

The second method of integration if S vanishes.   In the equation $R = \ddot{r} - r\dot{\theta}^2$, r is the dependent variable, and t the independent variable. In some problems, it may be an advantage to use $u = 1/r$ as the dependent variable and θ as the independent variable. We have

$$\dot{r} = \frac{dr}{dt} = \frac{dr}{du}\cdot\frac{du}{d\theta}\cdot\frac{d\theta}{dt} = -\frac{1}{u^2}\cdot\frac{du}{d\theta}\cdot\frac{h}{r^2} = -h\frac{du}{d\theta},$$

and

$$\ddot{r} = -h\frac{d^2u}{d\theta^2}\cdot\frac{d\theta}{dt} = -h\frac{d^2u}{d\theta^2}\cdot\frac{h}{r^2} = -h^2u^2\frac{d^2u}{d\theta^2}.$$

Hence the equation becomes

$$R\left(\frac{1}{u}\right) = -h^2 u^2 \frac{d^2 u}{d\theta^2} - h^2 u^3,$$

or
$$\frac{d^2 u}{d\theta^2} + u = -\frac{R(1/u)}{h^2 u^2}. \tag{21}$$

The solution of this differential equation yields the (u, θ) equation of the path.

The method of integration if $\dot\theta = constant = \omega$. If a constant angular velocity ω is prescribed, $\ddot\theta = 0$, and the total energy is not conserved. The equations become

$$R = \ddot r - r\omega^2, \qquad S = 2\dot r\omega$$

per unit mass. The first equation may be integrated with respect to r:

$$\int R\,dr = \tfrac{1}{2}\dot r^2 - \tfrac{1}{2}r^2\omega^2 + \text{constant}.$$

This equation gives $\dot r$ in terms of r; hence S is known in terms of r. Now $dr/dt = \omega\,dr/d\theta$ is expressed in terms of r; an integration yields the polar equation of the path.

Example 19   A bead can slide freely on a straight wire of length a, which is rotating with constant angular velocity ω about one end A. Initially the bead is projected along the wire with velocity V from A. When the bead leaves the wire, what is the angle between the line of the wire and the direction of motion of the bead?

The only force acting on the bead is the transverse normal reaction S per unit mass; moreover, since $\dot\theta$ is constant, the polar equations of motion reduce to

$$r - r\dot\theta^2 = 0, \qquad 2\dot r\dot\theta = S.$$

Rewriting the first equation in the form $\dot r\,d\dot r/dr = r\omega^2$, we obtain its first integral:

$$\tfrac{1}{2}\dot r^2 = r^2\omega^2 + \text{constant} = \tfrac{1}{2}r^2\omega^2 + \tfrac{1}{2}V^2.$$

Hence $\dot r = \sqrt{(r^2\omega^2 + V^2)}$; this relation gives S as a function of r if required.

When $r = a$, the radial velocity of the particle is $\dot r = \sqrt{(a^2\omega^2 + V^2)}$, while its transverse velocity is $a\omega$. Hence, if ϕ is the angle required, we have

$$\tan\phi = v_\theta/v_r = \omega a/\sqrt{(a^2\omega^2 + V^2)}.$$

Example 20★   A particle A is attached to one end of an inextensible string passing through a small hole in a smooth horizontal table, and it supports an equal mass B hanging beneath the table. The mass A is held on the table at a distance a from the hole, and then it is projected in a direction perpendicular to the string with velocity $\sqrt{(\tfrac{1}{3}ag)}$. Show that when the length of string on the table is $\tfrac{1}{2}a$, A is moving at right-angles to the portion of the string on the table.

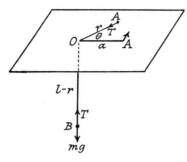

FIG. 185

Let T be the tension per unit mass in the string. If (r, θ) are the polar coordinates of the general position of A on the table, the radial equation of motion of A is

$$-T = \ddot{r} - r\dot{\theta}^2.$$

Since there is no transverse force acting on A, its moment of momentum about the hole O is conserved, namely

$$r^2\dot{\theta} = a\sqrt{(\tfrac{1}{3}ag)},$$

this being the initial value. Finally, the equation of motion vertically downwards of B is

$$g - T = d^2(l - r)/dt^2 = -\ddot{r}$$

per unit mass.

The tension T may be eliminated by subtracting:

$$-g = 2\ddot{r} - r\dot{\theta}^2 = 2\ddot{r} - \tfrac{1}{3}a^3g/r^3$$

when $\dot{\theta}$ is eliminated. Arranged for integration, this equation is

$$-g + \tfrac{1}{3}a^3g/r^3 = 2\ddot{r} = 2\dot{r}\,d\dot{r}/dr,$$

yielding

$$-gr - \tfrac{1}{6}a^3g/r^2 = \dot{r}^2 + \text{constant}.$$

Initially, $\dot{r} = 0$ when $r = a$, so

$$-gr - \tfrac{1}{6}a^3g/r^2 + ga + \tfrac{1}{6}ga = \dot{r}^2,$$

factorizing to

$$6r^2\dot{r}^2 = g(r - a)(3r + a)(-2r + a).$$

It follows that $\dot{r} = 0$ only when $r = a$ and $r = \tfrac{1}{2}a$. Motion of the particle is therefore confined between these two limits, and in particular, when $r = \tfrac{1}{2}a$, motion is perpendicular to OA.

23.7 Central orbits

A particle P is situated at the point whose polar coordinates are r, θ with respect to an initial line through a centre of force S. Let the radial *attractive* force on P due to S be $R(r)$ per unit mass.

The energy equation. The moment of momentum $r^2\dot\theta = h$ is conserved, its value being determined by the initial conditions of projection. The kinetic energy is

$$T = \tfrac{1}{2}(\dot r^2 + r^2\dot\theta^2) = \tfrac{1}{2}(\dot r^2 + h^2/r^2)$$

per unit mass. The potential energy per unit mass is the work done by the force $R(r)$ radially *outwards* as its point of application is moved from a standard position to the general position, namely

$$V = \int^r R(r)\,dr.$$

The equation of conservation of energy then becomes

$$\frac{1}{2}\left(\dot r^2 + \frac{h^2}{r^2}\right) + \int^r R(r)\,dr = E, \tag{22}$$

the value of E being determined by the initial conditions of projection. This equation yields the maximum and minimum values of r, found by equating $\dot r$ to zero. Moreover, this equation yields $\dot r$ in terms of r; taken with the relation $\dot\theta = h/r^2$, we may find by division $dr/d\theta$ in terms of r. Integration finally yields the polar equation of the orbit.

On the other hand, if p is the perpendicular distance from S to the velocity vector of the particle, we have $h = pv$; the energy equation then becomes

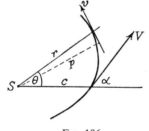

FIG. 186

$$\frac{h^2}{2p^2} + \int^r R(r)\,dr = E. \tag{23}$$

This equation is, of course, the p,r-equation of the orbit.

The areal velocity. If δA is the element of area $\tfrac{1}{2}r^2\,\delta\theta$, we have, upon division by δt,

$$dA/dt = \tfrac{1}{2}r^2\dot\theta = \tfrac{1}{2}h,$$

a constant. This result is known as *Kepler's second law*, namely that the radius vector sweeps out the area at a constant rate. If A is the total area within the closed orbit and T the periodic time, we have, upon integration, $A = \tfrac{1}{2}hT$, yielding $T = 2A/h$.

Example 21 Examine the orbits possible under an inverse square law of attraction. If the law of attraction is $R(r) = \mu/r^2$ per unit mass, the potential energy is

$$V = \int^r_\infty \frac{\mu\,dr}{r^2} = -\frac{\mu}{r},$$

where $r = \infty$ is chosen to be the standard position. Equation (23) becomes

$$\frac{h^2}{2p^2} - \frac{\mu}{r} = E,$$

or

$$\frac{1}{p^2} = \frac{2\mu}{h^2 r} + \frac{2E}{h^2}.$$

We compare this with the p,r-equations of the ellipse and hyperbola derived in sections 9.4,5, and we conclude that the orbits consist of conics with S as one focus; in particular orbits occurring naturally are ellipses (*Kepler's first law*).

Case i. If $E < 0$, we compare this with the p,r-equation of the ellipse

$$\frac{1}{p^2} = \frac{2a}{b^2 r} - \frac{1}{b^2}.$$

Comparing coefficients, we see that $\mu/h^2 = a/b^2$ and $2E/h^2 = -1/b^2$. Hence $a = -\mu/2E$, $b^2 = -h^2/2E$, giving the lengths of the axes of the ellipse. The eccentricity is given by

$$e^2 = 1 - \frac{b^2}{a^2} = 1 + \frac{2Eh^2}{\mu^2}.$$

In particular, we note that

$$v^2 = 2(E - V) = 2E + \frac{2\mu}{r} = \mu\left(\frac{2}{r} - \frac{1}{a}\right).$$

Case ii. If $E > 0$, in which case a finite real velocity U is possible at infinity, we compare the p,r-equation of the orbit with that of the hyperbola with respect to the focus on the concave side:

$$\frac{1}{p^2} = \frac{2a}{b^2 r} + \frac{1}{b^2}.$$

We conclude that $a = \mu/2E$, $b^2 = h^2/2E$.

In particular, if the velocity vector at infinity lies at a distance d from S, we have $E = \frac{1}{2}U^2$, $h = dU$. Hence $a = \mu/U^2$ and $b = d$. The angle between the asymptotes is then given by

$$2\tan^{-1}(b/a) = 2\tan^{-1}(dU^2/\mu).$$

Case iii. If $E = 0$, we compare the p,r-equation of the orbit with that of the parabola, namely $p^2 = ar$. The orbit must now be a parabola, with $a = h^2/2\mu$.

In each of these three cases, the length of the semi-latus rectum (b^2/a for an ellipse and hyperbola, and $2a$ for a parabola) has the value h^2/μ.

Case iv. If the force is repulsive and not attractive, we must change the sign of μ and compare the p,r-equation of the orbit with that of the hyperbola with respect to the focus on the convex side, namely

$$\frac{1}{p^2} = -\frac{2a}{b^2 r} + \frac{1}{b^2}.$$

E must be positive in this case, since it consists of two positive terms; comparing coefficients, we see that $a = \mu/2E$, $b^2 = h^2/2E$.

The periodic time for the ellipse. The area of the ellipse is πab, so

$$T^2 = \frac{4A^2}{h^2} = \frac{4\pi^2 a^2 b^2}{h^2} = \frac{4\pi a^3}{h^2} \cdot \frac{b^2}{a} = \frac{4\pi a^3}{h^2} \cdot \frac{h^2}{\mu} = \frac{4\pi a^3}{\mu}.$$

The greatest and least distances of P from S are $a(1 + e)$ and $a(1 - e)$ respectively; a is the mean distance. Hence

$$T^2 \propto \text{(mean distance)}^3,$$

a result known as *Kepler's third law*.

The apses of the orbit. The energy equation (22) yields

$$\dot{r}^2 = 2E + \frac{2\mu}{r} - \frac{h^2}{r^2}.$$

An *apse* occurs where $\dot{r} = 0$, that is, at points where the velocity of P is perpendicular to the radius vector. This implies that

$$2Er^2 + 2\mu r - h^2 = 0.$$

The roots of this equation must be $a(1 \pm e)$. The sum of the roots yields $2a = -\mu/E$, as before, while the product yields $a^2(1 - e^2) = -h^2/2E$, as before, since $a^2(1 - e^2) = b^2$.

The nearer apse is known as the *perihelion* and the more distant apse the *aphelion*.

Initial conditions. Let the particle be projected from a point distant c from S with velocity V at an angle α with the outward radius vector as shown in Fig. 186. Then $h = Vc \sin \alpha$ and $E = \frac{1}{2}V^2 - \mu/c$. Assuming an ellipse, we have

$$a = \frac{\mu}{2\mu/c - V^2}, \qquad b = \frac{Vc \sin \alpha}{\sqrt{(2\mu/c - V^2)}},$$

$$T = \frac{2\pi\mu}{(2\mu/c - V^2)^{3/2}}.$$

Circular orbits. If the velocity of P is v and if the radius is r, the attractive force μ/r^2 must be equal to v^2/r, the rate of change of momentum radially inwards. This yields $v^2 = \mu/r$, so the periodic time is $T = 2\pi r^{3/2}/\sqrt{\mu}$.

The use of the equations of motion. If $R(r)$ is the given attractive force, the equations of motion in polar coordinates are

$$-R(r) = \ddot{r} - r\dot{\theta}^2, \qquad r^2\dot{\theta} = h,$$

the latter equation being a first integral. Quoting equation (21), in which we use $r = 1/u$, we may use the transformed equation

$$\frac{d^2u}{d\theta^2} + u = \frac{R(1/u)}{h^2u^2}, \tag{24}$$

using a positive sign on the right-hand side for an attractive force. This is the differential equation for the polar equation of the path.

The law of force. Conversely, if the equation of the path is given, we may find the law of force necessary to produce this orbit.

If the p,r-equation of the orbit is given, we differentiate equation (23) with respect to r, obtaining

$$-\frac{h^2}{p^3}\frac{dp}{dr} + R(r) = 0 \, ,$$

yielding
$$R(r) = \frac{h^2}{r^2}\frac{dp}{dr} \, .$$

If the r,θ-equation of the orbit is given, equation (24) provides directly

$$R(r) = h^2\left(u^2\frac{d^2u}{d\theta^2} + u^3\right)_{r=1/u} \, .$$

Example 22   Integrate equation (24) for the inverse square law.
   Placing $R = \mu/r^2 = \mu u^2$, the equation for the orbit becomes

$$\frac{d^2u}{d\theta^2} + u = \frac{\mu}{h^2}$$

integrating to
$$u = \mu/h^2 + A\cos\theta,$$

chosen so that $du/d\theta = 0$ when $\theta = 0$. The initial line is chosen, in fact, through an apse. Hence

$$\frac{h^2/\mu}{r} = 1 + B\cos\theta.$$

The constant B is determined from the initial value of r, specified by $r = c$, say. Then $B = h^2/\mu c - 1$.
   Now this equation is merely the polar equation of a conic (see section 10.8). The latus rectum is h^2/μ and the eccentricity is B. These two parameters determine the conic completely.

Example 23   Investigate the orbit when the attractive force is proportional to distance.
   When $R(r) = n^2 r$ per unit mass, it is preferable to use Cartesian coordinates rather than polar coordinates. Resolving, we obtain

$$\ddot{x} = -R\cos\theta = -n^2x, \quad \ddot{y} = -R\sin\theta = -n^2y,$$

integrating to
$$x = A\cos nt + B\sin nt, \quad y = C\cos nt + D\sin nt.$$

Solving for $\sin nt$, $\cos nt$, squaring and adding, we obtain

$$(Cx - Ay)^2 + (Dx - By)^2 = (AD - BC)^2,$$

representing an ellipse whose centre is the centre of attraction S.
   If the lengths of the semi-axes of this ellipse are a and b, we must have $\dot{r} = 0$ when $r = a$ and b. The energy equation is

$$\tfrac{1}{2}(\dot{r}^2 + r^2\dot{\theta}^2) + \int_0^r R\,dr = E,$$

where the standard position is taken to be S. Hence

$$\dot{r}^2 + h^2/r^2 = 2E - n^2 r^2.$$

Placing $\dot{r}$ equal to zero, we obtain the quadratic equation

$$n^2 r^4 - 2Er^2 + h^2 = 0$$

whose roots must be $r^2 = a^2$ and $r^2 = b^2$. The sum and product of the roots yield the relations

$$a^2 + b^2 = 2E/n^2, \qquad a^2 b^2 = h^2/n^2,$$

or $h = nab$. Generally, we have

$$\dot{r}^2 = n^2(a^2 - r^2)(r^2 - b^2)/r^2.$$

The periodic time is obviously $2\pi/n$, seen from the values of x and y given above

EXERCISES

(1)*. Two particles, each of mass $2m$, are joined by a light string, which passes over two smooth fixed pulleys at a distance $2a$ apart on the same level. Midway between the pulleys, a mass $3m$ is attached to the string and then released from rest. Find the distance which it descends before first coming to rest. Determine the position of the mass $3m$ when the potential energy of the system is a minimum.

(2)*. A ring is threaded on a smooth flexible cord of length $2a$, whose ends are fixed to two points in the same vertical line at a distance a apart. The ring revolves in a horizontal circle with angular velocity ω. Show that (if ω is great enough) the ring divides the cord into two parts of lengths $a \pm 2g/3\omega^2$.

(3)*. A smooth wire bent into the form of a circle is fixed so that its plane is vertical. Two small beads, of masses m and $2m$, threaded on the wire are simultaneously released from rest at opposite ends of the horizontal diameter of the circle. Prove that, after the first collision, the greatest heights attained by the beads are in the ratio $(1 + 4e)^2:(1 - 2e)^2$ where e is the coefficient of restitution between the beads.

(4)*. A particle is released from rest at a point on a smooth fixed hemisphere which stands with its plane face on a horizontal table. Show that the particle leaves the hemisphere when its vertical distance from the table is two-thirds of its original value; and find its acceleration at this instant.

(5)*. Two particles A and B, of masses m and m' respectively are connected by a light inelastic string of length $2a$ and lie at rest on a smooth horizontal table at a distance a apart. The particle B is given a velocity u at right-angles to AB. Show that, immediately after the string has become taut, the speed of A is $m'u\sqrt{3}/2(m + m')$. Show that the loss of kinetic energy due to the tightening of the string is

$$3mm'u^2/8(m + m').$$

(6)*. Four particles, each of mass m, connected by equal inextensible strings of length a, lie in the form of a rhombus on a smooth horizontal table. One particle receives a blow P outwards along the diagonal. Prove that the angular velocities of the strings after the blow are $P \sin \alpha/2ma$, where $2\alpha(\alpha < \frac{1}{4}\pi)$ is the angle of the rhombus at the particle.

(7)*. A particle B is attached to a fixed point A by an inelastic string of length $2a$ and to a point C at the same level as A by an elastic string of natural length a. If, in the position of equilibrium, ABC is an equilateral triangle, prove that the period of small oscillations in the vertical plane is $4\pi\sqrt{(2\sqrt{3}a/11g)}$.

(8) ★. The total resistance to the motion of a car when the speed is v ft./sec. is $(a + bv^2)$ lb. wt., where a and b are constants. A car weighing 3,200 lb. travels at a steady speed of 45 m.p.h. when the power exerted is 15 h.p. and at 30 m.p.h. when the power is 8 h.p. Calculate the values of a and b. If the engine is switched off, show that the distance covered while the speed falls from 45 m.p.h. to 30 m.p.h. is 4,840 log (5/4) ft.

(9) ★. A car weighing 1 ton is driven by an engine, so that the H.P. available for acceleration, when allowance has been made for power losses and resistance to motion, is $H = av - bv^2$, where a and b are constants and v is the speed. It is found that when the speed is 30 m.p.h. the acceleration is 4 m.p.h. per second and when the speed is 60 m.p.h. the acceleration is 2 m.p.h. per second. Find the greatest speed which can be attained by the car and show that the time taken to reach a speed of 45 m.p.h. from rest is the same as it takes to accelerate from 30 m.p.h. to 60 m.p.h. Find the maximum value of H.

(10) ★. A particle of mass m moves in a straight line under no forces except a resistance mkv^3, where v is the velocity and k is a constant. If the initial velocity is u and x is the distance covered in time t, prove that

$$kx = (u - v)/uv, \qquad t = x/u + \tfrac{1}{2}kx^2.$$

The initial velocity of a bullet fired horizontally from a point O is 2500 ft./sec. and after moving 400 ft. its velocity is reduced to 2450 ft./sec. Neglecting gravity and assuming the air resistance to be proportional to the cube of the velocity, find the time for the bullet to cover a distance of 3000 ft. from O.

(11) ★. A particle starts from rest and moves in a horizontal straight line under the action of an accelerating force and a resistance so that the resultant acceleration has the form $(a - bv)$ ft./sec.^{2}, where a and b are constants and v ft./sec. is the velocity acquired in t secs. If the limiting velocity is V ft./sec., show that the particle attains half the limiting velocity in a distance $(V/2b)(2 \log 2 - 1)$.

(12) ★. A body falls from rest through water. Assuming that, in addition to the force of buoyancy, the water offers resistance proportional to velocity, show that the equation of motion may be put in the form

$$v\,dv/dx = g(1 - 1/s) - kv$$

where s is the specific gravity of the body and k is a constant.

If $s = 2$, $k = 4/5$ sec.$^{-1}$, show that the terminal velocity is 20 ft./sec. and that when the body has acquired a velocity equal to 99 per cent of this, it will have fallen about 90 ft. (Take g to be 32 ft./sec.^{2}).

(13) ★. A car of mass 5 cwt. stands at rest on a gradient of 1/10. When the brakes are released it descends under a resistance which is proportional to the velocity at any instant. This resistance is 12 lb. wt. when the velocity is 10 m.p.h. Show that the velocity can never exceed $46\tfrac{2}{3}$ m.p.h. and find, to the nearest foot, how far the car descends before the velocity reaches 20 m.p.h.

(14) ★. A 20 lb. shell is fired horizontally from a mountain top at a speed of 2,000 ft. sec. and the air resistance at velocity v ft./sec. is $v^2/4,000$ lb. wt. Neglecting the vertical motion, show that the initial velocity is halved in $1\tfrac{1}{4}$ seconds and find the time taken for the shell to travel the first mile.

(15) ★. A particle moving in a horizontal straight line is subject to a retardation $av(v^2 + u^2)$, where v is the velocity at any time. Show that, if it is started with

velocity u, the particle moves through a distance $\pi/12au$ before its velocity is reduced to $u/\sqrt{3}$, and find the time taken.

---

(16)*. A thin uniform square plate $ABCD$, of side l and mass $3M$, is free to turn with its plane vertical about a smooth horizontal axis through A, and has a particle of mass M attached to it at C. If the plate is released from rest when AC is horizontal, prove that when it has turned through an angle θ, its angular velocity is $\sqrt{(\frac{5}{4}\sqrt{2}g\sin\theta/l)}$, and find the components along and perpendicular to AC of the reaction at the axis.

(17)*. Three thin uniform rods, each of length l and mass m, are rigidly joined to form an equilateral triangle ABC. Show that the radius of gyration about an axis through A, perpendicular to the plane ABC, is $l/\sqrt{2}$.

The system can rotate freely in a vertical plane about a fixed horizontal axis through A, perpendicular to the plane. When in equilibrium with D, the mid-point of BC, vertically below A, the system is given an angular velocity ω_0 about the axis. Show that, when AD makes an angle θ with the downward vertical through A,

$$l(\omega_0^2 - \dot\theta^2) = \tfrac{4}{3}\sqrt{3}\,g(1 - \cos\theta).$$

Find the period of small oscillations about the equilibrium position.

(18)*. A non-uniform rod of length $2a$ has its centre of gravity at a distance $\frac{1}{2}a$ from one end. If the period of small oscillations under gravity about either end is the same, show that the radius of gyration of the rod about its centre of gravity is $\frac{1}{2}a\sqrt{3}$.

(19)*. A uniform circular disc, of mass 10 lb. and diameter 1 ft., is hanging in equilibrium with its plane vertical, supported by two equal light vertical rods which are rigidly attached to the disc at points of its rim and freely pivoted to a horizontal bar in the plane of the disc, so that the centre of the disc is 1 ft. below the bar. In this position, the disc receives a blow which imparts to it an angular velocity ω radians per sec. about the bar. Show that if $\omega^2 < 64g/17$ the disc comes to rest after turning through an angle θ given by $\cos\theta = 1 - 17\omega^2/32g$.

If $\omega^2 = 4g$ show that the disc makes complete revolutions round the bar. Find the stress in each of the light rods as they pass through the vertical positions and state whether the rods are in tension or compression.

(20)*. A uniform plate in the form of an equilateral triangle of altitude a swings as a compound pendulum about a smooth horizontal axis along one side of the plate, the extreme angle of swing being α on either side of the vertical. Prove that when the plate is inclined at angle θ to the vertical $\dot\theta^2 = 4g(\cos\theta - \cos\alpha)/a$. Prove also that the reaction on the axis is vertical when $\theta = 0$.

(21)*. Two uniform rods OA, AB, each of mass m and length $2l$, are smoothly jointed at A, and the end O is smoothly jointed to a fixed point on a horizontal table. Initially the rods are at rest and in line on the table. The rod AB is then given an angular velocity $\sqrt{(3g/l)}$ about A in a vertical plane. Prove that, so long as the rod OA remains on the table, the angular velocity of the rod AB is $\sqrt{[(3g/2l)(2 - \sin\theta)]}$ when it has turned through an angle θ. Find the vertical component of the reaction of OA on AB and hence find the value of θ at which the rod OA will begin to rise.

(22)*. A light frame consists of two equal rods AB, AC of length a and a third rod BC. A mass m is attached at B and a mass $2m$ at C and the frame is suspended so that it can rotate freely in a vertical plane about a horizontal axis through A. The angles between the rods AB, AC is 2θ.

If the system is released from rest with BC vertical, and C above B and comes to rest subsequently with AB vertical, show that $\sin \theta = \frac{3}{4}$. Calculate the angular velocity of the system when BC makes an angle ϕ with the horizontal, and the thrust in the rod BC, when $\phi = 0$.

(23)*. A uniform rod of mass M and length $2a$ can turn freely in a vertical plane about a pivot $\frac{1}{2}a$ from one end. The rod is held in the horizontal position and released from rest. Find the horizontal and vertical components of reaction at the pivot when the rod has turned through an angle θ. The pivot itself is of negligible mass and is free to slide on a rough horizontal track. Show that if the pivot has not slipped before the rod has turned through an angle $\tan^{-1}(2/\sqrt{13})$ it will not slip at all.

(24)*. A uniform rod AB of length $4a$ is in contact with a small rough horizontal peg at C, where AC is a. The rod is released from rest when it is horizontal. Show that it will begin to slip on the peg when it makes an angle $\tan^{-1}(4\mu/13)$ with the horizontal, where μ is the coefficient of friction between the rod and the peg.

(25). A uniform cube of mass $9(\sqrt{2}-1)m$ is at rest on a smooth horizontal table; the side of the cube is $2a$. A uniform rod, of mass m and length $2a\sqrt{2}$ is pivoted at a fixed point on the table distant $2a$ from the nearest edge of the base of the cube, and it rests symmetrically with its top end just on the corresponding top edge of the cube. The system is released from rest; show that the maximum velocity attained by the cube is $\sqrt{(\frac{1}{9}\sqrt{2}ag)}$.

(26). A uniform circular disc, with a length of thread wound round it, falls vertically by unwinding itself, one end of the string being fixed. Show that the tension in the string is one-third the weight of the disc.

(27). A uniform solid sphere of radius a rolls without slipping on a smooth horizontal plane with velocity V. Without the action of any impulsive forces, it then rolls down a gradient of vertical height $21V^2/5g$ to a lower horizontal plane. Show that its velocity is now $2V$.

(28)*. One end of a thin inelastic string is attached to the surface of a uniform hollow cylinder of internal radius a and external radius $2a$, and of mass M. The string is wrapped several times round the cylinder which is then held on a smooth plane of inclination β, the line of contact being horizontal. The free part of the string lies along an upward drawn line of greatest slope, and the end of the string is attached to the plane. A particle of mass m is held on the plane at a distance b from the line of contact with the cylinder and above it. If the cylinder and the particle are released at the same instant, after how long will the particle strike the cylinder? Find the tension in the string before this event.

(29)*. A uniform solid sphere is projected along a rough horizontal plane with a velocity V and no rotation. Show that it will slip for a distance $12V^2/49\mu g$, where μ is the coefficient of friction and that when it rolls its speed will be $5V/7$.

(30)*. A uniform solid circular cylinder of mass m and radius a moves with its axis horizontal up a rough inclined plane of inclination α by means of a constant couple L acting so that the cylinder rolls up the plane. Show that if the coefficient of friction between the cylinder and the plane is μ, then for rolling to take place

$$\mu \geqslant \frac{1}{3} \tan \alpha + (2L \sec \alpha)/(2 \, mag).$$

If this condition is satisfied and $L = 2mag \sin \alpha$ and moreover, the cylinder starts from rest at time $t = 0$, find its displacement at time t.

(31)★. The total mass of a car, including the wheels, is M. Each wheel is of mass m, radius a and radius of gyration k about is axis. The car is driven on horizontal ground by a torque T (not necessarily constant) applied to the back axle. Find the acceleration of the car, and the frictional force between each wheel and the ground, assuming there is no slipping.

(32)★. A uniform circular disc of mass m and radius a is at rest, with its plane vertical, on a rough horizontal table, the coefficient of friction at the point of contact being μ. A constant horizontal force P is applied to the disc in a line through its centre and in its plane. Prove that slipping will occur of $P > 3\mu mg$. If $P = 6\mu mg$ and the force is applied for a time T and then removed, prove that the disc will continue to slip for a further time T and find its velocity when slipping ceases.

(33)★. A uniform straight rod is placed with its ends in contact with a smooth vertical wall and a smooth horizontal plane, the vertical plane through the rod being perpendicular to the wall. If the rod is allowed to fall freely under gravity, show that it will lose contact with the wall when its centre has fallen through one-third of its original height above the plane.

(34)★. A uniform rod AB, of mass m and length r, slides with its ends on a smooth vertical circular wire with centre O and of radius r. The rod is released from the position in which its upper end B is on a horizontal line through O. Prove that, when AB makes an angle θ with the horizontal, $5r\dot\theta^2 = 3\sqrt3\,(2\cos\theta - 1)g$. Calculate the reaction between either end of the rod and the wire when AB is horizontal. Find the period of small oscillations of the rod when it is slightly displaced from its equilibrium position.

(35)★. A cubical block of mass M rests on a smooth horizontal plane. A uniform rod AB of mass $3M$ and length a is freely hinged to a fixed point A in the plane, while the end B rests against a smooth vertical face of the block, the vertical plane through the rod being a plane of symmetry of the block. If the system is released from rest, show that so long as contact between the rod and the block is maintained

$$a(1 + \sin^2\theta)\dot\theta^2 = 3g(\sin\alpha - \sin\theta),$$

where θ is the angle of inclination of the rod to the horizontal and α is the initial value of θ. Show also that the initial reaction at B is $3Mg \sin\alpha \cos\alpha/[2(1 + \sin^2\alpha)]$.

(36)★. A uniform plank of mass M is placed symmetrically upon two equal rough uniform cylindrical rollers, each of mass m, on a rough plane inclined at an angle α to the horizontal. Assuming no slipping and that the cylinders do not touch, find the initial values of the frictional forces on each cylinder and the acceleration of the plank.

(37)★. A uniform rod AB of mass m and length $2a$ lies at rest on a smooth horizontal plane when a constant horizontal force P is applied to B in a direction making an angle $\alpha(<\tfrac12\pi)$ with BA. Prove that when the rod makes an angle θ with the the direction of P, $ma\dot\theta^2 = 6P\,(\cos\alpha - \cos\theta)$. Prove, also, that the rod oscillates with amplitude $2(\pi - \alpha)$.

(38)★. A thin hollow cylinder of radius a has a particle of equal mass attached symmetrically to its inner surface. If the system is disturbed from its position of stable equilibrium on a rough horizontal table and then left to itself show that, when the radius to the particle makes an angle θ with the downward vertical, $a\dot\theta^2(2 - \cos\theta) - g\cos\theta = \text{constant}$. Hence prove that the period of small oscillations is $2\pi\sqrt{(2a/g)}$.

(39)*. A uniform solid cylinder of mass m and circular cross-section of radius a rolls without slipping along a horizontal plane with angular velocity ω and strikes a perfectly rough inelastic stop whose edge is parallel to the axis of the cylinder and at height $\frac{1}{4}a$ above the plane. Show that the angular velocity of the cylinder just after impact is $5\omega/6$.

Assuming that, in the subsequent motion, the cylinder remains in contact with the edge of the step and does not slip, show that the cylinder will surmount the step if $25a\omega^2 > 12g$.

(40)*. A uniform rod of length $2a$ swings under gravity about one end which is fixed at a height $h(>2a)$ above the floor. Its greatest inclination to the vertical is $\pi/3$. When the rod is passing through the vertical position the upper end is set free and the rod strikes the floor when it is next vertical. Prove that $h = 2a(\pi^2 + 3)/3$.

(41)*. A uniform circular disc of mass $2m$ and radius a has a particle of mass m fixed to the circumference. The disc is projected, with its plane vertical and the particle initially in its highest position, so as to roll without slipping on a horizontal rail. Prove that, when the radius to the particle makes an angle θ with the upward vertical,

$$a\dot{\theta}^2 = [7a\Omega^2 + 2g(1 - \cos\theta)]/(5 + 2\cos\theta)$$

where Ω is the angular speed of projection. Hence find the vertical reaction on the rail when the disc has turned through one right-angle.

(42)*. A uniform bar AB, of length a and of mass M, is at rest on a smooth horizontal table when it is struck a horizontal blow Mu at B and at right-angles to AB. Find the time that elapses before the bar is first parallel to its original position and in the same direction.

In this position the end A is suddenly fixed so that the bar rotates about A. Find the angular speed and the impulse at A.

(43)*. Three uniform rigid rods AB, BC, CD, each of mass m and length $2a$, are smoothly jointed at B and C. The system rests on a smooth horizontal table with A, B, C, D collinear when a horizontal impulse P is applied to the mid-point of BC in the direction perpendicular to the line of the rods. Show that the angular velocity of CD immediately after the impulse is $P/2ma$ and that the kinetic energy generated by the blow is $P^2/3m$. Find the angular velocity of CD when it has rotated through $90°$.

(44)*. Two equal uniform rods XY, YZ, each of mass m and length $2a$ are freely jointed at Y. XYZ is a straight line and the rods are moving on a smooth horizontal table with velocity v perpendicular to XYZ when XY impinges at its mid-point on an inelastic stop. Show that the angular velocity of each rod just after the impact is $3v/7a$. Find the impulsive force exerted on the stop and the loss of kinetic energy.

(45)*. A uniform solid cube of mass M and edge of length $2a$ rests on one face of a smooth horizontal table. It is given a horizontal impulse I at the mid-point of one edge of its top face perpendicular to that edge. Show that the impulsive reaction at the table is $3I/5$, and find the initial angular velocity of the cube. Show also that the cube will overturn in the subsequent motion if $I^2 > 10M^2ga(\sqrt{2} - 1)/3$.

(46)*. Two equal uniform straight rods AB, BC, each of mass m and length a, are jointed together at B. When the rods rest on a smooth horizontal table with AB, BC in line, C is jerked into motion with a velocity v perpendicular to the length of the rods. If ABC remains a straight line after motion begins, prove that friction at the joint B must supply an impulsive couple of magnitude $mva/8$.

(47)*. A thin uniform rod of mass m and length $2a$ falls freely with its length vertical. When the rod is moving with speed v the lower end strikes a smooth inelastic plane fixed at an angle of $30°$ to the horizontal. Prove that the magnitude of the impulsive reaction of the plane is $2\sqrt{3}\,mv/7$, and find the speed after impact of the end striking the plane.

(48)*. A uniform rod AB of mass m and length $2a$ is held in the horizontal position and is then allowed to fall freely. After falling through a height $8a$ the end A engages with a fixed smooth hinge. Prove that the rod begins to turn about A with angular velocity $3\sqrt{(g/a)}$. Find the velocity of B when it is vertically below A.

(49)*. A lamina is rotating with angular velocity ω about an axis through its mass-centre perpendicular to its plane when some other point of the lamina is suddenly fixed. Show that the kinetic energy is reduced in the same ratio as the angular velocity. If the lamina is a uniform square of side $2a$ and mass m and it is found that half the kinetic energy is lost, find the locus of the point which is pinned and the impulse on the pin.

(50)*. A uniform rod OA of mass m and length $2a$ turns freely in a horizontal plane about a fixed vertical axis through O. A similar rod AB is hinged to the first at A so that it turns in a horizontal plane. At the moment when OA, AB are in line and rotating with respective angular velocities ω, ω' in opposite senses, the hinge at A is suddenly locked. If the rods come to rest prove that $5\omega' = 11\omega$, and find the impulsive reaction on the axis through O in terms of ω.

---

(51)*. The acceleration of a particle P moving on a smooth horizontal table is always n^2OP directed away from the fixed point O on the table. If the particle is projected from the point $A(a, 0)$ at time $t = 0$ with velocity na at right-angles to OA, prove that $r^2\dot\theta = na^2$, $\ddot r = n^2(r + a^4/r^3)$. Hence prove that $r^2 = a^2 \cosh 2nt$.

(52)*. A narrow tube, of length $2a$, rotates about one end with constant angular velocity ω. Inside is a small bead of mass m, instantaneously at rest at the mid-point; the coefficient of friction is $\frac{3}{4}$. Find the reaction between the bead and the tube in terms of m, a, ω and t, neglecting the effect of gravity. Show that the particle reaches one end of the tube after the time $(2/\omega)\log_e 2\cdot5$ approximately.

(53)*. A fine smooth tube rotates about a fixed point O of itself with constant angular velocity ω in a horizontal plane. The tube contains a particle m, attached to O by an elastic thread of natural length a and modulus $2ma\omega^2$. At time $t = 0$, $r = a$, and the particle is at rest. Show that the particle makes one complete oscillation in the tube in each rotation, and that the greatest horizontal reaction is $2ma\omega^2$. Make a drawing of the path of the particle.

(54)*. An elastic string of natural length a and modulus λ is attached at one end to a fixed point O, and a mass m is attached at the other end. Motion takes place on a smooth horizontal table, and the mass is projected from a point distant $2a$ from O with velocity $\sqrt{(\lambda a/3m)}$ at right angles to the radius vector. Show that the string never becomes slack.

(55). P and Q are two particles, each of mass m, connected by a light inextensible string of length $2a$, passing through a small smooth hole O in a smooth horizontal table. Initially, $OQ = a$, and P is projected at right-angles to OP with speed $\sqrt{(8ga/3)}$. Show that Q will just reach the hole.

(56)*. A particle of unit mass is initially at an infinite distance from a point S and moving with a speed V_0 along a line which is at a perpendicular distance p_0 from S.

If the particle is attracted to S by a force of magnitude μ/PS^2, show that the semi-major axis of its orbit is μ/V_0^2, the eccentricity of its orbit is cosh α and the speed of the particle at the nearest approach to S is $V_0 \coth\frac{1}{2}\alpha$, where α is given by

$$\mu \sinh \alpha = p_0 V_0^2.$$

(57)⋆. A particle P, of mass m, moves in a plane under the action of a force mku^2/r^2 towards a fixed point S, where $SP = r$ and k, u are constants. When it is at a point A distant c from S it has a velocity u perpendicular to SA. Prove that it describes a conic with eccentricity $|k - c|/k$.

(58)⋆. If a central force is directed *from* O and is of magnitude μr per unit mass, where r is the distance of the particle from O, and the particle is projected from a point P in any direction with speed $\mu^{\frac{1}{2}}OP$, prove that its path is a rectangular hyperbola with its centre at O.

(59)⋆. If a particle describes a circle of radius a passing through O, and if the attractive force is directed towards the point O on the circumference of the circle, show that the p,r-equation of the circle is given by $p = r^2/2a$, and that the force F must be proportional to r^{-5}.

(60)⋆. A particle of unit mass moves under the action of a force F directed towards a fixed point O. Prove that

$$F = h^2u^2(d^2u/d\theta^2 + u)$$

where $(1/u, \theta)$ are the polar coordinates referred to O and h is a constant.
Find F as a function of u if $u^2 = a \cos^2 \theta + b \sin^2 \theta$.

(61)⋆. A particle is projected from P in a direction making an angle $\frac{1}{3}\pi$ with the line joining P to a centre of force O the force being proportional to OP. If the speed of projection is $\sqrt{2}$ times that which it would acquire in moving directly from rest at P to O, prove that the eccentricity of the orbit is $\sqrt{(\sqrt{3} - 1)}$.

(62)⋆. A particle projected with velocity $\sqrt{(2\mu/3a^3)}$ at right-angles to the radius vector at a distance a from the centre of an attracting force μ/r^4 per unit mass. Using the equation of energy, show that the equation of the path is $r = \frac{1}{2}a(1 + \cos \theta)$.

ANSWERS TO EXERCISES

(1). $24a/7, 3a/\sqrt{7}$ below initial position. (4) g vertically downwards.
(8). $a = 80, b = 5/484$. (9). $v = 90$ m.p.h., max. $H = 36\frac{24}{25}$.
(10). $(\frac{6}{5} + \frac{9}{98})$ secs. $= 1 \cdot 292$ secs. (13). 192 ft. (14). $9 \cdot 081$ secs.
(15). $(\log 2)/2au^2$. (16). $\frac{41}{4}Mg \sin \theta, \frac{7}{5}Mg \cos \theta$. (17). $2\pi\sqrt{(l\sqrt{3}/2g)}$.
(19). Tension: 25 lb. wt., thrust: $65/17$ lb. wt. (21). $\theta = \sin^{-1}\frac{3}{4}$.
(22). $2a\dot\phi^2 = g(1 + \sqrt{7} \cos \phi - \sin \phi)$; thrust $= \frac{1}{2}mg$. (23). $\frac{9}{7}Mg \sin \theta \cos \theta$,
$Mg - \frac{3}{7}Mg(3 \cos^2 \theta - 2)$. (28). $\sqrt{(18b/5g} \sin \beta), \frac{5}{9}Mg \sin \beta$.
(30). $\frac{1}{3}gt^2 \sin \alpha$. (31). $aT/(Ma^2 + 4mk^2)$, $mk^2T/a(Ma^2 + 4mk^2)$, $\frac{1}{2}T(Ma^2 + 2mk^2)/a(Ma^2 + 4mk^2)$. (32). $4\mu gT$. (34). $19mg/10\sqrt{3}, 2\pi\sqrt{(5r/3g\sqrt{3})}$.
(36). $\frac{1}{2}Mmg \sin \alpha/(4M + 3m), \frac{1}{2}mg \sin \alpha(3M + 2m)/(4M + 3m), 4(M + m)g \sin \alpha/ (4M + 3m)$. (41). $m(68g - 7a\Omega^2)/25$. (42). $\frac{1}{3}\pi a/u, 3u/a, \frac{1}{2}Mu$.
(43). $P/2am\sqrt{2}$. (44). $8mv/7$, loss $= \frac{4}{7}mv^2$.
(45). $3l/5aM$. (47). $8v/7$. (48). $\sqrt{(42ga)}$. (49). Circle radius $a\sqrt{\frac{2}{3}}$ about centre; $ma\omega/\sqrt{6}$. (50). $\frac{4}{5}ma\omega$.
(52). normal reaction: $\frac{4}{5}am\omega^2 (e^{\frac{1}{2}\omega t} - e^{-2\omega t})$. (60). $F = h^2ab/u$.

CHAPTER 24

STATISTICS

24.1 The mean

Measurements are usually of two distinct types, depending on the variable measured. In a controlled laboratory experiment for which one definite numerical value x is sought (such as a boiling point), repeated experiments produce a series of values x_1, x_2, ... closely clustered round the required value x. Not one of these measurements can be absolutely correct; they all differ slightly one from another on account of inherent experimental errors outside the control of the investigator. On the other hand, we may be given a collection of data, for which no unique number is expected, such as the number of visitors to a museum on each day throughout a month, or the number of defective manufactured articles found in various examined batches.

If n measurements or *observations* x_1, x_2, ..., x_n are made, their *mean* m is defined to be

$$m = (x_1 + x_2 + \ldots x_n)/n = \sum x/n. \tag{1}$$

This mean is a suitable representative value of the whole mass of information contained in the n measurements.

The *deviation* of a particular measurement x_i from its mean is $x_i - m$; the sum of these deviations is

$$\sum(x - m) = \sum x - \sum m = \sum x - nm = 0, \tag{2}$$

from equation (1).

If the observations are *weighted*, let x_i occur not merely once, but with a *frequency* f_i. Then

$$m = (f_1 x_1 + f_2 x_2 + \ldots)/(f_1 + f_2 + \ldots) = \sum fx / \sum f,$$

where all the observations are added together and divided by the total frequency. This formula is analogous to that for finding the centre of gravity of weights along a line; the f's correspond to the weights and the x's to their positions.

The addition of a series of large numbers may be avoided by the introduction of a *fictitious mean* M, its value being judged roughly by inspection. Let the n deviations $x_i - M$ from this fictitious mean be calculated; then

$$m = \sum x/n = \sum(x - M + M)/n = M + \sum(x - M)/n. \tag{3}$$

That is, we need only calculate the average of the deviations from M, and add this average to M to obtain the true mean m.

24.2 Variance and standard deviation

We seek to reduce a large mass of observational material to a small number of quantitative parameters. The mean m, a useful parameter, tells us nothing about the spread of the observations about the mean. The two distinct sets of observations

$$1, 99, 200, 301, 399; \qquad 198, 199, 200, 201, 202$$

both have a common mean 200, but obviously, the first set is widely scattered about m and the second is closely clustered about m. We need, therefore, a second parameter to measure *dispersion*.

The *mean deviation*, defined to be $\Sigma|x - m|/n$, is a useful numerical parameter measuring dispersion, but theoretically this average of the deviations, all taken positively, is not susceptible to further algebraical treatment.

We therefore define the *variance* σ^2 to be the average of the squares of the deviations from the mean:

$$\sigma^2 = \Sigma(x - m)^2/n. \tag{4}$$

Its square root σ is known as the *standard deviation*. The variance is always used in analytical theory, since a sum of squares is amenable to algebraical treatment. If σ is small, the observations are closely clustered around the mean m.

The numerical calculation of σ^2 as the sum of the squares of deviations $x_i - m$ from the true mean may often be simplified by using a fictitious mean M. For example, if all the x's are integers, decimals may be avoided in the calculation of σ^2 by choosing M to be an integer close to m. Let σ_M^2 denote the average of the squares of deviations from M. Then

$$\sigma_M{}^2 = \frac{\Sigma(x - M)^2}{n} = \frac{\Sigma[(x - m) + (m - M)]^2}{n}$$

$$= \frac{\Sigma(x - m)^2}{n} + \frac{2\Sigma(x - m)(m - M)}{n} + \frac{\Sigma(m - M)^2}{n}$$

$$= \sigma^2 + (m - M)^2 \tag{5}$$

since $\Sigma(x - m) = 0$ by equation (2). Hence

$$\sigma^2 = \sigma_M{}^2 - (m - M)^2 \tag{6}$$

a result that may be compared with the theorem of parallel axes in the theory of moments of inertia. As M is varied, we see from equation (5) that $\sigma_M{}^2$ has a minimum when $M = m$, its value being σ^2. This fact leads to an independent definition of the mean m. It is that value such that the sum of squares of deviations from it is a minimum.

In particular, if $M = 0$, we have

$$\sigma^2 = \sum x^2/n - m^2, \tag{7}$$

thereby expressing σ^2 in terms of the squares of the actual observations.

Example 1 Find the mean and variance of the first $2n$ positive integers.

We have

$$m = \sum r/2n = \tfrac{1}{2}.2n(2n+1)/2n = (n + \tfrac{1}{2}).$$

Using equation (7), we find for the variance

$$\sigma^2 = \sum r^2/n - m^2 = \tfrac{1}{6}.2n(2n+1)(4n+1)/2n - (n+\tfrac{1}{2})^2 = \tfrac{1}{12}(4n^2 - 1)$$

upon simplification. The standard deviation is $\sqrt{[\tfrac{1}{12}(4n^2 - 1)]}$.

Example 2 Find the standard deviation of the 40 observations

x	16	17	18	19	20	21	22
f	2	5	8	10	9	5	1

Vertical columns should always be used in numerical work requiring addition and subtraction. We choose a fictitious mean $M = 19$ as follows:

x	f	$x-19$	$(x-19)^2$	$f(x-19)$	$f(x-19)^2$
16	2	-3	9	-6	18
17	5	-2	4	-10	20
18	8	-1	1	-8	8
19	10	0	0	0	0
20	9	1	1	9	9
21	5	2	4	10	20
22	1	3	9	3	9
totals:	40			-2	84
totals/40:				-0.05	2·1

It follows that

$$m = M - 0.05 = 19 - 0.05 = 18.95$$
$$\sigma^2 = 2.1 - (-0.05)^2 = 2.1 - 0.0025 = 2.0975,$$

yielding $\sigma = 1.448$.

24.3 The combination of two sets of observations

Let set I consist of the n observations $x_1, x_2, \ldots, x_n$ whose mean and variance are given by

$$nm_x = \sum x, \quad n\sigma_n{}^2 = \sum x^2 - nm_x{}^2,$$

and let set II consist of the p observations $y_1, y_2, \ldots, y_p$, whose mean and variance are given by

$$pm_y = \sum y, \quad p\sigma_y{}^2 = \sum y^2 - pm_y{}^2.$$

Case i. We seek the mean m and the variance σ^2 of the combined set of $n + p$ observations $x_1, x_2, \ldots, x_n, y_1, y_2, \ldots, y_p$, in terms of $n, p, m_x, m_y, \sigma_x{}^2, \sigma_y{}^2$.

For the mean m, we have

$$m = \frac{\sum x + \sum y}{n + p} = \frac{nm_x + pm_y}{n + p}$$

expressed in terms of the two individual means.

The variance may be calculated using the sum of the squares of all the individual observations in both sets. We have

$$\sigma^2 = \frac{\sum x^2 + \sum y^2}{n + p} - m^2 = \frac{n\sigma_x{}^2 + nm_x{}^2 + p\sigma_y{}^2 + pm_y{}^2}{n + p} - \left(\frac{nm_x + pm_y}{n + p}\right)^2$$

$$= \frac{n\sigma_x{}^2 + p\sigma_y{}^2}{n + p} + \frac{(n + p)(nm_x{}^2 + pm_x{}^2) - (nm_x + pm_y)^2}{(n + p)^2}$$

$$= \frac{n\sigma_x{}^2 + p\sigma_y{}^2}{n + p} + \frac{np(m_x - m_y)^2}{(n + p)^2}.$$

Only if $m_x = m_y$ is a simpler formula obtained:

$$\sigma^2 = (n\sigma_x{}^2 + p\sigma_y{}^2)/(n + p).$$

In numerical work, three or more sets may easily be combined in a similar manner.

Case ii. Let us form a set of np observations by taking every observation in set I and adding to it λ times every observation of set II. In tabular form, these np observations are

$$x_1 + \lambda y_1, \quad x_2 + \lambda y_1, \ldots x_n + \lambda y_1,$$
$$x_1 + \lambda y_2, \quad x_2 + \lambda y_2, \ldots x_n + \lambda y_2,$$
$$\cdot \qquad\qquad \cdot \qquad \cdots \quad \cdot$$
$$x_1 + \lambda y_p, \quad x_2 + \lambda y_p, \ldots x_n + \lambda y_p.$$

The mean is given by

$$m = \frac{\sum(x + \lambda y)}{np} = \frac{p\sum x_i + \lambda n \sum y_i}{np} = m_x + \lambda m_y$$

since each x enters the table p times and each y, n times.

The variance is given by

$$\sigma^2 = \sum(x + \lambda y - m)^2/np = \sum[(x - m_x) + \lambda(y - m_y)]^2/np$$
$$= \sum[(x - m_x)^2 + 2\lambda(x - m_x)(y - m_y) + \lambda^2(y - m_y)^2]/np$$
$$= [p\sum(x_i - m_x)^2 + 2\lambda\sum(x_i - m_x)\sum(y_i - m_y) + \lambda^2 n\sum(y_i - m_y)^2]/np$$
$$= \sigma_x{}^2 + \lambda^2\sigma_y{}^2,$$

since $\Sigma(x_i - m_x) = \Sigma(y_i - m_y) = 0$, and since each x enters the table p times and each y, n times.

In particular, if $\lambda = \pm 1$, $m = m_x \pm m_y$, $\sigma^2 = \sigma_x{}^2 + \sigma_y{}^2$.

24.4   Frequency distributions

Graphical representation of a set of observations reduces a mass of numerical data to a visual and easily digestable form.

If only the n discrete observations $x_1, x_2, \ldots, x_n$ are possible, and if

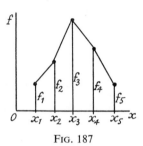

FIG. 187

their respective frequencies are $f_1, f_2, \ldots, f_n$, then we plot the points (x_i, f_i) on a graph with respect to Cartesian axes Ox, Of. The n points are then joined by straight lines, yielding a *frequency polygon*.

The parameters of this distribution are

(i) The *mean* $m = \Sigma xf/\Sigma f$.

(ii) The *mode*, namely that value of the observation for which the frequency is a maximum; in Fig. 187, the mode is x_3.

(iii) The *median*. If the $\Sigma f = n$ observations are placed side by side in order of magnitude, the median is the middle observation if n is odd, and the average of the two middle observations if n is even.

Such polygons may be either unsymmetrical or symmetrical about the mode; the mean may be either to the right or to the left of the mode, or perhaps they may be equal. Pearson's definition of *skewness* is

$$(\text{mean} - \text{mode})/\text{standard deviation}.$$

This is a dimensionless parameter, so it may be used to compare the skewness of polygons drawn for observations with different dimensions.

On the other hand, if all measurements of x are possible in the range $a < x < b$, and if we have n observations in this range, we draw a *histogram*. The range $a < x < b$ is subdivided into N equal *class-intervals* of equal width $h = (b - a)/N$. The class-intervals are

$$a = x_0 < x < x_1 = a + h,$$
$$a + h = x_1 < x < x_2 = a + 2h, \text{ etc.}$$

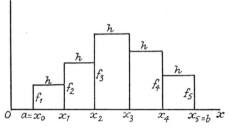

FIG. 188

Let f_i equal the number of observations that fall within the ith class-interval

$$a + (i - 1)h < x < a + ih;$$

we note that $\Sigma f_i = n$. A histogram is plotted as shown in Fig. 188, the height of the rectangle for the ith class-interval being f_i.

To find the mean, we use an approximate calculation. We associate the frequencies $f_1, f_2, \ldots$ with those values of x lying at the mid-point of each class-interval, namely $a + \frac{1}{2}h, a + \frac{3}{2}h, \ldots$. With this convention, the mean and variance follow by the usual calculations.

24.5 Continuous distributions

If all measurements are possible in the range $a \leqslant x \leqslant b$, we seek a representation of the distribution as the total number of observations n becomes indefinitely large. Clearly, a histogram as defined above is not possible, since all the f_i's would tend to infinity. Instead, we work in terms of an ordinate that refers to the *proportion* of observations rather than the actual number.

Let $f(x)\,\delta x$ denote the proportion of observations that fall within the small range $(x, x + \delta x)$. The actual number that fall within this range is $nf(x)\,\delta x$ if n is very large. It follows that the proportion of the observations falling in the range $c \leqslant x \leqslant d$ where $a \leqslant c < d \leqslant b$ is

$$\int_c^d f(x)\,dx;$$

when integrated over the whole range, we must have

$$\int_a^b f(x)\,dx = 1.$$

The actual number of observations falling in the range $c \leqslant x \leqslant d$ is

$$n \int_c^d f(x)\,dx.$$

The observation x is associated with the frequency $nf(x)\,\delta x$, so the mean is given by

$$m = \frac{1}{n} \int_a^b xnf(x)\,dx = \int_a^b xf(x)\,dx, \tag{8}$$

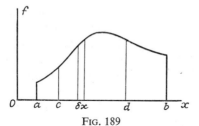

FIG. 189

where the number n does not enter the final formula. Formula (7) yields for the variance

$$\sigma^2 = \int_a^b x^2 f(x)\, dx - \left(\int_a^b x f(x)\, dx \right)^2.$$

The mean deviation is given by

$$\int_a^b |x - m| f(x)\, dx = \int_a^m (m - x) f(x)\, dx + \int_m^b (x - m) f(x)\, dx$$

where $|x - m| = m - x$ when $a < x < m$ and $|x - m| = x - m$ when $m < x < b$.

Either a or b or both a and b may be infinite in some distributions. If $f(x)$ is an even function, and if $a = -\infty$ and $b = \infty$, evidently $m = 0$ and the mean deviation simplifies to

$$2 \int_0^\infty x f(x)\, dx.$$

24.6   One fundamental problem of statistics

In example 1, we have seen that the mean of the first $2n$ integers is $n + \tfrac{1}{2}$ and that its standard deviation is $\sqrt{[\tfrac{1}{12}(4n^2 - 1)]}$. If n is large, we may write this approximately as $\sigma = n/\sqrt{3}$. Since

$$m + 2\sigma = n + \tfrac{1}{2} + 2n/\sqrt{3} > 2n,$$
$$m - 2\sigma = n + \tfrac{1}{2} - 2n/\sqrt{3} < 0,$$

we conclude that all the $2n$ integers lie within a range of width 2σ on each side of the mean m. In other words,

$$|x - m| < 2\sigma, \tag{9}$$

for all integers x considered.

This result is a general feature of all distributions, namely that *most* of the individual observations satisfy the inequality (9), while *few, if any*, satisfy the inequality $|x - m| > 3\sigma$.

If we have made an observation X, to what extent can we decide whether it forms part of a distribution with mean m and standard deviation σ? If more is known about the distribution, for example if the distribution is normal, a precise answer can be given to this question. But if *no* other information is available, we use the following *significance test*.

We make a *null hypothesis*, namely that X is a member of the given distribution. The theory of statistics can never prove such a hypothesis, all it can do is to offer evidence *against* the hypothesis. We postulate as reasonable:

If $|X - m| < 2\sigma$, no evidence exists against the hypothesis (compare equation (9)).

If $2\sigma < |X - m| < 3\sigma$, certain evidence exists against the hypothesis.

If $|X - m| > 3\sigma$, almost complete evidence exists against the hypothesis; we conclude (almost certainly, but perhaps with a shadow of doubt) that the hypothesis is wrong, and that X does not belong to the given distribution.

We say that the last result is *highly significant*; it compels us to take action to amend the hypothesis.

If the distribution is known to be approximately normal, the figures 2 and 3 are modified, and a precise interpretation may be placed upon the modified figures.

24.7 The elements of probability theory

The student should recall the following ideas from his previous Advanced Level Pure Mathematics course.

If, in an experiment or a *trial*, there are n equally likely results, and if we choose to call m of them *successes* and $n - m$ *failures*, then the *probability* of success in one trial is m/n and the probability of failure is $(n - m)/n$. We write

$$p = m/n, \qquad q = (n - m)/n,$$

and observe that $p + q = 1$.

For example, if we require the probability of a throw of a dice* being even, we call the results 2, 4, 6 successes and the results 1, 3, 5 failures. The probability of success is therefore $\frac{3}{6} = \frac{1}{2}$.

The addition law. Of the n alternative results just considered, let m_1 be designated as an event E_1 and a distinct m_2 be designated as an event E_2. Evidently $p_1 = m_1/n$ and $p_2 = m_2/n$ are the probabilities of E_1 and E_2 respectively. We seek the probability p that the result in one trial should be either event E_1 OR event E_2. Evidently $m_1 + m_2$ alternatives satisfy the criterion, so

$$p = (m_1 + m_2)/n = p_1 + p_2.$$

The multiplication law for independent events. Let the event E_1 occur m_1 times out of n_1 alternatives, and let the event E_2 occur m_2 times out of a second *distinct* set of n_2 alternatives. Evidently $p_1 = m_1/n_1$, $p_2 = m_2/n_2$. If one trial is made out of n_1 and one trial out of the independent set n_2, we seek the probability that the combined event E_1 AND E_2 occurs.

* Colloquially; strictly speaking, the singular is die.

The total number of ways in which selection may be made from the two complete sets is $n_1 n_2$, while the total number of ways in which selection may be made from the two groups regarded as successes is $m_1 m_2$. Hence

$$p = m_1 m_2 / n_1 n_2 = p_1 p_2.$$

The expected value. If the probabilities of the values $x_1, x_2, \ldots, x_n$ occurring in one trial are given to be $p_1, p_2, \ldots, p_n$, then out of a large number N of trials, we expect x_1 to occur $N p_1$ times, x_2 to occur $N p_2$ times, etc.

The *expected value* $E(x)$ of an event is defined to be the mean value of that event evaluated over a long series of trials; namely

$$E(x) = (N p_1 x_1 + N p_2 x_2 + \ldots)/N = p_1 x_1 + p_2 x_2 + \ldots = \sum px.$$

For example, the expected value of a single throw of a dice is

$$E(x) = \tfrac{1}{6}(1 + 2 + 3 + 4 + 5 + 6) = 3 \cdot 5;$$

this is the average result calculated over a long series of trials.

'*At least one*'. If p_1 and p_2 are the probabilities of two independent events E_1 and E_2, what is the probability that *at least one* occurs? This is understood as

The probability of (E_1 AND not E_2) OR (E_2 AND not E_1) OR (E_1 AND E_2)

$$\begin{aligned} &= p_1 q_2 + p_2 q_1 + p_1 p_2 \\ &= (1 - q_1)q_2 + (1 - q_2)q_1 + (1 - q_1)(1 - q_2) \\ &= 1 - q_1 q_2. \end{aligned}$$

'*Not more than*'. Let p_0 be the probability that a certain event does not occur, p_1 that it occurs once, p_2 that it occurs twice, etc. Then the probability that the event occurs *not more than* twice, say, equals

The probability of it not occurring OR of it occurring once
OR of it occurring twice $= p_0 + p_1 + p_2.$

The probability that the event occurs two or more times is

$$p_2 + p_3 + \ldots + p_n = 1 - p_0 - p_1.$$

24.8 The binomial distribution

In one trial, let p be the probability of success of an event E and $q = 1 - p$ the probability of failure. We make n such trials in succession, and we seek the probability p_r that there should be r successes and $n - r$ failures during these n trials.

The number of ways in which the r successes may be scattered amongst the n trials is $_nC_r$. The probability of any one of these arrangements is $p^r q^{n-r}$, the multiplication law being used since we require r successes AND $n - r$ failures. Finally, any one of the $_nC_r$ arrangements satisfies the requirements since we are not concerned with any particular order. The addition law must therefore be used; that is, the probability $p^r q^{n-r}$ is required $_nC_r$ times. Hence

the probability of r successes out of n trials $= p_r = {}_nC_r p^r q^{n-r}$.

The probabilities of 0, 1, 2, 3, . . . successes are therefore given by

$$p_0 = {}_nC_0 p^0 q^n = q^n, \qquad p_1 = {}_nC_1 pq^{n-1} = npq^{n-1},$$
$$p_2 = {}_nC_2 p^2 q^{n-2} = \tfrac{1}{2}n(n-1)p^2 q^{n-2}, \text{ etc.}$$

If this set of n trials is carried out a large number of times N, we obtain a frequency distribution; r successes occur $N_nC_r p^r q^{n-r}$ times approximately.

The generating function for the binomial distribution is defined to be

$$\sum_0^n p_r z^r \equiv p_0 + p_1 z + p_2 z^2 + \ldots + p_n z^n$$
$$\equiv q^n + z_n C_1 pq^{n-1} + z^2 {}_nC_2 p^2 q^{n-2} + \ldots + z^n p^n \equiv (q + pz)^n.$$

To find the expected value or the mean m, we differentiate with respect to z, obtaining

$$\sum r p_r z^{r-1} = np(q + pz)^{n-1}.$$

Placing $z = 1$, we find

$$m = \sum r p_r = np,$$

since $q + p = 1$.

Multiplying by z, we obtain

$$\sum r p_r z^r = npz(q + pz)^{n-1};$$

differentiation yields

$$\sum r^2 p_r z^{r-1} = np(q + pz)^{n-1} + n(n-1)p^2 z(q + pz)^{n-2}.$$

When $z = 1$, we have

$$\sum r^2 p_r = np + n(n-1)p^2.$$

Finally, the variance is given by

$$\sigma^2 = \sum r^2 p_r - m^2 = np + n(n-1)p^2 - n^2 p^2 = np(1-p) = npq.$$

We eliminate p from this formula, obtaining $\sigma^2 = m(1 - m/n)$, reducing to

$$n\sigma^2 = m(n - m) \tag{10}$$

as the special relationship existing between m and σ^2 for the binomial distribution.

A second distribution, but with the same probabilities, may be formed by considering the *proportion* of successes in n trials; in this case, the observation is r/n rather than r. Its mean and variance are found by dividing the previous results by n and n^2 respectively; namely $m = p$, $\sigma^2 = pq/n$.

Fitting a binomial distribution. Let us suppose that the set of observations 0, 1, 2, 3, ..., n has the given associated probabilities p_0, p_1, p_2, ..., p_n. Is this approximately a binomial distribution?

First, we find m and σ^2 for the given observations, and we test to ascertain whether the necessary condition $n\sigma^2 = m(n - m)$ is satisfied. If *not*, the given distribution cannot be a binomial distribution. But if the condition is satisfied exactly or approximately, the given distribution *may* be a binomial distribution. We calculate $p = m/n$, $q = 1 - m/n$, and evaluate the $n + 1$ probabilities $p_r' = {}_nC_r p^r q^{n-r}$. If these are all reasonably close to the given probabilities, then the fit is a good one.

Example 3* In an experiment the numbers $0, 1, 2, \ldots, 6$ were obtained with frequencies given by the table

0	1	2	3	4	5	6
8	58	250	656	976	784	268

Calculate their mean and standard deviation. According to theory, a binomial frequency distribution was expected with $q = 1/m$ for some integer m. Find the value of m suggested by the experiment and calculate the theoretical frequencies.

Choosing a fictitious mean $M = 3$, we prepare the following table

x	f	$x - M$	$(x - M)^2$	$f(x - M)$	$f(x - M)^2$
0	8	-3	9	-24	72
1	58	-2	4	-116	232
2	250	-1	1	-250	250
3	656	0	0	0	0
4	976	1	1	976	976
5	784	2	4	1568	3136
6	268	3	9	804	2412
totals:	3000			2958	7078
totals/3000				0·986	2·359

Hence

$$m = M + 0\cdot986 = 3\cdot986,$$

$$\sigma^2 = 2\cdot359 - (M - m)^2 = 1\cdot387,$$

yielding $\sigma = 1\cdot18$.

It may be checked that equation (10) is approximately satisfied, so we may choose $m = np$, $\sigma^2 = npq$ with $n = 6$. Dividing, we obtain

$$q = \sigma^2/m = 1\cdot387/3\cdot986 \doteqdot \tfrac{1}{3}$$

Fitting a Poisson distribution to given data. Let the frequencies $f_0, f_1, f_2, \ldots$ (total N) be associated with the observations $1, 2, 3, \ldots$. The probabilities $p_0, p_1, p_2, \ldots$ may be found by dividing the frequencies by N. Firstly, we calculate the mean and the variance of the distribution; unless $m = \sigma^2$, the distribution *cannot* be a Poisson distribution. If, however, $m \doteqdot \sigma^2$, the distribution *may* be a Poisson distribution. We then evaluate the theoretical frequencies

$$Ne^{-m}, \; Ne^{-m}m, \; Ne^{-m}m^2/2!, \; Ne^{-m}m^3/3!, \ldots$$

If these values are very close to the given frequencies, the fit is a good one. As an aid to rapid calculation, the student should note that each frequency may be obtained from the previous one by multiplying Ne^{-m} by $m, \frac{1}{2}m, \frac{1}{3}m, \frac{1}{4}m, \ldots$ respectively.

Example 6★ Fit a Poisson distribution to the following data:

r	0	1	2	3	4	5	6	7 and over
f	370	365	185	61	15	3	1	0

We prepare the following table:

r	f	rf	$r - m$	$(r - m)^2$	$f(r - m)^2$
0	370	0	-1	1	370
1	365	365	0	0	0
2	185	370	1	1	185
3	61	183	2	4	244
4	15	60	3	9	135
5	3	15	4	16	48
6	1	6	5	25	25
totals:	1000	999			1007
totals/1000		1·00			1·01

It follows that $m = 1$, $\sigma^2 = 1·01$, a satisfactory result. Then the theoretical frequencies are given by

$$1000 \times e^{-1}m^r/r! = 1000/er! = 368/r!,$$

yielding the following table that shows a very good fit:

r	0	1	2	3	4	5	6
theoretical f	368	368	184	61	15	3	1
given f	370	365	185	61	15	3	1

Example 7 *The use of the Poisson distribution in approximations.* If, in the binomial distribution, p is small but non-zero and if n is large but finite, we may use the Poisson formula to evaluate the binomial probabilities, namely

$$_nC_rp^r(1 - p)^{n-r} \doteqdot e^{-m}m^r/r! \quad \text{where } m = np.$$

(a) If the probability of an article being defective is 4%, find the probability that not more than one defective exists in a sample of ten.

Here, $p = \frac{4}{100} = 0.04$, $q = 0.96$, $n = 10$, so strictly speaking, we require the value of

$$(0.96)^{10} + 10 \times 0.04 \times (0.96)^9.$$

Instead, noting that $m = np = 0.4$, we use

$$e^{-0.4} + e^{-0.4}\, 0.4 = e^{-0.4} \times 1.4 = 0.938.$$

(b) If the probability of an article being defective is 0.8%, find the probability that five or more are defective in a batch of 200.

Here, $p = 0.008$, $n = 200$, $m = np = 1.6$. We therefore use the simpler result that the probability of r defectives is $e^{-1.6}(1.6)^r/r!$ When $r = 5, 6, 7$, this probability equals 0.018, 0.005, 0.001 respectively. Hence the required probability equals the sum of these values, namely 0.024, or $2\frac{1}{2}$%.

24.10   The normal distribution

If every value of a variable x in the range $a \leqslant x \leqslant b$ is a possible result in a trial, we define $p(x)\,\delta x$ to be the probability that a value of x falls within the range $(x, x + \delta x)$. This means that out of a large number N of trials, the variable x falls within this small range $Np(x)\,\delta x$ times. The curve $y = p(x)$ is the *probability curve* for the variable x. The probability that a value of x falls within the range $c \leqslant x \leqslant d$ is

$$\int_c^d p(x)\, dx.$$

As in section 24.5, we have the formulae

$$\int_a^b p(x)\, dx = 1, \qquad m = \int_a^b x p(x)\, dx, \qquad \sigma^2 = \int_a^b x^2 p(x)\, dx - m^2.$$

Example 8★   In a certain population, the probability of an individual aged t years dying between the ages of t and $t + \delta t$ years is $te^{-t/n}\delta t/n^2$. Show that the probability of an individual now aged $\frac{1}{2}n$ years still living in n years time is $\frac{1}{2}(2 - 3e^{-1/2} + 5e^{-3/2})$. Show also that the expectation of life at birth is $2n$ years.

The probability that an individual will not die in the time interval $(\frac{1}{2}n, \frac{3}{2}n)$ is 1 minus the probability that the individual will die, namely

$$1 - \frac{1}{n^2}\int_{\frac{1}{2}n}^{\frac{3}{2}n} te^{-t/n}\, dt = 1 - \frac{1}{n^2}\left[-nte^{-t/n} - n^2e^{-t/n} \right]_{\frac{1}{2}n}^{\frac{3}{2}n} \qquad \text{(by parts)}$$

$$= 1 - \tfrac{3}{2}e^{-1/2} + \tfrac{5}{2}e^{-3/2}$$

Of a large number N of individuals, $Nte^{-t/n}\delta t/n^2$ is the number who expect to die between t and $t + \delta t$ years; their length of life is t years. The expectation of life is the mean of this, namely

$$\frac{1}{n^2}\int_0^\infty t^2 e^{-t/n}\, dt = \frac{1}{n^2}\left[-nt^2 e^{-t/n} - 2n^2 te^{-t/n} - 2n^3 e^{-t/n} \right]_0^\infty \qquad \text{(by parts)}$$

$$= 2n.$$

The normal distribution. We define the *normal probability curve* to be

$$p(x) = e^{-\frac{1}{2}x^2/\sigma^2}/\sigma\sqrt{(2\pi)}.$$

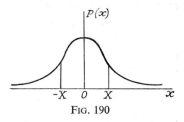

FIG. 190

The curve is symmetrical about $x = 0$, which is obviously the mean. It can be seen that the curve consists only of a central hump around the mean. It is found that errors in precise measurement are subject to such a distribution about their mean. If we require the same curve, but referred to the general mean m, we write

$$p(x) = e^{-\frac{1}{2}(x-m)^2/\sigma^2}/\sigma\sqrt{(2\pi)}. \qquad (11)$$

The variance of the distribution is given by

$$\int_{-\infty}^{\infty} x^2 p(x)\, dx = \frac{2}{\sigma\sqrt{(2\pi)}} \int_0^{\infty} x^2 e^{-\frac{1}{2}x^2/\sigma^2}\, dx$$

$$= \frac{2}{\sigma\sqrt{(2\pi)}} \left[-x\sigma^2 e^{-\frac{1}{2}x^2/\sigma^2} + \sigma^2 \int e^{-\frac{1}{2}x^2/\sigma^2}\, dx \right]_0^{\infty}$$

$$= \frac{2\sigma}{\sqrt{(2\pi)}} \int_0^{\infty} e^{-y^2}\sqrt{2}\sigma\, dy \qquad (x = \sqrt{2}\sigma y)$$

$$= \sigma^2, \text{ since } \int_0^{\infty} e^{-y^2}\, dy = \tfrac{1}{2}\sqrt{\pi} \qquad \text{(see section 17.2).}$$

The parameter σ occurring in the definition of $p(x)$ is therefore the standard deviation of the distribution.

The following table gives the values of the function $e^{-\frac{1}{2}t^2}/\sqrt{(2\pi)}$; the value of $p(x)$ may then be found by calculating $t = x/\sigma$, and dividing the tabulated value by σ.

t	$e^{-\frac{1}{2}t^2}/\sqrt{(2\pi)}$	t	$e^{-\frac{1}{2}t^2}/\sqrt{(2\pi)}$	t	$e^{-\frac{1}{2}t^2}/\sqrt{(2\pi)}$
0·0	0·399	1·0	0·242	2·0	0·054
0·1	0·397	1·1	0·218	2·1	0·044
0·2	0·391	1·2	0·194	2·2	0·035
0·3	0·381	1·3	0·171	2·3	0·028
0·4	0·368	1·4	0·150	2·4	0·022
0·5	0·352	1·5	0·129	2·5	0·017
0·6	0·333	1·6	0·111	2·6	0·014
0·7	0·312	1·7	0·094	2·7	0·011
0·8	0·290	1·8	0·079	2·8	0·008
0·9	0·266	1·9	0·066	2·9	0·006
				3·0	0·004

A normal distribution may be fitted to a given distribution merely by calculating the mean m and the standard deviation σ and then by using equation (11) together with the above table. (See example 9 for details.)

If the variable x is normally distributed about its mean $x = 0$, say, then the probability that a value of x lies within the range $-X < 0 < X$ is

$$p = \frac{1}{\sigma\sqrt{(2\pi)}} \int_{-X}^{X} e^{-\frac{1}{2}x^2/\sigma^2}\, dx,$$

reducing to the simpler integral

$$p = \frac{2}{\sqrt{\pi}} \int_{0}^{X/\sigma\sqrt{2}} e^{-t^2}\, dt$$

under the substitution $x = \sqrt{2}\sigma t$. This integral can only be evaluated numerically, and tables have been prepared of its value. To this end, we define the error function erf(y) to denote the integral

$$\mathrm{erf}(y) = \frac{2}{\sqrt{\pi}} \int_{0}^{y} e^{-t^2} dt,$$

yielding $p = \mathrm{erf}(X/\sigma\sqrt{2})$ as the probability that a value of x lies within the range $|x| < X$. Out of a large number N of random observations of the variable x, $N\,\mathrm{erf}(X/\sigma\sqrt{2})$ will lie within the range $|x| < X$, and $N[1 - \mathrm{erf}(X/\sigma\sqrt{2})]$ will lie outside the range.

The following table provides the values of erf(y).

y	erf(y)	y	erf(y)	y	erf(y)
0·0	0	1·0	0·843	2·0	0·995
0·1	0·112	1·1	0·880	2·1	0·997
0·2	0·223	1·2	0·910	2·2	0·998
0·3	0·329	1·3	0·934	2·3	0·999
0·4	0·428	1·4	0·952		
0·5	0·520	1·5	0·966		
0·6	0·604	1·6	0·976		
0·7	0·678	1·7	0·984		
0·8	0·742	1·8	0·989		
0·9	0·797	1·9	0·993		

Consider, now, some special values of X, namely σ, 2σ and 3σ. The probability that a value x lies within the range $-\sigma < x < \sigma$ is

$$p = \mathrm{erf}(\sigma/\sqrt{2}\sigma) = \mathrm{erf}(0\cdot707) = 0\cdot683;$$

the probability that it lies within the range $-2\sigma < x < 2\sigma$ is

$$p = \mathrm{erf}(2\sigma/\sqrt{2}\sigma) = \mathrm{erf}(1\cdot414) = 0\cdot954;$$

the probability that it lies within the range $-3\sigma < x < 3\sigma$ is

$$p = \text{erf}(3\sigma/\sqrt{2}\sigma) = \text{erf}(2{\cdot}121) = 0{\cdot}997.$$

This implies that out of 1000 observations,

683 lie within the range $\;-\sigma < x < \sigma\;$ and 317 lie outside;
954 lie within the range $-2\sigma < x < 2\sigma$ and $\;$ 46 lie outside;
997 lie within the range $-3\sigma < x < 3\sigma$ and $\;\;$ 3 lie outside.

These numbers are, however, not the most convenient in applications of the theory. Instead, we choose those values of X such that either 95% or 99% of a large number of observations lie within the range $-X < x < X$; this implies that either 5% or 1% lie outside the range respectively. For the two cases, we have

	$\text{erf}(X/\sqrt{2}\sigma) = 0{\cdot}95$	$\text{erf}(X/\sqrt{2}\sigma) = 0{\cdot}99,$
yielding	$X/\sqrt{2}\sigma = 1{\cdot}386$	$X/2\sigma = 1{\cdot}820$
or	$X = 1{\cdot}96\sigma,$	$X = 2{\cdot}58\sigma.$

(These values have been extracted from a table containing finer subdivisions than the table above.)

The student should notice that the equation $p = \text{erf}(X/\sqrt{2}\sigma)$ relates the three quantities p, X and σ. If any two of these are given, the third may be calculated; if p is given, the tables must of course be used backwards in order to find either X or σ.

Significance test. We wish to test whether it is likely that a random value x extracted from a normal distribution belongs in fact to a given normal distribution with mean m and standard deviation σ.

Now if x is extracted at random from this given normal distribution, then we know that $|x - m|$ is less than $1{\cdot}96\sigma$ for 95 random extractions out of 100 and that $|x - m|$ is less than $2{\cdot}58\sigma$ for 99 random extractions out of 100.

Hence we make the *null hypothesis* that the particular value x was extracted from the given normal distribution.

If $|x - m| < 1{\cdot}96\sigma$, there is no evidence against the hypothesis.

If $|x - m| > 1{\cdot}96\sigma$, we say that the result is significant at the 5% level; namely, we reject the null hypothesis but we are prepared to make a mistake in so doing 5 times out of 100.

If we are not prepared to take this risk, we accept the hypothesis, unless $|x - m| > 2{\cdot}58\sigma$. This result is significant at the 1% level; namely we reject the null hypothesis but we are prepared to make a mistake in so doing once out of 100 such tests.

Example 9 Rods are to be manufactured to a specified length of 8″; the lengths of 80 such rods selected at random are measured. A class-interval of 0·01″ is chosen; it is specified by its mid-point in the following table which also gives the corresponding frequencies for each interval:

Class-interval	7·96	7·97	7·98	7·99	8·00	8·01	8·02	8·03	8·04
Frequencies	2	2	8	16	20	18	8	4	2

Fit a normal curve to this distribution.

It is not sufficient merely to draw a histogram to an arbitrary scale; the area of each rectangle must correspond either to the probability or to the actual frequency. If y is the height of the rectangle above the class-interval whose frequency is f, we require $y \times 0{\cdot}01 = f$, or $y = 100f$.

The reader may check that the mean and standard deviation of the given distribution are 8·00 and 0·016 respectively. The normal frequency distribution is therefore given by

$$f(x) = \frac{N}{\sigma\sqrt{(2\pi)}} \exp\left[-\frac{1}{2}\left(\frac{x-m}{\sigma}\right)^2\right] = \frac{80}{0{\cdot}016}\cdot\frac{1}{\sqrt{(2\pi)}} \exp\left[-\frac{1}{2}\left(\frac{x-8}{0{\cdot}016}\right)^2\right]$$

$$= 5000\,\frac{1}{\sqrt{(2\pi)}} \exp\left[-\frac{1}{2}\left(\frac{x-8}{0{\cdot}016}\right)^2\right].$$

The following table is now prepared:

	7·96	7·97	7·98	7·99	8·00	8·01	8·02	8·03	8·04
$x-8$	−0·04	−0·03	−0·02	−0·01	0	0·01	0·02	0·03	0·04
$t = \lvert(x-8)/0{\cdot}016\rvert$	2·5	1·89	1·25	0·62	0	0·62	1·25	1·89	2·5
$\exp(-\tfrac{1}{2}t^2)/\sqrt{(2\pi)}$	0·017	0·067	0·182	0·329	0·399	0·329	0·182	0·067	0·017
$f(x)$ (2 sig. figs.)	85	330	910	1600	2000	1600	910	330	85
Given freqs. f	2	2	8	16	20	18	8	4	2
$y = 100f$	200	200	800	1600	2000	1600	800	400	200

It should be noticed that $f(x)$ and y compare favourably around the hump, but that the fit is not so good for the two tails.

Example 10 A certain mass-produced article is designed to be of length h. It is found that $P\%$ of the articles have a length greater than $h + \varepsilon$ and that $P\%$ of the articles are less than $h - \varepsilon$ in length. If the lengths are normally distributed about the mean h, find the standard deviation of the distribution. What percentage lie within the range $h - \eta$, $h + \eta$?

The probability that a value of the length lies within the range $h + \varepsilon$, $h - \varepsilon$ is

$$1 - 2P/100 = 1 - \tfrac{1}{50}P.$$

Knowing this probability and ε, we use the formula

$$1 - \tfrac{1}{50}P = \operatorname{erf}(\varepsilon/\sqrt{2}\sigma),$$

or, upon using the table of the error function backwards,

$$\varepsilon/\sqrt{2}\sigma = \operatorname{erf}^{-1}(1 - \tfrac{1}{50}P)$$

yielding $$\sigma = \frac{\varepsilon}{\sqrt{2}\,\operatorname{erf}^{-1}(1 - \tfrac{1}{50}P)}.$$

The probability that a value of the length lies within the range $h + \eta$, $h - \eta$ is now given by

$$p = \text{erf}(\eta/\sqrt{2}\sigma),$$

so the percentage that lie within this range is

$$100p = 100 \, \text{erf} \left[\frac{\eta}{\varepsilon} \, \text{erf}^{-1} \, (1 - \tfrac{1}{50}P) \right]$$

upon eliminating σ. Example 24 at the end of this chapter requires this method.

24.11 Sampling theory

We shall now be concerned with the following problem. A population consisting of N members is given; its mean m and variance σ^2 are defined by the relations

$$m = \Sigma_N x/N, \qquad \sigma^2 = \Sigma_N x^2/N - m^2,$$

where throughout this present section Σ_N denotes summation over all the N members of the given population. Later we shall take N to be infinite.

We now consider every possible *sample* of n members that may be selected from the given population; evidently there are $_NC_n = N!/[n! \, (N - n)!]$ such samples. In random sampling, each of these $_NC_n$ samples has an equal chance of being selected.

Each sample of size n has a mean m_s and a variance σ_s^2, defined by

$$m_s = \Sigma_n x/n, \qquad \sigma_s^2 = \Sigma_n x^2/n - m_s^2,$$

where Σ_n denotes summation from 1 to n. We have therefore $_NC_n$ values of m_s and $_NC_n$ values of σ_s^2, thereby forming two new populations.

We seek answers to the following six questions. The algebraic investigation of these questions given in small type below need not be read at a first reading; the answers are quoted after the questions.

(a) What is the mean of the $_NC_n$ values of m_s?   Ans. m.
(b) What is the value of this mean as $N \to \infty$?   Ans. m.
(c) What is the variance of these means about their mean?
$$\text{Ans. } (N - n)\sigma^2/(N - 1)n.$$
(d) What is the value of this variance as $N \to \infty$?   Ans. σ^2/n.
(e) What is the mean of the $_NC_n$ values of σ_s^2?
$$\text{Ans. } (n - 1)N\sigma^2/n(N - 1).$$
(f) What is the value of this mean as $N \to \infty$?
$$\text{Ans. } (n - 1)\sigma^2/n.$$

An identity. We have

$$(x_1 + x_2 + \ldots + x_N)^2 = x_1^2 + x_2^2 + \ldots + x_N^2 + 2(x_1 x_2 + \ldots + x_{N-1} x_N),$$

or

$$2(x_1 x_2 + \ldots + x_{N-1} x_N) = (x_1 + x_2 + \ldots + x_N)^2 - (x_1^2 + x_2^2 + \ldots + x_N^2)$$

$$= m^2 N^2 - N(\sigma^2 + m^2). \tag{12}$$

Calculation (a), the mean of the means. The required mean equals $\Sigma m_s / {}_N C_n$, where Σ denotes summation from 1 to ${}_N C_n$ for all samples. Expressed explicitly, this mean is

$$\Sigma(x_1 + x_2 + \ldots + x_n) / n {}_N C_n,$$

where $(x_1 + x_2 + \ldots + x_n)/n$ is a typical value of m_s. Owing to perfect symmetry, all the terms $x_1, x_2, \ldots, x_N$ occur an equal number of times in the final sum. The bracket contains n terms; the sum therefore contains $n {}_N C_n$ terms. In this sum each of the terms $x_1, x_2, \ldots, x_N$ must occur $n {}_N C_n / N$ times, yielding for the mean

$$\frac{(n {}_N C_n / N)(x_1 + x_2 + \ldots + x_N)}{n {}_N C_n} = \frac{\Sigma_N x}{N} = m.$$

We conclude that *the mean of the sample means equals the mean of the original population.*

Calculation (b). The value of this mean is independent of N, so it remains equal to m as $N \to \infty$.

Calculation (c), the variance of the means. The variance σ_n^2 of the sample means about their mean m is

$$\sigma_n^2 = \frac{\Sigma m_s^2}{{}_N C_n} - m^2 = \frac{\Sigma(x_1 + x_2 + \ldots + x_n)^2}{n^2 {}_N C_n} - m^2 \qquad \text{(typically)} \tag{13}$$

$$= \frac{\Sigma(x_1^2 + \ldots + x_n^2)}{n^2 {}_N C_n} + \frac{2\Sigma(x_1 x_2 + \ldots + x_{n-1} x_n)}{n^2 {}_N C_n} - m^2.$$

Using the same argument as in (a), we conclude that the first term on the right-hand side equals

$$\frac{(n {}_N C_n / N)(x_1^2 + \ldots + x_N^2)}{n^2 {}_N C_n} = \frac{(x_1^2 + \ldots + x_N^2)}{nN} = (\sigma^2 + m^2)/n.$$

The bracket in the second term on the right-hand side contains $\frac{1}{2}n(n-1)$ terms, so the sum contains ${}_N C_n \cdot \frac{1}{2}n(n-1)$ terms. In the final sum, owing to perfect symmetry, each of the $\frac{1}{2}N(N-1)$ terms $x_1 x_2, \ldots, x_{N-1} x_N$ must occur an equal number of times, namely ${}_N C_n \cdot \frac{1}{2}n(n-1)/[\frac{1}{2}N(N-1)]$ times. The second term then becomes

$$\frac{2 {}_N C_n n(n-1)}{N(N-1)} \cdot \frac{(x_1 x_2 + \ldots + x_{N-1} x_N)}{n^2 {}_N C_n} = \frac{(n-1)}{nN(N-1)} [m^2 N^2 - N(\sigma^2 + m^2)]$$

from equation (12). Hence

$$\sigma_n{}^2 = \frac{\sigma^2 + m^2}{n} + \frac{(n-1)}{nN(N-1)}\left[m^2N^2 - N(\sigma^2 + m^2)\right] - m^2$$

$$= \frac{\sigma^2}{n} + \frac{m^2}{n} + \frac{m^2(n-1)}{n} - \frac{(n-1)\sigma^2}{n(N-1)} - m^2$$

$$= \frac{\sigma^2}{n} - \frac{(n-1)\sigma^2}{n(N-1)} = \frac{(N-n)\sigma^2}{(N-1)n} .$$

σ_n is called the *standard error of the mean*.

Calculation (d). As $N \to \infty$, it is obvious that $\sigma_n{}^2 \to \sigma^2/n$.

Calculation (e), the mean of the variances. The individual sample variance $\sigma_s{}^2$ is given typically by

$$\sigma_s{}^2 = (x_1{}^2 + \ldots + x_n{}^2)/n - m_s{}^2.$$

The mean of $_NC_n$ similar quantities is

$$\frac{\Sigma\sigma_s{}^2}{_NC_n} = \frac{\Sigma(x_1{}^2 + \ldots + x_n{}^2)}{n_NC_n} - \frac{\Sigma m_s{}^2}{_NC_n} .$$

The value of the first term on the right-hand side equals, as before,

$$\frac{(n_NC_n/N)(x_1{}^2 + \ldots + x_N{}^2)}{n_NC_n} = \sigma^2 + m^2.$$

Equation (13) provides the value of the second term, namely $\sigma_n{}^2 + m^2$. The required mean therefore equals

$$(\sigma^2 + m^2) - (\sigma_n{}^2 + m^2) = \sigma^2 - \sigma_n{}^2$$

$$= \sigma^2 - \frac{(N-n)\sigma^2}{(N-1)n}$$

$$= \frac{N(n-1)\sigma^2}{(N-1)n} .$$

Calculation (f). As $N \to \infty$, this mean tends to $(n-1)\sigma^2/n$. For an infinite population, this implies that the mean of $n\sigma_s{}^2/(n-1)$ is σ^2.

Four problems may now be considered.

Problem (i). The mean m and the variance σ^2 of an infinite population are not known. One random sample of n members is taken; its mean is m_s and its variance is $\sigma_s{}^2$. What deductions may be made about the original population?

We define the sample mean m_s to be the best or *unbiased estimate* of the unknown population mean m. The word *unbiased* implies that if this experiment could be carried out a large number of times, the mean of all the estimates m_s would be m, the parameter required (calculation b above).

The unbiased estimate of the population variance is *not* σ_s^2, rather it is $n\sigma_s^2/(n-1)$, since the mean of this estimate over a large number of experiments would be σ^2 (calculation *f*). This estimate is therefore obtained by dividing the sum of the squares of deviations from m_s by $(n-1)$ and not by n as is usually done.

The standard error of the mean σ_n also requires an estimate. This would be given by

$$\sigma_n{}^2 = \frac{\sigma^2}{n} \doteqdot \frac{1}{n} \cdot \frac{n\sigma_s{}^2}{n-1} = \frac{\sigma_s{}^2}{n-1} = \frac{\sum_n(x-m_s)^2}{n(n-1)}.$$

Problem (ii). How accurate is this estimate of the population mean?

No one would dispute the fact that the above estimate m_s for the population mean cannot be accurate. We use the interesting fact (which we cannot prove here) that even if the original population is far from normal, nevertheless the new distribution of the sample means m_s is more normal in character, and that as n increases, the distribution of the sample means becomes more and more normal in character.

Then the distribution of m_s about its mean m (calculation *b*) may be taken to be normal, with variance $\sigma_n{}^2$ (calculation *d*), estimated as $\sigma_s{}^2/(n-1)$. We know that 95% of the values of m_s must lie in the range $|m-m_s| < 1{\cdot}96\sigma_n$ and that 99% of the values of m_s lie in the range $|m-m_s| < 2{\cdot}58\sigma_n$.

We conclude that m must lie within the range

$$m_s - 1{\cdot}96\sigma_n < m < m_s + 1{\cdot}96\sigma_n$$

at the 95% level, while at the 99% level, m must lie in the wider range

$$m_s - 2{\cdot}58\sigma_n < m < m_s + 2{\cdot}58\sigma_n.$$

Problem (iii). Given m, examine a sample of n members to see if it is likely that it has been selected from the original normal population. We calculate m_s and the standard error σ_n from the estimate of σ^2. Then if

$$|m-m_s| < 1{\cdot}96\sigma_n$$

no evidence exists against the null hypothesis that the sample was selected from the population, but if

$$|m-m_s| > 1{\cdot}96\sigma_n$$

the result is significant and the hypothesis can be rejected at the 5% level.

Problem (iv). In a controlled laboratory experiment, the value of a certain physical quantity is measured n times with the following results: $x_1, x_2, \ldots, x_n$. What conclusions may be drawn from this data?

Let m_s and $\sigma_s{}^2$ be the calculated mean and sample variance. Then the estimated mean and variance of the whole population of all such experimental results are m_s and $n\sigma_s{}^2/(n-1)$ respectively. The estimate of the standard error of the mean is $\sigma_n = \sqrt{[\sigma_s{}^2/(n-1)]}$.

The values m_s of all similar experiments are distributed normally around their mean m with standard deviation σ_n. Hence

$$m_s - 0.6745\sigma_n < m < m_s + 0.6745\sigma_n,$$

where we have chosen the 50% level usually applied to experimental results. This result is correct in 50 out of 100 such experiments. Hence we write

$$m = m_s \pm 0.6745\sigma_n$$

$$= \frac{\sum_n x}{n} \pm 0.6745 \frac{\sqrt{[\sum_n (x - \sum_n x/n)^2]}}{\sqrt{[n(n-1)]}}$$

in terms of the actual observations.

Example 11★ A new method is suggested for determining the melting-point of metals. Seven determinations for manganese (known to melt at 1260°C) were found to be 1267, 1262, 1267, 1263, 1258, 1263, 1268°C. Discuss whether these results provide evidence for supposing the new method to be biased.

In the infinite normal population of all such experimental results, the mean m is required to be 1260, while the variance σ^2 is unknown. It may be checked that the sample mean m_s is 1264 and that the sample variance is 10·86.

The estimate of σ^2 is therefore $\frac{7}{6} \times 10.86$, and the estimate of the variance of the means is $\frac{1}{7} \times \frac{7}{6} \times 10.86 = 1.81$. Hence $\sigma_n = 1.3$.

Now $$|m - m_s| = 4 > 2.58\sigma_n = 3.35.$$

There is therefore a probability of less than 1% that the given sample was selected from a normal distribution with mean 1260. At this level, we conclude that the method is definitely biased (on the high side).

Example 12★ Evaluate the mean and the standard deviation of the sample values 17·0, 16·8, 16·3, 17·2, 16·1, 16·4, 16·7, 17·1, 17·0, 16·3, 16·0. How many more values would you estimate to be needed to reduce the standard error of the mean to 0·1?

The student may check that the sample mean is 16·63 and that the sample variance is 0·160. Hence the population mean is estimated to be 16·63 and the population variance to be $\frac{11}{10} \times 0.160$. The variance of the means of sample of size 11 is therefore estimated to be $\frac{1}{11} \times \frac{11}{10} \times 0.160 = 0.016$.

Now we require σ_n to be less than 0·1 where n is to be found. Then

$$0.01 > \sigma_n{}^2 = \sigma^2/n = (\tfrac{11}{10} \times 0.160)/n,$$

or $$n > 11 \times 0.0160/0.01 = 17.6.$$

We conclude that $n = 18$, so 7 more sample values are required.

24.12   A note on quality control

In this somewhat wide subject, we shall explain theoretically to the reader only one application of the topic. To see how this, and other applications, are actually carried out in practice, text-books of a more specialized character should be consulted.

Bluntly speaking, *quality control* consists of a series of significance tests illustrated graphically. In the manufacture of a certain article, the dimension x, specified to be m, cannot be obtained exactly; there are (*a*) inherent errors in the manufacturing process such that the actual values of x are normally distributed about the mean, and (*b*) errors that can and must be recognized and corrected. The method of quality control indicates the presence of errors of type (*b*) immediately they occur, and action can then be taken to eliminate the cause of the error.

It is assumed that the mean m and the variance σ^2 of the distribution are known or estimated from prior measurements, when errors of type (*a*) only are operative.

Random samples of size n (from 4 to 10, say) are regularly selected from the manufactured articles. Their means m_s have mean m and variance σ^2/n. Now 95% of the values of m_s must lie in the range $|m - m_s| < 1 \cdot 96\sigma/\sqrt{n}$, and 99·8% of the values of m_s must lie in the range $|m - m_s| < 3 \cdot 09\sigma/\sqrt{n}$.

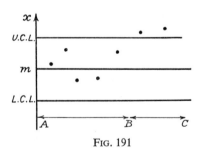

FIG. 191

A graph is now prepared, the vertical scale of which contains m, the *upper control limit* $m + 1 \cdot 96\sigma/\sqrt{n}$ (at the 95% level) and the *lower control limit* $m - 1 \cdot 96\sigma/\sqrt{n}$. When the process is under *statistical control*, all the sample means should lie within these control lines; it is highly improbable that a point will lie outside these limits. From A to B in the diagram the process is under control, but from B to C errors have entered the process which are not due merely to random fluctuations under the normal law. Immediate inspection of the process is called for, until once again the system is under control.

24.13 The method of least squares and correlation

A series of points $(x_1, y_1), \ldots, (x_n, y_n)$ is given with respect to axes Ox and Oy. These points may lie approximately on a straight line or on a curve, or they may be scattered more or less at random over the plane. Theoretical considerations may suggest that the relation between x and y takes such forms as $y = ax + b$ or $y = ax + bx^2$, etc. The object of the present analysis is to find the best values for the constants a and b.

In other problems, a curve such as $y = ax^b$ may be suggested theoretically. We replace this by

$$\log y = b \log x + \log a,$$

or

$$v = bu + c,$$

say, thereby reducing the problem to the above case.

More than two variables may be present. The given set of points (x, y, z) may be related theoretically by an equation of the form $z = a + bx + cy$, or by a more complicated function of x and y.

In other cases, the (three, say) variables x, y, z may be connected by various (slightly) inconsistent linear equations. The object now is to find the best values of x, y and z suggested by the data.

In all cases, the deviations are found of what is given numerically from what is postulated theoretically. The unknowns in the problem are then found by *minimizing the sum of the squares of these deviations.*

We shall illustrate the method for the straight line; other cases are considered in the examples at the end of the section.

Let the straight line be assumed to be $y = ax + b$. If the values of x are assumed to be exact, the straight line that we obtain is known as the *line of regression of y on x.* We now form the sum of the squares of all the deviations of the given numerical values of y from the theoretical values:

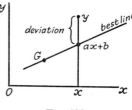

$$S = \Sigma(y - ax - b)^2,$$

Fig. 192

where the values of x and y are inserted.

S is a minimum when $\partial S/\partial a = \partial S/\partial b = 0$; that is when

$$\Sigma 2x(y - ax - b) = 0, \qquad \Sigma 2(y - ax - b) = 0,$$

or

$$a\Sigma x^2 + b\Sigma x = \Sigma xy, \qquad a\Sigma x + nb = \Sigma y. \qquad (14)$$

The fact that n multiplies b in the second equation should be noticed carefully, since it can easily be overlooked. These equations are known as the *normal equations* of the system; their solution is obviously

$$a = \frac{n\Sigma xy - \Sigma x \Sigma y}{n\Sigma x^2 - (\Sigma x)^2}, \qquad b = \frac{\Sigma y \Sigma x^2 - \Sigma x \Sigma xy}{n\Sigma x^2 - (\Sigma x)^2}. \qquad (15)$$

The importance of using vertical columns to calculate Σx, Σy, Σx^2, Σxy should be stressed.

Unique values of a and b are given by this method; S is obviously a minimum, since if a and b are large, S would be large and positive.

If m_x is the mean of the n values of x, and m_y the mean of the n values of y, we have $m_x = \Sigma x/n$; $m_y = \Sigma y/n$. Then the second equation (14) becomes

$$am_x + b = m_y,$$

showing that the point $G(m_x, m_y)$ lies on this line of regression.

Consider, now, the deviations of the values of x and y from their means m_x and m_y respectively. We write $x_i = m_x + X_i$, $y_i = m_y + Y_i$. The gradient of this line through G is then given by

$$a = \frac{n\Sigma(m_x + X)(m_y + Y) - \Sigma(m_x + X)\Sigma(m_y + Y)}{n\Sigma(m_x + X)^2 - [\Sigma(m_x + X)]^2}$$

$$= \frac{n(nm_x m_y + \Sigma XY) - nm_x \cdot nm_y}{n(nm_x^2 + \Sigma X^2) - (nm_x)^2}$$

$$= \frac{\Sigma XY}{\Sigma X^2} = \frac{\sigma_{xy}}{\sigma_x^2}, \tag{16}$$

where σ_x^2 denotes the variance of the values of x about their mean m_x, and σ_{xy} denotes the covariance of the values of x and y, defined by

$$\sigma_{xy} = \Sigma XY/n = \Sigma(x - m_x)(y - m_y)/n.$$

Finally, with this simpler value of a, the line of regression through G with this gradient is

$$(y - m_y) = a(x - m_x).$$

Numerically, it may be simpler to use this form rather than the results (15).

We may also calculate the standard deviation S_y of the given values of y from this best line. Since a typical deviation is $(y - ax - b)$, we have

$$S_y^2 = \Sigma(y - ax - b)^2/n$$

$$= \Sigma[(y - ax) - (m_y - am_x)]^2/n$$

$$= \Sigma(Y - aX)^2/n$$

$$= \Sigma Y^2/n - 2a\Sigma XY/n + a^2\Sigma X^2/n$$

$$= \sigma_y^2 - 2a\sigma_{xy} + a^2\sigma_x^2$$

$$= \sigma_y^2 - 2\sigma_{xy}\sigma_{xy}/\sigma_x^2 + (\sigma_{xy}/\sigma_x^2)^2\sigma_x^2$$

$$= (\sigma_x^2\sigma_y^2 - \sigma_{xy}^2)/\sigma_x^2. \tag{17}$$

When the line of regression of y on x is being calculated, both a and b must be found by minimizing the sum of squares $S = \Sigma(y - ax - b)^2$. Some investigators (though hardly statisticians!) have objected to finding the value of the constant b by this method, since graphically the given points may all be in the first quadrant, and the supposed extrapolation of the line beyond the given points to form the intercept on the y-axis may appear unjustifiable. Such investigators have rewritten the equation of the line in the form

$$\frac{y}{x} = \frac{b}{x} + a.$$

The same method now applied to the sum of squares $\Sigma(y/x - b/x - a)^2$ yields b as a gradient without the necessity of extrapolation, but obviously this new value of b is quite different from the original value. It is wrong to use the value of a calculated by the first method and this value of b found by the second method, since taken together these two values do not minimize either sum of squares.

Similarly, the line of regression of x on y is derived on the assumption that the given values of y are exact. The line may be written in the form $x = cy + d$, where, as before, it contains the point $G(m_x, m_y)$, and where the constant c is given by σ_{xy}/σ_y^2. The gradient of the line is σ_y^2/σ_{xy}.

Correlation. A given set of points in a plane may only exhibit a *trend* rather than a close approximation to a straight line. The extent to which the trend approximates to a straight line (that is, the extent to which the x and y coordinates of the points are linearly related) is specified quantitatively by the *correlation coefficient*.

The two lines of regression are considered; their gradients are σ_{xy}/σ_x^2 and σ_y^2/σ_{xy} respectively, and their point of intersection is $G(m_x, m_y)$. If the correlation is perfect, the two lines must be identical, so $\sigma_{xy}/\sigma_x^2 = \sigma_y^2/\sigma_{xy}$; that is, $\sigma_{xy}/\sigma_x\sigma_y = \pm 1$. If, however, the lines are perpendicular, we say that there is no correlation, in which case the product of the gradients $(\sigma_{xy}/\sigma_x^2)(\sigma_y^2/\sigma_{xy})$ must equal -1. This is impossible, since the product

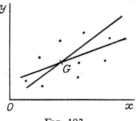

FIG. 193

obviously consists only of squared terms. In fact, the lines can only be perpendicular when $\sigma_{xy} = 0$; they are then parallel to Ox and Oy respectively.

These features are embodied in the correlation coefficient

$$\rho = \sigma_{xy}/\sigma_x\sigma_y.$$

In terms of the gradient a, this coefficient is given by $\rho = a\sigma_x/\sigma_y$. If $\rho = \pm 1$, correlation is perfect, while if $\rho = 0$, there is no correlation. Intermediate values of ρ indicate varying degrees of correlation.

Quoting equation (17), we have

$$0 \leqslant S_y^2 = \sigma_y^2\left(1 - \frac{\sigma_{xy}^2}{\sigma_x^2\sigma_y^2}\right) = \sigma_y^2(1 - \rho^2);$$

hence $\rho^2 \leqslant 1$, and $-1 \leqslant \rho \leqslant 1$.

Strictly speaking, the significance of the correlation coefficient should be examined, in order to determine whether it is merely a chance result due to the random errors inherent in the numerical data, or whether the result cannot be due to chance in which case it is accepted as a basis for discussion. The reader must refer to specialized texts for an investigation of this important question.

Example 13 The following measurements were made

x	0·2	1·20	2·61
y	17·3	15·93	11·32

Assuming that $y = ax + b$, calculate a and b, given that x is measured accurately. Find the correlation coefficient.

In order to use equations (15), we must calculate Σx, Σy, Σx^2, Σxy:

	x	y	x^2	xy
	0·2	17·3	0·04	3·46
	1·20	15·93	1·44	19·12
	2·61	11·32	6·81	29·55
Totals:	4·01	44·55	8·29	52·13

It follows that

$$a = \frac{3 \times 52\cdot13 - 4\cdot01 \times 44\cdot55}{3 \times 8\cdot29 - (4\cdot01)^2} = \frac{156\cdot39 - 178\cdot85}{24\cdot87 - 16\cdot08} = -\frac{22\cdot46}{8\cdot79} = -2\cdot56,$$

$$b = \frac{44\cdot55 \times 8\cdot29 - 4\cdot01 \times 52\cdot13}{8\cdot79} = \frac{369\cdot32 - 209\cdot04}{8\cdot79} = \frac{160\cdot28}{8\cdot79} = 18\cdot2.$$

The line of regression of y on x is therefore

$$y = -2\cdot56x + 18\cdot2.$$

We note that $m_x = 4\cdot01/3 = 1\cdot34$ and $m_y = 44\cdot55/3 = 14\cdot85$. Taking the deviations from their respective means, we find

$$\sigma_x^2 = \tfrac{1}{3}(1\cdot14^2 + 0\cdot14^2 + 1\cdot27)^2 = 0\cdot978, \qquad \sigma_x = 0\cdot989,$$
$$\sigma_y^2 = \tfrac{1}{3}(2\cdot45^2 + 1\cdot18^2 + 3\cdot53^2) = 6\cdot54, \qquad \sigma_y = 2\cdot56.$$

Hence
$$\rho = a\sigma_x/\sigma_y = -2\cdot56 \times 0\cdot989/2\cdot56 = -0\cdot989,$$

showing high correlation.

Example 14★ The points $(0, 1)$, $(1, 4)$, $(2, 11)$, $(3, 24)$, $(4, 40)$ appear to lie approximately on a parabola of the form $y = ax^2 + b$. Find the values of the constants a and b which will give the best fit.

We form the sum of the squares of the deviations of the given values of y from their theoretical values: $S = \Sigma(y - ax^2 - b)^2$. This sum is a minimum when

$$\partial S/\partial a \propto \Sigma x^2(y - ax^2 - b) = 0,$$
$$\partial S/\partial b \propto \Sigma(y - ax^2 - b) = 0,$$

namely
$$\Sigma x^2 y - a\Sigma x^4 - b\Sigma x^2 = 0, \quad \Sigma y - a\Sigma x^2 - nb = 0, \quad (n = 5).$$

We prepare the following table:

x	y	x^2	x^4	x^2y
0	1	0	0	0
1	4	1	1	4
2	11	4	16	44
3	24	9	81	216
4	40	16	256	640
Totals:	80	30	354	904

The equations become:
$$354a + 30b = 904, \qquad 30a + 5b = 80.$$
The first equation minus six times the second equation yields $174a = 424$, or $a = 212/87 = 2{\cdot}44$. The second equation then yields $b = 16 - 6a = 1{\cdot}36$.

Hence the parabola is
$$y = 2{\cdot}44x^2 + 1{\cdot}36$$

Example 15★ Find the values of x and y which nearly satisfy the equations
$$2x + y = 2{\cdot}76, \quad 4x + 3y = 3{\cdot}90, \quad 3x - y = 8{\cdot}62, \quad x + 2y = -1{\cdot}38.$$

If x and y denote the theoretical values, we form the sum of squares of deviations of $2x + y$, $4x + 3y$, $3x - y$, $x + 2y$ from their given numerical values, namely
$$S = (2x + y - 2{\cdot}76)^2 + (4x + 3y - 3{\cdot}90)^2$$
$$+ (3x - y - 8{\cdot}62)^2 + (x + 2y + 1{\cdot}38)^2.$$

We choose x and y so that S is a minimum, namely
$$\partial S/\partial x \propto 2(2x + y - 2{\cdot}76) + 4(4x + 3y - 3{\cdot}90)$$
$$+ 3(3x - y - 8{\cdot}62) + (x + 2y + 1{\cdot}38) = 0,$$
$$\partial S/\partial y \propto (2x + y - 2{\cdot}76) + 3(4x + 3y - 3{\cdot}90)$$
$$- (3x - y - 8{\cdot}62) + 2(x + 2y + 1{\cdot}38) = 0.$$

These equations simplify to
$$30x + 13y = 45{\cdot}60,$$
$$13x + 15y = 3{\cdot}08,$$
whose solution is $x = 2{\cdot}29$, $y = -1{\cdot}78$.

EXERCISES

(1)★. Two dice, each of which has its faces numbered from 1 to 6, are thrown together, and the score is found by squaring the difference between the numbers on the faces resting uppermost. Draw up a table showing the number of ways in which each possible score can be obtained. Determine the mean score, and calculate the standard deviation from this mean.

(2)★. Measurements are made to the nearest inch of the heights of 100 children. Draw the frequency polygon for the following distribution:

Height	60	61	62	63	64	65	66	67	68
Frequency	2	0	15	29	25	12	10	4	3

Calculate the mean, and the standard deviation from the mean.

(3)*. Find the mean and standard deviation of the set of numbers 8, 9, 10, 11, 12. From this set, ten samples each containing two numbers can be selected. Find the mean of each of these samples, and calculate the standard deviations of these means.

(4)*. The heights of 100 men of a certain regiment are given in the following table:

Height in inches	Frequency	Height in inches	Frequency
60·5 to 61·5	1	66·5 to 67·5	18
61·5 to 62·5	2	67·5 to 68·5	11
62·5 to 63·5	7	68·5 to 69·5	8
63·5 to 64·5	8	69·5 to 70·5	4
64·5 to 65·5	18	70·5 to 71·5	2
65·5 to 66·5	20	71·5 to 72·5	1

Draw the histogram and calculate the mean and the standard deviation of this distribution.

(5)*. The following table gives the number of boys in a class of 100 who obtained various marks between 0 and 10 in a test.

Mark	0	1	2	3	4	5	6	7	8	9	10
Number	1	4	7	8	10	20	15	12	11	8	4

Calculate the mean mark and the standard deviation.

(6)*. Four boys sit for an examination. The average of their marks is M and the standard deviation is σ. The marks are converted to a new scale by the formula $y = 50 - 20(M - x)/6$ where y is the new mark and x is the original mark. Find the mean and the standard deviation of the new marks. If the original marks were 47, 57, 65, 71, find the new marks each to the nearest integer.

(7). Set I of 280 observations has mean 45, standard deviation 6; set II of 350 observations has mean 54, standard deviation 4; set III of 630 observations has mean 49, standard deviation 8. If the three sets are combined yielding 1260 observations, find the combined mean and standard deviation.

(8)*. The mean of 50 readings of a variable was 7·43 and their standard deviation was 0·28. The following ten additional readings became available: 6·80, 7·81, 7·58, 7·70, 8·05, 6·98, 7·78, 7·85, 7·21, 7·40. If these are included with the original 50 readings, find (i) the mean, (ii) the standard deviation of the whole set of 60 readings.

(9)*. A sampling inspection scheme is as follows. From a large batch of components eight are selected at random. If they are all faultless, the batch is accepted; if more than one is faulty, the batch is rejected; if one (and only one) is faulty, twelve more components selected at random are inspected and the batch is accepted only if twelve are faultless. If, in fact, 5 per cent of the components in the batch are faulty, find (i) the probability that the batch is accepted, (ii) the probability that the first sample of eight is decisive, resulting in either immediate acceptance or immediate rejection of the batch.

(10)*. On an expedition, a machine is taken which fails to start on the average once in c attempts owing to the breakage of a certain part. If s spare parts of this kind are carried, show that the probability that the last spare part will fail at the nth attempt at starting is equal to the coefficient of t^s in the expansion of

$$[1 + (t - 1)/c]^{n-1}/c.$$

(11)★. An even number $2n$ of dice is cast. Show how to calculate the probability that more than half the number of dice show a one or a two. Calculate this probability for $n = 1, 2, 3, 4$ respectively.

(12)★. In the manufacture of screws by a certain process it was found that five per cent of the screws were rejected because they failed to satisfy tolerance requirements. What was the probability that a sample of 12 screws contained (a) exactly 2 (b) not more than 2 rejects?

(13)★. Metal sheets, when correctly inserted in a stamping machine, each produce five rows of four accurate pieces, but when incorrectly inserted, one row is entirely defective. Incorrect insertions average one per cent of the whole. After thoroughly mixing the pieces, large numbers of packets are made up, each containing 100 pieces. Show that only about one packet in 1000 is likely to contain more than two defective pieces.

(14)★. In a quality control procedure, the chance that a mass-produced article will fail to pass a gauge is 0·16. Calculate, to two decimal places, the chance that more than two of a sample of ten articles will fail to pass.

(15)★. A set of random digits (0, 1, ... , 9) is arranged in 100 rows, each containing 50 digits. In the following table n is the number of rows in which the digit 5 occurs p times.

p	0	1	2	3	4	5	6	7	8	9	10	11	12
n	1	3	5	19	20	15	18	5	10	2	1	0	1

Find the mean number of occurrences in a row and the standard deviation, and compare them with those to be expected for a binomial distribution.

(16)★. A competition consists of filling in a form which contains N spaces and each space has to be filled up in one of n ways. There is a unique correct solution. If the spaces are filled up in a random manner, prove that the probability of there being r mistakes is the coefficient of x^r in the expansion of $n^{-N}[1 + x(n - 1)]^N$. If $N = 12$ and $n = 3$ prove that the probability of there being *not more* than 2 mistakes is 289×3^{-12}.

(17)★. The probability that a pipe line develops n faults in a given time is believed to be $e^{-k}k^n/n!$, where k is proportional to the time and to the length of line. Show that the mean and standard deviation of the number of faults are k and $\sqrt{k}$ respectively. The following figures give the number of faults per month over a period of 5 years:

No. of faults	0	1	2	3	4	5
No. of months	16	21	15	5	2	1

Show that this agrees fairly well with that predicted if k is suitably chosen.

(18)★. The probabilities that a firm will require 0, 1, 2, 3, ... articles of a certain kind in a month are given by Poisson's distribution with mean 2. How many of the articles should the firm have in stock at the beginning of the month, if the probability of running out of stock during the month is to be less than 0·01?

(19)★. Samples containing a large number of seeds are examined and the number of seeds showing a certain rare defect are counted. It is found that the frequencies of occurrence of samples containing exactly 0, 1, 2, ... , s, ... defective seeds are approximately proportional to 1, m, $m^2/2!$, ... , $m^s/s!$, ... respectively. Show that the probability that a sample contains exactly s defective seeds is $e^{-m}m^s/s!$. If 0·2% of the seeds are defective, and the samples contain 5000 seeds, show that the probability that a sample contains exactly 6 defective seeds is about 1 in 16.

(20)★. If a probability distribution is defined by $dp = f(x^2)\,dx$, $-\infty < x < \infty$, the mean absolute deviation D is given by

$$D = 2\int_0^\infty xf(x^2)\,dx.$$

Show that, for the normal distribution $dp = \exp(-x^2/2\sigma^2)\,dx/[\sigma\sqrt{(2\pi)}]$, $D = 0.8\sigma$, very nearly.

(21)★. Nine pennies are tossed together and the number of heads noted. Calculate the probability of r heads being observed and plot the resulting probability distribution on squared paper. Plot on the same diagram the normal probability curve with the same mean and standard deviation.

(22)★. Five skilled operatives carrying out similar tasks were found to have the following times: 10·25, 10·12, 9·98, 9·84, 9·81 secs. Find their standard deviation Σ. By taking all possible groups of four operatives, verify that the standard deviation σ of their mean times satisfies the formula

$$n(N - 1)\sigma^2 = (N - n)\Sigma^2,$$

where N is the total number of operatives and n is the number in a group.

(23)★. Six values, constituting a sample drawn at random from a normal population, are 194, 185, 201, 190, 199, 189. Estimate the mean and variance of the parent population.

Given that, in a normal population, the probability of a value differing from the mean by more than the standard deviation is approximately $\tfrac{1}{3}$, find the probabilities that in a sample of six values, (a) exactly two, (b) not more than two so differ.

(24)★. Plastic trays are manufactured to be 18 in. in length, but they are acceptable if they are inside the limits $17\tfrac{15}{16}$, $18\tfrac{1}{16}$ in. It is observed that about $2\tfrac{1}{2}\%$ are rejected as oversize and about $2\tfrac{1}{2}\%$ as undersize. Assuming that the lengths are normally distributed about the mean value of 18 in., find the standard deviation of the distribution. Hence calculate what the proportion of rejections will be if the tolerance limits (i) are narrowed to $17\tfrac{61}{64}$, $18\tfrac{3}{64}$ in., (ii) widened to $17\tfrac{59}{64}$, $18\tfrac{5}{64}$ in.

(25)★. It is desired to estimate the magnitude of a certain physical quantity T secs. with a standard error of not more than one-fifth of a second. A preliminary set of eleven measurements was

1·76, 1·63, 1·79, 2·43, 0·88, 0·99, 1·12, 4·56, 2·11, 3·26, 2·73 secs.

The sum of these measurements is 23·26; the sum of their squares is 61·1986. Give a preliminary estimate of T, and attach a standard error to your estimate. How many further measurements would you recommend to be taken to achieve the desired accuracy in the final estimate?

(26)★. Find the equation of the straight line which satisfies the condition that $\Sigma(y_r - ax_r - b)^2$ is a minimum for the set of points with coordinates (0, 13), (3, 10), (6, 8), (9, 5), (12, 2).

(27)★. Values of y are measured for certain values of x:

x	1	2	3	4	5	6
y	12·2	18·9	23·5	30·4	35·6	42·5

If the relation $y = a + bx$ be assumed, find the best value of y when $x = 2.5$ using the method of least squares.

(28) ★. A low temperature process gave the following yields y in equal times at $\theta°C$.

$$\theta = 1 \quad 2 \quad 3 \quad 4$$
$$y = 0\cdot8 \quad 1\cdot5 \quad 1\cdot8 \quad 2\cdot0$$

It is believed that the variables are related in the form $y = a\theta + b\theta^2$. Find, correct to two decimal places, the values of a and b and the temperature at which the yield is likely to be most rapid.

(29) ★. The five pairs of numbers x, y tabulated below are believed to be connected by a relation of the form $y = Ca^x$.

x	1·0	1·2	1·4	1·6	1·8
y	11·84	14·57	17·93	22·06	27·15

Determine the values of C and a, each to three significant figures, which best fit the data.

(30) ★. The yield of a chemical process was measured at three temperatures, each with two concentrations of a particular reactant, as recorded in the table below:

Temperature $\theta°C$.	40	40	50	50	60	60
Concentration x	0·2	0·4	0·2	0·4	0·2	0·4
Yield y	38	42	41	46	46	49

Use the method of least squares to find the best values of the coefficients a, b, c in the equation $y = a + b\theta + cx$, and from your equation estimate the yield at $70°C$, with concentration 0·5.

(31) ★. Find, to three significant figures, the best values of x, y, z to fit the equations

$$x - y + 2z = 15, \, 2x + 3y + z = 5, \, x + y - z = -5, \, 3x - 2y - 2z = 0.$$

(32) ★. All possible combinations of three weights x, y and z gm. were measured with the following results: $x = 4\cdot75$, $x + y = 11\cdot34$, $x + z = 6\cdot38$, $x + y + z = 12\cdot92$, $y = 6\cdot57$, $y + z = 8\cdot20$, $z = 1\cdot55$. By the method of least squares find the best values to assign to x, y and z.

(33) ★. Find by the method of least squares the gradient a of the straight line $y = ax + b$ which best represents the observed values:

x	0	1	2	3	4	5	6	7	8	9
y	−4	−3	−1	−2	2	1	4	5	7	8

By means of the relation $a = \rho\sigma_2/\sigma_1$ where σ_1 is the standard deviation of the ten observed values of x and σ_2 that of the observed values of y, calculate the correlation coefficient ρ.

(34) ★. For the pairs tabulated below, calculate the correlation coefficient:

x	0	2	2	4	5	6	7	8	10	11
y	20	19	16	14	16	18	13	15	13	10

ANSWERS TO EXERCISES

(1). $5\frac{5}{6}$, 6·8. (2). 63·89, 1·6. (3). 10, $\sqrt{2}$, $\frac{1}{2}\sqrt{3}$. (4). 66·3, 2·1.

(5). 5·56, 2·35. (6). 50, 20; 21, 43, 61, 75. (7). 49·5, 7·4.

(8). (i) 7·444, (ii) 0·309. (9). (i) 0·814, (ii) 0·720. (ii). $\displaystyle\sum_{s=n+1}^{2n} {}_{2n}C_s(\tfrac{1}{3})^s(\tfrac{2}{3})^{2n-s}$;

$\frac{1}{9} = 0\cdot111$, $\frac{1}{9} = 0\cdot111$, $73/3^6 = 0\cdot100$, $577/3^8 = 0\cdot0879$.

(12). (a) $_{12}C_2(\frac{1}{20})^2(\frac{19}{20})^{10} = 66 \times 19^{10}/20^{12} = 0.0988$,

    (b) $\displaystyle\sum_{s=0}^{2} {}_{12}C_s(\frac{1}{20})^s(\frac{19}{20})^{12-s} = 655 \times 19^{10}/20^{12} = 0.980$.

(14). $1 - \displaystyle\sum_{s=0}^{2} {}_{10}C_s(0.84)^{10-s}(0.16)^s = 0.21$.   (15). $m = 4.88$, $\sigma = 2.11$; $m = 5$,

     $\sigma = 2.12$.   (17) $m = 1.32$, $\sigma^2 = 1.31$; let $k = 1.32$.   (18). 6.

(21). $_9C_r/2^9$, $m = \frac{9}{2}$, $\sigma^2 = \frac{9}{4}$.   (22) $\Sigma^2 = 0.0278$, $\Sigma = 0.167$.   (23). 193, 38;

     (a) $80 \times 3^{-5} = 0.3292$, (b) $496 \times 3^{-6} = 0.6804$.   (24). $\sigma = 0.032$, (i) 0.14,

     (ii) 0.015.   (25). $m_s = 2.11$, $\sigma_s^2 = 1.1114$; estimate $m = 2.11$, $\sigma^2 = \frac{11}{10}\sigma_s^2 =$

     1.22254; S.E. $= \sigma_n = \sqrt{(\sigma^2/n)} = 0.333$; 20 more.   (26). $y = -0.9x + 13$.

(27). 21.2.   (28). $y = 0.950 - 0.110^2$; $\theta = 4.21$.   (29). $a = 2.82$, $C = 4.19$.

(30). $y = 18.917 + 0.375\theta + 20x$; $y = 55.2$.   (31). $x = 6.08$, $y = -3.93$,

     $z = 8.97$.   (32). $x = 4.76$, $y = 6.58$, $z = 1.55$.

(33). $a = 1.36$, $\sigma_1 = 2.87$, $\sigma_2 = 4.00$, $\rho = 0.98$.   (34). -0.853.

INDEX